Symbol Tab

H	Kruskal-Wallis test statistic
R	sum of the ranks for a sample; used in the Wilcoxon rank-sum test
μ_R	expected mean rank; used in the Wilcoxon rank-sum test
σ_R	expected standard deviation of ranks; used in the Wilcoxon rank-sum test
G	number of runs in runs test for randomness
μ_G	expected mean number of runs; used in runs test for randomness
σ_G	expected standard deviation for the number of runs; used in runs test for randomness
$\mu_{\bar{x}}$	mean of the population of all possible sample means $\bar{x}$
$\sigma_{\bar{x}}$	standard deviation of the population of all possible sample means $\bar{x}$
E	margin of error of the estimate of a population parameter, or expected value
Q_1, Q_2, Q_3	quartiles
$D_1, D_2, \ldots, D_9$	deciles
$P_1, P_2, \ldots, P_{99}$	percentiles
x	data value

14th EDITION

ELEMENTARY STATISTICS

14th EDITION

ELEMENTARY STATISTICS

MARIO F. TRIOLA

Pearson

Content Development: Robert Carroll
Content Management: Suzanna Bainbridge, Amanda Brands
Content Production: Jean Choe, Peggy McMahon
Product Management: Karen Montgomery
Product Marketing: Alicia Wilson
Rights and Permissions: Tanvi Bhatia/Anjali Singh

Please contact https://support.pearson.com/getsupport/s/ with any queries on this content.

Cover Image by Bim/Getty Images

Library of Congress Cataloging-in-Publication Data
Names: Triola, Mario F., author.
Title: Elementary statistics / Mario F. Triola.
Description: 14th edition, annotated instructor's edition. | Hoboken :
    Pearson, [2022] | Includes index. | Summary: "Step-by-step guide to the
    important concepts of Statistics"-- Provided by publisher.
Identifiers: LCCN 2020040438 | ISBN 9780136803201 (hardcover)
Subjects: LCSH: Statistics--Textbooks.
Classification: LCC QA276.12 .T76 2022 | DDC 519.5--dc23
LC record available at https://lccn.loc.gov/2020040438

2 2021

Rental
ISBN-10: 0136803202
ISBN-13: 9780136803201

To Ginny
Marc, Dushana, and Marisa
Scott, Anna, Siena, and Kaia

ABOUT THE AUTHOR

Mario F. Triola is a Professor Emeritus of Mathematics at Dutchess Community College, where he has taught statistics for over 30 years. Marty is the author of *Essentials of Statistics*, 6th edition, *Elementary Statistics Using Excel™*, 7th edition, *Elementary Statistics Using the TI-83/84 Plus Calculator*, 5th edition, and he is a co-author of *Biostatistics for the Biological and Health Sciences*, 2nd edition, *Statistical Reasoning for Everyday Life*, 5th edition, and *Business Statistics*. *Elementary Statistics* is currently available as an International Edition, and it has been translated into several foreign languages. Marty designed the original Statdisk statistical software, and he has written several manuals and workbooks for technology supporting statistics education. He has been a speaker at many conferences and colleges. Marty's consulting work includes the design of casino slot machines and fishing rods. He has worked with attorneys in determining probabilities in paternity lawsuits, analyzing data in medical malpractice lawsuits, identifying salary inequities based on gender, and analyzing disputed election results. He has also used statistical methods in analyzing medical school surveys, and in analyzing survey results for the New York City Transit Authority, and analyzing COVID-19 virus data for government officials. Marty has testified as an expert witness in the New York State Supreme Court. The Text and Academic Authors Association has awarded Marty a "Texty" for Excellence for his work on *Elementary Statistics*. As of this writing, Marty's *Elementary Statistics* book has been the #1 statistics book in the United States for the past 25 consecutive years.

*Celebrating the past 25 years as
the #1 statistics textbook author!*

CONTENTS

PREFACE

The ancient Chinese philosopher Lao Tzu famously wrote: *A journey of a thousand miles must begin with a single step.* This textbook will lead you, step-by-step, on a journey through the important concepts of statistics and if you're reading this, you've already taken the first step! Thankfully, our journey will be much less physically taxing than a "journey of a thousand miles" and will only require use of your feet for determining skewness (see page 57).

We are now on the leading edge of a major revolution in technology, and the content of this text is key to that revolution. Artificial intelligence, machine learning, and deep learning are studied in data science, and the study of data science requires study of the discipline of statistics. Data science is now experiencing unprecedented growth. Projections indicate a 33% increased demand for statisticians in a few short years, and there is a projected shortage of workers with statistical skills. Also, as in past decades, statistics continues to be essential to a wide variety of disciplines, including medicine, polling, journalism, law, physical science, education, business, and economics. It is a gross understatement to suggest that it is now very wise to initiate a study of statistics.

Goals of This Fourteenth Edition

- Foster personal growth of students through critical thinking, use of technology, collaborative work, and development of communication skills.

- Incorporate the latest and best methods used by professional statisticians.

- Include features that address all of the recommendations included in the *Guidelines for Assessment and Instruction in Statistics Education* (GAISE) as recommended by the American Statistical Association.

- Provide an abundance of new and interesting data sets, examples, and exercises, such as those involving biometric security, cybersecurity, drones, and Internet traffic.

- Present topics used in data science and many other applications, and include very large data sets that have become so important in our current culture.

- Enhance teaching and learning with the most extensive and best set of supplements and digital resources.

Audience/Prerequisites

Elementary Statistics is written for students majoring in any subject. Algebra is used minimally. It is recommended that students have completed at least an elementary algebra course or that students should learn the relevant algebra components through an integrated or co-requisite course available through MyLab Statistics. In many cases, underlying theory is included, but this book does not require the mathematical rigor more appropriate for mathematics majors. Instead of being a "cookbook" devoid of any theory, this book includes the mathematics underlying important statistical methods, but the focus is on understanding and applying those methods along with interpreting results in a meaningful way.

Hallmark Features

Great care has been taken to ensure that each chapter of *Elementary Statistics* will help students understand the concepts presented. The following features are designed to help meet that objective of conceptual understanding.

Real Data

Thousands of hours have been devoted to finding data that are real, meaningful, and interesting to students. 94% of the examples are based on real data, and 93% of the exercises are based on real data. Some exercises refer to the 46 data sets listed in Appendix B, and 20 of those data sets are new to this edition. Exercises requiring use of the Appendix B data sets are located toward the end of each exercise set and are marked with a special data set icon ⏹⏹⏹. These data sets are also available in MyLab Statistics, including data sets for StatCrunch.

Appendix B includes descriptions of the 46 data sets that can be downloaded from www.TriolaStats.com in formats for Excel™, Minitab™, JMP, SPSS, and TI-83/84™ Plus calculators. (Because TI-83/84 Plus calculators have limited memory, several larger data sets have been truncated for TI users, and answers have been annotated when appropriate.)

Readability

Great care, enthusiasm, and passion have been devoted to creating a book that is readable, understandable, interesting, and relevant. Students pursuing any major are sure to find applications related to their future work.

Website

This textbook is supported by www.pearsonhighered.com/triola and the author's website www.TriolaStats.com which are continually updated to provide the latest digital resources for the *Triola Statistics Series,* including:

- Statdisk: A free and robust browser-based statistical program designed specifically for this book. This is the only statistics textbook with dedicated and comprehensive statistics software.

- Downloadable Appendix B data sets in a variety of technology formats.

- Downloadable textbook supplements including Section 1-4 *Ethics in Statistics,* Section 6-6 *Normal as Approximation to Binomial, Glossary of Statistical Terms,* and *Formulas and Tables.*

- Interactive flow charts for key statistical procedures.

- Online instructional videos created specifically for the 14th Edition that provide step-by-step technology instructions.

- Contact link providing one-click access for instructors and students to contact the author, Marty Triola, with questions and comments.

Chapter Features

Chapter Opening Features

- Chapters begin with a **Chapter Problem** that uses real data and motivates the chapter material.

- **Chapter Objectives** provide a summary of key learning goals for each section in the chapter.

Exercises Many exercises require the *interpretation* of results. Great care has been taken to ensure their usefulness, relevance, and accuracy. Exercises are arranged in order of increasing difficulty and exercises are also divided into two groups: (1) *Basic Skills and Concepts* and (2) *Beyond the Basics. Beyond the Basics* exercises address more difficult concepts or require a stronger mathematical background. In a few cases, these exercises introduce a new concept.

End-of-Chapter Features

- *Chapter Quick Quiz* provides 10 review questions that require brief answers.
- *Review Exercises* offer practice on the chapter concepts and procedures.
- *Cumulative Review Exercises* reinforce earlier material.
- *Technology Project* provides an activity that can be used with a variety of technologies.
- *Big (or Very Large) Data Projects* encourage use of large data sets.
- *From Data to Decision* is a capstone problem that requires critical thinking and writing.
- *Cooperative Group Activities* encourage active learning in groups.

Other Features

Margin Essays There are 133 margin essays designed to highlight real-world topics and foster student interest. 36 of them are new to this edition. There are also many *Go Figure* items that briefly describe interesting numbers or statistics.

Flowcharts The text includes flowcharts that simplify and clarify more complex concepts and procedures. Animated versions of the text's flowcharts are available within MyLab Statistics.

Formulas and Tables This summary of key formulas, organized by chapter, gives students a quick reference for studying, or can be printed for use when taking tests (if allowed by the instructor). It also includes the most commonly used tables. This is available for download in MyLab Statistics, via pearson.com/math-stats-resources, or TriolaStats.com.

Technology Integration

As in the preceding edition, there are many displays of screens from technology throughout the book, and some exercises are based on displayed results from technology. Where appropriate, sections end with a **Tech Center** subsection that includes detailed instructions for Statdisk, Minitab®, Excel®, StatCrunch, *R* (new to this edition), or a TI-83/84 Plus® calculator. (Throughout this text, "TI-83/84 Plus" is used to identify a TI-83 Plus or TI-84 Plus calculator). The Tech Centers also include references to new technology-specific instructional videos. The end-of-chapter features include a *Technology Project*.

The Statdisk statistical software package is designed specifically for this textbook and contains all Appendix B data sets. Statdisk is free to users of this book and it can be accessed at www.Statdisk.com.

Changes to This 14th Edition

New Features

New Content: This 14th edition includes an abundance of new exercises, new examples, and Chapter Problems, as summarized in the following table.

	Number	New to 14th Edition	Use Real Data
Exercises	1822	64% (1172)	93% (1703)
Examples	213	58% (124)	94% (201)
Chapter Problems	14	100% (14)	100% (14)

New Data Sets: This book includes a rich data set library in Appendix B so that professors and students have ready access to real and interesting data. Appendix B has been expanded from 32 data sets to 46 data sets. Twenty of those data sets are new, including *Internet Traffic, Queues, Car Data, Commute Times, Candies, Taxis,* and *Disney World Wait Times.*

Larger Data Sets: The largest data set in the previous edition had 600 cases. The data set library in this 14th edition includes data sets with 6068, 3982, 5755, 8959, and 1000 cases. In addition, there are *big* data sets with 465,506 cases and 31,784 cases. Working with such larger data sets is essential to students progressing into the age of big data and data science.

New Types of Exercises: To foster the development of critical thinking, the Cumulative Review Exercises near the end of Chapters 9, 10, and 11 consist of open-ended questions in which students are presented with a data set, and they are asked to pose a key question relevant to the data, identify a procedure for addressing that question, then analyze the data to form a conclusion.

New Margin Essays: This 14th edition of *Elementary Statistics* includes 36 new margin essays.

Big (or Very Large) Data Projects: New to this edition, these projects are located near the end of each chapter and ask students to think critically while using large data sets.

New Chapter Problem Icon: Examples that relate to the Chapter Problem are now highlighted with this icon (CP) to show how different statistical concepts and procedures can be applied to the real-world issue highlighted in the chapter.

Organization Changes

New Technology: The previous edition of *Elementary Statistics* introduced the resampling method of *bootstrapping* in Section 7-4. This 14th edition of *Elementary Statistics* includes these methods of resampling using bootstrapping and randomization:

> **Bootstrap One Proportion**
> **Bootstrap Two Proportions**
> **Bootstrap One Mean**
> **Bootstrap Two Means**
> **Bootstrap Matched Pairs**
> --
> **Randomization One Proportion**
> **Randomization Two Proportions**
> **Randomization One Mean**
> **Randomization Two Means**
> **Randomization Matched Pairs**
> **Randomization Correlation**

New Section 4-5: Simulations for Hypothesis Tests

New Resampling Methods: Resampling methods are new to Sections 8-2, 8-3, 8-4, 8-5, 9-5, and 10-1.

New Section 8-5: Resampling: Using Technology for Hypothesis Testing

New Section 9-5: Resampling: Using Technology for Inferences

New Subsection 10-1, Part 3: Randomization Test (for Correlation)

New Chapter 15: Holistic Statistics

Removed Section: *The content of Section 6-6 (Normal as Approximation to Binomial) has been removed from the text and is now available for download (MyLab Statistics, pearson.com/math-stats-resources, or TriolaStats.com).*

Removed Section: *Ethics in Statistics has been moved from Chapter 15 to Section 1-4, and is available for download (MyLab Statistics, pearson.com/math-stats-resources, or TriolaStats.com).*

Technology Changes

New to Statdisk: The previous version of Statdisk for *Elementary Statistics* included bootstrap resampling, but the new version of Statdisk for the 14th edition also includes all of the bootstrapping and randomization methods listed above under *"New Technology."*

Statdisk Online: Statdisk is now a browser-based program that can be used on any device with a modern web browser, including laptops (Windows, macOS), Chromebooks, tablets and smartphones. Statdisk Online includes all of the statistical functions from earlier versions of Statdisk and is continually adding new functions and features.

New Technology: Where it is appropriate, the end-of-section *Tech Centers* include *R* as an additional technology. (The technologies of Statdisk, Excel, StatCrunch, Minitab, and TI-83/84 Plus calculators continue to be included in the Tech Centers.)

Flexible Syllabus

This book's organization reflects the preferences of most statistics instructors, but there are two common variations:

- ***Early Coverage of Correlation and Regression:*** Some instructors prefer to cover the basics of correlation and regression early in the course. Section 2-4 includes basic concepts of scatterplots, correlation, and regression without the use of formulas and greater depth found in Sections 10-1 (*Correlation*) and 10-2 (*Regression*).

- ***Minimum Probability:*** Some instructors prefer extensive coverage of probability, while others prefer to include only basic concepts. Instructors preferring minimum coverage can include Section 4-1 while skipping the remaining sections of Chapter 4, as they are not essential for the chapters that follow. Many instructors prefer to cover the fundamentals of probability along with the basics of the addition rule and multiplication rule (Section 4-2).

GAISE This book reflects recommendations from the American Statistical Association and its *Guidelines for Assessment and Instruction in Statistics Education* (GAISE). Those guidelines suggest the following objectives and strategies.

1. ***Emphasize statistical literacy and develop statistical thinking:*** Each section exercise set begins with *Statistical Literacy and Critical Thinking* exercises. Many of the book's exercises are designed to encourage statistical thinking rather than the blind use of mechanical procedures.

2. ***Use real data:*** 94% of the examples and 93% of the exercises use real data.

3. ***Stress conceptual understanding rather than mere knowledge of procedures:*** Instead of seeking simple numerical answers, most exercises and examples involve conceptual understanding through questions that encourage practical interpretations of results. Also, each chapter includes a *From Data to Decision* project.

4. ***Foster active learning in the classroom:*** Each chapter ends with several *Cooperative Group Activities*.

5. *Use technology for developing conceptual understanding and analyzing data:* Computer software displays are included throughout the book. Special *Tech Center* subsections include instruction for using the software. Each chapter includes a *Technology Project*. When there are discrepancies between answers based on tables and answers based on technology, Appendix D provides *both* answers. The website www.TriolaStats.com includes free text-specific software (Statdisk), data sets formatted for several different technologies, and instructional videos for technologies. MyLab Statistics also includes support videos for different statistical software applications.

6. *Use assessments to improve and evaluate student learning:* Assessment tools include an abundance of section exercises, *Chapter Quick Quizzes*, *Chapter Review Exercises*, *Cumulative Review Exercises*, *Technology Projects*, *Big (or Very Large) Data Projects*, *From Data to Decision* projects, and *Cooperative Group Activities.*

Acknowledgments

I would like to thank the thousands of statistics professors and students who have contributed to the success of this book. I thank the reviewers for their suggestions for this fourteenth edition: Mary Kay Abbey, Vance Granville Community College; Kristin Cook, College of Western Idaho; Celia Cruz, Lehman College of CUNY; Don Davis, Lakeland Community College; Jean Ellefson, Alfred University; Matthew Harris, Ozarks Tech Community College; Stephen Krizan, Sait Polytechnic; Adam Littig, Los Angeles Valley College; Dr. Rick Silvey, University of Saint Mary – Leavenworth; Sasha Verkhovtseva, Anoka Ramsey Community College; William Wade, Seminole Community College. Special thanks to Laura Iossi of Broward College for her contributions to the Triola Statistics Series.

Other recent reviewers have included Raid W. Amin, University of West Florida; Robert Black, United States Air Force Academy; James Bryan, Merced College; Donald Burd, Monroe College; Keith Carroll, Benedictine University; Monte Cheney, Central Oregon Community College; Christopher Donnelly, Macomb Community College; Billy Edwards, University of Tennessee—Chattanooga; Marcos Enriquez, Moorpark College; Angela Everett, Chattanooga State Technical Community College; Joe Franko, Mount San Antonio College; Rob Fusco, Broward College; Sanford Geraci, Broward College; Eric Gorenstein, Bunker Hill Community College; Rhonda Hatcher, Texas Christian University; Laura Heath, Palm Beach State College; Richard Herbst, Montgomery County Community College; Richard Hertz; Diane Hollister, Reading Area Community College; Michael Huber, George Jahn, Palm Beach State College; Gary King, Ozarks Technical Community College; Kate Kozak, Coconino Community College; Dan Kumpf, Ventura College; Ladorian Latin, Franklin University; Mickey Levendusky, Pima County Community College; Mitch Levy, Broward College; Tristan Londre, Blue River Community College; Alma Lopez, South Plains College; Kim McHale, Heartland Community College; Carla Monticelli, Camden County Community College; Ken Mulzet, Florida State College at Jacksonville; Julia Norton, California State University Hayward; Michael Oriolo, Herkimer Community College; Jeanne Osborne, Middlesex Community College; Joseph Pick, Palm Beach State College; Ali Saadat, University of California—Riverside; Radha Sankaran, Passaic County Community College; Steve Schwager, Cornell University; Pradipta Seal, Boston University; Kelly Smitch, Brevard College; Sandra Spain, Thomas Nelson Community College; Ellen G. Stutes, Louisiana State University, Eunice; Sharon Testone, Onondaga Community College; Chris Vertullo, Marist College; Dave Wallach, University of Findlay; Cheng Wang, Nova Southeastern University; Barbara Ward,

Belmont University; Richard Weil, Brown College; Lisa Whitaker, Keiser University; Gail Wiltse, St. John River Community College; Claire Wladis, Borough of Manhattan Community College; Rick Woodmansee, Sacramento City College; Yong Zeng, University of Missouri at Kansas City; Jim Zimmer, Chattanooga State Technical Community College; Cathleen Zucco-Teveloff, Rowan University; Mark Z. Zuiker, Minnesota State University, Mankato.

This fourteenth edition of *Elementary Statistics* is truly a team effort, and I consider myself fortunate to work with the dedication and commitment of the Pearson team. I thank Suzy Bainbridge, Amanda Brands, Deirdre Lynch, Peggy McMahon, Vicki Dreyfus, Jean Choe, Robert Carroll, Joe Vetere, and Rose Kernan of RPK Editorial Services.

I thank the following for their help in checking the accuracy of text and answers in this 14th edition: Paul Lorczak, and Dirk Tempelaar.

I extend special thanks to Marc Triola, M.D., New York University School of Medicine, for his outstanding work on creating the new Statdisk Online software. I thank Scott Triola for his very extensive help throughout the entire production process for this 14th edition.

M.F.T.
Madison, Connecticut
September 2020

Resources for Success

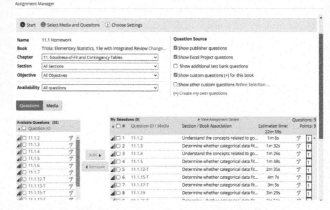

MyLab Statistics is available to accompany Pearson's market-leading text options, including Elementary Statistics, 14e by Mario F. Triola (access code required).

MyLab™ is the teaching and learning platform that empowers you to reach every student. MyLab Statistics combines trusted author content—including full eText and assessment with immediate feedback—with digital tools and a flexible platform to personalize the learning experience and improve results for each student. Integrated with StatCrunch®, Pearson's web-based statistical software program, students learn the skills they need to interact with data in the real world.

Expanded objective-based exercise coverage - Exercises in MyLab Statistics are designed to reinforce and support students' understanding of key statistical topics.

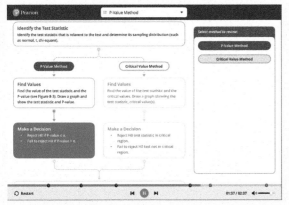

Enhanced video program to meet Introductory Statistics needs:

- **New! Animated Flow Charts -** Animated flow charts have been updated with a modern, interactive interface with assignable auto-graded assessment questions in MyLab Statistics.
- **New! Tech-Specific Video Tutorials -** These short, topical videos show how to use common statistical software to complete exercises.
- **Updated! Chapter Review Exercise Videos -** Watch the Chapter Review Exercises come to life with new review videos that help students understand key chapter concepts.

Real-World Data Examples - Help students understand how statistics applies to everyday life through the extensive current, real-world data examples and exercises provided throughout the text. MyLab Statistics allows students to easily launch data sets from their exercises to analyze real-world data.

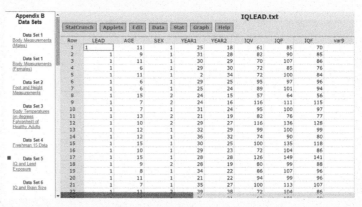

pearson.com/mylab/statistics

Resources for Success

Supplements

Student Resources

Student's Solutions Manual, by James Lapp (Colorado Mesa University), provides detailed, worked-out solutions to all odd-numbered text exercises. Available for download in MyLab Statistics.

Student Workbook for the Triola Statistics Series, by Laura Iossi (Broward College) offers additional examples, concept exercises, and vocabulary exercises for each chapter. Available for download in MyLab Statistics. Can also be purchased separately.
ISBN: 0137363435 | 9780137363438

The following technology manuals include instructions, examples from the main text, and interpretations to complement those given in the text. They are all available for download in MyLab Statistics.

Excel Student Laboratory Manual and Workbook, (Download Only) by Laurel Chiappetta (University of Pittsburgh).

Graphing Calculator Manual for the TI-83 Plus, TI-84 Plus, TI-84 Plus C and TI-84 Plus CE, (Download Only) by Kathleen McLaughlin (University of Connecticut) & Dorothy Wakefield (University of Connecticut Health Center).

Statdisk Student Laboratory Manual and Workbook (Download Only), by Mario F. Triola. Available at www.TriolaStats.com or within MyLab Statistics.

Instructor Resources

Annotated Instructor's Edition, by Mario F. Triola, contains answers to exercises in the margin, plus recommended assignments, and teaching suggestions.
(ISBN-13: 9780136803065; ISBN-10: 0136803067)

Instructor's Solutions Manual (Download Only), by James Lapp (Colorado Mesa University), contains solutions to all the exercises. These files are available to qualified instructors through Pearson Education's online catalog at www.pearsonhighered.com/irc or within MyLab Statistics.

Insider's Guide to Teaching with the Triola Statistics Series, (Download Only) by Mario F. Triola, contains sample syllabi and tips for incorporating projects, as well as lesson overviews, extra examples, minimum outcome objectives, and recommended assignments for each chapter.

TestGen® Computerized Test Bank (www.pearsoned.com/testgen), enables instructors to build, edit, print, and administer tests using a computerized bank of questions developed to cover all the objectives of the text. TestGen is algorithmically based, allowing instructors to create multiple but equivalent versions of the same question or test with the click of a button. Instructors can also modify test bank questions or add new questions. The software and testbank are available for download from Pearson Education's online catalog at www.pearsonhighered.com. Test Forms (Download Only) are also available from the online catalog.

PowerPoint® Lecture Slides: These files are available to instructors through Pearson's online catalog at www.pearsonhighered.com/irc or within MyLab Statistics.

Accessibility—Pearson works continuously to ensure our products are as accessible as possible to all students. Currently we work toward achieving WCAG 2.0 AA for our existing products (2.1 AA for future products) and Section 508 standards, as expressed in the Pearson Guidelines for Accessible Educational Web Media.

pearson.com/mylab/statistics

Get the Most Out of
MyLab Statistics®

MyLab™ is the teaching and learning platform that empowers you to reach every student. MyLab Statistics combines trusted author content — including full eText and assessment with immediate feedback — with digital tools and a flexible platform to personalize the learning experience and improve results for each student. Integrated with StatCrunch®, Pearson's web-based statistical software program, students learn the skills they need to interact with data in the real world.

Integrated Review

Integrated Review in MyLab Statistics provides embedded and personalized review of prerequisite topics within relevant chapters.

- Students begin each chapter with a premade, assignable Skills Check assignment to check each student's understanding of prerequisite skills needed to be successful in that chapter.

- For any gaps in skill that are identified, a personalized review homework is populated. Students practice on the topics they need to focus on-no more, no less.

- A suite of resources are available to help students understand the objectives they missed on the Skills Check quiz, including worksheets and videos to help remediate.

Integrated Review in the MyLab is ideal for corequisite courses, where students are enrolled in a statistics course while receiving just-in-time remediation. But it can also be used simply to get underprepared students up to speed on prerequisite skills in order to be more successful in the Statistics content.

Used by nearly one million students a year, MyLab Statistics is the world's leading online program for teaching and learning statistics.

pearson.com/mylab/statistics

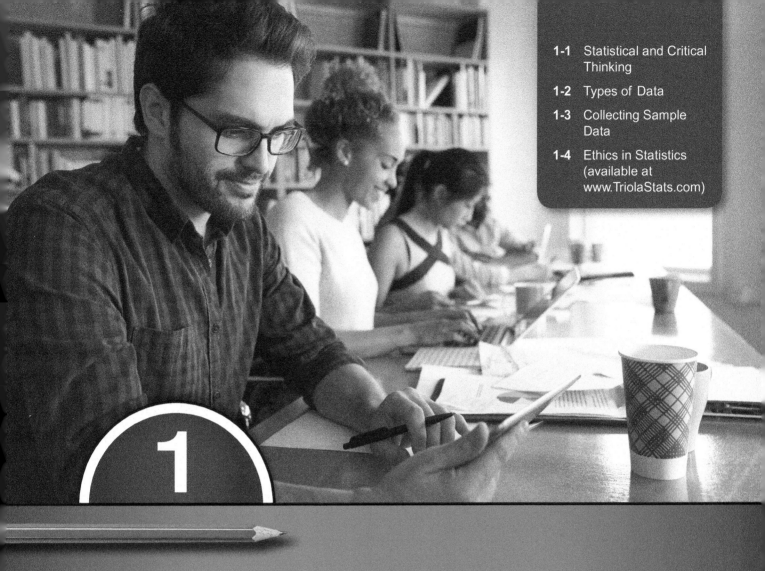

1

INTRODUCTION TO STATISTICS

CHAPTER PROBLEM — **Is YouTube Becoming a More Important Learning Tool?**

Surveys provide data that enable us to better understand the world in which we live and identify changes in the opinions, habits, and behaviors of others. Survey data guide public policy, influence business and educational practices, and affect many aspects of our daily lives. A recent Pearson survey, conducted by The Harris Poll, examined how technology has shaped students' learning habits and compared the responses from Gen-Z (ages 14–23) and millennials (ages 24–40). Among

other topics, this survey asked respondents to identify their preferred learning tools, and YouTube was identified as one of the top tools by both Gen-Z and millennials. Figure 1-1 includes a graph that depicts the percentage of Gen-Z and millennials who identified YouTube as a preferred learning tool.

Critical Thinking Figure 1-1 on the next page makes it appear that Gen-Z is more than twice as likely to prefer YouTube as a learning tool compared to millennials. A quick glance might also

1

give the impression that most millennials *do not* prefer YouTube as a learning tool. But wait! Look carefully at Figure 1-1 and see that the vertical axis has a scale that ranges from 52% to 60%. The graph in Figure 1-1 is *misleading* because it uses the scale of 52% to 60% instead of a scale that begins with 0%. As a result, the difference between the two bars is visually exaggerated in Figure 1-1. In Figure 1-2, the same data are shown in the graph, but we use a scale that begins with 0%. Figure 1-2 shows that the Gen-Z prefers YouTube as a learning tool only *slightly* more than millennials (actually 4% more to be exact). Figure 1-1 is misleading, whereas Figure 1-2 depicts the data fairly.

We might now consider how these survey data can be used to improve the learning experience for *Elementary Statistics*! Figure 1-2 shows that the majority of both Gen-Z and millennials prefer YouTube as a learning tool and this percentage has increased from one generation to the next. Knowing that YouTube and other videos are increasingly preferred learning tools, the author has created a YouTube channel with custom instructional videos to support this textbook (visit www.TriolaStats.com for the link). In addition, MyLab includes additional instructional videos and interactive content to support students.

The flaw shown in Figure 1-1 is among the most commonly used tactics to present misleading arguments, so it is especially important to recognize. Here are brief descriptions of common flaws:

Flaw 1: Misleading Graphs

The bar chart in Figure 1-1 is very deceptive. By using a vertical scale that does not start at zero, the difference between the two percentages is grossly exaggerated. Deceptive graphs are discussed in more detail in Section 2-3.

Flaw 2: Bad Sampling Method

Figure 1-1 and Figure 1-2 are based on data from the Pearson survey cited earlier. This study included 2587 respondents from a nationally representative sample, and the sampling method appears to be sound based on the description provided in the report. However, many other surveys obtain participants by using methods that are inappropriate and may lead to biased results, such as these:

- **Voluntary response sample:** Participants decide themselves whether to participate. *Example:* A survey question is posted on a website, and then Internet users decide whether to respond. With a voluntary response sample, it often happens

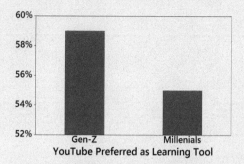

FIGURE 1-1   YouTube as a Preferred Learning Tool

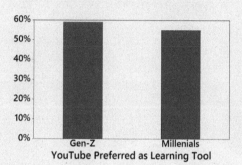

FIGURE 1-2   Same as Figure 1-1 but with scale beginning with 0%

that those with a strong interest in the topic are more likely to participate, so the results are very questionable.

- **Convenience sample:** Participants are selected because they are easy to reach and are readily available. *Example:* A student conducts a survey of fellow students relaxing in the cafeteria.

When using sample data to learn something about a population, it is *extremely* important to obtain sample data that are representative of the population from which the data are drawn. As we proceed through this chapter and discuss types of data and sampling methods, we should focus on these key concepts:

- **Sample data must be collected in an appropriate way, such as through a process of *random* selection.**

- **If sample data are not collected in an appropriate way, the data may be so completely useless that no amount of statistical torturing can salvage them.**

It is all too easy to analyze sample data without thinking critically about how the data were collected. We could then develop conclusions that are fundamentally wrong and misleading. Instead, we should develop skills in statistical thinking and critical thinking so that we can distinguish between collections of sample data that are good and those that are seriously flawed.

CHAPTER OBJECTIVES

Here is the single most important concept presented in this chapter: When using methods of statistics with sample data to form conclusions about a population, it is absolutely essential to collect sample data in a way that is appropriate. Here are the chapter objectives:

1-1 Statistical and Critical Thinking

- Analyze sample data relative to context, source, and sampling method.
- Understand the difference between *statistical significance* and *practical significance*.
- Define and identify a *voluntary response sample* and know that statistical conclusions based on data from such a sample are generally not valid.

1-2 Types of Data

- Distinguish between a *parameter* and a *statistic.*
- Distinguish between *quantitative data* and *categorical* (or *qualitative* or *attribute*) *data*.
- Distinguish between *discrete* data and *continuous* data.
- Determine whether basic statistical calculations are appropriate for a particular data set.

1-3 Collecting Sample Data

- Define and identify a *simple random sample.*
- Understand the importance of sound sampling methods and the importance of good design of experiments.

1-4 Ethics in Statistics (available at www.TriolaStats.com)

- Analyze ethical issues in statistics, including those related to data collection, analysis, and reporting.

1-1   Statistical and Critical Thinking

Key Concept In this section we begin with a few very basic definitions, and then we consider an *overview* of the process involved in conducting a statistical study. This process consists of "prepare, analyze, and conclude." "Preparation" involves consideration of the *context*, the *source* of data, and *sampling method*. In future chapters we construct suitable graphs, explore the data, and execute computations required for the statistical method being used. In future chapters we also form conclusions by determining whether results have statistical significance and practical significance.

Statistical thinking involves critical thinking and the ability to make sense of results. Statistical thinking demands so much more than the ability to execute complicated calculations. Through numerous examples, exercises, and discussions, this text will help you develop the statistical thinking skills that are so important in today's world.

We begin with some very basic definitions.

DEFINITIONS

Data are collections of observations, such as measurements, genders, or survey responses. (A single data value is called a *datum*, a term rarely used. The term "data" is plural, so it is correct to say "data *are* . . ." not "data *is* . . .")

Statistics is the science of planning studies and experiments; obtaining data; and organizing, summarizing, presenting, analyzing, and interpreting those data and then drawing conclusions based on them.

A **population** is the complete collection of *all* measurements or data that are being considered.

A **census** is the collection of data from *every* member of the population.

A **sample** is a *subcollection* of members selected from a population.

Because populations are often very large, a common objective of the use of statistics is to obtain data from a sample and then use those data to form a conclusion about the population.

EXAMPLE 1 **Watch What You Post Online**

In a survey of 410 human resource professionals, 148 of them said that job candidates were disqualified because of information found on social media postings (based on data from *The Society for Human Resource Management*). In this case, the population and sample are as follows:

> **Population:** All human resource professionals
> **Sample:** The 410 human resource professionals who were surveyed

The objective is to use the sample as a basis for drawing a conclusion about the population of all human resource professionals, and methods of statistics are helpful in drawing such conclusions.

 YOUR TURN. Do part (a) of Exercise 2 "Reported Versus Measured."

We now proceed to consider the process involved in a statistical study. See Figure 1-3 for a summary of this process and note that the focus is on critical thinking, not mathematical calculations. Thanks to wonderful developments in technology, we have powerful tools that effectively do the number crunching so that we can focus on understanding and interpreting results.

Prepare

Context Figure 1-3 suggests that we begin our preparation by considering the *context* of the data, so let's start with context by considering the data in Table 1-1. Table 1-1 includes shoe print lengths and heights of eight males. Forensic scientists measure shoe print lengths at burglary scenes and other crime scenes in order to estimate the height of the criminal. The format of Table 1-1 suggests the following goal: Determine whether there is a *relationship* between shoe print lengths and heights of males. This goal suggests a reasonable hypothesis: Males with larger shoe print lengths tend to be taller. (We are using data for males only because 84% of burglaries are committed by males.)

TABLE 1-1 Shoe Print Lengths and Heights of Men

Shoe Print (cm)	27.6	29.7	29.7	31.0	31.3	31.4	31.8	34.5
Height (cm)	172.7	175.3	177.8	175.3	180.3	182.3	177.8	193.7

Source of the Data The second step in our preparation is to consider the source (as indicated in Figure 1-3). The data in Table 1-1 are from Data Set 9 "Foot and Height" in Appendix B, where the source is identified. The source certainly appears to be reputable.

Sampling Method Figure 1-3 suggests that we conclude our preparation by considering the sampling method. For the data in Table 1-1, individuals were randomly selected, so the sampling method appears to be sound.

Sampling methods and the use of random selection will be discussed in Section 1-3, but for now, we stress that a sound sampling method is absolutely essential for good results in a statistical study. It is generally a bad practice to use voluntary response (or self-selected) samples, even though their use is common.

Prepare

1. **Context**
   - What do the data represent?
   - What is the goal of study?
2. **Source of the Data**
   - Are the data from a source with a special interest so that there is pressure to obtain results that are favorable to the source?
3. **Sampling Method**
   - Were the data collected in a way that is unbiased, or were the data collected in a way that is biased (such as a procedure in which respondents volunteer to participate)?

↓

Analyze

1. **Graph the Data**
2. **Explore the Data**
   - Are there any outliers (numbers very far away from almost all of the other data)?
   - What important statistics summarize the data (such as the mean and standard deviation described in Chapter 3)?
   - How are the data distributed?
   - Are there missing data?
   - Did many selected subjects refuse to respond?
3. **Apply Statistical Methods**
   - Use technology to obtain results.

↓

Conclude

1. **Significance**
   - Do the results have statistical significance?
   - Do the results have practical significance?

FIGURE 1-3   Statistical and Critical Thinking

Survivorship Bias

In World War II, statistician Abraham Wald saved many lives with his work on the Applied Mathematics Panel. Military leaders asked the panel how they could improve the chances of aircraft bombers returning after missions. They wanted to add some armor for protection, and they recorded locations on the bombers where damaging holes were found. They reasoned that armor should be placed in locations with the most holes, but Wald said that strategy would be a big mistake. He said that armor should be placed where returning bombers were *not* damaged. His reasoning was this: The bombers that made it back with damage were *survivors*, so the damage they suffered could be survived. Locations on the aircraft that were not damaged were the most vulnerable, and aircraft suffering damage in those vulnerable areas were the ones that did not make it back. The military leaders would have made a big mistake with survivorship bias by studying the planes that survived instead of thinking about the planes that did not survive.

Origin of "Statistics"

The word *statistics* is derived from the Latin word *status* (meaning "state"). Early uses of statistics involved compilations of data and graphs describing various aspects of a state or country. In 1662, John Graunt published statistical information about births and deaths. Graunt's work was followed by studies of mortality and disease rates, population sizes, incomes, and unemployment rates. Households, governments, and businesses rely heavily on statistical data for guidance. For example, unemployment rates, inflation rates, consumer indexes, and birth and death rates are carefully compiled on a regular basis, and the resulting data are used by business leaders to make decisions affecting future hiring, production levels, and expansion into new markets.

> **DEFINITION**
>
> A **voluntary response sample** (or **self-selected sample**) is one in which the respondents themselves decide whether to be included.

The following types of polls are common examples of voluntary response samples. By their very nature, all are seriously flawed because we should not make conclusions about a population on the basis of samples with a strong possibility of bias.

- Internet polls, in which people online decide whether to respond
- Mail-in polls, in which people decide whether to reply
- Telephone call-in polls, in which newspaper, radio, or television announcements ask that you voluntarily call a special number to register your opinion

See the following Example 2.

EXAMPLE 2 **Voluntary Response Sample**

The ABC television show *Nightline* asked viewers to call with their opinion about whether the United Nations headquarters should remain in the United States. Viewers then decided themselves whether to call with their opinions, and 67% of 186,000 respondents said that the United Nations should be moved out of the United States. In a separate and independent survey, 500 respondents were randomly selected and surveyed, and 38% of this group wanted the United Nations to move out of the United States. The two polls produced dramatically different results. Even though the *Nightline* poll involved 186,000 volunteer respondents, the much smaller poll of 500 randomly selected respondents is more likely to provide better results because of the far superior sampling method.

YOUR TURN. Do Exercise 1 "Computer Virus."

Analyze

Figure 1-3 indicates that after completing our preparation by considering the context, source, and sampling method, we begin to *analyze* the data.

Graph and Explore An analysis should begin with appropriate graphs and explorations of the data. Graphs are discussed in Chapter 2, and important statistics are discussed in Chapter 3.

Apply Statistical Methods Later chapters describe important statistical methods, but application of these methods is often made easy with technology (calculators and/or statistical software packages). A good statistical analysis does not require strong computational skills. A good statistical analysis does require using common sense and paying careful attention to sound statistical methods.

Conclude

Figure 1-3 shows that the final step in our statistical process involves conclusions, and we should develop an ability to distinguish between *statistical significance* and *practical significance*.

Statistical Significance *Statistical significance* is achieved in a study when we get a result that is very unlikely to occur by chance. A common criterion has been this: We have statistical significance if the likelihood of an event occurring by chance is 5% or less.

- Getting 98 girls in 100 random births *is* statistically significant because such an extreme outcome is not likely to result from random chance.

- Getting 52 girls in 100 births *is not* statistically significant because that event could easily occur with random chance.

> **CAUTION** An outcome can be statistically significant, and it may or may not be *important*. Don't associate statistical significance with importance.

Practical Significance It is possible that some treatment or finding is effective, but common sense might suggest that the treatment or finding does not make enough of a difference to justify its use or to be practical, as illustrated in Example 3.

EXAMPLE 3 **Statistical Significance Versus Practical Significance**

In a trial of weight loss programs, 21 subjects on the Atkins program lost an average (mean) of 2.1 kg (or 4.6 lb) after one year (based on data from "Comparison of the Atkins, Ornish, Weight Watchers, and Zone Diets for Weight Loss and Heart Disease Reduction," by Dansinger et al., *Journal of the American Medical Association*, Volume 93, Number 1). The results show that this loss is *statistically significant* and is not likely to occur by chance. However, many dieters believe that after following this diet for a year, a loss of only 2.1 kg is not worth the time, cost, and effort so that for these people, this diet does not have *practical significance*.

 **YOUR TURN.** Do Exercise 13 "Diet and Exercise Program."

Example 3 includes a small sample of only 21 subjects, but with very large data sets (e.g., "big data"), statistically significant differences can often be found with very small differences. We should be careful to avoid the mistake of thinking that those small differences have practical significance.

Analyzing Data: Potential Pitfalls

Here are a few more items that could cause problems when analyzing data.

Misleading Conclusions When forming a conclusion based on a statistical analysis, we should make statements that are clear even to those who have no understanding of statistics and its terminology. We should carefully avoid making statements not justified by the statistical analysis. For example, later in this book we introduce the concept of a correlation, or association between two variables, such as shoe print lengths and heights of males. A statistical analysis might justify the statement that there is a correlation between shoe print length and height, but it would not justify a statement that an increase in the shoe print length *causes* an increase in height. Such a statement about causality can be justified by physical evidence, not by statistical analysis.

Correlation does not imply causation.

Sample Data *Reported* Instead of Measured When collecting data from people, it is better to take measurements yourself instead of asking subjects to *report* results. Ask people what they weigh and you are likely to get their *desired* weights, not their

actual weights. People tend to round, usually down, sometimes *way* down. When asked, someone with a weight of 187 lb might respond that he or she weighs 160 lb. Accurate weights are collected by using a scale to *measure* weights, not by asking people what they weigh.

Loaded Questions If survey questions are not worded carefully, the results of a study can be misleading. Survey questions can be "loaded," or intentionally worded to elicit a desired response. Here are the actual rates of "yes" responses for the two different wordings of a question:

> 97% yes: "Should the President have the line item veto to eliminate waste?"

> 57% yes: "Should the President have the line item veto, or not?"

Order of Questions Sometimes survey questions are unintentionally loaded by such factors as the order of the items being considered. See the following two questions from a poll conducted in Germany, along with the very different response rates:

> "Would you say that traffic contributes more or less to air pollution than industry?" (45% blamed traffic; 27% blamed industry.)

> "Would you say that industry contributes more or less to air pollution than traffic?" (24% blamed traffic; 57% blamed industry.)

In addition to the order of items within a question, as illustrated above, the order of separate questions could also affect responses.

Nonresponse A *nonresponse* occurs when someone either refuses to respond to a survey question or is unavailable. When people are asked survey questions, some firmly refuse to answer. The refusal rate has been growing in recent years, partly because many persistent telemarketers try to sell goods or services by beginning with a sales pitch that initially sounds as though it is part of an opinion poll. (This "selling under the guise" of a poll is called *sugging*.) In *Lies, Damn Lies, and Statistics*, author Michael Wheeler makes this very important observation:

> **People who refuse to talk to pollsters are likely to be different from those who do not. Some may be fearful of strangers and others jealous of their privacy, but their refusal to talk demonstrates that their view of the world around them is markedly different from that of those people who will let poll-takers into their homes.**

Low Response Rates Related to the preceding item of nonresponses is the issue of low response rates. If a survey has a low response rate, the reliability of the results decreases. In addition to having a smaller sample size, there is an increased likelihood of having a bias among those who do respond. Some steps to help prevent a low response rate: (1) A survey should present an engaging argument for its importance; (2) a survey should not be very time consuming; (3) it is helpful to provide a reward for completing a survey, such as cash or a chance to win a prize. There are not definitive guidelines for acceptable response rates. A very good response rate is 80% or higher. Some suggest that response rates of at least 40% are acceptable. Pew Research Center reports that its typical telephone surveys have a response rate around 9%, but their surveys tend to be quite good. Sections 7-1, 7-2, and 7-3 include procedures for determining the sample size needed to estimate characteristics (proportion, mean, standard deviation) of a population, and those methods require sound sampling methods.

Percentages Some studies cite misleading or unclear percentages. Note that 100% of some quantity is *all* of it, but if there are references made to percentages that exceed 100%, such references are often not justified. If an advertiser claims that your utility costs can be reduced by 200%, that claim is misleading. Eliminating all utility costs would be a reduction of 100%, and a reduction of 200% doesn't make sense.

The following list identifies some key principles to apply when dealing with percentages. These principles all use the basic concept that % or "percent" really means "divided by 100." The first principle that follows is used often in this book.

Percentage of: To find a percentage of an amount, replace the % symbol with division by 100, and then interpret "of" to be multiplication. This example shows that 6% of 1200 is 72:

$$6\% \text{ of } 1200 \text{ responses} = \frac{6}{100} \times 1200 = 72$$

Decimal → Percentage: To convert from a decimal to a percentage, multiply by 100%. This example shows that 0.25 is equivalent to 25%:

$$0.25 \rightarrow 0.25 \times 100\% = 25\%$$

Fraction → Percentage: *To convert from a fraction to a percentage,* divide the denominator into the numerator to get an equivalent decimal number; then multiply by 100%. This example shows that the fraction $3/4$ is equivalent to 75%:

$$\frac{3}{4} = 0.75 \rightarrow 0.75 \times 100\% = 75\%$$

Percentage → Decimal: To convert from a percentage to a decimal number, replace the % symbol with division by 100. This example shows that 85% is equivalent to 0.85:

$$85\% = \frac{85}{100} = 0.85$$

1-1 Basic Skills and Concepts

Statistical Literacy and Critical Thinking

1. Computer Virus In an AOL survey of Internet users, this question was posted online: "Have you ever been hit by a computer virus?" Among the 170,063 responses, 63% answered "yes." What term is used to describe this type of survey in which the people surveyed consist of those who chose to respond? What is wrong with this type of sampling method?

2. Reported Versus Measured In a survey of 1046 adults conducted by Bradley Corporation, subjects were asked how often they wash their hands when using a public restroom, and 70% of the respondents said "always."

a. Identify the sample and the population.

b. Why would better results be obtained by observing the hand washing instead of asking about it?

3. Statistical Significance Versus Practical Significance When testing a new treatment, what is the difference between statistical significance and practical significance? Can a treatment have statistical significance, but not practical significance?

4. Correlation One study showed that for a recent period of 10 years, there was a strong correlation (or association) between the per capita consumption of margarine and the divorce rate in Maine (based on data from National Vital Statistics reports and the U.S. Department of Agriculture). Does this imply that increasing margarine consumption is the cause of an increase in the divorce rate in Maine? Why or why not?

Consider the Source.   *In Exercises 5–8, determine whether the given source has the potential to create a bias in a statistical study.*

5. AAA The American Automobile Association (AAA) is a not-for-profit federation of motor clubs that provides automotive and travel services. AAA conducts a survey of its members about their use of public transportation versus private automobiles.

6. Body Data Data Set 1 "Body Data" in Appendix B includes pulse rates of subjects, and those pulse rates were recorded by examiners as part of a study conducted by the National Center for Health Statistics.

7. Brain Size A data set in Appendix B includes brain volumes from 10 pairs of monozygotic (identical) twins. The data were collected by researchers at Harvard University, Massachusetts General Hospital, Dartmouth College, and the University of California at Davis.

8. Chocolate An article in *Journal of Nutrition* (Vol. 130, No. 8) noted that chocolate is rich in flavonoids. The article notes "regular consumption of foods rich in flavonoids may reduce the risk of coronary heart disease." The study received funding from Mars, Inc., the candy company, and the Chocolate Manufacturers Association.

Sampling Method.   *In Exercises 9–12, determine whether the sampling method appears to be sound or is flawed.*

9. Nuclear Power Plants In a survey of 1368 subjects, the following question was posted on the *USA Today* website: "In your view, are nuclear plants safe?" The survey subjects were Internet users who chose to respond to the question posted on the electronic edition of *USA Today*.

10. Clinical Trials Researchers at Yale University conduct a wide variety of clinical trials by using subjects who volunteer after reading advertisements soliciting paid volunteers.

11. Sharing Passwords In a Password Boss survey of 2030 randomly selected adults, 39% said that they never share passwords with anyone.

12. Social Media Usage In a survey of social media usage, the Pew Research Center randomly selected 2002 adults in the United States.

Statistical Significance and Practical Significance.   *In Exercises 13–20, determine whether the results appear to have statistical significance, and also determine whether the results appear to have practical significance.*

13. Diet and Exercise Program In a study of the Ornish weight loss program, 40 subjects lost a mean of 3.3 lb after 12 months (based on data from "Comparison of the Atkins, Ornish, Weight Watchers, and Zone Diets for Weight Loss and Heart Disease Risk Reduction," by Dansinger et al., *Journal of the American Medical Association*, Vol. 293, No. 1). Methods of statistics can be used to show that if this diet had no effect, the likelihood of getting these results is roughly 3 chances in 1000.

14. Surgery versus Splints A study compared surgery and splinting for subjects suffering from carpal tunnel syndrome. It was found that among 73 patients treated with surgery, there was a 92% success rate. Among 83 patients treated with splints, there was a 72% success rate. Calculations using those results showed that if there really is no difference in success rates between surgery and splints, then there is about one chance in a thousand of getting success rates like the ones obtained in this study.

15. Mendel's Genetics Experiments One of Gregor Mendel's famous hybridization experiments with peas yielded 580 offspring with 152 of those peas (or 26%) having yellow pods. According to Mendel's theory, 25% of the offspring peas should have yellow pods.

16. IQ Scores Most people have IQ scores between 70 and 130. For $39.99, you can purchase a PC or Mac program from HighIQPro that is claimed to increase your IQ score by 10 to 20 points. The program claims to be "the only proven IQ increasing software in the brain training market," but the author of your text could find no substantial data supporting that claim, so let's suppose that these results were obtained: In a study of 12 subjects using the program, the average increase in IQ score is 3 IQ points. There is a 25% chance of getting such results if the program has no effect.

17. Election Fraud The County Clerk in Essex County, New Jersey, was responsible for randomly assigning the order in which candidates' names appeared on a recent election ballot. Among 41 different ballots, a Democrat was placed on the first line 40 times, and a Republican was placed on the first line once.

18. Football Overtime Games In "The Overtime Rule in the National Football League: Fair or Unfair?" by Gorgievski et al., *MathAMATYC Educator*, Vol. 2, No. 1, the authors report that among 414 football games won in overtime (prior to the overtime rule change in 2012), 235 were won by the team that won the coin toss at the beginning of overtime. If winning the coin toss does not provide an advantage, there is a 0.3% chance of getting such results.

19. Bias in Jury Selection In the case of *Casteneda v. Partida*, it was found that during a period of 11 years in Hidalgo County, Texas, 870 people were selected for grand jury duty, and 39% of them were Americans of Mexican ancestry. Among the people eligible for grand jury duty, 79.1% were Americans of Mexican ancestry.

20. Misleading Survey Responses In one presidential election, voting records showed that 61% of eligible voters actually did vote. In a survey of 1002 people, 70% *said* that they voted in that election (based on data from ICR Research Group). If survey respondents answered honestly and with accurate recall, there is about a 0.0000006% chance of getting such results.

In Exercises 21–24, refer to the sample of body temperatures (degrees Fahrenheit) in the table below. (The body temperatures are from Data Set 5 in Appendix B.)

	Subject				
	1	2	3	4	5
8 AM	97.0	98.5	97.6	97.7	98.7
12 AM	97.6	97.8	98.0	98.4	98.4

21. Context of the Data Refer to the table of body temperatures. Is there some meaningful way in which each body temperature recorded at 8 AM is matched with the 12 AM temperature?

22. Source The listed body temperatures were obtained from Dr. Steven Wasserman, Dr. Philip Mackowiak, and Dr. Myron Levine, who were researchers at the University of Maryland. Is the source of the data likely to be biased?

23. Conclusion Given the body temperatures in the table, what issue can be addressed by conducting a statistical analysis of the data?

24. Conclusion If we analyze the listed body temperatures with suitable methods of statistics, we conclude that when the differences are found between the 8 AM body temperatures and the 12 AM body temperatures, there is a 64% chance that the differences can be explained by random results obtained from populations that have the same 8 AM and 12 AM body temperatures. What should we conclude about the statistical significance of those differences?

In Exercises 25–28, refer to the data in the table below. The entries are for five different years, and they consist of weights (metric tons) of lemons imported from Mexico and U.S. car crash fatality rates per 100,000 population [based on data from "The Trouble with QSAR (or How I Learned to Stop Worrying and Embrace Fallacy)" by Stephen Johnson, **Journal of Chemical Information and Modeling,** *Vol. 48, No. 1].*

Lemon Imports	230	265	358	480	530
Crash Fatality Rate	15.9	15.7	15.4	15.3	14.9

25. Context Given that the data are matched and considering the units of the data, does it make sense to use the difference between each pair of values? Why or why not?

26. Analysis Given the context of the data in the table, what issue can be addressed by conducting a statistical analysis of the measurements?

27. Source of the Data Considering the source of the data, does that source appear to be biased in some way?

28. Conclusion If we were to use the sample data and conclude that there is a correlation or association between lemon imports and crash fatality rates, does it follow that lemon imports are the cause of fatal crashes?

What's Wrong?   *In Exercises 29–36, identify what is wrong.*

29. Potatoes In a poll sponsored by the Idaho Potato Commission, 1000 adults were asked to select their favorite vegetables, and the favorite choice was potatoes, which were selected by 26% of the respondents.

30. Healthy Water In a *USA Today* online poll, 951 Internet users chose to respond, and 57% of them said that they prefer drinking bottled water instead of tap water.

31. Motorcycles and Sour Cream In recent years, there has been a strong correlation between per capita consumption of sour cream and the numbers of motorcycle riders killed in noncollision accidents. Therefore, consumption of sour cream causes motorcycle fatalities.

32. Smokers The electronic cigarette maker V2 Cigs sponsored a poll showing that 55% of smokers surveyed say that they feel ostracized "sometimes," "often," or "always."

33. Cell Phones and Pirates In recent years, the numbers of cell phones and the numbers of pirates have both increased, so there is a correlation, or association, between those two variables. Therefore, pirates cause increases in cell phones.

34. Storks and Babies In the years following the end of World War II, it was found that there was a strong correlation, or association, between the number of human births and the stork population. It therefore follows that storks cause babies.

35. Future Optimism Survey The software package StatCrunch coordinated a "Future Optimism Survey" that included this question: Do you expect to be better off than your parents were over their lifetime? StatCrunch users could choose to complete the survey and obtain results. Among 1019 StatCrunch users, 587 said that they expected to be better off than their parents.

36. Diet Research Twelve nutritionists are each paid $100,000 to try a new celebrity diet on ten of their clients and then write a report summarizing the results. Based on the sample results, it is found that the diet is effective for 118 of the 120 people.

Percentages.   *In Exercises 37–44, answer the given questions, which are related to percentages.*

37. Workplace Attire In a survey conducted by Opinion Research Corporation, 1000 adults were asked to identify "what is inappropriate in the workplace." Of the 1000 subjects, 70% said that miniskirts were not appropriate in the workplace.

a. What is 70% of 1000?

b. Among the 1000 respondents, 550 said that shorts are unacceptable in the workplace. What percentage of respondents said that shorts are unacceptable in the workplace?

38. Checking Job Applicants In a study conducted by the Society for Human Resource Management, 347 human resource professionals were surveyed. Of those surveyed, 73% said that their companies conduct criminal background checks on all job applicants.

a. What is the exact value that is 73% of the 347 survey subjects?

b. Could the result from part (a) be the actual number of survey subjects who said that their companies conduct criminal background checks on all job applicants? Why or why not?

c. What is the actual number of survey subjects who said that their company conducts criminal background checks on all job applicants?

d. Assume that 112 of the survey subjects are females. What percentage of those surveyed are females?

39. Marriage Proposals In a survey conducted by TheKnot.com, 1165 engaged or married women were asked about the importance of a bended knee when making a marriage proposal. Among the 1165 respondents, 48% said that the bended knee was essential.

a. What is the exact value that is 48% of 1165 survey respondents?

b. Could the result from part (a) be the actual number of survey subjects who said that a bended knee is essential? Why or why not?

c. What is the actual number of survey respondents saying that the bended knee is essential?

d. Among the 1165 respondents, 93 said that a bended knee is corny and outdated. What percentage of respondents said that a bended knee is corny and outdated?

40. Texting While Driving *USA Today* reported results from an Arity survey in which 2018 drivers were asked if they text while driving.

a. Among the respondents, 42% said that they text while driving. What is the exact value that is 42% of the number of respondents?

b. Could the result from part (a) be the actual number of respondents who said that they text while driving? Why or why not?

c. What is the actual number of respondents who said that they text while driving?

d. What do the results suggest about highway safety?

41. Percentages in Advertising An ad for Big Skinny wallets included the statement that one of their wallets "reduces your filled wallet size by 50%–200%." What is wrong with this statement?

42. Percentages in Advertising Continental Airlines ran ads claiming that lost baggage is "an area where we've already improved 100% in the past six months." What is wrong with this statement?

43. Percentages in Advertising A *New York Times* editorial criticized a chart caption that described a dental rinse as one that "reduces plaque on teeth by over 300%." What is wrong with this statement?

44. Percentages in Advertising In an actual ad for the Club, a device used to discourage car thefts, it was stated that "The Club reduces your odds of car theft by 400%." What is wrong with this statement?

1-1   Beyond the Basics

45. Percentages in Negotiations When the author was negotiating a contract for the faculty and administration at a college, a dean presented the argument that if faculty receive a 4% raise and administrators receive a 4% raise, that's an 8% raise and it would never be approved. What's wrong with that argument?

46. What's Wrong with This Picture? The *Newport Chronicle* ran a survey by asking readers to call in their response to this question: "Do you support the development of atomic weapons that could kill millions of innocent people?" It was reported that 20 readers responded and that 87% said "no," while 13% said "yes." Identify four major flaws in this survey.

47. Falsifying Data A researcher at the Sloan-Kettering Cancer Research Center was once criticized for falsifying data. Among his data were figures obtained from 6 groups of mice, with 20 individual mice in each group. The following values were given for the percentage of successes in each group: 53%, 58%, 63%, 46%, 48%, 67%. What's wrong with those values?

1-2   Types of Data

Key Concept Because a major use of statistics is to collect and use sample data to make conclusions about populations, we should know and understand the meanings of the terms *statistic* and *parameter*, as defined below. In this section we describe a few different types of data. The type of data is one of the key factors that determine the statistical methods we use in our analysis.

In Part 1 of this section we describe the basics of different types of data, and then in Part 2 we consider "big data" and missing data.

PART 1   Basic Types of Data

Parameter / Statistic

> **DEFINITIONS**
>
> A **parameter** is a numerical measurement describing some characteristic of a *population*.
>
> A **statistic** is a numerical measurement describing some characteristic of a *sample*.

HINT The alliteration in "population parameter" and "sample statistic" helps us remember the meanings of these terms.

If we have more than one statistic, we have "statistics." Another meaning of "statistics" was given in Section 1-1, where we defined *statistics* to be the science of planning studies and experiments; obtaining data; organizing, summarizing, presenting, analyzing, and interpreting those data; and then drawing conclusions based on them. We now have two different definitions of statistics, but we can determine which of these two definitions applies by considering the context in which the term *statistics* is used. The following example uses the first meaning of *statistics* as given on the previous page.

EXAMPLE 1   **Parameter / Statistic**

There are 250,342,875 adults in the United States. In a survey of 1659 randomly selected adults, 28% of them said that they own a credit card.

1. **Parameter:** The population size of 250,342,875 adults is a *parameter*, because it is the entire population of all adults in the United States. (If we somehow knew the percentage of all 250,342,875 adults who have a credit card, that percentage would also be a parameter.)

2. **Statistic:** The sample size of 1659 adults is a statistic, because it is based on a sample, not the entire population of all adults in the United States. The value of 28% is another statistic, because it is also based on the sample, not on the entire population.

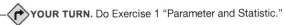 **YOUR TURN.** Do Exercise 1 "Parameter and Statistic."

Quantitative / Categorical

Some data are numbers representing counts or measurements (such as heights of adults), whereas others are attributes (such as eye color of green or brown) that are not counts or measurements. The terms quantitative data and categorical data distinguish between these types.

DEFINITIONS

Quantitative (or numerical) data consist of *numbers* representing counts or measurements.

Categorical (or qualitative or attribute) data consist of names or labels (not numbers that represent counts or measurements).

CAUTION Categorical data are sometimes coded with numbers, with those numbers replacing names. Although such numbers might appear to be quantitative, they are actually categorical data. See the third part of Example 2 that follows.

Include Units of Measurement With quantitative data, it is important to use the appropriate units of measurement, such as dollars, hours, feet, or meters. We should carefully observe information given about the units of measurement, such as "all amounts are in *thousands of dollars*" or "all units are in *kilograms*." Ignoring such units of measurement can be very costly. The National Aeronautics and Space Administration (NASA) lost its $125 million Mars Climate Orbiter when the orbiter crashed

because the controlling software had acceleration data in *English* units, but they were incorrectly assumed to be in *metric* units.

Hopefully, the day will soon come when the United States adopts the metric system and joins almost all of the rest of the countries on planet Earth.

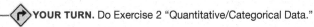

EXAMPLE 2 **Quantitative / Categorical**

1. **Quantitative Data:** The ages (in years) of subjects enrolled in a clinical trial
2. **Categorical Data as Labels:** The genders (male / female) of subjects enrolled in a clinical trial
3. **Categorical Data as Numbers:** The identification numbers 1, 2, 3, . . . , 25 are assigned randomly to the 25 subjects in a clinical trial. Those numbers are substitutes for names. They don't measure or count anything, so they are categorical data.

YOUR TURN. Do Exercise 2 "Quantitative/Categorical Data."

Discrete / Continuous

Quantitative data can be further described by distinguishing between *discrete* and *continuous* types.

DEFINITIONS

Discrete data result when the data values are quantitative and the number of values is finite, or "countable." (If there are infinitely many values, the collection of values is countable if it is possible to count them individually, such as the number of tosses of a coin before getting tails.)

Continuous (numerical) data result from infinitely many possible quantitative values, where the collection of values is not countable. (That is, it is impossible to count the individual items because at least some of them are on a continuous scale, such as the lengths of distances from 0 cm to 12 cm.)

CAUTION The concept of countable data plays a key role in the preceding definitions, but it is not a particularly easy concept to understand. Continuous data can be measured, but not counted. If you select a particular data value from continuous data, there is no "next" data value. See Example 3.

Continuous Data   **Discrete Data**

┌─ **EXAMPLE 3** **Discrete / Continuous**

1. **Discrete Data of the Finite Type:** A statistics professor counts the number of students in attendance at each of her classes. The numbers are discrete because they are finite numbers resulting from a counting process.

2. **Discrete Data of the Infinite Type:** A statistics student plans to toss a fair coin until it turns up heads. It is theoretically possible to toss the coin forever without ever getting heads, but the number of tosses can be counted, even though the counting could go on forever. Because such numbers result from a counting procedure, the numbers are discrete.

3. **Continuous Data:** Burmese pythons are invading Florida. Researchers capture pythons and measure their lengths. So far, the largest python captured in Florida was 17 feet long. If the python lengths are between 0 feet and 17 feet, there are infinitely many values between 0 feet and 17 feet. Because it is impossible to count the number of different possible values on such a continuous scale, these lengths are continuous data.

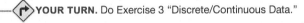 **YOUR TURN.** Do Exercise 3 "Discrete/Continuous Data."

GRAMMAR: FEWER VERSUS LESS When describing smaller amounts, it is correct grammar to use "fewer" for discrete amounts and "less" for continuous amounts. It is correct to say that we drank *fewer* cans of cola and that, in the process, we drank *less* cola. The numbers of cans of cola are discrete data, whereas the volume amounts of cola are continuous data.

Levels of Measurement

Another common way of classifying data is to use four levels of measurement: nominal, ordinal, interval, and ratio, all defined below. (Also see Table 1-2 on page 19 for brief descriptions of the four levels of measurements.) When we are applying statistics to real problems, the level of measurement of the data helps us decide which procedure to use. There will be references to these levels of measurement in this book, but the important point here is based on common sense: *Don't do computations and don't use statistical methods that are not appropriate for the data.* For example, it would not make sense to compute an average (mean) of Social Security numbers, because those numbers are data that are used for identification, and they don't represent measurements or counts of anything.

> **DEFINITION**
>
> The **nominal level of measurement** is characterized by data that consist of names, labels, or categories only. The data cannot be arranged in some order (such as low to high).

┌─ **EXAMPLE 4** **Nominal Level**

Here are examples of sample data at the nominal level of measurement.

1. **Yes / No / Undecided:** Survey responses of *yes*, *no*, and *undecided*

2. **Coded Survey Responses:** For an item on a survey, respondents are given a choice of possible answers, and they are coded as follows: "I agree" is coded as 1; "I disagree" is coded as 2; "I don't care" is coded as 3; "I refuse to answer" is coded as 4; "Go away and stop bothering me" is coded as 5. The numbers 1, 2, 3, 4, 5 don't measure or count anything.

 YOUR TURN. Do Exercise 21 "College Students."

Measuring Disobedience

How are data collected about something that doesn't seem to be measurable, such as people's level of disobedience? Psychologist Stanley Milgram devised the following experiment: A researcher instructed a volunteer subject to operate a control board that gave increasingly painful "electrical shocks" to a third person. Actually, no real shocks were given, and the third person was an actor. The volunteer began with 15 volts and was instructed to increase the shocks by increments of 15 volts. The disobedience level was the point at which the subject refused to increase the voltage. Surprisingly, two-thirds of the subjects obeyed orders even when the actor screamed and faked a heart attack.

Big Data Study of Measles Vaccine and Autism

In 2019, there were measles outbreaks in U.S. geographic regions with large numbers of children who did not receive the MMR (measles, mumps, rubella) vaccine. Many parents opposed those vaccinations because they believed that they were associated with autism. Much of that belief was fueled by a 1998 "study" of 12 subjects showing an autism and MMR link that was reported in *Lancet*, but that article was later retracted. Based on a new ten-year study of 657,461 children, the *Annals of Internal Medicine* reported that the "MMR vaccination does not increase the risk for autism, does not trigger autism in susceptible children, and is not associated with clustering of autism cases after vaccination." An article in *The New York Times* reported about this study and emphasized the key point with this headline: "One More Time, With Big Data: Measles Vaccine Doesn't Cause Autism." In this case, the use of big data is being used to help overcome misunderstandings that result in unnecessary measles outbreaks.

Because nominal data lack any ordering or numerical significance, they should not be used for calculations. Numbers such as 1, 2, 3, and 4 are sometimes assigned to the different categories (especially when data are coded for computers), but these numbers have no real computational significance and any average (mean) calculated from them is meaningless and possibly misleading.

> **DEFINITION**
>
> Data are at the **ordinal level of measurement** if they can be arranged in some order, but differences (obtained by subtraction) between data values either cannot be determined or are meaningless.

EXAMPLE 5 Ordinal Level

Here is an example of sample data at the ordinal level of measurement.

Course Grades: A college professor assigns grades of A, B, C, D, or F. These grades can be arranged in order, but we can't determine differences between the grades. For example, we know that A is higher than B (so there is an ordering), but we cannot subtract B from A (so the difference cannot be found).

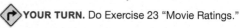

YOUR TURN. Do Exercise 23 "Movie Ratings."

Ordinal data provide information about relative comparisons but not the *magnitudes* of the differences. Ordinarily, ordinal data (such as course grades of A, B, C, D, F) should not be used for calculations such as the average (mean), but calculations are commonly used for some ordinal data, such as data from a survey question with a rating scale of 0 to 10. (A *Likert scale* is used to measure attitudes or opinions with a scale used for the level of agreement, usually with five to ten choices ranging from one extreme opinion to the opposite extreme.)

> **DEFINITION**
>
> Data are at the **interval level of measurement** if they can be arranged in order, and differences between data values can be found and are meaningful. *Data at the interval level do not have a natural zero starting point at which none of the quantity is present.*

EXAMPLE 6 Interval Level

These examples illustrate the interval level of measurement.

1. **Temperatures:** The lowest and highest temperatures recorded on earth are $-129°F$ and $134°F$. Those values are examples of data at the interval level of measurement. Those values are ordered, and we can determine that their difference is $263°F$. However, there is no natural starting point. The value of $0°F$ is arbitrary and does not represent the total absence of heat (negative temperatures are common).

2. **Years:** The years 1492 and 1776 can be arranged in order, and the difference of 284 years can be found and is meaningful. However, time did not begin in the year 0, so the year 0 is arbitrary instead of being a natural zero starting point representing "no time." The years of 1492 and 1776 are therefore at the interval level of measurement.

3. **Shoe Sizes:** The shoe sizes of 10 and 5 can be arranged in order, and the difference is the same as the difference in shoe sizes of 8 and 13. However, size 0 is arbitrary.

YOUR TURN. Do Exercise 25 "Baseball."

DEFINITION

Data are at the **ratio level of measurement** if they can be arranged in order, differences can be found and are meaningful, and *there is a natural zero starting point* (where zero indicates that none of the quantity is present). For data at this level, differences and ratios are both meaningful.

EXAMPLE 7   Ratio Level

The following are examples of data at the ratio level of measurement. Note the presence of the natural zero value, and also note the use of meaningful ratios of "twice" and "three times."

1. **Heights of Students:** Heights of 180 cm and 90 cm for a high school student and a preschool student (0 cm represents no height, and 180 cm is *twice* as tall as 90 cm.)
2. **Class Times:** The times of 50 min and 100 min for a statistics class (0 min represents no class time, and 100 min is *twice* as long as 50 min.)

 **YOUR TURN.** Do Exercise 27 "Areas of States."

TABLE 1-2 Levels of Measurement

Level of Measurement	Brief Description	Example
Ratio	There is a natural zero starting point and ratios make sense.	Heights, lengths, distances, volumes
Interval	Differences are meaningful, but there is no natural zero starting point and ratios are meaningless.	Body temperatures in degrees Fahrenheit or Celsius
Ordinal	Data can be arranged in order, but differences either can't be found or are meaningless.	Ranks of colleges in *U.S. News & World Report*
Nominal	Categories only. Data cannot be arranged in order.	Eye colors

HINT The distinction between the interval and ratio levels of measurement can be a bit tricky. Here are two tools to help with that distinction:

1. **Ratio Test** Focus on the term "ratio" and know that the term "twice" describes the ratio of one value to be double the other value. To distinguish between the interval and ratio levels of measurement, use a "ratio test" by asking this question: Does use of the term "twice" make sense? "Twice" makes sense for data at the ratio level of measurement, but it does not make sense for data at the interval level of measurement.
2. **True Zero** For ratios to make sense, there must be a value of "true zero," where the value of zero indicates that none of the quantity is present, and zero is not simply an arbitrary value on a scale. The temperature of 0°F is arbitrary and does not indicate that there is no heat, so temperatures on the Fahrenheit scale are at the interval level of measurement, not the ratio level.

Six Degrees of Separation

Social psychologists, historians, political scientists, and communications specialists are interested in "The Small World Problem": Given any two people in the world, how many intermediate links are necessary to connect the two original people? In the 1950s and 1960s, social psychologist Stanley Milgram conducted an experiment in which subjects tried to contact other target people by mailing an information folder to an acquaintance who they thought would be closer to the target. Among 160 such chains that were initiated, only 44 were completed, so the failure rate was 73%. Among the successes, the number of intermediate acquaintances varied from 2 to 10, with a median of 6 (hence "six degrees of separation"). The experiment has been criticized for its high failure rate and its disproportionate inclusion of subjects with above-average incomes. A more recent study conducted by Microsoft researcher Eric Horvitz and Stanford Assistant Professor Jure Leskovec involved 30 billion instant messages and 240 million people. This study found that for instant messages that used Microsoft, the mean length of a path between two individuals is 6.6, suggesting "seven degrees of separation." Work continues in this important and interesting field.

Big Data Instead of a Clinical Trial

Nicholas Tatonetti of Columbia University searched Food and Drug Administration databases for adverse reactions in patients that resulted from different pairings of drugs. He discovered that the Paxil (paroxetine) drug for depression and the pravastatin drug for high cholesterol interacted to create increases in glucose (blood sugar) levels. When taken separately by patients, neither drug raised glucose levels, but the increase in glucose levels occurred when the two drugs were taken together. This finding resulted from a general database search of interactions from many pairings of drugs, not from a clinical trial involving patients using Paxil and pravastatin.

EXAMPLE 8 **Distinguishing Between the Ratio Level and Interval Level**

For each of the following, determine whether the data are at the ratio level of measurement or the interval level of measurement:

a. Times (minutes) it takes students to complete a statistics test.

b. Body temperatures (Celsius) of statistics students.

SOLUTION

a. Apply the "ratio test" described in the preceding hint. If one student completes the test in 40 minutes and another student completes the test in 20 minutes, does it make sense to say that the first student used *twice* as much time? Yes! So the times are at the ratio level of measurement. We could also apply the "true zero" test. A time of 0 minutes does represent "no time," so the value of 0 is a true zero indicating that no time was used.

b. Apply the "ratio test" described in the preceding hint. If one student has a body temperature of 40°C and another student has a body temperature of 20°C, does it make sense to say that the first student is *twice* as hot as the second student? (Ignore subjective amounts of attractiveness and consider only science.) No! So the body temperatures are not at the ratio level of measurement. Because the difference between 40°C and 20°C is the same as the difference between 90°C and 70°C, the differences are meaningful, but because ratios do not make sense, the body temperatures are at the interval level of measurement. Also, the temperature of 0°C does not represent "no heat" so the value of 0 is not a true zero indicating that no heat is present.

YOUR TURN. Do Exercise 28 "Body Temperatures."

PART 2 Big Data and Missing Data: Too Much and Not Enough

When working with data, we might encounter some data sets that are ginormous, and we might also encounter some data sets with individual elements missing. Here in Part 2 we briefly discuss both cases.

Big Data

UPS delivers 20 million packages every day. UPS analyzes massive amounts of data in order to optimize routes and plan maintenance for its truck and aircraft fleets. Data analysis and optimization efforts to-date have enabled UPS to save 40 million gallons of fuel and shorten travel distances by 370 million miles. The need to analyze large data sets has led to the birth of *data science*. There is not universal agreement on the following definitions, and various other definitions can be easily found elsewhere.

DEFINITIONS

Big data refers to data sets so large and so complex that their analysis is beyond the capabilities of traditional software tools. Analysis of big data may require software simultaneously running in parallel on many different computers.

Data science involves applications of statistics, computer science, and software engineering, along with some other relevant fields (such as sociology or finance).

Examples of Data Set Magnitudes We can see from the definition of big data that there isn't a fixed number that serves as an exact boundary for determining whether a data set qualifies as being big data, but big data typically involves amounts of data such as the following:

- Terabytes (10^{12} or 1,000,000,000,000 bytes) of data
- Petabytes (10^{15} bytes) of data
- Exabytes (10^{18} bytes) of data
- Zettabytes (10^{21} bytes) of data
- Yottabytes (10^{24} bytes) of data

Examples of Applications of Big Data The following are a few other examples involving big data:

- Google provides live traffic maps by recording and analyzing GPS (global positioning system) data collected from the smartphones of people traveling in their vehicles.
- Netflix collects data on viewing records and uses the data to create original programming as well as identifying which movies to acquire.
- Attempts to forecast flu epidemics are made by analyzing Internet searches of flu symptoms.
- The Sloan Digital Sky Survey started in the year 2000, and it quickly collected more astronomy data than in the history of mankind up to 2000. It now has more than 140 terabytes of astronomy data.
- Walmart processes 2.5 petabytes (2,500,000,000,000,000 bytes) of data every hour. For online sales, Walmart developed the Polaris search engine that increased sales by 10% to 15%, worth billions of dollars.
- Amazon monitors and tracks about 6 million items shipped daily from its stores that are distributed across hundreds of fulfillment centers around the world.
- Uber feeds driver and customer data into algorithms that identify the most profitable driver/passenger matches.

Examples of Jobs According to Analytic Talent, there are 6000 companies hiring data scientists, and here are some job posting examples:

- Facebook: Data Scientist
- IBM: Data Scientist
- PayPal: Data Scientist
- The College Board: SAS Programmer/Data Scientist
- Netflix: Senior Data Engineer/Scientist

It was noted in the Preface that we are experiencing a new major revolution in technology that uses artificial intelligence, machine learning, and deep learning—topics studied in Data Science, which requires a study of statistics. Data Science and statistics are now experiencing unprecedented growth.

Statistics in Data Science The modern data scientist has a solid background in statistics and computer systems as well as expertise in fields that extend beyond statistics. The modern data scientist might be skilled with software of *R*, Python or Hadoop. The modern data scientist might also have a strong background in some other field

Statistics for Online Dating

The four founders of the online dating site OkCupid are mathematicians who use methods of statistics to analyze results from their website. The chief executive officer of OkCupid has been quoted as saying, "We're not psychologists. We're math guys" (from "Looking for a Date? A Site Suggests You Check the Data," by Jenna Wortham, *New York Times*). The OkCupid website is unique in its use of methods of statistics to match people more effectively.

By analyzing the photos and responses of 7000 users, analysts at OkCupid found that when creating a profile photo, men should not look directly at the camera, and they should not smile. For women, the appearance of being interesting produces much better results than the appearance of being sexy. They found that brevity is good for the first posted message; the ideal length of the first posted message is 40 words—about what a typical person can type in 1 minute.

Hawthorne and Experimenter Effects

The well-known placebo effect occurs when an untreated subject incorrectly believes that he or she is receiving a real treatment and reports an improvement in symptoms. The Hawthorne effect occurs when treated subjects somehow respond differently simply because they are part of an experiment. (This phenomenon was called the "Hawthorne effect" because it was first observed in a study of factory workers at Western Electric's Hawthorne plant.) An experimenter effect (sometimes called a Rosenthal effect) occurs when the researcher or experimenter unintentionally influences subjects through such factors as facial expression, tone of voice, or attitude.

such as psychology, biology, medicine, chemistry, or economics. Because of the wide range of disciplines required, a data science project might typically involve a team of collaborating individuals with expertise in different fields. An introductory statistics course is a great first step in becoming a data scientist.

Missing Data

When collecting sample data, it is quite common to find that some values are missing. Ignoring missing data can sometimes create misleading results. If you make the mistake of skipping over a few different sample values when you are manually typing them into a statistics software program, the missing values are not likely to have a serious effect on the results. However, if a survey includes many missing salary entries because those with very low incomes are reluctant to reveal their salaries, those missing low values will have the serious effect of making salaries appear higher than they really are.

For an example of missing data, see the following table. The body temperature for Subject 2 at 12 AM on Day 2 is missing. (The table below includes the first three rows of data from Data Set 5 "Body Temperatures" in Appendix B.)

Body Temperatures (in degrees Fahrenheit) of Healthy Adults

Subject	Sex	Smoke	Temperature Day 1		Temperature Day 2	
			8 AM	12 AM	8 AM	12 AM
1	M	Y	98.0	98.0	98.0	98.6
2	M	Y	97.0	97.6	97.4	----
3	M	Y	98.6	98.8	97.8	98.6

There are different categories of missing data, as described in the following definitions.

> **DEFINITION**
>
> A data value is **missing completely at random** if the likelihood of its being missing is independent of its value or any of the other values in the data set. That is, any data value is just as likely to be missing as any other data value.

(*NOTE:* More complete discussions of missing data will distinguish between *missing completely at random* and *missing at random*, which means that the likelihood of a value being missing is independent of its value after controlling for another variable. There is no need to know this distinction in this book.)

Example of Missing Data—Random: When using a keyboard to manually enter ages of survey respondents, the operator is distracted by a colleague singing "Daydream Believer" and makes the mistake of failing to enter the age of 37 years. This data value is missing completely at random.

> **DEFINITION**
>
> A data value is **missing not at random** if the missing value is related to the reason that it is missing.

Example of Missing Data—Not at Random A survey question asks each respondent to enter his or her annual income, but respondents with very low incomes skip this question because they find it embarrassing.

Biased Results? Based on the two definitions and examples from the previous page, it makes sense to conclude that if we ignore data *missing completely at random*, the remaining values are not likely to be biased and good results should be obtained. However, if we ignore data that are *missing not at random*, it is very possible that the remaining values are biased and results will be misleading.

Correcting for Missing Data There are different methods for dealing with missing data.

1. **Delete Cases:** One very common method for dealing with missing data is to delete all subjects having any missing values.

   - If the data are missing completely at random, the remaining values are not likely to be biased and good results can be obtained, but with a smaller sample size.

   - If the data are missing not at random, deleting subjects having any missing values can easily result in a bias among the remaining values, so results can be misleading.

2. **Impute Missing Values:** We "impute" missing data values when we substitute values for them. There are different methods of determining the replacement values, such as using the mean of the other values, or using a randomly selected value from other similar cases, or using a method based on regression analysis (which will make more sense after studying Chapter 10).

In this book we do not work much with missing data, but it is important to understand this:

> When analyzing sample data with missing values, try to determine *why* they are missing, then decide whether it makes sense to treat the remaining values as being representative of the population. If it appears that there are missing values that are *missing not at random* (that is, their values are related to the reasons why they are missing), know that the remaining data may well be biased and any conclusions based on those remaining values may well be misleading.

1-2 Basic Skills and Concepts

Statistical Literacy and Critical Thinking

1. Parameter and Statistic In a Citrix Security survey of 1001 adults in the United States, it was found that 69% of those surveyed believe that having their personal information stolen is inevitable. Identify the population and sample. Is the value of 69% a statistic or a parameter?

2. Quantitative/Categorical Data Identify each of the following as quantitative data or categorical data.

a. The platelet counts in Data Set 1 "Body Data" in Appendix B

b. The cigarette brands in Data Set 16 "Cigarette Contents" in Appendix B

c. The colors of the M&M candies in Data Set 38 "Candies" in Appendix B

d. The weights of the M&M candies in Data Set 38 "Candies" in Appendix B

3. Discrete/Continuous Data Which of the following describe discrete data?

a. The exact heights of all NBA basketball players

b. The numbers of people surveyed in each of the Gallup polls preceding the next Presidential election

c. The exact times that randomly selected students spend on smart phones during the preceding week

4. E-Cigarette Survey In a survey of 36,000 adults, 3.7% said that they regularly use E-cigarettes (based on data from the National Center for Health Statistics).

a. Identify the sample and population.

b. Is the value of 3.7% a statistic or parameter?

c. What is the level of measurement of the value of 3.7%? (nominal, ordinal, interval, ratio)

d. Are the numbers of subjects in such surveys discrete or continuous?

In Exercises 5–12, identify whether the given value is a statistic or a parameter.

5. Lost Wallets A survey of a sample of consumers in the United States showed that among those who have found a wallet or purse, 89% either turned it in or located the owner (based on a Toluna Quicksurveys poll).

6. Drivers According to the Federal Highway Administration, there are 212 million licensed drivers in the United States.

7. Titanic Deaths The sinking of the Titanic on April 15, 1912, is one of the most infamous disasters in history. A population of 1503 passengers and crew died when the Titanic sank approximately 400 miles south of Newfoundland, Canada.

8. Birth Weight In a study of a sample of babies born at hospitals in New York State, it was found that the average (mean) weight at birth was 3152.0 grams.

9. Birth Genders In the same study cited in the preceding exercise, 51% of the babies were girls.

10. Smart Phones In a Pew Research Center poll, a sample of adults in the United States was obtained, and it was found that 72% of them own smart phones.

11. Super Bowl A study was conducted of all 70,081 people who attended Super Bowl LIII at Mercedes-Benz Stadium in Atlanta, Georgia.

12. Prisoners According to the U.S. Bureau of Justice, there are 2,227,318 prisoners in the United States.

In Exercises 13–20, determine whether the data are from a discrete or continuous data set.

13. Freshman 15 In a study of weight gains by college students in their freshman year, researchers record the amounts of weight gained by randomly selected students (as in Data Set 13 "Freshman 15" in Appendix B).

14. Fraud Detection While monitoring Internet traffic in order to detect fraudulent activity, a researcher records the interarrival times (sec) between incoming Internet queries.

15. House Attendance The Clerk of the U.S. House of Representatives records the number of representatives present at each session.

16. Students Your statistics professor records the number of students who pass each of her courses.

17. Amazon Sales In a study of service times at an Amazon fulfillment center, the times (minutes) it takes to process orders are recorded.

18. Texting Fatalities The Insurance Institute for Highway Safety collects data consisting of the numbers of motor vehicle fatalities caused by driving while texting.

19. Statistics Classes In each of her classes, a statistics professor records the number of students who earned a grade of A.

20. Criminal Forensics When studying the relationship between lengths of feet and heights so that footprint evidence at a crime scene can be used to estimate the height of the suspect, a researcher records the exact lengths of feet from a large sample of random subjects.

In Exercises 21–28, determine which of the four levels of measurement (nominal, ordinal, interval, ratio) best describes the given data.

21. College Students In order to better plan for the incoming freshman class, a college dean asks each newly admitted student to identify their likely major (physics, business, math, psychology, engineering, law, etc.).

22. Medical School Rankings *U.S. News & World Report* periodically provides its rankings of medical schools, and in a recent year the ranks for Harvard, Johns Hopkins, and New York University were 1, 2, and 3, respectively.

23. Movie Ratings In a college film studies course, students rate ten documentaries using a scale of 0 to 5 stars.

24. Criminology In a criminology study, the lengths of prison sentences are obtained for randomly selected subjects convicted of auto theft.

25. Baseball Baseball statistician Bill James records the years in which the baseball World Series is won by a team from the National League.

26. Art History In an art history course, students are asked to identify the painting styles (abstract, classical, expressionism, etc.) of several paintings.

27. Areas of States A data set consists of the areas (km^2) of each of the 50 United States.

28. Body Temperatures Body temperatures (in degrees Fahrenheit) listed in Data Set 5 "Body Temperatures" in Appendix B

In Exercises 29–32, identify the level of measurement of the data as nominal, ordinal, interval, or ratio. Also, explain what is wrong with the given calculation.

29. Super Bowl The first Super Bowl attended by the author was Super Bowl XLVIII. On the first play of the game, the Seattle defense scored on a safety. The defensive players wore jerseys numbered 31, 28, 41, 56, 25, 54, 69, 50, 91, 72, 29, and the average (mean) of those numbers is 49.6.

30. Social Security Numbers As part of a project in a statistics class, students report the last four digits of their Social Security numbers, and the average (mean) of those digits is computed to be 4.7.

31. Temperatures As this exercise is being written, it is 80°F in Paris, France, and it is 40°F in Anchorage, Alaska, so it is twice as warm in Paris as it is in Anchorage.

32. College Ranks As of this writing, *U.S. News & World Report* ranked the best global universities, including these results: Harvard (1), MIT (2), Stanford (3), University of California at Berkeley (4), and University of Oxford (5). The difference between Harvard and MIT is the same as the difference between Stanford and the University of California at Berkeley.

1-2 Beyond the Basics

33. Countable For each of the following, categorize the nature of the data using one of these three descriptions: (1) discrete because the number of possible values is finite; (2) discrete because the number of possible values is infinite but countable; (3) continuous because the number of possible values is infinite and not countable.

a. Exact lengths of the feet of members of the band the Monkees

b. Shoe sizes of members of the band the Monkees (such as 9, 9½, and so on)

c. The number of albums sold by the Monkees band

d. The numbers of monkeys sitting at keyboards before one of them randomly types the lyrics for the song "Daydream Believer."

34. Directions in Degrees Standard navigation systems used for aviation and boating are based on directions measured in degrees, with north represented by 0°. Relative to north, east is 90°, south is 180°, and west is 270°. What is the level of measurement of such directions measured in degrees?

1-3 Collecting Sample Data

Key Concept When analyzing sample data, it is essential to use an appropriate method for collecting those sample data. This section includes comments about various methods and sampling procedures. Of particular importance is the method of using a *simple random sample*. We will make frequent use of this sampling method throughout the remainder of this book.

As you read this section, remember this:

If sample data are not collected in an appropriate way, the data may be so utterly useless that no amount of statistical torturing can salvage them.

PART 1 Basics of Design of Experiments and Collecting Sample Data

The Gold Standard Randomness with placebo/treatment groups is sometimes called the "gold standard" because it is so effective.

DEFINITION

A **placebo** is a harmless and ineffective pill, medicine, or procedure sometimes used for psychological benefit or sometimes used by researchers for comparison to other treatments.

The following example describes how the gold standard was used in the largest health experiment ever conducted.

EXAMPLE 1 The Salk Vaccine Experiment

In 1954, an experiment was designed to test the effectiveness of the Salk vaccine in preventing polio, which had killed or paralyzed thousands of children. By random selection, 401,974 children were randomly assigned to two groups: (1) 200,745 children were given a *treatment* consisting of Salk vaccine injections; (2) 201,229 children were injected with a *placebo* that contained no drug. Children were assigned to the treatment or placebo group through a process of random selection, equivalent to flipping a coin. Among the children given the Salk vaccine, 33 later developed paralytic polio, and among the children given a placebo, 115 later developed paralytic polio.

— **YOUR TURN.** Do Exercise 1 "Magnet Treatment of Pain."

Example 1 describes an *experiment* because subjects were given a treatment, but ethical, cost, time, and other considerations sometimes prohibit the use of an experiment. We would never want to conduct a driving/texting experiment in which we ask subjects to text while driving—some of them could die. It would be far better to observe past crash results to understand the effects of driving while texting. See the following definitions.

> **DEFINITIONS**
>
> In an **experiment**, we apply some *treatment* and then proceed to observe its effects on the individuals. (The individuals in experiments are called **experimental units**, and they are often called **subjects** when they are people.)
>
> In an **observational study**, we observe and measure specific characteristics, but we don't attempt to *modify* the individuals being studied.

Experiments are often better than observational studies because well-planned experiments typically reduce the chance of having the results affected by some variable that is not part of a study. A *lurking variable* is one that affects the variables included in the study, but it is not included in the study.

EXAMPLE 2 Ice Cream and Drownings

Observational Study: Observe past data to incorrectly conclude that ice cream causes drownings (based on data showing that increases in ice cream sales are associated with increases in drownings). The mistake is to miss the lurking variable of temperature and the failure to see that as the temperature increases, ice cream sales increase and drownings increase because more people swim.

Experiment: Conduct an *experiment* with one group treated with ice cream while another group gets no ice cream. We would see that the rate of drowning victims is about the same in both groups, so ice cream consumption has no effect on drownings.

Here, the experiment is clearly better than the observational study.

— **YOUR TURN.** Do Exercise 6 "Experiment or Observational Study."

Clinical Trials Versus Observational Studies

In a *New York Times* article about hormone therapy for women, reporter Denise Grady wrote about randomized clinical trials that involve subjects who were randomly assigned to a treatment group and another group not given the treatment. Such randomized clinical trials are often referred to as the "gold standard" for medical research. In contrast, observational studies can involve patients who decide themselves to undergo some treatment. Subjects who decide themselves to undergo treatments are often healthier than other subjects, so the treatment group might appear to be more successful simply because it involves healthier subjects, not necessarily because the treatment is effective. Researchers criticized observational studies of hormone therapy for women by saying that results might appear to make the treatment more effective than it really is.

There is a variety of different ways that polls can be conducted, and the way that a particular poll is conducted can strongly influence the responses. Survey questions on sensitive topics can be greatly influenced by the survey mode that was used. For example, Pew reports that when asked about their personal financial situation, 20% of those responding online reported that it was in poor shape, but 14% of those responding by phone gave that same response. When given multiple choices to a question, respondents tend to favor the first choice when they are reading it in an online poll, but they tend to favor the last choice when they hear the choices in a live phone interview. These are examples of the mode effect—the way that a poll is conducted has an effect on the responses that people give.

Design of Experiments

Good design of experiments includes *replication, blinding,* and *randomness.*

- **Replication** is the repetition of an experiment on more than one individual. Good use of replication requires sample sizes that are large enough so that we can see effects of treatments. In the Salk experiment in Example 1, the experiment used sufficiently large sample sizes, so the researchers could see that the Salk vaccine was effective.

- **Blinding** is used when the subject doesn't know whether he or she is receiving a treatment or a placebo. Blinding is a way to get around the **placebo effect,** which occurs when an untreated subject reports an improvement in symptoms. (The reported improvement in the placebo group may be real or imagined.) The Salk experiment in Example 1 was **double-blind,** which means that blinding occurred at two levels: (1) The children being injected didn't know whether they were getting the Salk vaccine or a placebo, and (2) the doctors who gave the injections and evaluated the results did not know either. Codes were used so that the researchers could objectively evaluate the effectiveness of the Salk vaccine.

- **Randomness** is used when individuals are assigned to different groups through a process of random selection, as in the Salk vaccine experiment in Example 1. The logic behind randomness is to use chance as a way to create two groups that are similar. The following definition refers to one common and effective way to collect sample data in a way that uses randomness.

DEFINITION

A **simple random sample** of *n* subjects is selected in such a way that every possible *sample of the same size n* has the same chance of being chosen. (A simple random sample is often called a random sample, but strictly speaking, a *random sample* has the weaker requirement that all members of the population have the same chance of being selected. That distinction is not so important in this text. See Exercise 37 "Simple Random Sample vs. Random Sample".)

Throughout, we will use various statistical procedures, and we often have a requirement that we have collected a *simple random sample*, as defined above.

Unlike careless or haphazard sampling, random sampling usually requires very careful planning and execution. Wayne Barber of Chemeketa Community College is quite correct when he tells his students that "randomness needs help."

Other Sampling Methods In addition to simple random sampling, here are some other sampling methods commonly used for surveys. Figure 1-4 illustrates these different sampling methods.

DEFINITIONS

With **systematic sampling**, we select some starting point and then select every *k*th (such as every 50th) element in the population.

With **convenience sampling**, we simply use data that are very easy to get.

With **stratified sampling**, we subdivide the population into at least two different subgroups (or strata) so that subjects within the same subgroup share the same characteristics (such as gender). Then we draw a sample from each subgroup (or stratum).

With **cluster sampling**, we first divide the population area into sections (or clusters). Then we randomly select some of those clusters and choose *all* the members from those selected clusters.

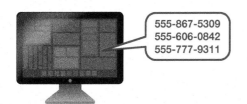

Simple Random Sample
A sample of *n* subjects is selected so that every sample of the same size *n* has the same chance of being selected.

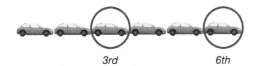

3rd   *6th*

Systematic Sample
Select every *k*th subject.

Convenience Sample
Use data that are very easy to get.

Men   Women

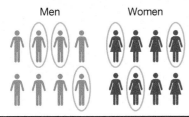

Stratified Sample
Subdivide population into strata (groups) with the same characteristics, then randomly sample within those strata.

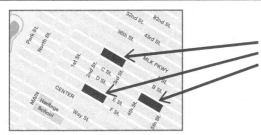

Cluster Sample
Partition the population in clusters (groups), then randomly select some clusters, then select all members of the selected clusters.

FIGURE 1-4   **Common Sampling Methods**

HINT Because it's difficult to remember the distinction between stratified sampling and cluster sampling, picture your entire class as one cluster among all classes at your college. Remember the alliteration of "cluster class" to recall that with cluster sampling, you choose *all* of the members of selected clusters. Associate "cluster" with "all." Then, stratified sampling is the other method of choosing samples from selected classes or subgroups.

Multistage Sampling Professional pollsters and government researchers often collect data by using some combination of the preceding sampling methods. In a multistage sample design, pollsters select a sample in different stages, and each stage might use different methods of sampling, as in the following example.

EXAMPLE 3 Multistage Sample Design

The U.S. government's unemployment statistics are based on surveys of households. It is impractical to personally survey each household in a simple random sample, because they would be scattered all over the country, making it nearly

continued

Wording in Surveys Can Affect Results

Pew Research Center pollsters conduct experiments to better understand how wording in questions can affect the responses of survey subjects. In a Pew Research Center survey of 1505 adults in the United States, half of the respondents were asked about finding "jobs" while the other half were asked about "*good* jobs." For the "jobs" group, 33% said that jobs were difficult to find. For the "*good* jobs" group, 45% said that good jobs were difficult to find.

The Human Project

Started in 2014, the Human Project is a *prospective study* in which 10,000 New Yorkers will be followed for decades. The goal of this ambitious study is to "*provide new insights and understanding into how our biology, our environment, and our behavior interact to determine our health.*" The subjects in the study will be the basis for collecting medical records, education records, data from physical examinations, patterns of physical activity, environmental measurements, and a wide variety of other measurements. The hope is that big data analysis will enable researchers to generate new insights into the biological, behavioral, and environmental factors that influence our health. The Human Project was started by the Kavli Foundation and the New York University Institute for Interdisciplinary Study of Decision Making.

impossible to contact each of them. Instead, the U.S. Census Bureau and the Bureau of Labor Statistics collaborate to conduct a survey called the Current Population Survey. A recent survey incorporates a multistage sample design, roughly following these steps:

1. The entire United States is partitioned into 2025 different regions called *primary sampling units* (PSUs). The primary sampling units are metropolitan areas, large counties, or combinations of smaller counties. The 2025 primary sampling units are then grouped into 824 different strata.

2. In each of the 824 different strata, one of the primary sampling units is selected so that the probability of selection is proportional to the size of the population in each primary sampling unit.

3. Among the 824 selected primary sampling units, census data are used to randomly select about 60,000 households.

4. A responsible person in each of the 60,000 selected households is interviewed about the employment status of each household member of age 16 or older.

This multistage sample design includes a combination of random, stratified, and cluster sampling at different stages. The end result is a very complicated sampling design, but it is much more practical, less expensive, and faster than using a simpler design, such as a simple random sample. (Using a simple random sample would result in households that are far apart and difficult to contact.)

PART 2 Beyond the Basics of Design of Experiments and Collecting Sample Data

In Part 2 of this section, we discuss different types of observational studies and different ways of designing experiments.

Observational Studies The following definitions identify the standard terminology used in professional journals for different types of observational studies. These definitions are illustrated in Figure 1-5.

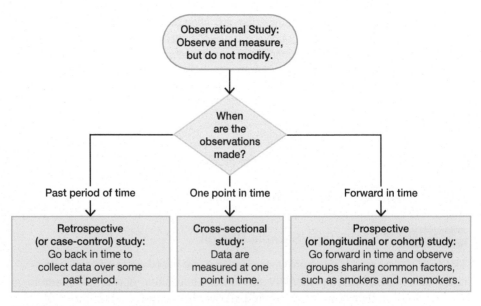

FIGURE 1-5   Types of Observational Studies

DEFINITIONS

In a **cross-sectional study**, data are observed, measured, and collected at *one point in time*, not over a period of time.

In a **retrospective (or case-control) study**, data are collected from a *past time period* by going back in time (through examination of records, interviews, and so on).

In a **prospective (or longitudinal or cohort) study**, data are collected in the *future* from groups that share common factors (such groups are called *cohorts*).

Experiments In an experiment, **confounding** occurs when we can see some effect, but we can't identify the specific factor that caused it, as in the ice cream and drowning observational study in Example 2. See also the bad experimental design illustrated in Figure 1-6(a) on the next page, where confounding can occur when the treatment group of women shows strong positive results. Because the treatment group consists of women and the placebo group consists of men, confounding has occurred because we cannot determine whether the positive results are attributable to the treatment or to the gender of the subjects. The Salk vaccine experiment in Example 1 illustrates one method for controlling the effect of the treatment variable: Use a *completely randomized experimental design*, whereby randomness is used to assign subjects to the treatment group and the placebo group. A completely randomized experimental design is just one of the following methods that are used to control effects of variables.

Completely Randomized Experimental Design: Assign subjects to different treatment groups through a process of *random selection*, as illustrated in Figure 1-6(b) on the next page.

Randomized Block Design: See Figure 1-6c on the next page. A **block** is a group of subjects that are similar, but blocks differ in ways that might affect the outcome of the experiment. Use the following procedure, as illustrated in Figure 1-6(c):

1. Form blocks (or groups) of subjects with similar characteristics.

2. Randomly assign treatments to subjects within each block.

For example, in designing an experiment to test the effectiveness of aspirin treatments on heart disease, we might form a block of men and a block of women, because it is known that the hearts of men and women can behave differently. By controlling for gender, this randomized block design eliminates gender as a possible source of confounding.

A randomized block design uses the same basic idea as stratified sampling, but randomized block designs are used when designing experiments, whereas stratified sampling is used for surveys.

Matched Pairs Design: Compare two treatment groups (such as treatment and placebo) by using subjects matched in pairs that are somehow related or have similar characteristics, as in the following cases.

- Before/After: Matched pairs might consist of measurements from subjects before and after some treatment, as illustrated in Figure 1-6(d) on the next page. Each subject yields a "before" measurement and an "after" measurement, and each before/after pair of measurements is a matched pair.

Value of a Statistical Life

The *value of a statistical life* (VSL) is a measure routinely calculated and used for making decisions in fields such as medicine, insurance, environmental health, and transportation safety. As of this writing, the value of a statistical life is $7.4 million.

Many people oppose the concept of putting a value on a human life, but the word *statistical* in the "value of a statistical life" is used to ensure that we don't equate it with the true worth of a human life. Some people legitimately argue that every life is priceless, but others argue that there are conditions in which it is impossible or impractical to save every life, so a value must be somehow assigned to a human life in order that sound and rational decisions can be made. Not far from the author's home, a parkway was modified at a cost of about $3 million to improve safety at a location where car occupants had previously died in traffic crashes. In the cost-benefit analysis that led to this improvement in safety, the value of a statistical life was surely considered.

■ **Twins:** A test of Crest toothpaste used matched pairs of twins, where one twin used Crest and the other used another toothpaste.

Rigorously Controlled Design: Carefully assign subjects to different treatment groups, so that those given each treatment are similar in the ways that are important to the experiment. This can be extremely difficult to implement, and often we can never be sure that we have accounted for all of the relevant factors.

(a)
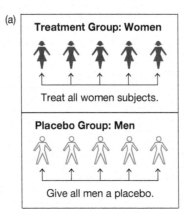

Bad experimental design:
Treat all women subjects and give the men a placebo. (Problem: We don't know if effects are due to gender or to treatment.)

(b)
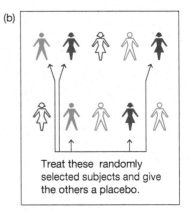

Completely randomized experimental design:
Use randomness to determine who gets the treatment and who gets the placebo.

(c)
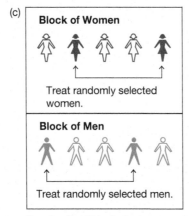

Randomized block design:
1. Form a block of women and a block of men.
2. Within each block, randomly select subjects to be treated.

(d)
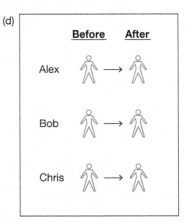

Matched pairs design:
Get measurements from the same subjects before and after some treatment.

FIGURE 1-6   Designs of Experiments

Sampling Errors

In statistics, you could use a good sampling method and do everything correctly, and yet it is possible to get wrong results. No matter how well you plan and execute the sample collection process, there is likely to be some error in the results. The different types of sampling errors are described here.

DEFINITIONS

A **sampling error** (or **random sampling error**) occurs when the sample has been selected with a random method, but there is a discrepancy between a sample result and the true population result; such an error results from chance sample fluctuations.

A **nonsampling error** is the result of human error, including such factors as wrong data entries, computing errors, questions with biased wording, false data provided by respondents, forming biased conclusions, or applying statistical methods that are not appropriate for the circumstances.

A **nonrandom sampling error** is the result of using a sampling method that is not random, such as using a convenience sample or a voluntary response sample.

Experimental design requires much more thought and care than we can describe in this relatively brief section. Taking a complete course in the design of experiments is a good start in learning so much more about this important topic.

1-3 Basic Skills and Concepts

Statistical Literacy and Critical Thinking

1. Magnet Treatment of Pain Researchers conducted a study to determine whether magnets are effective in treating back pain. Pain was measured using the visual analog scale, and the results given below are among the results obtained in the study (based on data from "Bipolar Permanent Magnets for the Treatment of Chronic Lower Back Pain: A Pilot Study," by Collacott, Zimmerman, White, and Rindone, *Journal of the American Medical Association*, Vol. 283, No. 10). Higher scores correspond to greater pain levels.

Reduction in Pain Level After Magnet Treatment: $n = 20, \bar{x} = 0.49, s = 0.96$

Reduction in Pain Level After Sham Treatment: $n = 20, \bar{x} = 0.44, s = 1.4$

Is this study an experiment or an observational study? Explain.

2. Blinding What does it mean when we say that the study cited in Exercise 1 was "double-blind"?

3. Replication In what specific way was replication applied in the study cited in Exercise 1?

4. Sampling Method The patients were recruited among those at a Veterans Affairs hospital. What type of sampling best describes the way in which the subjects were chosen: simple random sample, systematic sample, convenience sample, stratified sample, cluster sample? Does the method of sampling appear to adversely affect the quality of the results?

Exercises 5–8 refer to the study of an association between which ear is used for cell phone calls and whether the subject is left-handed or right-handed. The study is reported in "Hemispheric Dominance and Cell Phone Use," by Seidman et al., **JAMA Otolaryngology—Head & Neck Surgery,** *Vol. 139, No. 5. The study began with a survey e-mailed to 5000 people belonging to an otology online group, and 717 surveys were returned.* **(Otology** *relates to the ear and hearing.)*

5. Sampling Method What type of sampling best describes the way in which the 717 subjects were chosen: simple random sample, systematic sample, convenience sample, stratified sample, cluster sample? Does the method of sampling appear to adversely affect the quality of the results?

6. Experiment or Observational Study Is the study an experiment or an observational study? Explain.

7. Response Rate What percentage of the 5000 surveys were returned? Does that response rate appear to be low? In general, what is a problem with a very low response rate?

8. Sampling Method Assume that the population consists of all students currently in your statistics class. Describe how to obtain a sample of six students so that the result is a sample of the given type.

a. Simple random sample

b. Systematic sample

c. Stratified sample

d. Cluster sample

e. Convenience sample

In Exercises 9–20, identify which of these types of sampling is used: random, systematic, convenience, stratified, or cluster.

9. Cormorant Density Cormorant bird population densities were studied by using the "line transect method" with aircraft observers flying along the shoreline of Lake Huron and collecting sample data at intervals of every 20 km (based on data from *Journal of Great Lakes Research*).

10. Sexuality of Women The sexuality of women was discussed in Shere Hite's book *Women and Love: A Cultural Revolution*. Her conclusions were based on sample data that consisted of 4500 mailed responses from 100,000 questionnaires that were sent to women.

11. UFO Poll In a Kelton Research poll, 1114 Americans 18 years of age or older were called after their telephone numbers were randomly generated by a computer, and 36% of the respondents said that they believe in the existence of UFOs.

12. Reported and Observed Results A Harris Interactive study involved 1013 adults who were interviewed about washing their hands in restrooms and another 6336 adults who were observed in public restrooms.

13. Books The author collected data by randomly selecting 35 pages from the previous edition of this book and then counting the number of words on each of those pages.

14. Acupuncture Study In a study of treatments for back pain, 641 subjects were randomly assigned to the four different treatment groups of individualized acupuncture, standardized acupuncture, simulated acupuncture, and usual care (based on data from "A Randomized Trial Comparing Acupuncture, Simulated Acupuncture, and Usual Care for Chronic Low Back Pain," by Cherkin et al., *Archives of Internal Medicine*, Vol. 169, No. 9).

15. Criminology Researchers randomly selected 50 convicted felons from each category of burglary, auto theft, and assault.

16. Deforestation Rates Satellites are used to collect sample data for estimating deforestation rates. The Forest Resources Assessment of the United Nations (UN) Food and Agriculture Organization uses a method of selecting a sample of a 10-km-wide square at every 1° intersection of latitude and longitude.

17. Testing Lipitor In a clinical trial of the cholesterol drug Lipitor (atorvastatin), subjects were partitioned into groups given a placebo or Lipitor doses of 10 mg, 20 mg, 40 mg, or 80 mg. The subjects were randomly assigned to the different treatment groups (based on data from Pfizer, Inc.).

18. Exit Polls During the last presidential election, CNN conducted an exit poll in which specific polling stations were randomly selected and all voters were surveyed as they left the premises.

19. *Literary Digest* Poll In 1936, *Literary Digest* magazine mailed questionnaires to 10 million people and obtained 2,266,566 responses. The responses indicated that Alf Landon would win the presidential election. He didn't.

20. Highway Strength The New York State Department of Transportation evaluated the quality of the New York State Thruway by testing core samples collected at regular intervals of 1 mile.

Critical Thinking: What's Wrong? *In Exercises 21–28, determine whether the study is an experiment or an observational study, and then identify a major problem with the study.*

21. Online News In a survey conducted by *USA Today*, 1465 Internet users chose to respond to this question posted on the *USA Today* electronic edition: "Is news online as satisfying as print and TV news?" 52% of the respondents said "yes."

22. Physicians' Health Study The Physicians' Health Study involved 22,071 male physicians. Based on random selections, 11,037 of them were treated with aspirin and the other 11,034 were given placebos. The study was stopped early because it became clear that aspirin reduced the risk of myocardial infarctions by a substantial amount.

23. Drinking and Driving A researcher for a consortium of insurance companies plans to test for the effects of drinking on driving ability by randomly selecting 1000 drivers and then randomly assigning them to two groups: One group of 500 will drive in New York City after no alcohol consumption, and the second group will drive in New York City after consuming three shots of Jim Beam bourbon whiskey.

24. School Suspensions The Children's Defense Fund reported that among secondary school students suspended in one region, 67% were suspended at least three times. That statistic was based on three students.

25. Sleep Study When designing the study of a new treatment for insomnia in adults, researchers were criticized because their test subjects consisted of 75 college students. They then expanded the study so that 750 college students were given the treatment.

26. Atkins Weight Loss Program An independent researcher tested the effectiveness of the Atkins weight loss program by randomly selecting 1000 subjects using that program. Each of the subjects was called to report their weight before the diet and after the diet.

27. Crime Research A sociologist has created a brief survey to be given to 2000 adults randomly selected from the U.S. population. Here are her first two questions: (1) Have you ever been the victim of a felony crime? (2) Have you ever been convicted of a felony?

28. Medications The Pharmaceutical Research and Manufacturers of America wants information about the consumption of various medications. An independent researcher conducts a survey by mailing 10,000 questionnaires to randomly selected adults in the United States, and she receives 152 responses.

1-3 Beyond the Basics

In Exercises 29–32, indicate whether the observational study used is cross-sectional, retrospective, or prospective.

29. Nurses' Health Study II Phase II of the Nurses' Health Study was started in 1989 with 116,000 female registered nurses. The study is ongoing.

30. Heart Health Study Samples of subjects with and without heart disease were selected, and then researchers looked back in time to determine whether they took aspirin on a regular basis.

31. Marijuana Study Researchers from the National Institutes of Health want to determine the current rates of marijuana consumption among adults living in states that have legalized the use of marijuana. They conduct a survey of 500 adults in those states.

32. Framingham Heart Study The Framingham Heart Study was started in 1948 and is ongoing. Its focus is on heart disease.

In Exercises 33–36, identify which of these designs is most appropriate for the given experiment: completely randomized design, randomized block design, or matched pairs design.

33. Lunesta Lunesta is a drug designed to treat insomnia. In a clinical trial of Lunesta, amounts of sleep each night are measured before and after subjects have been treated with the drug.

34. Lipitor A clinical trial of Lipitor treatments is being planned to determine whether its effects on diastolic blood pressure are different for men and women.

35. West Nile Vaccine Currently, there is no approved vaccine for the prevention of infection by West Nile virus. A clinical trial of a possible vaccine is being planned to include subjects treated with the vaccine while other subjects are given a placebo.

36. HIV Vaccine The HIV Trials Network is conducting a study to test the effectiveness of two different experimental HIV vaccines. Subjects will consist of 80 pairs of twins. For each pair of twins, one of the subjects will be treated with the DNA vaccine and the other twin will be treated with the adenoviral vector vaccine.

37. Simple Random Sample vs. Random Sample Refer to the definition of *simple random sample* on page 28 and its accompanying definition of *random sample* enclosed within parentheses. Determine whether each of the following is a simple random sample and a random sample.

a. In Major League Baseball, there are 30 teams, each with an active roster of 25 players. The names of the teams are printed on 30 separate index cards, the cards are shuffled, and one card is drawn. The sample consists of the 25 players on the active roster of the selected team.

b. For the same Major League Baseball population described in part (a), the 750 names of the players are printed on 750 separate index cards, and the cards are shuffled. Twenty-five different cards are selected from the top. The sample consists of the 25 selected players.

c. For the same Major League Baseball population described in part (a), a sample is constructed by selecting the 25 youngest players.

1-4 Ethics in Statistics

The website www.TriolaStats.com includes a downloadable section that discusses ethical issues in statistics, including those related to data collection, analysis, and reporting.

Chapter Quick Quiz

1. Survey An example in this chapter referred to a survey of 410 human resource professionals. If those subjects are identified with numbers from 1 through 410, does it make sense to calculate the average (mean) of those numbers?

2. Survey Which of the following best describes the level of measurement of the numbers 1, 2, 3, . . . , 410 described in Exercise 1: nominal, ordinal, interval, ratio?

3. Survey In the same survey cited in Exercise 1, are the exact unrounded ages of the 410 subjects discrete data or continuous data?

4. Survey In the same survey cited in Exercise 1, are the exact unrounded ages of the 410 subjects quantitative data or categorical data?

5. Survey Which of the following best describes the level of measurement of the exact unrounded ages of the 410 survey subjects from Exercise 1: nominal, ordinal, interval, ratio?

6. Birth Weights For 100 randomly selected births from Bellevue Hospital Center, the birth weights are added and then divided by 100. The result is 3240 g. Is the value of 3240 g a statistic or a parameter?

7. Birth Weights Refer to the sample described in Exercise 6. Because Bellevue Hospital Center agreed to provide the 100 birth weights, does the sample of birth weights constitute a voluntary response sample?

8. Birth Weights Are the data described in Exercise 6 the result of an observational study or an experiment?

9. Physicians' Health Study In the Physicians' Health Study, some of the subjects were treated with aspirin while others were given a placebo. For the subjects in this experiment, what is *blinding*?

10. Sampling In a statistical study, which of the following types of samples is generally best: convenience sample, voluntary response sample, simple random sample, biased sample?

Review Exercises

1. Online Medical Info *USA Today* posted this question on its website: "How often do you seek medical information online?" Of 1072 Internet users who chose to respond, 38% of them responded with "frequently." What term is used to describe this type of survey in which the people surveyed consist of those who decided to respond? What is wrong with this type of sampling method?

2. Paying for First Dates *USA Today* posted this question on the electronic version of its newspaper: "Should guys pay for the first date?" Of the 1148 subjects who decided to respond, 85% of them said "yes."

a. What is wrong with this survey?

b. Is the value of 85% a statistic or a parameter?

c. Does the survey constitute an experiment or an observational study?

3. Sample Design Literacy In "High-Flow Oxygen for Treatment of Cluster Headache" (*Journal of the American Medical Association*, Vol. 302, No. 22), the authors explain that 150 patients were treated with oxygen, and 148 patients were given a placebo. The authors summarize the sample design as "randomized and double-blind." Describe the meaning of "randomized" and "double-blind" in the context of this study.

4. Divorces and Margarine One study showed that there is a very high correlation between the divorce rate in Maine and per capita consumption of margarine in the United States. Can we conclude that either one of those two variables is the cause of the other?

5. Sampling For each of the following, identify the term that best describes the type of sample: *systematic*, *convenience*, *stratified*, *cluster*, or *simple random sample*.

a. As Lipitor pills are being manufactured, a quality control plan is to select every 500th pill and test it to confirm that it contains 80 mg of atorvastatin.

b. To test for a gender difference in the way that men and women make online purchases, Gallup surveys 500 randomly selected men and 500 randomly selected women.

c. A list of all 1,736,997 adults in Manhattan is obtained; the list is numbered from 1 to 1,736,997; and then a computer is used to randomly generate 500 different numbers between 1 and 1,736,997. The sample consists of the adults corresponding to the selected numbers.

d. A statistics student creates a survey and presents it to fellow statistics students.

e. The Commissioner of Major League Baseball obtains a sample by randomly selecting one team from the American League and one team from the National League, and all players on the selected teams are surveyed.

6. Defense of Marriage Act Both of the following questions are essentially the same. Does the difference in wording seem as though it could affect the way that people respond?

• Are you in favor of the "Defense of Marriage Act"?

• Are you in favor of an act that for federal and state aid, only heterosexual marriages should be recognized?

7. State Populations Currently, California has the largest population with 39,776,830 residents, and Wyoming has the smallest population with 573,520 residents.

a. Are the population sizes of the different states discrete or continuous?

b. What is the level of measurement for the numbers of residents in the different states? (nominal, ordinal, interval, ratio)

c. What is wrong with surveying state residents by mailing questionnaires to 10,000 of them who are randomly selected?

d. If we randomly select 50 full-time workers in each of the 50 states, what type of sample is obtained? (random, systematic, convenience, stratified, cluster)

e. If we randomly select two states and survey all of their adult residents, what type of sample is obtained? (random, systematic, convenience, stratified, cluster)

8. Percentages

a. The labels on U-Turn protein energy bars include the statement that these bars contain "125% less fat than the leading chocolate candy brands" (based on data from *Consumer Reports* magazine). What is wrong with that claim?

b. In a Pew Research Center poll on driving, 58% of the 1182 respondents said that they like to drive. What is the actual number of respondents who said that they like to drive?

c. In a Pew Research Center poll on driving, 331 of the 1182 respondents said that driving is a chore. What percentage of respondents said that driving is a chore?

9. Types of Data In each of the following, identify the level of measurement of the sample data (nominal, ordinal, interval, ratio) and the type of sampling used to obtain the data (random, systematic, convenience, stratified, cluster).

a. At Albany Medical Center, every 10th newborn baby is selected and the body temperature is measured (degrees Fahrenheit).

b. In each of the 50 states, 50 voters are randomly selected and their political party affiliations are identified.

c. A pollster stops each person passing her office door and asks the person to rate the last movie that he or she saw (on a scale of 1 star to 4 stars).

10. Statistical Significance and Practical Significance The Genetics and IVF Institute developed a procedure designed to increase the likelihood that a baby would be a boy. In a clinical trial of their procedure, 239 boys were born among 291 births. If the method has no effect, there is less than a 1% chance that such extreme results would occur. Does the procedure appear to have statistical significance? Does the procedure appear to have practical significance?

Cumulative Review Exercises

For Chapter 2 through Chapter 14, the Cumulative Review Exercises include topics from preceding chapters. For this chapter, we present a few calculator warm-up exercises, with expressions similar to those found throughout this book. Use your calculator to find the indicated values.

1. IQ Scores Listed below are the IQ scores of randomly selected statistics professors. What value is obtained when those IQ scores are added and the total is divided by the number of scores? (This result, called the *mean*, is discussed in Chapter 3.) What is notable about these values?

$$135 \quad 149 \quad 145 \quad 129 \quad 118 \quad 119 \quad 115 \quad 133 \quad 107 \quad 188 \quad 127 \quad 131$$

2. Streak of Boys Jay and Kateri Schwandt had 13 children—all boys! The probability that 13 randomly selected children are all boys is found by evaluating 0.5^{13}. Find that value and round the result to six decimal places.

3. LeBron James LeBron James, one of the best professional basketball players ever, has a height of 203 cm. The expression below converts his height of 203 cm (or 6' 8") to a standardized score. Find this value and round the result to two decimal places. Such standardized scores are considered to be significantly high if they are greater than 2 or 3. Is the result significantly high?

$$\frac{203 - 176}{6}$$

4. Body Temperature The given expression is used for determining the likelihood that the average (mean) human body temperature is different from the value of 98.6°F that is commonly used. Find the given value and round the result to two decimal places.

$$\frac{98.2 - 98.6}{\frac{0.62}{\sqrt{106}}}$$

5. Determining Sample Size The given expression is used to determine the size of the sample necessary to estimate the proportion of college students who have the profound wisdom to take a statistics course. Find the value and round the result up to the next larger whole number.

$$\frac{1.95996^2 \cdot 0.25}{0.03^2}$$

6. Standard Deviation One way to get a very rough approximation of the value of a standard deviation of sample data is to find the range, then divide it by 4. The range is the difference between the highest sample value and the lowest sample value. In using this approach, what value is obtained from the sample data listed in Exercise 1 "IQ Scores"?

7. Standard Deviation The standard deviation is an extremely important concept introduced in Chapter 3. Using the sample data from Exercise 1 "IQ Scores," part of the calculation of the standard deviation is shown in the expression below. Evaluate this expression and round the result to three decimal places. (Fortunately, calculators and software are designed to automatically execute such expressions, so our future work with standard deviations will not be burdened with cumbersome calculations.)

$$\frac{(135 - 133.0)^2}{11}$$

8. Standard Deviation The given expression is used to compute the standard deviation of three randomly selected body temperatures. Perform the calculation and round the result to two decimal places.

$$\sqrt{\frac{(98.4 - 98.6)^2 + (98.6 - 98.6)^2 + (98.8 - 98.6)^2}{3 - 1}}$$

Scientific Notation. *In Exercises 9–12, the given expressions are designed to yield results expressed in a form of scientific notation. For example, the calculator-displayed result of 1.23E5 can be expressed as 123,000, and the result of 1.23E-4 can be expressed as 0.000123. Perform the indicated operation and express the result as an ordinary number that is not in scientific notation.*

9. 0.3^6 **10.** 8^{12} **11.** 85^6 **12.** 0.2^{12}

Technology Project

1. Missing Data The focus of this project is to download a data set and manipulate it to work around the issue of missing data.

a. First, download Data Set 5 "Body Temperatures" in Appendix B from TriolaStats.com. Choose the download format that matches your technology.

b. Some statistical procedures, such as those involved with correlation and regression (discussed in later chapters) require data that consist of matched pairs of values, and those procedures ignore pairs in which at least one of the data values in a matched pair is missing. Assume that we want to conduct analyses for correlation and regression on the last two columns of data in Data Set 5: body temperatures measured at 8 AM on day 2 and again at 12 AM on day 2. For those last two columns, identify the rows with at least one missing value. Note that in some technologies, such as TI-83/84 Plus calculators, missing data must be represented by a constant such as −9 or 999.

c. Here are two different strategies for reconfiguring the data set to work around the missing data in the last two columns (assuming that we need matched pairs of data with no missing values):

i. Manual Deletion Highlight rows with at least one missing value in the last two columns, then delete those rows. This can be tedious if there are many rows with missing data and those rows are interspersed throughout instead of being adjacent rows.

ii. Sort Most technologies have a Sort feature that allows you to rearrange all rows using one particular column as the basis for sorting (TI-83/84 Plus calculators *do not* have this type of sort feature). The result is that all rows remain the same but they are in a different order. First use the technology's Sort feature to rearrange all rows using the "8 AM day 2" column as the basis for sorting (so that all missing values in the "8 AM day 2" column are at the beginning); then highlight and delete all of those rows with missing values in the "8 AM day 2" column. Next, use the technology's Sort feature to rearrange all rows using the "12 AM day 2" column as the basis for sorting (so that all missing values in the "12 AM day 2" column are at the beginning); then highlight and delete all of those rows with missing values in the "12 AM day 2" column. The remaining rows will include matched pairs of body temperatures, and those rows will be suitable for analyses such as correlation and regression. Print the resulting reconfigured data set that now has no missing data.

Big (or Very Large) Data Project

Refer to Data Set 45 "Births in New York" in Appendix B, with records from 465,506 births. Find the number of males and find the number of females. What percentage of births are males? How does that result compare to the value of 51.2%, which is believed to be the proportion of male births in the population? Based on these results, does it appear that the sample accurately reflects the population?

FROM DATA TO DECISION

Critical Thinking: Is Being a Student More Dangerous or Unhealthy Than Being a Carpenter?

In 1835, the Swiss physician H. C. Lombard compiled longevity data for different professions. Over a period of 50 years, he collected 8496 death certificates from Geneva that included name, age at death, and profession. He calculated the average (mean) length of life for different professions, and some of his results are listed on the right. The table shows that among the five professions listed, being a student is most dangerous or unhealthy with an average (mean) age of death of only 20.2 years. Similar results would be obtained if the same data were collected today. (See "A Selection of Selection Anomalies" by Wainer, Palmer, and Bradlow in *Chance*, Volume 11, No. 2.) Using common sense, the most indispensable tool for statistical thinking, it should not seem reasonable that being a student is substantially more dangerous or unhealthy than being a carpenter or barber.

Profession	Average (Mean) Age at Death
Carpenters	55.1
Bakers	49.8
Barbers	47.4
Shoemakers	54.2
Students	20.2

Analysis

1. Consider the population of students. About how many people do you know who are students aged 50 years or older?

2. Estimate the age at which people stop being students.

3. Why is it that being a student is actually no more dangerous or unhealthy than being a carpenter or barber?

4. How are samples of carpenters, bakers, barbers, shoemakers, and students fundamentally different?

Cooperative Group Activities

1. In-class activity For each student in the class, collect the number of children in his or her immediate family, including the student. Combine the results and find the average (mean). Compare the result to the value of 1.9 reported in the *World Factbook* by the Central Intelligence Agency. Use a class discussion to explain the discrepancy.

2. In-class activity Working in groups of three or four, design an experiment to determine whether pulse rates of college students are the same while the students are standing and sitting. Conduct the experiment and collect the data. Save the data so that they can be analyzed with methods presented in the following chapters.

3. In-class activity Working in groups of three or four, construct a brief survey that includes only a few questions that can be quickly asked. Include some objective questions along with some that are biased, such as the first question below.

• Should your college force all students to pay a $100 activity fee?

• Should your college fund activities by collecting a $100 fee?

Conduct the survey and try to detect the effect that the biased wording has on the responses.

4. In-class activity Identify problems with a mailing from *Consumer Reports* magazine that included an annual questionnaire about cars and other consumer products. Also included were a request for a voluntary contribution of money and a voting ballot for the board of directors. Responses were to be mailed back in envelopes that required postage stamps.

5. Out-of-class activity Find a report of a survey that used a voluntary response sample. Describe how it is quite possible that the results do not accurately reflect the population.

6. Out-of-class activity Find a professional journal with an article that includes a statistical analysis of an experiment. Describe and comment on the design of the experiment. Identify one particular issue addressed by the study, and determine whether the results were found to be statistically significant. Determine whether those same results have practical significance.

7. Out-of-class activity Obtain 18 straws from the cafeteria or supermarket. Cut 6 of them in half, cut 6 of them into quarters, and leave the other 6 as they are. There should now be 42 straws of different lengths. Put them in a bag, mix them up, then select one straw, find its length, then replace it. Repeat this until 20 straws have been selected. *Important:* Select the straws without looking into the bag and select the first straw that is touched. Find the average (mean) of the sample of 20 straws. Now remove all of the straws and find the average (mean) of the population. Did the sample provide an average (mean) that was close to the true population average (mean)? Why or why not?

EXPLORING DATA WITH TABLES AND GRAPHS

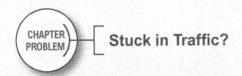

CHAPTER PROBLEM — **Stuck in Traffic?**

Does it seem like traffic is getting worse and that rush hour has expanded to include most of the day? If your commute to work or college seems like it is getting longer, that's because it probably is! Recent data from the U.S. Census Bureau's American Community Survey found that the average American's commute time increased from 26.6 minutes to 26.9 minutes over a one-year period. That increase may seem small, but it means the average American spends 2.5 hours

more in traffic per year! Even minor changes in daily commute times can have major impacts on productivity, the environment, mental health, and more.

In this Chapter Problem we will consider daily commute times in different cities. It is important that commute times be analyzed at both the national and local levels so that undesirable trends can be identified and mitigated. Table 2-1 lists 50 reported daily commute times (to work) from residents of the city of Los Angeles, which is infamous for its traffic. These data are from Data Set 31 "Commute Times" in Appendix B.

It is an exceptionally rare person who can simply look at the data in Table 2-1 and form meaningful conclusions. We mere mortals must work at describing, exploring, and comparing such data to gain meaningful insights. In this chapter we present methods that focus on organizing and summarizing the data and using graphs that enable us to understand important characteristics of the data, especially the *distribution* of the data.

TABLE 2-1 Daily Commute Time (minutes) in Los Angeles

18	25	45	75	60	40	25	8	50	10	10	30	15	25	50	20	30	20	45	30	60	30	20	15	30
60	30	15	35	40	5	30	40	20	10	45	30	15	25	25	5	90	30	15	60	20	60	30	25	25

CHAPTER OBJECTIVES

HINT Remember the sentence "**C**omputer **V**iruses **D**estroy **O**r **T**erminate" to recall the first letters of the characteristics (CVDOT).

This chapter and the following chapter focus on important characteristics of data, including the following:

Important Characteristics of Data

1. **Center:** A representative value that shows us where the middle of the data set is located.

2. **Variation:** A measure of the amount that the data values vary.

3. **Distribution:** The nature or shape of the spread of the data over the range of values (such as bell-shaped).

4. **Outliers:** Sample values that lie very far away from the vast majority of the other sample values.

5. **Time:** Any change in the characteristics of the data over time.

This chapter provides tools that enable us to gain insight into data by organizing, summarizing, and representing them in ways that enable us to see important characteristics of the data. Here are the chapter objectives:

2-1 Frequency Distributions for Organizing and Summarizing Data

- Develop an ability to summarize data in the format of a frequency distribution and a relative frequency distribution.

- For a frequency distribution, identify values of class width, class midpoint, class limits, and class boundaries.

2-2 Histograms

- Develop the ability to picture the distribution of data in the format of a histogram or relative frequency histogram.

- Examine a histogram and identify common distributions, including a uniform distribution and a normal distribution.

2-3 Graphs That Enlighten and Graphs That Deceive

- Develop an ability to graph data using a dotplot, stemplot, time-series graph, Pareto chart, pie chart, and frequency polygon.

- Determine when a graph is deceptive through the use of a nonzero axis or a pictograph that uses an object of area or volume for one-dimensional data.

2-4 Scatterplots, Correlation, and Regression

- Develop an ability to construct a scatterplot of paired data.

- Analyze a scatterplot to determine whether there appears to be a correlation between two variables.

Frequency Distributions for Organizing and Summarizing Data

2-1

Key Concept When working with large data sets, a *frequency distribution* (or *frequency table*) is often helpful in organizing and summarizing data. A frequency distribution helps us to understand the nature of the *distribution* of a data set. Also, construction of a frequency distribution is often the first step in constructing a histogram, which is a graph used to help visualize the distribution of data.

TABLE 2-2 Daily Commute Time in Los Angeles

Daily Commute Time in Los Angeles (minutes)	Frequency
0–14	6
15–29	18
30–44	14
45–59	5
60–74	5
75–89	1
90–104	1

DEFINITION

A **frequency distribution** (or **frequency table**) shows how data are partitioned among several categories (or *classes*) by listing the categories along with the number (frequency) of data values in each of them.

Let's use the commute times listed in Table 2-1 from the Chapter Problem. Table 2-2 is a frequency distribution summarizing those times. The **frequency** for a particular class is the number of original values that fall into that class. For example, the first class in Table 2-2 has a frequency of 6, so 6 of the commute times are between 0 and 14 minutes, inclusive. Examining the list of frequencies, we see that the commute times are distributed with most of the times being at the lower end.

The following standard terms are often used in constructing frequency distributions and graphs.

DEFINITIONS

Lower class limits are the smallest numbers that can belong to each of the different classes. (Table 2-2 has lower class limits of 0, 15, 30, 45, 60, 75, and 90.)

Upper class limits are the largest numbers that can belong to each of the different classes. (Table 2-2 has upper class limits of 14, 29, 44, 59, 74, 89, and 104.)

Class boundaries are the numbers used to separate the classes, but without the gaps created by class limits. Figure 2-1 on the next page shows the gaps created by the class limits from Table 2-2. In Figure 2-1 we see that the values of 14.5, 29.5, 44.5, 59.5, 74.5, and 89.5 are in the centers of those gaps. Following the pattern of those class boundaries, we see that the lowest class boundary is −0.5 and the highest class boundary is 104.5. The complete list of class boundaries is −0.5, 14.5, 29.5, 44.5, 59.5, 74.5, 89.5, and 104.5.

Class midpoints are the values in the middle of the classes. Table 2-2 has class midpoints of 7, 22, 37, 52, 67, 82, and 97. Each class midpoint can be found by adding the lower class limit to the upper class limit and dividing the sum by 2.

Class width is the difference between two consecutive lower class limits (or two consecutive lower class boundaries) in a frequency distribution. Table 2-2 uses a class width of 15. (The first two lower class limits are 0 and 15, and their difference is 15.)

CAUTION Finding the correct class width can be tricky. For class width, don't make the most common mistake of using the difference between a lower class limit and an upper class limit. See Table 2-2 and note that the class width is 15, not 14.

CAUTION For class boundaries, remember that they split the difference between the end of one class and the beginning of the next class, as shown in Figure 2-1.

STEP 1: List the class limits from Table 2-2.

STEP 2: Split the difference as shown.

STEP 3: Find the first and last values of −0.5 and 104.5 by projecting the same pattern from Step 2.

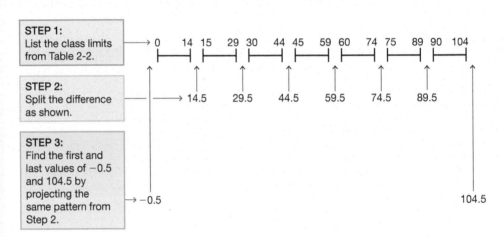

FIGURE 2-1   Finding Class Boundaries from Class Limits in Table 2-2

Procedure for Constructing a Frequency Distribution

We construct frequency distributions to (1) summarize large data sets, (2) see the distribution of the data, (3) identify outliers, and (4) have a basis for constructing graphs (such as *histograms,* introduced in Section 2-2). Technology can generate frequency distributions, but here are the steps for manually constructing them:

1. Select the number of classes, usually between 5 and 20. The number of classes might be affected by the convenience of using round numbers. (According to "Sturges' guideline," the ideal number of classes for a frequency distribution can be approximated by $1 + (\log n)/(\log 2)$ where n is the number of data values. We don't use this guideline in this book.)

2. Calculate the class width.

$$\text{Class width} \approx \frac{(\text{maximum data value}) - (\text{minimum data value})}{\text{number of classes}}$$

Round this result to get a convenient number. (It's usually best to round *up.*) Using a specific number of classes is not too important, and it's usually wise to change the number of classes so that they use convenient values for the class limits.

3. Choose the value for the first lower class limit by using either the minimum value or a convenient value below the minimum.

4. Using the first lower class limit and the class width, list the other lower class limits. (Do this by adding the class width to the first lower class limit to get the second lower class limit. Add the class width to the second lower class limit to get the third lower class limit, and so on.)

5. List the lower class limits in a vertical column and then determine and enter the upper class limits.

6. Take each individual data value and put a tally mark in the appropriate class. Add the tally marks to find the total frequency for each class.

When constructing a frequency distribution, be sure the classes do not overlap. Each of the original values must belong to exactly one class. Include all classes, even those with a frequency of zero. Try to use the same width for all classes, although it is sometimes impossible to avoid open-ended intervals, such as "65 years or older."

(CP) **EXAMPLE 1** Daily Commute Time in Los Angeles

Using the daily commute times in Los Angeles in Table 2-1 from the Chapter Problem, follow the above procedure to construct the frequency distribution shown in Table 2-2. Use seven classes.

SOLUTION

Step 1: Select 7 as the number of desired classes.

Step 2: Calculate the class width as shown below. Note that we round 12 up to 15, which is a more convenient number for commute time measurements.

$$\text{Class width} \approx \frac{(\text{maximum data value}) - (\text{minimum data value})}{\text{number of classes}}$$

$$= \frac{90 - 5}{7} = 12.1 \approx 15 \,(\text{rounded up to a more convenient number})$$

Step 3: Let's select 0 as the first lower class limit because it is below the value of 5 and is a very convenient starting point for commute time.

Step 4: Add the class width of 15 to the starting value of 0 to get the second lower class limit of 15. Continue to add the class width of 15 until we have seven lower class limits. The lower class limits are therefore 0, 15, 30, 45, 60, 75, and 90.

Step 5: List the lower class limits vertically, as shown in the margin. From this list, we identify the corresponding upper class limits as 14, 29, 44, 59, 74, 89, and 104.

Step 6: Enter a tally mark for each data value in the appropriate class. Then add the tally marks to find the frequencies shown in Table 2-2.

↪ **YOUR TURN.** Do Exercise 13 "Chicago Commute Time."

Categorical Data So far we have discussed frequency distributions using only quantitative data sets, but frequency distributions can also be used to summarize categorical (or qualitative or attribute) data, as illustrated in Example 2.

⌐ **EXAMPLE 2** Causes of Fatal Plane Crashes

Table 2-3 on the next page lists data for the causes of fatal plane crashes from 1960 until a recent year. The causes are categorical data at the nominal level of measurement, but we can create the frequency distribution as shown. We can see that pilot error is the major cause of fatal plane crashes. Such information is helpful to regulatory agencies, such as the Federal Aviation Administration, as they develop strategies for reducing such crashes.

continued

| 0– |
| 15– |
| 30– |
| 45– |
| 60– |
| 75– |
| 90– |

TABLE 2-3 Causes of Fatal Plane Crashes

Cause	Frequency
Pilot Error	640
Mechanical	195
Sabotage	95
Weather	63
Other	111

➤YOUR TURN. Do Exercise 27 "Software Piracy."

Relative Frequency Distribution

A variation of the basic frequency distribution is a **relative frequency distribution** or **percentage frequency distribution**, in which each class frequency is replaced by a relative frequency (or proportion) or a percentage. In this text we use the term "relative frequency distribution" whether we use relative frequencies or percentages. Relative frequencies and percentages are calculated as follows.

$$\text{Relative frequency for a class} = \frac{\text{frequency for a class}}{\text{sum of all frequencies}}$$

$$\text{Percentage for a class} = \frac{\text{frequency for a class}}{\text{sum of all frequencies}} \times 100\%$$

TABLE 2-4 Relative Frequency Distribution of Daily Commute Times in Los Angeles

Daily Commute Time in Los Angeles (minutes)	Relative Frequency
0–14	12%
15–29	36%
30–44	28%
45–59	10%
60–74	10%
75–89	2%
90–104	2%

Table 2-4 is an example of a relative frequency distribution. It is a variation of Table 2-2 in which each class frequency is replaced by the corresponding percentage value. The sum of the frequencies in Table 2-2 is 50, so the percentages for the classes can be found by dividing each class frequency by 50, and then multiplying by 100%. The first class of Table 2-2 has a frequency of 6, so divide 6 by 50 to get 0.12, and then multiply by 100% to get 12%. The sum of the percentages should be 100%, with a small discrepancy allowed for rounding errors, so a sum such as 99% or 101% is usually acceptable. The sum of the percentages in Table 2-4 is 100%.

The sum of the percentages in a relative frequency distribution must be very close to 100% (with a little wiggle room for rounding errors).

Comparisons Example 3 illustrates this principle:

Combining two or more relative frequency distributions in one table makes comparisons of different data sets much easier.

CP)— **EXAMPLE 3** Comparing Daily Commute Time in New York, NY and Boise, ID

Now let's shift gears (pun intended) and compare commute times of two different cities. Table 2-5 shows the relative frequency distributions for 1000 commute times in New York and Boise from Data Set 31. Because of the different sizes of these two cities, we might expect the commute times to be very different. By comparing the relative frequencies in Table 2-5, we see that there are major differences. The Boise commute times appear to be lower than the New York commute times. (See that for Boise, the lowest two classes have 75.8% of all commute times, compared to only 28.9% for New York.) This is not surprising given the relative size and population density of these cities.

TABLE 2-5 Daily Commute Times in New York, NY and Boise, ID (minutes)

Daily Commute Time (minutes)	New York, NY	Boise, ID
0–14	8.6%	30.3%
15–29	20.3%	45.5%
30–44	24.8%	17.0%
45–59	17.2%	3.5%
60–74	18.5%	2.2%
75–89	3.3%	0.3%
90–104	4.7%	0.3%
105–119	0.1%	0.0%
120–134	0.0%	0.0%
135–149	2.5%	0.9%

YOUR TURN. Do Exercise 23 "Oscar Winners."

Cumulative Frequency Distribution

Another variation of a frequency distribution is a **cumulative frequency distribution** in which the frequency for each class is the sum of the frequencies for that class and all previous classes. Let's return to the Los Angeles commute times provided at the beginning of this chapter. Table 2-6 is the cumulative frequency distribution found from Table 2-2. Using the original frequencies of 6, 18, 14, 5, 5, 1, 1, we add 6 + 18 to get the second cumulative frequency of 24, then we add 6 + 8 + 14 to get the third, and so on. See Table 2-6, and note that in addition to the use of cumulative frequencies, the class limits are replaced by "less than" expressions that describe the new ranges of values.

TABLE 2-6 Cumulative Frequency Distribution of Daily Commute Times in Los Angeles

Daily Commute Times in Los Angeles (minutes)	Cumulative Frequency
Less than 15	6
Less than 30	24
Less than 45	38
Less than 60	43
Less than 75	48
Less than 90	49
Less than 105	50

Critical Thinking: Using Frequency Distributions to Understand Data

At the beginning of this section we noted that a frequency distribution can help us understand the *distribution* of a data set, which is the nature or shape of the spread of the data over the range of values (such as bell-shaped). In statistics we are often interested in determining whether the data have a *normal distribution*. (Normal distributions are discussed extensively in Chapter 6.) Data that have an approximately normal distribution are characterized by a frequency distribution with the following features.

Normal Distribution

1. The frequencies start low, then increase to one or two high frequencies, and then decrease to a low frequency.

2. The distribution is approximately symmetric: Frequencies preceding the maximum frequency should be roughly a mirror image of those that follow the maximum frequency.

Table 2-7 satisfies these two conditions. The frequencies start low, increase to the maximum of 18, and then decrease to a low frequency. Also, the frequencies of 2, 4, and 10 that precede the maximum are a mirror image of the frequencies 10, 4, and 2 that follow the maximum. Real data sets are usually not so perfect as Table 2-7, and judgment must be used to determine whether the distribution comes close enough to satisfying those two conditions. (There are more objective procedures described later.)

If we consider the Los Angeles commute times from Table 2-1 and their frequency distribution summarized in Table 2-2, we see that the frequencies start low at 6, increase to a maximum of 18 and then decrease to a low frequency of 1. The distribution is far from symmetric, so the data do not satisfy the criteria for being a normal distribution. The Los Angeles commute times have some other distribution that is clearly not a normal distribution.

TABLE 2-7 Frequency Distribution Showing a Normal Distribution

Time	Frequency	Normal Distribution
0–14	2	← Frequencies start low, . . .
15–29	4	
30–44	10	
45–59	18	← Increase to this maximum, . . .
60–74	10	
75–89	4	
90–104	2	← Decrease to become low again.

Analysis of Last Digits Example 4 illustrates this principle:

Frequencies of last digits sometimes reveal how the data were collected or measured.

TABLE 2-8 Last Digits of Pulse Rates from the National Health and Examination Survey

Last Digit of Pulse Rate	Frequency
0	455
1	0
2	461
3	0
4	479
5	0
6	425
7	0
8	399
9	0

EXAMPLE 4 **Exploring Data: How Were the Pulse Rates Measured?**

Upon examination of measured pulse rates from 2219 adults included in the National Health and Examination Survey, the last digits of the recorded pulse rates are identified and the frequency distribution for those last digits is as shown in Table 2-8. Here is an important observation of those last digits: All of the last digits are *even* numbers. If the pulse rates were counted for 1 full minute, there would surely be a large number of them ending with an *odd* digit. So what happened?

One reasonable explanation is that even though the pulse rates are the number of heartbeats in 1 minute, they were likely counted for 30 seconds and the number of beats was doubled. (The original pulse rates are not all multiples of 4, so we can rule out a procedure of counting for 15 seconds and then multiplying by 4.) Analysis of these last digits reveals to us the method used to obtain these data.

In many surveys, we can determine that surveyed subjects were asked to *report* some values, such as their heights or weights, because disproportionately many values end in 0 or 5. This is a strong clue that the respondent is rounding instead of being physically measured. Fascinating stuff!

YOUR TURN. Do Exercise 21 "Analysis of Last Digits."

Gaps Example 5 illustrates this principle:

> **The presence of gaps can suggest that the data are from two or more different populations.**

The converse of this principle is not true, because data from different populations do not necessarily result in gaps.

TABLE 2-9 Randomly Selected Pennies

Weight (grams) of Penny	Frequency
2.40–2.49	18
2.50–2.59	19
2.60–2.69	0
2.70–2.79	0
2.80–2.89	0
2.90–2.99	2
3.00–3.09	25
3.10–3.19	8

EXAMPLE 5 Exploring Data: What Does a Gap Tell Us?

Table 2-9 is a frequency distribution of the weights (grams) of randomly selected pennies. Examination of the frequencies reveals a large *gap* between the lightest pennies and the heaviest pennies. This suggests that we have two different populations: Pennies made before 1983 are 95% copper and 5% zinc, but pennies made after 1983 are 2.5% copper and 97.5% zinc, which explains the large gap between the lightest pennies and the heaviest pennies represented in Table 2-9.

YOUR TURN. Do Exercise 21 "Analysis of Last Digits" and determine whether there is a gap. If so, what is a reasonable explanation for it?

TECH CENTER

Frequency Distributions
Access tech supplements, videos, and data sets at **www.TriolaStats.com**

Frequency distributions are often easy to obtain after generating a histogram, as described in Section 2-2. With Statdisk, for example, we can generate a histogram with a desired starting point and class width, then move the cursor over the histogram to see the frequency for each class. If histograms are not used, "sort" the data (arrange them in order) so that we can see the maximum data value and the minimum data value used for computing the class width. Once the class limits are established, it is easy to find the frequency for each class using sorted data. Every statistics software package includes a sort feature.

2-1 Basic Skills and Concepts

Statistical Literacy and Critical Thinking

1. Boston Commute Time The accompanying table summarizes daily commute times in Boston. How many commute times are included in the summary? Is it possible to identify the exact values of all of the original data amounts?

2. Boston Commute Time Refer to the accompanying frequency distribution. What problem would be created by using classes of 0–30, 30–60, . . . , 120–150?

3. Relative Frequency Distribution Use percentages to construct the relative frequency distribution corresponding to the accompanying frequency distribution for daily commute time in Boston.

Table for Exercises 1, 2 & 3.

Daily Commute Time in Boston (minutes)	Frequency
0–29	468
30–59	422
60–89	92
90–119	10
120–149	8

Table for Exercise 4

Height (cm)	Relative Frequency
130–144	23%
145–159	25%
160–174	22%
175–189	27%
190–204	28%

4. What's Wrong? Heights of adult males are known to have a normal distribution, as described in this section. A researcher claims to have randomly selected adult males and measured their heights with the resulting relative frequency distribution as shown in the margin. Identify two major flaws with these results.

In Exercises 5–8, identify the class width, class midpoints, and class boundaries for the given frequency distribution. Also identify the number of individuals included in the summary. The frequency distributions are based on real data from Appendix B.

5.

Age (yr) of Best Actress When Oscar Was Won	Frequency
20–29	31
30–39	34
40–49	15
50–59	3
60–69	6
70–79	1
80–89	1

6.

Age (yr) of Best Actor When Oscar Was Won	Frequency
20–29	1
30–39	29
40–49	38
50–59	16
60–69	6
70–79	1

7.

Blood Platelet Count of Males	Frequency
0–99	1
100–199	51
200–299	90
300–399	10
400–499	0
500–599	0
600–699	1

8.

Blood Platelet Count of Females	Frequency
100–199	25
200–299	92
300–399	28
400–499	0
500–599	2

Normal Distributions. *In Exercises 9–12, using a loose interpretation of the criteria for determining whether a frequency distribution is approximately a normal distribution, determine whether the given frequency distribution is approximately a normal distribution. Give a brief explanation.*

9. Best Actresses Refer to the frequency distribution from Exercise 5.

10. Best Actors Refer to the frequency distribution from Exercise 6.

11. Blood Platelet Counts of Males Refer to the frequency distribution from Exercise 7.

12. Blood Platelet Counts of Females Refer to the frequency distribution from Exercise 8.

Constructing Frequency Distributions. *In Exercises 13–20, use the indicated data to construct the frequency distribution. (The data for Exercises 17–20 can be downloaded at TriolaStats.com.)*

13. Chicago Commute Time Listed below are the first 50 Chicago commute times from Data Set 31. Construct a frequency distribution. Use a class width of 15 minutes and begin with a lower class limit of 0 minutes. Do the data amounts appear to have a normal distribution? Examine the data and identify anything appearing to be unique.

60	15	35	30	15	45	10	15	15	30
12	30	30	45	30	20	20	15	25	45
60	15	28	30	30	60	30	45	30	12
45	20	10	15	45	45	35	60	20	20
20	30	4	80	45	30	60	45	25	30

14. Presidents Listed below are the ages (years) of presidents of the United States at the times of their first inaugurations (from Data Set 22 "Presidents" in Appendix B). Presidents who took office as a result of an assassination or resignation are not included. The data are current as of this writing. Use these ages to construct a frequency distribution. Use a class width of 5 years and begin with a lower class limit of 40 years. Do the ages appear to have a normal distribution?

57 61 57 57 58 57 61 54 68 49 64 48 65 52 46 54 49 47 55 54
42 51 56 55 51 54 51 60 62 43 55 56 52 69 64 46 54 47 70

15. Old Faithful Listed below are sorted duration times (seconds) of eruptions of the Old Faithful geyser in Yellowstone National Park. Use these times to construct a frequency distribution. Use a class width of 25 seconds and begin with a lower class limit of 125 seconds.

125 203 205 221 225 229 233 233 235 236 236 237 238 238 239 240 240
240 240 241 241 242 242 242 243 243 244 245 245 245 245 246 246 248
248 248 249 249 250 251 252 253 253 255 255 256 257 258 262 264

16. Tornadoes Listed below are the F-scale intensities of recent tornadoes in the United States. Construct a frequency distribution. Do the intensities appear to have a normal distribution?

0 4 0 0 1 1 1 0 0 0 1 2 0 1 1 0 1 0 1 1 1 1 0
0 1 0 0 1 0 0 1 1 1 3 0 0 0 2 0 3 0 0 0 0 0

17. Burger King Lunch Service Times Refer to Data Set 36 "Fast Food" and use the drive-through service times for Burger King lunches. Begin with a lower class limit of 70 seconds and use a class width of 40 seconds.

18. Burger King Dinner Service Times Refer to Data Set 36 "Fast Food" and use the drive-through service times for Burger King dinners. Begin with a lower class limit of 30 seconds and use a class width of 40 seconds.

19. Freshman 15 Refer to Data Set 13 "Freshman 15" and use the second column, which lists weights (kg) in September of college freshmen. Begin with a lower class limit of 40 kg and use a class width of 10 kg. Does the distribution appear to be a normal distribution?

20. Hershey Kisses Refer to Data Set 38 "Candies" and use the weights (grams) of Hershey's Kisses. Begin with a lower class limit of 4.300 g and use a class width of 0.100 g. Does this distribution appear to be a normal distribution?

21. Analysis of Last Digits Heights of statistics students were obtained by the author as part of an experiment conducted for class. The last digits of those heights are listed below. Construct a frequency distribution with 10 classes. Based on the distribution, do the heights appear to be reported or actually measured? Does there appear to be a gap in the frequencies and, if so, how might that gap be explained? What do you know about the accuracy of the results?

0 0 0 0 0 0 0 0 0 1 1 2 3 3 3 4 5 5 5
5 5 5 5 5 5 5 5 5 5 5 5 5 6 6 8 8 8 9

22. Analysis of Last Digits Weights of respondents were recorded as part of the California Health Interview Survey. The last digits of weights from 50 randomly selected respondents are listed below. Construct a frequency distribution with 10 classes. Based on the distribution, do the weights appear to be reported or actually measured? Does there appear to be a gap in the frequencies and, if so, how might that gap be explained? What do you know about the accuracy of the results?

5 0 1 0 2 0 5 0 5 0 3 8 5 0 5 0 5 6 0 0 0 0 0 0 8
5 5 0 4 5 0 0 4 0 0 0 0 8 0 9 5 3 0 5 0 0 0 5 8

Relative Frequencies for Comparisons.   *In Exercises 23 and 24, construct the relative frequency distributions and answer the given questions.*

23. Oscar Winners Construct one table (similar to Table 2-5 on page 49) that includes relative frequencies based on the frequency distributions from Exercises 5 and 6, and then compare the ages of Oscar-winning actresses and actors. Are there notable differences?

24. Blood Platelet Counts Construct one table (similar to Table 2-5 on page 49) that includes relative frequencies based on the frequency distributions from Exercises 7 and 8, and then compare them. Are there notable differences?

Cumulative Frequency Distributions.   *In Exercises 25 and 26, construct the cumulative frequency distribution that corresponds to the frequency distribution in the exercise indicated.*

25. Exercise 5 (Age of Best Actress When Oscar Was Won)

26. Exercise 6 (Age of Best Actor When Oscar Was Won)

Categorical Data.   *In Exercises 27 and 28, use the given categorical data to construct the relative frequency distribution.*

27. Software Piracy Here are the countries with the five highest estimated costs of software piracy: United States ($9.1 billion), China ($8.7 billion), India ($2.7 billion), France ($2.1 billion), United Kingdom ($1.9 billion). Among these five countries, the United States has 37.1% of the cost of piracy. Is it correct to conclude that the United States has 37.1% of the total cost of piracy for all countries? What do these results tell us about the costs of piracy in the other countries not included here?

28. Births Natural births randomly selected from four hospitals in New York State occurred on the days of the week (in the order of Monday through Sunday) with these frequencies: 52, 66, 72, 57, 57, 43, 53. Does it appear that such births occur on the days of the week with equal frequency?

Large Data Sets.   *Exercises 29–34 involve large sets of data, so technology should be used. Complete lists of the data are not listed in Appendix B, but they can be downloaded from the website TriolaStats.com. Use the indicated data and construct the frequency distribution.*

29. Los Angeles Commute Time Refer to Data Set 31 "Commute Times" in Appendix B and use the 1000 Los Angeles commute times. Use a class width of 15 minutes and begin with a lower class limit of 0 minutes. How does the frequency distribution compare to Table 2-2?

30. Dallas Commute Time Refer to Data Set 31 "Commute Times" in Appendix B and use the 1000 Dallas commute times. Use a class width of 30 minutes and begin with a lower class limit of 0 minutes. How does the frequency distribution compare to the Boston commute time frequency distribution given for Exercise 1?

31. Systolic Blood Pressure Use the systolic blood pressures of the 300 subjects included in Data Set 1 "Body Data." Use a class width of 20 mm Hg and begin with a lower class limit of 80 mm Hg. Does the frequency distribution appear to be a normal distribution?

32. Diastolic Blood Pressure Use the diastolic blood pressures of the 300 subjects included in Data Set 1 "Body Data." Use a class width of 15 mm Hg and begin with a lower class limit of 40 mm Hg. Does the frequency distribution appear to be a normal distribution?

33. Earthquake Magnitudes Use the magnitudes of the 600 earthquakes included in Data Set 24 "Earthquakes." Use a class width of 0.5 and begin with a lower class limit of 1.00. Does the frequency distribution appear to be a normal distribution?

34. Earthquake Depths Use the depths (km) of the 600 earthquakes included in Data Set 24 "Earthquakes." Use a class width of 10.0 km and begin with a lower class limit of 0.0 km. Does the frequency distribution appear to be a normal distribution?

2-1 Beyond the Basics

 35. Interpreting Effects of Outliers Refer to Data Set 41 "Aluminum Cans" in Appendix B for the axial loads of aluminum cans that are 0.0111 in. thick. An axial load is the force at which the top of a can collapses. The load of 504 lb is an *outlier* because it is very far away from all of the other values. Construct a frequency distribution that includes the value of 504 lb, and then construct another frequency distribution with the value of 504 lb excluded. In both cases, start the first class at 200 lb and use a class width of 20 lb. State a generalization about the effect of an outlier on a frequency distribution.

2-2 Histograms

PART 1 Basic Concepts of Histograms

Key Concept While a frequency distribution is a useful tool for summarizing data and investigating the distribution of data, an even better tool is a *histogram*, which is a graph that is easier to understand and interpret than a table of numbers.

> **DEFINITION**
>
> A **histogram** is a graph consisting of bars of equal width drawn adjacent to each other (unless there are gaps in the data). The horizontal scale represents classes of quantitative data values, and the vertical scale represents frequencies. The heights of the bars correspond to frequency values.

Important Uses of a Histogram

- Visually displays the shape of the *distribution* of the data
- Shows the location of the *center* of the data
- Shows the *spread* of the data
- Identifies *outliers*

A histogram is basically a graph of a frequency distribution. For example, Figure 2-2 on the next page shows the Minitab-generated histogram corresponding to the frequency distribution given in Table 2-2 on page 45.

Class frequencies should be used for the vertical scale and that scale should be labeled as in Figure 2-2. There is no universal agreement on the procedure for selecting which values are used for the bar locations along the horizontal scale, but it is common to use class midpoints (as shown in Figure 2-2) or class boundaries or class limits or something else. It is often easier for us mere mortals to use class midpoints for the horizontal scale. Histograms can usually be generated using technology.

Relative Frequency Histogram

A **relative frequency histogram** has the same shape and horizontal scale as a histogram, but the vertical scale uses relative frequencies (as percentages or proportions) instead of actual frequencies. Figure 2-3 on the next page is the relative frequency histogram corresponding to Figure 2-2.

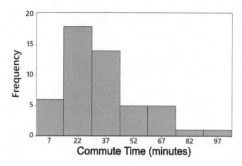

FIGURE 2-2   Histogram of Commute Time in Los Angeles from Table 2-1

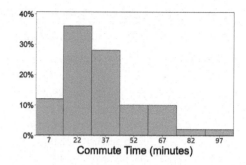

FIGURE 2-3   Relative Frequency Histogram of Commute Time in Los Angeles from Table 2-1

Critical Thinking: Interpreting Histograms

Even though creating histograms is more fun than human beings should be allowed to have, the ultimate objective is to *understand* characteristics of the data. Explore the data by analyzing the histogram to see what can be learned about "CVDOT": the *center* of the data, the *variation* (which will be discussed at length in Section 3-2), the *shape of the distribution*, whether there are any *outliers* (values far away from the other values), and *time* (whether there is any change in the characteristics of the data over time). Examining Figure 2-2, we see that the histogram is centered roughly around 30 minutes, and the shape of the distribution is a bit lopsided.

Common Distribution Shapes

The histograms shown in Figure 2-4 depict four common distribution shapes.

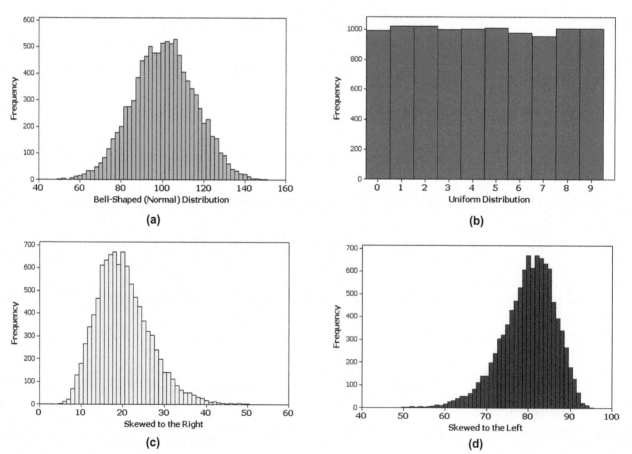

FIGURE 2-4   Common Distributions

Normal Distribution

When graphed as a histogram, a normal distribution has a "bell" shape similar to the one superimposed in Figure 2-5. Many statistical methods require that sample data come from a population having a distribution that is approximately a normal distribution, and we can often use a histogram to judge whether this requirement is satisfied. There are more advanced and less subjective methods for determining whether the distribution is close to being a normal distribution. Normal quantile plots can be very helpful for assessing normality: see Part 2 of this section.

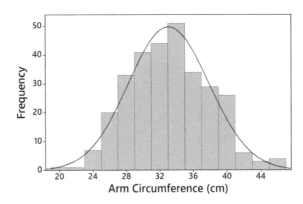

FIGURE 2-5   Bell-Shaped Distribution of Arm Circumferences
Because this histogram is roughly bell-shaped, we say that the data have a *normal distribution*. (A more rigorous definition will be given in Chapter 6.)

Uniform Distribution

With data having a uniform distribution, the different possible values occur with approximately the same frequency, so the heights of the bars in the histogram are approximately uniform, as in Figure 2-4(b). Figure 2-4(b) depicts outcomes of digits from state lotteries.

Skewness

A distribution of data is **skewed** if it is not symmetric and extends more to one side than to the other. Data **skewed to the right** (also called *positively skewed*) have a longer right tail, as in Figure 2-2 and Figure 2-4(c). Commute times in Los Angeles are skewed to the right. Annual incomes of adult Americans are also skewed to the right. Data **skewed to the left** (also called *negatively skewed*) have a longer left tail, as in Figure 2-4(d). Life span data in humans are skewed to the left. (Here's a mnemonic for remembering skewness: A distribution skewed to the right resembles the toes on your right foot, and one skewed to the left resembles the toes on your left foot.) Distributions skewed to the right are more common than those skewed to the left because it's often easier to get exceptionally large values than values that are exceptionally small. With annual incomes, for example, it's impossible to get values below zero, but there are a few people who earn millions or billions of dollars in a year. Annual incomes therefore tend to be skewed to the right.

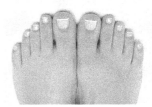

Remembering Skewness:
Skewed Left: Resembles toes on left foot
Skewed Right: Resembles toes on right foot

PART 2 Assessing Normality with Normal Quantile Plots

Some really important methods presented in later chapters have a requirement that sample data must be from a population having a normal distribution. Histograms can be helpful in determining whether the normality requirement is satisfied, but they are not very helpful with small data sets. Section 6-5 discusses methods for *assessing normality*—that is, determining whether the sample data are from a normally distributed population. Section 6-5 includes a procedure for constructing *normal quantile plots*, which are easy to generate using technology such as Statdisk, Minitab, XLSTAT, StatCrunch, or a TI-83/84 Plus calculator. Interpretation of a normal quantile plot is based on the following criteria:

Criteria for Assessing Normality with a Normal Quantile Plot

Normal Distribution: The population distribution is normal if the pattern of the points in the normal quantile plot is reasonably close to a straight line, and the points do not show some other systematic pattern that is not a straight-line pattern.

Not a Normal Distribution: The population distribution is *not* normal if the normal quantile plot has either or both of these two conditions:

- The points do not lie reasonably close to a straight-line pattern.
- The points show some *systematic pattern* that is not a straight-line pattern.

The following are examples of normal quantile plots. Procedures for creating such plots are described in Section 6-5.

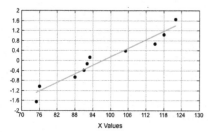

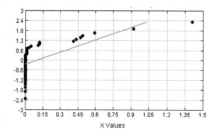

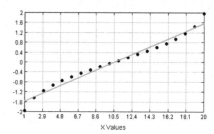

Normal Distribution: The points are reasonably close to a straight-line pattern, and there is no other systematic pattern that is not a straight-line pattern.

Not a Normal Distribution: The points do not lie reasonably close to a straight line.

Not a Normal Distribution: The points show a systematic pattern that is not a straight-line pattern.

TECH CENTER

 ### Histograms

Access tech supplements, videos, and data sets at **www.TriolaStats.com**

Statdisk	Minitab	StatCrunch
1. Click **Data** in top menu.	1. Click **Graph** in top menu.	1. Click **Graph** in the top menu.
2. Select **Histogram** from the dropdown menu.	2. Select **Histogram** from the dropdown menu.	2. Select **Histogram** from the dropdown menu.
3. Select the desired data column.	3. Select **Simple** histogram and click **OK**.	3. Select the desired data column.
4. Click **Plot**.	4. Click on the desired data column, then click **Select** and click **OK**.	4. To customize the histogram enter desired starting point and class width under **Bins**.
5. Move the cursor over the histogram to view frequencies.	5. Change default class width and starting point as needed by right-clicking on the graph and selecting **Edit Graph**. Right-click on the horizontal axis and select **Edit X Scale**.	5. Click **Compute!**.
6. Select **User Defined** under *Plot Options* to use your own class width and starting point.	–Select the **Scale** tab to enter the location of the tick marks.	
Tip: This procedure is also an easy way to identify frequencies in a frequency distribution.	–Select the **Binning** tab to enter the class midpoints.	

TECH CENTER *continued*

Histograms
Access tech supplements, videos, and data sets at **www.TriolaStats.com**

TI-83/84 Plus Calculator

1. Open the **STAT PLOTS** menu by pressing **2ND**, **Y=**.
2. Press **ENTER** to access the *Plot 1* settings screen as shown:
   a. Select **ON** and press **ENTER**.
   b. Select the bar chart option, then press **ENTER**.
   c. Enter the name of list containing data.
3. Press **ZOOM**, then **9** (ZoomStat) to generate the default histogram.
4. Press **TRACE** and use ◁ ▷ to view the class boundaries and frequencies for each class.
5. Press **WINDOW** to customize class width and boundaries. Press **GRAPH** to view histogram.

Tip: The list name *L1* (and *L2* . . . *L6*) can be quickly entered by pressing **2ND** **1**.

```
NORMAL FLOAT AUTO REAL RADIAN MP
Plot1 Plot2 Plot3
On Off
Type: ⌃ ⌃ ▥ ▥ ▥ ⌃
Xlist: MCDL
Freq: 1
Color: BLUE
```

Excel

It is extremely difficult to generate histograms in Excel; the XLSTAT add-in should be used:
1. Select the **XLSTAT** tab in the Ribbon.
2. Click the **Visualizing Data** button.
3. Select **Histograms** from the dropdown menu.
4. Enter the range of cells containing the desired data. Click **Variable labels** if the first cell contains a data name.
5. Click **OK** to generate a default histogram.

Tip: To customize, enter the desired class boundaries in a column, select the **Options** tab, click **User Defined**, and enter the range of cells containing the boundaries in the box.

R

R command: **hist(x)**

A complete list of R statistical commands is available at TriolaStats.com

2-2   Basic Skills and Concepts

Statistical Literacy and Critical Thinking

1. IQ Scores IQ scores of adults are normally distributed. If a large sample of adults is randomly selected and the IQ scores are illustrated in a histogram, what is the shape of that histogram?

2. More IQ Scores The population of IQ scores of adults is normally distributed. If we obtain a voluntary response sample of 5000 of those IQ scores, will a histogram of the sample be bell-shaped?

3. Cell Phone Radiation Listed below are radiation levels (W/kg) from Samsung Galaxy cell phones (based on data from Samsung). Why does it *not* make sense to construct a histogram for this data set?

$$0.87 \quad 1.18 \quad 1.47 \quad 1.25 \quad 1.59 \quad 1.55$$

4. Cell Phone Radiation If we collect a sample of cell phone radiation amounts much larger than the sample included with Exercise 3, and if our sample includes a single outlier, how will that outlier appear in a histogram?

Interpreting a Histogram.   In Exercises 5–8, answer the questions by referring to the following Minitab-generated histogram, which depicts the weights (grams) of all quarters listed in Data Set 40 "Coin Weights" in Appendix B. (Grams are actually units of mass and the values shown on the horizontal scale are rounded.)

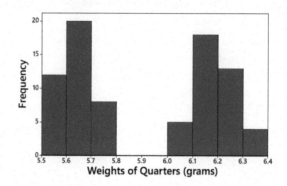

5. Sample Size What is the approximate number of quarters depicted in the three bars farthest to the left?

6. Class Width and Class Limits Give the approximate values of the class width, and the lower and upper class limits of the class depicted in the bar farthest to the left.

7. Relative Frequency Histogram How would the shape of the histogram change if the vertical scale uses relative frequencies expressed in percentages instead of the actual frequency counts as shown here?

8. Gap What is a reasonable explanation for the gap between the quarters with weights between 5.5 grams and 5.8 grams and the group of quarters with weights between 6.0 grams and 6.4 grams? (*Hint:* Refer to the columns of quarters in Data Set 40 "Coin Weights" in Appendix B.)

Constructing Histograms.   *In Exercises 9–18, construct the histograms and answer the given questions.*

9. Chicago Commute Time Use the frequency distribution from Exercise 13 in Section 2-1 on page 52 to construct a histogram. Does it appear to be the graph of data from a population with a normal distribution?

10. Presidents Use the frequency distribution from Exercise 14 in Section 2-1 on page 53 to construct a histogram. Does it appear to be the graph of data from a population with a normal distribution?

11. Old Faithful Use the frequency distribution from Exercise 15 in Section 2-1 on page 53 to construct a histogram. Does it appear to be the graph of data from a population with a normal distribution?

12. Tornadoes Use the frequency distribution from Exercise 16 in Section 2-1 on page 53 to construct a histogram. Does the histogram appear to be skewed? If so, identify the type of skewness.

13. Burger King Lunch Service Times Use the frequency distribution from Exercise 17 in Section 2-1 on page 53 to construct a histogram. Does the histogram appear to be normal?

14. Burger King Dinner Service Times Use the frequency distribution from Exercise 18 in Section 2-1 on page 53 to construct a histogram. Using a strict interpretation of the criteria for being a normal distribution, does the histogram appear to depict data from a population with a normal distribution?

15. Freshman 15 Use the frequency distribution from Exercise 19 in Section 2-1 on page 53 to construct a histogram. Does the histogram appear to depict a normal distribution?

16. Hershey's Kisses Use the frequency distribution from Exercise 20 in Section 2-1 on page 53 to construct a histogram. In using a strict interpretation of the criteria for being a normal distribution, does the histogram appear to depict data from a population with a normal distribution?

17. Analysis of Last Digits Use the frequency distribution from Exercise 21 in Section 2-1 on page 53 to construct a histogram. What can be concluded from the distribution of the digits? Specifically, do the heights appear to be reported or actually measured?

18. Analysis of Last Digits Use the frequency distribution from Exercise 22 in Section 2-1 on page 53 to construct a histogram. What can be concluded from the distribution of the digits? Specifically, do the heights appear to be reported or actually measured?

2-2 Beyond the Basics

19. Interpreting Normal Quantile Plots Which of the following normal quantile plots appear to represent data from a population having a normal distribution? Explain.

a.
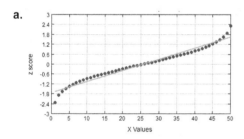

b.
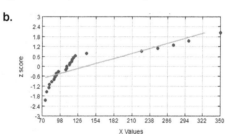

c.
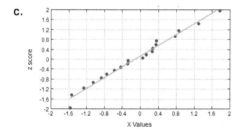

d.
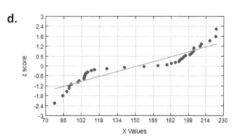

20. Comparing Histograms Refer to the data in Data Set 20 "Alcohol and Tobacco in Movies" and construct histograms for the movie lengths, the times of tobacco use, and the times of alcohol use. Compare the three histograms. Are there any differences in the *distributions* of the data?

2-3   Graphs That Enlighten and Graphs That Deceive

Key Concept Section 2-2 introduced the histogram, and this section introduces other common graphs that foster understanding of data. We also discuss some graphs that are deceptive because they create impressions about data that are somehow misleading or wrong.

The era of charming and primitive hand-drawn graphs has passed, and technology now provides us with powerful tools for generating a wide variety of graphs. Here we go.

The Power of a Graph

With annual sales around $13 billion and with roughly 50 million people using it, Pfizer's prescription drug Lipitor (generic name, atorvastatin) has become the most profitable and most widely used prescription drug ever marketed. In the early stages of its development, Lipitor was compared to other drugs (Zocor [simvastatin], Mevacor [lovastatin], Lescol [fluvastatin], and Pravachol [pravastatin]) in a process that involved controlled trials. The summary report included a graph showing a Lipitor curve that had a steeper rise than the curves for the other drugs, visually showing that Lipitor was more effective in reducing cholesterol than the other drugs. Pat Kelly, who was then a senior marketing executive for Pfizer, said, "I will never forget seeing that chart . . . . It was like 'Aha!' Now I know what this is about. We can communicate this!" The Food and Drug Administration approved Lipitor and allowed Pfizer to include the graph with each prescription. Pfizer sales personnel also distributed the graph to physicians.

Graphs That Enlighten

Dotplots

A **dotplot** consists of a graph of *quantitative* data in which each data value is plotted as a point (or dot) above a horizontal scale of values. Dots representing equal values are stacked.

Features of a Dotplot

- Displays the shape of the distribution of data.
- It is usually possible to recreate the original list of data values.

> **EXAMPLE 1   Dotplot of Pulse Rates of Males**
>
> Figure 2-6 shows a dotplot of the pulse rates (beats per minute) of males from Data Set 1 "Body Data" in Appendix B. The two stacked dots above the position at 50 indicate that two of the pulse rates are 50. (In this dotplot, the horizontal scale allows even numbers only, but the original pulse rates are all even numbers.)
>
> For instructional purposes, this dotplot includes a fictional pulse rate of 10 beats per minute which is not part of the original data set. The lowest pulse rate ever recorded in a living healthy person is 28 beats per minute, so this value is clearly an error. In this case, the pulse rate of 10 beats per minute is an *outlier*, because it is very far from the other data values. See how that outlier becomes easy to identify when included as part of the dotplot.
>
> In this example, the dotplot allows us to see that the general shape of the distribution is approximately normal, and there is an outlier present.
>
>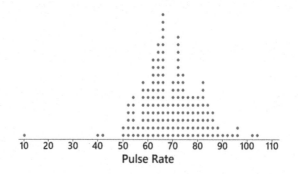
>
> **FIGURE 2-6   Dotplot of Pulse Rates of Males**

 YOUR TURN. Do Exercise 5 "Pulse Rates."

Jitter Some dotplots and other graphs don't work too well when many data values are the same. One way to improve these graphs is to add *jitter*, which randomly nudges points so that they don't overlap. Instead of the identical data values being plotted on top of each other, adding jitter allows us to see them as separate points that are close together.

Stemplots

A **stemplot** (or **stem-and-leaf plot**) represents *quantitative* data by separating each value into two parts: the stem (such as the leftmost digit) and the leaf (such as the rightmost digit). Better stemplots are often obtained by first rounding the original data values. Also, stemplots can be *expanded* to include more rows and can be *condensed* to include fewer rows, as in Exercise 21.

Features of a Stemplot

- Shows the shape of the distribution of the data.
- Retains the original data values.
- The sample data are sorted (arranged in order).

> **EXAMPLE 2** Stemplot of Male Pulse Rates
>
> The following stemplot displays the pulse rates of the males in Data Set 1 "Body Data" in Appendix B. (The fictional outlier of 10 beats per minute included in Example 1 is not included in this example.) The lowest pulse rate of 40 is separated into the stem of 4 and the leaf of 0. The stems and leaves are arranged in increasing order, not the order in which they occur in the original list. If you turn the stemplot on its side, you can see distribution of the pulse rates in the same way you would see it in a histogram or dotplot.
>
> See also that in the stemplot, the data are now sorted (arranged in order). It is easy to see that the lowest value is 40 beats per minute and the highest value is 104 beats per minute. It is easy to see that the middle value of the sorted data is around 68 beats per minute.
>
> ```
>  4 | 02       ←——————— Pulse rates are 40 and 42
>  5 | 0022222444446688888888
>  6 | 000000022222222224444444444444466666666666666666688888
>  7 | 000000002222222222222244444444446666666888888
>  8 | 00000022222222444444666688
>  9 | 02466    ←——————— Pulse rates are 90, 92, 94, 96, 96
> 10| 24
> ```
>
> ↱**YOUR TURN.** Do Exercise 7 "Pulse Rates."

Time-Series Graph

A **time-series graph** is a graph of *time-series data,* which are quantitative data that have been collected at different points in time, such as monthly or yearly.

Feature of a Time-Series Graph

- Reveals information about trends over time

EXAMPLE 3   **Time-Series Graph of Global PC Shipments**

The time-series graph shown in Figure 2-7 depicts the yearly number (millions) of PC computers that were shipped. See that shipments rose steadily until 2011 when they reached a peak and began to decline. Ignoring such important trends could be catastrophic for businesses trying to remain competitive.

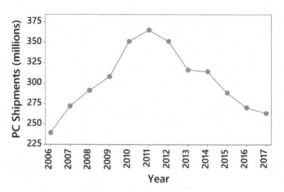

FIGURE 2-7   Time-Series Graph of Global PC Shipments

YOUR TURN. Do Exercise 9 "Gender Pay Gap."

Bar Graphs

A **bar graph** uses bars of equal width to show frequencies of categories of *categorical* (or qualitative) data. The bars may or may not be separated by small gaps.

Feature of a Bar Graph

- Shows the relative distribution of categorical data so that it is easier to compare the different categories

Pareto Charts

A **Pareto chart** is a bar graph for categorical data, with the added stipulation that the *bars are arranged in descending order* according to frequencies, so the bars decrease in height from left to right.

Features of a Pareto Chart

- Shows the relative distribution of categorical data so that it is easier to compare the different categories

- Draws attention to the more important categories

EXAMPLE 4   **Pareto Chart of Causes of Fatal Plane Crashes**

Example 2 in Section 2-1 included a frequency distribution describing the causes of fatal plane crashes. Figure 2-8 shows the Pareto chart based on Table 2-3 in that example. Figure 2-8 and Table 2-3 contain the same basic data, but Figure 2-8 is a graph that allows for better understanding the data. Note that Figure 2-8 draws attention to the fact that pilot error is by far the most serious cause of fatal plane crashes. Note also that Figure 2-8 does not strictly follow the requirement that the heights of the bars decrease from left to right, but it makes sense to locate the category of "other" at the far right part of the graph.

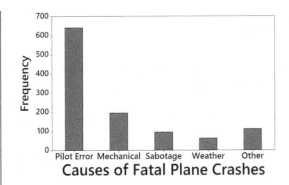

FIGURE 2-8   Pareto Chart of Causes of Fatal
Plane Crashes

Cause	Frequency
Pilot Error	640
Mechanical	195
Sabotage	95
Weather	63
Other	111

TABLE 2-3 Causes of Fatal
Plane Crashes

YOUR TURN. Do Exercise 11 "Box Office Boffo."

***One Reason Why
Statisticians Are
Successful***

"If you say
that there are
elephants
flying in the
sky, people
are not going
to believe
you. But if you say that there
are four hundred and twenty-
five elephants flying in the sky,
people will probably believe you."
—Gabriel García Márquez

Pie Charts

A **pie chart** is a very common graph that depicts categorical data as slices of a
circle, in which the size of each slice is proportional to the frequency count for the
category. Although pie charts are very common, they are not as effective as Pareto
charts.

Feature of a Pie Chart

- Shows the distribution of categorical data in a commonly used format.

EXAMPLE 5   Pie Chart of Causes of Fatal Plane Crashes

Figure 2-9a is a pie chart of the same data from Example 4. Construction of a pie
chart involves slicing up the circle into the proper proportions that represent relative
frequencies. For example, the category of pilot error accounts for 640/1104 or 58%
of the total, so the slice representing pilot error should be 58% of the total (with a
central angle of $0.58 \times 360° = 209°$).

Figure 2-9b speaks for itself.

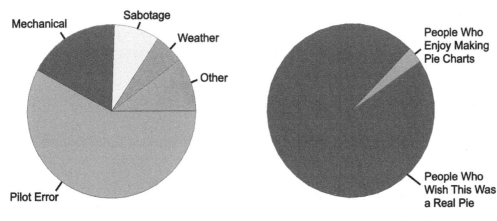

FIGURE 2-9a   Pie Chart of Causes of Fatal
Plane Crashes

FIGURE 2-9b   Pie Chart That Speaks for Itself

 YOUR TURN. Do Exercise 13 "Box Office Boffo."

The Pareto chart in Figure 2-8 and the pie chart in Figure 2-9a depict the same data in different ways, but the Pareto chart does a better job of showing the relative sizes of the different components. Graphics expert Edwin Tufte makes the following suggestion:

> **Never use pie charts because they waste ink on components that are not data, and they lack an appropriate scale.**

Frequency Polygon

A **frequency polygon** uses line segments connected to points located directly above *class midpoint* values. A frequency polygon is very similar to a histogram, but a frequency polygon uses line segments instead of bars.

A variation of the basic frequency polygon is the **relative frequency polygon**, which uses relative frequencies (proportions or percentages) for the vertical scale. An advantage of relative frequency polygons is that two or more of them can be combined on a single graph for easy comparison, as in Figure 2-11.

(CP) **EXAMPLE 6** **Frequency Polygon of Daily Commute Time in Los Angeles**

See Figure 2-10 for the frequency polygon corresponding to the daily Los Angeles commute time summarized in the frequency distribution of Table 2-2 on page 45 (based on the data from the Chapter Problem). The heights of the points correspond to the class frequencies, and the line segments are extended to the right and left so that the graph begins and ends on the horizontal axis.

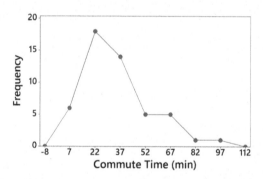

FIGURE 2-10   Frequency Polygon of Daily Commute Time in Los Angeles (minutes)

▶ **YOUR TURN.** Do Exercise 15 "Chicago Commute Times."

(CP) **EXAMPLE 7** **Relative Frequency Polygons: Daily Commute Times in Los Angeles and Boise**

Figure 2-11 shows the relative frequency polygons for the daily commute times in Los Angeles, California, and Boise, Idaho, from Data Set 31 "Commute Times". Figure 2-11 uses all of the 1000 commute times for Los Angeles and Boise and it is not based on the smaller sample of 50 Los Angeles commute times used in Table 2-2 and Example 6. Figure 2-11 shows that the Los Angeles commute times are somewhat longer (farther to the right in the graph) than those in Boise. This is expected, given the larger population density of Los Angeles.

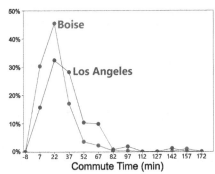

FIGURE 2-11   Relative Frequency Polygons for Commute Time in Los Angeles and Boise (minutes)

Go Figure

4,574,150,134: Number of Internet users in the world.

Graphs That Deceive

Deceptive graphs are commonly used to mislead people, and we really don't want statistics students to be among those susceptible to such deceptions. Graphs should be constructed in a way that is fair and objective. The readers should be allowed to make their own judgments, instead of being manipulated by misleading graphs. We present two of the ways in which graphs are commonly used to misrepresent data.

Nonzero Vertical Axis

A common deceptive graph involves using a vertical scale that starts at some value greater than zero to exaggerate differences between groups.

NONZERO AXIS Always examine a graph carefully to see whether a vertical axis begins at some point other than zero so that differences are exaggerated.

EXAMPLE 8 **Nonzero Axis**

Figure 2-12(a) and Figure 2-12(b) on the next page are based on the same data from a clinical trial of OxyContin (oxycodone), a drug used to treat moderate to severe pain. The results of that clinical trial included the percentage of subjects who experienced nausea in an OxyContin treatment group and the percentage in a group given a placebo.

By using a vertical scale that starts at 10% instead of 0%, Figure 2-12(a) grossly exaggerates the difference between the two groups. Figure 2-12(a) makes it appear that those using OxyContin experience nausea at a rate that is about 12 times higher than the rate for those using a placebo, but Figure 2-12(b) shows that the true ratio is about 2:1, not 12:1. Perhaps someone wants to discourage recreational use of OxyContin by misleading people into thinking that the problem with nausea is much greater than it really is. The objective might be sincere, but the use of a misleading graph is not the way to achieve that objective.

YOUR TURN. Do Exercise 17 "Self-Driving Vehicles."

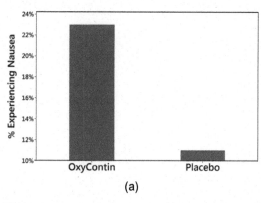 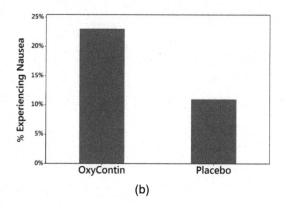

(a)　　　　　　　　　　　　　　　　　　(b)

FIGURE 2-12 Nausea in a Clinical Trial

Pictographs

Drawings of objects, called *pictographs,* are often misleading. Data that are one-dimensional in nature (such as budget amounts) are often depicted with two-dimensional objects (such as dollar bills) or three-dimensional objects (such as stacks of dollar bills). By using pictographs, artists can create false impressions that grossly distort differences by using these simple principles of basic geometry: (1) When you double each side of a square, its area doesn't merely double; it increases by a factor of *four*. (2) When you double each side of a cube, its volume doesn't merely double; it increases by a factor of *eight*.

> **PICTOGRAPHS** When examining data depicted with a pictograph, determine whether the graph is misleading because objects of area or volume are used to depict amounts that are actually one-dimensional. (Histograms and bar charts represent one-dimensional data with two-dimensional bars, but they use bars with the same width so that the graph is not misleading.)

EXAMPLE 9 **Pictograph of U.S. Phone Records Collected**

In two recent and consecutive years, the number of phone records collected by the U.S. National Security Agency jumped from 151 million to 534 million, and 534 million is roughly 3.5 times 151 million. Refer to Figure 2-13 and see that the larger phone is about 3.5 times as tall and 3.5 times as wide as the smaller phone. The larger phone *appears* to be about 12 times as large as the smaller phone, but it should be only 3.5 times as large as the smaller phone. (Brief explanation: If you double the sides of a square, the area becomes four times as large.)

Figure 2-13 therefore misleads readers into thinking that the increase is dramatically more substantial than it really is. A better graph would be a simple bar chart (vertical scale starting at zero) with two bars for the two years.

Year 1 - 151 million　　　　　　Year 2 -534 million

FIGURE 2-13 Pictograph of U.S. National Security Agency Collected Phone Records

 YOUR TURN. Do Exercise 19 "Cost of Giving Birth."

Concluding Thoughts

In addition to the graphs we have discussed in this section, there are many other useful graphs—some of which have not yet been created. The world desperately needs more people who can create original graphs that enlighten us about the nature of data. In *The Visual Display of Quantitative Information,* Edward Tufte offers these principles:

- For small data sets of 20 values or fewer, use a table instead of a graph.

- A graph of data should make us focus on the true nature of the data, not on other elements, such as eye-catching but distracting design features (as in the telephones in Figure 2-13).

- Do not distort data; construct a graph to reveal the true nature of the data.

- Almost all of the ink in a graph should be used for the data, not for other design elements.

TECH CENTER

 ### Graphing Capabilities
Access tech supplements, videos, and data sets at **www.TriolaStats.com**

Instead of listing instructions for each type of graph, the following lists identify the graphs that can be generated with the different technologies.

Statdisk	**Minitab**	**StatCrunch**
• Histograms • Scatterplots	• Histograms • Dotplots • Stemplots • Time-Series Graphs • Bar Graphs • Pareto Charts • Pie Charts • Frequency Polygons • Scatterplots	• Histograms • Dotplots • Stemplots • Bar Graphs • Pie Charts • Scatterplots

TI-83/84 Plus Calculator	**Excel**	**R**
• Histograms • Time-Series Graphs • Frequency Polygons • Scatterplots	• Histograms • Time-Series Graphs • Bar Graphs • Pareto Charts • Pie Charts • Scatterplots	• Histograms • Dotplots • Stemplots • Time-Series Graphs • Bar Graphs • Pareto Charts • Pie Charts • Frequency Polygons • Scatterplots

2-3   Basic Skills and Concepts

Statistical Literacy and Critical Thinking

1. Jaws Listed below are the numbers of unprovoked shark attacks worldwide for the last several years. Why is it that a dotplot of these data would not be very effective in helping us understand the data? Which of the following graphs would be most effective for these data: dotplot, stemplot, time-series graph, Pareto chart, pie chart, frequency polygon?

$$70 \quad 54 \quad 68 \quad 82 \quad 79 \quad 83 \quad 76 \quad 73 \quad 98 \quad 81$$

2. Stemplot Construct a stemplot of the data listed in Exercise 1. If given only the stemplot, can the original data values be found?

3. Ethics There are data showing that smoking is detrimental to good health. Given that people could be helped and lives could be saved by reducing smoking, is it ethical to graph the data in a way that is misleading by exaggerating the health risks of smoking?

4. Voluntary Response Data If we have a large voluntary response sample consisting of weights of subjects who chose to respond to a survey posted on the Internet, can a graph help to overcome the deficiency of having a voluntary response sample?

Dotplots.   *In Exercises 5 and 6, construct the dotplot.*

5. Pulse Rates Listed below are pulse rates (beats per minute) of females selected from Data Set 1 "Body Data" in Appendix B. All of those pulse rates are even numbers. Is there a pulse rate that appears to be an outlier? What is its value?

$$80 \quad 94 \quad 58 \quad 66 \quad 56 \quad 82 \quad 78 \quad 86 \quad 88 \quad 56 \quad 36 \quad 66 \quad 84 \quad 76 \quad 78 \quad 64 \quad 66 \quad 78 \quad 60 \quad 64$$

6. Diastolic Blood Pressure Listed below are diastolic blood pressure measurements (mm Hg) of females selected from Data Set 1 "Body Data" in Appendix B. All of the values are even numbers. Are there any outliers? If so, identify their values.

$$62 \quad 70 \quad 72 \quad 88 \quad 70 \quad 66 \quad 68 \quad 70 \quad 82 \quad 74 \quad 90 \quad 62$$
$$70 \quad 76 \quad 90 \quad 86 \quad 60 \quad 78 \quad 82 \quad 78 \quad 84 \quad 76 \quad 60 \quad 64$$

Stemplots.   *In Exercises 7 and 8, construct the stemplot.*

7. Pulse Rates Refer to the data listed in Exercise 5. How are the data sorted in the stemplot?

8. Diastolic Blood Pressure Refer to the data listed in Exercise 6. Identify the two values that are closest to the middle when the data are sorted in order from lowest to highest. (These values are often used to find the *median*, which is defined in Section 3-1.)

Time-Series Graphs.   *In Exercises 9 and 10, construct the time-series graph.*

9. Gender Pay Gap Listed below are women's median earnings as a percentage of men's median earnings for recent years beginning with 1997 (listed in order by row). Is there a trend? How does it appear to affect women?

$$74.4 \quad 76.3 \quad 76.5 \quad 76.9 \quad 76.4 \quad 77.9 \quad 79.4 \quad 80.4 \quad 81.0 \quad 80.8$$
$$80.2 \quad 79.9 \quad 80.2 \quad 81.2 \quad 82.2 \quad 80.9 \quad 82.1 \quad 82.5 \quad 81.1 \quad 81.9$$

10. Home Runs Listed below are the numbers of home runs in Major League Baseball for each year beginning with 1993 (listed in order by row). Is there a trend?

$$4030 \quad 3306 \quad 4081 \quad 4962 \quad 4640 \quad 5064 \quad 5528 \quad 5693 \quad 5458 \quad 5059 \quad 5207 \quad 5451 \quad 5017$$
$$5386 \quad 4957 \quad 4878 \quad 5042 \quad 4613 \quad 4552 \quad 4934 \quad 4661 \quad 4186 \quad 4909 \quad 5610 \quad 6105$$

Pareto Charts.   *In Exercises 11 and 12 construct the Pareto chart.*

11. Box Office Boffo Recent annual gross revenue (millions of dollars) for the leading movie studios are as follows: 20th Century Fox (1082), Buena Vista (3092), Paramount (757), Sony/Columbia (1304), Universal (1772), Warner Brothers (1941). Are these data likely to be reasonably accurate?

12. Getting a Job In a survey, subjects seeking a job were asked to whom they should send a thank-you note after having a job interview. Results were as follows: 40 said only the person they spent the most time with, 396 said everyone they met, 40 said only the most senior-level person, 15 said the person that they had the best conversation with, and 10 said that they don't send thank-you notes (based on data from TheLadders.com). Comment on the results.

Pie Charts.   *In Exercises 13 and 14, construct the pie chart.*

13. Box Office Boffo Use the data from Exercise 11 "Box Office Boffo."

14. Getting a Job Use the data from Exercise 12 "Getting a Job."

Frequency Polygon.   *In Exercises 15 and 16, construct the frequency polygons.*

15. Chicago Commute Times Use the frequency distribution from Exercise 13 in Section 2-1 on page 52 to construct a frequency polygon. Does the graph suggest that the distribution is skewed? If so, how?

16. Presidents Use the frequency distribution from Exercise 14 in Section 2-1 on page 53 to construct a frequency polygon. Does the graph suggest that the distribution is skewed? If so, how?

Deceptive Graphs.   *In Exercises 17–20, identify how the graph is deceptive.*

17. Self-Driving Vehicles In a survey of adults, subjects were asked if they felt comfortable being in a self-driving vehicle. The accompanying graph depicts the results (based on data from TE Connectivity).

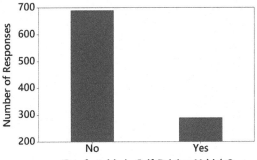

18. Subway Fare In 1986, the New York City subway fare cost $1, and as of this writing, the current cost is $2.50, so the 1986 price was multiplied by 2.5. In the accompanying graph, the large bill is 2.5 times as tall and 2.5 times as wide as the smaller bill.

1986 Subway Fare   **Current Subway Fare**

19. Cost of Giving Birth According to the Agency for Healthcare Research and Quality Healthcare Cost and Utilization Project, the typical cost of a C-section baby delivery is $4500, and the typical cost of a vaginal delivery is $2600. See the following illustration.

Cost of C-Section Delivery: $4500   **Cost of Vaginal Delivery: $2600**

20. Incomes and Academic Degrees The accompanying graph depicts workers with various academic degrees along with their income levels.

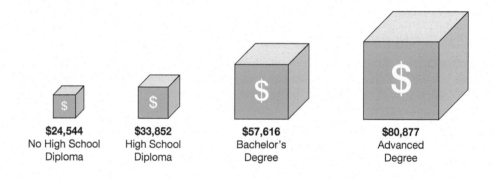

| **$24,544** | **$33,852** | **$57,616** | **$80,877** |
| No High School Diploma | High School Diploma | Bachelor's Degree | Advanced Degree |

2-3 Beyond the Basics

21. Expanded Stemplots A stemplot can be *condensed* by combining adjacent rows. We could use a stem of "6–7" instead of separate stems of 6 and 7. Every row in the condensed stemplot should include an asterisk to separate digits associated with the different stem values. A stemplot can be *expanded* by subdividing rows into those with leaves having digits 0 through 4 and those with leaves having digits 5 through 9. Using the body temperatures from 12 AM on Day 2 listed in Data Set 5 "Body Temperatures" in Appendix B, we see that the first three rows of an expanded stemplot have stems of 96 (for leaves between 5 and 9 inclusive), 97 (for leaves between 0 and 4 inclusive), and 97 (for leaves between 5 and 9 inclusive). Construct the complete expanded stemplot for the body temperatures from 12 AM on Day 2 listed in Data Set 5 "Body Temperatures" in Appendix B.

22. TV and Digital Ads Listed below are amounts (billions of dollars) spent on TV and digital advertising. The amounts are listed in order by year ending with the year 2022. The last few years are projected amounts (based on data from Magna Global). Construct a graph that reveals the story that the data are trying to tell. What story does the graph depict?

TV Ads:	94.5	106.3	103.7	109.6	114.3	125.5	131.0	137.6	142.0	143.2
	133.1	151.2	157.3	165.6	169.7	176.2	176.2	178.4	178.5	183.0
	179.8	183.8	180.0	183.4						

Digital Ads:	4.8	9.3	8.5	8.1	11.1	15.5	22.2	32.0	43.3	50.6
	52.7	62.6	75.5	89.0	105.2	125.6	150.7	178.4	208.8	236.8
	263.9	291.3	319.4	347.7						

2-4 Scatterplots, Correlation, and Regression

Key Concept This section introduces the analysis of *paired* sample data. In Part 1 of this section we discuss *correlation* and the role of a graph called a *scatterplot*. In Part 2 we provide an introduction to the use of the *linear correlation coefficient*. In Part 3 we provide a very brief discussion of *linear regression*, which involves the equation and graph of the straight line that best fits the sample paired data.

All of the principles discussed in this section are discussed more fully in Chapter 10, but this section serves as a quick introduction to some important concepts of correlation and regression. This section does not include details for executing manual calculations, which are rarely done. Instructions for using technology to obtain results are included in Chapter 10.

PART 1 Scatterplot and Correlation

Our objective in this section is to explore whether there is a *correlation*, or association, between two variables. We begin with basic definitions.

DEFINITIONS

A **correlation** exists between two variables when the values of one variable are somehow associated with the values of the other variable.

A **linear correlation** exists between two variables when there is a correlation and the plotted points of paired data result in a pattern that can be approximated by a *straight line*.

A **scatterplot** (or **scatter diagram**) is a plot of paired (*x, y*) quantitative data with a horizontal *x*-axis and a vertical *y*-axis. The horizontal axis is used for the first variable (*x*), and the vertical axis is used for the second variable (*y*).

CAUTION The presence of a correlation between two variables is not evidence that one of the variables *causes* the other. We might find a correlation between beer consumption and weight, but we cannot conclude from the statistical evidence that drinking beer has a direct effect on weight.

Correlation does not imply causality!

A scatterplot can be very helpful in determining whether there is a correlation (or relationship) between the two variables. (This issue is discussed at length when the topic of correlation is considered in Section 10-1.)

EXAMPLE 1   Correlation: Weighing Seals with a Camera

Listed below are the overhead widths (cm) of seals measured from aerial photographs and the weights (kg) of these same seals (based on "Mass Estimation of Weddell Seals Using Techniques of Photogrammetry," by R. Garrott of Montana State University). The purpose of the study was to determine if weights of seals could be determined from overhead photographs. Figure 2-14 is a scatterplot of the paired overhead width and weight measurements. The points show a distinct pattern of increasing values from left to right. This pattern suggests that there is a correlation between overhead widths and weights of seals. This suggests that we can "weigh" seals with a camera.

Overhead Width	7.2	7.4	9.8	9.4	8.8	8.4
Weight	116	154	245	202	200	191

> **YOUR TURN.** Do Exercise 7 "Cigarette Tar and Nicotine."

EXAMPLE 2   No Correlation: Heights of Presidents and Heights of their Main Opponents

Data Set 22 in Appendix B includes heights (cm) of presidents and heights (cm) of their main opponents in the election. Figure 2-15 is a scatterplot of the paired heights. The points in Figure 2-15 do not show any obvious pattern, and this lack of a pattern suggests that there is no correlation between heights of presidents and heights of their opponents.

> **YOUR TURN.** Do Exercise 5 "Forecast and Actual Temperatures."

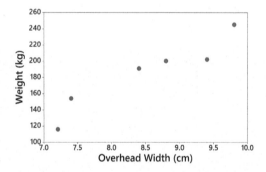

FIGURE 2-14   Overhead Widths and Weights of Seals

Correlation: The distinct pattern of the plotted points suggests that there is a correlation between overhead widths and weights of seals.

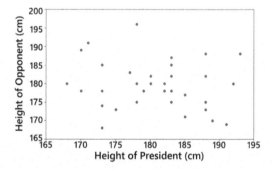

FIGURE 2-15   Heights of Presidents and Heights of Their Main Opponents

No Correlation: The plotted points do not show a distinct pattern, so it appears that there is no correlation between heights of presidents and heights of their main opponents.

EXAMPLE 3   Clusters and a Gap

Consider the scatterplot in Figure 2-16. It depicts paired data consisting of the weight (grams) and year of manufacture for each of 72 pennies. This scatterplot shows two very distinct clusters separated by a gap, which can be explained by the inclusion of two different populations: Pre-1983 pennies are 97% copper and 3% zinc, but post-1983 pennies are 2.5% copper and 97.5% zinc. If we ignored the characteristic of the clusters, we might incorrectly think that there is a relationship between the weight of a penny and the year it was made. If we examine the two groups separately, we see that there does *not* appear to be a relationship between the weights of pennies and the years they were produced.

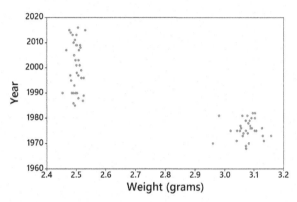

FIGURE 2-16   Weights of Pennies and Years of Production

The preceding three examples involve making decisions about a correlation based on subjective judgments of scatterplots, but Part 2 introduces the *linear correlation coefficient* as a numerical measure that can help us make such decisions more objectively. Using paired data, we can calculate the value of the *linear correlation coefficient r*.

PART 2 Linear Correlation Coefficient *r*

DEFINITION

The **linear correlation coefficient** is denoted by *r*, and it measures the strength of the linear association between two variables.

The value of a linear correlation coefficient *r* can be manually computed by applying Formula 10-1 or Formula 10-2 found in Section 10-1 on page 511, but in practice, *r* is almost always found by using statistics software or a suitable calculator.

Using *r* for Determining Correlation

The computed value of the linear correlation coefficient is always between −1 and 1. If *r* is close to −1 or close to 1, there appears to be a correlation, but if *r* is close to 0, there does not appear to be a linear correlation. For the data depicted in the scatterplot of Figure 2-14, *r* = 0.948 (close to 1), and the data in the scatterplot of Figure 2-15 result in *r* = −0.144 (pretty close to 0). These descriptions of "close to" −1 or 1 or 0 are vague, but there are other objective criteria. For now we will use a table of special values (Table 2-11 on page 77) for deciding whether there is a linear correlation. See the following example illustrating the interpretation of the linear correlation coefficient *r*.

EXAMPLE 4   Correlation Between Shoe Print Lengths and Heights?

Consider the data in Table 2-10 (using data from Data Set 9 "Foot and Height" in Appendix B). From the accompanying scatterplot of the paired data in Table 2-10, it isn't very clear whether there is a linear correlation. The Statdisk display of the results shows that the linear correlation coefficient has the value of $r = 0.591$ (rounded).

TABLE 2-10 Shoe Print Lengths and Heights of Males

Shoe Print Length (cm)	29.7	29.7	31.4	31.8	27.6
Height (cm)	175.3	177.8	185.4	175.3	172.7

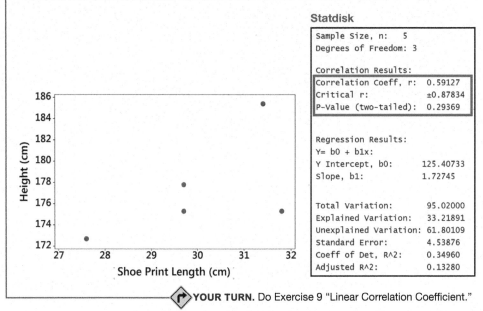

Statdisk

```
Sample Size, n:   5
Degrees of Freedom: 3

Correlation Results:
Correlation Coeff, r:  0.59127
Critical r:           ±0.87834
P-Value (two-tailed):  0.29369


Regression Results:
Y= b0 + b1x:
Y Intercept, b0:       125.40733
Slope, b1:             1.72745


Total Variation:        95.02000
Explained Variation:    33.21891
Unexplained Variation: 61.80109
Standard Error:         4.53876
Coeff of Det, R^2:      0.34960
Adjusted R^2:           0.13280
```

YOUR TURN. Do Exercise 9 "Linear Correlation Coefficient."

In Example 4, we know from the Statdisk display that in using the five pairs of data from Table 2-10, the linear correlation coefficient is computed to be $r = 0.591$. Use the following criteria for interpreting such values.

Using Table 2-11 to Interpret r: Consider critical values from Table 2-11 as being both positive and negative, and draw a graph similar to Figure 2-17. Use the values in the table for determining whether a value of a linear correlation coefficient r is "close to" 0 or "close to" −1 or "close to" 1 by applying the following criteria:

Correlation   If the computed linear correlation coefficient r lies in the left or right tail region bounded by the table value for that tail, conclude that there is sufficient evidence to support the claim of a linear correlation.

No Correlation   If the computed linear correlation coefficient r lies between the two critical values, conclude that there is not sufficient evidence to support the claim of a linear correlation.

Figure 2-17 shows that the linear correlation coefficient of $r = 0.591$ computed from the paired sample data is a value that lies between the critical values of $r = -0.878$ and $r = 0.878$ (found from Table 2-11). Figure 2-17 shows that we can consider the value of $r = 0.591$ to be close to 0 instead of being close to −1 or close to 1. Therefore, there is not sufficient evidence to conclude that there is a linear correlation between shoe print lengths and heights of males.

TABLE 2-11 Critical Values of the Linear Correlation Coefficient r

Number of Pairs of Data n	Critical Value of r
4	0.950
5	**0.878**
6	0.811
7	0.754
8	0.707
9	0.666
10	0.632
11	0.602
12	0.576

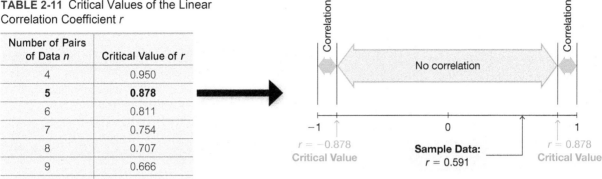

FIGURE 2-17   Critical Values from Table 2-11 and the Computed Value of r

P-Values for Determining Linear Correlation

In Example 4, we used the computed value of the linear correlation coefficient $r = 0.591$ and compared it to the critical r values of ± 0.878 found from Table 2-11. (See Figure 2-17.) In the real world of statistics applications, the use of such tables is almost obsolete. Section 10-1 describes a more common approach that is based on "P-values" instead of tables. The Statdisk display accompanying Example 4 shows that the P-value is 0.29369, or 0.294 when rounded. P-values are first introduced in Chapter 8, but here is a preliminary definition suitable for the context of this section:

DEFINITION

If there really is no linear correlation between two variables, the **P-value** is the probability of getting paired sample data with a linear correlation coefficient r that is at least as extreme as the one obtained from the paired sample data.

Based on Example 4 and the Statdisk displayed results showing a P-value of 0.294, we know that there is a 0.294 probability (or a 29.4% chance) of getting a linear correlation coefficient of $r = 0.591$ or more extreme, assuming that there is no linear correlation between shoe print length and height. (The values of r that are "at least as extreme" as 0.591 are the values greater than or equal to 0.591 and the values less than or equal to -0.591.)

Interpreting a P-Value The P-value of 0.294 from Example 4 is high. It shows that there is a high chance of getting a linear correlation coefficient of $r = 0.591$ (or more extreme) by chance when there is no linear correlation between the two variables. Because the likelihood of getting $r = 0.591$ or a more extreme value is so high (29.4% chance), we conclude that there is not sufficient evidence to conclude that there is a linear correlation between shoe print lengths and heights of males.

Only a *small P*-value, such as 0.05 or less (or a 5% chance or less), suggests that the sample results are *not* likely to occur by chance when there is no linear correlation, so a small P-value supports a conclusion that there is a linear correlation between the two variables.

Police Deaths in Car Chases

USA Today investigated the annual reporting of the numbers of police who were killed during car chases. It was found that the Federal Bureau of Investigation (FBI) counted 24 deaths in the past 35 years, but other records show that there were 371 deaths during that time period. *USA Today* reporter Thomas Frank wrote that "the undercount is one of the most extreme examples of the federal government's inability to accurately track violent deaths and has led the FBI to minimize the danger of police chasing motorists." Apparently, the FBI was categorizing these deaths as automobile accidents instead of designating them as police deaths that occurred during a car chase.

EXAMPLE 5   Correlation Between Shoe Print Lengths and Heights?

Example 4 used only five pairs of data from Data Set 9 "Foot and Height" in Appendix B. If we use the shoe print lengths and heights from all of the 40 subjects listed in Data Set 9 in Appendix B, we get the scatterplot shown in Figure 2-18 and we get the Minitab results shown in the accompanying display. The scatterplot does show a distinct pattern instead of having points scattered about willy-nilly. Also, we see that the value of the linear correlation coefficient is $r = 0.813$, and the *P*-value is 0.000 when rounded to three decimal places. Because the *P*-value of 0.000 is *small*, we have sufficient evidence to conclude that there is a linear correlation between shoe print lengths and heights.

In Example 4 with only five pairs of data, we did not have enough evidence to conclude that there is a linear correlation, but in this example with 40 pairs of data, we have sufficient evidence to conclude that there is a linear correlation between shoe print lengths and heights.

Minitab

```
Pearson correlation of Shoe Print Length and Height = 0.813
P-Value = 0.000
```

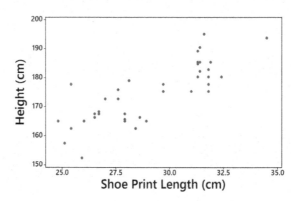

FIGURE 2-18   Scatterplot of 40 Pairs of Data

▶ **YOUR TURN.** Do Exercise 13 "*P*-Values."

PART 3   Regression

When we do conclude that there appears to be a linear correlation between two variables (as in Example 5), we can find the equation of the straight line that best fits the sample data, and that equation can be used to predict the value of one variable when given a specific value of the other variable. Based on the results from Example 5, we can predict someone's height given the length of their shoe print (which may have been found at a crime scene).

Instead of using the straight-line equation format of $y = mx + b$ that we have all come to know and love from prior math courses, we use the format that follows.

DEFINITION

Given a collection of paired sample data, the **regression line** (or *line of best fit*, or *least-squares line*) is the straight line that "best" fits the scatterplot of the data. (The specific criterion for the "best"-fitting straight line is the "least squares" property described in Section 10-2.)

The **regression equation**

$$\hat{y} = b_0 + b_1 x$$

where b_0 is the y-intercept of the line and b_1 is the slope of the line. This equation algebraically describes the regression line.

Section 10-2 gives a good reason for using the format of $\hat{y} = b_0 + b_1 x$ instead of the format of $y = mx + b$. Section 10-2 also provides formulas that could be used to identify the values of the y-intercept b_0 and the slope b_1, but those values are usually found by using statistics software or a suitable calculator.

EXAMPLE 6 **Regression Line**

Example 5 included a scatterplot of the 40 pairs of shoe print lengths and heights from Data Set 9 "Foot and Height" in Appendix B. Figure 2-19 is that same scatterplot with the graph of the regression line included. Also shown is the Statdisk display from the 40 pairs of data.

From the Statdisk display, we see that the general form of the regression equation has a y-intercept of $b_0 = 80.9$ (rounded) and slope $b_1 = 3.22$ (rounded), so the equation of the regression line shown in Figure 2-19 is $\hat{y} = 80.9 + 3.22x$. It might be helpful to express that equation more clearly by using the names of the variables:

$$\text{Height} = 80.9 + 3.22\,(\text{Shoe Print Length})$$

Note that the *equation* shows the y-intercept of 80.9 that does not appear on the vertical scale in the *graph*. The leftmost vertical scale in Figure 2-19 is not the actual y-axis that passes through 0 on the x-axis. If the graph were extended to the left, the regression line would intercept the actual y-axis at the height of $y = 80.9$ cm.

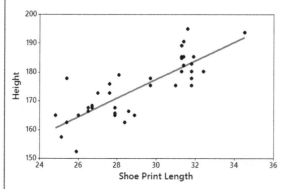

Statdisk

```
Correlation Results:
Correlation Coeff, r:     0.81295
Critical r:               ±0.31201
P-Value (two-tailed):     0.00000


Regression Results:
Y= b0 + b1x:
Y Intercept, b0:          80.93041
Slope, b1:                3.21856
```

FIGURE 2-19 **Regression Line**

2-4 Basic Skills and Concepts

Statistical Literacy and Critical Thinking

1. Linear Correlation In this section we use r to denote the value of the linear correlation coefficient. Why do we refer to this correlation coefficient as being *linear*?

2. Causation A study has shown that there is a correlation between body weight and blood pressure. Higher body weights are associated with higher blood pressure levels. Can we conclude that gaining weight is a cause of increased blood pressure?

3. Scatterplot What is a scatterplot and how does it help us?

4. Estimating *r* For each of the following, estimate the value of the linear correlation coefficient *r* for the given paired data obtained from 50 randomly selected adults.

a. Their heights are measured in inches (x) and those same heights are recorded in centimeters (y).

b. Their IQ scores (x) are measured and their heights (y) are measured in centimeters.

c. Their pulse rates (x) are measured and their IQ scores are measured (y).

d. The 50 adults all drove cars from Jacksonville, Florida, to Richmond, Virginia. Their average (mean) speeds (x) are recorded along with the times (y) it took to complete that trip.

Scatterplot.   *In Exercises 5–8, use the sample data to construct a scatterplot. Use the first variable for the x-axis. Based on the scatterplot, what do you conclude about a linear correlation?*

5. Forecast and Actual Temperatures The table lists actual high temperatures and the high temperatures that were previously forecasted for these same days. The table includes data for ten different days near the author's home. What does the result suggest about the accuracy of five-day predicted high temperatures?

Actual High	80	77	81	85	73	73	80	72	83	81
Predicted High	56	57	59	56	64	57	61	63	59	61

6. Airport Data Speeds Listed below are the cellular data speeds (Mbps) from Sprint and Verizon measured at nine different airports (based on data from CNN). What would the presence of a correlation suggest about Sprint and Verizon?

Sprint	13.0	30.4	15.2	2.4	2.7	2.1	0.8	1.6	5.6
Verizon	38.5	55.6	22.4	14.1	23.1	24.5	6.5	21.5	25.7

7. Cigarette Tar and Nicotine The table below lists amounts of tar per cigarette (milligrams) and amounts of nicotine (milligrams) from different cigarettes (from Data Set 16 "Cigarette Contents").

Tar	5.0	16	17.0	13.0	9.0	14	15.0	2.0	7.0
Nicotine	0.4	1	1.2	0.8	0.8	1	1.1	0.2	0.6

8. Pulse Rates The table lists pulse rates (beats per minute) from randomly selected females and randomly selected males (based on Data Set 1 "Body Data"). What is a major and fundamental flaw with this exercise?

Female	66	56	82	78	86	88	56	36	84	76
Male	60	52	62	52	76	52	62	72	64	78

Linear Correlation Coefficient   *In Exercises 9–12, the linear correlation coefficient r is provided. Use Table 2-11 on page 77 to find the critical values of r. Based on a comparison of the linear correlation coefficient r and the critical values, what do you conclude about a linear correlation?*

9. Using the data from Exercise 5 "Forecast and Actual Temperatures," the linear correlation coefficient is $r = -0.475$.

10. Using the data from Exercise 6 "Airport Data Speeds," the linear correlation coefficient is $r = 0.866$.

11. Using the data from Exercise 7 "Cigarette Tar and Nicotine," the linear correlation coefficient is $r = 0.971$.

12. Using the data from Exercise 8 "Pulse Rates," the linear correlation coefficient is $r = -0.076$. As in Exercise 8, identify the major flaw with these data.

2-4   Beyond the Basics

P-Values   In Exercises 13–16, write a statement that interprets the P-value and includes a conclusion about linear correlation.

13. Using the data from Exercise 5 "Forecast and Actual Temperatures," the *P*-value is 0.166.

14. Using the data from Exercise 6 "Airport Data Speeds," the *P*-value is 0.003.

15. Using the data from Exercise 7 "Cigarette Tar and Nicotine," the *P*-value is 0.000.

16. Using the data from Exercise 8 "Pulse Rates," the *P*-value is 0.835.

Chapter Quick Quiz

1. Tornado Alley Refer to the accompanying frequency distribution that summarizes the number of tornadoes in Oklahoma in each year for the past several years. What is the class width? Is it possible to identify the original data values?

2. Tornado Alley Using the same frequency distribution from Exercise 1, identify the class limits of the first class and the class boundaries of the first class.

3. Tornado Alley Using the same frequency distribution from Exercise 1, how many years are included?

4. Tornado Alley Construct the relative frequency distribution corresponding to the frequency distribution in Exercise 1.

5. Tornado Alley A stemplot of the same data summarized in Exercise 1 is created, and one of the rows of that stemplot is 3 | 000144669. Identify the values represented by that row of the stemplot.

Annual Tornadoes in Oklahoma	Frequency (Number of Years)
0–19	3
20–39	18
40–59	21
60–79	15
80–99	6
100–119	5
120–139	0
140–159	1

6. Computers As a quality control manager at Texas Instruments, you find that defective calculators have various causes, including worn machinery, human error, bad supplies, and packaging mistreatment. Which of the following graphs would be best for describing the causes of defects: histogram; scatterplot; Pareto chart; dotplot; pie chart?

7. Health Test In an investigation of a relationship between systolic blood pressure and diastolic blood pressure of adult females, which of the following graphs is most helpful: histogram; pie chart; scatterplot; stemplot; dotplot?

8. Lottery In Florida's Play 4 lottery game, four digits between 0 and 9 inclusive are randomly selected each day. We normally expect that each of the 10 different digits will occur about $1/10$ of the time, and an analysis of last year's results shows that this did happen. Because the results are what we normally expect, is it correct to say that the distribution of selected digits is a normal distribution?

9. Seatbelts The Beams Seatbelts company manufactures—well, you know. When a sample of seatbelts is tested for breaking point (measured in kilograms), the sample data are explored. Identify the important characteristic of data that is missing from this list: center, distribution, outliers, changing characteristics over time.

10. Normal Distribution If the following data are randomly selected, which are expected to have a normal distribution?

a. Weights of Reese's Peanut Butter Cups

b. Numbers selected in the Florida Pick 4 lottery, in which four whole numbers between 0 and 9 inclusive are randomly selected in each lottery

c. Numbers that turn up when a fair die is rolled

d. Exact volumes of Coke in 12 oz cans

e. Weights of McIntosh apples harvested from the same orchard

Review Exercises

1. Email Data Listed below are the interarrival times (minutes) of email arriving at the author's computer. Construct a frequency distribution. Use a class width of 10 minutes and begin with a lower class limit of 0 minutes. Compare the distribution of these interarrival times to the distribution of the commute times listed in the Chapter Problem (Table 2-1) and summarized in the frequency distribution of Table 2-2.

19	58	39	3	61	17	21	13	1	20	1	12	13	7	8	33	3	2	34	18
1	20	16	18	37	25	15	1	1	6	29	5	5	3	7	9	7	5	6	38
19	6	37	18	24	53	1	41	2	6	9	9	35	1	10	11	28	15	8	18

2. Histogram of Interarrival Times Construct the histogram that corresponds to the frequency distribution from Exercise 1. Use class midpoint values for the horizontal scale. Does the histogram suggest that the data are from a population having a normal distribution? Why or why not?

3. Dotplot of Interarrival Times Construct a dotplot of the interarrival times listed in Exercise 1. Which does a better job of illustrating the distribution of the data: the histogram from Exercise 2 or the dotplot?

4. Stemplot of Interarrival Times Construct a stemplot of the interarrival times listed in Exercise 1. Are there any outliers?

5. Body Temperatures Listed below are the temperatures from nine males measured at 8 AM and again at 12 AM (from Data Set 5 "Body Temperatures" in Appendix B). Construct a scatterplot. Based on the graph, does there appear to be a relationship between 8 AM temperatures and 12 AM temperatures?

8 AM	98.0	97.0	98.6	97.4	97.4	98.2	98.2	96.6	97.4
12 AM	98.0	97.6	98.8	98.0	98.8	98.8	97.6	98.6	98.6

6. Environment

a. After collecting the average (mean) global temperatures for each of the most recent 100 years, we want to construct the graph that is most appropriate for these data. Which graph is best?

b. After collecting the average (mean) global temperature and the amount of carbon monoxide emissions for the most recent 100 years, we want to construct a graph to investigate the association between those two variables. Which graph is best?

c. An investigation of carbon monoxide sources includes motor vehicles, furnaces, fires, coal-burning power plants, and tobacco smoke. If we want to construct a graph that illustrates the relative importance of these sources, which graph is best?

7. It's Like Time to Do This Exercise In a Marist survey of adults, these are the words or phrases that subjects find most annoying in conversation (along with their frequencies of response): like (127); just sayin' (81); you know (104); whatever (219); obviously (35). Construct a pie chart. Identify one disadvantage of a pie chart.

8. Whatever Use the same data from Exercise 7 to construct a Pareto chart. Which graph does a better job of illustrating the data: Pareto chart or pie chart?

Cumulative Review Exercises

In Exercises 1–5, use the data listed in the margin, which are magnitudes (Richter scale) and depths (km) of earthquakes from Data Set 24 "Earthquakes" in Appendix B.

1. Frequency Distribution Construct a frequency distribution of the magnitudes. Use a class width of 0.50 and use a starting value of 1.00.

2. Frequency Distribution For the frequency distribution from Exercise 1, find the following.

a. Class limits of the first class

b. Class boundaries of the first class

c. Class midpoint of the first class

3. Histogram Construct the histogram corresponding to the frequency distribution from Exercise 1. For the values on the horizontal axis, use the class midpoint values. Which of the following comes closest to describing the distribution: uniform, normal, skewed left, skewed right?

4. Data Type

a. The listed earthquake *depths* (km) are all rounded to one decimal place. Before rounding, are the exact depths discrete data or continuous data?

b. For the listed earthquake depths, are the data categorical or quantitative?

c. Identify the level of measurement of the listed earthquake depths: nominal, ordinal, interval, or ratio.

d. Given that the listed earthquake depths are part of a larger collection of depths, do the data constitute a sample or a population?

5. Correlation Between Magnitudes and Depths Using the paired magnitude/depth data, construct the graph that is helpful in determining whether there is a correlation between earthquake magnitudes and depths. Based on the result, does there appear to be a correlation?

Magnitude	Depth (km)
2.45	0.7
3.62	6.0
3.06	7.0
3.30	5.4
1.09	0.5
3.10	0.0
2.99	7.0
2.58	17.6
2.44	7.0
2.91	15.9
3.38	11.7
2.83	7.0
2.44	7.0
2.56	6.9
2.79	17.3
2.18	7.0
3.01	7.0
2.71	7.0
2.44	8.1
1.64	7.0

Technology Project

Graphs It was stated in this chapter that the days of charming and primitive hand-drawn graphs are well behind us, and technology now provides us with powerful tools for generating a wide variety of different graphs. This project therefore serves as a good preparation for professional presentations that will be inevitably made in the future.

The complete data sets in Appendix B are already included in Statdisk. Also, those data sets can be downloaded from www.TriolaStats.com. They can be opened by statistical software packages, such as Minitab, Excel, SPSS, and JMP. Use a statistical software package to open Data Set 1 "Body Data." Use this software with the methods of this chapter to explore and compare the pulse rates of females and the pulse rates of males.

• Obtain a printed copy of the two histograms. In both cases, use a class width of 10 beats per minute and use 30 beats per minute as the lower class limit of the first class.

• Describe the natures of the two distributions (uniform, normal, skewed left, skewed right), and identify possible outliers.

continued

• *Carefully* identify the value at the center of each histogram. Does there appear to be a difference? (Such comparisons will become much easier and much less subjective in future chapters.)

• Write a brief description of your results.

Hint: The genders are coded as 1 for male and 0 for female, so *sort* (arrange in order) all of the rows using the gender column as the basis for sorting. Then the rows for males can be separated from the rows for females by using the copy/paste and cut functions of the software.

Big (or Very Large) Data Project

Refer to Data Set 45 "Births in New York" in Appendix B, which contains records from 465,506 births. Generate a histogram of the birth weights, then describe the shape of the histogram.

FROM DATA TO DECISION

Were the subjects weighed or did they report their weights?

One fascinating aspect of statistics is that we can sometimes learn how data were collected by analyzing the data. Table 2-12 and Table 2-13 both include weights (pounds) of 50 randomly selected adult male subjects. When subjects are included in the National Health and Interview Survey, there is a requirement that subjects must be weighed on a scale.

One of the two data sets was obtained by using a scale to actually weigh the subjects, but the other data set consists of weights that were *reported* by the subjects when they were asked how much they weighed. With a clever use of common sense, we know that when subjects *report* their weights, the results are often rounded to a value conveniently ending in a 0 or 5. Given this, we are able to deduce how the data were collected by analyzing the *last digits* of the weights.

TABLE 2-12 Weights (lbs) of 50 Adult Males

129	172	115	125	240	124	183	147	195	200
217	180	185	170	217	160	140	232	215	165
196	228	225	165	210	145	200	210	225	200
160	250	185	140	120	250	150	172	200	131
160	205	255	205	145	180	195	230	155	200

TABLE 2-13 Weights (lbs) of 50 Adult Males

155	200	256	166	179	202	170	196	256	165
231	143	174	164	147	200	182	228	195	208
203	125	221	229	130	230	212	218	254	149
129	183	187	212	144	160	199	197	187	144
221	166	174	119	213	158	243	124	226	124

Critical Thinking

Use the methods from this chapter to address the following questions.

1. Construct a frequency distribution and histogram of the *last digits* of the weights in Table 2-12.

2. Construct a frequency distribution and histogram of the *last digits* of the weights in Table 2-13.

3. Compare the results from questions 1 and 2. Determine which table includes weights obtained by using a scale and which table includes weights that were reported by the subjects.

4. Which table appears to include data that are more accurate? Explain.

Cooperative Group Activities

1. Out-of-class activity Record the arrival times of your incoming emails (email timestamps can be used). Then find your email interarrival times and compare the distribution to the author's email interarrival times which are provided in Review Exercise 1 on page 82.

2. Out-of-class activity Data Set 36 "Fast Food" in Appendix B includes measured service times of different fast food restaurants. Go to one or more fast food restaurants and collect your own service times. Compare the results to those found in Data Set 36 in Appendix B.

3. In-class activity Using a package of purchased chocolate chip cookies, each student should be given two or three cookies. Proceed to count the number of chocolate chips in each cookie. Not all of the chocolate chips are visible, so "destructive testing" must be used through a process involving consumption. Record the numbers of chocolate chips for each cookie and combine all results. Construct a frequency distribution, histogram, dotplot, and stemplot of the results. Given that the cookies were made through a process of mass production, we might expect that the numbers of chips per cookie would not vary much. Is that indicated by the results? Explain.

4. In-class activity For each student in the class, measure shoe print length and height. Construct a scatterplot of the paired data. Does there appear to be a correlation? Explain.

5. In-class activity Divide into groups of 8 to 12 people. For each group member, measure one or more of the distances below. Construct a scatterplot of the paired data for each type of measurement. Does there appear to be a correlation?

• Measure each person's height and also measure his or her navel height, which is the height from the floor to the navel.

• Measure each person's height and arm span. For the arm span, the subject should stand with arms extended, like the wings on an airplane.

• Measure each person's head circumference and forearm length using a string and ruler.

6. In-class activity Use a ruler as a device for measuring reaction time. One person should suspend the ruler by holding it at the top while the subject holds his or her thumb and forefinger at the bottom edge, ready to catch the ruler when it is released. Record the distance that the ruler falls before it is caught. Convert that distance to the time (in seconds) that it took the subject to react and catch the ruler. (If the distance is measured in inches, use $t = \sqrt{d/192}$. If the distance is measured in centimeters, use $t = \sqrt{d/487.68}$.) Test each subject once with the right hand and once with the left hand, and record the paired data. Construct a scatterplot of the paired data. Does there appear to be a correlation? Explain.

7. In-class activity In class, each student should record two pulse rates by counting the number of her or his heartbeats in 1 minute. The first pulse rate should be measured while the student is seated, and the second pulse rate should be measured while the student is standing. Using the pulse rates measured while seated, construct a frequency distribution and histogram for the pulse rates of males, and then construct another frequency distribution and histogram for the pulse rates of females. Using the pulse rates measured while standing, construct a frequency distribution and histogram for the pulse rates of males, and then construct another frequency distribution and histogram for the pulse rates of females. Compare the results. Do males and females appear to have different pulse rates? Do pulse rates measured while seated appear to be different from pulse rates measured while standing? Use an appropriate graph to determine whether there is a relationship between sitting pulse rate and standing pulse rate.

8. Out-of-class activity Search newspapers and magazines to find an example of a graph that is misleading. Describe how the graph is misleading. Redraw the graph so that it depicts the information correctly. If possible, please submit your graph to www.TriolaStats.com.

9. Out-of-class activity Find Charles Joseph Minard's graph describing Napoleon's march to Moscow and back, and explain why Edward Tufte says that "it may well be the best graphic ever drawn." (See *The Visual Display of Quantitative Information* by Edward Tufte, Graphics Press). Minard's graph can be seen at www.TriolaStats.com under "Textbook Supplements."

10. Out-of-class activity In *The Visual Display of Quantitative Information* by Edward Tufte (Graphics Press), find the graph that appeared in *American Education*, and explain why Tufte says that "this may well be the worst graphic ever to find its way into print." The graph can be seen at www.TriolaStats.com under "Textbook Supplements." Construct a graph that is effective in depicting the same data.

3

DESCRIBING, EXPLORING, AND COMPARING DATA

CHAPTER PROBLEM | **It's a Small World After All!**

Data Set 33 "Disney World Wait Times" in Appendix B includes wait times for several popular Walt Disney World rides at both 10 AM and 5 PM. (The author collected these data using Disney's "My Disney Experience" app.) What rides have the longest wait times? How much do wait times vary for an individual ride? How do morning wait times compare to the evening wait times? These are important questions to Disney World visitors and those that are responsible for its ongoing management and operation.

A *queue* is a line of people or vehicles or objects waiting to be serviced, and *queueing theory* is a complex but important field of study with applications that we all experience on a daily basis. It should be noted that the psychology of queues (or waiting lines) is often more important than the statistics. Here are three examples:

- Airline passengers arriving at Houston International Airport complained about the waiting time required to get their baggage. Increasing the number of baggage handlers greatly reduced the waiting time, but complaints persisted. The airplane arrival gates were then moved farther away from the baggage claim area, so passengers had to walk farther. Passengers now spend more time walking than waiting in place, and complaints have fallen dramatically.

- Many DMV locations now provide visitors with an estimated wait time and queue number. The current status of the queue is displayed on clearly visible screens. Research has shown that providing people with this queue information defuses the stress, anxiety and uncertainty of waiting in line.

- The queue for Harry Potter and the Escape from Gringotts at Universal Orlando Resort features many attractions including the Great Hall of Gringotts bank with animatronic goblins, a pre-ride show featuring the character of Bill Weasley, and an elevator that creates the illusion of descending deep down into underground vaults. All of these attractions keep guests happily distracted (and cool) as they wait in long summer lines.

We will proceed to examine the statistics of wait times, but we should always keep in mind that many effective strategies require common sense in addition to a knowledge of statistics.

Let's consider 10 AM wait times at two of the most popular Disney World Rides: "Space Mountain" and "Avatar Flight of Passage."

Examination of the dotplots in Figure 3-1 suggests that "Space Mountain" has a shorter wait time than "Avatar Flight of Passage." The difference between the minimum and maximum wait time for "Space Mountain" is also less than that for "Avatar Flight of Passage." Instead of relying solely on subjective interpretations of a graph like Figure 3-1, this chapter introduces measures that are essential to any study of statistics. This chapter introduces the mean, median, standard deviation, and variance, which are among the most important statistics presented in this book, and they are essential to any study of statistics. We will use these statistics for describing, exploring, and comparing the wait times for popular Disney World rides as listed in Data Set 33.

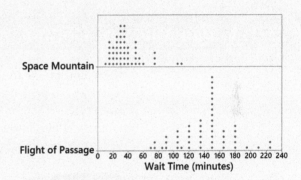

FIGURE 3-1   Disney World Wait Times

CHAPTER OBJECTIVES

Critical Thinking and Interpretation: Going Beyond Formulas and Arithmetic

In this modern statistics course, the emphasis is not on memorizing formulas or manually doing messy arithmetic. We can get results with a calculator or software so that we can focus on making practical sense of results through critical thinking. Although this chapter includes detailed steps for important procedures, it isn't always necessary to master those steps. It is, however, generally helpful to perform a few manual calculations before using technology so that understanding is enhanced.

The methods and tools presented in this chapter are often called methods of **descriptive statistics,** because they summarize or *describe* relevant characteristics of data. In later chapters we use **inferential statistics** to make *inferences,* or generalizations, about populations. Here are the chapter objectives:

3-1 Measures of Center

- Develop the ability to measure the center of data by finding the mean, median, mode, and midrange.

- Determine whether an outlier has a substantial effect on the mean and median.

3-2 Measures of Variation

- Develop the ability to measure variation in a set of sample data by finding values of the range, variance, and standard deviation.

- Develop the ability to interpret values of the standard deviation by applying the *range rule of thumb* to determine whether a particular value is *significantly low* or *significantly high*.

3-3 Measures of Relative Standing and Boxplots

- Develop the ability to compute a *z* score and use the result to determine whether a given value *x* is *significantly low* or *significantly high*.

- Identify *percentile* values and *quartile* values from a set of data.

- Develop the ability to construct a boxplot from a set of data.

3-1 Measures of Center

Key Concept The focus of this section is to obtain a value that measures the *center* of a data set. In particular, we present measures of center, including *mean* and *median*. Our objective here is not only to find the value of each measure of center, but also to interpret those values. Part 1 of this section includes core concepts that should be understood before considering Part 2.

PART 1 Basic Concepts of Measures of Center

In Part 1 of this section, we introduce the mean, median, mode, and midrange as different measures of center. Measures of center are widely used to provide representative values that "summarize" data sets.

> **DEFINITION**
>
> A **measure of center** is a value at the center or middle of a data set.

There are different approaches for measuring the center, so we have different definitions for those different approaches. We begin with the mean.

Mean

The mean (or arithmetic mean) is generally the most important of all numerical measurements used to describe data, and it is what many people call an *average*.

> **CAUTION** Never use the term *average* when referring to a measure of center. The word *average* is often used for the mean, but it is sometimes used for other measures of center. The term *average* is not used by statisticians and it will not be used throughout the remainder of this book when referring to a specific measure of center. The term *average* is not used by the statistics community or professional journals. From this point forward, it would be wise to abandon use of the term *average* when referring to a measure of center.

Go Figure

$3.70: Mean amount left by the tooth fairy, based on a survey by Visa. An unlucky 10% of kids get nothing.

DEFINITION

The **mean** (or **arithmetic mean**) of a set of data is the measure of center found by adding all of the data values and dividing the total by the number of data values.

Important Properties of the Mean

- Sample means drawn from the same population tend to vary less than other measures of center.

- The mean of a data set uses every data value.

- A disadvantage of the mean is that just one extreme value (outlier) can change the value of the mean substantially. (Using the following definition, we say that the mean is not *resistant*.)

DEFINITION

A statistic is **resistant** if the presence of extreme values (outliers) does not cause it to change very much.

Calculation and Notation of the Mean

The definition of the mean can be expressed as Formula 3-1, in which the Greek letter Σ (uppercase sigma) indicates that the data values should be added, so Σx represents the sum of all data values. The symbol n denotes the **sample size,** which is the number of data values.

FORMULA 3-1

$$\text{Mean} = \frac{\Sigma x}{n} \quad \begin{array}{l}\leftarrow \text{sum of all data values} \\ \leftarrow \text{number of data values}\end{array}$$

If the data are a *sample* from a population, the mean is denoted by $\bar{x}$ (pronounced "*x*-bar"); if the data are the entire population, the mean is denoted by μ (lowercase Greek mu).

NOTATION *Hint:* Sample statistics are usually represented by English letters, such as $\bar{x}$, and population parameters are usually represented by Greek letters, such as μ.

Σ	denotes the *sum* of a set of data values.
x	is the *variable* usually used to represent the individual data values.
n	represents the number of data values in a *sample*.
N	represents the number of data values in a *population*.
$\bar{x} = \dfrac{\Sigma x}{n}$	is the mean of a set of *sample* values.
$\mu = \dfrac{\Sigma x}{N}$	is the mean of all values in a *population*.

Class Size Paradox

There are at least two ways to obtain the mean class size, and they can have very different results. At one college, if we take the numbers of students in 737 classes, we get a mean of 40 students. But if we were to compile a list of the class sizes for each student and use this list, we would get a mean class size of 147. This large discrepancy is because there are many students in large classes, while there are few students in small classes. Without changing the number of classes or faculty, we could reduce the mean class size experienced by students by making all classes about the same size. This would also improve attendance, which is better in smaller classes.

Redefining Units of Measure

In 1983, the meter was redefined to be the distance traveled by a beam of light in 1/299,792,458 of a second. In 1967, the time unit of one second was redefined to be the amount of time it takes an atom of cesium-133 to vibrate 9,192,631,770 times.

From 1889 to 2018, the kilogram was defined to be the mass of the International Prototype Kilogram—a chunk of platinum-iridium metal that was stored in a vault in Paris. The kilogram has now been redefined in terms of the Planck constant—a physical constant in nature. The actual definition is complicated, but the new definition completes the goal of having the basic units of the International System of Units (S.I.) defined by constants of nature instead of physical objects.

As of this writing, these are the only countries that have not yet adopted the S.I. system as their official system of weights and measures: Liberia, Myanmar, and the United States!

(CP) **EXAMPLE 1** **Mean**

Data Set 33 "Disney World Wait Times" in Appendix B includes wait times (minutes) for six popular rides. Find the mean of the first eleven wait times for "Space Mountain" at 10 AM:

$$50 \quad 25 \quad 75 \quad 35 \quad 50 \quad 25 \quad 30 \quad 50 \quad 45 \quad 25 \quad 20$$

SOLUTION

The mean is computed by using Formula 3-1. First add the data values, and then divide by the number of data values:

$$\bar{x} = \frac{\Sigma x}{n} = \frac{50 + 25 + 75 + 35 + 50 + 25 + 30 + 50 + 45 + 25 + 20}{11}$$

$$= \frac{430}{11} = 39.1 \, \text{min}$$

The mean of the wait times for "Space Mountain" is 39.1 minutes.

YOUR TURN. Find the mean in Exercise 5 "Super Bowl Jersey Numbers."

Median

The median can be thought of loosely as a "middle value" in the sense that about half of the values in a data set are less than the median and half are greater than the median. The following definition is more precise.

> **DEFINITION**
>
> The **median** of a data set is the measure of center that is the *middle value* when the original data values are arranged in order of increasing (or decreasing) magnitude.

Important Properties of the Median

- The median does not change by large amounts when we include just a few extreme values, so the median is a *resistant* measure of center.

- The median does not directly use every data value. (For example, if the largest value is changed to a much larger value, the median does not change.)

Calculation and Notation of the Median

The median of a sample is sometimes denoted by $\tilde{x}$ (pronounced "x-tilde") or M or Med; there isn't a commonly accepted notation, and there isn't a special symbol for the median of a population. To find the median, first *sort* the values (arrange them in order) and then follow one of these two procedures:

1. If the number of data values is *odd*, the median is the number located in the exact middle of the sorted list.

2. If the number of data values is *even*, the median is found by computing the mean of the two middle numbers in the sorted list.

EXAMPLE 2 Median with an *Odd* Number of Data Values

Find the median of the first eleven wait times (mins) for "Space Mountain" at 10 AM:

50   25   75   35   50   25   30   50   45   25   20

SOLUTION

First sort the data values by arranging them in ascending order, as shown below:

20   25   25   25   30   35   45   50   50   50   75

Because the number of data values is an odd number (11), the median is the data value that is in the exact middle of the sorted list. The median is therefore 35.0 minutes. Note that the *median* of 35.0 minutes is different from the *mean* of 39.1 minutes found in Example 1.

YOUR TURN. Find the median in Exercise 17 "Diamonds at the Diamonds."

 EXAMPLE 3 Median with an *Even* Number of Data Values

Repeat Example 2 after including the twelfth wait time for "Space Mountain" at 10 AM. That is, find the median of these wait times (minutes).

50   25   75   35   50   25   30   50   45   25   20   50

SOLUTION

First sort the data values by arranging them in ascending order, as shown below:

20   25   25   25   30   35   45   50   50   50   50   75

Because the number of data values is an even number (12), the median is found by computing the mean of the two data values in the middle of the sorted list, which are 35 and 45. The median is therefore $(35 + 45)/2 = 40.0$ minutes.

YOUR TURN. Find the median in Exercise 7 "Celebrity Net Worth."

Mode

The mode isn't used much with quantitative data, but it's the only measure of center that can be used with qualitative data (consisting of names, labels, or categories only).

DEFINITION

The **mode** of a data set is the value(s) that occur(s) with the greatest frequency.

Important Properties of the Mode

- The mode can be found with qualitative data.
- A data set can have no mode or one mode or multiple modes.

Finding the Mode: A data set can have one mode, more than one mode, or no mode.

- When two data values occur with the same greatest frequency, each one is a mode, and the data set is said to be **bimodal.**

What the Median Is Not

Harvard biologist Stephen Jay Gould wrote, "The Median Isn't the Message." In it, he describes how he learned that he had abdominal mesothelioma, a form of cancer. He went to the library to learn more, and he was shocked to find that mesothelioma was incurable, with a median survival time of only *eight months* after it was discovered. Gould wrote this: "I suspect that most people, without training in statistics, would read such a statement as 'I will probably be dead in eight months' - the very conclusion that must be avoided, since it isn't so, and since attitude (in fighting the cancer) matters so much." Gould went on to carefully interpret the value of the median. He knew that his chance of living longer than the median was good because he was young, his cancer was diagnosed early, and he would get the best medical treatment. He also reasoned that some could live much longer than eight months, and he saw no reason why he could not be in that group. Armed with this thoughtful interpretation of the median and a strong positive attitude, Gould lived for *20 years* after his diagnosis. He died of another cancer not related to the mesothelioma.

continued

- When more than two data values occur with the same greatest frequency, each is a mode, and the data set is said to be **multimodal.**
- When no data value is repeated, we say that there is **no mode.**
- When you have ice cream with your pie, it is "à la mode."

CP | EXAMPLE 4   Mode

Find the mode of the first eleven wait times for "Tower of Terror" at 10 AM.

35   35   20   50   95   75   45   50   30   35   30

SOLUTION

Sort the list to make it easier to find values that occur more than once:

20   30   30   35   35   35   45   50   50   75   95

The mode is 35 minutes, because it is the value occurring most often (three times).

YOUR TURN. Find the mode in Exercise 7 "Celebrity Net Worth."

In Example 4, the mode is a single value. Here are other possible circumstances:

Two modes: The wait times (mins) of 30, 30, 50, 50, and 75 have two modes: 30 mins and 50 mins.

No mode: The wait times (mins) of 20, 30, 35, 50, and 75 have no mode because no value is repeated.

Midrange

Another measure of center is the midrange.

> **DEFINITION**
>
> The **midrange** of a data set is the measure of center that is the value midway between the maximum and minimum values in the original data set. It is found by adding the maximum data value to the minimum data value and then dividing the sum by 2, as in the following formula:
>
> $$\text{Midrange} = \frac{\text{maximum data value} + \text{minimum data value}}{2}$$

Important Properties of the Midrange

- Because the midrange uses only the maximum and minimum values, it is very sensitive to those extremes so the midrange is not *resistant*.
- In practice, the midrange is rarely used, but it has three redeeming features:
  1. The midrange is very easy to compute.
  2. The midrange helps reinforce the very important point that there are several different ways to define the center of a data set.
  3. The value of the midrange is sometimes used incorrectly for the median, so confusion can be reduced by clearly defining the midrange along with the median.

(CP) **EXAMPLE 5** Midrange

Find the midrange of the first eleven wait times for "Space Mountain" at 10 AM (from Example 1):

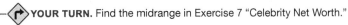

50   25   75   35   50   25   30   50   45   25   20

SOLUTION

The midrange is found as follows:

$$\text{Midrange} = \frac{\text{maximum data value} + \text{minimum data value}}{2}$$

$$= \frac{75 + 20}{2} = 47.5 \text{ minutes}$$

The midrange is 47.5 minutes.

▶ **YOUR TURN.** Find the midrange in Exercise 7 "Celebrity Net Worth."

Rounding Measures of Center

When calculating measures of center, we often need to round the result. We use the following rule.

Round-Off Rules for Measures of Center:

- **For the mean, median, and midrange, carry one more decimal place than is present in the original set of values.**

- **For the mode, leave the value as is without rounding** (because values of the mode are the same as some of the original data values).

When applying any rounding rules, round only the final answer, *not intermediate values that occur during calculations.* See these examples:

- The mean of 2, 3, and 5 is 3.333333 . . . , which is rounded to 3.3, which has one more decimal place than the original values of 2, 3, and 5.

- The mean of 80.4 and 80.6 is 80.50 (one more decimal place than was used for the original values).

Mode: Because the mode is one or more of the original data values, we do not round values of the mode; we simply use the same original values that are modes.

Critical Thinking

We can always calculate measures of center from a sample of numbers, but we should always think about whether it makes sense to do that. In Section 1-2 we noted that it makes no sense to do numerical calculations with data at the nominal level of measurement, because those data consist of names, labels, or categories only, so statistics such as the mean and median are meaningless. We should also think about the sampling method used to collect the data. If the sampling method is not sound, the statistics we obtain may be very misleading.

Simpson's Paradox

Consider these data: When playing a basketball game, Bart makes 4 of 10 shots in the first half (40% success) and 3 of 4 shots in the second half (75% success), while Homer makes 1 of 4 shots in the first half (25% success) and 7 of 10 shots in the second half (70% success). See that Bart was better than Homer in each half, but for the entire game, Homer made 8 of 14 shots (57.1% success), while Bart made 7 of 14 shots (50% success). Bart was better than Homer in each half, but Homer was better overall. This is a good example of Simpson's paradox, which states that groups can have means that show one trend, but the trend is reversed when the groups are combined.

One classic and real situation occurred when the Berkeley graduate program admitted 44% of male applicants and 35% of female applicants (bias in favor of males), but when looking at individual departments, there appeared to be a bias in favor of female applicants.

EXAMPLE 6 **Critical Thinking and Measures of Center**

See each of the following illustrating situations in which the mean and median are *not* meaningful statistics.

a. Zip codes of the Gateway Arch in St. Louis, White House, Air Force division of the Pentagon, Empire State Building, and Statue of Liberty: 63102, 20500, 20330, 10118, 10004. (The zip codes don't measure or count anything. The numbers are just labels for geographic locations.)

b. Ranks of selected medical schools of Harvard, Johns Hopkins, New York University, Stanford University, and Duke University: 1, 2, 3, 4 10. (The ranks reflect an ordering, but they don't measure or count anything.)

c. Numbers on the jerseys of the starting offense for the New England Patriots when they won Super Bowl LIII: 12, 26, 46, 15, 11, 87, 77, 62, 60, 69, 61. (The numbers on the football jerseys don't measure or count anything; they are just substitutes for names.)

d. Top 5 annual compensation of chief executive officers (in millions of dollars): 513.3, 256.0, 146.6, 141.7, 130.7. (Such "top 5" or "top 10" lists include data that are not at all representative of the larger population.)

e. The 50 mean ages computed from the means in each of the 50 states. (If you calculate the mean of those 50 values, the result is not the mean age of people in the entire United States. The population sizes of the 50 different states must be taken into account, as described in the *weighted mean* introduced in Part 2 of this section.)

> **YOUR TURN.** For Exercise 5 "Super Bowl Jersey Numbers," determine why the mean and median are not meaningful.

In the spirit of describing, exploring, and comparing data, let's examine the data in Table 3-1 and their dotplots in Figure 3-2, which includes 10 AM wait times on different days for "Rock 'n' Roller Coaster" and "Tower of Terror." These data are taken from Data Set 33 "Disney World Wait Times" in Appendix B. The wait times for each ride have been sorted from shortest to longest.

TABLE 3-1 Wait Times (min) For Rock 'n' Roller Coaster and Tower of Terror

Rock 'n' Roller Coaster	15	20	45	45	45	55	55	70	75	95	110
Tower of Terror	45	45	45	50	50	55	60	60	65	75	80

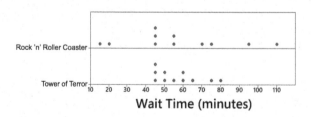

FIGURE 3-2   Dotplots of "Rock 'n' Roller Coaster" and "Tower of Terror" Wait Times

Table 3-2 summarizes the different measures of center for the "Rock 'n' Roller Coaster" and "Tower of Terror" wait times shown above.

TABLE 3-2 Comparison of Disney Wait Times (minutes)

	Mean	Median	Mode	Midrange
Rock 'n' Roller Coaster	57.3	55.0	45	62.5
Tower of Terror	57.3	55.0	45	62.5

Well, how can that be? The wait times for both rides have the *same* measures of center! Instead of being a phenomenon that commonly occurs, the wait times from Figure 3-2 have been carefully selected. Because the wait times for the two different rides have the same measures of center, they appear to be behaving the same, but this is really, really important: Go back and examine the two sets of wait times in Figure 3-2 and try to identify a fundamental and dramatic difference that is not identified by the measures of center. Find it? If not, SPOILER ALERT: Section 3-2 identifies and investigates this important difference. (See Example 8 on page 114.)

PART 2 Beyond the Basics of Measures of Center

Calculating the Mean from a Frequency Distribution

Formula 3-2 is the same calculation for the mean that was presented in Part 1, but it incorporates this approach: When working with data summarized in a frequency distribution, we make calculations possible by pretending that all sample values in each class are equal to the class midpoint. Formula 3-2 is not really a new concept; it is simply a variation of Formula 3-1 (mean).

FORMULA 3-2   MEAN FROM A FREQUENCY DISTRIBUTION

First multiply each frequency and
class midpoint; then add the products.
↓

$$\bar{x} = \frac{\Sigma (f \cdot x)}{\Sigma f} \quad \text{(Result is an approximation)}$$

↑
Sum of frequencies
(equal to n)

Example 7 illustrates the procedure for finding the mean from a frequency distribution.

EXAMPLE 7   Computing the Mean from a Frequency Distribution

The first two columns of Table 3-3 shown here are the same as the Los Angeles commute time frequency distribution of Table 2-2 from Chapter 2. Use the frequency distribution in the first two columns of Table 3-3 to find the mean.

TABLE 3-3 Daily Commute Time in Los Angeles

Daily Commute Times in Los Angeles (minutes)	Frequency f	Class Midpoint x	$f \cdot x$
0–14	6	7.0	42.0
15–29	18	22.0	396.0
30–44	14	37.0	518.0
45–59	5	52.0	260.0
60–74	5	67.0	335.0
75–89	1	82.0	82.0
90–104	1	97.0	97.0
Totals:	$\Sigma f = 50$		$\Sigma (f \cdot x) = 1730.0$

continued

SOLUTION

Remember, when working with data summarized in a frequency distribution, we make calculations possible by pretending that all sample values in each class are equal to the class midpoint. For example, consider the first class interval of 0–14 with a frequency of 6. We pretend that each of the 6 commute times is 7 minutes (the class midpoint). With the commute time of 7 minutes repeated 6 times, we have a total of $7.0 \cdot 6.0 = 42.0$, as shown as the first entry in the rightmost column of Table 3-3. We can then add those results to find the sum of all sample values.

The bottom row of Table 3-3 shows the two components we need for the calculation of the mean (as in Formula 3-2): $\Sigma f = 50$ and $\Sigma (f \cdot x) = 1730.0$. We calculate the mean using Formula 3-2 as follows:

$$\bar{x} = \frac{\Sigma (f \cdot x)}{\Sigma f} = \frac{1730.0}{50} = 34.6 \text{ minutes}$$

The result of $\bar{x} = 34.6$ minutes is an *approximation* because it is based on the use of class midpoint values instead of the original list of 50 commute times. The mean of 31.4 minutes (rounded from 31.42) found by using all of the original commute times is a more accurate result.

 YOUR TURN. Do Exercise 29 "Frequency Distribution."

Calculating a Weighted Mean

When different x data values are assigned different weights w, we can compute a **weighted mean**. Formula 3-3 can be used to compute the weighted mean.

FORMULA 3-3

$$\text{Weighted mean: } \bar{x} = \frac{\Sigma (w \cdot x)}{\Sigma w}$$

Formula 3-3 tells us to first multiply each weight w by the corresponding value x, then to add the products, and then finally to divide that total by the sum of the weights, Σw.

EXAMPLE 8 **Computing Grade-Point Average**

In her first semester of college, a student of the author took five courses. Her final grades, along with the number of credits for each course, were A (3 credits), A (4 credits), B (3 credits), C (3 credits), and F (1 credit). The grading system assigns quality points to letter grades as follows: A = 4; B = 3; C = 2; D = 1; F = 0. Compute her grade-point average.

SOLUTION

Use the numbers of credits as weights: $w = 3, 4, 3, 3, 1$. Replace the letter grades of A, A, B, C, and F with the corresponding quality points: $x = 4, 4, 3, 2, 0$. We now use Formula 3-3 as shown below. The result is a first-semester grade-point average of 3.07. (In using the preceding round-off rule, the result should be rounded to 3.1, but it is common to round grade-point averages to two decimal places.)

$$\bar{x} = \frac{\Sigma (w \cdot x)}{\Sigma w}$$
$$= \frac{(3 \times 4) + (4 \times 4) + (3 \times 3) + (3 \times 2) + (1 \times 0)}{3 + 4 + 3 + 3 + 1}$$
$$= \frac{43}{14} = 3.07$$

 YOUR TURN. Do Exercise 33 "Weighted Mean."

TECH CENTER

 ## Descriptive Statistics Display Examples
Access tech supplements, videos, and data sets at **www.TriolaStats.com**

The following displays are based on Space Mountain 10AM wait times from Data Set 33 "Disney World Wait Times."

Statdisk

```
Explore Data -  Column 1
Sample Size, n:                50
Mean:                          38.00000
Median:                        35.00000
Midrange:                      60.00000
RMS:                           43.39355
Variance, s^2:                 447.95918
Standard Deviation, s:         21.16505
Mean Absolute Deviation:       15.24000
Range:                         100
Coefficient of Variance:       55.69749%

Minimum:                       10
1st Quartile:                  25.00000
2nd Quartile:                  35.00000
3rd Quartile:                  50.00000
Maximum:                       110

Sum:                           1900.00000
Sum of Squares:                94150.00000

95% CI for the Mean:
31.98496 < mean < 44.01504

95% CI for the standard Deviation:
17.67987 < SD < 26.37446

95% CI for the variance:
312.57797 < VAR < 695.61209
```

TI-83/84 Plus

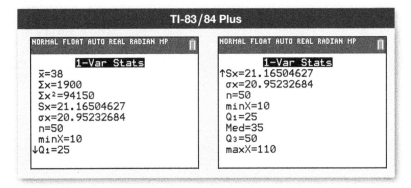

```
NORMAL FLOAT AUTO REAL RADIAN MP

      1-Var Stats
x̄=38
Σx=1900
Σx²=94150
Sx=21.16504627
σx=20.95232684
n=50
minX=10
↓Q₁=25
```

```
NORMAL FLOAT AUTO REAL RADIAN MP

      1-Var Stats
↑Sx=21.16504627
σx=20.95232684
n=50
minX=10
Q₁=25
Med=35
Q₃=50
maxX=110
```

Minitab

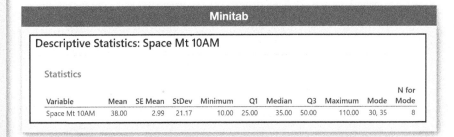

Descriptive Statistics: Space Mt 10AM

Statistics

Variable	Mean	SE Mean	StDev	Minimum	Q1	Median	Q3	Maximum	Mode	N for Mode
Space Mt 10AM	38.00	2.99	21.17	10.00	25.00	35.00	50.00	110.00	30, 35	8

R

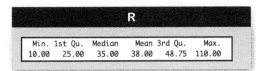

Min.	1st Qu.	Median	Mean	3rd Qu.	Max.
10.00	25.00	35.00	38.00	48.75	110.00

StatCrunch

Summary statistics:

Column	n	Mean	Variance	Std. dev.	Std. err.	Median	Range	Min	Max	Q1	Q3
SPACE MT 10AM	50	38	447.95918	21.165046	2.9931895	35	100	10	110	25	50

Excel - Data Analysis Toolpak

SPACE MT 10AM	
Mean	38
Standard Error	2.9931895
Median	35
Mode	35
Standard Deviation	21.165046
Sample Variance	447.95918
Kurtosis	3.2209206
Skewness	1.6409566
Range	100
Minimum	10
Maximum	110
Sum	1900
Count	50

Excel - XLSTAT Add-In

Statistic	SPACE MT 10AM
Nbr. of observations	50
Minimum	10.000
Maximum	110.000
Range	100.000
1st Quartile	25.000
Median	35.000
3rd Quartile	48.750
Sum	1900.000
Mean	38.000
Variance (n)	439.000
Variance (n-1)	447.959
Standard deviation (n)	20.952
Standard deviation (n-1)	21.165

TECH CENTER

Descriptive Statistics
Access tech supplements, videos, and data sets at **www.TriolaStats.com**

Statdisk
1. Click **Data** in the top menu.
2. Select **Explore Data-Descriptive Statistics** from the dropdown menu.
3. Select the desired data column.
4. Click **Evaluate** to view descriptive statistics.

Minitab
1. Click **Stat** in the top menu.
2. Select **Basic Statistics** from the drop-down menu, and then select **Display Descriptive Statistics**.
3. Double click on the desired data column so that it appears in the *Variables* window.
4. Click **OK** to view descriptive statistics.
TIP: Click the **Statistics** button above **OK** to select individual statistics you want displayed.

StatCrunch
1. Click on **Stat** in the top menu.
2. Select **Summary Stats** from the dropdown menu, then select **Columns**.
3. Select the desired data column.
4. Click **Compute!** to view descriptive statistics.
TIP: Customize descriptive statistics by selecting items under **Statistics**.

TI-83/84 Plus Calculator
1. Press **STAT**, then select **CALC** from the top menu.
2. Select **1-Var Stats** and press **ENTER**.
3. Enter the name of list that includes the desired data (e.g., L1).
4. Select **Calculate** and press **ENTER** to view descriptive statistics.
TIP: Press ⌄ to view additional statistics that don't fit on the initial screen.

Excel
XLSTAT Add-In
1. Click on the **XLSTAT** tab in the Ribbon, and then click **Describing Data**.
2. Select **Descriptive statistics** from the dropdown menu.
3. Check the **Quantitative data** box and enter the desired data range. If the first row of data contains a label, also check the **Variable labels** box.
4. Click **OK** to view descriptive statistics.
TIP: Click the **Outputs** tab to select which statistics are shown.
Excel Data Analysis Add-In
1. Click on the **Data** tab in the Ribbon, and then select **Data Analysis** in the top menu.
2. Select **Descriptive Statistics** under *Analysis Tools*.
3. Enter the desired data range for **Input Range**. If the first row of data contains a label, also check the **Labels in First Row** box.
4. Check the **Summary Statistics** box and click **OK** to view descriptive statistics.

R
R commands:
Mean, 5-Number Summary: **summary(x)**
Standard Deviation: **sd(x)**
Variance: **var(x)**
A complete list of R statistical commands is available at TriolaStats.com

3-1 Basic Skills and Concepts

Statistical Literacy and Critical Thinking

1. Average The Social Security Administration lists "the national average wage index" for a recent year as 50,321.89. What is the role of the term *average* in statistics? Should another term be used in place of *average*?

2. What's Wrong? *Education Week* magazine published a list consisting of the mean teacher salary in each of the 50 states for a recent year. If we add the 50 means and then divide by 50, we get $56,479. Is the value of $56,479 the mean teacher salary for the population of all teachers in the 50 United States? Why or why not?

3. Measures of Center In what sense are the mean, median, mode, and midrange measures of "center"?

4. Resistant Measures Listed below are 10 wait times (minutes) for "Rock 'n' Roller Coaster" at 10 AM (from Data Set 33 "Disney World Wait Times"). The data are listed in order from lowest to highest. Find the mean and median of these ten values. Then find the mean and median after excluding the value of 180, which appears to be an outlier. Compare the two sets of results. How much was the mean affected by the inclusion of the outlier? How much is the median affected by the inclusion of the outlier?

15   20   25   30   30   35   45   50   50   180

Critical Thinking.   *For Exercises 5–20, watch out for these little buggers. Each of these exercises involves some feature that is somewhat tricky. Find the (a)* **mean**, *(b)* **median**, *(c)* **mode**, *(d)* **midrange**, *and then answer the given question.*

5. Super Bowl Jersey Numbers Listed below are the jersey numbers of the 11 offensive players on the starting roster of the New England Patriots when they won Super Bowl LIII. Find the mean and median. What do the results tell us?

12   26   46   15   11   87   77   62   60   69   61

6. Super Bowl Ages Listed below are the ages of the same 11 players used in the preceding exercise. How are the resulting statistics fundamentally different from those found in the preceding exercise?

41   24   30   31   32   29   25   26   26   25   30

7. Celebrity Net Worth Here are the celebrities with the top 8 net worths (in millions of dollars) in a recent year: George Lucas (5500), Steven Spielberg (3700), Oprah Winfrey (3200), Michael Jordan (1700), Paul McCartney (1200), J. K. Rowling (1000), David Copperfield (1000), and Jerry Seinfeld (950). Find the mean and median. What do the results tell us about the population of all celebrities? Based on the nature of the amounts, what can be inferred about their precision?

8. Geography Majors The data listed below are estimated incomes (dollars) of students who graduated from the University of North Carolina (UNC) after majoring in geography. The data are based on graduates in the year 1984. The income of basketball superstar Michael Jordan (a 1984 UNC graduate and geography major) is included. Does his income have much of an effect on the measures of center? Based on these data, would the college have been justified by saying that the mean income of a graduate in their geography program is greater than $250,000?

17,466   18,085   17,875   19,339   19,682   19,610   18,259   16,354   2,200,000

9. Jaws 2 Listed below are the number of unprovoked shark attacks worldwide for the last several years. What extremely important characteristic of the data is not considered when finding the measures of center?

70   54   68   82   79   83   76   73   98   81

10. Peas in a Pod Biologists conducted experiments to determine whether a deficiency of carbon dioxide in the soil affects the phenotypes of peas. Listed below are the phenotype codes, where 1 = smooth-yellow, 2 = smooth-green, 3 = wrinkled-yellow, and 4 = wrinkled-green. Can the measures of center be obtained for these values? Do the results make sense?

2   1   1   1   1   1   1   4   1   2   2   1   2   3   3   2   3   1   3   1   3   1   3   2   2

11. Smart Thermostats Listed below are selling prices (dollars) of smart thermostats tested by *Consumer Reports* magazine. If you decide to buy one of these smart thermostats, what statistic is most relevant, other than the measures of central tendency?

250   170   225   100   250   250   130   200   150   250   170   200   180   250

12. Cell Phone Radiation Listed below are the measured radiation levels (in W/kg) corresponding to these cell phones: iPhone X, iPhone 7, Google Pixel, Samsung Galaxy S8, One-Plus 5, Motorola VE465, LG G3, and HTC Desire 310. The data are from the Federal Communications Commission. The media often report about the dangers of cell phone radiation as a cause of cancer. The Federal Communications Commission (FCC) has a standard that a cell phone radiation rate must be 1.6 W/kg or less. If you are planning to purchase a cell phone, are any of the measures of center the most important statistic? Is there another statistic that is most relevant? If so, which one?

0.97   1.38   0.93   1.52   1.37   1.09   0.48   0.65

13. Caffeine in Soft Drinks Listed below are measured amounts of caffeine (mg per 12 oz of drink) obtained in one can from each of 20 brands (7-UP, A&W Root Beer, Cherry Coke, . . . , Tab). Are the statistics representative of the population of all cans of the same 20 brands consumed by Americans?

0   0   34   34   34   45   41   51   55   36   47   41   0   0   53   54   38   0   41   47

14. Gender Pay Gap Listed below are women's median earnings as a percentage of men's median earnings for recent years beginning with 1997 (listed in order by row). What extremely important characteristic of the data is not considered when finding the measures of center?

74.4   76.3   76.5   76.9   76.4   77.9   79.4   80.4   81.0   80.8

80.2   79.9   80.2   81.2   82.2   80.9   82.1   82.5   81.1   81.9

15. Writing Hand Listed below are the writing hands (1 = right; 2 = left) of randomly selected Army women examined in 1988 for the Anthropometric Survey (ANSUR). Identify two problems with the results.

1   1   1   1   1   1   1   1   2   2

16. Most Expensive Colleges Listed below are the annual costs (dollars) of tuition and fees at the 10 most expensive colleges in the United States for a recent year (based on data from *U.S. News & World Report*). The colleges listed in order are Columbia, Vassar, Harvey Mudd, University of Chicago, Trinity, Franklin and Marshall, Tufts, Amherst, University of Southern California, and Sarah Lawrence. What does this "top 10" list tell us about those costs for the population of all U.S. college tuitions?

57,208   55,210   54,886   54,825   54,770   54,380   54,318   54,310   54,259   54,010

17. Diamonds at the Diamonds Listed below in dollars are the amounts it costs for marriage proposal packages at the different Major League Baseball stadiums. Five of the teams don't allow proposals. Are there any outliers?

39   50   50   50   55   55   75   85   100   115   175   175   200

209   250   250   350   400   450   500   500   500   500   1500   2500

18. Sales of LP Vinyl Record Albums Listed below are annual U.S. sales of vinyl record albums (millions of units). The numbers of albums sold are listed in chronological order, and the last entry represents the most recent year. Do the measures of center give us any information about a changing trend over time?

0.3   0.6   0.8   1.1   1.1   1.4   1.4   1.5   1.2   1.3   1.4   1.2   0.9   0.9

1.0   1.9   2.5   2.8   3.9   4.6   6.1   9.2   11.9   13.1   14.3

19. California Smokers In the California Health Interview Survey, randomly selected adults are interviewed. One of the questions asks how many cigarettes are smoked per day, and results are listed below for 50 randomly selected respondents. How well do the results reflect the smoking behavior of California adults?

9   10   10   20   40   50   0   0   0   0   0   0   0   0   0

0   0   0   0   0   0   0   0   0   0   0   0   0   0

0   0   0   0   0   0   0   0   0   0   0   0   0   0

0   0   0   0   0

20. Big Mac Index Listed below in order are prices in dollars for a Big Mac hamburger in the United States, Canada, Mexico, China, Japan, Russia, Switzerland, Italy, Spain, Britain, India, and Egypt. Such data are used to compare currency exchange rates and the costs of goods in different countries. Do these data suggest that the prices are roughly the same, or do they appear to vary by large amounts? Do any of the measures of center reveal anything about the variation of the prices?

$$5.3 \quad 5.3 \quad 2.6 \quad 3.2 \quad 3.4 \quad 2.3 \quad 6.8 \quad 5.1 \quad 4.8 \quad 4.4 \quad 2.8 \quad 1.9$$

In Exercises 21–24, find the **mean** *and* **median** *for each of the two samples, then compare the two sets of results.*

21. Blood Pressure A sample of blood pressure measurements is taken from Data Set 1 "Body Data" in Appendix B, and those values (mm Hg) are listed below. The values are matched so that 10 subjects each have systolic and diastolic measurements. (Systolic is a measure of the force of blood being pushed through arteries, but diastolic is a measure of blood pressure when the heart is at rest between beats.) Are the measures of center the best statistics to use with these data? What else might be better?

Systolic:	118	128	158	96	156	122	116	136	126	120
Diastolic:	80	76	74	52	90	88	58	64	72	82

22. Parking Meter Theft Listed below are amounts (in millions of dollars) collected from parking meters by Brinks and others in New York City during similar time periods. A larger data set was used to convict five Brinks employees of grand larceny. The data were provided by the attorney for New York City, and they are listed on the Data and Story Library (DASL) website. Do the limited data listed here show evidence of stealing by Brinks employees?

Collection Contractor Was Brinks	1.3	1.5	1.3	1.5	1.4	1.7	1.8	1.7	1.7	1.6
Collection Contractor Was Not Brinks	2.2	1.9	1.5	1.6	1.5	1.7	1.9	1.6	1.6	1.8

23. Pulse Rates Listed below are pulse rates (beats per minute) from samples of adult males and females (from Data Set 1 "Body Data" in Appendix B). Does there appear to be a difference?

Male:	86	72	64	72	72	54	66	56	80	72	64	64	96	58	66
Female:	64	84	82	70	74	86	90	88	90	90	94	68	90	82	80

24. It's a Small Wait After All Listed below are the wait times (minutes) at 10 AM for the rides "It's a Small World" and "Avatar Flight of Passage." These data are found in Data Set 33 "Disney World Wait Times." Does a comparison between the means and medians reveal that there is a difference between the two sets of data?

It's a Small World

10   5   5 10 10 10 10 15 10 10 10 10 10 10   5 10 10 10   5   5   5 10 10   5 10
 5 10 15   5   5 10   5   5   5 15 10 10 30 10   5 10 10 10   5 10 15 10 20 15 15

Avatar Flight of Passage 180 195 110 150 180 150 150 180 150 150 165 150 120 165 135
150 75 90 85 105 75 135 120 150 105 135 105 105 150 90 70 120 90 120 135
210 135 150 225 150 165 150 135 150 180 120 150 180 225 165

Large Data Sets from Appendix B. *In Exercises 25–28, refer to the indicated data set in Appendix B. Use software or a calculator to find the* **means** *and* **medians.**

25. Weights Use the weights of the males listed in Data Set 2 "ANSUR I 1988," which were measured in 1988 and use the weights of the males listed in Data Set 3 "ANSUR II 2012," which were measured in 2012. Does it appear that males have become heavier?

26. Earthquakes Use the magnitudes (Richter scale) of the 600 earthquakes listed in Data Set 24 "Earthquakes" in Appendix B. In 1989, the San Francisco Bay Area was struck with an earthquake that measured 7.0 on the Richter scale. That earthquake occurred during the warm-up period for the third game of the baseball World Series. Is the magnitude of that World Series earthquake an *outlier* when considered in the context of the sample data given in Data Set 24? Explain.

27. Body Temperatures Refer to Data Set 5 "Body Temperatures" in Appendix B and use the body temperatures for 12:00 AM on day 2. Do the results support or contradict the common belief that the mean body temperature is 98.6°F?

28. Births Use the birth weights (grams) of the 400 babies listed in Data Set 6 "Births" in Appendix B. Examine the list of birth weights to make an observation about those numbers. How does that observation affect the way that the results should be rounded?

*In Exercises 29–32, compute the **mean** of the data summarized in the frequency distribution. Also, compare the **computed means** to the **actual means** obtained by using the original list of data values, which are as follows: (Exercise 29) 31.4 minutes; (Exercise 30) 140.6 minutes; (Exercise 31) 55.2 years; (Exercise 32) 240.2 seconds.*

29.

Daily Commute Time in Los Angeles (minutes)	Frequency
0–14	6
15–29	18
30–44	14
45–59	5
60–74	5
75–89	1
90–104	1

30.

Avatar Flight of Passage Wait Times 10 AM (minutes)	Frequency
70–89	4
90–109	7
110–129	6
130–149	6
150–169	18
170–189	5
190–209	1
210–229	3

31.

Age of President at First Inauguration (years)	Frequency
40–44	2
45–49	7
50–54	10
55–59	10
60–64	6
65–69	3
70–74	1

32.

Duration of Old Faithful Eruptions (sec)	Frequency
125–149	1
150–174	0
175–199	0
200–224	3
225–249	34
250–274	12

33. Weighted Mean A student of the author earned grades of A, C, B, A, and D. Those courses had these corresponding numbers of credit hours: 3, 3, 3, 4, and 1. The grading system assigns quality points to letter grades as follows: A = 4; B = 3; C = 2; D = 1; F = 0. Compute the grade-point average (GPA) and round the result with two decimal places. If the dean's list requires a GPA of 3.00 or greater, did this student make the dean's list?

34. Weighted Mean A student of the author earned grades of 63, 91, 88, 84, and 79 on her five regular statistics tests. She earned grades of 86 on the final exam and 90 on her class projects. Her combined homework grade was 70. The five regular tests count for 60% of the final grade, the final exam counts for 10%, the project counts for 15%, and homework counts for 15%. What is her weighted mean grade? What letter grade did she earn (A, B, C, D, or F)? Assume that a mean of 90 or above is an A, a mean of 80 to 89 is a B, and so on.

3-1   Beyond the Basics

35. Degrees of Freedom Five recent U.S. presidents had a mean age of 56.2 years at the time of their inauguration. Four of these ages are 64, 46, 54, and 47.

a. Find the missing value.

b. We need to create a list of n values that have a specific known mean. We are free to select any values we desire for some of the n values. How many of the n values can be freely assigned before the remaining values are determined? (The result is referred to as the *number of degrees of freedom*.)

 36. Censored Data Data Set 22 "Presidents" in Appendix B lists the numbers of years that U.S. presidents lived after their first inauguration. As of this writing, five of the presidents are still alive, and after their first inauguration they have lived 44 years, 28 years, 20 years, 12 years, and 4 years so far. We might use the values of 44+, 28+, 20+, 12+, and 4+, where the positive signs indicate that the actual value is equal to or greater than the current value. (These values are said to be *censored* at the current time that this list was compiled.) If you use the values in Data Set 22 and ignore the presidents who are still alive, what is the mean? If you use the values given in Data Set 22 along with the additional values of 44+, 28+, 20+, 12+, and 4+, what do we know about the mean? Do the two results differ by much?

37. Trimmed Mean Because the mean is very sensitive to extreme values, we say that it is not a *resistant* measure of center. By deleting some low values and high values, the **trimmed mean** is more resistant. To find the 10% trimmed mean for a data set, first arrange the data in order, then delete the bottom 10% of the values and delete the top 10% of the values, then calculate the mean of the remaining values. Use the axial loads (pounds) of aluminum cans listed below (from Data Set 41 "Aluminum Cans" in Appendix B) for cans that are 0.0111 in. thick. An axial load is the force at which the top of a can collapses. Identify any outliers, then compare the median, mean, 10% trimmed mean, and 20% trimmed mean.

> 247 260 268 273 276 279 281 283 284 285 286 288
> 289 291 293 295 296 299 310 504

38. Harmonic Mean The **harmonic mean** is often used as a measure of center for data sets consisting of rates of change, such as speeds. It is found by dividing the number of values n by the sum of the *reciprocals* of all values, expressed as

$$\frac{n}{\sum \frac{1}{x}}$$

(No value can be zero.)

a. A bicycle trip of 30 miles is traveled at a mean speed of 30 mi/h, and the return trip is traveled at a mean speed of 10 mi/h. What is the total time required to travel the 60 miles? What was the harmonic mean speed for the round trip?

b. The author drove 1163 miles to a conference in Orlando, Florida. For the trip to the conference, the author stopped overnight, and the mean speed from start to finish was 38 mi/h. For the return trip, the author stopped only for food and fuel, and the mean speed from start to finish was 56 mi/h. Find the harmonic mean of 38 mi/h and 56 mi/h. How does the result compare to the (arithmetic) mean of 38 mi/h and 56 mi/h found using Formula 3-1? Which of those two means is the actual mean speed for the round trip?

39. Geometric Mean The **geometric mean** is often used in business and economics for finding average rates of change, average rates of growth, or average ratios. To find the geometric mean of n values (all of which are positive), first multiply the values, then find the nth root of the product. For a 6-year period, money deposited in annual certificates of deposit had annual interest rates of 0.58%, 0.29%, 0.13%, 0.14%, 0.15%, and 0.19%. Identify the single percentage growth rate that is the same as the six consecutive growth rates by computing the geometric mean of 1.0058, 1.0029, 1.0013, 1.0014, 1.0015, and 1.0019.

40. Quadratic Mean The **quadratic mean** (or **root mean square**, or **R.M.S.**) is used in physical applications, such as power distribution systems. The quadratic mean of a set of values is obtained by squaring each value, adding those squares, dividing the sum by the number of values n, and then taking the square root of that result, as indicated below:

$$\text{Quadratic mean} = \sqrt{\frac{\Sigma x^2}{n}}$$

Find the R.M.S. of these voltages measured from household current: 0, 60, 110, −110, −60, 0. How does the result compare to the mean?

41. Median When data are summarized in a frequency distribution, the median can be found by first identifying the *median class*, which is the class that contains the median. We then assume that the values in that class are evenly distributed and we interpolate. Letting n denote the sum of all class frequencies, and letting m denote the sum of the class frequencies that *precede* the median class, the median can be estimated as shown below.

$$(\text{lower limit of median class}) + (\text{class width}) \left(\frac{\left(\frac{n+1}{2} \right) - (m+1)}{\text{frequency of median class}} \right)$$

Use this procedure to find the median of the frequency distribution given in Table 3-3 on page 95. How far is that result from the median found from the original list of 1000 Los Angeles commute times listed in Data Set 31 "Commute Times" in Appendix B?

3-2 Measures of Variation

Key Concept Variation is the single most important topic in statistics, so this is the single most important section in this book. This section presents three important measures of variation: *range, standard deviation,* and *variance.* These statistics are numbers, but our focus is not just computing those numbers but developing the ability to *interpret* and *understand* them. This section is not a study of arithmetic; it is about understanding and interpreting measures of variation, especially the standard deviation.

STUDY HINT Part 1 of this section presents basic concepts of variation, and Part 2 presents additional concepts related to the standard deviation. Part 1 and Part 2 both include formulas for computation, but do not spend too much time memorizing formulas or doing arithmetic calculations. Instead, focus on *understanding* and *interpreting* values of standard deviation.

PART 1 Basic Concepts of Variation

Visualizing Variation See Figure 3-3, which shows histograms and dotplots comparing volumes of cola in cans of (1) regular Coke and (2) Special Cola. (The volumes of regular Coke are real data from Data Set 37 in Appendix B.) Recall from Section 2-3 that a *dotplot* is a graph of quantitative data in which each data value is plotted as a point (or dot) above a horizontal scale of values, and dots representing equal values are stacked vertically. To visualize the property of variation, refer to Figure 3-3 and note these extremely important observations about the two data sets:

- Both data sets have the *same mean* of 12.2 ounces.
- The two data sets have very different amounts of *variation*, as indicated by the dramatically different amounts of spread in the two histograms and the dramatically different amounts of spread in the two dotplots. (Compare the two dotplots to see that the points in the dotplot of regular Coke volumes are very close together, but the points in the dotplot of Special Cola volumes are spread much farther apart.)

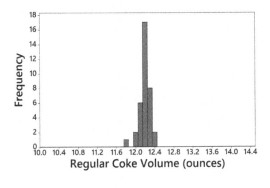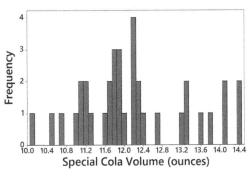

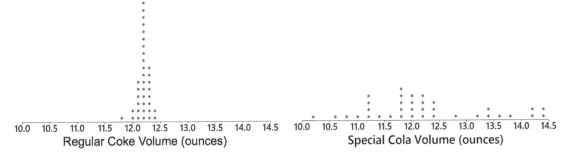

FIGURE 3-3   Volumes of Regular Coke and Special Cola

The volumes of regular Coke appear to vary very little about the mean of 12.2 oz, but the volumes of Special Cola appear to vary substantially about the mean of 12.2 oz. Continuing production of the Special Cola with such excessive variation would eventually result in disaster for the Special Cola company. It is likely that the company would not be able to stay in business with such a poor product. Consequently, companies often have this important goal:

Improve quality by reducing *variation* in goods and/or services.

We can subjectively compare the variation in the volumes of cola illustrated in Figure 3-3, but this concept of variation is so critically important that we need objective measures instead of relying on subjective judgments. We will now proceed to consider such measures of variation. To keep our round-off rules as consistent and as simple as possible, we will round the measures of variation using this rule, which is the same round-off rule used for the mean, median, and midrange:

ROUND-OFF RULE FOR MEASURES OF VARIATION When rounding the value of a measure of variation, carry one more decimal place than is present in the original set of data.

Range

Let's begin with the range because it is quick and easy to compute, but it is not as important as other measures of variation.

> **DEFINITION**
>
> The **range** of a set of data values is the difference between the maximum data value and the minimum data value.
>
> Range = (maximum data value) − (minimum data value)

Important Property of the Range

- The range uses only the maximum and the minimum data values, so it is very sensitive to extreme values. The range is not *resistant*.

- Because the range uses only the maximum and minimum values, it does not take every value into account and therefore does not truly reflect the variation among all of the data values.

(CP) **EXAMPLE 1** **Range**

Find the range of these wait times (minutes) for Space Mountain. (These are the first eleven "Space Mountain" 10 AM wait times from Data Set 33 "Disney World Wait Times" in Appendix B.)

50 25 75 35 50 25 30 50 45 25 20

SOLUTION

The range is found by subtracting the lowest value from the largest value, so we get

$$\text{Range} = (\text{maximum value}) - (\text{minimum value}) = 75 - 20 = 55.0 \text{ minutes}$$

The range of 55.0 minutes is shown with one more decimal place than is present in the original data values.

 **YOUR TURN.** Find the range in Exercise 7 "Celebrity Net Worth."

Standard Deviation of a Sample

The *standard deviation* is the measure of variation most commonly used in statistics.

> **DEFINITION**
>
> The **standard deviation** of a set of sample values, denoted by s, is a measure of how much data values deviate away from the mean. It is calculated by using Formula 3-4 or 3-5. Formula 3-5 is just a different version of Formula 3-4; both formulas are algebraically the same.

The standard deviation found from sample data is a statistic denoted by s, but the standard deviation found from population data is a parameter denoted by σ. The formula for σ is slightly different with division by the population size N used instead of division by $n - 1$. The population standard deviation σ will be discussed later.

Notation

$s = $ *sample* standard deviation

$\sigma = $ *population* standard deviation

FORMULA 3-4

$$s = \sqrt{\frac{\Sigma(x - \bar{x})^2}{n - 1}} \quad \text{sample standard deviation}$$

FORMULA 3-5

$$s = \sqrt{\frac{n(\Sigma x^2) - (\Sigma x)^2}{n(n - 1)}} \quad \begin{array}{l}\text{shortcut formula for sample standard}\\ \text{deviation (used by calculators and software)}\end{array}$$

Later we give the reasoning behind these formulas, but for now we recommend that you use Formula 3-4 for an example or two, and then learn how to find standard deviation values using a calculator or software.

Important Properties of Standard Deviation

■ The standard deviation is a measure of how much data values deviate away from the *mean*.

■ The value of the standard deviation s is never negative. It is zero only when all of the data values are exactly the same.

■ Larger values of s indicate greater amounts of variation.

■ The standard deviation s can increase dramatically with one or more outliers.

■ The units of the standard deviation s (such as minutes, feet, pounds) are the same as the units of the original data values.

■ The sample standard deviation s is a **biased estimator** of the population standard deviation σ, which means that values of the sample standard deviation s do not center around the value of σ. (This is explained in Part 2.)

Example 2 illustrates a calculation using Formula 3-4 because that formula better illustrates that the standard deviation is based on deviations of sample values away from the mean.

CP ▸ **EXAMPLE 2** Calculating Standard Deviation with Formula 3-4

Use Formula 3-4 to find the standard deviation of these "Space Mountain" wait times (minutes) from Example 1: 50, 25, 75, 35, 50, 25, 30, 50, 45, 25, 20.

SOLUTION

The left column of Table 3-4 on the next page summarizes the general procedure for finding the standard deviation using Formula 3-4, and the right column illustrates that procedure for the specific sample values 50, 25, 75, 35, 50, 25, 30, 50, 45, 25, 20. The result shown in Table 3-4 is 16.6 minutes, which is rounded to one more decimal place than is present in the original list of sample values. Also, the units for the standard deviation are the same as the units of the original data. Because the original data all have units of minutes, the standard deviation is 16.6 minutes.

▸ **YOUR TURN.** Find the standard deviation in Exercise 7 "Celebrity Net Worth."

More Stocks, Less Risk

In their book *Investments*, authors Zvi Bodie, Alex Kane, and Alan Marcus state that "the average standard deviation for returns of portfolios composed of only one stock was 0.554. The average portfolio risk fell rapidly as the number of stocks included in the portfolio increased." They note that with 32 stocks, the standard deviation is 0.325, indicating much less variation and risk. They make the point that with only a few stocks, a portfolio has a high degree of "firm-specific" risk, meaning that the risk is attributable to the few stocks involved. With more than 30 stocks, there is very little firm-specific risk; instead, almost all of the risk is "market risk," attributable to the stock market as a whole. They note that these principles are "just an application of the well-known law of averages."

TABLE 3-4

General Procedure for Finding Standard Deviation with Formula 3-4	Specific Example Using These Sample Values: 50, 25, 75, 35, 50, 25, 30, 50, 45, 25, 20
Step 1: Compute the mean $\bar{x}$.	The sum of 50, 25, 75, 35, 50, 25, 30, 50, 45, 25, 20 is 430; therefore: $$\bar{x} = \frac{\Sigma x}{n}$$ $$= \frac{50+25+75+35+50+25+30+50+45+25+20}{11}$$ $$= \frac{430}{11} = 39.1$$
Step 2: Subtract the mean from each individual sample value. [The result is a list of deviations of the form $(x - \bar{x})$.]	Subtract the mean of 39.1 from each sample value to get these deviations away from the mean: 10.9, −14.1, 35.9, −4.1, 10.9, −14.1, −9.1, 10.9, 5.9, −14.1, −19.1.
Step 3: Square each of the deviations obtained from Step 2. [This produces numbers of the form $(x - \bar{x})^2$.]	The squares of the deviations from Step 2 are: 118.81, 198.81, 1288.81, 16.81, 118.81, 198.81, 82.81, 118.81, 34.81, 198.81, 364.81.
Step 4: Add all of the squares obtained from Step 3. The result is $\Sigma(x - \bar{x})^2$.	The sum of the squares from Step 3 is 2740.91.
Step 5: Divide the total from Step 4 by the number $n - 1$, which is 1 less than the total number of sample values present.	With $n = 11$ data values, $n - 1 = 10$, so we divide 2740.91 by 10 to get this result: $\frac{2740.91}{10} = 274.091$.
Step 6: Find the square root of the result of Step 5. The result is the standard deviation, denoted by s.	The standard deviation is $\sqrt{274.091} = 16.556$. Expressing the result with one more decimal place than the original data, we get $s = 16.6$ minutes.

CP EXAMPLE 3 Calculating Standard Deviation with Formula 3-5

Use Formula 3-5 to find the standard deviation of these "Space Mountain" wait times (minutes) from Example 1: 50, 25, 75, 35, 50, 25, 30, 50, 45, 25, 20.

SOLUTION

Here are the components needed in Formula 3-5.

$n = 11$ (because there are 11 values in the sample)

$\Sigma x = 430$ (found by adding the original sample values)

$\Sigma x^2 = 19{,}550$ (found by adding the squares of the sample values, as in
$$50^2 + 25^2 + 75^2 + 35^2 + 50^2 + 25^2 + 30^2 + 50^2 + 45^2 + 25^2 + 20^2$$
$$= 19{,}550)$$

Using Formula 3-5, we get

$$s = \sqrt{\frac{n(\Sigma x^2) - (\Sigma x)^2}{n(n-1)}} = \sqrt{\frac{11(19{,}550) - (430)^2}{11(11-1)}} = \sqrt{\frac{30{,}150}{110}} = 16.6 \text{ minutes}$$

The result of $s = 16.6$ minutes is the same as the result in Example 2. (Because Formulas 3-4 and 3-5 are equivalent, those two results should always be the same.)

 YOUR TURN. Find the standard deviation in Exercise 7 "Celebrity Net Worth."

Range Rule of Thumb for Understanding Standard Deviation

The **range rule of thumb** is a crude but simple tool for understanding and interpreting standard deviation. It is based on the principle that for many data sets, the vast majority (such as 95%) of sample values lie within 2 standard deviations of the mean. We could improve the accuracy of this rule by taking into account such factors as the size of the sample and its distribution, but here we sacrifice accuracy for the sake of simplicity. The concept of *significance* that follows will be enhanced in later chapters, especially those that include the topic of hypothesis tests, which are also called tests of significance. The following range rule of thumb is based on the population mean μ and the population standard deviation σ, but for large and representative samples, we could use $\bar{x}$ and s instead.

Range Rule of Thumb for Identifying Significant Values

Significantly low values are $\mu - 2\sigma$ or lower.

Significantly high values are $\mu + 2\sigma$ or higher.

Values not significant: Between $(\mu - 2\sigma)$ and $(\mu + 2\sigma)$

See Figure 3-4, which illustrates the above criteria.

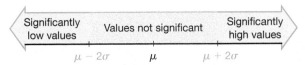

FIGURE 3-4   Range Rule of Thumb for Identifying Significant Values

> **CAUTION** An outcome can be statistically significant, and it may or may not be *important.* Don't associate statistical significance with importance.

Range Rule of Thumb for Estimating a Value of the Standard Deviation s

To roughly estimate the standard deviation from a collection of known sample data, use

$$s \approx \frac{\text{range}}{4}$$

EXAMPLE 4 Range Rule of Thumb for Interpreting s

Using the 147 pulse rates of females in Data Set 1 "Body Data" in Appendix B, the mean is 74.0 beats per minute and the standard deviation is 12.5 beats per minute. Use the range rule of thumb to find the limits separating values that are significantly low or significantly high, and then determine whether the pulse rate of 102 beats per minute is significantly high.

SOLUTION

With a mean of 74.0 and a standard deviation of 12.5, we use the range rule of thumb to find the limits separating values that are significantly low or significantly high, as follows:

Significantly low values are $(74.0 - 2 \times 12.5)$ or lower,

so significantly low values are 49.0 beats per minute or lower.

Significantly high values are $(74.0 + 2 \times 12.5)$ or higher,

so significantly high values are 99.0 beats per minute or higher.

Values not significant between 49.0 beats per minute and 99.0 beats per minute

INTERPRETATION

Based on these results, we expect that typical pulse rates of females are between 49.0 beats per minute and 99.0 beats per minute. Because the given value of 102 beats per minute falls above 99.0 beats per minute, we can consider it to be significantly high. (The Mayo Clinic website states that "a normal resting heart rate for adults ranges from 60 to 100 beats a minute.")

▶**YOUR TURN.** Do Exercise 33 "U.S. Presidents."

EXAMPLE 5 **Range Rule of Thumb for Estimating *s***

Use the range rule of thumb to *estimate* the standard deviation of the sample of 147 pulse rates of females in Data Set 1 "Body Data" in Appendix B. Those 147 pulse rates have a minimum of 36 beats per minute and a maximum of 104 beats per minute.

SOLUTION

The range rule of thumb indicates that we can estimate the standard deviation by finding the range and dividing it by 4. With a minimum of 36 and a maximum of 104, the range rule of thumb can be used to estimate the standard deviation *s*, as follows:

$$s \approx \frac{\text{range}}{4} = \frac{104 - 36}{4} = 17.0 \text{ beats per minute}$$

INTERPRETATION

The actual value of the standard deviation is $s = 12.5$ beats per minute, so the estimate of 17.0 beats per minute is in the general neighborhood of the exact result. Because this estimate is based on only the minimum and maximum values, it is generally a rough estimate that could be off by a considerable amount.

 **YOUR TURN.** Do Exercise 29 "Estimating Standard Deviation."

Standard Deviation of a Population

The definition of standard deviation and Formulas 3-4 and 3-5 apply to the standard deviation of *sample* data. A slightly different formula is used to calculate the standard deviation σ (lowercase sigma) of a *population*: Instead of dividing by $n - 1$, we divide by the population size N, as shown here:

$$\text{Population standard deviation } \sigma = \sqrt{\frac{\Sigma(x - \mu)^2}{N}}$$

Because we generally deal with sample data, we will usually use Formula 3-4, in which we divide by $n - 1$. Many calculators give both the sample standard deviation and the population standard deviation, but they use a variety of different notations.

> **CAUTION** When using a calculator to find standard deviation, identify the notation used by your particular calculator so that you get the *sample* standard deviation, not the *population* standard deviation.

Variance of a Sample and a Population

So far, we have used the term *variation* as a general description of the amount that values vary among themselves. (The terms *dispersion* and *spread* are sometimes used instead of *variation*.) The term *variance* has a specific meaning.

DEFINITION

The **variance** of a set of values is a measure of variation equal to the square of the standard deviation.

• Sample variance: $s^2 = $ square of the standard deviation *s*.

• Population variance: $\sigma^2 = $ square of the population standard deviation σ.

Notation Here is a summary of notation for the standard deviation and variance:

s = *sample* standard deviation

s^2 = *sample* variance

σ = *population* standard deviation

σ^2 = *population* variance

Note: Articles in professional journals and reports often use SD for standard deviation and VAR for variance.

Important Properties of Variance

- The units of the variance are the *squares* of the units of the original data values. (If the original data values are in feet, the variance will have units of ft^2; if the original data values are in seconds, the variance will have units of sec^2.)

- The value of the variance can increase dramatically with the inclusion of outliers. (The variance is not a *resistant* measure of variation.)

- The value of the variance is never negative. It is zero only when all of the data values are the same number.

- The sample variance s^2 is an **unbiased estimator** of the population variance σ^2, as described in Part 2 of this section.

The variance is a statistic used in some statistical methods, but for our present purposes, the variance has the serious disadvantage of using units that are *different than the units of the original data set*. This makes it difficult to understand variance as it relates to the original data set. Because of this property, it is better to first focus on the standard deviation when trying to develop an understanding of variation.

PART 2 Beyond the Basics of Variation

In Part 2, we focus on making sense of the standard deviation so that it is not some mysterious number devoid of any practical significance. We begin by addressing common questions that relate to the standard deviation.

Why Is Standard Deviation Defined as in Formula 3-4?

In measuring variation in a set of sample data, it makes sense to begin with the individual amounts by which values deviate from the mean. For a particular data value x, the amount of **deviation** is $x - \bar{x}$. It makes sense to somehow combine those deviations into one number that can serve as a measure of the variation. Adding the deviations isn't good, because the sum will always be zero. To get a statistic that measures variation, it's necessary to avoid the canceling out of negative and positive numbers. One approach is to add absolute values, as in $\Sigma |x - \bar{x}|$. If we find the mean of that sum, we get the **mean absolute deviation** (or **MAD**), which is the mean distance of the data from the mean:

$$\text{Mean absolute deviation} = \frac{\Sigma |x - \bar{x}|}{n}$$

Why Not Use the Mean Absolute Deviation Instead of the Standard Deviation?

Computation of the mean absolute deviation uses absolute values, so it uses an operation that is not "algebraic." (The algebraic operations include addition, multiplication, extracting roots, and raising to powers that are integers or fractions.) The use of absolute values would be simple, but it would create algebraic difficulties in inferential

Geographical Center of North America

Geography professor Peter Rogerson calculated the geographical center of North America to be in the aptly named town of Center, North Dakota. The method used by Dr. Rogerson involved finding the point at which the sum of the squares of the distances to all other points in the region is the smallest possible sum. The calculation of the standard deviation is based on a sum of squares, as are some other measures in statistics.

methods of statistics discussed in later chapters. The standard deviation has the advantage of using only algebraic operations. Because it is based on the square root of a sum of squares, the standard deviation closely parallels distance formulas found in algebra. There are many instances where a statistical procedure is based on a similar sum of squares. Consequently, instead of using absolute values, we *square* all deviations $(x - \bar{x})$ so that they are nonnegative, and those squares are used to calculate the standard deviation.

Why Divide by $n - 1$? After finding all of the individual values of $(x - \bar{x})^2$ we combine them by finding their sum. We then divide by $n - 1$ because there are only $n - 1$ values that can assigned without constraint. With a given mean, we can use any numbers for the first $n - 1$ values, but the last value will then be automatically determined. With division by $n - 1$, sample variances s^2 tend to center around the value of the population variance σ^2; with division by n, sample variances s^2 tend to *underestimate* the value of the population variance σ^2.

How Do We Make Sense of a Value of Standard Deviation? Part 1 of this section included the range rule of thumb for interpreting a known value of a standard deviation or estimating a value of a standard deviation. (See Examples 4 and 5.) Two other approaches for interpreting standard deviation are the empirical rule and Chebyshev's theorem.

Empirical (or 68-95-99.7) Rule for Data with a Bell-Shaped Distribution

A concept helpful in interpreting the value of a standard deviation is the **empirical rule.** This rule states that *for data sets having a distribution that is approximately bell-shaped,* the following properties apply. (See Figure 3-5.)

- About 68% of all values fall within 1 standard deviation of the mean.
- About 95% of all values fall within 2 standard deviations of the mean.
- About 99.7% of all values fall within 3 standard deviations of the mean.

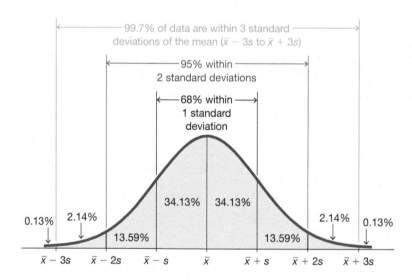

FIGURE 3-5   The Empirical Rule

EXAMPLE 6 The Empirical Rule

IQ scores have a bell-shaped distribution with a mean of 100 and a standard deviation of 15. What percentage of IQ scores are between 70 and 130?

SOLUTION

The key to solving this problem is to recognize that 70 and 130 are each exactly 2 standard deviations away from the mean of 100, as shown below:

$$2 \text{ standard deviations} = 2s = 2\,(15) = 30$$

Therefore, 2 standard deviations from the mean is

$$100 - 30 = 70$$
$$\text{or} \quad 100 + 30 = 130$$

The empirical rule tells us that about 95% of all values are within 2 standard deviations of the mean, so about 95% of all IQ scores are between 70 and 130.

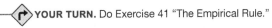 **YOUR TURN.** Do Exercise 41 "The Empirical Rule."

Another concept helpful in understanding or interpreting a value of a standard deviation is **Chebyshev's theorem**. The empirical rule applies only to data sets with bell-shaped distributions, but Chebyshev's theorem applies to *any* data set. Unfortunately, results from Chebyshev's theorem are only approximate. Because the results are lower limits ("at least"), Chebyshev's theorem has limited usefulness.

Chebyshev's Theorem

The proportion of any set of data lying within K standard deviations of the mean is always *at least* $1 - 1/K^2$, where K is any positive number greater than 1. For $K = 2$ and $K = 3$, we get the following statements:

- At least $3/4$ (or 75%) of all values lie within 2 standard deviations of the mean.
- At least $8/9$ (or 89%) of all values lie within 3 standard deviations of the mean.

EXAMPLE 7 Chebyshev's Theorem

IQ scores have a mean of 100 and a standard deviation of 15. What can we conclude from Chebyshev's theorem?

SOLUTION

Applying Chebyshev's theorem with a mean of 100 and a standard deviation of 15, we can reach the following conclusions:

- At least $3/4$ (or 75%) of IQ scores are within 2 standard deviations of the mean (between 70 and 130).
- At least $8/9$ (or 89%) of all IQ scores are within 3 standard deviations of the mean (between 55 and 145).

YOUR TURN. Do Exercise 43 "Chebyshev's Theorem."

Comparing Variation in Different Samples or Populations

In Section 3-1 we included sample wait time data from "Rock 'n' Roller Coaster" and "Tower of Terror," and those two data sets had the same means, medians, modes, and midranges. However, those two data sets have very different amounts of variation, as illustrated in the following example.

CP **EXAMPLE 8** Wait Times for "Rock 'n' Roller Coaster" and "Tower of Terror"

Table 3-5 includes measures of center and variation for the two data sets in Figure 3-2 on page 94. The measures of center fail to "see" the dramatic difference in variation between the two data sets. The table shows that the measure of center are identical, but the standard deviations of 28.8 and 12.1 are dramatically different. It would be a major error to make the comparison based on measures of center alone.

TABLE 3-5 Comparison of Disney Wait Times (minutes)

	Mean	Median	Mode	Midrange	Standard Deviation	Variance
Rock 'n' Roller Coaster	57.3	55.0	45	62.5	28.8	831.8
Tower of Terror	57.3	55.0	45	62.5	12.1	146.8

It's a good practice to compare two sample standard deviations only when the sample means are approximately the same. When comparing variation in samples or populations with very different means, it is better to use the *coefficient of variation*. Also use the coefficient of variation to compare variation from two samples or populations with different scales or units of values, such as the comparison of variation of *heights* of adult males and *weights* of adult males.

DEFINITION

The **coefficient of variation** (or **CV**) for a set of nonnegative sample or population data, expressed as a percent, describes the standard deviation relative to the mean, and is given by the following:

Sample	Population
$CV = \dfrac{s}{\bar{x}} \cdot 100$	$CV = \dfrac{\sigma}{\mu} \cdot 100$

ROUND-OFF RULE FOR THE COEFFICIENT OF VARIATION Round the coefficient of variation to one decimal place (such as 25.3%).

EXAMPLE 9 Heights of Adult Males and Weights of Adult Males

Use the data from Data Set 1 "Body Data" to compare the variation of heights (cm) of adult males and weights (kg) of adult males. For the *heights* of the males included in Data Set 1, $\bar{x} = 174.12$ cm and $s = 7.10$ cm. For the *weights* of those same adult males, $\bar{x} = 85.54$ kg and $s = 17.65$ kg. Note that we want to compare variation among heights (cm) and weights (kg), and we are working with different units of measure.

SOLUTION

We can directly compare the standard deviations if the same scales and units are used and the two means are approximately equal, but here we have different scales and different units of measurement, so we use the coefficients of variation:

Heights: $CV = \dfrac{s}{\bar{x}} \cdot 100\% = \dfrac{7.10 \text{ cm}}{174.12 \text{ cm}} \cdot 100\% = 4.1\%$

Weights: $CV = \dfrac{s}{\bar{x}} \cdot 100\% = \dfrac{17.65 \text{ kg}}{85.54 \text{ kg}} \cdot 100\% = 20.6\%$

We can now see that the weights of adult males (with $CV = 20.6\%$) vary considerably more than heights of adult males (with $CV = 4.1\%$).

 **YOUR TURN.** Do Exercise 21 "Blood Pressure."

Biased and Unbiased Estimators

The sample standard deviation s is a **biased estimator** of the population standard deviation σ, which means that values of the sample standard deviation s do *not* tend to center around the value of the population standard deviation σ. While individual values of s could equal or exceed σ, values of s generally tend to *underestimate* the value of σ. For example, consider an IQ test designed so that the population standard deviation is 15. If you repeat the process of randomly selecting 100 subjects, giving them IQ tests, and calculating the sample standard deviation s in each case, the sample standard deviations that you get will tend to be less than 15, which is the population standard deviation. There is no correction that allows us to fix the bias for all distributions of data. There is a correction that allows us to fix the bias for normally distributed populations, but it is rarely used because it is too complex and makes relatively minor corrections.

The sample variance s^2 is an **unbiased estimator** of the population variance σ^2, which means that values of s^2 tend to center around the value of σ^2 instead of systematically tending to overestimate or underestimate σ^2. Consider an IQ test designed so that the population variance is 225. If you repeat the process of randomly selecting 100 subjects, giving them IQ tests, and calculating the sample variance s^2 in each case, the sample variances that you obtain will tend to center around 225, which is the population variance.

Biased estimators and unbiased estimators will be discussed more in Section 6-3.

TECH CENTER

 ### Measures of Variation
Access tech supplements, videos, and data sets at **www.TriolaStats.com**

Statdisk, Minitab, StatCrunch, Excel, R, and the TI-83/84 Plus Calculator can be used for the important calculations of this section. Use the same **Descriptive Statistics** procedures given at the end of Section 3-1 on page 98.

3-2 Basic Skills and Concepts

Statistical Literacy and Critical Thinking

1. Range Rule of Thumb for Estimating s The 153 heights of males from Data Set 1 "Body Data" in Appendix B vary from a low of 155.0 cm to a high of 193.3 cm. Use the range rule of thumb to estimate the standard deviation s and compare the result to the standard deviation of 7.10 cm calculated using the 153 heights. What does the result suggest about the accuracy of estimates of s found using the range rule of thumb?

2. Range Rule of Thumb for Interpreting *s* The 153 heights of males from Data Set 1 "Body Data" in Appendix B have a mean of 174.12 cm and a standard deviation of 7.10 cm. Use the range rule of thumb to identify the limits separating values that are significantly low or significantly high. For such data, would a height of 190 cm be significantly high?

3. Variance The 153 heights of males from Data Set 1 "Body Data" in Appendix B have a standard deviation of 7.10 cm. What is the variance of their heights? Be sure to include the appropriate units with the result.

4. Symbols Identify the symbols used for each of the following: (a) sample standard deviation; (b) population standard deviation; (c) sample variance; (d) population variance. If sample data consist of weights measured in grams, what units are used for these statistics and parameters?

*In Exercises 5–20, find the **range, variance,** and **standard deviation** for the given sample data. Include appropriate units (such as "minutes") in your results. (The same data were used in Section 3-1, where we found measures of center. Here we find measures of variation.) Then answer the given questions.*

5. Super Bowl Jersey Numbers Listed below are the jersey numbers of the 11 offensive players on the starting roster of the New England Patriots when they won Super Bowl LIII. What do the results tell us?

12   26   46   15   11   87   77   62   60   69   61

6. Super Bowl Ages Listed below are the ages of the same 11 players used in the preceding exercise. How are the resulting statistics fundamentally different from those found in the preceding exercise?

41   24   30   31   32   29   25   26   26   25   30

7. Celebrity Net Worth Here are the celebrities with the top 8 net worths (in millions of dollars) in a recent year: George Lucas (5500), Steven Spielberg (3700), Oprah Winfrey (3200), Michael Jordan (1700), Paul McCartney (1200), J. K. Rowling (1000), David Copperfield (1000), and Jerry Seinfeld (950). What do the results tell us about the population of all celebrities? Based on the nature of the amounts, what can be inferred about their precision?

8. Geography Majors The data listed below are estimated incomes (dollars) of students who graduated from the University of North Carolina (UNC) after majoring in geography. The data are based on graduates from the year 1984, and the income of basketball superstar Michael Jordan (a 1984 UNC graduate and geography major) is included. Does his income have much of an effect on the results?

17,466   18,085   17,875   19,339   19,682   19,610   18,259   16,354   2,200,000

9. Jaws 3 Listed below are the number of unprovoked shark attacks worldwide for the last several years. What extremely important characteristic of the data is not considered when finding the measures of variation?

70   54   68   82   79   83   76   73   98   81

10. Peas in a Pod Biologists conducted experiments to determine whether a deficiency of carbon dioxide in the soil affects the phenotypes of peas. Listed below are the phenotype codes, where 1 = smooth-yellow, 2 = smooth-green, 3 = wrinkled-yellow, and 4 = wrinkled-green. Can the measures of variation be obtained for these values? Do the results make sense?

2   1   1   1   1   1   1   4   1   2   2   1   2   3   3   2   3   1   3   1   3   1   3   2   2

11. Smart Thermostats Listed below are selling prices (dollars) of smart thermostats tested by *Consumer Reports* magazine. Are any of the resulting statistics helpful in selecting a smart thermostat for purchase?

250   170   225   100   250   250   130   200   150   250   170   200   180   250

12. Cell Phone Radiation Listed below are the measured radiation rates (in W/kg) corresponding to these cell phones: iPhone X, iPhone 7, Google Pixel, Samsung Galaxy S8, OnePlus 5,

Motorola VE465, LG G3, and HTC Desire 310. The data are from the Federal Communications Commission. Are any of the resulting statistics helpful in selecting a cell phone for purchase?

$$0.97 \quad 1.38 \quad 0.93 \quad 1.52 \quad 1.37 \quad 1.09 \quad 0.48 \quad 0.65$$

13. Caffeine in Soft Drinks Listed below are measured amounts of caffeine (mg per 12 oz of drink) obtained in one can from each of 20 brands (7-UP, A&W Root Beer, Cherry Coke, . . . , Tab). Are the statistics representative of the population of all cans of the same 20 brands consumed by Americans?

$$0 \quad 0 \quad 34 \quad 34 \quad 34 \quad 45 \quad 41 \quad 51 \quad 55 \quad 36 \quad 47 \quad 41 \quad 0 \quad 0 \quad 53 \quad 54 \quad 38 \quad 0 \quad 41 \quad 47$$

14. Gender Pay Gap Listed below are women's median earnings as a percentage of men's median earnings listed in order by row for recent years beginning with 1997. What extremely important characteristic of the data is not considered when finding the measures of variation?

$$74.4 \quad 76.3 \quad 76.5 \quad 76.9 \quad 76.4 \quad 77.9 \quad 79.4 \quad 80.4 \quad 81.0 \quad 80.8$$
$$80.2 \quad 79.9 \quad 80.2 \quad 81.2 \quad 82.2 \quad 80.9 \quad 82.1 \quad 82.5 \quad 81.1 \quad 81.9$$

15. Writing Hand Listed below are the writing hands (1 = right; 2 = left) of randomly selected Army women examined in 1988 for the Anthropometric Survey (ANSUR). Are the results useful?

$$1 \quad 1 \quad 1 \quad 1 \quad 1 \quad 1 \quad 1 \quad 1 \quad 2 \quad 2$$

16. Most Expensive Colleges Listed below are the annual costs (dollars) of tuition and fees at the ten most expensive colleges in the United States for a recent year (based on data from *U.S. News & World Report*). The colleges listed in order are Columbia, Vassar, Harvey Mudd, University of Chicago, Trinity, Franklin and Marshall, Tufts, Amherst, University of Southern California, and Sarah Lawrence. What do the results tell us about the variation of costs for the population of all U.S. college tuitions?

$$57{,}208 \quad 55{,}210 \quad 54{,}886 \quad 54{,}825 \quad 54{,}770 \quad 54{,}380 \quad 54{,}318 \quad 54{,}310 \quad 54{,}259 \quad 54{,}010$$

17. Diamonds at the Diamonds Listed below are the amounts (dollars) it costs for marriage proposal packages at the different Major League Baseball stadiums. Five of the teams don't allow proposals. Are there any outliers, and are they likely to have much of an effect on the measures of variation?

$$39 \quad 50 \quad 50 \quad 50 \quad 55 \quad 55 \quad 75 \quad 85 \quad 100 \quad 115 \quad 175 \quad 175 \quad 200$$
$$209 \quad 250 \quad 250 \quad 350 \quad 400 \quad 450 \quad 500 \quad 500 \quad 500 \quad 500 \quad 1500 \quad 2500$$

18. Sales of LP Vinyl Record Albums Listed below are annual U.S. sales of vinyl record albums (millions of units). The numbers of albums sold are listed in chronological order, and the last entry represents the most recent year. Do the measures of variation give us any information about a changing trend over time?

$$0.3 \quad 0.6 \quad 0.8 \quad 1.1 \quad 1.1 \quad 1.4 \quad 1.4 \quad 1.5 \quad 1.2 \quad 1.3 \quad 1.4 \quad 1.2 \quad 0.9$$
$$0.9 \quad 1.0 \quad 1.9 \quad 2.5 \quad 2.8 \quad 3.9 \quad 4.6 \quad 6.1 \quad 9.2 \quad 11.9 \quad 13.1 \quad 14.3$$

19. California Smokers In the California Health Interview Survey, randomly selected adults are interviewed. One of the questions asks how many cigarettes are smoked per day, and results are listed below for 50 randomly selected respondents. How well do the results reflect the smoking behavior of California adults?

$$9 \quad 10 \quad 10 \quad 20 \quad 40 \quad 50 \quad 0 \quad 0 \quad 0 \quad 0 \quad 0 \quad 0 \quad 0 \quad 0 \quad 0$$
$$0 \quad 0 \quad 0 \quad 0 \quad 0 \quad 0 \quad 0 \quad 0 \quad 0 \quad 0 \quad 0 \quad 0 \quad 0 \quad 0 \quad 0$$
$$0 \quad 0 \quad 0 \quad 0 \quad 0 \quad 0 \quad 0 \quad 0 \quad 0 \quad 0 \quad 0 \quad 0 \quad 0 \quad 0 \quad 0$$
$$0 \quad 0 \quad 0 \quad 0 \quad 0$$

20. Big Mac Index Listed below in order are prices in dollars for a Big Mac hamburger in the United States, Canada, Mexico, China, Japan, Russia, Switzerland, Italy, Spain, Britain, India, and Egypt. Such data are used to compare currency exchange rates and the costs of goods in different countries. What do the measures of variation tell us about the prices of a Big Mac in different countries?

5.3   5.3   2.6   3.2   3.4   2.3   6.8   5.1   4.8   4.4   2.8   1.9

In Exercises 21–24, find the **coefficient of variation** *for each of the two samples; then compare the variation. (The same data were used in Section 3-1.)*

21. Blood Pressure A sample of blood pressure measurements is taken from Data Set 1 "Body Data" in Appendix B, and those values (mm Hg) are listed below. The values are matched so that 10 subjects each have a systolic and diastolic measurement.

Systolic:	118	128	158	96	156	122	116	136	126	120
Diastolic:	80	76	74	52	90	88	58	64	72	82

22. Parking Meter Theft Listed below are amounts (in millions of dollars) collected from parking meters by Brinks and others in New York City during similar time periods. A larger data set was used to convict five Brinks employees of grand larceny. The data were provided by the attorney for New York City, and they are listed on the Data and Story Library (DASL) website. A difference in variation suggests theft may have occurred. Do the two samples appear to have different amounts of variation?

Collection Contractor Was Brinks	1.3	1.5	1.3	1.5	1.4	1.7	1.8	1.7	1.7	1.6
Collection Contractor Was Not Brinks	2.2	1.9	1.5	1.6	1.5	1.7	1.9	1.6	1.6	1.8

23. Pulse Rates Listed below are pulse rates (beats per minute) from samples of adult males and females (from Data Set 1 "Body Data" in Appendix B). Does there appear to be a difference?

Male:	86	72	64	72	72	54	66	56	80	72	64	64	96	58	66
Female:	64	84	82	70	74	86	90	88	90	90	94	68	90	82	80

24. It's a Small Wait After All Listed below are the fifty wait times (minutes) at 10 AM for the rides "It's a Small World" and "Avatar Flight of Passage." These data are found in Data Set 33 "Disney World Wait Times." Do the two rides appear to have different amounts of variation?

It's a Small World

10   5   5   10   10   10   10   15   10   10   10   10   10   10   5   10   10   10   5   5   5   10   10   5   10
5   10   15   5   5   10   5   5   5   15   10   10   30   10   5   10   10   10   5   10   15   10   20   15   15

Avatar Flight of Passage   180   195   110   150   180   150   150   180   150   150   165   150   120   165   135
150   75   90   85   105   75   135   120   150   105   135   105   105   150   90   70   120   90   120   135
210   135   150   225   150   165   150   135   150   180   120   150   180   225   165

Large Data Sets from Appendix B. *In Exercises 25–28, refer to the indicated data set in Appendix B. Use software or a calculator to find the* **range, variance,** *and* **standard deviation.** *Express answers using appropriate units, such as "minutes."*

25. Body Temperatures Refer to Data Set 5 "Body Temperatures" in Appendix B and use the body temperatures for 12:00 AM on day 2.

26. Earthquakes Use the magnitudes (Richter scale) of the 600 earthquakes listed in Data Set 24 "Earthquakes" in Appendix B. In 1989, the San Francisco Bay Area was struck with an earthquake that measured 7.0 on the Richter scale. If we add that value of 7.0 to those listed in the data set, do the measures of variation change much?

27. Audiometry Use the hearing measurements from Data Set 7 "Audiometry." Does it appear that the amounts of variation are different for the right threshold measurements and the left threshold measurements?

28. Weights Use the weights of the males listed in Data Set 2 "ANSUR I 1988," which were measured in 1988 and use the weights of the males listed in Data Set 3 "ANSUR II 2012," which were measured in 2012. Does it appear that amounts of variation have changed from 1988 to 2012?

Estimating Standard Deviation with the Range Rule of Thumb. *In Exercises 29–32, refer to the data in the indicated exercise. After finding the* **range** *of the data, use the range rule of thumb to estimate the value of the* **standard deviation.** *Compare the result to the standard deviation computed using all of the data.*

 29. Exercise 25 "Body Temperatures"   **30.** Exercise 26 "Earthquakes"

 31. Exercise 27 "Audiometry"   **32.** Exercise 28 "Weights"

Identifying Significant Values with the Range Rule of Thumb. *In Exercises 33–36, use the range rule of thumb to identify the limits separating values that are* **significantly low** *or* **significantly high.**

33. U.S. Presidents Based on Data Set 22 "Presidents" in Appendix B, at the time of their first inauguration, presidents have a mean age of 55.2 years and a standard deviation of 6.9 years. Is the minimum required 35-year age for a president significantly low?

34. Pulse Rates of Males Based on Data Set 1 "Body Data" in Appendix B, males have pulse rates with a mean of 69.6 beats per minute and a standard deviation of 11.3 beats per minute. Is a pulse rate of 50 beats per minute significantly low, significantly high, or neither? (All of these pulse rates are measured at rest.) Explain.

35. Foot Lengths Based on Data Set 9 "Foot and Height" in Appendix B, adult males have foot lengths with a mean of 27.32 cm and a standard deviation of 1.29 cm. Is the adult male foot length of 30 cm significantly low, significantly high, or neither? Explain.

36. Body Temperatures Based on Data Set 5 "Body Temperatures" in Appendix B, body temperatures of adults have a mean of 98.20°F and a standard deviation of 0.62°F. (The data from 12 AM on day 2 are used.) Is an adult body temperature of 100°F significantly low, significantly high, or neither?

Finding Standard Deviation from a Frequency Distribution. *In Exercises 37–40, refer to the frequency distribution in the given exercise and compute the* **standard deviation** *by using the formula below, where x represents the class midpoint, f represents the class frequency, and n represents the total number of sample values. Also, compare the computed standard deviations to these standard deviations obtained by using Formula 3-4 with the original list of data values: (Exercise 37) 18.5 minutes; (Exercise 38) 36.7 minutes; (Exercise 39) 6.9 years; (Exercise 40) 20.4 seconds.*

Standard deviation for frequency distribution

$$s = \sqrt{\frac{n\left[\Sigma\left(f \cdot x^2\right)\right] - \left[\Sigma\left(f \cdot x\right)\right]^2}{n(n-1)}}$$

37.

Daily Commute Time in Los Angeles, CA (minutes)	Frequency
0–14	6
15–29	18
30–44	14
45–59	5
60–74	5
75–89	1
90–104	1

38.

"Avatar Flight of Passage" Wait Times 10 AM (minutes)	Frequency
70–89	4
90–109	7
110–129	6
130–149	6
150–169	18
170–189	5
190–209	1
210–229	3

39.

Age of President at First Inauguration (years)	Frequency
40–44	2
45–49	7
50–54	10
55–59	10
60–64	6
65–69	3
70–74	1

40.

Duration of Old Faithful Eruptions (sec)	Frequency
125–149	1
150–174	0
175–199	0
200–224	3
225–249	34
250–274	12

41. The Empirical Rule Based on Data Set 1 "Body Data" in Appendix B, blood platelet counts of women have a bell-shaped distribution with a mean of 255.1 and a standard deviation of 65.4. (All units are 1000 cells/μL.) Using the empirical rule, what is the approximate percentage of women with platelet counts

a. within 2 standard deviations of the mean, or between 124.3 and 385.9?

b. between 189.7 and 320.5?

42. The Empirical Rule Based on Data Set 5 "Body Temperatures" in Appendix B, body temperatures of healthy adults have a bell-shaped distribution with a mean of 98.20°F and a standard deviation of 0.62°F. Using the empirical rule, what is the approximate percentage of healthy adults with body temperatures

a. within 1 standard deviation of the mean, or between 97.58°F and 98.82°F?

b. between 96.34°F and 100.06°F?

43. Chebyshev's Theorem Based on Data Set 1 "Body Data" in Appendix B, blood platelet counts of women have a bell-shaped distribution with a mean of 255.1 and a standard deviation of 65.4. (All units are 1000 cells/μL.) Using Chebyshev's theorem, what do we know about the percentage of women with platelet counts that are within 3 standard deviations of the mean? What are the minimum and maximum platelet counts that are within 3 standard deviations of the mean?

44. Chebyshev's Theorem Based on Data Set 5 "Body Temperatures" in Appendix B, body temperatures of healthy adults have a bell-shaped distribution with a mean of 98.20°F and a standard deviation of 0.62°F (using the data from 12 AM on day 2). Using Chebyshev's theorem, what do we know about the percentage of healthy adults with body temperatures that are within 2 standard deviations of the mean? What are the minimum and maximum body temperatures that are within 2 standard deviations of the mean?

3-2   Beyond the Basics

45. Why Divide by $n - 1$? Let a *population* consist of the values 9 cigarettes, 10 cigarettes, and 20 cigarettes smoked in a day (based on data from the California Health Interview Survey). Assume that samples of two values are randomly selected *with replacement* from this population. (That is, a selected value is replaced before the second selection is made.)

a. Find the variance σ^2 of the population {9 cigarettes, 10 cigarettes, 20 cigarettes}.

b. After listing the nine different possible samples of two values selected with replacement, find the sample variance s^2 (which includes division by $n - 1$) for each of them; then find the mean of the nine sample variances s^2.

c. For each of the nine different possible samples of two values selected with replacement, find the variance by treating each sample as if it is a population (using the formula for population variance, which includes division by n); then find the mean of those nine population variances.

d. Which approach results in values that are better estimates of σ^2: part (b) or part (c)? Why? When computing variances of samples, should you use division by n or $n - 1$?

e. The preceding parts show that s^2 is an unbiased estimator of σ^2. Is s an unbiased estimator of σ? Explain.

46. Mean Absolute Deviation Use the same population of {9 cigarettes, 10 cigarettes, 20 cigarettes} from Exercise 45. Show that when samples of size 2 are randomly selected with replacement, the samples have mean absolute deviations that do not center about the value of the mean absolute deviation of the population. What does this indicate about a sample mean absolute deviation being used as an estimator of the mean absolute deviation of a population?

3-3   Measures of Relative Standing and Boxplots

Key Concept This section introduces measures of relative standing, which are numbers showing the location of data values relative to the other values within the same data set. The most important concept in this section is the *z score*, which will be used often in following chapters. We also discuss percentiles and quartiles, which are common statistics, as well as another statistical graph called a boxplot.

PART 1   Basics of *z* Scores, Percentiles, Quartiles, and Boxplots

z Scores

A *z* score is found by converting a value to a standardized scale, as given in the following definition. This definition shows that a *z* score is *the number of standard deviations that a data value is away from the mean.* The *z* score is used often in Chapter 6 and later chapters.

DEFINITION

A **z score** (or **standard score** or **standardized value**) is the number of standard deviations that a given value x is above or below the mean. The *z* score is calculated by using one of the following:

Sample		Population
$z = \dfrac{x - \bar{x}}{s}$	or	$z = \dfrac{x - \mu}{\sigma}$

ROUND-OFF RULE FOR *z* SCORES Round *z* scores to two decimal places (such as 2.31).

This round-off rule is motivated by the format of standard tables in which *z* scores are expressed with two decimal places, as in Table A-2 in Appendix A. Example 1 illustrates how *z* scores can be used to compare values, even if they come from different populations.

Important Properties of *z* Scores

   1. A *z* score is the number of standard deviations that a given value x is above or below the mean.

continued

2. z scores are expressed as numbers with no units of measurement.

3. Using the same range rule of thumb introduced in the preceding section, a data value is *significantly low* if its z score is less than or equal to -2 or the value is *significantly high* if its z score is greater than or equal to $+2$.

4. If an individual data value is less than the mean, its corresponding z score is a negative number.

EXAMPLE 1 **Comparing Adult Body Temperature and Weight of a Quarter**

Which of the following two data values is more extreme relative to the data set from which it came?

- The 99°F temperature of an adult (among 106 adults with sample mean $\bar{x} = 98.20°F$ and sample standard deviation $s = 0.62°F$)

- The 5.7790 g weight of a quarter (among 40 quarters with sample mean $\bar{x} = 5.63930\,g$ and sample standard deviation $s = 0.06194\,g$)

SOLUTION

The 99°F body temperature and the 5.7790 g weight of a quarter can be standardized by converting each of them to z scores as shown below.

99°F body temperature:

$$z = \frac{x - \bar{x}}{s} = \frac{99°F - 98.20°F}{0.62\,°F} = 1.29$$

5.7790 g weight of a quarter:

$$z = \frac{x - \bar{x}}{s} = \frac{5.7790\,g - 5.63930\,g}{0.06194\,g} = 2.26$$

INTERPRETATION

The z scores show that the 99°F body temperature is 1.29 standard deviations above the mean, and the 5.7790 g weight of the quarter is 2.26 standard deviations above the mean. Because the weight of the quarter is farther above the mean, it is the more extreme value. A weight of 5.7790 g of a quarter is more extreme than a 99°F body temperature.

YOUR TURN. Do Exercise 13 "Tallest and Shortest Men."

Using z Scores to Identify Significant Values In Section 3-2 we used the range rule of thumb to conclude that a value is significantly low or significantly high if it is at least 2 standard deviations away from the mean. It follows that significantly low values have z scores less than or equal to -2 and significantly high values have z scores greater than or equal to $+2$, as illustrated in Figure 3-6. Using this criterion with the two individual values used in Example 1, we see that the weight of the quarter is *significantly high* because its z score is greater than $+2$, but the body temperature is neither significantly low nor significantly high because its z score is between -2 and $+2$.

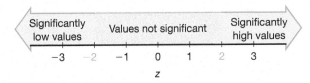

FIGURE 3-6   Interpreting z Scores Using the Range Rule of Thumb

- Significantly low values: $z \leq -2$
- Significantly high values: $z \geq 2$
- Values not significant: $-2 < z < 2$

EXAMPLE 2 **Is an Earthquake Magnitude of 4.01 Significantly High?**

Among the earthquakes listed in Data Set 24 "Earthquakes," one of the stronger earthquakes had a magnitude of 4.01. The magnitudes are measured on the Richter scale, and only earthquakes of magnitude 1.00 or higher are included. The 600 magnitudes in the data set have a mean of 2.572 and a standard deviation of 0.651. For this data set, is the magnitude of 4.01 significantly high?

SOLUTION

The magnitude of 4.01 is converted to a z score as shown below:

$$z = \frac{x - \bar{x}}{s} = \frac{4.01 - 2.572}{0.651} = 2.21$$

INTERPRETATION

The magnitude of 4.01 converts to the z score of 2.21. Because the z score of 2.21 is greater than or equal to $+2$, that magnitude is significantly high. (Refer to Figure 3-6.)

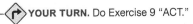 **YOUR TURN.** Do Exercise 9 "ACT."

A z score is a measure of position, in the sense that it describes the location of a value (in terms of standard deviations) relative to the mean. Percentiles and quartiles are other measures of position useful for comparing values within the same data set or between different sets of data.

Percentiles

Beyond the importance of their use in ordinary situations, percentiles play an important role in many *resampling* procedures, some of which are included in this book. It is therefore important to develop an ability to find percentile values.

Percentiles are one type of *quantiles*—or *fractiles*—which partition data into groups with roughly the same number of values in each group.

DEFINITION

Percentiles are measures of location, denoted $P_1, P_2, \ldots, P_{99}$, which divide a set of data into 100 groups with about 1% of the values in each group.

Cost of Laughing Index

There really is a Cost of Laughing Index (CLI), which tracks costs of such items as rubber chickens, Groucho Marx glasses, admissions to comedy clubs, and 13 other leading humor indicators. This is the same basic approach used in developing the Consumer Price Index (CPI), which is based on a weighted average of goods and services purchased by typical consumers. While standard scores and percentiles allow us to compare different values, they ignore any element of time. Index numbers, such as the CLI and CPI, allow us to compare the value of some variable to its value at some base time period. The value of an index number is the current value, divided by the base value, multiplied by 100.

The 50th percentile, denoted P_{50}, has about 50% of the data values below it and about 50% of the data values above it, so the 50th percentile is the same as the median. There is not universal agreement on a single procedure for calculating percentiles, but we will describe relatively simple procedures for (1) finding the percentile of a data value and (2) converting a percentile to its corresponding data value. We begin with the first procedure.

Finding the Percentile of a Data Value

The process of finding the percentile that corresponds to a particular data value x is given by the following (round the result to the nearest whole number):

$$\text{Percentile of value } x = \frac{\text{number of values less than } x}{\text{total number of values}} \cdot 100$$

CP | **EXAMPLE 3** Finding a Percentile

Table 3-6 lists the fifty "Space Mountain" 10 AM wait times from Data Set 33 "Disney World Wait Times." These wait times are arranged in increasing order in Table 3-6. Find the percentile for the wait time of 45 minutes.

TABLE 3-6 *Sorted* "Space Mountain" 10 AM Wait Times

10	15	15	15	15	15	20	20	20	20
25	25	25	25	25	25	30	30	30	30
30	30	30	30	35	35	35	35	35	35
35	35	40	40	40	40	45	50	50	50
50	50	55	55	60	75	75	75	105	110

SOLUTION

From the sorted list of wait times in Table 3-6, we see that there are 36 wait times less than 45 minutes, so

$$\text{Percentile of } 45 = \frac{36}{50} \cdot 100 = 72$$

INTERPRETATION

A wait time of 45 minutes is in the 72nd percentile. This can be interpreted loosely as this: A wait time of 45 minutes separates the lowest 72% of values from the highest 28% of values. We have $P_{72} = 45$ minutes.

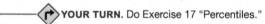 **YOUR TURN.** Do Exercise 17 "Percentiles."

Example 3 shows how to convert from a given sample value to the corresponding percentile. There are several different methods for the reverse procedure of converting a given percentile to the corresponding value in the data set. The procedure we will use is summarized in Figure 3-7, which uses the following notation.

Notation

n total number of values in the data set

k percentile being used (Example: For the 25th percentile, $k = 25$.)

L locator that gives the *position* of a value (Example: For the 12th value in the sorted list, $L = 12$.)

P_k kth percentile (Example: P_{25} is the 25th percentile.)

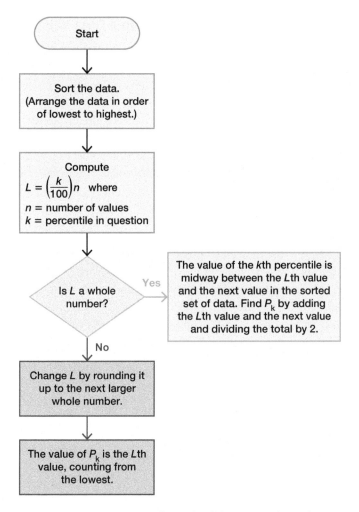

FIGURE 3-7   **Converting from the *k*th percentile to the corresponding data value**

CP ▸ **EXAMPLE 4**   Converting a Percentile to a Data Value

Refer to the fifty sorted "Space Mountain" wait times in Table 3-6 and use the procedure in Figure 3-7 to find the value of the 25th percentile, P_{25}.

SOLUTION

From Figure 3-7, we see that the sample data are already sorted, so we can proceed to find the value of the locator L. In this computation we use $k = 25$ because we are trying to find the value of the 25th percentile. We use $n = 50$ because there are 50 data values.

$$L = \frac{k}{100} \cdot n = \frac{25}{100} \cdot 50 = 12.5$$

Since $L = 12.5$ is not a whole number, we proceed to the next lower box in Figure 3-7, where we change L by rounding it up from 12.5 to the next larger whole number: 13. (In this book we typically round off the usual way, but this is one of two cases where we round *up* instead of rounding *off*.) From the bottom box we see that the value of P_{25} is the 13th value, counting from the lowest. In Table 3-6, the 13th value is 25. That is, $P_{25} = 25$ minutes. Roughly speaking, about 25% of the wait times are less than 25 minutes and 75% of the wait times are more than 25 minutes.

▸ **YOUR TURN.** Do Exercise 27 "Percentile."

$$Q_1 = P_{25}$$
$$Q_2 = P_{50}$$
$$Q_3 = P_{75}$$

CP **EXAMPLE 5** Converting a Percentile to a Data Value

Refer to the fifty sorted "Space Mountain" wait times in Table 3-6. Use Figure 3-7 to find the 90th percentile, denoted by P_{90}.

SOLUTION

Referring to Figure 3-7, we see that the sample data are already sorted, so we can proceed to compute the value of the locator L. In this computation, we use $k = 90$ because we are attempting to find the value of the 90th percentile, and we use $n = 50$ because there are 50 data values.

$$L = \frac{k}{100} \cdot n = \frac{90}{100} \cdot 50 = 45$$

Since $L = 45$ is a whole number, we proceed to the box in Figure 3-7 located at the right. We now see that the value of the 90th percentile is midway between the Lth (45th) value and the next value in the original set of data. That is, the value of the 90th percentile is midway between the 45th value and the 46th value. The 45th value in Table 3-6 is 60 and the 46th value is 75, so the value midway between them is 67.5 minutes. We conclude that the 90th percentile is $P_{90} = 67.5$ minutes.

 YOUR TURN. Do Exercise 21 "Percentile."

Quartiles

Just as there are 99 percentiles that divide the data into 100 groups, there are three quartiles that divide the data into four groups.

DEFINITION

Quartiles are measures of location, denoted Q_1, Q_2, and Q_3, which divide a set of data into four groups with about 25% of the values in each group.

Here are descriptions of quartiles that are more accurate than those given in the preceding definition:

Q_1 **(First quartile):**   Same value as P_{25}. It separates the bottom 25% of the sorted values from the top 75%. (To be more precise, at least 25% of the sorted values are less than or equal to Q_1, and at least 75% of the values are greater than or equal to Q_1.)

Q_2 **(Second quartile):**   Same as P_{50} and same as the median. It separates the bottom 50% of the sorted values from the top 50%.

Q_3 **(Third quartile):**   Same as P_{75}. It separates the bottom 75% of the sorted values from the top 25%. (To be more precise, at least 75% of the sorted values are less than or equal to Q_3, and at least 25% of the values are greater than or equal to Q_3.)

Finding values of quartiles can be accomplished with the same procedure used for finding percentiles. Simply use the relationships shown in the margin. In Example 4 we found that $P_{25} = 25$ minutes, so it follows that $Q_1 = 25$ minutes.

CAUTION Just as there is not universal agreement on a procedure for finding percentiles, there is not universal agreement on a single procedure for calculating quartiles, and different technologies often yield different results. If you use a calculator or software for exercises involving quartiles, you may get results that differ somewhat from the answers obtained by using the procedures described here.

In earlier sections of this chapter we described several statistics, including the mean, median, mode, range, and standard deviation. Some other statistics are defined using quartiles and percentiles, as in the following:

Interquartile range (or IQR) $= Q_3 - Q_1$

Semi-interquartile range $= \dfrac{Q_3 - Q_1}{2}$

Midquartile $= \dfrac{Q_3 + Q_1}{2}$

10–90 percentile range $= P_{90} - P_{10}$

5-Number Summary and Boxplot

The values of the minimum, maximum and three quartiles (Q_1, Q_2, Q_3) are used for the 5-number summary and the construction of boxplot graphs.

DEFINITION

For a set of data, the **5-number summary** consists of these five values:

1. Minimum

2. First quartile, Q_1

3. Second quartile, Q_2 (same as the median)

4. Third quartile, Q_3

5. Maximum

CP ─ **EXAMPLE 6** **Finding a 5-Number Summary**

Use the "Space Mountain" wait times in Table 3-6 to find the 5-number summary.

SOLUTION

Because the "Space Mountain" wait times in Table 3-6 are sorted, it is easy to see that the minimum is 10 minutes and the maximum is 110 minutes. The value of the first quartile is $Q_1 = 25$ minutes (from Example 4). The median is equal to Q_2, and it is 35 minutes. Also, we can find that $Q_3 = 50$ minutes by using the same procedure for finding P_{75} (as summarized in Figure 3-7). The 5-number summary is therefore 10, 25, 35, 50, and 110 (all in minutes).

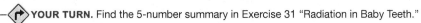 **YOUR TURN.** Find the 5-number summary in Exercise 31 "Radiation in Baby Teeth."

The values from the 5-number summary are used for the construction of a boxplot, defined as follows.

DEFINITION

A **boxplot** (or **box-and-whisker diagram**) is a graph of a data set that consists of a line extending from the minimum value to the maximum value, and a box with lines drawn at the first quartile Q_1, the median, and the third quartile Q_3. (See Figure 3-8 on the next page.)

Procedure for Constructing a Boxplot

1. Find the 5-number summary (minimum value, Q_1, Q_2, Q_3, maximum value).

2. Construct a line segment extending from the minimum data value to the maximum data value.

3. Construct a box (rectangle) extending from Q_1 to Q_3, and draw a line in the box at the value of Q_2 (median).

> **CAUTION** Because there is not universal agreement on procedures for finding quartiles, and because boxplots are based on quartiles, different technologies may yield different boxplots.

 EXAMPLE 7 **Constructing a Boxplot**

Use the "Space Mountain" wait times listed in Table 3-6 to construct a boxplot.

SOLUTION

The boxplot uses the 5-number summary found in Example 6: 10, 25, 35, 50, and 110 (all in minutes). Figure 3-8 is the boxplot representing the "Space Mountain" wait times listed in Table 3-6.

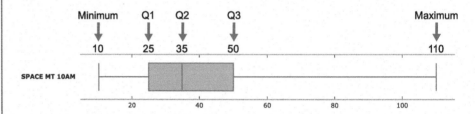

FIGURE 3-8   Boxplot of "Space Mountain" Wait Times (minutes)

 YOUR TURN. Construct the boxplot in Exercise 31 "Radiation in Baby Teeth."

Skewness A boxplot can often be used to identify skewness. Recall that in Section 2-2 we stated that a distribution of data is **skewed** if it is not symmetric and extends more to one side than to the other. In a histogram of data skewed to the right (also called *positively skewed*), there is a longer right tail showing that relatively few data values are high data values; most of the data values are located at the left. The boxplot in Figure 3-8 shows that the data are skewed to the right, and most of the data values are located at the left.

Because the shape of a boxplot is determined by the five values from the 5-number summary, a boxplot is not a graph of the distribution of the data, and it doesn't show as much detailed information as a histogram or stemplot. However, boxplots are often great for comparing two or more data sets. When using two or more boxplots for comparing different data sets, graph the boxplots on the same scale so that comparisons can be easily made. Methods discussed later in this book allow us to analyze comparisons of data sets more formally than subjective conclusions based on a graph. It is always wise to construct suitable graphs, such as histograms, dotplots, and boxplots, but we should not rely solely on subjective judgments based on graphs.

EXAMPLE 8 **Comparing the Wait Times at Popular Walt Disney World Rides**

Data Set 33 "Disney World Wait Times" includes wait times for several popular rides at 10 AM on fifty different days. Use the same scale to construct the boxplots for "Space Mountain," "Tower of Terror," and "Avatar Flight of Passage"; then compare the results.

SOLUTION

The Statdisk-generated boxplots shown in Figure 3-9 suggest that "Avatar Flight of Passage" has the longest wait time, and that "Space Mountain" and "Tower of Terror" wait times are similar to each other in both their measures of center and variation.

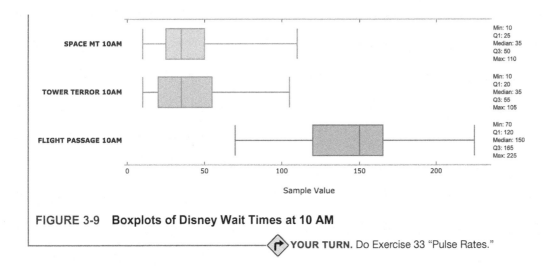

FIGURE 3-9   **Boxplots of Disney Wait Times at 10 AM**

➤ **YOUR TURN.** Do Exercise 33 "Pulse Rates."

Now refer to Figure 3-10 for three examples of histograms and their corresponding boxplots.

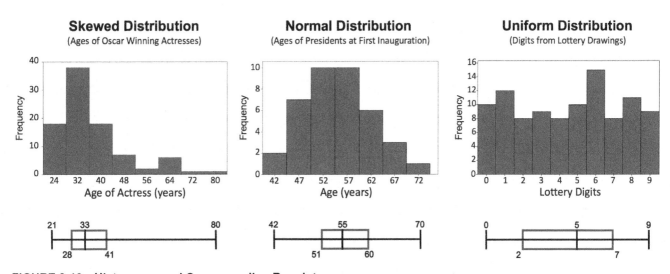

FIGURE 3-10   **Histograms and Corresponding Boxplots**

Skewed: The first case of the skewed histogram shows the boxplot as being lopsided.

Normal: The second case of a normal distribution shows the boxplot as being symmetric.

Uniform: The third case of a uniform distribution shows the boxplot as being symmetric.

From the second and third cases, we see that a boxplot gives us information about the symmetry of data, but it does not reveal the shape of the distribution.

Outliers

When analyzing data, it is important to identify and consider outliers because they can strongly affect values of some important statistics (such as the mean and standard deviation), and they can also strongly affect important methods discussed later in this book. In Chapter 2 we described outliers as sample values that lie very far away from the vast majority of the other values in a set of data, but that description is vague and it does not provide specific objective criteria. Part 2 of this section includes a description of *modified boxplots* along with a more precise definition of outliers used in the context of creating modified boxplots.

CAUTION When analyzing data, always identify outliers and consider their effects, which can be substantial.

PART 2 Outliers and Modified Boxplots

We noted that the description of outliers is somewhat vague, but for the purposes of constructing *modified boxplots*, we can consider outliers to be data values meeting specific criteria based on quartiles and the interquartile range. (The interquartile range is often denoted by IQR, where IQR $= Q_3 - Q_1$.)

Identifying Outliers for Modified Boxplots

1. Find the quartiles Q_1, Q_2, and Q_3.

2. Find the interquartile range (IQR), where IQR $= Q_3 - Q_1$.

3. Evaluate $1.5 \times$ IQR.

4. **In a modified boxplot, a data value is an *outlier* if it is**

        above Q_3, by an amount greater than $1.5 \times$ IQR

  or   **below Q_1, by an amount greater than $1.5 \times$ IQR**

Modified Boxplots

The boxplots described earlier are called **skeletal (or regular) boxplots**, but some statistical software packages provide modified boxplots, which represent outliers as special points. A **modified boxplot** is a regular boxplot constructed with these modifications:

1. A special symbol (such as an asterisk or point) is used to identify outliers as defined above.

2. The solid horizontal line extends only as far as the minimum data value that is not an outlier and the maximum data value that is not an outlier.

(*Note: Exercises involving modified boxplots are found in the "Beyond the Basics" exercises only.*)

CP)—**EXAMPLE 9** Constructing a Modified Boxplot

Use the fifty "Space Mountain" 10 AM wait times in Table 3-6 on page 124 (Data Set 33 "Disney World Wait Times" in Appendix B) to construct a modified boxplot.

SOLUTION

Let's begin with the above four steps for identifying outliers in a modified boxplot.

1. Using the "Space Mountain" wait times, the three quartiles are $Q_1 = 25$, the median is $Q_2 = 35$, and $Q_3 = 50$. (All values are in minutes, and these quartiles were found in Example 6.)

2. The interquartile range is IQR $= Q_3 - Q_1 = 50 - 25 = 25$.

3. $1.5 \times$ IQR $= 1.5 \times 25 = 37.5$

4. Any outliers are above $Q_3 = 50$ by more than 37.5, or below $Q_1 = 25$ by more than 37.5. This means that any outliers are greater than 87.5, or less than -12.5 (which is impossible, so there can be no outliers at the low end in this example).

We can now examine the original "Space Mountain" wait times to identify any wait times greater than 87.5, and we find these values: 105 and 110. The only outliers are 105 and 110.

   We can now construct the modified boxplot shown in Figure 3-11. In Figure 3-11, the two outliers are identified as special points, the three quartiles are shown as in a regular boxplot, and the horizontal line extends from the lowest data value that is not an outlier (10) to the highest data value that is not an outlier (75).

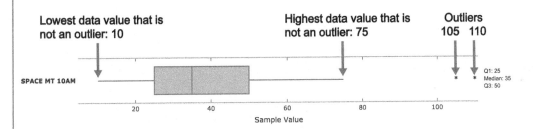

FIGURE 3-11   Modified Boxplot of "Space Mountain" 10 AM Wait Times

➤ **YOUR TURN.** Do Exercise 37 "Outliers and Modified Boxplots."

CAUTION Because there is not universal agreement on procedures for finding quartiles, and because modified boxplots are based on quartiles, different technologies may yield different modified boxplots.

TECH CENTER

 Boxplots, 5-Number Summary, Outliers
Access tech supplements, videos, and data sets at www.TriolaStats.com

Statdisk

5-Number Summary
Use **Descriptive Statistics** procedure given at the end of Section 3-1 on page 98.

Boxplots
1. Click **Data** in the top menu.
2. Select **Boxplot** from the dropdown menu.
3. Select the desired data columns.
4. Click **Boxplot** or **Modified Boxplot**.

Outliers
Create a modified boxplot using the above procedure or sort as follows:
1. Click **Data** in the top menu.
2. Select **Sort Data** from the dropdown menu.
3. Click **Sort** after making desired choices in the sort menu.
4. Examine minimum and maximum values to determine if they are far from other values.

Minitab

5-Number Summary
Use **Descriptive Statistics** procedure given at the end of Section 3-1 on page 98.

Boxplots
1. Click **Graph** in the top menu
2. Select **Boxplot** from the dropdown menu
3. Select **Simple** option for one boxplot or multiple boxplots, then click **OK**.
4. Double click on the desired data column(s) so that it appears in the *Graph variables* window, then click **OK**.

Outliers
Create a modified boxplot using the above procedure or sort as follows:
1. Click **Data** in the top menu.
2. Select **Sort** from the dropdown menu.
3. Double click the desired data column so that it appears in the first row of the *Columns to sort by* window.
4. Under *Columns to sort* select **All columns**. Click **OK**.
5. Examine minimum and maximum sorted values to determine if they are far from other values.

StatCrunch

5-Number Summary
Use **Descriptive Statistics** procedure given at the end of Section 3-1 on page 98.

Boxplots
1. Click on **Graph** in the top menu.
2. Select **Boxplot** from the dropdown menu.
3. Select the desired data column. For a modified boxplot, check the *Use fences to idenfity outliers* box.
4. Click **Compute!**

Outliers
Create a modified boxplot using the above procedure or sort as follows:
1. Click **Data** in top menu.
2. Select **Sort** from the dropdown menu.
3. Select the desired data column.
4. Click **Compute!**
5. Examine minimum and maximum values to determine if they are far from other values.

TI-83/84 Plus Calculator

5-Number Summary
Use **Descriptive Statistics** procedure given at the end of Section 3-1 on page 98.

Boxplots
1. Open the **STAT PLOTS** menu by pressing **2ND**, **Y=**
2. Press **ENTER** to access the *Plot 1* settings screen as shown:
   a. Select **ON** and press **ENTER**.
   b. Select the second boxplot icon, press **ENTER**. Select the first boxplot icon for a modified boxplot.
   c. Enter name of list containing data.
3. Press **ZOOM** then **9** (ZoomStat) to display the boxplot.
4. Press **TRACE** and use **◁ ▷** to view values.

Outliers
Create a modified boxplot using the above procedure or sort as follows:
1. Press **STAT**, select **SortA** (sort ascending) from the menu and press **ENTER**.
2. Enter the name of the list to be sorted and press **ENTER**.
3. To view the sorted list, press **STAT**, select **Edit** and press **ENTER**.
4. Highlight the top cell in an empty column, enter the list name and press **ENTER**.
5. Use **⌃ ⌄** to examine minimum and maximum values to determine if they are far from other values.

TIP: The list name *L1* (and *L2 . . . L6*) can be quickly entered by pressing **2ND** **1**.

TECH CENTER *continued*

 Boxplots, 5-Number Summary, Outliers
Access tech supplements, videos, and data sets at **www.TriolaStats.com**

Excel

5-Number Summary
Use **Descriptive Statistics** procedure given at the end of Section 3-1 on page 98.

XLSTAT Add-In
- After Step 3 in the Descriptive Statistics procedure, click the **Outputs** tab and select **Minimum**, **Maximum**, **1st Quartile**, **Median**, **3rd Quartile**. Click **OK**.

Excel
The Data Analysis add-in provides only the minimum, maximum and median. To obtain quartiles use the following procedure:
1. Click on **Insert Function** f_x, select the category **Statistical** and select the function **QUARTILE.INC**.
2. Enter the range of data values in the *Array* box.
3. In the *Quart* box enter **0** to find the minimum, **1** to find the first 1st Quartile and **2,3,4** to find the remaining values.

Boxplots
XLSTAT Add-In (Required)
1. Click on the **XLSTAT** tab in the Ribbon and then click **Describing Data**.
2. Select **Descriptive Statistics** from the dropdown menu.
3. Check the **Quantitative data** box and enter the desired data range. Selecting two or more columns will generate multiple boxplots. If the first row of data contains a label, also check the **Variable labels** box.
4. Click on the **Charts (1)** tab and checkmark the **Box plots** box under *Quantitative data*.
5. Click **OK**.

Outliers
Create a modified boxplot using the above XLSTAT procedure or sort as follows:
1. Click **Data** tab in the top menu and select the desired range of data values.
2. Click the **Sort Smallest to Largest** (A → Z) button in the ribbon.
3. Examine minimum and maximum values to determine if they are far from other values.

R

R commands:

5-Number Summary:
  summary*(x)*

Boxplots:
  boxplots*(x,y,z)*

Outliers:
Outliers are displayed on boxplots (see R command above), or sort data as follows:

1. Use **sort(x)** command to sort the data in ascending order.
2. Examine minimum and maximum values to determine if they are far from other values.

A complete list of R statistical commands is available at TriolaStats.com

3-3   Basic Skills and Concepts

Statistical Literacy and Critical Thinking

1. z Scores Professional football quarterback Tom Brady is 193 cm tall. Based on statistics for the males from Data Set 1 "Body Data" in Appendix B, his height converts to the z score of 2.66. How many standard deviations is his height above the mean?

2. Waiting Times The boxplots shown below represent customer waiting times (minutes) for two different waiting lines. Which line would you prefer, or does it not make a difference? Explain.

3. Boxplot Comparison Refer to the boxplots shown below that are drawn on the same scale. The top boxplot represents weights (kg) of male U.S. Army personnel in 1988, and the bottom boxplot represents weights (kg) of male U.S. Army personnel in 2012. What story is told by these boxplots?

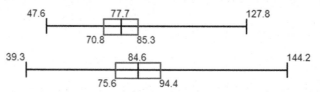

4. z Scores If your score on your next statistics test is converted to a z score, which of these z scores would you prefer: −2.00, −1.00, 0, 1.00, 2.00? Why?

z Scores.   *In Exercises 5–8, express all z scores with two decimal places.*

5. Diastolic Blood Pressure of Females For the diastolic blood pressure measurements of females listed in Data Set 1 "Body Data" in Appendix B, the highest measurement is 98 mm Hg. The 147 diastolic blood pressure measurements of females have a mean of $\bar{x} = 70.2$ mm Hg and a standard deviation of $s = 11.2$ mm Hg.

a. What is the difference between the highest diastolic blood pressure and the mean of the diastolic blood pressures for females?

b. How many standard deviations is that [the difference found in part (a)]?

c. Convert the highest diastolic blood pressure to a z score.

d. Using the criteria summarized in Figure 3-6 on page 123, is the highest blood pressure significantly low, significantly high, or neither?

6. Diastolic Blood Pressure of Males For the diastolic blood pressure measurements of males listed in Data Set 1 "Body Data" in Appendix B, the lowest measurement is 40 mm Hg. The 153 males have a mean of $\bar{x} = 71.3$ mm Hg and a standard deviation of $s = 12.0$ mm Hg.

a. For males, what is the difference between the lowest diastolic blood pressure and the mean of the diastolic blood pressures?

b. How many standard deviations is that [the difference found in part (a)]?

c. Convert the lowest diastolic blood pressure to a z score.

d. Using the criteria summarized in Figure 3-6 on page 123, is the lowest blood pressure significantly low, significantly high, or neither?

7. New York City Commute Time New York City commute times (minutes) are listed in Data Set 31 "Commute Times" in Appendix B. The 1000 times have a mean of 42.6 minutes and a standard deviation of 26.2 minutes. Consider the commute time of 95.0 minutes.

a. What is the difference between the commute time of 95.0 minutes and the mean commute time?

b. How many standard deviations is that [the difference found in part (a)]?

c. Convert the commute time of 95.0 minutes to a z score.

d. Using the criteria summarized in Figure 3-6 on page 123, is the commute time of 95 minutes significantly low, significantly high, or neither?

8. Word Counts Data Set 14 "Word Counts" includes counts of the numbers of words spoken in a day by couples ranging in age from 18 to 29. The males have a mean of 16,576.1 words with a standard deviation of 7871.5 words. The minimum for the males is 1411 words.

a. What is the difference between the 1411 words and the mean number of words?

b. How many standard deviations is that [the difference found in part (a)]?

c. Convert the count of 1411 words to a z score.

d. Using the criteria summarized in Figure 3-6 on page 123, is 1411 words significantly low, significantly high, or neither?

Significant Values. *In Exercises 9–12, use the range rule of thumb to identify (a) the values that are significantly low, (b) the values that are significantly high, and (c) the values that are neither significantly low nor significantly high.*

9. ACT The ACT test is used to assess readiness for college. In a recent year, the mean ACT score was 21.1 and the standard deviation was 5.2.

10. IQ Scores The Wechsler test is used to measure intelligence of adults aged 16 to 80. The mean test score is 100 and the standard deviation is 15.

11. Designing a Work Station In designing a work desk, it is found that males have sitting knee heights with a mean of 21.4 in. and a standard deviation of 1.2 in. (based on data from the Department of Transportation).

12. Designing Aircraft Seats In the process of designing aircraft seats, it was found that men have hip widths with a mean of 36.6 cm and a standard deviation of 2.5 cm (based on anthropometric survey data from Gordon, Clauser et al.).

Comparing Values. *In Exercises 13–16, use z scores to compare the given values.*

13. Tallest and Shortest Men The tallest adult male was Robert Wadlow, and his height was 272 cm. The shortest adult male was Chandra Bahadur Dangi, and his height was 54.6 cm. Heights of men have a mean of 174.12 cm and a standard deviation of 7.10 cm. Which of these two men has the height that is more extreme?

14. Pulse Rates Based on Data Set 1 "Body Data" in Appendix B, males have pulse rates with a mean of 69.6 and a standard deviation of 11.3; females have pulse rates with a mean of 74.0 and a standard deviation of 12.5. All pulse rates are measured in beats per minute. Which pulse rate is more extreme: A male with a pulse rate of 50 or a female with a pulse rate of 99?

15. Birth Weights Based on Data Set 6 "Births" in Appendix B, newborn males have weights with a mean of 3272.8 g and a standard deviation of 660.2 g. Newborn females have weights with a mean of 3037.1 g and a standard deviation of 706.3 g. Who has the weight that is more extreme relative to the group from which they came: a male who weighs 1500 g or a female who weighs 1500 g?

16. Candy Based on Data Set 38 "Candies" in Appendix B, Hershey's Kisses have a mean weight of 4.5338 g and a standard deviation of 0.1039 g, and Reese's Cups have a mean weight of 8.8637 g and a standard deviation of 0.1608 g. Which candy has the more extreme weight: A Hershey's Kiss with a weight of 4.794 g or a Reese's Cup with a weight of 8.413 g?

Percentiles. *In Exercises 17–20, use the following radiation levels (in W/kg) for 50 different cell phones. Find the percentile corresponding to the given radiation level.*

0.24	0.24	0.31	0.48	0.60	0.60	0.61	0.65	0.75	0.85
0.91	0.91	0.91	0.91	0.93	0.97	0.98	1.00	1.09	1.09
1.10	1.13	1.13	1.15	1.15	1.16	1.16	1.17	1.18	1.19
1.19	1.23	1.27	1.27	1.28	1.28	1.28	1.28	1.30	1.32
1.35	1.37	1.38	1.40	1.45	1.46	1.47	1.48	1.49	1.52

17. 0.48 W/kg   **18.** 1.47 W/kg   **19.** 1.10 W/kg   **20.** 0.98 W/kg

In Exercises 21–28, use the same list of cell phone radiation levels given for Exercises 17–20. Find the indicated percentile or quartile.

21. P_{30} **22.** Q_1 **23.** Q_3 **24.** P_{40} **25.** P_{50} **26.** P_{75} **27.** P_{25} **28.** P_{85}

Boxplots. *In Exercises 29–32, use the given data to construct a boxplot and identify the 5-number summary.*

29. Speed Dating In a study of speed dating conducted at Columbia University, female subjects were asked to rate the attractiveness of their male dates, and a sample of the results is listed below (1 = not attractive; 10 = extremely attractive).

2.0 3.0 4.0 5.0 6.0 6.0 7.0 7.0 7.0 7.0 7.0 7.0 8.0 8.0 8.0 8.0 9.0 9.5 10.0 10.0

30. Taxis Listed below are times (minutes) of a sample of taxi rides in New York City. The data are from the New York City Taxi and Limousine Commission.

15 12 31 3 11 33 62 4

31. Radiation in Baby Teeth Listed below are amounts of strontium-90 (in millibecquerels, or mBq) in a simple random sample of baby teeth obtained from Pennsylvania residents born after 1979 (based on data from "An Unexpected Rise in Strontium-90 in U.S. Deciduous Teeth in the 1990s," by Mangano et al., *Science of the Total Environment*).

128 130 133 137 138 142 142 144 147 149 151 151 151 155
156 161 163 163 166 172

32. Blood Pressure Measurements Fourteen different second-year medical students at Bellevue Hospital measured the blood pressure of the same person. The systolic readings (mm Hg) are listed below.

138   130   135   140   120   125   120   130   130   144   143   140   130   150

Boxplots from Large Data Sets in Appendix B. *In Exercises 33–36, use the given data sets in Appendix B. Use the boxplots to compare the two data sets.*

33. Pulse Rates Use the same scale to construct boxplots for the pulse rates of males and females from Data Set 1 "Body Data" in Appendix B.

34. Ages of Oscar Winners Use the same scale to construct boxplots for the ages of the best actresses and best actors from Data Set 21 "Oscar Winner Age" in Appendix B.

35. Weights Use the weights (kg) of males from Data Set 2 "ANSUR I 1988" and the weights of males (kg) from Data Set 3 "ANSUR II 2012." The ANSUR I data are from 1988 and the ANSUR II data are from 2012.

36. Lead and IQ Use the same scale to construct boxplots for the full IQ scores (IQF) for the low lead level group (group 1) and the high lead level group (group 3) in Data Set 11 "IQ and Lead" in Appendix B. The low lead level group consists of children with low levels of lead in their blood, and the high lead level group consists of children with high levels of lead in their blood. What do the boxplots suggest about the effect of exposure to lead?

3-3   Beyond the Basics

37. Outliers and Modified Boxplots Repeat Exercise 33 "Pulse Rates" using modified boxplots. Identify any outliers as defined in Part 2 of this section.

38. Outliers and Modified Boxplots Repeat Exercise 34 "Ages of Oscar Winners" using modified boxplots. Identify any outliers as defined in Part 2 of this section.

Chapter Quick Quiz

1. Mean of Roller Coaster Speeds Listed below are maximum speeds (km/h) of randomly selected roller coasters in the United States. Find the mean.

70   76   97   81   57   151   194   65   117   65   45   105

2. Median of Roller Coaster Speeds What is the median of the sample values listed in Exercise 1?

3. Mode of Roller Coaster Speeds What is the mode of the sample values listed in Exercise 1?

4. Variance of Roller Coaster Speeds The standard deviation of the sample values in Exercise 1 is 43.1 km/h. What is the variance (including units)?

5. Roller Coaster Speed Outlier Identify any outliers among the data listed for Exercise 1.

6. Roller Coaster z Score A larger sample of 92 roller coaster maximum speeds has a mean of 85.9 km/h and a standard deviation of 28.7 km/h. What is the z score for a speed of 34 km/h? Does the z score suggest that the speed of 34 km/h is *significantly low*?

7. Q_3 for Roller Coaster Speeds For the sample of 92 roller coaster maximum speeds, approximately how many of those speeds are less than Q_3?

8. Roller Coaster Speed 5-Number Summary For the sample of 92 roller coaster maximum speeds, give the *names* of the values that constitute the 5-number summary. (The actual values can't be identified; just give the *names* of those values.)

9. Estimating s The sample of 92 roller coaster maximum speeds includes values ranging from a low of 10 km/h to a high of 194 km/h. Use the range rule of thumb to estimate the standard deviation.

10. Roller Coaster Speed Notation Consider a sample of roller coaster maximum speeds taken from the population of all roller coasters operating on our planet. Identify the symbols used for the sample mean, population mean, sample standard deviation, population standard deviation, sample variance, and the population variance.

Review Exercises

1. Reported and Measured Heights Listed below are self-reported heights of males aged 16 and over and their corresponding measured heights (based on data from the National Health and Nutrition Examination Survey). All heights are in inches. First find the differences (reported height–measured height), and then use those differences to find the (a) mean, (b) median, (c) mode, (d) midrange, (e) range, (f) standard deviation, (g) variance, (h) Q_1, (i) Q_3.

Reported	68.0	71.0	63.0	70.0	71.0	60.0	65.0	64	54.0	63.0	66	72.0
Measured	67.9	69.9	64.9	68.3	70.3	60.6	64.5	67	55.6	74.2	65	70.8

2. Outliers Identify any of the differences found from Exercise 1 that appear to be outliers. For any outliers, how much of an effect do they have on the mean, median, and standard deviation?

3. z Score Using the differences from Exercise 1, find the z score corresponding to the difference of $-11.2\,\text{in}$. Is that difference significantly low, significantly high, or neither?

4. Boxplot Using the same differences from Exercise 1, construct a boxplot and include the values of the 5-number summary.

5. ER Codes In an analysis of activities that resulted in brain injuries presenting at hospital emergency rooms, the following activities were identified by the codes shown in parentheses: bicycling (12); football (14); playground (22); basketball (27); swimming (40). Find the mean of 12, 14, 22, 27, and 40. What is wrong with this result?

6. MCAT In a recent year, applicants to medical schools achieved scores on the Medical College Admission Test (MCAT) with a mean of 504.7 and a standard deviation of 9.4. Identify the MCAT scores that are significantly low or high.

7. Interpreting a Boxplot Shown below is a boxplot of a sample of 30 maximal skull widths (mm) measured from Egyptian skulls from around 4000 B.C. What do the numbers in the boxplot represent?

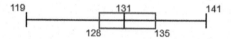

8. Estimating Standard Deviation Listed below are sorted weights (g) of a sample of M&M plain candies randomly selected from one bag. Use the range rule of thumb to estimate the value of the standard deviation of all 345 M&Ms in the bag. Compare the result to the standard deviation of 0.0366 g computed from all of the 345 M&Ms in the bag.

0.799 0.843 0.849 0.855 0.870 0.872 0.874 0.875 0.879 0.886

0.887 0.889 0.894 0.901 0.902 0.902 0.926 0.940 0.943 0.944

9. Percentiles Use the sorted weights of M&Ms from the preceding exercise to find the value of P_{25}. How does the result compare to the value of Q_1?

10. Comparing Birth Weights The birth weights of a sample of females have a mean of 3037.1 g and a standard deviation of 706.3 g. The birth weights of a sample of males have a mean of 3272.8 g and a standard deviation of 660.2 g (based on Data Set 6 "Births" in Appendix B). When considered among members of the same gender, which baby has the relatively larger birth weight: a female with a birth weight of 3200 g or a male with a birth weight of 3400 g? Why?

Cumulative Review Exercises

1. Sugar Listed below are measured weights (mg) of sugar in Domino packets labelled as containing 3500 mg (or 3.5 g).

a. Are the data qualitative or quantitative?

b. What is the level of measurement of the data (nominal, ordinal, interval, or ratio)?

c. Before any rounding, are the weights discrete or continuous?

d. Given that the weights are from Domino sugar packets selected from a much larger population, are the weights a sample or a population?

e. If we calculate the mean of the listed values, is the result a statistic or a parameter?

3511 3516 3521 3531 3532 3545 3583 3588 3590 3617

3621 3635 3638 3643 3645 3647 3666 3673 3678 3723

2. Frequency Distribution Using the data from Exercise 1, construct a frequency distribution using a class width of 50 mg and a first class with a lower class limit of 3500 mg.

3. Histogram Use the frequency distribution from Exercise 2 to construct a histogram. Use class midpoint values for the horizontal scale.

4. Percentile Use the weights from Exercise 1 to find the percentile for 3647 mg.

5. Descriptive Statistics Use the weights of the Domino sugar packets from Exercise 1 and find the following: (a) mean, (b) median, (c) standard deviation, (d) variance, (e) range. Include the appropriate units of measurement.

6. Histogram The accompanying histogram depicts outcomes of digits from the Florida Play 4 lottery. What is the major flaw in this histogram?

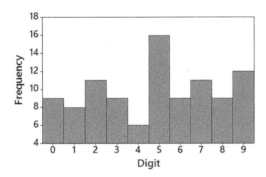

7. Normal Distribution Examine the distribution shown in the histogram from Exercise 6. Does it appear that the sample data are from a population with a normal distribution? Why or why not?

8. Correlation of Heights of Fathers and Sons Listed below are heights (in.) of fathers and their first sons (based on Data Set 10 "Family Heights" in Appendix B). Construct a scatterplot and then make a judgment to determine whether there appears to be a correlation between heights of fathers and heights of their first sons.

Father	70.5	69.0	68.7	70.0	68.0	65.0	69.0	68.7	67.0	66.0
Son	74.0	68.0	67.7	68.0	67.5	66.5	71.0	71.0	69.0	66.0

Technology Project

Words Spoken by Men and Women Refer to Data Set 14 "Word Counts" in Appendix B, which includes counts of words spoken by males and females. That data set includes 12 columns of data, but first stack all of the male word counts in one column and stack all of the female word counts in another column. Then proceed to generate histograms, any other suitable graphs, and find appropriate statistics that allow you to compare the two sets of data. Are there any outliers? Do both data sets have properties that are basically the same? Are there any significant differences? What would be a consequence of having significant differences? Write a brief report including your conclusions and supporting graphs.

Big (or Very Large) Data Project

a. Use the birth weights in Data Set 6 "Births" to complete the following table.

	n	$\bar{x}$	s	Minimum	Maximum
Male					
Female					

b. Repeat part (a) using Data Set 45 "Births in New York" in Appendix B, which contains records from 465,506 births.

c. Use the preceding results to compare the birth weights of males and females.

d. Do the results from Data Set 6 "Births" differ much from the very large "Births in New York" data set with 465,506 records?

FROM DATA TO DECISION

Second-Hand Smoke

Data Set 15 "Passive and Active Smoke" in Appendix B lists measures of cotinine from three groups of subjects: (1) smokers; (2) nonsmokers exposed to environmental tobacco smoke; (3) nonsmokers not exposed to environmental tobacco smoke. Cotinine is an indicator of nicotine absorption.

Critical Thinking

Use the methods from this chapter to explore and compare the cotinine measures in the three groups. Are there any notable differences? Are there any outliers? What do you conclude about the effects that smokers have on nonsmokers? Write a brief report of your conclusions, and provide supporting statistical evidence.

Cooperative Group Activities

1. In-class activity In class, each student should record two pulse rates by counting the number of heartbeats in 1 minute. The first pulse rate should be measured while the student is seated, and the second pulse rate should be measured while the student is standing. Use the methods of this chapter to compare results. Do males and females appear to have different pulse rates? Do pulse rates measured while seated appear to be different from pulse rates measured while standing?

2. Out-of-class activity In the article "Weighing Anchors" in *Omni* magazine, author John Rubin observed that when people estimate a value, their estimate is often "anchored" to (or influenced by) a preceding number, even if that preceding number is totally unrelated to the quantity being estimated. To demonstrate this, he asked people to give a quick estimate of the value of $8 \times 7 \times 6 \times 5 \times 4 \times 3 \times 2 \times 1$. The mean of the answers given was 2250, but when the order of the numbers was reversed, the mean became 512. Rubin explained that when we begin calculations with larger numbers (as in $8 \times 7 \times 6$), our estimates tend to be larger. He noted that both 2250 and 512 are far below the correct product, 40,320. The article suggests that irrelevant numbers can play a role in influencing real estate appraisals, estimates of car values, and estimates of the likelihood of nuclear war. Conduct an experiment to test this theory.

Record the estimates along with the particular order used. Carefully design the experiment so that conditions are uniform and the two sample groups are selected in a way that minimizes any bias. Don't describe the theory to subjects until after they have provided their estimates. Compare the two sets of sample results by using the methods of this chapter. Provide a printed report that includes the data collected, the detailed methods used, the method of analysis, any relevant graphs and/or statistics, and a statement of conclusions. Include a critique of the experiment, with reasons why the results might not be correct, and describe ways in which the experiment could be improved.

3. In-class activity Each student should estimate the number of tennis balls that can fit in the classroom that is currently being used. (A similar activity is often used to assess the problem-solving skills of job applicants.) Combine the estimates into one data set. Describe the distribution of the estimates, find the mean, and find the standard deviation. Is it likely that the mean of the estimates is reasonably close to the correct number of tennis balls?

4. Out-of-class activity Each student should obtain a sample of pennies. For each penny, find its age by subtracting the year that the penny was produced from the current year. Those ages should be combined into one data set. Identify the distribution of the ages, then find the mean and standard deviation. What do the results indicate about the pennies in circulation?

5. Out-of-class activity Each student should obtain a sample of data from a line of people waiting for a service. For each person, record the arrival time, the time waiting in line, and the time it took to complete the transaction. For each person, calculate the interarrival time, which is the difference in time between the person's arrival and the arrival of the preceding person. For each of the following sets of sample data, describe the distribution and then find the mean and standard deviation: interarrival times, waiting times, service times.

6. In-class activity Complete the following table, and then compare variation for each ride at 10 AM. See Data Set 33 "Disney World Wait Times."

	Space Mountain	It's a Small World	Rock 'n' Roller Coaster	Tower of Terror	Avatar Flight of Passage	Na'vi River Journey
Standard Deviation						
Range						

7. Out-of-class activity Record the times that cars are parked at a gas pump, and describe important characteristics of those times.

8. Out-of-class activity Several websites, such as www.gasbuddy.com, are designed to provide a list of local gas prices. Obtain a list of local gas prices and explore the data using the methods of this chapter and Chapter 2.

9. Out-of-class activity Data Set 39 "Chocolate Chip Cookies" in Appendix B includes counts of chocolate chips in five different brands of cookies. Obtain your own sample of chocolate chip cookies and proceed to count the number of chocolate chips in each cookie. Use the data to generate a histogram and any other suitable graphs. Find the descriptive statistics. Compare your chocolate chip counts to those given in Data Set 39. Are there any differences? Explain.

10. Out-of-class activity Appendix B includes many real and interesting data sets. In each group of three or four students, select a data set from Appendix B and analyze it using the methods discussed so far in this book. Write a brief report summarizing key conclusions.

11. Out-of-class activity In each group of three or four students, collect an original data set of values at the interval or ratio level of measurement. Provide the following: (1) a list of sample values; (2) software results of descriptive statistics and graphs; and (3) a written description of the nature of the data, the method of collection, and important characteristics.

4

PROBABILITY

CHAPTER PROBLEM — **Probability for Significance**

In Chapter 3 we introduced the concepts of *significantly low* or *significantly high* sample values. In that chapter, determination of whether values are significantly low or significantly high was based on the range rule of thumb or the use of *z* scores. Both the range rule of thumb and the use of *z* scores indicate that a value is significantly low if it is at least two standard deviations below the mean (or $z \leq -2$), and a value is significantly high if

it is at least two standard deviations above the mean (or $z \geq 2$). Those criteria are based on the values of the mean and standard deviation, but those statistics could be greatly affected by outliers and the distributions of the data. In many cases (such as correlation), we don't work with a single mean and standard deviation, so the range rule of thumb can't be used. We can better identify significant results by using *probability* values.

Caution: An outcome can be statistically significant, and it may or may not be *important.* Don't associate statistical significance with importance.

The Microsort XSORT gender selection technique was designed to increase the likelihood that a baby will be a girl. At one point before clinical trials of the XSORT gender selection technique were discontinued, 945 births consisted of 879 baby girls and 66 baby boys (based on data from the Genetics & IVF Institute). The *probability* of getting such results by chance with no treatment is 0.00000000 when rounded to eight decimal places. We can now interpret that probability to conclude that 879 girls in 945 births is a *significantly high* number of girls.

For now, let's consider this simpler problem that can be easily solved using the methods of this chapter: If a test of the XSORT method of gender selection involves 20 couples who give birth to 20 babies, what is the probability that the 20 babies are all girls? Does the result of 20 girls suggest that the XSORT technique is effective? We will address these questions in this chapter.

In addition to being great fun, the topic of probability is critically important because it serves as a foundation for later concepts of statistics, such as hypothesis testing introduced in Chapter 8. Probability is not an independent and unrelated topic stuck in here for the sole purpose of being a fun distraction. Instead, probability plays an important role in helping us to determine whether results are *significant.*

CHAPTER OBJECTIVES

The main objective of this chapter is to develop a sound understanding of probability values, and then use those values to identify when results are *significant.* Probability values constitute the underlying foundation on which methods of inferential statistics are built. The important methods of hypothesis testing commonly use *P-values*, which are probability values expressed as numbers between 0 and 1, inclusive. Smaller probability values, such as 0.01, correspond to events that are very unlikely. Larger probability values, such as 0.99, correspond to events that are very likely. Here are the chapter objectives:

4-1 Basic Concepts of Probability

- Identify probabilities as values between 0 and 1, and interpret those values as expressions of likelihood of events.

- Develop the ability to calculate probabilities of events.

- Understand and apply the *rare event rule for inferential statistics* to determine when results are *significant.*

- Define the *complement* of an event and calculate the probability of that complement.

4-2 Addition Rule and Multiplication Rule

- Develop the ability to calculate the probability that in a single trial, some event *A* occurs or some event *B* occurs or they both occur. Apply the addition rule by correctly adjusting for events that are not disjoint (or are overlapping).

- Develop the ability to calculate the probability of an event *A* occurring in a first trial and an event *B* occurring in a second trial. Apply the multiplication rule by adjusting for events that are not independent.

- Distinguish between independent events and dependent events.

4-3 Complements, Conditional Probability, and Bayes' Theorem

- Compute the probability of "at least one" occurrence of an event *A*.

- Apply the multiplication rule by computing the probability of some event, given that some other event has already occurred.

4-4 Counting

- Develop the ability to apply the fundamental counting rule, factorial rule, permutations rule, and combinations rule.

- Distinguish between circumstances requiring the permutations rule and those requiring the combinations rule.

4-5 Simulations for Hypothesis Tests

- Use simulations to determine when sample results are significantly low or significantly high, so that claims about population parameters can be tested.

4-1   Basic Concepts of Probability

Key Concept Part 1 of this section includes basic concepts of probability. The single most important objective of this section is to learn how to *interpret* probability values, which are expressed as values between 0 and 1. A small probability, such as 0.001, corresponds to an event that rarely occurs. When interpreting probability values, it is also important to understand the *rare event rule for inferential statistics*, which is described later in Part 1 of this section.

Part 2 of this section includes *odds* and how they relate to probabilities. Concepts related to odds are not needed for topics in the following chapters, but odds are commonly used in situations such as lotteries and gambling.

PART 1   Basic Concepts of Probability

Role of Probability in Statistics

Probability plays a central role in the important statistical method of *hypothesis testing* introduced later in Chapter 8. Statisticians make decisions using data by rejecting explanations (such as chance) based on very low *probabilities*. See the following example illustrating the role of probability and a fundamental way that statisticians think.

CP EXAMPLE 1   Analyzing a Claim

Researchers have made this claim (really, they have):

Claim: "We have developed a gender selection method that greatly increases the likelihood of a baby being a girl."

Hypothesis Used When Testing the Preceding Claim: The method of gender selection has *no effect*, so that for couples using this method, about 50% of the births result in girls.

Figure 4-1 shows the sample data from two tests of couples using the gender selection method and the conclusion reached for each test.

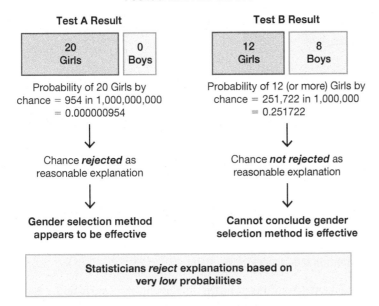

FIGURE 4-1   Gender Selection Method Test Data and Conclusions

INTERPRETATION

Among the 20 babies, 20 girls and 12 girls are both greater than the 10 girls that we typically expect, but only the event of 20 girls leads us to believe that the gender selection method is effective. Even though there is a chance of getting 20 girls in 20 births with no special treatment, the probability of that happening is so small (0.000000954) that we should reject chance as a reasonable explanation. Instead, it would be generally recognized that the results provide strong support for the claim that the gender selection method is effective. This is exactly how statisticians think: They reject explanations (such as chance) based on very low *probabilities*.

 **YOUR TURN.** Do Exercise 37 "Predicting Gender."

Basics of Probability

In probability, we deal with procedures (such as generating male/female births or answering a multiple choice test question) that produce outcomes.

DEFINITIONS

An **event** is any collection of results or outcomes of a procedure.

A **simple event** is an outcome or an event that cannot be further broken down into simpler components.

The **sample space** for a procedure consists of all possible *simple* events. That is, the sample space consists of all outcomes that cannot be broken down any further.

Example 2 illustrates the concepts defined above.

Probabilities That Challenge Intuition

In certain cases, our subjective estimates of probability values are dramatically different from the actual probabilities. Here is a classical example: If you take a deep breath, there is better than a 99% chance that you will inhale a molecule that was exhaled in dying Caesar's last breath. In that same morbid and unintuitive spirit, if Socrates' fatal cup of hemlock was mostly water, then the next glass of water you drink will likely contain one of those same molecules. Here's another, less morbid example that can be verified: In classes of 25 students, there is better than a 50% chance that at least 2 students will share the same birthday (day and month).

CP ▸ **EXAMPLE 2**   Simple Events and Sample Spaces

In the following display, we use "b" to denote a baby boy and "g" to denote a baby girl.

Procedure	Example of Event	Sample Space: Complete List of Simple Events
Single birth	1 girl (simple event)	{b, g}
3 births	2 boys and 1 girl (bbg, bgb, and gbb are all simple events resulting in 2 boys and 1 girl)	{bbb, bbg, bgb, bgg, gbb, gbg, ggb, ggg}

Simple Events:

- With one birth, the result of 1 girl is a *simple event* and the result of 1 boy is another simple event. They are individual simple events because they cannot be broken down any further.

- With three births, the result of 2 girls followed by a boy (ggb) is a simple event.

- When rolling a single die, the outcome of 5 is a simple event, but the outcome of an even number is not a simple event.

Not a Simple Event: With three births, the event of "2 girls and 1 boy" is *not a simple event* because it can occur with these different simple events: ggb, gbg, bgg.

Sample Space: With three births, the *sample space* consists of the eight different simple events listed in the lower right cell of the above table.

⬦ **YOUR TURN.** Do Exercise 31 "Four Children."

Three Common Approaches to Finding the Probability of an Event

We first list some basic notation, then we present three common approaches to finding the probability of an event.

> **Notation for Probabilities**
>
> P denotes a probability.
>
> A, B, and C denote specific events.
>
> $P(A)$ denotes the "probability of event A occurring."

The following three approaches for finding probabilities result in values between 0 and 1: $0 \leq P(A) \leq 1$. Figure 4-2 shows the possible values of probabilities and the more familiar and common expressions of likelihood.

1. **Relative Frequency Approximation of Probability** Conduct (or observe) a procedure and count the number of times that event A occurs. $P(A)$ is then *approximated* as follows:

$$P(A) = \frac{\text{number of times } A \text{ occurred}}{\text{number of times the procedure was repeated}}$$

When referring to relative frequency approximations of probabilities, this text will not distinguish between results that are exact probabilities and

FIGURE 4-2   Possible Values for Probabilities

(Scale from bottom to top: 0 — Impossible; Unlikely; 0.5 — 50–50 Chance; Likely; 1 — Certain)

those that are approximations, so an instruction to "find the probability" could actually mean "*estimate* the probability."

2. **Classical Approach to Probability (Requires Equally Likely Outcomes)** If a procedure has *n* different simple events that are *equally likely*, and if event *A* can occur in *s* different ways, then

$$P(A) = \frac{\text{number of ways } A \text{ occurs}}{\text{number of different simple events}} = \frac{s}{n}$$

CAUTION When using the classical approach, always confirm that the outcomes are *equally likely*.

---

3. **Subjective Probabilities** $P(A)$, the probability of event *A*, is *estimated* by using knowledge of the relevant circumstances.

Figure 4-3 illustrates the approaches of the preceding three definitions.

1. Relative Frequency Approach: When trying to determine the probability that an individual car crashes in a year, we must examine past results to determine the number of cars in use in a year and the number of them that crashed; then we find the ratio of the number of cars that crashed to the total number of cars. For a recent year, the result is a probability of 0.0480. (See Example 3.)

2. Classical Approach: When trying to determine the probability of winning the grand prize in a lottery by selecting six different numbers between 1 and 60, each combination has an equal chance of occurring. The probability of winning is 0.0000000200, which can be found by using methods presented in Section 4-4. (See Example 4.)

3. Subjective Probability: When trying to estimate the probability of getting stuck in the next elevator that you ride, we know from personal experience that the probability is quite small. Let's estimate it to be, say, 0.001 (equivalent to 1 chance in 1000). (See Example 5.)

FIGURE 4-3   Three Approaches to Finding a Probability

Understanding Chances of Winning the Lottery

In the New York State Lottery Mega Millions game, you must choose five different numbers from 1 to 75, and you must also select another "Mega Ball" number from 1 to 15. To win the jackpot, you must get the correct five numbers *and* the correct Mega Ball number. The chance of winning the jackpot with one ticket is 1/258,890,850. Commercials for this lottery state that "all you need is a little bit of luck," but in reality you need a ginormous amount of luck. The probability of 1/258,890,850 is not so easy to understand, so let's consider a helpful analogy suggested by Brother Donald Kelly of Marist College. A stack of 258,890,850 quarters is about 282 miles high. Commercial jets typically fly about 7 miles high, so this stack of quarters is about 40 times taller than the height of a commercial jet when it is at cruising altitude. The chance of winning the Mega Millions lottery game is equivalent to the chance of randomly selecting *one* specific quarter from that pile of quarters that is 282 miles high. Any of us who spend money on this lottery should understand that the chance of winning the jackpot is very, very, very close to zero.

Simulations Sometimes none of the preceding three approaches can be used. A *simulation* of a procedure is a process that behaves in the same ways as the procedure itself so that similar results are produced. Probabilities can sometimes be found by using a simulation. See Section 4-5.

ROUNDING PROBABILITIES

It is difficult to provide a universal rule for rounding probability values, but this guide will apply to most problems in this text: When expressing the value of a probability, use this rounding rule: **Either give the *exact* fraction or decimal, or round off final decimal results to *three* significant digits.**

(*Suggestion:* When a probability is not a simple fraction such as 2/3 or 5/9, express it as a decimal so that the number can be better understood.) All digits in a number are significant except for the zeros that are included for proper placement of the decimal point. See the following examples.

- The probability of 0.1827259111333 (from Example 6) has thirteen significant digits (1827259111333), and it can be rounded to three significant digits as 0.183.

- The probability of 1/3 can be left as a fraction or rounded to 0.333. (Do *not* round to 0.3, because 0.3 has only one significant digit instead of three.)

- The probability of 2/8 can be expressed as 1/4 or 0.25. (Because 0.25 is exact, there's no need to express it with three significant digits as 0.250.)

Probabilities Expressed as Percentages? Mathematically, a probability of 0.25 is equivalent to 25%, but there are good reasons for working with fractions and decimals and not using percentages. Professional journals almost universally express probabilities as decimals, not as percentages. Later in this book, we will use probability values generated from statistical software, and they will always be in the form of decimals. Also, calculations using probability values, such as 0.25 × 0.25, are easy when working with decimals, but 25% × 25% can cause major problems.

When finding probabilities with the relative frequency approach, we obtain an *approximation* instead of an exact value. As the total number of observations increases, the corresponding approximations tend to get closer to the actual probability. This property is commonly referred to as the *law of large numbers*.

LAW OF LARGE NUMBERS

As a procedure is repeated again and again, the relative frequency probability of an event tends to approach the actual probability.

The law of large numbers tells us that relative frequency approximations tend to get better with more observations. This law reflects a simple notion supported by common sense: A probability estimate based on only a few trials can be off by a substantial amount, but with a very large number of trials, the estimate tends to be much more accurate.

CAUTIONS

1. The law of large numbers applies to behavior over a large number of trials, and it does not apply to any one individual outcome. Gamblers sometimes foolishly lose large sums of money by incorrectly thinking that a string of losses increases the chances of a win on the next bet, or that a string of wins is likely to continue.

2. If we know nothing about the likelihood of different possible outcomes, we should not assume that they are equally likely. For example, we should not think that the probability of passing the next statistics test is 1/2, or 0.5 (because we either pass the test or do not). The actual probability depends on factors such as the amount of preparation and the difficulty of the test.

EXAMPLE 3 **Relative Frequency Probability: Airline Crashes**

Find the probability that a commercial airliner will crash on any given flight.

SOLUTION

In a recent year, there were about 39 million commercial airline flights, and 16 of them crashed. We use the relative frequency approach as follows:

$$P(\text{airline crash}) = \frac{\text{number of airline crashes}}{\text{total number of airline flights}} = \frac{16}{39,000,000} = 0.000000410$$

Here, the classical approach cannot be used because the two outcomes (crashing, not crashing) are not equally likely. A subjective probability can be estimated in the absence of historical data.

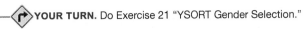**YOUR TURN.** Do Exercise 21 "YSORT Gender Selection."

EXAMPLE 4 **Classical Probability: Three Children of the Same Gender**

When three children are born, the sample space of genders is as shown in Example 2: {bbb, bbg, bgb, bgg, gbb, gbg, ggb, ggg}. If boys and girls are equally likely, then those eight simple events are equally likely. Assuming that boys and girls are equally likely, find the probability of getting three children all of the same gender when three children are born. (In reality, the probability of a boy is 0.512 instead of 0.5.)

SOLUTION

The sample space {bbb, bbg, bgb, bgg, gbb, gbg, ggb, ggg} includes eight equally likely outcomes, and there are exactly two outcomes in which the three children are of the same gender: bbb and ggg. We can use the classical approach to get

$$P(\text{three children of the same gender}) = \frac{2}{8} = \frac{1}{4} \text{ or } 0.25$$

YOUR TURN. Do Exercise 29 "Three Children."

EXAMPLE 5 **Subjective Probability: Earning a grade of A in this Statistics Course**

What is the probability that you will earn a grade of A in the statistics course you are currently taking?

SOLUTION

Earning a grade of A depends on many factors including these: How much you study; the difficulty of the tests; attendance in class; best in class textbook (✓); skill of your professor. There is no way to calculate an accurate probability, so we use subjective judgment. You might observe that you enjoy learning statistical concepts and are highly motivated to master this valuable subject which has countless applications in today's data-driven world! This passion for statistics and your success in previous math courses might all suggest that there is a good chance of earning an A, so you might assign a probability of 0.8 to that event.

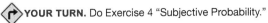**YOUR TURN.** Do Exercise 4 "Subjective Probability."

How Probable?

How do we interpret such terms as *probable*, *improbable*, or *extremely improbable*? The Federal Aviation Administration (FAA) interprets these terms as follows.

- *Probable:* A probability on the order of 0.00001 or greater for each hour of flight. Such events are expected to occur several times during the operational life of each airplane.

- *Improbable:* A probability on the order of 0.00001 or less. Such events are not expected to occur during the total operational life of a single airplane of a particular type, but may occur during the total operational life of all airplanes of a particular type.

- *Extremely improbable:* A probability on the order of 0.000000001 or less. Such events are so unlikely that they need not be considered to ever occur.

EXAMPLE 6   Ghosts!

In a Pew Research Center survey, randomly selected adults were asked if they have seen or have been in the presence of a ghost. 366 of the respondents answered "yes," and 1637 of the respondents answered "no". Based on these results, find the probability that a randomly selected adult says that they have seen or been in the presence of a ghost.

SOLUTION

> **CAUTION** A common *mistake* is to blindly plug in numbers to get the wrong probability of $366/1637 = 0.224$. We should *think* carefully about what we are doing, as follows.

Instead of trying to determine an answer directly from the given statement, first summarize the information in a format that allows clear understanding, such as this format:

$$366 \quad \text{responses of "yes"}$$
$$\underline{1637 \quad \text{responses of "no"}}$$
$$2003 \quad \text{total number of responses}$$

We can now use the relative frequency approach as follows:

$$P(\text{response of "yes"}) = \frac{\text{number of "yes" responses}}{\text{total number of responses}} = \frac{366}{2003}$$
$$= 0.183$$

INTERPRETATION

There is a 0.183 probability that a randomly selected adult says that they have seen or been in the presence of a ghost.

 **YOUR TURN.** Do Exercise 23 "Mendelian Genetics."

> **CAUTION** Don't make the common mistake of finding a probability value by mind-lessly dividing a smaller number by a larger number. Instead, *think* carefully about the numbers involved and what they represent. Carefully identify the total number of items being considered, as illustrated in Example 6.

EXAMPLE 7   Thanksgiving Day

If a year is selected at random, find the probability that Thanksgiving Day in the United States will be (a) on a Wednesday or (b) on a Thursday.

SOLUTION

a. In the United States, Thanksgiving Day always falls on the fourth Thursday in November. It is therefore impossible for Thanksgiving to be on a Wednesday. When an event is impossible, its probability is 0. $P(\text{Thanksgiving on Wednesday}) = 0$.

b. It is certain that a Thanksgiving Day in the United States will be on a Thursday. When an event is certain to occur, its probability is 1. $P(\text{Thanksgiving on Thursday}) = 1$.

Because any event imaginable is impossible, certain, or somewhere in between, it follows that the mathematical probability of any event A is 0, 1, or a number between 0 and 1 (as shown in Figure 4-2). For those of us into mathematical notation, we can express this as $0 \le P(A) \le 1$.

▶ **YOUR TURN.** Do Exercises 19 "Square Peg" and 20 "Death and Taxes."

Go Figure

10^{80}: Number of particles in the observable universe. The probability of a monkey randomly hitting keys and typing Shakespeare's *Hamlet* is $10^{-216,159}$.

Complementary Events

Sometimes we need to find the probability that an event A does *not* occur.

DEFINITION

The **complement** of event A, denoted by $\overline{A}$, consists of all outcomes in which event A does *not* occur.

EXAMPLE 8 **Complement of Internet User**

In a Pew Research Center survey of 2002 randomly selected adults, 1782 of those respondents said that they use the Internet. Find the probability that a randomly selected adult does *not* use the Internet.

SOLUTION

Among 2002 survey subjects, 1782 use the Internet, so it follows that the other 220 do *not* use the Internet. We get the following

$$P(\text{not using the Internet}) = \frac{220}{2002} = 0.110$$

INTERPRETATION

The probability of randomly selecting an adult who does *not* use the Internet is 0.110.

▶ **YOUR TURN.** Do Exercise 25 "Social Networking."

Relationship Between $P(A)$ and $P(\overline{A})$ If we denote the event of an adult using the Internet by I, we get $P(I) = 1782/2002 = 0.890$ and $P(\overline{I}) = 0.110$. $P(\overline{I})$ could be found by just subtracting $P(I)$ from 1.

Identifying Significant Results with Probabilities: The Rare Event Rule for Inferential Statistics

If, under a given assumption, the probability of a particular observed event is very small and the observed event occurs *significantly less than* or *significantly greater than* what we typically expect with that assumption, we conclude that the assumption is probably not correct.

We can use probabilities to identify values that are *significantly low* or *significantly high* as follows.

Using Probabilities to Determine When Results Are Significantly High or Significantly Low

- **Significantly *high* number of successes:** x successes among n trials is a *significantly high* number of successes if the probability of x or more successes is unlikely with a probability of 0.05 or less. That is, x is a significantly high number of successes if $P(x \text{ or more}) \leq 0.05$.*

- **Significantly *low* number of successes:** x successes among n trials is a *significantly low* number of successes if the probability of x or fewer successes is unlikely with a probability of 0.05 or less. That is, x is a significantly low number of successes if $P(x \text{ or fewer}) \leq 0.05$.*

*The value 0.05 is not absolutely rigid. Other values, such as 0.01, could be used to distinguish between results that are not significant and those that are significantly high or low.

See Example 1 on pages 144–145, which illustrates the following:

- Among 20 births, 20 girls is *significantly high* because the probability of 20 or more girls is 0.000000954, which is less than or equal to 0.05 (so the gender selection method appears to be effective).

- Among 20 births, 12 girls is *not significantly high* because the probability of 12 or more girls is 0.251722, which is greater than 0.05 (so the gender selection does not appear to be effective).

Probability Review

- **The probability of an event is a fraction or decimal number between 0 and 1 inclusive.**

- **The probability of an impossible event is 0.**

- **The probability of an event that is certain to occur is 1.**

- **Notation: $P(A) = $ the probability of event A.**

- **Notation: $P(\overline{A}) = $ the probability that event A does *not* occur.**

PART 2   Odds

Expressions of likelihood are often given as *odds*, such as 50:1 (or "50 to 1"). Here are advantages of probabilities and odds:

- Odds make it easier to deal with money transfers associated with gambling. (That is why odds are commonly used in casinos, lotteries, and racetracks.)

- Probabilities make calculations easier. (That is why probabilities tend to be used by statisticians, mathematicians, scientists, and researchers in all fields.)

In the three definitions that follow, the *actual odds against* and the *actual odds in favor* reflect the actual likelihood of an event, but the *payoff odds* describe the payoff amounts that are determined by casino, lottery, and racetrack operators. Racetracks and casinos are in business to make a profit, so the payoff odds will not be the same as the actual odds.

DEFINITIONS

The **actual odds against** event A occurring are the ratio $P(\overline{A})/P(A)$, usually expressed in the form of *a:b* (or "*a* to *b*"), where *a* and *b* are integers. (Reduce using the largest common factor; if $a = 16$ and $b = 4$, express the odds as 4:1 instead of 16:4.)

The **actual odds in favor** of event A occurring are the ratio $P(A)/P(\overline{A})$, which is the reciprocal of the actual odds against that event. If the odds against an event are *a:b*, then the odds in favor are *b:a*.

The **payoff odds** against event A occurring are the ratio of net profit (if you win) to the amount bet:

$$\text{Payoff odds against event A} = (\text{net profit}):(\text{amount bet})$$

EXAMPLE 9 **Actual Odds Versus Payoff Odds**

If you bet \$5 on the number 13 in roulette, your probability of winning is 1/38, but the payoff odds are given by the casino as 35:1.

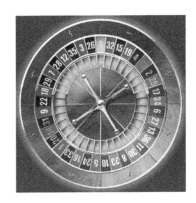

a. Find the actual odds against the outcome of 13.

b. How much net profit would you make if you win by betting \$5 on 13?

c. If the casino was not operating for profit and the payoff odds were changed to match the actual odds against 13, how much would you win if the outcome were 13?

SOLUTION

a. With $P(13) = 1/38$ and $P(\text{not } 13) = 37/38$, we get

$$\text{Actual odds against 13} = \frac{P(\text{not } 13)}{P(13)} = \frac{37/38}{1/38} = \frac{37}{1} \text{ or } 37:1$$

b. Because the casino payoff odds against 13 are 35:1, we have

$$35:1 = (\text{net profit}):(\text{amount bet})$$

So there is a \$35 profit for each \$1 bet. For a \$5 bet, the net profit is \$175 (which is 5 × \$35). The winning bettor would collect \$175 plus the original \$5 bet. After winning, the total amount collected would be \$180, for a net profit of \$175.

c. If the casino were not operating for profit, the payoff odds would be changed to 37:1, which are the actual odds against the outcome of 13. With payoff odds of 37:1, there is a net profit of \$37 for each \$1 bet. For a \$5 bet, the net profit would be \$185. (The casino makes its profit by providing a profit of only \$175 instead of the \$185 that would be paid with a roulette game that is fair instead of favoring the casino.)

YOUR TURN. Do Exercise 41 "Florida Pick 3."

4-1 Basic Skills and Concepts

Statistical Literacy and Critical Thinking

1. California Lottery Let A denote the event of placing a $1 straight bet on the California Daily 4 lottery and winning. There are 10,000 different ways that you can select the four digits (with repetition allowed) in this lottery, and only one of those four-digit numbers will be the winner. What is the value of $P(A)$? What is the value of $P(\overline{A})$?

2. Probability Rewrite the following statement so that the likelihood of rain is expressed as a value between 0 and 1: "The probability of rain today is 25%."

3. Dice and Coins

a. Find the probability that when a single six-sided die is rolled, the outcome is 5.

b. Find the probability that when a coin is tossed, the result is heads.

c. Find the probability that when a six-sided die is rolled, the outcome is 7.

4. Subjective Probability Estimate the probability that the next time that you approach an escalator, you find it to be in operation.

5. Identifying Probability Values Which of the following are probabilities?

$$0 \quad 3/5 \quad 5/3 \quad -0.25 \quad 250\% \quad 7{:}3 \quad 1 \quad 50{-}50 \quad 5{:}1 \quad 0.135 \quad 2.017$$

6. Penicillin "Who discovered penicillin: Marcel Bich, William Penn, Jonas Salk, Alexander Fleming, or Louis Pasteur?" If you make a random guess for the answer to that question, what is the probability that your answer is the correct answer of Alexander Fleming?

7. Planck's Constant If you are asked on a quiz to give the first digit of the Planck constant and, not knowing the answer, you make a random guess, what is the probability that your answer is the correct answer of 6?

8. Sample Space for Births Example 2 in this section includes the sample space for genders from three births. Identify the sample space for the genders from two births.

In Exercises 9–12, assume that 100 births are randomly selected. Use subjective judgment to describe the given number of girls as (a) significantly low, (b) significantly high, or (c) neither significantly low nor significantly high.

9. 53 girls.   **10.** 35 girls.   **11.** 75 girls.   **12.** 48 girls.

In Exercises 13–20, express the indicated degree of likelihood as a probability value between 0 and 1.

13. Testing If you make a random guess for the answer to a true/false test question, there is a 50–50 chance of being correct.

14. SAT Test When making a random guess for an answer to a multiple choice question on an SAT test, the possible answers are a, b, c, d, e, so there is 1 chance in 5 of being correct.

15. Movies Based on a study of the movies made in a recent year, 33 out of every 100 movies have a female lead or co-lead.

16. Online Shopping Based on a National Retail Federation survey, 47% of consumers turn down an online purchase if shipping is not free.

17. Randomness When using a computer to randomly generate the last digit of a phone number to be called for a survey, there is 1 chance in 10 that the last digit is zero.

18. Job Applicant Mistakes Based on an Adecco survey of hiring managers who were asked to identify the biggest mistakes that job candidates make during an interview, there is a 50–50 chance that they will identify "inappropriate attire."

19. Square Peg Sydney Smith wrote in "On the Conduct of the Understanding" that it is impossible to fit a square peg in a round hole.

20. Death and Taxes Benjamin Franklin said that death is a certainty of life.

In Exercises 21–28, find the probability and answer the questions.

21. YSORT Gender Selection MicroSort's YSORT gender selection technique is designed to increase the likelihood that a baby will be a boy. At one point before clinical trials of the YSORT gender selection technique were discontinued, 291 births consisted of 239 baby boys and 52 baby girls (based on data from the Genetics & IVF Institute). Based on these results, what is the probability of a boy born to a couple using MicroSort's YSORT method? Does it appear that the technique is effective in increasing the likelihood that a baby will be a boy?

22. Cash In a Circle survey of 3000 adults, it was found that 17% of the respondents do not carry any cash. Based on these results, what is the probability that a randomly selected adult carries no cash? Does it appear that most adults carry some cash?

23. Mendelian Genetics When Mendel conducted his famous genetics experiments with peas, one sample of offspring consisted of 428 green peas and 152 yellow peas. Based on those results, estimate the probability of getting an offspring pea that is green. Is the result reasonably close to the expected value of $3/4$, as Mendel claimed?

24. Guessing Birthdays On their first date, Kelly asks Mike to guess the date of her birth, not including the year.

a. What is the probability that Mike will guess correctly? (Ignore leap years.)

b. Would it be unlikely for him to guess correctly on his first try?

c. If you were Kelly, and Mike did guess correctly on his first try, would you believe his claim that he made a lucky guess, or would you be convinced that he already knew when you were born?

d. If Kelly asks Mike to guess her age, and Mike's guess is too high by 15 years, what is the probability that Mike and Kelly will have a second date?

25. Social Networking In a Pew Research Center survey of Internet users, 3732 respondents say that they use social networking sites and 1380 respondents say that they *do not* use social networking sites. What is the probability that a randomly selected person uses a social networking site? Does that result suggest that it is likely (with a probability of 0.5 or greater) for someone to use social networking sites?

26. Car Rollovers In a recent year in the United States, 83,600 passenger cars rolled over when they crashed, and 5,127,400 passenger cars did not roll over when they crashed. Find the probability that a randomly selected passenger car crash results in a rollover. Is it unlikely (with a probability of 0.5 or less) for a car to roll over in a crash?

27. Genetics: Eye Color Each of two parents has the genotype brown/blue, which consists of the pair of alleles that determine eye color, and each parent contributes one of those alleles to a child. Assume that if the child has at least one brown allele, that color will dominate and the eyes will be brown. (The actual determination of eye color is more complicated than that.)

a. List the different possible outcomes. Assume that these outcomes are equally likely.

b. What is the probability that a child of these parents will have the blue/blue genotype?

c. What is the probability that the child will have brown eyes?

28. X-Linked Genetic Disease Men have XY (or YX) chromosomes and women have XX chromosomes. X-linked recessive genetic diseases (such as juvenile retinoschisis) occur when there is a defective X chromosome that occurs *without* a paired X chromosome that is *not* defective. In the following, represent a defective X chromosome with lowercase x, so a child with the xY or Yx pair of chromosomes will have the disease and a child with XX or XY or YX or xX or Xx will not have the disease. Each parent contributes one of the chromosomes to the child.

a. If a father has the defective x chromosome and the mother has good XX chromosomes, what is the probability that a son will inherit the disease?

b. If a father has the defective x chromosome and the mother has good XX chromosomes, what is the probability that a daughter will inherit the disease?

c. If a mother has one defective x chromosome and one good X chromosome and the father has good XY chromosomes, what is the probability that a son will inherit the disease?

d. If a mother has one defective x chromosome and one good X chromosome and the father has good XY chromosomes, what is the probability that a daughter will inherit the disease?

Probability from a Sample Space. *In Exercises 29–32, use the given sample space or construct the required sample space to find the indicated probability.*

29. Three Children Use this sample space listing the eight simple events that are possible when a couple has three children (as in Example 2 on page 146): {bbb, bbg, bgb, bgg, gbb, gbg, ggb, ggg}. Assume that boys and girls are equally likely, so that the eight simple events are equally likely. Find the probability that when a couple has three children, there is exactly one girl.

30. Three Children Using the same sample space and assumption from Exercise 29, find the probability that when a couple has three children, there are exactly two girls.

31. Four Children Exercise 29 lists the sample space for a couple having three children. After identifying the sample space for a couple having four children, find the probability of getting three girls and one boy (in any order).

32. Four Children Using the same sample space and assumption from Exercise 31, find the probability that when a couple has four children, all four are of the same gender.

Using Probability for Signifiance. *In Exercises 33–40, use the given probability value to determine whether the sample results are* **significant.**

33. Voting The County Clerk in Essex, New Jersey, was supposed to use randomness to assign the order in which candidates' names appeared on voting ballots. Among 41 different ballots, Democratic candidate names were placed on the first line 40 times. The probability of a result that high is 0.0000000000191. Assuming randomness was used, is the result of 40 Democratic candidate names being placed on the first line significantly low, significantly high, or neither?

34. Voting Repeat the preceding Exercise 33 after replacing 40 Democrats being placed on the first line of voting ballots with 26 Democrats being placed on the first line. The probability of getting a result as high as 26 is 0.058638.

35. Voting Repeat Exercise 33 after replacing 40 Democrats being placed on the first line of voting ballots with 14 Democrats being placed on the first line. The probability of getting a result as low as 14 is 0.029792.

36. Voting Repeat Exercise 33 after replacing 40 Democrats being placed on the first line of voting ballots with 27 Democrats being placed on the first line. The probability of getting a result as high as 27 is 0.029792.

37. Predicting Gender A study addressed the issue of whether pregnant women can correctly predict the gender of their baby. Among 104 pregnant women, 57 correctly predicted the gender of their baby (based on data from "Are Women Carrying 'Basketballs' . . . ," by Perry, DiPietro, Constigan, *Birth*, Vol. 26, No. 3). If pregnant women have no such ability, there is a 0.189 probability of getting 57 or more correct predictions in 104 births. Is 57 correct predictions significantly low, significantly high, or neither? What do you conclude about the ability of pregnant women to correctly predict the gender of their baby?

38. Getting a Job In an SHRM survey of 410 human resource workers, it was found that 148 of these workers have turned down job applicants because of information they found on social media.

A job recruiter claims that less than 50% of human resource professionals have turned down job applicants because of information found on social media. If the true rate is 50%, there is a 0.00000000978 probability of getting 148 or fewer human resource professionals who turn down job applicants because of information found on social media. If the true rate is 50%, is the result of 148 significantly low? What does that suggest about the claim that the rate is less than 50%?

39. Online Friends In a Pew Research Center survey of 1060 teens aged 13 to 17, it was found that 604 (or 57.0%) of those respondents have made new friends online. If the true rate is 50%, there is a probability of 0.00000306 of getting 604 or more respondents who have made new friends online. Is 604 significantly low, significantly high, or neither? What does the result suggest about the true rate being 50%?

40. Selfie Deaths Based on Priceonomics data describing 49 deaths while taking selfies, it was found that 37 of those deaths were males. Assuming that males and females are equally likely to have selfie deaths, there is a 0.000235 probability of getting 37 or more males. Is the result of 37 males significantly low, significantly high, or neither? Does the result suggest that male selfie deaths are more likely than female selfie deaths?

4-1 Beyond the Basics

Odds. *In Exercises 41–44, answer the given questions that involve odds.*

41. Florida Pick 3 In the Florida Pick 3 lottery, you can place a "straight" bet of $1 by selecting the exact order of three digits between 0 and 9 inclusive (with repetition allowed), so the probability of winning is 1/1000. If the same three numbers are drawn in the same order, you collect $500, so your net profit is $499.

a. Find the actual odds against winning.

b. Find the payoff odds.

c. Is there much of a difference between the actual odds against winning and the payoff odds?

42. Finding Odds in Roulette A roulette wheel has 38 slots. One slot is 0, another is 00, and the others are numbered 1 through 36, respectively. You place a bet that the outcome is an odd number.

a. What is your probability of winning?

b. What are the actual odds against winning?

c. When you bet that the outcome is an odd number, the payoff odds are 1:1. How much profit do you make if you bet $18 and win?

d. How much profit would you make on the $18 bet if you could somehow convince the casino to change its payoff odds so that they are the same as the actual odds against winning? (*Recommendation:* Don't actually try to convince any casino of this; their sense of humor is remarkably absent when it comes to things of this sort.)

43. Kentucky Derby Odds When the horse Justify won the 144th Kentucky Derby, a $2 bet on a Justify win resulted in a winning ticket worth $7.80.

a. How much net profit was made from a $2 win bet on Justify?

b. What were the payoff odds against a Justify win?

c. Based on preliminary wagering before the race, bettors collectively believed that Justify had a 0.1935 probability of winning. Assuming that 0.1935 was the true probability of a Justify victory, what were the actual odds against his winning?

d. If the payoff odds were the actual odds found in part (c), what would be the worth of a $2 win ticket after the Justify win?

44. Relative Risk and Odds Ratio In a clinical trial of 2103 subjects treated with Nasonex, 26 reported headaches. In a control group of 1671 subjects given a placebo, 22 reported headaches. Denoting the proportion of headaches in the treatment group by p_t and denoting the proportion of headaches in the control (placebo) group by p_c, the *relative risk* is p_t/p_c. The relative risk is a measure of the strength of the effect of the Nasonex treatment. Another such measure is the *odds ratio*, which is the ratio of the odds in favor of a headache for the treatment group to the odds in favor of a headache for the control (placebo) group, found by evaluating the following:

$$\frac{p_t/(1 - p_t)}{p_c/(1 - p_c)}$$

The relative risk and odds ratios are commonly used in medicine and epidemiological studies. Find the relative risk and odds ratio for the headache data. What do the results suggest about the risk of a headache from the Nasonex treatment?

4-2 Addition Rule and Multiplication Rule

Key Concepts In this section we present the *addition rule* as a tool for finding $P(A \text{ or } B)$, which is the probability that either event A occurs or event B occurs (or they both occur) as the single outcome of a procedure. To find $P(A \text{ or } B)$, we begin by adding the number of ways that A can occur and the number of ways that B can occur, but add without double counting. The word "or" in the addition rule is associated with the addition of probabilities.

This section also presents the basic *multiplication rule* used for finding $P(A \text{ and } B)$, which is the probability that event A occurs and event B occurs. If the outcome of event A somehow affects the probability of event B, it is important to adjust the probability of B to reflect the occurrence of event A. The rule for finding $P(A \text{ and } B)$ is called the *multiplication rule* because it involves the multiplication of the probability of event A and the probability of event B (where, if necessary, the probability of event B is adjusted because of the outcome of event A). The word "and" in the multiplication rule is associated with the multiplication of probabilities.

In Section 4-1 we considered only *simple* events, but in this section we consider *compound events*.

> **DEFINITION**
>
> A **compound event** is any event combining two or more simple events.

Addition Rule

Notation for Addition Rule

$P(A \text{ or } B) = P(\text{in a single trial, event } A \text{ occurs or event } B \text{ occurs or they both occur})$

The word "or" used in the preceding notation is the *inclusive or*, which means either one or the other or both. The formal addition rule is often presented as a formula, but blind use of formulas is not recommended. Instead, *understand* the spirit of the rule and use that understanding, as in the intuitive addition rule that follows.

INTUITIVE ADDITION RULE

To find $P(A \text{ or } B)$, add the number of ways event A can occur and the number of ways event B can occur, but *add in such a way that every outcome is counted only once*. $P(A \text{ or } B)$ is equal to that sum, divided by the total number of outcomes in the sample space.

FORMAL ADDITION RULE

$$P(A \text{ or } B) = P(A) + P(B) - P(A \text{ and } B)$$

where $P(A \text{ and } B)$ denotes the probability that A and B both occur at the same time as an outcome in a trial of a procedure.

One way to apply the addition rule is to add the probability of event A and the probability of event B and, if there is any overlap that causes double-counting, compensate for it by subtracting the probability of outcomes that are included twice. This approach is reflected in the above formal addition rule.

EXAMPLE 1   Drug Testing of Job Applicants

Refer to Table 4-1. If 1 subject is randomly selected from the 555 subjects given a drug test, find the probability of selecting a subject who had a positive test result *or* uses drugs.

TABLE 4-1 Results from Drug Tests of Job Applicants

	Positive Test Result (Test shows drug use.)	Negative Test Result (Test shows no drug use.)
Subject Uses Drugs	45 (True Positive)	5 (False Negative)
Subject Does Not Use Drugs	25 (False Positive)	480 (True Negative)

Numbers in red correspond to positive test results or subjects who use drugs, and the total of those numbers is 75.

SOLUTION

Refer to Table 4-1 and carefully count the number of subjects who tested positive (first column) or use drugs (first row), but be careful to count subjects exactly once, not twice. *When adding the frequencies from the first column and the first row, include the frequency of 45 only once.* In Table 4-1, there are $45 + 25 + 5 = 75$ subjects who had positive test results or use drugs. We get this result:

$$P(\text{positive test result or subject uses drugs}) = 75/555 = 0.135$$

YOUR TURN. Do Exercise 11 "Texting or Drinking."

Disjoint Events and the Addition Rule

The addition rule is simplified when the events are *disjoint*.

DEFINITION

Events A and B are **disjoint** (or **mutually exclusive**) if they cannot occur at the same time. (That is, disjoint events do not overlap.)

EXAMPLE 2   Disjoint Events

Disjoint events:

Event A—Randomly selecting someone for a clinical trial who is a male

Event B—Randomly selecting someone for a clinical trial who is a female

(The selected person *cannot* be both.)

Events that are *not* disjoint:

Event A—Randomly selecting someone taking a statistics course

Event B—Randomly selecting someone who is a female

(The selected person *can* be both.)

▶ **YOUR TURN.** Do Exercise 12 "Texting or Not Drinking."

Whenever A and B are disjoint, $P(A \text{ and } B)$ becomes zero in the formal addition rule, so for disjoint events A and B we have $P(A \text{ or } B) = P(A) + P(B)$. But again, instead of blind use of a formula, it is better to *understand* and use the intuitive addition rule.

Here is a summary of the key points of the addition rule:

1. **To find $P(A \text{ or } B)$, first associate the word *or* with addition.**

2. **To find the value of $P(A \text{ or } B)$, add the number of ways A can occur and the number of ways B can occur, but be careful to add without double counting.**

Complementary Events and the Addition Rule

In Section 4-1 we used $\overline{A}$ to indicate that event A does not occur. Common sense dictates this principle: We are certain (with probability 1) that either an event A occurs *or* it does not occur, so it follows that $P(A \text{ or } \overline{A}) = 1$. Because events A and $\overline{A}$ must be disjoint, we can use the addition rule to express this principle as follows:

$$P(A \text{ or } \overline{A}) = P(A) + P(\overline{A}) = 1$$

This result of the addition rule leads to the following three expressions that are "equivalent" in the sense that they are just different forms of the same principle.

RULE OF COMPLEMENTARY EVENTS

$$P(A) + P(\overline{A}) = 1 \qquad P(\overline{A}) = 1 - P(A) \qquad P(A) = 1 - P(\overline{A})$$

EXAMPLE 3   Smartphone Home

Based on survey results from the Consumer Technology Association, the probability of randomly selecting a household in the United States and getting one with a smartphone is 0.87, so $P(\text{smartphone}) = 0.87$. If a household is randomly selected, find the probability of getting one that does *not* have a smartphone.

SOLUTION

Using the rule of complementary events, we get

$P(\text{household } not \text{ having a smartphone}) = 1 - P(\text{household with a smartphone})$
$$= 1 - 0.87 = 0.13$$

The probability of randomly selecting a household *not* having a smartphone is 0.13.

 **YOUR TURN.** Do Exercise 7 "Laundry Symbols."

Multiplication Rule

Notation for Multiplication Rule

We begin with basic notation followed by the multiplication rule. We strongly suggest using the *intuitive* multiplication rule, because it is based on understanding instead of blind use of a formula.

Notation

$P(A \text{ and } B) = P(\text{event } A \text{ occurs in a first trial and event } B \text{ occurs in a second trial})$

$P(B|A)$ represents the probability of event B occurring after it is assumed that event A has already occurred. (Interpret $B|A$ as "event B occurs after event A has already occurred.")

CAUTION The notation $P(A \text{ and } B)$ has two meanings, depending on its context. For the multiplication rule, $P(A \text{ and } B)$ denotes that event A occurs in one trial and event B occurs in another trial; for the addition rule we use $P(A \text{ and } B)$ to denote that events A and B both occur in the same trial.

INTUITIVE MULTIPLICATION RULE

To find the probability that event A occurs in one trial and event B occurs in another trial, multiply the probability of event A by the probability of event B, but *be sure that the probability of event B is found by assuming that event A has already occurred.*

FORMAL MULTIPLICATION RULE

$$P(A \text{ and } B) = P(A) \cdot P(B \mid A)$$

Independence and the Multiplication Rule

When applying the multiplication rule and considering whether the probability of event B must be adjusted to account for the previous occurrence of event A, we are focusing on whether events A and B are *independent*.

DEFINITIONS

Two events A and B are **independent** if the occurrence of one does not affect the *probability* of the occurrence of the other. (Several events are independent if the occurrence of any does not affect the probabilities of the occurrence of the others.) If A and B are not independent, they are said to be **dependent.**

CAUTION Don't think that *dependence* of two events means that one is the direct *cause* of the other. Having a working light in your kitchen and having a working light in your bedroom are dependent events because they share the same power source. One of the lights may stop working for many reasons, but if one light is out, there is a higher probability that the other light will be out (because of the common power source).

EXAMPLE 4   **Drug Screening and the Basic Multiplication Rule**

Let's use only the 50 test results from the subjects who use drugs (from Table 4-1), as shown below:

Positive Test Results:	45
Negative Test Results:	5
Total:	50

a. If 2 of these 50 subjects who use drugs are randomly selected *with replacement*, find the probability that the first selected person had a positive test result and the second selected person had a negative test result.

b. Repeat part (a) by assuming that the two subjects are selected *without replacement*.

SOLUTION

a. *With Replacement:* First selection (with 45 positive results among 50 total results):

$$P(\text{positive test result}) = \frac{45}{50}$$

Second selection (with 5 negative test results among the same 50 total results):

$$P(\text{negative test result}) = \frac{5}{50}$$

We now apply the multiplication rule as follows:

$$P(\text{1st selection is positive and 2nd is negative}) = \frac{45}{50} \cdot \frac{5}{50} = 0.0900$$

b. *Without Replacement:* Without replacement of the first subject, the calculations are the same as in part (a), except that the second probability must be adjusted to reflect the fact that the first selection was positive and is not available for the second selection. After the first positive result is selected, we have 49 test results remaining, and 5 of them are negative. The second probability is therefore 5/49, as shown below:

$$P(\text{1st selection is positive and 2nd is negative}) = \frac{45}{50} \cdot \frac{5}{49} = 0.0918$$

YOUR TURN. Do Exercise 13 "Drinking and Driving."

The key point of part (b) in Example 4 is this: *We must adjust the probability of the second event to reflect the outcome of the first event.* Because selection of the second subject is made *without* replacement of the first subject, the second probability must take into account the fact that the first selection removed a subject who tested positive, so only 49 subjects are available for the second selection, and 5 of them had a negative test result. Part (a) of Example 4 involved sampling with replacement, so the events are independent; part (b) of Example 4 involved sampling without replacement, so the events are dependent. See the following.

Sampling

In the wonderful world of statistics, sampling methods are critically important, and the following relationships hold:

- Sampling *with replacement:* Selections are *independent* events.
- Sampling *without replacement:* Selections are *dependent* events.

Exception: Treating Dependent Events as Independent

Some cumbersome calculations can be greatly simplified by using the common practice of treating events as independent when *small samples* are drawn without replacement from *large populations.* (In such cases, it is rare to select the same item twice.) Here is a common guideline routinely used with applications such as analyses of survey results:

TREATING DEPENDENT EVENTS AS INDEPENDENT:

5% GUIDELINE FOR CUMBERSOME CALCULATIONS

When sampling without replacement and the sample size is no more than 5% of the size of the population, treat the selections as being *independent* (even though they are actually dependent).

Example 5 illustrates use of the above "5% guideline for cumbersome calculations" and it also illustrates that the basic multiplication rule extends easily to three or more events.

EXAMPLE 5 **Drug Screening and the 5% Guideline for Cumbersome Calculations**

In a recent year, there were 130,639,273 full-time employees in the United States. If one of those employees is randomly selected and tested for illegal drug use, there is a 0.042 probability that the test will yield a positive result, indicating that the employee is using illegal drugs (based on data from Quest Diagnostics). Assume that three employees are randomly selected *without replacement* from the 130,639,273 employees in the United States. Find the probability that the three selected employees all test positive for drug use.

SOLUTION

Because the three employees are randomly selected without replacement, the three events are dependent, but here we can treat them as being independent by applying

continued

continued

Independent Jet Engines

Soon after departing from Miami, Eastern Airlines Flight 855 had one engine shut down because of a low oil pressure warning light. As the L-1011 jet turned to Miami for landing, the low pressure warning lights for the other two engines also flashed. Then an engine failed, followed by the failure of the last working engine. The jet descended without power from 13,000 ft to 4000 ft, when the crew was able to restart one engine, and the 172 people on board landed safely. With independent jet engines, the probability of all three failing is only 0.0001^3, or about one chance in a trillion. The FAA found that the same mechanic who replaced the oil in all three engines failed to replace the oil plug sealing rings. The use of a single mechanic caused the operation of the engines to become dependent, a situation corrected by requiring that the engines be serviced by different mechanics.

Redundancy

Reliability of systems can be greatly improved with redundancy of critical components. Race cars in the NASCAR Winston Cup series have two ignition systems so that if one fails, the other will keep the car running. Airplanes have two independent electrical systems, and aircraft used for instrument flight typically have two separate radios. The following is from a *Popular Science* article about stealth aircraft: "One plane built largely of carbon fiber was the Lear Fan 2100 which had to carry two radar transponders. That's because if a single transponder failed, the plane was nearly invisible to radar." Such redundancy is an application of the multiplication rule in probability theory. If one component has a 0.001 probability of failure, the probability of two independent components both failing is only 0.000001.

the 5% guideline for cumbersome calculations. The sample size of 3 is clearly no more than 5% of the population size of 130,639,273. We get

$$P(\text{all 3 employees test positive}) = P(\text{first tests positive } and \text{ second tests positive}$$
$$and \text{ third tests positive})$$

$$= P(\text{first tests positive}) \cdot P(\text{second tests positive}) \cdot P(\text{third tests positive})$$

$$= (0.042)(0.042)(0.042) = 0.0000741$$

There is a 0.0000741 probability that all three selected employees test positive.

YOUR TURN. Do Exercise 29 "Medical Helicopters."

In Example 5, if we treat the events as dependent without using the 5% guideline, we get the following cumbersome calculation that begins with 130,639,273 employees, with 4.2% of them (or 5,486,849) testing positive:

$$\left(\frac{5{,}486{,}849}{130{,}639{,}273}\right)\left(\frac{5{,}486{,}848}{130{,}639{,}272}\right)\left(\frac{5{,}486{,}847}{130{,}639{,}271}\right) = 0.0000740879$$

$$= 0.0000741 \,(\text{rounded})$$

Just imagine randomly selecting 1000 employees instead of just 3, as is commonly done in typical polls. Extending the above calculation to include 1000 factors instead of 3 factors: I mean, come on!

CAUTION In any probability calculation, it is extremely important to carefully identify the event being considered. See Example 6, where parts (a) and (b) might seem quite similar but their solutions are very different.

EXAMPLE 6 Birthdays

When two different people are randomly selected from those in your class or friend group, find the indicated probability by assuming that birthdays occur on the days of the week with equal frequencies.

    a. Find the probability that the two people are born on the *same day of the week*.

    b. Find the probability that the two people are both born on *Monday*.

SOLUTION

    a. Because no particular day of the week is specified, the first person can be born on any one of the seven weekdays. The probability that the second person is born on the same day as the first person is 1/7. The probability that two people are born on the same day of the week is therefore 1/7.

    b. The probability that the first person is born on Monday is 1/7 and the probability that the second person is also born on Monday is 1/7. Because the two events are independent, the probability that both people are born on Monday is

$$\frac{1}{7} \cdot \frac{1}{7} = \frac{1}{49}$$

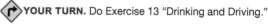 **YOUR TURN.** Do Exercise 13 "Drinking and Driving."

WATCH YOUR LANGUAGE! Example 6 illustrates that finding correct or relevant probability values often requires greater language skills than computational skills. In Example 6, what exactly do we mean by "same day of the week"? See how parts (a) and (b) in Example 6 are very different.

(CP) **EXAMPLE 7** Using Probability for *Significance*

Let's now revisit the Chapter Problem and apply what we have learned about independence and the multiplication rule. The Chapter Problem describes how the XSORT method of gender selection was developed to help couples have baby girls when they have children. If a test of the XSORT method of gender selection involves 20 couples who give birth to 20 babies, what is the probability that the 20 babies are all girls? Does the result of 20 girls suggest that the XSORT technique is effective?

SOLUTION

We assume that the XSORT method has no effect so that $P(\text{girl}) = 1/2$. Because the 20 births are all independent, we can apply the multiplication rule as follows:

$$P(20 \text{ girls}) = P(\text{1st baby is a girl}) \cdot P(\text{2nd baby is a girl})$$

$$\cdot \ldots \cdot P(\text{20th baby is a girl})$$

$$= \frac{1}{2} \cdot \frac{1}{2} \cdot \frac{1}{2} \cdot \ldots \cdot \frac{1}{2} \ (20 \text{ times})$$

$$= \left(\frac{1}{2}\right)^{20} = 0.000000954$$

Notice that this result of 0.000000954 matches the probability given for the Test A Result (probability of 20 girls born by chance) in Figure 4-1 on page 145. We love it when a plan comes together!

Now we must make a decision: Is the result of 20 girls in 20 births likely to occur with random chance, or does it appear that the XSORT method is effective in enabling couples to have baby girls? Because the probability of getting 20 girls by chance (with no effect from the XSORT method) is only 0.000000954, it makes sense to eliminate chance as a viable explanation. The result of 20 girls in 20 births is a *significantly high* number of girls (probability 0.05 or less), so it does appear that the XSORT method is effective.

YOUR TURN. Do Exercise 4 "Probability for Significance."

Redundancy: Important Application of Multiplication Rule

The principle of *redundancy* is used to increase the reliability of many systems. Our eyes have passive redundancy in the sense that if one of them fails, we continue to see. An important finding of modern biology is that genes in an organism can often work in place of each other. Engineers often design redundant components so that the whole system will not fail because of the failure of a single component, as in the following example.

To Win, Bet Boldly

The *New York Times* published an article by Andrew Pollack in which he reported lower than expected earnings for the Mirage casino in Las Vegas. He wrote that "winnings for Mirage can be particularly volatile, because it caters to high rollers, gamblers who might bet $100,000 or more on a hand of cards. The law of averages does not work as consistently for a few large bets as it does for thousands of smaller ones. . ." This reflects the most fundamental principle of gambling: To win, place one big bet instead of many small bets! With the right game, such as craps, you have just under a 50% chance of doubling your money if you place one big bet. With many small bets, your chance of doubling your money drops substantially.

Go Figure

13: Current record for the number of folds of a sheet of paper; very thin paper was used and the sheet was almost 2 miles long. If you could fold a sheet of paper 42 times, it would have a height that would reach to the moon. If you could fold a sheet of paper 103 times, it would have a height roughly equal to the diameter of the observable universe.

EXAMPLE 8   Seagate Hard Drive: *Redundancy* for Better Reliability

The Seagate hard drive model ST4000DM000 has a failure rate of 2.89% in a year (based on data from Backblaze, Inc.).

a. If your computer has only the Seagate hard drive model ST4000DM000, what is the probability that it will work for a year?

b. If your computer has two Seagate model ST4000DM000 hard drives, what is the probability at least one of them will work for a year?

SOLUTION

a. The failure rate of 2.89% converts to a probability of 0.0289 for failure, so the probability that the hard drive will not fail during the year is found as follows:

$$P(\text{hard drive } does\ not\ fail) = 1 - P(\text{failure}) = 1 - 0.0289 = 0.971$$

b. With two independent hard drives, the computer will work if both hard drives don't fail. That is, the computer will work if at least one of the hard drive works.

$$P(\text{at least one hard drive } does\ not\ fail) = 1 - P(\text{both hard drives fail})$$
$$= 1 - (0.0289)(0.0289) = 0.999$$

INTERPRETATION

With only one hard drive, there is a 0.0289 probability of failure, but with two independent hard drives, there is only a 0.001 probability that the computer will not work with at least one operating hard drive. By using two hard drives instead of just one, the risk of failure decreased by a factor of 1/28.9. By using two independent hard drives, the risk of a serious failure is dramatically decreased and reliability of the computer is dramatically increased. Redundancy at work!

 YOUR TURN. Do Exercise 25 "Redundancy in Computer Hard Drives."

Rationale for the Multiplication Rule

To see the reasoning that underlies the multiplication rule, consider a pop quiz consisting of these two questions:

1. True or false: A pound of feathers is heavier than a pound of gold.

2. Who said, "By a small sample, we may judge of the whole piece"? (a) Judge Judy; (b) Judge Dredd; (c) Miguel de Cervantes; (d) George Gallup; (e) Gandhi

The answers are T (true) and c. (The first answer is true, because weights of feathers are in avoirdupois units where a pound is 453.59 g, but weights of gold and other precious metals are in troy units where a pound is 373.24 g. The second answer is from *Don Quixote* by Cervantes.)

Here is the sample space for the different possible answers:

Ta   Tb   Tc   Td   Te   Fa   Fb   Fc   Fd   Fe

If both answers are random guesses, then the above 10 possible outcomes are equally likely, so

$$P(\text{both correct}) = P(T \text{ and } c) = \frac{1}{10} = 0.1$$

With $P(T \text{ and } c) = 1/10$, $P(T) = 1/2$, and $P(c) = 1/5$, we see that

$$\frac{1}{10} = \frac{1}{2} \cdot \frac{1}{5}$$

A *tree diagram* is a graph of the possible outcomes of a procedure, as in Figure 4-4. Figure 4-4 shows that if both answers are random guesses, all 10 branches are equally likely and the probability of getting the correct pair (T,c) is 1/10. For each response to the first question, there are 5 responses to the second. *The total number of outcomes is 5 taken 2 times, or 10.* The tree diagram in Figure 4-4 therefore provides a visual illustration for using multiplication.

Summary of Addition Rule and Multiplication Rule

Addition Rule for *P(A or B)*: The word *or* suggests addition, and when adding $P(A)$ and $P(B)$, we must add in such a way that every outcome is counted only once.

Multiplication Rule for *P(A and B)*: The word *and* for two trials suggests multiplication, and when multiplying $P(A)$ and $P(B)$, we must be sure that the probability of event B takes into account the previous occurrence of event A.

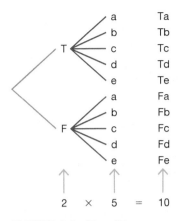

FIGURE 4-4 Tree Diagram of Test Answers

4-2 Basic Skills and Concepts

Statistical Literacy and Critical Thinking

1. Notation When randomly selecting a new smartphone, D denotes the event that it has a manufacturing defect. What do $P(D)$ and $P(\overline{D})$ represent?

2. Notation When randomly selecting adults, let M denote the event of randomly selecting a male and let B denote the event of randomly selecting someone with blue eyes. What does $P(M|B)$ represent? Is $P(M|B)$ the same as $P(B|M)$?

3. Sample for a Poll There are 30,488,983 Californians aged 18 or older. If The Gallup organization randomly selects 1068 adults without replacement, are the selections independent or dependent? If the selections are dependent, can they be treated as being independent for the purposes of calculations?

4. Probability for Significance The drug Lipitor (atorvastatin) is used to treat high cholesterol. In a clinical trial of Lipitor, 47 of 863 treated subjects experienced headaches (based on data from Pfizer). A claim is made that fewer than 10% of subjects treated with Lipitor experience headaches. If the actual rate of headaches is 10%, there is a probability of 0.000000987 of getting a result of 47 or lower. Does 47 appear to be significantly low? Does it appear that the claim is supported by the data?

Finding Complements. *In Exercises 5–8, find the indicated complements.*

5. Women in Movies In a recent year, speaking characters in movies were 68.2% male. What is the probability of randomly selecting a character with a speaking part and getting a female? What *should* be the value of that probability?

6. Smartwatch Based on a survey by Consumer Technology Association, smartwatches are used in 18% of U.S. households. Find the probability that a randomly selected U.S. household has no smartwatches.

7. Laundry Symbols Based on a New Generation of Stains survey, 13% of U.S. adults know that the care-instruction symbol Δ on clothing means that any bleach can be used. Find the probability of randomly selecting an adult in the U.S. who does not know that.

8. Sobriety Checkpoint When the author observed a sobriety checkpoint conducted by the Dutchess County Sheriff Department, he saw that 676 drivers were screened and 6 were arrested for driving while intoxicated. Based on those results, we can estimate that $P(I) = 0.00888$, where I denotes the event of screening a driver and getting someone who is intoxicated. What does $P(\overline{I})$ denote, and what is its value?

In Exercises 9–20, use the data in the following table, which lists survey results from high school drivers at least 16 years of age (based on data from "Texting While Driving and Other Risky Motor Vehicle Behaviors Among U.S. High School Students," by O'Malley, Shults, and Eaton, **Pediatrics,** *Vol. 131, No. 6). Assume that subjects are randomly selected from those included in the table.* **Hint:** *Be very careful to read the question correctly.*

	Drove When Drinking Alcohol?	
	Yes	No
Texted While Driving	731	3054
No Texting While Driving	156	4564

9. Drinking and Driving If one of the high school drivers is randomly selected, find the probability of getting one who drove when drinking alcohol.

10. Texting and Driving If one of the high school drivers is randomly selected, find the probability of getting one who did *not* text while driving.

11. Texting or Drinking If one of the high school drivers is randomly selected, find the probability of getting one who texted while driving or drove when drinking alcohol.

12. Texting or Not Drinking If one of the high school drivers is randomly selected, find the probability of getting one who did not text while driving or drove when drinking alcohol. Are those two events disjoint?

13. Drinking and Driving If two of the high school drivers are randomly selected, find the probability that they both drove when drinking alcohol.

a. Assume that the selections are made with replacement. Are the events independent?

b. Assume that the selections are made without replacement. Are the events independent?

c. Are the preceding results the same?

14. Texting While Driving If two of the high school drivers are randomly selected, find the probability that they both texted while driving.

a. Assume that the selections are made with replacement. Are the events independent?

b. Assume that the selections are made without replacement. Are the events independent?

c. Are the preceding results the same?

15. Texting and Alcohol If two of the high school drivers are randomly selected from the 887 subjects who drove when drinking, find the probability that neither of them texted while driving.

a. Assume that the selections are made with replacement. Are the events independent?

b. Assume that the selections are made without replacement. Are the events independent?

16. Texting and Alcohol If three of the high school drivers are randomly selected from the 4720 subjects who did not text while driving, find the probability that all three drove when drinking.

a. Assume that the selections are made with replacement. Are the events independent?

b. Assume that the selections are made without replacement. Are the events independent?

17. Texting and Alcohol If *one* of the high school drivers is randomly selected, find the probability that the selected driver texted while driving and drove when drinking alcohol.

18. Texting and Alcohol If *one* of the high school drivers is randomly selected, find the probability that the selected driver did not text while driving and did not drive when drinking.

19. Texting and Alcohol If four *different* high school drivers are randomly selected, find the probability that they all drove when drinking alcohol.

20. Texting and Alcohol If four *different* high school drivers are randomly selected, find the probability that they all texted while driving.

In Exercises 21–24, use these results from the "1-Panel-THC" test for marijuana use, which is provided by the company Drug Test Success: Among 143 subjects with positive test results, there are 24 false positive (incorrect) results; among 157 negative results, there are 3 false negative (incorrect) results. (Hint: Construct a table similar to Table 4-1 on page 159.)

21. Testing for Marijuana Use

a. How many subjects are included in the study?

b. How many of the subjects had a true negative result?

c. What is the probability that a randomly selected subject had a true negative result?

22. Testing for Marijuana Use If one of the test subjects is randomly selected, find the probability that the subject tested negative or used marijuana.

23. Testing for Marijuana Use If one of the test subjects is randomly selected, find the probability that the subject tested positive or did not use marijuana.

24. Testing for Marijuana Use If one of the test subjects is randomly selected, find the probability that the subject did not use marijuana. Do you think that the result reflects the general population rate of subjects who do not use marijuana?

Redundancy. *Exercises 25 and 26 involve redundancy.*

25. Redundancy in Computer Hard Drives It is generally recognized that it is wise to backup computer data. Assume that the following refer to use of Western Digital model WD60EFRX hard drives, which have an annual failure rate of 3.66% (based on data from Backblaze, Inc.).

a. If you store all of your computer data on a single hard drive, what is the probability that the drive will fail during a year?

b. If all of your computer data are stored on a hard drive with a copy stored on a second hard disk drive, what is the probability that both drives will fail during a year?

c. If copies of all of your computer data are stored on three independent hard drives, what is the probability that all three will fail during a year?

d. Describe the improved reliability that is gained with backup drives.

26. Alarm Clock Life Hack Each of us must sometimes wake up early for something really important, such as a final exam, job interview, or an early flight. (Professional golfer Jim Furyk was disqualified from a tournament when his cellphone lost power and he overslept.) Assume that a battery-powered alarm clock has a 0.005 probability of failure, a smartphone alarm clock has a 0.052 probability of failure, and an electric alarm clock has a 0.001 probability of failure.

a. What is the probability that your single battery-powered alarm clock works successfully when you need it?

b. If you use a battery-powered alarm clock and a smartphone alarm clock, what is the probability that they both fail? What is the probability that both of them do not fail?

c. If you use a battery-powered alarm clock and a smartphone alarm clock and an electric alarm clock, what is the probability that they all fail? What is the probability that they don't all fail? Express both of these answers using eight decimal places.

d. What configuration gives you the best chance to wake up for something really important?

Acceptance Sampling.   *With one method of a procedure called acceptance sampling, a sample of items is randomly selected without replacement and the entire batch is accepted if every item in the sample is found to be okay. Exercises 27 and 28 involve acceptance sampling.*

27. Defective Pacemakers Among 8834 cases of heart pacemaker malfunctions, 504 were found to be caused by firmware, which is software programmed into the device (based on data from "Pacemaker and ICD Generator Malfunctions," by Maisel et al., *Journal of the American Medical Association*, Vol. 295, No. 16). If the firmware is tested in three *different* pacemakers randomly selected from this batch of 8834 and the entire batch is accepted if there are no failures, what is the probability that the firmware in the entire batch will be accepted? Is this procedure likely to result in the entire batch being accepted?

28. Acceptance Sampling The Telektronics Company manufactured a batch of 400 backup power supply units for computers, and 8 of them are defective. If three of these units are randomly selected for testing (without replacement), what is the probability that the entire batch will be accepted?

In Exercises 29 and 30, find the probabilities and indicate when the "5% guideline for cumbersome calculations" is used.

29. Medical Helicopters In a study of helicopter usage and patient survival, results were obtained from 47,637 patients transported by helicopter and 111,874 patients transported by ground (based on data from "Association Between Helicopter vs Ground Emergency Medical Services and Survival for Adults with Major Trauma," by Galvagno et al., *Journal of the American Medical Association*, Vol. 307, No. 15).

a. If 1 of the 159,511 patients in the study is randomly selected, what is the probability that the subject was transported by helicopter?

b. If 5 of the subjects in the study are randomly selected without replacement, what is the probability that all of them were transported by helicopter?

30. Medical Helicopters In the same study cited in the preceding exercise, among the 47,637 patients transported by helicopter, 188 of them left the treatment center against medical advice, and the other 47,449 did not leave against medical advice. If 40 of the subjects transported by helicopter are randomly selected without replacement, what is the probability that none of them left the treatment center against medical advice?

4-2   Beyond the Basics

31. Surge Protectors Refer to the accompanying figure showing surge protectors *p* and *q* used to protect an expensive television. If there is a surge in the voltage, the surge protector reduces it to a safe level. Assume that each surge protector has a 0.985 probability of working correctly when a voltage surge occurs.

a. If the two surge protectors are arranged in series, what is the probability that a voltage surge will not damage the television? (Do not round the answer.)

b. If the two surge protectors are arranged in parallel, what is the probability that a voltage surge will not damage the television? (Do not round the answer.)

c. Which arrangement should be used for better protection?

Series configuration   Parallel configuration

32. Same Birthdays If 25 people are randomly selected, find the probability that no 2 of them have the same birthday. Ignore leap years.

33. Exclusive Or The *exclusive or* means either one or the other event occurs, but not both.

a. For the formal addition rule, rewrite the formula for $P(A \text{ or } B)$ assuming that the addition rule uses the *exclusive or* instead of the *inclusive or.*

b. Repeat Exercise 11 "Texting or Drinking" using the *exclusive or* instead of the *inclusive or.*

34. Complements and the Addition Rule Refer to the table used for Exercises 9–20. Assume that one driver is randomly selected. Let A represent the event of getting a driver who texted while driving and let B represent the event of getting a driver who drove when drinking alcohol. Find $P(\overline{A \text{ or } B})$, find $P(\overline{A} \text{ or } \overline{B})$, and then compare the results. In general, does $P(\overline{A \text{ or } B}) = P(\overline{A} \text{ or } \overline{B})$?

4-3 Complements, Conditional Probability, and Bayes' Theorem

Key Concept In Part 1 of this section we extend the use of the multiplication rule to include the probability that among several trials, we get *at least one* of some specified event. In Part 2 we consider *conditional probability:* the probability of an event occurring when we have additional information that some other event has already occurred. In Part 3 we provide a brief introduction to Bayes' theorem.

PART 1 Complements: The Probability of "At Least One"

When finding the probability of some event occurring "at least once," we should understand the following:

- "At least one" = "one or more."
- *Complement* of "at least one" particular event = *no* occurrences of that event.

For example, not getting at least 1 girl in 10 births is the same as getting no girls, which is also the same as getting 10 boys.

Not getting at least 1 girl in 10 births = Getting no girls = Getting 10 boys

The following steps describe the details of finding the probability of getting at least one of some event:

Finding the probability of getting *at least one* of some event:

1. **Let A = getting *at least one* of some event.**
2. **Then $\overline{A}$ = getting *none* of the event being considered.**
3. **Find $P(\overline{A})$ = probability that event A does not occur.** (This is relatively easy using the multiplication rule.)
4. **Subtract the result from 1:**

$$P(\text{\textit{at least one} occurrence of event } A)$$

$$= 1 - P(\text{\textit{no} occurrences of event } A)$$

EXAMPLE 1 **Manufacturing**

A factory of the Global Manufacturing Company was manufacturing products with a defect rate of 15% (based on data from the *Harvard Business Review*). If a customer purchases 12 of the products, what is the probability of getting at least one that is defective?

SOLUTION

Step 1: Let A = at least 1 of the 12 products is defective.

Step 2: Identify the event that is the complement of A.

$$\overline{A} = \textit{not} \text{ getting at least 1 defect among the 12 items}$$

$$= \text{all 12 items are good with no defects}$$

Step 3: Find the probability of the complement by evaluating $P(\overline{A})$.

$$P(\overline{A}) = P(\text{all 12 items are good})$$

$$= 0.85 \cdot 0.85 \cdot 0.85 \cdot 0.85 \cdot 0.85 \cdot 0.85 \cdot 0.85 \cdot 0.85 \cdot 0.85 \cdot 0.85 \cdot 0.85 \cdot 0.85$$

$$= 0.85^{12} = 0.142$$

Step 4: Find $P(A)$ by evaluating $1 - P(\overline{A})$.

$$P(A) = 1 - P(\overline{A}) = 1 - 0.142 = 0.858$$

INTERPRETATION

For a group of 12 products, there is a 0.858 probability of getting at least 1 that is defective. As quality control goes, this is too high. The company needs to improve its manufacturing process so that the defect rate is lowered.

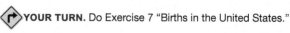 **YOUR TURN.** Do Exercise 7 "Births in the United States."

PART 2 **Conditional Probability**

We now consider the principle that the probability of an event is often affected by knowledge that some other event has occurred. According to *Golf Digest*, the probability of a golfer making a hole in one is $1/12{,}500$, but if you have the additional information that the golfer is a professional, the probability changes to $1/2500$. In general, a *conditional probability* of an event is used when the probability is calculated with some additional knowledge, such as the knowledge that some other event has occurred. (Conditional probabilities were used in Section 4-2 with situations in which samples were selected without replacement.)

> **DEFINITION**
>
> A **conditional probability** of an event is a probability obtained with the additional information that some other event occurred.

Notation

$P(B|A)$ denotes the conditional probability of event B occurring, given that event A has already occurred.

INTUITIVE APPROACH FOR FINDING $P(B|A)$

The conditional probability of B occurring given that A has occurred can be found by *assuming that event A occurred* and then calculating the probability that event B will occur, as illustrated in Example 2.

Convicted by Probability

A witness described a Los Angeles robber as a Caucasian woman with blond hair in a ponytail who escaped in a yellow car driven by an African-American male with a mustache and beard. Janet and Malcolm Collins fit this description, and they were convicted based on testimony that there is only about 1 chance in 12 million that any couple would have these characteristics. It was estimated that the probability of a yellow car is 1/10, and the other probabilities were estimated to be 1/10, 1/3, 1/10, and 1/1000. The convictions were later overturned when it was noted that no evidence was presented to support the estimated probabilities or the independence of the events. Also, because the couple was not randomly selected, a serious error was made in not considering the probability of *other* couples being in the same region with the same characteristics.

FORMAL APPROACH FOR FINDING $P(B|A)$

The probability $P(B|A)$ can be found by dividing the probability of events A and B both occurring by the probability of event A:

$$P(B|A) = \frac{P(A \text{ and } B)}{P(A)}$$

The preceding formula is a formal expression of conditional probability, but blind use of formulas is not recommended. Instead, we recommend the intuitive approach, as illustrated in Example 2.

EXAMPLE 2   **Pre-Employment Drug Screening**

Refer to Table 4-1 to find the following:

a. If 1 of the 555 test subjects is randomly selected, find the probability that the subject had a positive test result, given that the subject actually uses drugs. That is, find P(positive test result | subject uses drugs).

b. If 1 of the 555 test subjects is randomly selected, find the probability that the subject actually uses drugs, given that he or she had a positive test result. That is, find P(subject uses drugs | positive test result).

TABLE 4-1 Results from Drug Tests of Job Applicants

	Positive Test Result (Test shows drug use.)	Negative Test Result (Test shows no drug use.)
Subject Uses Drugs	45 (True Positive)	5 (False Negative)
Subject Does Not Use Drugs	25 (False Positive)	480 (True Negative)

SOLUTION

a. Intuitive Approach: We want P(positive test result | subject uses drugs), the probability of getting someone with a positive test result, *given that the selected subject uses drugs*. Here is the key point: If we assume that the selected subject actually uses drugs, we are dealing only with the 50 subjects in the first row of Table 4-1. Among those 50 subjects, 45 had positive test results, so we get this result:

$$P(\text{positive test result} \mid \text{subject uses drugs}) = \frac{45}{50} = 0.900$$

Formal Approach: The same result can be found by using the formula for $P(B|A)$ given with the formal approach. We use the following notation.

$$P(B|A) = P(\text{positive test result} \mid \text{subject uses drugs})$$

where B = positive test result and A = subject uses drugs.

In the following calculation, we use P(subject uses drugs and had a positive test result) = 45/555 and P(subject uses drugs) = 50/555 to get the following results:

$$P(B|A) = \frac{P(A \text{ and } B)}{P(A)}$$

continued

becomes

$$P(\text{positive test result} \mid \text{subject uses drugs})$$

$$= \frac{P(\text{subject uses drugs and had a positive test result})}{P(\text{subject uses drugs})}$$

$$= \frac{45/555}{50/555} = 0.900$$

By comparing the intuitive approach to the formal approach, it should be clear that the intuitive approach is much easier to use, and it is also less likely to result in errors. The intuitive approach is based on an *understanding* of conditional probability, instead of manipulation of a formula, and understanding is so much better.

b. Here we want P(subject uses drugs | positive test result). This is the probability that the selected subject uses drugs, *given that the subject had a positive test result.* If we assume that the subject had a positive test result, we are dealing with the 70 subjects in the first column of Table 4-1. Among those 70 subjects, 45 use drugs, so

$$P(\text{subject uses drugs} \mid \text{positive test result}) = \frac{45}{70} = 0.643$$

Again, the same result can be found by applying the formula for conditional probability, but we will leave that for those with a special fondness for manipulations with formulas.

INTERPRETATION

The first result of P(positive test result | subject uses drugs) = 0.900 indicates that a subject who uses drugs has a 0.900 probability of getting a positive test result. The second result of P(subject uses drugs | positive test result) = 0.643 indicates that for a subject who gets a positive test result, there is a 0.643 probability that this subject actually uses drugs. Note that P(positive test result | subject uses drugs) $\neq$ P(subject uses drugs | positive test result). This shows that in general, $P(B \mid A) \neq P(A \mid B)$. See "Confusion of the Inverse" that follows.

 **YOUR TURN.** Do Exercise 13 "Denomination Effect."

Confusion of the Inverse

Note that in Example 2, P(positive test result | subject uses drugs) $\neq$ P(subject uses drugs | positive test result). This example proves that in general, $P(B \mid A) \neq P(A \mid B)$. There could be individual cases where $P(A \mid B)$ and $P(B \mid A)$ are equal, but they are generally not equal.

DEFINITION

Confusion of the inverse is to incorrectly think that $P(B \mid A)$ and $P(A \mid B)$ are equal or to incorrectly use one value in place of the other.

EXAMPLE 3 Confusion of the Inverse

Consider these events:

D: It is dark outdoors.

M: It is midnight.

In the following, we conveniently ignore the Alaskan winter and other such anomalies.

$$P(D|M) = 1 \text{ (It is certain to be dark given that it is midnight.)}$$

$$P(M|D) = 0 \text{ (The probability that it is exactly midnight given}$$
$$\text{that it is dark is almost zero.)}$$

Here, $P(D|M) \neq P(M|D)$. Confusion of the inverse occurs when we incorrectly switch those probability values or think that they are equal.

PART 3 Bayes' Theorem

In this section we extend the discussion of conditional probability to include applications of *Bayes' theorem* (or *Bayes' rule*), which we use for revising a probability value based on additional information that is later obtained.

Let's consider a study showing that physicians often give very misleading information when they experience confusion of the inverse. They tended to confuse $P(\text{cancer}|\text{positive test result})$ with $P(\text{positive test result}|\text{cancer})$. (A positive test result indicates the patient has cancer; a negative test result indicates the patient is cancer-free.) About 95% of physicians estimated $P(\text{cancer}|\text{positive test result})$ to be about 10 times too high, with the result that patients were given diagnoses that were very misleading, and patients were unnecessarily distressed by the incorrect information. Let's take a closer look at this example, and let's hope that we can give physicians information in a better format that is easy to understand.

EXAMPLE 4 **Interpreting Medical Test Results**

Assume cancer has a 1% prevalence rate, meaning that 1% of the population has cancer. Denoting the event of having cancer by C, we have $P(C) = 0.01$ for a subject randomly selected from the population. This result is included with the following performance characteristics of the test for cancer (based on *Probabilistic Reasoning in Clinical Medicine* by David Eddy, Cambridge University Press).

- $P(C) = 0.01$ (There is a 1% prevalence rate of the cancer.)
- The false positive rate is 10%. That is, P(positive test result given that cancer is not present) $= 0.10$.
- The true positive rate is 80%. That is, P(positive test result given that cancer is present) $= 0.80$.

Find $P(C|\text{positive test result})$. That is, find the probability that a subject actually has cancer given that he or she has a positive test result.

SOLUTION

Using the given information, we can construct a hypothetical population with the above characteristics. We can find the entries in Table 4-2 on the next page, as follows.

- Assume that we have 1000 subjects. With a 1% prevalence rate, 10 of the subjects are expected to have cancer. The sum of the entries in the first row of values is therefore 10.
- The other 990 subjects do not have cancer. The sum of the entries in the second row of values is therefore 990.

continued

- Among the 990 subjects without cancer, 10% get positive test results, so 10% of the 990 cancer-free subjects in the second row get positive test results. See the entry of 99 in the second row.

- For the 990 subjects in the second row, 99 test positive, so the other 891 must test negative. See the entry of 891 in the second row.

- Among the 10 subjects with cancer in the first row, 80% of the test results are positive, so 80% of the 10 subjects in the first row test positive. See the entry of 8 in the first row.

- The other 2 subjects in the first row test negative. See the entry of 2 in the first row.

To find $P(C \mid \text{positive test result})$, see that the first column of values includes the positive test results. In that first column, the probability of randomly selecting a subject with cancer is 8/107 or 0.0748, so $P(C \mid \text{positive test result}) = 0.0748$.

INTERPRETATION

For the data given in this example, a randomly selected subject has a 1% chance of cancer, but for a randomly selected subject given a test with a positive result, the chance of cancer increases to 7.48%. Based on the data given in this example, a positive test result should not be devastating news, because there is still a good chance that the test is wrong.

 YOUR TURN. Do Exercise 19 "Positive Predictive Value."

TABLE 4-2 Test Results

	Positive Test Result (Test shows cancer.)	Negative Test Result (Test shows no cancer.)	Total
Cancer	8 (True Positive)	2 (False Negative)	10
No Cancer	99 (False Positive)	891 (True Negative)	990

The solution in Example 4 is not very difficult. Another approach is to compute the probability using this formula commonly given with Bayes' theorem:

$$P(A \mid B) = \frac{P(A) \cdot P(B \mid A)}{[P(A) \cdot P(B \mid A)] + [P(\overline{A}) \cdot P(B \mid \overline{A})]}$$

If we replace A with C and replace B with "positive," we get this solution for Example 4:

$$P(C \mid \text{positive}) = \frac{P(C) \cdot P(\text{positive} \mid C)}{P(C) \cdot P(\text{positive} \mid C) + P(\overline{C}) \cdot P(\text{positive} \mid \overline{C})}$$

$$= \frac{0.01 \cdot 0.80}{(0.01 \cdot 0.80) + (0.99 \cdot 0.10)} = 0.0748$$

Study Results Here is a truly fascinating fact: When 100 physicians were given the information in Example 4, 95 of them estimated $P(C \mid \text{positive})$ to be around 0.70 to 0.80, so they were wrong by a factor of 10. Physicians are extremely intelligent, but here they likely suffered from confusion of the inverse. The given rate of 80% for positive test results among those who are true positives implies that $P(\text{positive} \mid C) = 0.80$, but this is very different from $P(C \mid \text{positive})$. The physicians would have done much better if they had seen the given information in the form of a table like Table 4-2.

The importance and usefulness of Bayes' theorem is that it can be used with *sequential* events, whereby new additional information is obtained for a subsequent event, and that new information is used to revise the probability of the initial event. In this context, the terms *prior probability* and *posterior probability* are commonly used.

DEFINITIONS

A **prior probability** is an initial probability value originally obtained before any additional information is obtained.

A **posterior probability** is a probability value that has been revised by using additional information that is later obtained.

Relative to Example 4, $P(C) = 0.01$, which is the probability that a randomly selected subject has cancer. $P(C)$ is an example of a *prior probability*. Using the additional information that the subject has received a positive test result, we found that $P(C \mid \text{positive test result}) = 0.0748$, and this is a *posterior probability* because it uses that additional information of the positive test result.

4-3   Basic Skills and Concepts

Statistical Literacy and Critical Thinking

1. Language: Complement of "At Least One" Let $A =$ the event of getting at least one defective calculator when four are randomly selected with replacement from a batch. Write a statement describing event $\overline{A}$.

2. Probability of At Least One Let $A =$ the event of getting at least 1 malfunctioning iPhone when 3 iPhones are randomly selected with replacement from a batch. Based on data from Statista, the malfunction rate is 7.5%. Which of the following are correct?

a. $P(\overline{A}) = (0.925)(0.925)(0.925) = 0.791$

b. $P(A) = 1 - (0.925)(0.925)(0.925) = 0.209$

c. $P(A) = (0.075)(0.075)(0.075) = 0.000422$

3. Notation For a polygraph (lie detector) used when a subject is presented with a question, let $L =$ the subject lied and let $Y =$ the polygraph indicated that the subject told a lie. Use your own words to translate the notation $P(Y \mid L)$ into a verbal statement.

4. Confusion of the Inverse Using the same events L and Y described in Exercise 3, describe confusion of the inverse.

At Least One.   *In Exercises 5–12, find the probability.*

5. Four Girls Find the probability that when a couple has four children, at least one of them is a girl. (Assume that boys and girls are equally likely.)

6. Probability of a Girl Assuming that boys and girls are equally likely, find the probability of a couple having a boy when their third child is born, given that the first two children were both girls.

7. Births in the United States In the United States, the true probability of a baby being a boy is 0.512 (based on the data available at this writing). For a family having three children, find the following.

a. The probability that the first child is a girl.

b. The probability that all three children are boys.

continued

c. The probability that all three children are girls.

d. The probability that at least one of the children is a girl.

8. Births in Vietnam In Vietnam, the probability of a baby being a boy is 0.526 (based on the data available at this writing). For a family having four children, find the following.

a. The probability that the first child is a girl.

b. The probability that all four children are girls.

c. The probability that all four children are boys.

d. The probability that at least one of the children is a girl.

9. California Lottery In the California Daily 4 lottery, the probability of winning with one ticket is 0.0001. Someone buys one ticket on each of 10 different days.

a. What is the probability that all ten tickets are losing tickets?

b. What is the probability that at least one of the tickets is a winner?

10. At Least One Correct Answer If you make random guesses for 10 multiple choice SAT test questions (each with five possible answers), what is the probability of getting at least 1 correct? If these questions are part of a practice test and an instructor says that you must get at least one correct answer before continuing, is there a good chance you will continue?

11. At Least One Defective iPhone It has been reported that 20% of iPhones manufactured by Foxconn for a product launch did not meet Apple's quality standards. An engineer needs at least one defective iPhone so she can try to identify the problem(s). If she randomly selects 15 iPhones from a very large batch, what is the probability that she will get at least 1 that is defective? Is that probability high enough so that she can be reasonably sure of getting a defect for her work?

12. Drunk Driving In the United States, 31% of road crash deaths involve alcohol (based on data from the Global Status Report on Road Safety). What is the probability that among five randomly selected road crash deaths, at least one involved alcohol? If a researcher plans to conduct an in-depth study of road crash deaths that involve alcohol, can she be reasonably confident that the five road crash deaths will include at least one that involved alcohol?

Denomination Effect.   *In Exercises 13–16, use the data in the following table. In an experiment to study the effects of using four quarters versus a $1 bill, some college students were given four quarters and others were given a $1 bill, and they could either keep the money or spend it on gum. The results are summarized in the table (based on data from "The Denomination Effect," by Priya Raghubir and Joydeep Srivastava,* **Journal of Consumer Research,** *Vol. 36).*

	Purchased Gum	Kept the Money
Students Given Four Quarters	27	16
Students Given a $1 bill	12	34

13. Denomination Effect

a. Find the probability of randomly selecting a student who spent the money, given that the student was given four quarters.

b. Find the probability of randomly selecting a student who kept the money, given that the student was given four quarters.

c. What do the preceding results suggest?

14. Denomination Effect

a. Find the probability of randomly selecting a student who spent the money, given that the student was given a $1 bill.

b. Find the probability of randomly selecting a student who kept the money, given that the student was given a $1 bill.

c. What do the preceding results suggest?

15. Denomination Effect

a. Find the probability of randomly selecting a student who spent the money, given that the student was given four quarters.

b. Find the probability of randomly selecting a student who spent the money, given that the student was given a $1 bill.

c. What do the preceding results suggest?

16. Denomination Effect

a. Find the probability of randomly selecting a student who kept the money, given that the student was given four quarters.

b. Find the probability of randomly selecting a student who kept the money, given that the student was given a $1 bill.

c. What do the preceding results suggest?

In Exercises 17–20, refer to the accompanying table showing results from experiments conducted by researchers Charles R. Honts (Boise State University) and Gordon H. Barland (Department of Defense Polygraph Institute). In each case, it was known whether or not the subject lied, so the table indicates when the polygraph (lie detector) test was correct.

	Subject Did Not Lie	Subject Lied
Polygraph indicated that the subject lied.	15	42
Polygraph indicated that the subject did not lie.	32	9

17. False Positive Find the probability of selecting a subject with a positive polygraph test result, given that the subject did not lie. Why is this particular case problematic for test subjects?

18. False Negative Find the probability of selecting a subject with a negative polygraph result, given that the subject lied. What would be an unfavorable consequence of this error?

19. Positive Predictive Value Find the positive predictive value for the test. That is, find the probability that a subject lied, given that the polygraph indicated lying. Does the result make the polygraph appear to be effective?

20. Negative Predictive Value Find the negative predictive value for the polygraph. That is, find the probability that a subject did not lie, given that the polygraph indicates that the subject did not lie. Does the result make the test appear to be effective?

21. Redundancy in Computer Hard Drives The Seagate ST8000NM0055 hard drive has a 1.22% rate of failures in a year (based on data from Backblaze, Inc.). For the following, assume that all hard drives are that Seagate model.

a. If all of your computer data are stored on a hard disk drive with a copy stored on a second hard disk drive, what is the probability that during a year, you can avoid catastrophe with at least one working drive? Express the result with six decimal places.

b. If copies of all of your computer data are stored on three independent hard disk drives, what is the probability that during a year, you can avoid catastrophe with at least one working drive? Express the result with six decimal places. What is wrong with using the usual round-off rule for probabilities in this case?

22. Redundancy in Stadium Generators Large stadiums rely on backup generators to provide electricity in the event of a power failure. Assume that emergency backup generators fail 22% of the times when they are needed (based on data from Arshad Mansoor, senior vice president with the Electric Power Research Institute). A stadium has three backup generators so that power is available if at least one of them works in a power failure. Find the probability of having at least one of the backup generators working given that a power failure has occurred. Does the result appear to be adequate for the stadium's needs?

23. Composite Drug Test Based on the data in Table 4-1 on page 159, assume that the probability of a randomly selected person testing positive for drug use is 0.126. If drug screening samples are collected from 5 random subjects and combined, find the probability that the combined sample will reveal a positive result. Is that probability low enough so that further testing of the individual samples is rarely necessary?

24. Composite Water Samples The Fairfield County Department of Public Health tests water for the presence of *E. coli* (*Escherichia coli*) bacteria. To reduce laboratory costs, water samples from 10 public swimming areas are combined for one test, and further testing is done only if the combined sample tests positive. Based on past results, there is a 0.005 probability of finding *E. coli* bacteria in a public swimming area. Find the probability that a combined sample from 10 public swimming areas will reveal the presence of *E. coli* bacteria. Is that probability low enough so that further testing of the individual samples is rarely necessary?

4-3   Beyond the Basics

25. Shared Birthdays Find the probability that of 25 randomly selected people, at least 2 share the same birthday.

26. Unseen Coins A statistics professor tosses two coins that cannot be seen by any students. One student asks this question: "Did one of the coins turn up heads?" Given that the professor's response is "yes," find the probability that both coins turned up heads.

4-4   Counting

Key Concept Probability problems typically require that we know the total number of simple events, but finding that number often requires one of the five rules presented in this section. In Section 4-2 with the addition rule, multiplication rule, and conditional probability, we encouraged intuitive rules based on understanding and we discouraged blind use of formulas, but this section requires much greater use of formulas as we consider five different methods for counting the number of possible outcomes in a variety of situations. Not all counting problems can be solved with these five methods, but they do provide a strong foundation for the most common real applications.

1. Multiplication Counting Rule

The *multiplication counting rule* is used to find the total number of possibilities from some sequence of events.

MULTIPLICATION COUNTING RULE

For a sequence of events in which the first event can occur n_1 ways, the second event can occur n_2 ways, the third event can occur n_3 ways, and so on, the total number of outcomes is $n_1 \cdot n_2 \cdot n_3 \ldots$.

EXAMPLE 1 **Multiplication Counting Rule: Hacker Guessing a Password**

A computer hacker finds that a password is entered as •••••, so the characters are hidden, but we can see that there are five characters. We can use 92 different characters with a typical keyboard. How many different passwords are possible using five characters? If the hacker starts to generate all different possibilities, what is the probability of guessing the correct password on the first attempt?

SOLUTION

There are 92 different possibilities for each character, so the total number of different possible passwords is $n_1 \cdot n_2 \cdot n_3 \cdot n_4 \cdot n_5 = 92 \cdot 92 \cdot 92 \cdot 92 \cdot 92 = 6{,}590{,}815{,}232$.

Because all of the passcodes are equally likely, the probability of getting the correct passcode on the first attempt is $1/6{,}590{,}815{,}232$ or 0.000000000152. Unfortunately, there are sophisticated programs that allow hackers to try large numbers of likely possibilities, beginning with the commonly used but highly ineffective password of "password."

 **YOUR TURN.** Do Exercise 5 "Pin Numbers."

2. Factorial Rule

The factorial rule is used to find the total number of ways that n different items can be rearranged (order of items matters). The factorial rule uses the following notation.

NOTATION

The **factorial symbol** (!) denotes the product of decreasing positive whole numbers. For example, $4! = 4 \cdot 3 \cdot 2 \cdot 1 = 24$. By special definition, $0! = 1$.

FACTORIAL RULE

The number of different *arrangements* (order matters) of n different items when all n of them are selected is **$n!$**.

The factorial rule is based on the principle that the first item may be selected n different ways, the second item may be selected $n - 1$ ways, and so on. This rule is really the multiplication counting rule modified for the elimination of one item on each selection.

EXAMPLE 2 **Factorial Rule: Scrambling Letters**

Some words consist of letters which can be rearranged to form other words. Consider the word "steam."

a. How many different ways can the letters of "steam" be arranged?

b. If the letters of "steam" are arranged randomly, what is the probability that the letters will be in alphabetical order?

c. How many different words can be formed with the letters in "steam"?

continued

Changes to Mega Millions Lottery

The old Mega Millions lottery cost $1 and a player would select 5 numbers from 1 to 75 and a Mega number from 1 to 15; there is 1 chance in 258,890,850 of winning the jackpot. With the new format introduced on October 28, 2017, a ticket costs $2 and a player selects 5 numbers from 1 to 70 and a Mega number from 1 to 25; there is 1 chance in 302,575,350 of winning the jackpot. The change was motivated by psychological factors based on reasoning that with a much lower chance of winning the jackpot, the jackpot would grow to much larger amounts. Larger jackpots generate more lottery ticket sales, resulting in greater income from the lottery. In October of 2018, one player won the jackpot of $1.6 billion. The winner taking the lump sum payout would get about $904 million before taxes, and about $500 million after taxes.

SOLUTION

a. For the 5 different letters, the number of different arrangements is
$5! = 5 \cdot 4 \cdot 3 \cdot 2 \cdot 1 = 120$.

Note that this solution could have been done by applying the multiplication counting rule. The first letter can be any one of the 5 letters in "steam," the second letter can be any one of the 4 remaining letters, and so on. The result is again $5 \cdot 4 \cdot 3 \cdot 2 \cdot 1 = 120$. Use of the factorial rule has the advantage of including the factorial symbol, which is sure to impress.

b. There is only one arrangement with the letters listed in alphabetical order (aemst), so the probability is 1/120.

c. The letters of "steam" can be arranged to form these other words: teams, meats, mates, and tames, so there are five different words that can be formed. This is found by trial and error, and statistics is no help here.

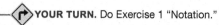 **YOUR TURN.** Do Exercise 1 "Notation."

Permutations and Combinations: Does *Order* Count?

When using different counting methods, it is essential to know whether different arrangements of the same items are counted only once or are counted separately. The terms *permutations* and *combinations* are standard in this context, and they are defined as follows:

DEFINITIONS

Permutations of items are arrangements in which different sequences of the same items are counted *separately*. (The letter arrangements of abc, acb, bac, bca, cab, and cba are all counted *separately* as six different permutations.)

Combinations of items are arrangements in which different sequences of the same items are counted as being the *same*. (The letter arrangements of abc, acb, bac, bca, cab, and cba are all considered to be the *same* combination.)

Mnemonics for Permutations and Combinations

- Remember "**P**ermutations **P**osition," where the alliteration reminds us that with permutations, the positions of the items makes a difference.

- Remember "**C**ombinations **C**ommittee," which reminds us that with members of a committee, rearrangements of the same members result in the same committee, so order does not count.

3. Permutations Rule (When All of the Items Are Different)

The permutations rule is used when there are n different items available for selection, we must select r of them without replacement, and the sequence of the items matters. The result is the total number of arrangements (or permutations) that are possible. (Remember, rearrangements of the same items are counted as different permutations.)

PERMUTATIONS RULE

When *n* different items are available and *r* of them are selected without replacement, the number of different permutations (order counts) is given by

$$_nP_r = \frac{n!}{(n-r)!}$$

EXAMPLE 3 **Permutations Rule (with Different Items): Trifecta Bet**

In a horse race, a *trifecta* bet is won by correctly selecting the horses that finish first and second and third, and you must select them in the correct order. The 144th running of the Kentucky Derby had a field of 20 horses.

a. How many different trifecta bets are possible?

b. If a bettor randomly selects three of those horses for a trifecta bet, what is the probability of winning by selecting Justify to win, Good Magic to finish second, and Audible to finish third, as they did? Do all of the different possible trifecta bets have the same chance of winning? (Ignore "dead heats" in which horses tie for a win.)

SOLUTION

a. There are $n = 20$ horses available, and we must select $r = 3$ of them without replacement. The number of different sequences of arrangements is found as shown:

$$_nP_r = \frac{n!}{(n-r)!} = \frac{20!}{(20-3)!} = 6840$$

b. There are 6840 different possible arrangements of 3 horses selected from the 20 that are available. If one of those arrangements is randomly selected, there is a probability of $1/6840$ that the winning arrangement is selected.

There are 6840 different possible trifecta bets, but not all of them have the same chance of winning, because some horses tend to be faster than others. (Because the "favorite" horses all finished in the top three, a winning $2 trifecta bet in this race won only $282.80.)

 **YOUR TURN.** Do Exercise 11 "Scheduling Routes."

4. Permutations Rule (When Some Items Are Identical to Others)

When *n* items are all selected without replacement, but *some items are identical*, the number of possible permutations (order matters) is found by using the following rule.

PERMUTATIONS RULE (WHEN SOME ITEMS ARE IDENTICAL TO OTHERS)

The number of different permutations (order counts) when *n* items are available and all *n* of them are selected *without replacement*, but some of the items are identical to others, is found as follows:

$$\frac{n!}{n_1! n_2! \ldots n_k!}$$ where n_1 are alike, n_2 are alike, . . . , and n_k are alike.

EXAMPLE 4   Permutations Rule (with Some Identical Items): Good Survey Design

When designing surveys, pollsters often repeat a question to see if a subject is thoughtlessly providing answers just to finish quickly. For one survey with 10 questions, 2 of the questions are identical to each other (with superficial differences in wording), and 3 other questions are also identical to each other (with superficial differences in wording). For this survey, how many different arrangements are possible? Is it practical to survey enough subjects so that every different possible arrangement is used?

SOLUTION

We have 10 questions with 2 that are identical to each other and 3 others that are also identical to each other, and we want the number of permutations. Using the rule for permutations with some items identical to others, we get

$$\frac{n!}{n_1!n_2! \ldots n_k!} = \frac{10!}{2!3!} = \frac{3{,}628{,}800}{2 \cdot 6} = 302{,}400$$

INTERPRETATION

There are 302,400 different possible arrangements of the 10 questions. It is not practical to accommodate every possible permutation. For typical surveys, the number of respondents is somewhere around 1000.

YOUR TURN. Do Exercise 9 "Statistics Counts."

5. Combinations Rule

The combinations rule is used when there are *n* different items available for selection, only *r* of them are selected without replacement, and order does not matter. The result is the total number of combinations that are possible. (*Remember:* Rearrangements of the same items are considered to be the same combination.)

> **COMBINATIONS RULE**
>
> When *n* different items are available, but only *r* of them are selected *without replacement,* the number of different combinations (order does not matter) is found as follows:
>
> $$_nC_r = \frac{n!}{(n-r)!r!}$$

EXAMPLE 5   Combinations Rule: Lottery

In Florida's Cash 5 lottery game, winning the jackpot requires that you select 5 different numbers from 1 to 35, and the same 5 numbers must be drawn in the lottery. The winning numbers can be drawn in any order, so order does not make a difference.

   a. How many different lottery tickets are possible?

   b. Find the probability of winning the jackpot when one ticket is purchased.

SOLUTION

a. There are $n = 35$ different numbers available, and we must select $r = 5$ of them without replacement (because the selected numbers must be different). Because order does not count, we need to find the number of different possible *combinations*. We get

$$_nC_r = \frac{n!}{(n-r)!r!} = \frac{35!}{(35-5)!5!} = \frac{35!}{30! \cdot 5!} = 324{,}632$$

b. If you select one 5-number combination, your probability of winning is $1/324{,}632$. Typical lotteries rely on the fact that people rarely know the value of this probability and have no realistic sense for how small that probability is. This is why the lottery is often called a "tax on people who are bad at math."

 **YOUR TURN.** Do Exercise 29 "Mega Millions."

Permutations or Combinations? Because choosing between permutations and combinations can often be tricky, we provide the following example that emphasizes the difference between them.

EXAMPLE 6 **Permutations and Combinations: Corporate Officers and Committees**

The Google company must appoint three corporate officers: chief executive officer (CEO), executive chairperson, and chief operating officer (COO). It must also appoint a Planning Committee with three different members. There are eight qualified candidates, and officers can also serve on the Planning Committee.

a. How many different ways can the officers be appointed?

b. How many different ways can the committee be appointed?

SOLUTION

Note that in part (a), order is important because the officers have very different functions. However, in part (b), the order of selection is irrelevant because the committee members all serve the same function.

a. Because order *does* count, we want the number of *permutations* of $r = 3$ people selected from the $n = 8$ available people. We get

$$_nP_r = \frac{n!}{(n-r)!} = \frac{8!}{(8-3)!} = 336$$

b. Because order does *not* count, we want the number of *combinations* of $r = 3$ people selected from the $n = 8$ available people. We get

$$_nC_r = \frac{n!}{(n-r)!r!} = \frac{8!}{(8-3)!3!} = 56$$

With order taken into account, there are 336 different ways that the officers can be appointed, but without order taken into account, there are 56 different possible committees.

 **YOUR TURN.** Do Exercise 23 "Corporate Officers and Committees."

How to Choose Lottery Numbers

Many books and suppliers of computer programs claim to be helpful in predicting winning lottery numbers. Some use the theory that particular numbers are "due" (and should be selected) because they haven't been coming up often; others use the theory that some numbers are "cold" (and should be avoided) because they haven't been coming up often; and still others use astrology, numerology, or dreams. Because selections of winning lottery number combinations are independent events, such theories are worthless. A valid approach is to choose numbers that are "rare" in the sense that they are not selected by other people, so that if you win, you will not need to share your jackpot with many others. The combination of 1, 2, 3, 4, 5, 6 is a poor choice because many people tend to select it. In a Florida lottery with $105 million in prizes, 52,000 tickets had 1, 2, 3, 4, 5, 6; if that combination had won, the top prize would have been only $1000. It's wise to pick combinations not selected by many others. Avoid combinations that form a pattern on the entry card.

Go Figure

43,252,003,274,489,856,000: Number of possible positions on a Rubik's cube.

4-4   Basic Skills and Concepts

Statistical Literacy and Critical Thinking

1. Notation What does the symbol ! represent? The five starting players of an NBA basketball team can stand in a line 5! different ways, so what is the actual number of ways that the five players can stand in a line?

2. Delaware Multi-Win Lotto In the Delaware Multi-Win Lotto game, a bettor selects six *different* numbers, each between 1 and 35. Winning the top prize requires that the selected numbers match those that are drawn, but the order does not matter. Do calculations for winning this lottery involve permutations or combinations? Why?

3. Delaware Play 3 In the Delaware Play 3 lottery game, a bettor selects three numbers between 0 and 9 and any selected number can be used more than once. Winning the top prize requires that the selected numbers match those and are drawn in the same order. Do calculations for this lottery involve the combinations rule or either of the two permutation rules presented in this section? Why or why not? If not, what rule does apply?

4. Combination Lock The typical combination lock uses three numbers, each between 0 and 49. Opening the lock requires entry of the three numbers in the correct order. Is the name "combination" lock appropriate? Why or why not?

In Exercises 5–36, express all probabilities as fractions.

5. Pin Numbers Use of ATM cards and hotel safes typically requires a four-digit (each 0 through 9) code, such as 3312. Digits can be repeated, but they must be entered in the correct order. If someone gains access and enters a code that was randomly selected, what is the probability of getting the correct code on the first try?

6. Social Security Numbers A Social Security number consists of nine digits in a particular order, and repetition of digits is allowed. After seeing the last four digits printed on a receipt, if you randomly select the other digits, what is the probability of getting the correct Social Security number of the person who was given the receipt?

7. Quinela In a horse race, a quinela bet is won if you selected the two horses that finish first and second, and they can be selected in any order. The 144th running of the Kentucky Derby had a field of 20 horses. What is the probability of winning a quinela bet if you randomly select the horses?

8. Soccer Shootout In the FIFA Women's World Cup 2019, a tie at the end of two overtime periods leads to a "shootout" with five kicks taken by each team from the penalty mark. Each kick must be taken by a different player. How many ways can 5 players be selected from the 11 eligible players? For the 5 selected players, how many ways can they be designated as first, second, third, fourth, and fifth?

9. Statistics Counts How many different ways can the letters of "statistics" be arranged? If the letters of "statistics" are arranged in a random order, what is the probability that the result will be "statistics"?

10. Radio Station Call Letters Radio and Television station call letters must begin with either K (for stations west of the Mississippi River) or W (for stations east of the Mississippi River) and must include either two or three additional letters. How many different possibilities are there?

11. Scheduling Routes A presidential candidate plans to begin her campaign by visiting the capitals of 4 of the 50 states. If the four capitals are randomly selected without replacement, what is the probability that the route is Sacramento, Juneau, Hartford, and Bismarck, in that order?

12. Survey Cross Validation One way to identify survey subjects who don't take the survey seriously is to repeat a question with similar wording. If a survey with 10 questions includes three questions that are the same except for minor differences in wording, how many different ways can the 10 questions be arranged?

13. Safety with Numbers The author owns a safe in which he stores all of his great ideas for the next edition of this book. The safe "combination" consists of four numbers, with each number from 0 to 99. The safe is designed so that numbers can be repeated. If another author breaks in and tries to steal these ideas, what is the probability that he or she will get the correct combination on the first attempt? Assume that the numbers are randomly selected. Given the number of possibilities, does it seem feasible to try opening the safe by making random guesses for the combination?

14. Electricity When testing for current in a cable with five color-coded wires, the author used a meter to test two wires at a time. How many different tests are required for every possible pairing of two wires?

15. Jumble Many newspapers carry "Jumble," a puzzle in which the reader must unscramble letters to form words. The letters MHRHTY were included in newspapers on the day this exercise was written. How many ways can those letters be arranged? Identify the correct unscrambling, then determine the probability of getting that result by randomly selecting one arrangement of the given letters.

16. DNA Nucleotides DNA (deoxyribonucleic acid) is made of nucleotides. Each nucleotide can contain any one of these nitrogenous bases: A (adenine), G (guanine), C (cytosine), T (thymine). If one of those four bases (A, G, C, T) must be selected three times to form a linear triplet, how many different triplets are possible? All four bases can be selected for each of the three components of the triplet.

17. Powerball As of this writing, the Powerball lottery is run in 44 states. Winning the jackpot requires that you select the correct five different numbers between 1 and 69 and, in a separate drawing, you must also select the correct single number between 1 and 26. Find the probability of winning the jackpot.

18. Teed Off When four golfers are about to begin a game, they often toss a tee to randomly select the order in which they tee off. What is the probability that they tee off in alphabetical order by last name?

19. ZIP Code If you randomly select five digits, each between 0 and 9, with repetition allowed, what is the probability you will get the author's ZIP code?

20. Age Discrimination The Cytertonics Communications Company reduced its management staff from 15 managers to 10. The company claimed that five managers were randomly selected for job termination. However, the five managers chosen are the five oldest managers among the 15 that were employed. Find the probability that when five managers are randomly selected from a group of 15, the five oldest are selected. Is that probability low enough to charge that instead of using random selection, the company actually fired the oldest employees?

21. Phone Numbers Current rules for telephone *area codes* allow the use of digits 2–9 for the first digit, and 0–9 for the second and third digits, but the last two digits cannot both be 1 (to avoid confusion with area codes such as 911). How many different area codes are possible with these rules? That same rule applies to the *exchange* numbers, which are the three digits immediately preceding the last four digits of a phone number. Given both of those rules, how many 10-digit phone numbers are possible? Given that these rules apply to the United States and Canada and a few islands, are there enough possible phone numbers? (Assume that the combined population is about 400,000,000.)

22. One Mississippi The counting sequence of "one Mississippi, two Mississippi, three Mississippi, . . ." is often used because saying a number with "Mississippi" takes about one second. A classic counting problem is to determine the number of different ways that the letters of "Mississippi" can be arranged. Find that number. If the letters are mixed up in a random sequence, what is the probability that the letters will be in alphabetical order?

23. Corporate Officers and Committees The Self Driving Unicycle Company was recently successfully funded via Kickstarter and must now appoint a president, chief executive officer (CEO), chief operating officer (COO), and chief financial officer (CFO), and chief human resources officer (CHR). It must also appoint a strategic planning committee with five different members. There are 15 qualified candidates, and officers can also serve on the committee.

a. How many different ways can the five officers be appointed?

b. How many different ways can a committee of five be appointed?

c. What is the probability of randomly selecting the committee members and getting the five youngest of the qualified candidates?

24. ATM You want to obtain cash by using an ATM, but it's dark and you can't see your card when you insert it. The card must be inserted with the front side up and the printing configured so that the beginning of your name enters first.

a. What is the probability of selecting a random position and inserting the card with the result that the card is inserted correctly?

b. What is the probability of randomly selecting the card's position and finding that it is incorrectly inserted on the first attempt, but it is correctly inserted on the second attempt? (Assume that the same position used for the first attempt could also be used for the second attempt.)

c. How many random selections are required to be absolutely sure that the card works because it is inserted correctly?

25. Is the Researcher Cheating? You become suspicious when a genetics researcher "randomly" selects numerous groups of 20 newborn babies and seems to consistently get 10 girls and 10 boys. The researcher claims that it is common to get 10 girls and 10 boys in such cases.

a. If 20 newborn babies are randomly selected, how many different gender sequences are possible?

b. How many different ways can 10 girls and 10 boys be arranged in sequence?

c. What is the probability of getting 10 girls and 10 boys when 20 babies are born?

d. Based on the preceding results, do you agree with the researcher's explanation that it is common to get 10 girls and 10 boys when 20 babies are randomly selected?

26. Identity Theft with Credit Cards Credit card numbers typically have 16 digits, but not all of them are random.

a. What is the probability of randomly generating 16 digits and getting *your* MasterCard number?

b. Receipts often show the last four digits of a credit card number. If only those last four digits are known, what is the probability of randomly generating the other digits of your MasterCard number?

c. Discover cards begin with the digits 6011. If you know that the first four digits are 6011 and you also know the last four digits of a Discover card, what is the probability of randomly generating the other digits and getting all of them correct? Is this something to worry about?

27. What a Word! One of the longest words in standard statistics terminology is "homoscedasticity." How many ways can the letters in that word be arranged?

28. Phase I of a Clinical Trial A clinical test on humans of a new drug is normally done in three phases. Phase I is conducted with a relatively small number of healthy volunteers. For example, a phase I test of bexarotene involved only 14 subjects. Assume that we want to treat 14 healthy humans with this new drug and we have 16 suitable volunteers available.

a. If the subjects are selected and treated one at a time *in sequence*, how many different sequential arrangements are possible if 14 people are selected from the 16 that are available?

b. If 14 subjects are selected from the 16 that are available, and the 14 selected subjects are all treated at the same time, how many different treatment groups are possible?

c. If 14 subjects are randomly selected and treated at the same time, what is the probability of selecting the 14 youngest subjects?

29. Mega Millions As of this writing, the Mega Millions lottery is run in 44 states. Winning the jackpot requires that you select the correct five different numbers from 1 to 70 and, in a separate drawing, you must also select the correct single number from 1 to 25.

a. Find the probability of winning the jackpot.

b. How does the result compare to the probability of being struck by lightning in a year, which the National Weather Service estimates to be 1/960,000?

c. How does the probability compare to the probability for the old Mega Millions game which involved the selection of five different numbers between 1 and 75 and a separate single number between 1 and 15?

30. Medicare Identifiers In 2019, the Social Security Numbers used on Medicare cards were replaced with new Medicare Benefit Identifiers (MBI). Here is the format for these new MBIs:

- Each MBI consists of 11 characters.
- The character in position 1 will be a digit 1 through 9.
- The characters in positions 4, 7, 10, 11 will be digits 0 through 9.
- The characters in positions 2, 5, 8, and 9 will be uppercase letters, but the letters S, L, O, I, B, Z will not be used.

The characters in positions 3 and 6 can be digits or letters (excluding S, L, O, I, B, Z). How many different MBIs are possible? Given that the current population of the United States is around 325,000,000, is the number of different possible MBIs sufficient? How does the number of different possible MBIs compare to the number of different possible Social Security Numbers used for Medicare cards before 2019? What is a major advantage of the new MBIs?

31. Morse Codes The International Morse code is a way of transmitting coded text by using sequences of on/off tones. Each character is 1 or 2 or 3 or 4 or 5 segments long, and each segment is either a dot or a dash. For example, the letter G is transmitted as two dashes followed by a dot, as in — — • . How many different characters are possible with this scheme? Are there enough characters for the alphabet and numbers?

32. Mendel's Peas Mendel conducted some of his famous experiments with peas that were either smooth yellow plants or wrinkly green plants. If four peas are randomly selected from a batch consisting of four smooth yellow plants and four wrinkly green plants, find the probability that the four selected peas are of the same type.

33. Change for a Quarter How many different ways can you make change for a quarter? (Different arrangements of the same coins are not counted separately.)

34. Counting with Fingers How many different ways can you touch two or more fingers to each other on one hand?

35. Design Your Own Lottery You have been given the task of creating a new lottery. For each $1 ticket, the player will select 6 different numbers from 1 to 25 (without replacement), and the only prize will be the jackpot won by players who select the six numbers (in any order) that are later drawn.

a. What is the probability of winning with one ticket?

b. What should be the winning prize if you want to average a profit of 50%, which is common for lotteries?

c. Would this lottery have much appeal?

36. Design Your Own Lottery Repeat the preceding exercise for a lottery with 6 numbers selected from 1 to 50.

a. What is the probability of winning with one ticket?

b. What should be the winning prize if you want to average a profit of 50%, which is common for lotteries?

c. Would this lottery have much appeal?

4-4   Beyond the Basics

37. Computer Variable Names A common computer programming rule was that names of variables must be between one and eight characters long. The first character can be any of the 26 letters, while successive characters can be any of the 26 letters or any of the 10 digits. For example, allowable variable names include A, BBB, and M3477K. How many different variable names are possible? (Ignore the difference between uppercase and lowercase letters.)

38. High Fives

a. Ten "mathletes" celebrate after solving a particularly challenging problem during competition. If each mathlete high fives each other mathlete exactly once, what is the total number of high fives?

b. If n mathletes shake hands with each other exactly once, what is the total number of handshakes?

c. How many different ways can ten mathletes be seated at a round table? (Assume that if everyone moves to the right, the seating arrangement is the same.)

d. How many different ways can n mathletes be seated at a round table?

39. Pick 10 Lottery For the New York Pick 10 lottery, the player first selects 10 numbers from 1 to 80. Then there is an official drawing of 20 numbers from 1 to 80. The prize of $500,000 is won if the 10 numbers selected by the player are all included in the 20 numbers that are drawn. Find the probability of winning that prize.

40. Stirling's Approximation Stirling's approximation given below can be used to approximate values of factorials. Use it to approximate the number of different ways that 60 ticket holders can stand in a line. How does the result compare to the exact value of $8.320987113 \times 10^{81}$?

$$\text{Stirling's approximation: } n! \approx \sqrt{2\pi n}\left(\frac{n}{e}\right)^n \text{ where } e = 2.718281828459\ldots$$

4-5   Simulations for Hypothesis Tests

Key Concept In this section we use simulations as one approach to determining when sample results are significantly low or high, so that claims about population parameters can be tested. Simulations can also be used for solving many probability problems that cannot be easily solved using the methods from the preceding sections of this chapter.

We begin by defining a simulation.

> **DEFINITION**
>
> A **simulation** of a procedure is a process that behaves the same way as the procedure, so that similar results are produced.

Here are two good uses of simulations:

1. **Test a Claim** Use a simulation to test some claim about a population parameter. (*Example:* Use the body temperatures from Data Set 5 "Body Temperatures" to test the common belief that the mean body temperature is 98.6°F. See Example 1.)

2. **Find a Probability** Use a simulation to find a probability that would be difficult to find using the methods presented earlier in this chapter. (*Example:* Find the probability that among 100 randomly selected people, at least three of them share the same birthday. See Example 2.)

> **EXAMPLE 1** **Test the Claim That the Mean Body Temperature is 98.6°F**

Data Set 5 "Body Temperatures" includes samples of body temperatures. Using the last column of body temperatures, we get the following:

$$n = 106 \quad \bar{x} = 98.20°F \quad s = 0.62°F \quad \textit{Distribution: Approximately normal}$$

If humans have a mean body temperature of 98.6°F as is commonly believed, is the above sample result of $\bar{x} = 98.20°F$ *significantly low*? If $\bar{x} = 98.20°F$ is significantly low, what does that suggest about the common belief that the mean body temperature is 98.6°F?

Simulation Method Used in This Example:

1. Assume that the mean body temperature is 98.6°F and randomly generate many samples of 106 body temperatures from a normal distribution. (Random generators in technology typically require that we specify the *normal* distribution, the mean, the standard deviation, and the sample size. For the mean, enter the *assumed* value of 98.6, for the standard deviation enter the value of 0.62 from the sample in Data Set 5, and enter 106 for the sample size.)

2. Find the mean $\bar{x}$ for each generated sample and construct a list of those sample means.

3. Examine the list of sample means to see whether the sample mean of 98.2°F can easily occur or whether a value such as 98.2°F is very unlikely, so that 98.2°F appears to be *significantly low*.

4. If it appears that a sample mean such as 98.2°F is significantly low, then its actual occurrence suggests that the assumed mean of 98.6°F is likely to be incorrect. (Chapter 8 will introduce another procedure for testing the belief that 98.6°F is the mean body temperature.)

> **SOLUTION**

Use a technology to repeat the process of randomly generating samples from a normally distributed population having the assumed mean of 98.6°F, the standard deviation of 0.62°F, and the sample size of $n = 106$. Obtain the mean of each generated sample.

Using the above procedure, we obtain 50 sample means that have been sorted and listed below.

98.5	98.5	98.5	98.5	98.5	98.5	98.5	98.5	98.5	98.6
98.6	98.6	98.6	98.6	98.6	98.6	98.6	98.6	98.6	98.6
98.6	98.6	98.6	98.6	98.6	98.6	98.6	98.6	98.6	98.6
98.6	98.6	98.6	98.6	98.6	98.6	98.6	98.6	98.7	98.7
98.7	98.7	98.7	98.7	98.7	98.7	98.7	98.7	98.7	98.7

continued

Cheating the Lottery

Eddie Tipton was hired as director of security for the Multi-State Lottery Association, even though he was a known convicted felon. Tipton managed to write and install a computer program for generating "random" lottery numbers, and this allowed him to reduce his odds against winning from 5 million to 1 down to 200 to 1. He was then able to acquire more than $24 million in winnings. He was caught and sentenced to up to 25 years in prison. Better luck next time, Eddie!

Examine this list of 50 simulated sample means with this question in mind: "How common is the Data Set 5 sample mean of 98.2°F?" The list of 50 sample means shows that if the population mean is actually 98.6°F as assumed, then such means will typically fall between 98.5°F and 98.7°F, so the sample mean of 98.2°F appears to be significantly low. It appears that if the population mean is actually 98.6°F, then a sample mean of 98.2°F is highly unlikely.

Probability Value We can also use the 50 sample means listed above to estimate the probability of getting a sample mean of 98.20°F or lower, assuming that the population mean is equal to 98.6°F. Because none of the 50 sample means is 98.2°F or lower, the estimated probability of getting a sample mean of 98.2°F or lower is $0/50 = 0$. Using more advanced methods, the actual probability can be found to be 0.00000000002.

> ### INTERPRETATION
>
> With the assumption that the mean body temperature is 98.6°F, we have found that the sample mean of 98.2°F is highly unlikely and is significantly low. *Because we did get the sample mean of 98.2°F from Data Set 5, we have strong evidence suggesting that the assumed population mean of 98.6°F is likely to be wrong!*

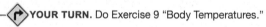YOUR TURN. Do Exercise 9 "Body Temperatures."

The simulation method used in Example 1 can be generalized as follows.

Simulation Method for Testing a Claim About a Population Mean

1. Assume that the population mean is the value that is being claimed. Obtain the sample statistics of n, $\bar{x}$, s, and identify the distribution (such as normal). Use technology to randomly generate many samples with these properties: The sample size is n (same as the sample being used), the standard deviation is s (the same standard deviation as the sample being used), and use the same distribution (such as normal) that was identified from the sample. For the mean, use the *assumed* (or claimed) value of the population mean.

2. Find the mean $\bar{x}$ for each generated sample, and construct a list of those sample means.

3. Examine the list of sample means to see whether the value of $\bar{x}$ from the sample can easily occur or whether the value of $\bar{x}$ is significantly low or significantly high (because it rarely occurs in the randomly generated samples). *Hint:* Sort the means from the randomly generated samples.

4. If it appears that a sample mean of $\bar{x}$ is significantly low or significantly high, then its occurrence suggests that the assumed mean is likely to be incorrect.

The following example illustrates the use of a simulation for finding a probability that would be very difficult to find using the methods presented in the preceding sections of this chapter.

EXAMPLE 2   Probability of Three Birthdays That Are the Same

Find the probability that among 100 randomly selected people, at least three share the same birthday.

SOLUTION

Although the probability problem is easy to state and understand, its solution can be quite difficult using the methods discussed in the previous sections of this chapter. Instead, a simulation can be used whereby different samples of 100 birthdays are randomly generated, then the samples are analyzed to determine whether three or more birthdays are the same. Instead of using actual birthdays, we can use the integers $1, 2, 3, \ldots, 365$, where $1 =$ January 1, $2 =$ January 2, ..., $365 =$ December 31. A computer can be used to generate such samples of 100 simulated birthdays. (Most statistics software packages provide a feature for generating random integers.) Here is one sample, with the simulated birthdays *sorted* so that it becomes easy to see whether three or more are the same:

4	7	7	9	10	11	14	15	16	18
21	25	34	36	37	45	46	61	65	70
75	79	87	92	97	101	105	107	109	110
113	**113**	**113**	114	116	123	130	139	142	142
148	149	157	162	173	173	174	174	181	183
185	186	**192**	**192**	**192**	197	201	203	206	211
215	215	225	234	234	235	237	238	240	241
243	245	247	247	252	265	269	270	272	272
273	273	304	315	318	320	321	321	323	327
332	333	337	340	340	357	358	361	363	364

Because the birthdays have been sorted, it is easy to scan through the above sample to see that there are three (or more) simulated birthdays that are the same. (For this sample, there are two birthdays that occur three times: 113 and 192). We could now continue to generate more samples and, in each case, determine whether three or more birthdays are the same. We can repeat as often as needed to get a good estimate of the probability that among 100 randomly selected people, at least three share the same birthday.

 YOUR TURN. Do Exercise 13 "Simulating the Monty Hall Problem."

TECH CENTER

 ### Generating Simulated Data
Access tech supplements, videos, and data sets at **www.TriolaStats.com**

Statdisk	Minitab	StatCrunch
1. Click **Data** in the top menu.	1. Click **Calc** in the top menu.	1. Click **Data** in the top menu.
2. Select the desired type of data generator from the dropdown menu. Options include: • **Normal Generator** • **Uniform Generator** • **Binomial Generator**	2. Select **Random Data** from the dropdown menu.	2. Select **Simulate** in the drop-down menu.
3. Enter the required inputs (varies depending on the type of generator selected).	3. Select the desired type of data generator from the dropdown menu. Options include: • **Normal** • **Uniform** • **Integer** (uniform distribution) • **Binomial**	3. Select the desired type of data generator from the dropdown menu. Options include: • **Normal** • **Uniform** • **Binomial**
4. Click **Generate**.	4. Enter the required inputs (varies depending on the type of generator selected).	4. Enter the required inputs (varies depending on the type of generator selected).
	5. Click **OK**.	5. Click **Compute**.

continued

TECH CENTER *continued*

Generating Simulated Data
Access tech supplements, videos, and data sets at **www.TriolaStats.com**

TI-83/84 Plus Calculator	**Excel**	**R**
1. Press **MATH** then select **PROB** (or **PRB**) from the menu. 2. Select the desired type of data generator from the dropdown menu. Options include: • **randNorm** (normal distribution) • **randInt** (uniform distribution) • **randBin** (binomial distribution) 3. Enter the required inputs (varies depending on the type of generator selected). *See tip below for TI-83 plus calculators.* 4. Select **Paste** and press **ENTER** twice. *TIP: Use the following format for TI-83 Plus calculators: **randNorm(μ, σ, trials); randInt(lower, upper, n); randBin(n, p, repetitions).** Press* **ENTER** *when complete.*	**XLSTAT Add-In** 1. Click the **XLSTAT** tab in the Ribbon and then click **Preparing data**. 2. Select **Distribution sampling** from dropdown menu. 3. In the *Theoretical distribution* box, select the desired type of data generator. Options include: • **Normal** • **Uniform** and **Uniform Discrete** • **Binomial** 4. Enter the required inputs (varies depending on the type of generator selected). 5. Click **OK**. **Excel** 1. Click on **Insert Function** f_x, select the category **Math & Trig** and select the function **RANDBETWEEN**. 2. Enter the desired bottom and top values and click **OK**. One random value will be generated. 3. Copy the cell with the random data value to additional cells as needed.	R commands: Normal Distribution: **rnorm(n, mean, sd)** Uniform Distribution: **runif (n, min, max)** Binomial Distribution: **rbinom(n, size, prob)** *A complete list of R statistical commands is available at TriolaStats.com*

4-5   Basic Skills and Concepts

Statistical Literacy and Critical Thinking

1. Simulating Dice When two dice are rolled, the total is between 2 and 12 inclusive. A student simulates the rolling of two dice by randomly generating numbers between 2 and 12. Does this simulation behave in a way that is similar to actual dice? Why or why not?

2. Simulating Dice Assume that you have access to a computer that can randomly generate whole numbers between any two values. Describe how this computer can be used to simulate the rolling of a pair of dice.

3. Simulating Birthdays A student wants to conduct the simulation described in Example 2, but no calculator or computer is available, so the student uses 365 individual index cards to write the individual numbers between 1 and 365. The student then shuffles the cards, selects one, and records the result. That card is replaced, the cards are again shuffled and a second number is drawn. This process is repeated until 100 birthdays are generated. Does this simulation behave the same way as the process of selecting 100 people and recording their birthdays? Why or why not?

4. Simulating Body Temperatures If Example 1 is repeated with a different sample and it is found that for 100 randomly generated samples, 40 of these generated samples have a mean that is as extreme as the mean of the actual sample, what should be concluded about the assumed mean of 98.6°F?

In Exercises 5–8, describe the simulation procedure. (For example, to simulate 10 births, use a random number generator to generate 10 integers between 0 and 1 inclusive, and consider 0 to be a male and 1 to be a female.)

5. Brand Recognition The probability of randomly selecting an adult who recognizes the brand name of McDonald's is 0.95 (based on data from Franchise Advantage). Describe a procedure for using software or a TI-83/84 Plus calculator to simulate the random selection of 50 adult consumers. Each individual outcome should be an indication of one of two results: (1) The consumer recognizes the brand name of McDonald's; (2) the consumer does not recognize the brand name of McDonald's.

6. Lefties Ten percent of people are left-handed. In a study of dexterity, 15 people are randomly selected. Describe a procedure for using software or a TI-83/84 Plus calculator to simulate the random selection of 15 people. Each of the 15 outcomes should be an indication of one of two results: (1) Subject is left-handed; (2) subject is not left-handed.

7. Tom Brady Tom Brady gained fame as the quarterback for the New England Patriots until 2020 when he left. As of this writing, he threw 9375 passes and 6004 of them were caught, so his success rate is 0.640. Describe a procedure for using software or a TI-83/84 Plus calculator to simulate his next pass. The outcome should be an indication of one of two results: (1) The pass is caught; (2) the pass is not caught.

8. Simulating Hybridization When Mendel conducted his famous hybridization experiments, he used peas with green pods and yellow pods. One experiment involved crossing peas in such a way that 75% of the offspring peas were expected to have green pods, and 25% of the offspring peas were expected to have yellow pods. Describe a procedure for using software or a TI-83/84 Plus calculator to simulate 20 peas in such a hybridization experiment. Each of the 20 individual outcomes should be an indication of one of two results: (1) The pod is green; (2) the pod is yellow.

In Exercises 9–12, use a suitable technology to conduct the simulation.

9. Body Temperatures Repeat Example 1 using these statistics from the 8 AM temperatures on Day 2 from Data Set 5 "Body Temperatures": $n = 70$, $\bar{x} = 97.49°F$, $s = 0.70°F$. As in Example 1, assume that the temperatures are from a normally distributed population.

10. Body Temperatures Repeat Example 1 using these statistics from *hypothetical* data with these statistics: $n = 50$, $\bar{x} = 98.5°F$, $s = 0.7°F$. Assume that the sample temperatures are from a normally distributed population.

11. Got a Minute? Students of the author estimated the length of one minute without reference to a watch or clock, and the times (seconds) are listed below. Assuming that the times are from a normally distributed population, use a simulation to determine whether these times are from a population with a mean equal to 60 seconds.

    69 81 39 65 42 21 60 63 66 48 64 70 96 91 65

12. IQ Scores New York City cab drivers are randomly selected for IQ tests, and the results are listed below. Assuming that IQ scores are from a normally distributed population, use a simulation to determine whether these IQ scores are from a population with a mean equal to 100.

    88 115 74 123 93 98 99 93 82 106

4-5   Beyond the Basics

13. Simulating the Monty Hall Problem A problem that once attracted much attention is the *Monty Hall problem*, based on the old television game show *Let's Make a Deal*, hosted by Monty Hall. Suppose you are a contestant who has selected one of three doors after being told that two of them conceal nothing, but that a new red Corvette is behind one of the three. Next, the host opens one of the doors you didn't select and shows that there is nothing behind it. He then offers you the choice of sticking with your first selection or switching to the other unopened door. Should you stick with your first choice or should you switch? Develop a simulation of this game and determine whether you should stick or switch. (According to *Chance* magazine, business schools at such institutions as Harvard and Stanford use this problem to help students deal with decision making.)

14. Simulating Birthdays

a. Develop a simulation for finding the probability that when 50 people are randomly selected, at least 2 of them have the same birth date. Describe the simulation and estimate the probability.

b. Develop a simulation for finding the probability that when 50 people are randomly selected, at least 3 of them have the same birth date. Describe the simulation and estimate the probability.

15. Genetics: Simulating Population Control A classical probability problem involves a king who wanted to increase the proportion of women by decreeing that after a mother gives birth to a son, she is prohibited from having any more children. The king reasons that some families will have just one boy, whereas other families will have a few girls and one boy, so the proportion of girls will be increased. Conduct a simulation to determine whether his reasoning is correct, and to determine whether the proportion of girls will increase.

Chapter Quick Quiz

1. ESP A psychologist tells you that in an ESP (extrasensory perception) experiment, there is a 20% chance of answering a question correctly. What is the *probability* of answering a question correctly?

2. Standard Tests Standard tests, such as the SAT or ACT or MCAT, tend to make extensive use of multiple-choice questions because they are easy to grade using software. If one such multiple choice question has possible correct answers of a, b, c, d, e, what is the probability of a wrong answer if the answer is a random guess?

3. Birthday If a day of a year (not a leap year) is randomly selected, what is the probability it is the author's birthday?

4. Online Courses Based on data from a survey sponsored by Sallie Mae, 10% of undergraduate students take online courses only. If two undergraduate students are randomly selected, what is the probability that they both take online courses only?

5. Subjective Probability Estimate the probability that the next time you watch a TV news report, it includes a story about a plane crash.

In Exercises 6–10, use the following results from tests of an experiment to test the effectiveness of an experimental vaccine for children (based on data from USA Today). Express all probabilities in decimal form.

	Developed Flu	Did Not Develop Flu
Vaccine Treatment	14	1056
Placebo	95	437

6. If 1 of the 1602 subjects is randomly selected, find the probability of getting 1 that developed flu.

7. If 1 of the 1602 subjects is randomly selected, find the probability of getting 1 who had the vaccine treatment or developed flu.

8. If 1 of the 1602 subjects is randomly selected, find the probability of getting 1 who had the vaccine treatment and developed flu.

9. Find the probability of randomly selecting 2 subjects without replacement and finding that they both developed flu.

10. Find the probability of randomly selecting 1 of the subjects and getting 1 who developed flu, given that the subject was given the vaccine treatment.

Review Exercises

In Exercises 1–10, use the data in the accompanying table and express all results in decimal form. (The data are from "The Left-Handed: Their Sinister History," by Elaine Fowler Costas, Education Resources Information Center, Paper 399519.)

	Writes with Left Hand?	
	Yes	No
Male	23	217
Female	65	455

1. Female If one of the subjects in the study is randomly selected, find the probability of getting a female. Does it appear that the proportion of females is reasonably close to the proportion of females in the general population?

2. Lefty Given Female Find the probability of randomly selecting one of the study subjects and getting someone who writes with their left hand given that the selected person is a female.

3. Female Given Lefty Find the probability of randomly selecting one of the study subjects and getting a female given that the selected person writes with their left hand.

4. Lefty or Female Find the probability of randomly selecting one of the study subjects and getting someone who writes with their left hand or is a female.

5. Lefty or Male Find the probability of randomly selecting one of the study subjects and getting someone who writes with their left hand or is a male.

6. Both Lefties If two of the study subjects are randomly selected *without replacement*, find the probability that they both write with their left hand.

7. Both Lefties If two of the study subjects are randomly selected *with replacement*, find the probability that they both write with their left hand.

8. Complement If L represents the event of randomly selecting one of the study subjects and getting someone who writes with their left hand, what does $\overline{L}$ represent? Find the value of $P(\overline{L})$.

9. Complement If M represents the event of randomly selecting one of the study subjects and getting someone who is a male, what does $\overline{M}$ represent? Find the value of $P(\overline{M})$.

10. All Three Lefties If three of the study subjects are randomly selected *without replacement*, find the probability that they all write with their left hand. If we did get three lefties when three subjects were randomly selected, would that be a significantly high number of lefties?

11. Random Seats on Ryanair When four researchers checked into a Ryanair flight from Manchester to Dublin, there were 65 seats available, and 15 of them were middle seats (based on data from "How 'Random' is Ryanair's Seating Allocation" by Jennifer Rogers, *Significance*). All four researchers were assigned middle seats. If the four researchers were assigned seats randomly, what is the probability that they are all given middle seats? What does the result suggest about Ryanair's claim that seats are randomly assigned?

12. Vision Correction About 75% of the U.S. population uses some type of vision correction (such as glasses or contact lenses).

a. If someone is randomly selected, what is the probability that he or she does not use vision correction?

b. If four different people are randomly selected, what is the probability that they all use vision correction?

c. What is the general criterion for using probability to determine whether a number of successes among *n* trials is *significantly high*?

d. If you randomly select four people, is a result of all four using vision correction significantly high? Why or why not?

13. National Statistics Day

a. If a person is randomly selected, find the probability that his or her birthday is October 18, which is National Statistics Day in Japan. Ignore leap years.

b. If a person is randomly selected, find the probability that his or her birthday is in October. Ignore leap years.

c. Estimate a subjective probability for the event of randomly selecting an adult American and getting someone who knows that October 18 is National Statistics Day in Japan.

d. If ten adult Americans are randomly selected and nine of them know that October 18 is National Statistics Day in Japan, is that result of nine significantly high?

14. Composite Sampling for Diabetes Currently, the rate for new cases of diabetes in a year is 4.3 per 1000 (based on data from the Centers for Disease Control and Prevention). When testing for the presence of diabetes, the Newport Diagnostics Laboratory saves money by combining blood samples for tests. The combined sample tests positive if at least one person has diabetes. If the combined sample tests positive, then the individual blood tests are performed. In a test for diabetes, blood samples from 10 randomly selected subjects are combined. Find the probability that the combined sample tests positive with at least 1 of the 10 people having diabetes. Is it likely that such combined samples test positive?

15. Texas Two Step In the Texas Two Step lottery, winning the top prize requires that you select the correct four different numbers from 1 to 35 (in any order and without replacement) and you must also select the correct additional "Bonus Ball" number between 1 and 35, which is drawn separately. The additional Bonus Ball number could be the same as one of the first four selected numbers. What is the probability of winning the top prize? (Express the answer as a fraction.) As this exercise was written, the jackpot was advertised to be $200,000; does that seem fair?

Cumulative Review Exercises

1. Cloud Seeding The "Florida Area Cumulus Experiment" was conducted by using silver iodide to seed clouds with the objective of increasing rainfall. For the purposes of this exercise, let the daily amounts of rainfall be represented by units of rnfl. (The actual rainfall amounts are in cubic meters $\times$ 10,000,000 or $m^3 \times 10^7$.)

Find the value of the following statistics and include appropriate units based on rnfl as the unit of measurement.

   15.53   7.27   7.45   10.39   4.70   4.50   3.44   5.70   8.24   7.30   4.05   4.46

a. mean   **b.** median   **c.** midrange

d. range   **e.** standard deviation   **f.** variance

2. Cloud Seeding Use the same data given in Exercise 1.

a. Identify the 5-number summary. As in Exercise 1, use rnfl to represent the units of measurement.

b. Construct a boxplot.

c. Identify any values that appear to be outliers.

3. Organ Donors *USA Today* provided information about a survey (conducted for Donate Life America) of 5100 adult Internet users. Of the respondents, 2346 said they are willing to donate organs after death. In this survey, 100 adults were surveyed in each state and the District of Columbia, and results were weighted to account for the different state population sizes.

a. What percentage of respondents said that they are willing to donate organs after death?

b. Based on the poll results, what is the probability of randomly selecting an adult who is willing to donate organs after death?

c. What term is used to describe the sampling method of randomly selecting 100 adults from each state and the District of Columbia?

4. Sampling Eye Color Based on a study by Dr. P. Sorita Soni at Indiana University, assume that eye colors in the United States are distributed as follows: 40% brown, 35% blue, 12% green, 7% gray, 6% hazel.

a. A statistics instructor collects eye color data from her students. What is the name for this type of sample?

b. Identify one factor that might make the sample from part (a) biased and not representative of the general population of people in the United States.

c. If one person is randomly selected, what is the probability that this person will have brown or blue eyes?

d. If two people are randomly selected, what is the probability that at least one of them has brown eyes?

5. Heights of Presidents Theories have been developed about the heights of winning candidates for the U.S. presidency and the heights of candidates who were runners up. Listed below are heights (cm) from recent presidential elections. Construct a graph suitable for exploring an association between heights of presidents and the heights of the presidential candidates who were runners-up. What does the graph suggest about that association?

Winner	182	177	185	188	188	183	188	191
Runner-Up	180	183	177	173	188	185	175	169

Technology Project

Simulations Calculating probabilities are sometimes painfully difficult, but *simulations* provide us with a very practical alternative to calculations based on formal rules. A **simulation** of a procedure is a process that behaves the same way as the procedure so that similar results are produced. Instead of calculating the probability of getting exactly 5 boys in 10 births, you could repeatedly toss 10 coins and count the number of times that exactly 5 heads (or simulated "boys") occur. Better yet, you could do the simulation with a random number generator on a computer or calculator to randomly generate 1s (or simulated "boys") and 0s (or simulated "girls"). Let's consider this probability exercise:

> **Find the probability that among 40 randomly selected people, at least 3 have the same birthday.**

For the above problem, a simulation begins by representing birthdays by integers from 1 through 365, where 1 represents a birthday of January 1, and 2 represents January 2, and so on. We can simulate 40 birthdays by using a calculator or computer to generate 40 random numbers (with repetition allowed) between 1 and 365. Those numbers can then be sorted, so it becomes easy to examine the list to determine whether any 3 of the simulated birth dates are the same. (After sorting, equal numbers are adjacent.) We can repeat the process as many times as we wish, until we are satisfied that we have a good estimate of the probability. Use technology to simulate 20 different groups of 40 birthdays. Use the results to estimate the probability that among 40 randomly selected people, at least 3 have the same birthday.

Summary of Simulation Functions (see Tech Center at the end of Section 4-5):

Statdisk:	Select **Data** from the top menu, select **Uniform Generator** from the dropdown menu.
Excel:	Click **Insert Function** f_x, select **Math & Trig,** select **RANDBETWEEN.** Copy to additional cells.
TI-83/84 Plus:	Press **MATH**, select **PROB** from the top menu, select **randInt** from the menu.
StatCrunch:	Select **Data** from the top menu, select **Simulate** from the dropdown menu, select **Uniform** or **Discrete Uniform** from the submenu.
Minitab:	Select **Calc** from the top menu, select **Random Data** from the dropdown menu, select **Integer** from the submenu.

Big (or Very Large) Data Project

a. Use Data Set 6 "Births" from Appendix B to estimate the following probabilities.

P(male with a birth weight greater than 3200 grams)

P(female with a birth weight greater than 3200 grams)

b. Repeat part (a) using Data Set 45 "Births in New York" from Appendix B, which contains records from 465,506 births.

c. Compare the results from the relatively small sample in part (a) to the results from the large sample in part (b). Does the larger data set have much of an effect on the results?

FROM DATA TO DECISION

Critical Thinking: Interpreting results from a test for smoking

It is estimated that roughly half of smokers lie when asked about their smoking involvement. Pulse CO-oximeters may be a way to get information about smoking without relying on patients' statements. Pulse CO-oximeters use light that shines through a fingernail, and it measures carbon monoxide in blood. These devices are used by firemen and emergency departments to detect carbon monoxide poisoning, but they can also be used to identify smokers. The accompanying table lists results from people aged 18–44 when the pulse CO-oximeter is set to detect a 6% or higher level of carboxyhemoglobin (based on data from "Carbon Monoxide Test Can Be Used to Identify Smoker," by Patrice Wendling, *Internal Medicine News*, Vol. 40., No. 1, and Centers for Disease Control and Prevention).

CO-Oximetry Test for Smoking

	Positive Test Result	Negative Test Result
Smoker	49	57
Nonsmoker	24	370

Analyzing the Results

1. False Positive Based on the results in the table, find the probability that a subject is not a smoker, given that the test result is positive.

2. True Positive Based on the results in the table, find the probability that a subject smokes, given that the test result is positive.

3. False Negative Based on the results in the table, find the probability that a subject smokes, given that the test result is negative.

4. True Negative Based on the results in the table, find the probability that a subject does not smoke, given that the test result is negative.

5. Sensitivity Find the *sensitivity* of the test by finding the probability of a true positive, given that the subject actually smokes.

6. Specificity Find the *specificity* of the test by finding the probability of a true negative, given that the subject does not smoke.

7. Positive Predictive Value Find the *positive predictive value* of the test by finding the probability that the subject smokes, given that the test yields a positive result.

8. Negative Predictive Value Find the *negative predictive value* of the test by finding the probability that the subject does not smoke, given that the test yields a negative result.

9. Confusion of the Inverse Find the following values, then compare them. In this case, what is confusion of the inverse?

- $P(\text{smoker} \mid \text{positive test result})$
- $P(\text{positive test result} \mid \text{smoker})$

10. Effectiveness of the Test Based on the results found, what do you conclude about the effectiveness of pulse CO-oximeters used to identify smokers?

Cooperative Group Activities

1. Out-of-class activity Divide into groups of three or four and create a new carnival game. Determine the probability of winning. Determine how much money the operator of the game can expect to gain each time the game is played.

2. In-class activity Divide into groups of three or four and use coin flipping to develop a simulation that emulates the kingdom that abides by this decree: After a mother gives birth to a son, she will not have any other children. If this decree is followed, does the proportion of girls increase?

3. In-class activity Divide into groups of three or four and use actual thumbtacks or Hershey's Kisses candies or paper cups to estimate the probability that when dropped, they will land with the point (or open side) up. How many trials are necessary to get a result that appears to be reasonably accurate when rounded to the first decimal place?

4. Out-of-class activity Marine biologists often use the *capture-recapture method* as a way to estimate the size of a population, such as the number of fish in a lake. This method involves capturing a sample from the population, tagging each member in the sample, then returning it to the population. A second sample is later captured, and the tagged members are counted along with the total size of this second sample. The results can be used to estimate the size of the population.

Instead of capturing real fish, simulate the procedure using some uniform collection of items such as colored beads, M&Ms, or index cards. Start with a large collection of at least 200 of such items. Collect a sample of 50 and use a marker to "tag" each one. Replace the tagged items, mix the whole population, then select a second sample and proceed to estimate the population size. Compare the result to the actual population size obtained by counting all of the items.

5. Out-of-class activity Divide into groups of three or four. First, use subjective estimates for the probability of randomly selecting a car and getting each of these car colors: black, white, blue, red, silver, other. Then design a sampling plan for obtaining car colors through observation. Execute the sampling plan and obtain revised probabilities based on the observed results. Write a brief report of the results.

6. In-class activity The manufacturing process for a new computer integrated circuit has a yield of 1/6, meaning that 1/6 of the circuits are good and the other 5/6 are defective. Use a die to simulate this manufacturing process, and consider an outcome of 1 to be a good integrated circuit, while outcomes of 2, 3, 4, 5, or 6 represent defective integrated circuits. Find the mean number of circuits that must be manufactured to get one that is good.

7. Out-of-class activity In Cumulative Review Exercise 4, it was noted that eye colors in the United States are distributed as follows: 40% brown, 35% blue, 12% green, 7% gray, 6% hazel. That distribution can form the basis for probabilities. Conduct a survey by asking fellow students to identify the color of their eyes. Does the probability of 0.4 for brown eyes appear to be consistent with your results? Why would a large sample be required to confirm that $P(\text{hazel eyes}) = 0.06$?

8. In-class activity Each student should survey people to determine whether they have the ability to raise one eyebrow without raising the other. All results can be combined to estimate the probability that a randomly selected person can raise one eyebrow without raising the other.

9. Out-of-class activity Have each student announce the 4th and 5th digits of their Social Security numbers. After all of those numbers have been recorded, analyze them and try to identify any features suggesting that those numbers are not random.

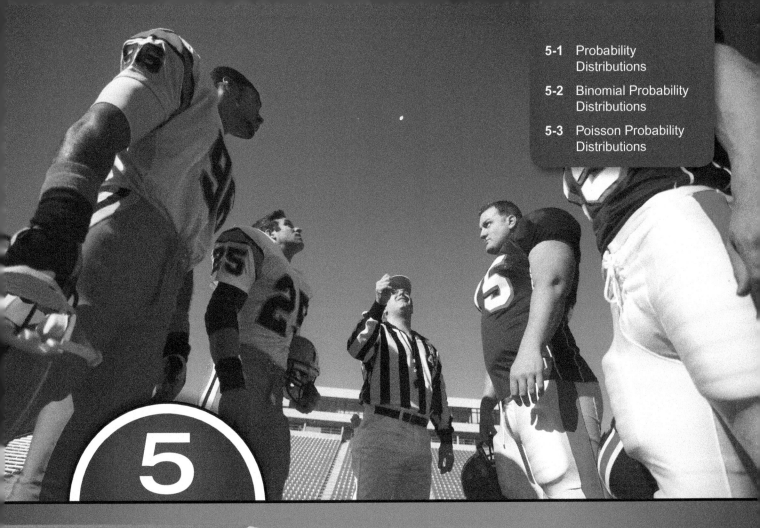

5

DISCRETE PROBABILITY DISTRIBUTIONS

CHAPTER PROBLEM

Is the NFL Overtime Coin-Toss Rule Fair?

Overtime in National Football League (NFL) football games begin with a coin toss. The team winning this coin toss has the option of receiving the ball or kicking the ball. Between 1974 and 2011, there were 477 overtime games, and 17 of them ended in a tie after overtime play. Here, we consider the 460 overtime games that did not end in a tie. Among those 460 games that were decided in overtime, 252 were won by the same team that won the overtime coin toss; the teams that lost the overtime coin toss went on to win 208 games. The NFL overtime rules were changed in 2012 to be more fair, and as of this writing, there have been 121 games since 2012 with winners decided in overtime. 67 of the teams that won in overtime also won the overtime coin toss. These results are shown in Table 5-1 on the next page.

continued

TABLE 5-1 NFL Games Decided in Overtime

	Before 2012	Since 2012
Team Won Overtime Coin Toss and Won Game	252	67
Team Won Overtime Coin Toss and Lost Game	208	54

Based on the data, has the NFL overtime rule change in 2012 resulted in outcomes that are more fair? Under the old rules for overtime, does winning the coin toss become an advantage? The result of 252 wins in 460 games is a winning rate of 54.8% for the teams that won the coin toss. Is that about the same as random chance, or is 54.8% *significantly* greater than 50%, so that teams winning the coin toss have an advantage? The methods of this chapter can be used to answer such questions.

Since 2012, there is a 55.4% winning rate for the teams that won the overtime coin toss. The overtime winning rate of 55.4% since 2012 does not appear to be significantly different from the winning rate of 54.8% before 2012, suggesting that the rule change in 2012 did not have a significant effect. (Using methods presented in Section 9-1 or Section 11-2, we can determine that the two winning rates of 54.8% and 55.4% are not significantly different.)

CHAPTER OBJECTIVES

Figure 5-1 provides a visual illustration of what this chapter accomplishes. When investigating the numbers of heads in two coin tosses, we can use the following two different approaches:

- **Use real sample data to find *actual* results:** Collect numbers of heads in tosses of two coins, summarize them in a frequency distribution, and find the mean $\bar{x}$ and standard deviation s (as in Chapters 2 and 3).

- **Find probabilities for each *possible* outcome:** Find the probability for each possible number of heads in two tosses (as in Chapter 4), then summarize the results in a table representing a probability distribution, and then find the mean μ and standard deviation σ.

In this chapter we merge the above two approaches as in this third approach:

- **Create a table of what we *expect* to happen:** Create a table describing what we *expect* to happen (instead of what did happen), then find the population mean μ and population standard deviation σ.

The table at the extreme right in Figure 5-1 is a *probability distribution,* because it describes the distribution using *probabilities* instead of frequency counts. The remainder

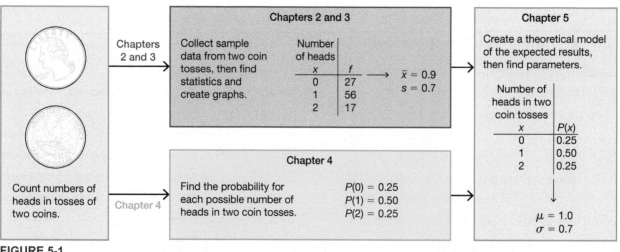

FIGURE 5-1

of this book and the core of inferential statistics are based on applications of probability distributions. In this chapter we focus on *discrete* probability distributions.

Here are the chapter objectives:

5-1 Probability Distributions

- Define *random variable* and *probability distribution*.

- Determine whether the requirements of a *probability distribution* are satisfied when given values of a random variable along with their corresponding probabilities.

- Compute the mean and standard deviation of a probability distribution. The mean and standard deviation can then be used to determine whether results are *significantly low* or *significantly high*.

5-2 Binomial Probability Distributions

- Describe a binomial probability distribution and find probability values for a binomial distribution.

- Compute the mean and standard deviation for a binomial distribution, and then use those results to determine whether results are *significantly low* or *significantly high*.

5-3 Poisson Probability Distributions

- Describe a Poisson probability distribution and find probability values for a Poisson distribution.

5-1   Probability Distributions

Key Concept This section introduces the concept of a *random variable* and the concept of a *probability distribution*. We illustrate how a *probability histogram* is a graph that visually depicts a probability distribution. We show how to find the important parameters of mean, standard deviation, and variance for a probability distribution. Most importantly, we describe how to determine whether outcomes are *significantly low* or *significantly high* or neither. We begin with the related concepts of *random variable* and *probability distribution*.

PART 1   Basic Concepts of a Probability Distribution

DEFINITIONS

A **random variable** is a variable (typically represented by *x*) that has a single numerical value, determined by chance, for each outcome of a procedure.

A **probability distribution** is a description that gives the probability for each value of the random variable. It is often expressed in the format of a table, formula, or graph.

In Section 1-2 we made a distinction between discrete and continuous data. Random variables may also be discrete or continuous, and the following two definitions are consistent with those given in Section 1-2.

> **DEFINITIONS**
>
> A **discrete random variable** has a collection of values that is finite or countable. (If there are infinitely many values, the number of values is countable if it is possible to count them individually, such as the number of tosses of a coin before getting heads.)
>
> A **continuous random variable** has infinitely many values, and the collection of values is not countable. (That is, it is impossible to count the individual items because at least some of them are on a continuous scale, such as body temperatures.)

This chapter deals exclusively with discrete random variables, but the following chapters deal with continuous random variables.

Probability Distribution: Requirements

Every probability distribution must satisfy each of the following three requirements.

1. There is a *numerical* (not categorical) random variable x, and its numerical values are associated with corresponding probabilities.

2. $\Sigma P(x) = 1$ where x assumes all possible values. (The sum of all probabilities must be 1, but sums such as 0.999 or 1.001 are acceptable because they result from rounding errors.)

3. $0 \leq P(x) \leq 1$ for every individual value of the random variable x. (That is, each probability value must be between 0 and 1 inclusive.)

The second requirement comes from the simple fact that the random variable x represents all possible events in the entire sample space, so we are certain (with probability 1) that one of the events will occur. The third requirement comes from the basic principle that any probability value must be 0 or 1 or a value between 0 and 1.

TABLE 5-2 Probability Distribution for the Number of Females in Two Births

x: Number of Females in Two Births	P(x)
0	0.25
1	0.50
2	0.25

EXAMPLE 1 Births

For the purposes of this example, assume that male births and female births are equally likely. [In reality, $P(\text{male birth}) = 0.512$.] Let's consider two births, with the following random variable:

$$x = \text{number of females when two babies are born}$$

The above x is a random variable because its numerical values depend on chance. With two births, the number of females can be 0, 1, or 2, and Table 5-2 is a probability distribution because it gives the probability for each value of the random variable x and it satisfies the three requirements listed earlier:

1. The variable x is a *numerical* random variable, and its values are associated with probabilities, as in Table 5-2.

2. $\Sigma P(x) = 0.25 + 0.50 + 0.25 = 1$

3. Each value of $P(x)$ is between 0 and 1. (Specifically, 0.25 and 0.50 and 0.25 are each between 0 and 1 inclusive.)

The random variable x in Table 5-2 is a *discrete* random variable, because it has three possible values $(0, 1, 2)$, and three is a finite number, so this satisfies the requirement of being finite or countable.

 YOUR TURN. Do Exercise 7 "Plane Crashes."

Notation for 0+

In tables such as Table 5-2 or the binomial probabilities listed in Table A-1 in Appendix A, we sometimes use 0+ to represent a probability value that is positive but very small, such as 0.000000123. (When rounding a probability value for inclusion in such a table, rounding to 0 would be misleading because it would incorrectly suggest that the event is impossible, so we use 0+ instead.)

Probability Histogram: Graph of a Probability Distribution

There are various ways to graph a probability distribution, but for now we will consider only the **probability histogram**. Figure 5-2 is a probability histogram corresponding to Table 5-2. Notice that it is similar to a relative frequency histogram (described in Section 2-2), but the vertical scale shows *probabilities* instead of relative frequencies based on actual sample results.

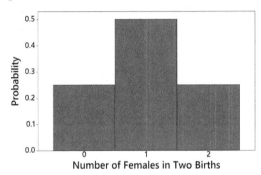

FIGURE 5-2   Probability Histogram for Number of Females in Two Births

Looking Ahead In Figure 5-2, we see that the values of 0, 1, 2 along the horizontal axis are located at the centers of the rectangles. This implies that the rectangles are each 1 unit wide, so the areas of the rectangles are 0.25, 0.50, and 0.25. The *areas* of these rectangles are the same as the *probabilities* in Table 5-2. We will see in Chapter 6 and future chapters that such a correspondence between areas and probabilities is very useful.

Probability Formula Example 1 involves a table, but a probability distribution could also be in the form of a formula. Consider the formula $P(x) = \dfrac{1}{2(2-x)!x!}$ (where x can be 0, 1, or 2). Using that formula, we find that $P(0) = 0.25$, $P(1) = 0.50$, and $P(2) = 0.25$. The probabilities found using this formula are the same as those in Table 5-2. This formula does describe a probability distribution because the three requirements are satisfied, as shown in Example 1.

EXAMPLE 2 **Software Piracy**

Table 5-3 lists countries along with the proportion of unlicensed software in each country (based on data from Business Software Alliance). Does Table 5-3 describe a probability distribution?

SOLUTION

Table 5-3 violates the first requirement because x is not a *numerical* random variable. Instead, the "values" of x are categorical data, not numbers. Table 5-3 also violates the second requirement because the sum of the "probabilities" is 2.09, but that sum should be 1. Because the three requirements are not all satisfied, we conclude that Table 5-3 does *not* describe a probability distribution.

 YOUR TURN. Do Exercise 11 "Cell Phone Use."

Not at Home

Pollsters cannot simply ignore those who were not at home when they were called the first time. One solution is to make repeated callback attempts until the person can be reached. Alfred Politz and Willard Simmons describe a way to compensate for those missed calls without making repeated callbacks. They suggest weighting results based on how often people are not at home. For example, a person at home only two days out of six will have a 2/6 or 1/3 probability of being at home when called the first time. When such a person is reached the first time, his or her results are weighted to count three times as much as someone who is always home. This weighting is a compensation for the other similar people who are home two days out of six and were not at home when called the first time. This clever solution was first presented in 1949.

TABLE 5-3 Software Piracy

Country	Proportion of Unlicensed Software
United States	0.17
China	0.70
India	0.58
Russia	0.64
Total	2.09

Parameters of a Probability Distribution

Remember that with a probability distribution, we have a description of a *population* instead of a sample, so the values of the mean, standard deviation, and variance are *parameters,* not statistics. The mean, variance, and standard deviation of a discrete probability distribution can be found with the following formulas:

FORMULA 5-1   Mean μ for a probability distribution

$$\mu = \Sigma [\, x \cdot P(x)\,]$$

FORMULA 5-2   Variance σ^2 for a probability distribution

$$\sigma^2 = \Sigma [\, (x - \mu)^2 \cdot P(x)\,] \text{ (This format is easier to understand.)}$$

FORMULA 5-3   Variance σ^2 for a probability distribution

$$\sigma^2 = \Sigma [\, x^2 \cdot P(x)\,] - \mu^2 \text{ (This format is easier for manual calculations.)}$$

FORMULA 5-4   Standard deviation σ for a probability distribution

$$\sigma = \sqrt{\Sigma [\, x^2 \cdot P(x)\,] - \mu^2}$$

When applying Formulas 5-1 through 5-4, use the following rule for rounding results.

Round-Off Rule for μ, σ, and σ^2 from a Probability Distribution

Round results by carrying *one more decimal place* than the number of decimal places used for the random variable x. If the values of x are integers, round μ, σ, and σ^2 to one decimal place.

Exceptions to Round-Off Rule In some special cases, the above round-off rule results in values that are misleading or inappropriate. For example, with four-engine jets the mean number of jet engines working successfully throughout a flight is 3.999714286, which becomes 4.0 when rounded, but that is misleading because it suggests that all jet engines always work successfully. Here we need more precision to correctly reflect the true mean, such as the precision in 3.999714.

Expected Value

The mean of a discrete random variable x is the theoretical mean outcome for infinitely many trials. We can think of that mean as the *expected value* in the sense that it is the average value that we would expect to get if the trials could continue indefinitely.

DEFINITION

The **expected value** of a discrete random variable x is denoted by E, and it is the mean value of the outcomes, so $E = \mu$ and E can also be found by evaluating $E = \Sigma [\, x \cdot P(x)\,]$, as in Formula 5-1.

CAUTION An expected value need not be a whole number, even if the different possible values of *x* might all be whole numbers. The expected number of girls in five births is 2.5, even though five particular births can never result in 2.5 girls. If we were to survey many couples with five children, we *expect* that the mean number of girls will be 2.5.

Meta-Analysis

The term *meta-analysis* refers to a technique of conducting a study that essentially combines results of other studies. It has the advantage that separate smaller samples can be combined into one big sample, making the collective results more meaningful. It also has the advantage of using work that has already been done. Meta-analysis has the disadvantage of being only as good as the studies that are used. If the previous studies are flawed, the "garbage in, garbage out" phenomenon can occur. The use of meta-analysis is currently popular in medical research and psychological research. As an example, a study of migraine headache treatments was based on data from 46 other studies. (See "Meta-Analysis of Migraine Headache Treatments: Combining Information from Heterogeneous Designs," by Dominici et al., *Journal of the American Statistical Association*, Vol. 94, No. 445.)

EXAMPLE 3 **Finding the Mean, Variance, and Standard Deviation**

Table 5-2 on page 206 describes the probability distribution for the number of females in two births. Find the mean, variance, and standard deviation for the probability distribution described in Table 5-2 from Example 1.

SOLUTION

In Table 5-4, the two columns at the left describe the probability distribution given earlier in Table 5-2. We create the two columns at the right for the purposes of the calculations required.

Using Formulas 5-1 and 5-2 and the table results, we get

Mean: $\mu = \Sigma[x \cdot P(x)] = 1.0$

Variance: $\sigma^2 = \Sigma[(x - \mu)^2 \cdot P(x)] = 0.5$

The standard deviation is the square root of the variance, so

Standard deviation: $\sigma = \sqrt{0.5} = 0.707107 = 0.7$ (rounded)

Rounding: In Table 5-4, we use $\mu = 1.0$. If μ had been the value of 1.23456, we might round μ to 1.2, but we should use its *unrounded* value of 1.23456 in Table 5-4 calculations. Rounding in the middle of calculations can lead to results with errors that are too large.

TABLE 5-4 Calculating μ and σ for a Probability Distribution

x	*P(x)*	*x · P(x)*	$(x - \mu)^2 \cdot P(x)$
0	0.25	$0 \cdot 0.25 = 0.00$	$(0 - 1.0)^2 \cdot 0.25 = 0.25$
1	0.50	$1 \cdot 0.50 = 0.50$	$(1 - 1.0)^2 \cdot 0.50 = 0.00$
2	0.25	$2 \cdot 0.25 = 0.50$	$(2 - 1.0)^2 \cdot 0.25 = 0.25$
Total		1.00	0.50
		$\uparrow$	$\uparrow$
		$\mu = \Sigma[x \cdot P(x)]$	$\sigma^2 = \Sigma[(x - \mu)^2 \cdot P(x)]$

INTERPRETATION

In two births, the mean number of females is 1.0 female, the variance is 0.5 female², and the standard deviation is 0.7 female. Also, the expected value for the number of females in two births is 1.0 female, which is the same value as the mean. If we were to collect data on a large number of trials with two births in each trial, we expect to get a mean of 1.0 female.

 **YOUR TURN.** Do Exercise 15 "Mean and Standard Deviation."

Making Sense of Results: Significant Values

We present the following two different approaches for determining whether a value of a random variable *x* is significantly low or significantly high.

Identifying Significant Results with the Range Rule of Thumb

The following range rule of thumb (from Section 3-2) is based on the principle that the vast majority of values should lie within 2 standard deviations of the mean.

> **Range Rule of Thumb for Identifying Significant Values**
>
> **Significantly low** values are $(\mu - 2\sigma)$ or lower.
>
> **Significantly high** values are $\mu + 2\sigma$ or higher.
>
> **Values not significant**: Between $(\mu - 2\sigma)$ and $(\mu + 2\sigma)$

Figure 5-3 (repeated from Figure 3-4 in Section 3-2) illustrates the above criteria:

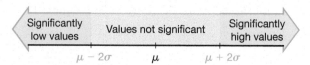

FIGURE 5-3 **Range Rule of Thumb for Identifying Significant Values**

> **CAUTION** Know that the use of the number 2 in the range rule of thumb is somewhat arbitrary, and this is a guideline, not an absolutely rigid rule.

EXAMPLE 4 **Identifying Significant Results with the Range Rule of Thumb**

In Example 3 we found that for two births, the mean number of females is $\mu = 1.0$ female and the standard deviation is $\sigma = 0.7$ female. Use those results and the range rule of thumb to determine if 2 females in 2 births is significantly high.

SOLUTION

Using the range rule of thumb, the outcome of 2 females is significantly high if it is greater than or equal to $\mu + 2\sigma$. With $\mu = 1.0$ female and $\sigma = 0.7$ female, we get

$$\mu + 2\sigma = 1 + 2(0.7) = 2.4 \text{ females}$$

Significantly high numbers of females are 2.4 and above.

INTERPRETATION

Based on these results, we conclude that 2 females is not a significantly high number of females (because 2 is not greater than or equal to 2.4).

YOUR TURN. Do Exercise 17 "Range Rule of Thumb for Significant Events."

Identifying Significant Results with Probabilities:

- **Significantly *high* number of successes:** x successes among n trials is a *significantly high* number of successes if the probability of x or more successes is 0.05 or less. That is, x is a significantly high number of successes if $P(x \text{ or more}) \leq 0.05$.*

- **Significantly *low* number of successes:** x successes among n trials is a *significantly low* number of successes if the probability of x or fewer successes is 0.05 or less. That is, x is a significantly low number of successes if $P(x \text{ or fewer}) \leq 0.05$.*

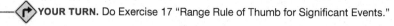

*The value 0.05 is not absolutely rigid. Other values, such as 0.01, could be used to distinguish between results that are significant and those that are not significant.

Identification of significantly low or significantly high numbers of successes is sometimes used for the purpose of rejecting assumptions, as stated in the following rare event rule.

The Rare Event Rule for Inferential Statistics

If, under a given assumption, the probability of a particular outcome is very small and the outcome occurs *significantly less than* or *significantly greater than* what we expect with that assumption, we conclude that the assumption is probably not correct.

For example, if testing the assumption that boys and girls are equally likely, the outcome of 20 girls in 100 births is significantly low and would be a basis for rejecting that assumption.

(CP)— **EXAMPLE 5** Identifying Significant Results with Probabilities

Is 252 heads in 460 coin tosses a significantly high number of heads?

What does the result suggest about the Chapter Problem, which includes results from 460 overtime games between 1974 and 2011? (Among the 460 teams that won the coin toss, 252 of them won the game. Is 252 wins in those 460 games *significantly high*?)

SOLUTION

A result of 252 heads in 460 coin tosses is greater than we expect with random chance, but we need to determine whether 252 heads is *significantly high*. Here, the relevant probability is the probability of getting *252 or more* heads in 460 coin tosses. Using methods covered later in Section 5-2, we can find that $P(252 \text{ or more heads in } 460 \text{ coin tosses}) = 0.0224$ (rounded). Because the probability of getting 252 or more heads is less than or equal to 0.05, we conclude that 252 heads in 460 coin tosses is a *significantly high* number of heads. See Figure 5-4, which is a probability histogram showing the probability for the different numbers of heads.

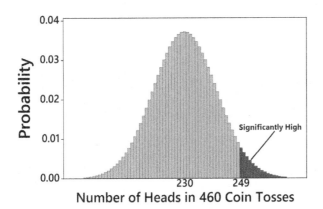

FIGURE 5-4 Probability Histogram of Heads in 460 Coin Tosses

continued

> **INTERPRETATION**
>
> It is unlikely that we would get 252 or more heads in 460 coin tosses by chance. It follows that 252 wins by teams that won the overtime coin toss is significantly high, so winning the coin toss is an advantage. This is justification for changing the overtime rules, as was done in 2012.

 YOUR TURN. Do Exercise 19 "Using Probabilities for Significant Events."

Not *Exactly,* but "At Least as Extreme"

It should be obvious that among 1000 tosses of a coin, 502 heads is not significantly high, whereas 900 heads is significantly high. What makes 900 heads significantly high while 502 heads is not significantly high? It is not the *exact* probabilities of 900 heads and 502 heads (they are both less than 0.026). It is the fact that the probability of 502 *or more* heads (0.462) is not low, but the probability of 900 *or more* heads (0+) is very low.

PART 2 Expected Value and Rationale for Formulas

Expected Value

In Part 1 of this section we noted that the expected value of a random variable x is equal to the mean μ. We can therefore find the expected value by computing $\Sigma\left[x \cdot P(x)\right]$, just as we do for finding the value of μ. We also noted that the concept of expected value is used in *decision theory.* In Example 6 we illustrate this use of expected value with a situation in which we must choose between two different bets. Example 6 involves a real and practical decision.

EXAMPLE 6 Be a Better Bettor

You have $5 to place on a bet in the Golden Nugget casino in Las Vegas. You have narrowed your choice to one of two bets:

Roulette: Bet on the number 7 in roulette.

Craps: Bet on the "pass line" in the dice game of craps.

a. If you bet $5 on the number 7 in roulette, the probability of losing $5 is 37/38 and the probability of making a net gain of $175 is 1/38. (The prize is $180, including your $5 bet, so the net gain is $175.) Find your expected value if you bet $5 on the number 7 in roulette.

b. If you bet $5 on the pass line in the dice game of craps, the probability of losing $5 is 251/495 and the probability of making a net gain of $5 is 244/495. (If you bet $5 on the pass line and win, you are given $10 that includes your bet, so the net gain is $5.) Find your expected value if you bet $5 on the pass line.

Which of the preceding two bets is better in the sense of producing higher expected value?

SOLUTION

a. Roulette The probabilities and payoffs for betting $5 on the number 7 in roulette are summarized in Table 5-5. Table 5-5 also shows that the expected value is $\Sigma\left[x \cdot P(x)\right] = -26\cancel{c}$. That is, for every $5 bet on the number 7, you can expect to *lose* an average of 26¢.

TABLE 5-5 Roulette

Event	x	P(x)	x · P(x)
Lose	−$5	37/38	−$4.868421
Win (net gain)	$175	1/38	$4.605263
Total			−$0.26 (rounded) (or −26¢)

b. **Craps Game** The probabilities and payoffs for betting $5 on the pass line in craps are summarized in Table 5-6. Table 5-6 also shows that the expected value is $\Sigma[x \cdot P(x)] = -7¢$. That is, for every $5 bet on the pass line, you can expect to lose an average of 7¢.

TABLE 5-6 Craps Game

Event	x	P(x)	x · P(x)
Lose	−$5	251/495	−$2.535353
Win (net gain)	$5	244/495	$2.464646
Total			−$0.07 (rounded) (or −7¢)

INTERPRETATION

The $5 bet in roulette results in an expected value of −26¢ and the $5 bet in craps results in an expected value of −7¢. Because you are better off losing 7¢ instead of losing 26¢, the craps game is better in the long run, even though the roulette game provides an opportunity for a larger payoff when playing the game once.

▶ **YOUR TURN.** Do Exercise 29 "Expected Value for the Florida Pick 3 Lottery."

Rationale for Formulas 5-1 Through 5-4

Instead of blindly accepting and using formulas, it is much better to have some understanding of why they work. When computing the mean from a frequency distribution, f represents class frequency and N represents population size. In the expression that follows, we rewrite the formula for the mean of a frequency table so that it applies to a population. In the fraction f/N, the value of f is the frequency with which the value x occurs and N is the population size, so f/N is the probability for the value of x. When we replace f/N with $P(x)$, we make the transition from relative frequency based on a limited number of observations to probability based on infinitely many trials. This result shows why Formula 5-1 is as given earlier in this section.

$$\mu = \frac{\Sigma(f \cdot x)}{N} = \Sigma\left[\frac{f \cdot x}{N}\right] = \Sigma\left[x \cdot \frac{f}{N}\right] = \Sigma[x \cdot P(x)]$$

Similar reasoning enables us to take the variance formula from Chapter 3 and apply it to a random variable for a probability distribution; the result is Formula 5-2. Formula 5-3 is a shortcut version that will always produce the same result as Formula 5-2. Although Formula 5-3 is usually easier to work with, Formula 5-2 is easier to understand directly. Based on Formula 5-2, we can express the standard deviation as

$$\sigma = \sqrt{\Sigma[(x - \mu)^2 \cdot P(x)]}$$

or as the equivalent form given in Formula 5-4.

5-1 Basic Skills and Concepts

Statistical Literacy and Critical Thinking

1. Random Variable The accompanying table lists probabilities for the corresponding numbers of unlicensed software packages when four software packages are randomly selected in China. What is the random variable, what are its possible values, and are its values numerical?

Number of Unlicensed Software Packages x	P(x)
0	0.008
1	0.076
2	0.265
3	0.412
4	0.240

2. Discrete or Continuous? Is the random variable given in the table from Exercise 1 discrete or continuous? Explain.

3. Probability Distribution For the table from Exercise 1, is the sum of the values of $P(x)$ equal to 1, as required for a probability distribution? Does the table describe a probability distribution?

4. Significant For 100 births, $P(\text{exactly 56 girls}) = 0.0390$ and $P(\text{56 or more girls}) = 0.136$. Is 56 girls in 100 births a significantly high number of girls? Which probability is relevant to answering that question?

Identifying Discrete and Continuous Random Variables. *In Exercises 5 and 6, refer to the given values, then identify which of the following is most appropriate:* **discrete random variable, continuous random variable,** *or* **not a random variable.**

5. a. IQ scores of statistics students

b. Exact heights of statistics students

c. Shoe sizes (such as 8 or 8½) of statistics students

d. Majors (such as history) of statistics students

e. The number of rolls of a die required for a statistics student to get the number 4

6.a. Numbers of students in statistics classes

b. Grades (A, B, C, D, F) earned in statistics classes

c. Number of times a statistic student must draw a card from a shuffled deck before getting an ace

d. Social Security numbers of statistics students

e. Exact unrounded ages of statistics students

Identifying Probability Distributions. *In Exercises 7–14, determine whether a probability distribution is given. If a probability distribution is given, find its mean and standard deviation. If a probability distribution is not given, identify the requirements that are not satisfied.*

7. Plane Crashes The table lists causes of fatal plane crashes with their corresponding probabilities.

Cause	Probability
Pilot Error	0.58
Mechanical	0.17
Weather	0.06
Sabotage	0.09
Other	0.10

8. Password Protection Results from a survey of mobile device users are listed in the table, where x is the number in a group who said that they do not use passwords to protect their mobile devices (based on data from a Kaspersky Lab survey).

x	P(x)
0	0.012
1	0.079
2	0.215
3	0.311

9. Online Courses College students are randomly selected and arranged in groups of three. The random variable x is the number in the group who say that they take one or more online courses (based on data from Sallie Mae).

x	P(x)
0	0.104
1	0.351
2	0.396
3	0.149

10. Genetic Disorder Five males with an X-linked genetic disorder have one child each. The random variable x is the number of children among the five who inherit the X-linked genetic disorder.

x	P(x)
0	0.031
1	0.156
2	0.313
3	0.313
4	0.156
5	0.031

11. Cell Phone Use In a survey, cell phone users were asked which ear they use to hear their cell phone, and the table is based on their responses (based on data from "Hemispheric Dominance and Cell Phone Use," by Seidman et al., *JAMA Otolaryngology—Head & Neck Surgery*, Vol. 139, No. 5).

	P(x)
Left	0.636
Right	0.304
No preference	0.060

12. Fear of Heights The table lists results from a survey of 285 subjects who were asked, "Are you afraid of heights in tall buildings?" The results are from *USA Today*.

Response x	P(x)
Yes	0.46
No	0.54

13. Printer Usage Households are randomly selected and partitioned into groups of four. For those groups, the random variable x is the number of households with a printer (based on data from the Consumer Technology Association).

x	P(x)
0	0.023
1	0.145
2	0.340
3	0.354
4	0.138

14. Self-Driving Vehicle Groups of adults are randomly selected and arranged in groups of three. The random variable x is the number in the group who say that they would feel comfortable in a self-driving vehicle (based on a TE Connectivity survey).

x	P(x)
0	0.358
1	0.439
2	0.179
3	0.024

Lottery. *In Exercises 15–20, refer to the accompanying table, which describes probabilities for the California Daily 4 lottery. The player selects four digits with repetition allowed, and the random variable x is the number of digits that match those in the same order that they are drawn (for a "straight" bet).*

Number of Matching Digits	P(x)
0	0.656
1	0.292
2	0.049
3	0.004
4	0+

15. Mean and Standard Deviation Find the mean and standard deviation for the numbers of correct matches.

16. Range Rule of Thumb for Significant Events Use the range rule of thumb to determine whether 0 matches is a significantly low number of matches.

17. Range Rule of Thumb for Significant Events Use the range rule of thumb to determine whether 4 matches is a significantly high number of matches.

18. Using Probabilities for Significant Events

a. Find the probability of getting exactly 2 matches.

b. Find the probability of getting 2 or more matches.

c. Which probability is relevant for determining whether 2 is a significantly high number of matches: the result from part (a) or part (b)?

d. Is 2 a significantly high number of matches? Why or why not?

19. Using Probabilities for Significant Events

a. Find the probability of getting exactly 3 matches.

b. Find the probability of getting 3 or more matches.

c. Which probability is relevant for determining whether 3 is a significantly high number of matches: the result from part (a) or part (b)?

d. Is 3 a significantly high number of matches? Why or why not?

20. Using Probabilities for Significant Events

a. Find the probability of getting exactly 1 match.

b. Find the probability of getting 1 or fewer matches.

c. Which probability is relevant for determining whether 1 is a significantly low number of matches: the result from part (a) or part (b)?

d. Is 1 a significantly low number of matches? Why or why not?

Texting and Driving. *In Exercises 21–26, refer to the accompanying table, which describes probabilities for groups of five drivers. The random variable x is the number of drivers in a group who say that they text while driving (based on data from an Arity survey of drivers).*

Number of Drivers Who Say That They Text While Driving	P(x)
0	0.066
1	0.238
2	0.344
3	0.249
4	0.090
5	0.013

21. Mean and Standard Deviation For groups of five drivers, find the mean and standard deviation for the numbers of drivers who say that they text while driving.

22. Range Rule of Thumb for Significant Events Use the range rule of thumb to determine whether 4 is a significantly high number of drivers who say that they text while driving.

23. Range Rule of Thumb for Significant Events Use the range rule of thumb to determine whether 1 is a significantly low number of drivers who say that they text while driving.

24. Using Probabilities for Significant Events

a. Find the probability of getting exactly 3 drivers who say that they text while driving.

b. Find the probability of getting 3 or more drivers who say that they text while driving.

c. Which probability is relevant for determining whether 3 is a significantly high number of drivers who say that they text while driving: the result from part (a) or part (b)?

d. Is 3 a significantly high number of drivers who say that they text while driving? Why or why not?

25. Using Probabilities for Significant Events

a. Find the probability of getting exactly 2 drivers who say that they text while driving.

b. Find the probability of getting 2 or fewer drivers who say that they text while driving.

c. Which probability is relevant for determining whether 2 is a significantly low number of drivers who say that they text while driving: the result from part (a) or part (b)?

d. Is 2 a significantly low number of drivers who say that they text while driving? Why or why not?

26. Using Probabilities for Significant Events

a. Find the probability of getting exactly 4 drivers who say that they text while driving.

b. Find the probability of getting 4 or more drivers who say that they text while driving.

c. Which probability is relevant for determining whether 4 is a significantly high number of drivers who say that they text while driving: the result from part (a) or part (b)?

d. Is 4 a significantly high number of drivers who say that they text while driving? Why or why not?

27. Biometric Security In a *USA Today* survey of 510 people, 270 (or 53%) said that we should replace passwords with biometric security, such as fingerprints. Use the following probabilities related to determining whether the result of 270 is significantly high (assuming the true rate is 50%). Is 270 significantly high? What should be concluded about the claim that the majority of the population says that we should replace passwords with biometric security? Explain.

- P(respondent says to use biometrics) = 0.5
- P(among 510, exactly 270 say to use biometrics) = 0.0146
- P(among 510, 270 or more say to use biometrics) = 0.0995.

28. Stem Cell Survey In a *Newsweek* poll of 882 adults, 481 (or 55%) said that they were in favor of using federal tax money to fund medical research using stem cells obtained from human embryos. A politician claims that people don't really understand the stem cell issue and their responses to such questions are random responses equivalent to a coin toss. Use the following probabilities related to determining whether the result of 481 is significantly high (assuming the true rate is 50%). Is 481 significantly high? What should be concluded about the politician's claim? Explain.

- P(respondent says to use the federal tax money) = 0.5
- P(among 882, exactly 481 say to use federal tax money) = 0.000713
- P(among 882, 481 or more say to use federal tax money) = 0.00389

5-1 Beyond the Basics

29. Expected Value for the Florida Pick 3 Lottery In the Florida Pick 3 lottery, you can bet $1 by selecting three digits, each between 0 and 9 inclusive. If the same three numbers are drawn in the same order, you win and collect $500.

a. How many different selections are possible?

b. What is the probability of winning?

c. If you win, what is your net profit?

d. Find the expected value for a $1 bet.

e. If you bet $1 on the pass line in the casino dice game of craps, the expected value is −1.4¢. Which bet is better in the sense of producing a higher expected value: a $1 bet in the Florida Pick 3 lottery or a $1 bet on the pass line in craps?

30. Expected Value in North Carolina's Pick 4 Game In North Carolina's Pick 4 lottery game, you can pay $1 to select a four-digit number from 0000 through 9999. If you select the same sequence of four digits that are drawn, you win and collect $5000.

a. How many different selections are possible?

b. What is the probability of winning?

c. If you win, what is your net profit?

d. Find the expected value.

e. If you bet $1 in North Carolina's Pick 3 game, the expected value is −50¢. Which bet is better in the sense of a producing a higher expected value: A $1 bet in the North Carolina Pick 4 game or a $1 bet in the North Carolina Pick 3 game?

31. Expected Value in Roulette When playing roulette at the Venetian casino in Las Vegas, a gambler is trying to decide whether to bet $5 on the number 27 or to bet $5 that the outcome is any one of these five possibilities: 0, 00, 1, 2, 3. The expected value of the $5 bet for a single number is −26¢. For the $5 bet that the outcome is 0, 00, 1, 2, or 3, there is a probability of 5/38 of making a net profit of $30 and a 33/38 probability of losing $5.

a. Find the expected value for the $5 bet that the outcome is 0, 00, 1, 2, or 3.

b. Which bet is better: a $5 bet on the number 27 or a $5 bet that the outcome is any one of the numbers 0, 00, 1, 2, or 3? Why?

32. Life Insurance There is a 0.99963 probability that a randomly selected 20-year-old female lives through the year (based on data from the U.S. Department of Health and Human Services). An insurance company wants to offer her a one-year policy with a death benefit of $1,000,000. How much should the company charge for this policy if it wants an expected return of $400 from all similar policies?

5-2 Binomial Probability Distributions

Key Concept Section 5-1 introduced the important concept of a discrete probability distribution. Among the various discrete probability distributions that exist, the focus of this section is the *binomial probability distribution*. Part 1 of this section introduces the binomial probability distribution along with methods for finding probabilities. Part 2 presents easy methods for finding the mean and standard deviation of a binomial distribution. As in other sections, we stress the importance of *interpreting* probability values to determine whether events are *significantly low* or *significantly high*.

PART 1 Basics of Binomial Probability Distribution

Binomial probability distributions allow us to deal with circumstances in which the outcomes belong to *two* categories, such as heads/tails or acceptable/defective or survived/died.

DEFINITION

A **binomial probability distribution** results from a procedure that meets these four requirements:

1. The procedure has a *fixed number of trials.* (A trial is a single observation.)

2. The trials must be *independent*, meaning that the outcome of any individual trial doesn't affect the probabilities in the other trials.

3. Each trial must have all outcomes classified into exactly *two categories,* commonly referred to as *success* and *failure* (but a "success" is not necessarily something good).

4. The probability of a success remains the same in all trials.

Notation for Binomial Probability Distributions

S and F (success and failure) denote the two possible categories of all outcomes.

$P(S) = p$	(p = probability of a success)
$P(F) = 1 - p = q$	(q = probability of a failure)
n	the fixed number of trials
x	a specific number of successes in n trials, so x can be any whole number between 0 and n, inclusive
p	probability of *success* in *one* of the n trials
q	probability of *failure* in *one* of the n trials
$P(x)$	probability of getting exactly x successes among the n trials

---

CAUTION The word *success* as used here is arbitrary and does not necessarily represent something good. Either of the two possible categories may be called the success S as long as its probability is identified as p. (The value of q can always be found from $q = 1 - p$. If $p = 0.95$, then $q = 1 - 0.95 = 0.05$.)

CAUTION When using a binomial probability distribution, always be sure that x and p are *consistent* in the sense that they both refer to the *same* category being called a success.

EXAMPLE 1 Cash

When an adult smartphone owner is randomly selected (with replacement), there is a 0.05 probability that this person is cashless (*never* carries cash) (based on a U.S. Bank survey of over 2003 adult smartphone owners in the U.S.). We want to find the probability that among ten randomly selected adults, exactly two of them are cashless.

a. Does this procedure result in a binomial distribution?

b. If this procedure does result in a binomial distribution, identify the values of n, x, p, and q.

continued

SOLUTION

a. This procedure does satisfy the requirements for a binomial distribution, as shown below.

1. The number of trials (10) is fixed.
2. The 10 trials are independent because the probability of any random adult smartphone owner being cashless is not affected by the results from the other randomly selected adults.
3. Each of the 10 trials has two categories of outcomes: The selected person is either cashless or is not.
4. For each randomly selected adult smartphone owner, there is a 0.05 probability that this person is cashless, and that probability remains the same for each of the ten selected people.

b. Having concluded that the given procedure does result in a binomial distribution, we now proceed to identify the values of n, x, p, and q.

1. With ten randomly selected adults, we have $n = 10$.
2. We want the probability of exactly two who are cashless, so $x = 2$.
3. The probability of success (getting someone who is cashless) for one selection is 0.05, so $p = 0.05$.
4. The probability of failure (not getting someone who is cashless) is 0.95, so $q = 0.95$.

Consistent Notation Again, it is very important to be sure that x and p both refer to the same concept of "success." In this example, we use x to count the number of people who are cashless, so p must be the probability that the selected person is cashless. Therefore, x and p do use the same concept of success: being cashless.

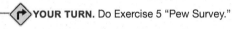

YOUR TURN. Do Exercise 5 "Pew Survey."

Treating Dependent Events as Independent

When selecting a sample (as in a survey), we usually sample *without replacement*. Sampling without replacement results in dependent events, which violates a requirement of a binomial distribution. However, we can often treat the events as if they were independent by applying the following 5% guideline introduced in Section 4-2:

5% Guideline for Cumbersome Calculations

When sampling without replacement and the sample size is no more than 5% of the size of the population, treat the selections as being *independent* (even though they are actually dependent).

Methods for Finding Binomial Probabilities

We now proceed with three methods for finding the probabilities corresponding to the random variable x in a binomial distribution. The first method involves calculations using the *binomial probability formula* and is the basis for the other two methods. The second method involves the use of software or a calculator, and the third method involves the use of the Appendix Table A-1. (With technology so widespread, such tables are becoming obsolete.) If using technology that automatically produces binomial probabilities, we recommend that you solve one or two exercises using Method 1 to better understand the basis for the calculations.

Method 1: Using the Binomial Probability Formula In a binomial probability distribution, probabilities can be calculated by using Formula 5-5.

FORMULA 5-5   Binomial Probability Formula

$$P(x) = \frac{n!}{(n - x)!x!} \cdot p^x \cdot q^{n-x} \qquad \text{for } x = 0, 1, 2, \ldots, n$$

where

n = number of trials

x = number of successes among n trials

p = probability of success in any one trial

q = probability of failure in any one trial $(q = 1 - p)$

Fun Stuff for Formula-Loving Readers

Formula 5-5 can also be expressed as $P(x) = {}_nC_x \, p^x \, q^{n-x}$. With x items identical to themselves, and $n - x$ other items identical to themselves, the number of permutations is $_nC_x = n!/[(n - x)!x!]$, so the two sides of this equation are interchangeable. The factorial symbol !, introduced in Section 4-4, denotes the product of decreasing factors. Two examples of factorials are $3! = 3 \cdot 2 \cdot 1 = 6$ and $0! = 1$ (by definition).

EXAMPLE 2   Cash

Given that there is a 0.05 probability that a randomly selected adult smartphone owner is cashless, use the binomial probability formula to calculate the probability that when ten adults are randomly selected, exactly two of them are cashless. That is, apply the binomial probability formula (Formula 5-5) to find $P(2)$ given that $n = 10$, $x = 2$, $p = 0.05$, and $q = 0.95$.

SOLUTION

Using the given values of n, x, p, and q in the binomial probability formula (Formula 5-5), we get

$$P(2) = \frac{10!}{(10 - 2)!2!} \cdot 0.05^2 \cdot 0.95^{10-2}$$

$$= \frac{10!}{8!2!} \cdot 0.0025 \cdot 0.663420$$

$$= (45)(0.0025)(0.663420) = 0.074635$$

$$= 0.0746 \text{ (rounded to three significant digits)}$$

The probability of getting exactly two cashless adults is 0.0746.

YOUR TURN. Do Exercise 13 "Guessing Answers."

Calculation hint: When computing a probability with the binomial probability formula, it's helpful to get a single number for $n!/[(n - x)!x!]$ or $_nC_x$, a single number for p^x, and a single number for q^{n-x}, then simply multiply the three factors together as shown in the third line of the calculation in the preceding example. Don't round when you find those three factors; round only at the end, and round the final result to three significant digits.

Method 2: Using Technology Technologies can be used to find binomial probabilities. The screen displays list binomial probabilities for $n = 10$ and $p = 0.05$, as in Example 2. Notice that in each display, the probability distribution is given as a table. Example 2 showed that $P(2) = 0.0746$, and that same result can be easily obtained from technology; see the probability of 0.0746 corresponding to 2 successes in the displays.

Statdisk

x	P(x)	P(x or fewer)	P(x or greater)
0	0.5987369	0.5987369	1.0000000
1	0.3151247	0.9138616	0.4012631
2	0.0746348	0.9884964	0.0861384
3	0.0104751	0.9989715	0.0115036
4	0.0009648	0.9999363	0.0010285
5	0.0000609	0.9999972	0.0000637
6	0.0000027	0.9999999	0.0000028
7	0.0000001	1.0000000	0.0000001
8	0.0000000	1.0000000	0.0000000
9	0.0000000	1.0000000	0.0000000
10	0.0000000	1.0000000	0.0000000

Minitab

x	P(X = x)
0	0.598737
1	0.315125
2	0.074635
3	0.010475
4	0.000965
5	0.000061
6	0.000003
7	0.000000
8	0.000000
9	0.000000
10	0.000000

Excel

	A	B
1	0	0.598736939
2	1	0.315124705
3	2	0.074634799
4	3	0.010475059
5	4	0.000964808
6	5	6.09352E-05
7	6	2.6726E-06
8	7	8.03789E-08
9	8	1.58643E-09
10	9	1.85547E-11
11	10	9.76563E-14

TI-85 Plus CE

```
NORMAL FLOAT AUTO REAL RADIAN MP

L1    L2      L3     L4     L5     3
0     0.5987  ------ ------ ------
1     0.3151
2     0.0746
3     0.0105
4     9.6E-4
5     6.1E-5
6     2.7E-6
7     8E-8
8     1.6E-9
9     2E-11
10    1E-13

L3(1)=
```

CP — **EXAMPLE 3** **Overtime Rule in Football**

In the Chapter Problem, we noted that between 1974 and 2011, there were 460 NFL football games decided in overtime, and 252 of them were won by the team that won the overtime coin toss. Is the result of 252 wins in the 460 games equivalent to random chance, or is 252 wins *significantly high?* We can answer that question by finding the probability of 252 wins or more in 460 games, assuming that wins and losses are equally likely.

SOLUTION

Using the notation for binomial probabilities, we have $n = 460$, $p = 0.5$, $q = 0.5$, and we want to find the sum of all probabilities for each value of x from 252 through 460. The formula is not practical here, because we would need to apply it 209 times—we don't want to go there. Table A-1 (Binomial Probabilities) doesn't apply because $n = 460$, which is way beyond the scope of that table. Instead, we wisely choose to use technology.

   The Statdisk display on the next page shows that the probability of 252 or more wins in 460 overtime games is 0.0224 (rounded), which is low (such as less than 0.05). This shows that it is unlikely that we would get 252 or more wins by chance. If we effectively rule out chance, we are left with the more reasonable explanation that the team winning the overtime coin toss has a better chance of winning the game.

Statdisk

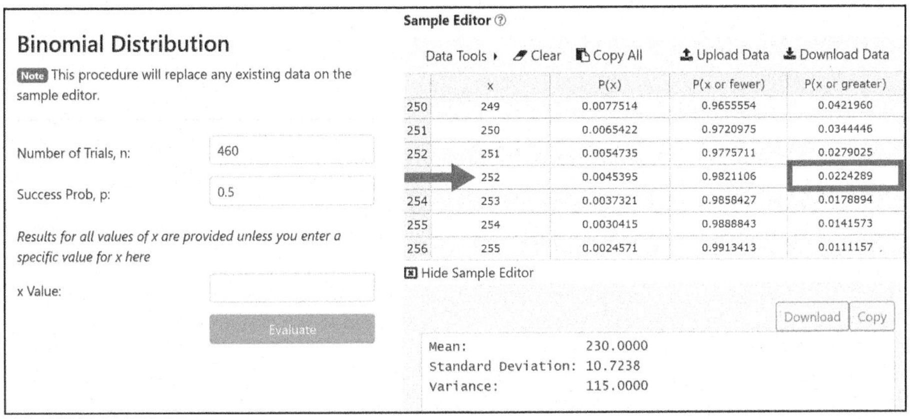

Binomial Distribution

Note This procedure will replace any existing data on the sample editor.

Number of Trials, n: 460

Success Prob, p: 0.5

Results for all values of x are provided unless you enter a specific value for x here

x Value:

Evaluate

Sample Editor ⑦

Data Tools ▸   ✐ Clear   🗋 Copy All   ⬆ Upload Data   ⬇ Download Data

	x	P(x)	P(x or fewer)	P(x or greater)
250	249	0.0077514	0.9655554	0.0421960
251	250	0.0065422	0.9720975	0.0344446
252	251	0.0054735	0.9775711	0.0279025
	252	0.0045395	0.9821106	0.0224289
254	253	0.0037321	0.9858427	0.0178894
255	254	0.0030415	0.9888843	0.0141573
256	255	0.0024571	0.9913413	0.0111157

☒ Hide Sample Editor

Download   Copy

Mean: 230.0000
Standard Deviation: 10.7238
Variance: 115.0000

↱ **YOUR TURN.** Do Exercise 27 "Internet Voting."

Example 3 illustrates the power and ease of using technology. Example 3 also illustrates the rare event rule of statistical thinking: If under a given assumption (such as the assumption that winning the overtime coin toss has no effect), the probability of a particular observed event (such as 252 or more wins in 460 games) is extremely small (such as 0.05 or less), we conclude that the assumption is probably not correct.

Method 3: Using Table A-1 in Appendix A This method can be skipped if technology is available. Table A-1 in Appendix A lists binomial probabilities for select values of n and p. Table A-1 cannot be used if $n > 8$ or if the probability p is not one of the 13 values included in the table.

To use Table A-1 we must first locate n and the desired corresponding value of x. At this stage, one row of numbers should be isolated. Now align that row with the desired probability of p by using the column across the top. The isolated number represents the desired probability. A very small probability, such as 0.000064, is indicated by 0+.

EXAMPLE 4   Veggies

Based on a Gallup poll, 5% of U.S. adults are vegetarians. If we randomly select five adults, find the following probabilities by using Table A-1.

   a. The probability that exactly two of the five adults are vegetarians

   b. The probability that there are fewer than three vegetarians

SOLUTION

   a. The following excerpt from Table A-1 shows that when $n = 5$ and $p = 0.05$, the probability for $x = 2$ is given by $P(2) = 0.021$.

   TABLE A-1 Binomial Probabilities

n	x	.01	.05	.10	x	P(x)
5	0	.951	.774	.590	0	.774
	1	.048	.204	.328	1	.204
	2	.001	.021	.073	2	.021
	3	0+	.001	.008	3	.001
	4	0+	0+	0+	4	0+
	5	0+	0+	0+	5	0+

p (heading spanning .01, .05, .10 columns)

continued

Proportions of Males/Females

It is well known that when a baby is born, boys and girls are not equally likely. It is currently believed that 105 boys are born for every 100 girls, so the probability of a boy is 0.512. Kristen Navara of the University of Georgia conducted a study showing that around the world, more boys are born than girls, but the difference becomes smaller as people are located closer to the equator. She used latitudes, temperatures, unemployment rates, gross and national products from 200 countries and conducted a statistical analysis showing that the proportions of boys appear to be affected only by latitude and its related weather. So far, no one has identified a reasonable explanation for this phenomenon.

b. The phrase "fewer than three" vegetarians means that the number of vegetarians is 0 or 1 or 2. (See the bottom of the preceding page for the probability values.)

$$P(\text{fewer than 3 vegetarians}) = P(0 \text{ or } 1 \text{ or } 2)$$
$$= P(0) + P(1) + P(2)$$
$$= 0.774 + 0.204 + 0.021$$
$$= 0.999$$

YOUR TURN. Do Exercise 15 "Cashless Society" using Table A-1.

PART 2 Using Mean and Standard Deviation for Critical Thinking

Section 5-1 included formulas for finding the mean, variance, and standard deviation from *any* discrete probability distribution. A binomial distribution is a particular type of discrete probability distribution, so we could use those same formulas, but if we know the values of *n* and *p*, it is much easier to use the following:

For Binomial Distributions

FORMULA 5-6   Mean: $\mu = np$

FORMULA 5-7   Variance: $\sigma^2 = npq$

FORMULA 5-8   Standard Deviation: $\sigma = \sqrt{npq}$

As in earlier sections, finding values for μ and σ can be great fun, but it is especially important to *interpret* and *understand* those values, so the range rule of thumb and the rare event rule for inferential statistics can be very helpful. Here is a brief summary of the range rule of thumb: Values are significantly low or high if they differ from the mean by more than 2 standard deviations, as described by the following:

> **Range Rule of Thumb**
> ***Significantly low*** values $\leq (\mu - 2\sigma)$
> ***Significantly high*** values $\geq (\mu + 2\sigma)$
> ***Values not significant***: Between $(\mu - 2\sigma)$ *and* $(\mu + 2\sigma)$

CP EXAMPLE 5 Using Parameters to Determine Significance

The Chapter Problem and Example 3 involve $n = 460$ overtime wins in NFL football games. We get $p = 0.5$ and $q = 0.5$ by assuming that winning the overtime coin toss does not provide an advantage, so both teams have the same 0.5 chance of winning the game in overtime.

a. Find the mean and standard deviation for the number of wins in groups of 460 games.

b. Use the range rule of thumb to find the values separating the numbers of wins that are significantly low or significantly high.

c. Is the result of 252 overtime wins in 460 games significantly high?

SOLUTION

a. With $n = 460$, $p = 0.5$, and $q = 0.5$, Formulas 5-6 and 5-8 can be applied as follows:

$$\mu = np = (460)(0.5) = 230.0 \text{ games}$$

$$\sigma = \sqrt{npq} = \sqrt{(460)(0.5)(0.5)} = 10.7 \text{ games (rounded)}$$

For random groups of 460 overtime games, the mean number of wins is 230.0 games, and the standard deviation is 10.7 games.

b. The values separating numbers of wins that are significantly low or significantly high are the values that are two standard deviations away from the mean. With $\mu = 230.0$ games and $\sigma = 10.7$ games, we get

Significantly low $\leq \mu - 2\sigma = 230.0 - 2(10.7) = 208.6$ games

Significantly high $\geq \mu + 2\sigma = 230.0 + 2(10.7) = 251.4$ games

Significantly low numbers of wins are 208.6 games or fewer, significantly high numbers of wins are 251.4 games or greater, and values not significant are between 208.6 games and 251.4 games.

c. The result of 252 wins is significantly high because it is greater than the value of 251.4 games found in part (b).

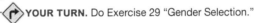 **YOUR TURN.** Do Exercise 29 "Gender Selection."

Instead of the range rule of thumb, we could also use probabilities to determine when values are significantly high or low.

Using Probabilities to Determine When Results Are Significantly High or Low

■ **Significantly *high* number of successes:** x successes among n trials is *significantly high* if the probability of x or more successes is 0.05 or less. That is, x is a significantly high number of successes if $P(x \text{ or more}) \leq 0.05$.*

■ **Significantly *low* number of successes:** x successes among n trials is *significantly low* if the probability of x or fewer successes is 0.05 or less. That is, x is a significantly low number of successes if $P(x \text{ or fewer}) \leq 0.05$.*

*The value 0.05 is not absolutely rigid. Other values, such as 0.01, could be used to distinguish between results that are significant and those that are not significant.

Rationale for the Binomial Probability Formula

The binomial probability formula is the basis for all three methods presented in this section. Instead of accepting and using that formula blindly, let's see why it works.

In Example 2, we used the binomial probability formula to find the probability of getting exactly two adult smartphone owners who are cashless (never use cash) when ten adult smartphone owners are randomly selected. With $P(\text{one person is cashless}) = 0.05$, we can use the multiplication rule from Section 4-2 to find the probability that the first two adults are cashless and the last eight adults are not cashless. We get the following result:

$P(2 \text{ adults are cashless followed by 8 adults who are not cashless})$

$= 0.05 \cdot 0.05 \cdot 0.95 \cdot 0.95 \cdot 0.95 \cdot 0.95 \cdot 0.95 \cdot 0.95 \cdot 0.95 \cdot 0.95$

$= 0.05^2 \cdot 0.95^8$

$= 0.00165855$

This result gives a probability of randomly selecting ten adult smartphone owners and finding that the first two are cashless and the last eight are not. However, the probability of

0.00165855 is not the probability of getting exactly two adults who are cashless because it was found by assuming a particular sequence. Other different sequences are possible.

In Section 4-4 we saw that with two subjects identical to each other (such as adults who are cashless) and eight other subjects identical to each other (such as adults who are not cashless), the total number of arrangements, or permutations, is $10!/[(10 - 2)!\,2!]$ or 45. Each of those 45 different arrangements has a probability of $0.05^2 \cdot 0.95^8$, so the total probability is as follows:

$$P(2 \text{ adults are cashless among } 10) = \frac{10!}{(10 - 2)!\,2!} \cdot 0.05^2 \cdot 0.95^8 = 0.0746$$

This particular result can be generalized as the binomial probability formula (Formula 5-5). That is, the binomial probability formula is a combination of the multiplication rule of probability and the counting rule for the number of arrangements of n items when x of them are identical to each other and the other $n - x$ are identical to each other.

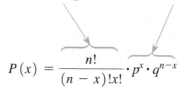

The number of outcomes with exactly x successes among n trials

The probability of x successes among n trials for any one particular order

$$P(x) = \frac{n!}{(n - x)!\,x!} \cdot p^x \cdot q^{n-x}$$

TECH CENTER

Binomial Distributions

Access tech supplements, videos, and data sets at **www.TriolaStats.com**

Statdisk

1. Click **Analysis** in the top menu.
2. Select **Probability Distributions** from the dropdown menu and select **Binomial Distribution** from the submenu.
3. Enter the values for *n, p* and click **Evaluate.**

Tip: Enter a specific value for *x* to get a single probability.

Minitab

1. Enter the values of *x* for which you want probabilities (such as 0, 1, 2, 3, 4, 5) in column C1.
2. Select **Calc** from the top menu.
3. Select **Probability Distributions** from the dropdown menu and **Binomial** from the submenu.
4. Select **Probability,** enter the number of trials, enter the event probability, and select **C1** for *Input Column.*
5. Click **OK.**

StatCrunch

1. Click **Stat** in the top menu.
2. Select **Calculators** from the dropdown menu and **Binomial** from the submenu.
3. In the dialog box, enter the desired values for *n, p, x.* Select = or the desired inequality for *x.*
4. Click **Compute.**

TI-83/84 Plus Calculator

1. Press **2ND** then **VARS** keys to access the *DISTR* (distributions) menu.
2. Select **binompdf** and click **ENTER**.
3. Enter the values for trials *n*, probability *p*, and number of successes *x* to complete the command **binompdf(n, p, x)**. Press **ENTER**.

Tip: Omitting a value for *x* provides a list for all probabilities corresponding to *x = 0, 1, 2…n*. Press **STO** then **2ND** then **2** to save the probabilities as list *L2*. You can then manually enter the values of *x* in list *L1* for calculations.

Tip: Select **binomcdf** in Step 2 for *cumulative* probabilities.

Excel

1. Enter the values of *x* for which you want probabilities (such as 0, 1, 2, 3, 4, 5) in column A.
2. Select cell **B1**, click **Insert Function** *fx*, select the category **Statistical**, select the function **BINOM.DIST** and click **OK.**
3. Enter **A1** for *Number_s* and then enter the number of trials *n* and probability *p*.
4. Enter **0** in the *Cumulative* box.
5. Click **OK** and the probability will appear in cell B1.
6. Copy **B1** down the column to obtain the probability for each value of *x* listed in column A.

Tip: Enter **1** in Step 4 for the *cumulative* binomial distribution.

R

R command:
dbinom(x,n,p)

TIP: Use the R command **pbinom(x,n,p)** for *cumulative* probabilities.

A complete list of R statistical commands is available at TriolaStats.com

5-2 Basic Skills and Concepts

Statistical Literacy and Critical Thinking

1. Movies When randomly selecting a speaking character in a movie, the probability of getting a female is 0.331 (based on data from "Inequality in 1200 Popular Films," by Smith, et al., Annenberg Foundation). If we want to find the probability that among five randomly selected speaking characters in movies, there are exactly two females, what is wrong with this solution:

$$P(2 \text{ females among 5 speaking characters}) =$$
$$P(\text{female}) \cdot P(\text{female}) \cdot P(\text{male}) \cdot P(\text{male}) \cdot P(\text{male}) =$$
$$(0.331)(0.331)(1 - 0.331)(1 - 0.331)(1 - 0.331) = 0.0328$$

2. Notation Assume that we want to find the probability that when five speaking characters in movies are randomly selected, exactly two of them are females. Also assume that when randomly selecting a speaking character in a movie, the probability of getting a female is 0.331. Identify the values of n, x, p, and q.

3. Independent Events Again assume that when randomly selecting a speaking character in a movie, the probability of getting a female is 0.331, as in Exercise 1. If we want to find the probability of 20 females when 50 *different* speaking characters are randomly selected from a population of 1500 speaking characters, are the 50 selections independent? Using the 5% guideline for cumbersome calculations, can they be treated as being independent?

4. Notation of 0+ Using the same survey described in Exercise 1, the probability of randomly selecting 50 speaking characters from movies and getting 40 females is expressed as 0+. Does 0+ indicate that it is impossible to get 40 females among the 50 speaking characters? What does 0+ indicate?

Identifying Binomial Distributions. *In Exercises 5–12, determine whether the given procedure results in a binomial distribution or a distribution that can be treated as binomial (by applying the 5% guideline for cumbersome calculations). For those that are not binomial and cannot be treated as binomial, identify at least one requirement that is not satisfied.*

5. Pew Survey In a Pew Research Center survey of 3930 subjects, the ages of the respondents are recorded.

6. Pew Survey In a Pew Research Center survey, 3930 subjects were asked if they have ever fired a gun, and the responses consist of "yes" or "no."

7. LOL In a U.S. Cellular survey of 500 smartphone users, subjects are asked if they find abbreviations (such as LOL or BFF) annoying, and each response was recorded as "yes," "no," or "not sure."

8. Clinical Trial of YSORT The YSORT method of gender selection, developed by the Genetics & IVF Institute, was designed to increase the likelihood that a baby will be a boy. When 291 couples use the YSORT method and give birth to 291 babies, the genders of the babies are recorded.

9. Surveying Senators The Senate members of the 116th Congress include 75 males and 25 females. Forty different senators are randomly selected without replacement, and the gender of each selected senator is recorded.

10. Surveying Senators Ten different senators from the 116th Congress are randomly selected without replacement, and the numbers of terms that they have served are recorded.

11. Smart TV In a comScore survey, 3600 different households were randomly selected without replacement, and respondents were asked whether the household had a smart TV. Answers of "yes" and "no" were recorded.

12. Credit Cards In a CreditCards.com survey, 1659 different adults with credit cards were randomly selected without replacement, and respondents were asked if they have ever changed their primary credit card. Responses of "yes" and "no" were recorded.

Binomial Probability Formula. *In Exercises 13 and 14, answer the questions designed to help understand the rationale for the binomial probability formula.*

13. Guessing Answers Standard tests, such as the SAT, ACT, or Medical College Admission Test (MCAT), typically use multiple choice questions, each with five possible answers (a, b, c, d, e), one of which is correct. Assume that you guess the answers to the first three questions.

a. Use the multiplication rule to find the probability that the first two guesses are wrong and the third is correct. That is, find $P(WWC)$, where W denotes a wrong answer and C denotes a correct answer.

b. Beginning with WWC, make a complete list of the different possible arrangements of two wrong answers and one correct answer, and then find the probability for each entry in the list.

c. Based on the preceding results, what is the probability of getting exactly one correct answer when three guesses are made?

14. Porch Pirates An InsuranceQuotes.com survey showed that 8% of Americans had a holiday package stolen from outside their front door. Consider the random selection of four Americans.

a. Use the multiplication rule to find the probability that the first three did not have a package stolen from outside their front door and the fourth subject did have a package stolen from outside their front door. That is, find $P(NNNS)$, where N denotes that no package was stolen and S indicates that a package was stolen.

b. Beginning with NNNS, make a complete list of the different possible arrangements of those four letters, then find the probability for each entry in the list.

c. Based on the preceding results, what is the probability of getting exactly three Americans who did not have a package stolen from outside their front porch and one American who did have a package stolen from outside their front porch.

Cashless Society. *40% of consumers believe that cash will be obsolete in the next 20 years (based on a survey by J.P. Morgan Chase). In each of Exercises 15–20, assume that 8 consumers are randomly selected. Find the indicated probability.*

15. Find the probability that exactly 6 of the selected consumers believe that cash will be obsolete in the next 20 years.

16. Find the probability that at least 6 of the selected consumers believe that cash will be obsolete in the next 20 years.

17. Find the probability that fewer than 3 of the selected consumers believe that cash will be obsolete in the next 20 years.

18. Find the probability that no more than 3 of the selected consumers believe that cash will be obsolete in the next 20 years.

19. Find the probability that none of the selected consumers believes that cash will be obsolete in the next 20 years.

20. Find the probability that at least one of the selected consumers believes that cash will be obsolete in the next 20 years.

In Exercises 21–24, assume that when human resource managers are randomly selected, 65% of them say that after submitting a résumé, job applicants should follow up within two weeks.

21. If 10 human resource managers are randomly selected, find the probability that exactly 6 of them say job applicants should follow up within two weeks.

22. If 16 human resource managers are randomly selected, find the probability that exactly 12 of them say job applicants should follow up within two weeks.

23. If 20 human resource managers are randomly selected, find the probability that at least 18 of them say job applicants should follow up within two weeks.

24. If 14 human resource managers are randomly selected, find the probability that fewer than 3 of them say job applicants should follow up within two weeks.

In Exercises 25–28, find the probabilities and answer the questions.

25. Whitus v. Georgia In the classic legal case of *Whitus v. Georgia*, a jury pool of 90 people was supposed to be randomly selected from a population in which 27% were minorities. Among the 90 people selected, 7 were minorities. Find the probability of getting 7 or fewer minorities if the jury pool was randomly selected. Is the result of 7 minorities significantly low? What does the result suggest about the jury selection process?

26. Social Media and Job Applicants Based on a Society for Human Resource Management survey, 36% of human resource professionals are at companies that rejected job candidates because of information found on their social media. If 25 human resource professionals are randomly selected, would 14 be a significantly high number to be at companies that rejected job candidates because of information found on their social media? Why or why not?

27. Internet Voting Based on a Consumer Reports survey, 39% of likely voters would be willing to vote by Internet instead of the in-person traditional method of voting. For each of the following, assume that 15 likely voters are randomly selected.

a. What is the probability that exactly 12 of those selected would do Internet voting?

b. If 12 of the selected voters would do Internet voting, is 12 significantly high? Why or why not?

c. Find the probability that at least one of the selected likely voters would do Internet voting.

28. Too Young to Tat Based on a Harris poll, among adults who regret getting tattoos, 20% say that they were too young when they got their tattoos. Assume that five adults who regret getting tattoos are randomly selected, and find the indicated probability.

a. Find the probability that none of the selected adults say that they were too young to get tattoos.

b. Find the probability that exactly one of the selected adults says that he or she was too young to get tattoos.

c. Find the probability that the number of selected adults saying they were too young is 0 or 1.

d. If we randomly select five adults, is 1 a significantly low number who say that they were too young to get tattoos?

Significance with Range Rule of Thumb. *In Exercises 29 and 30, assume that different groups of couples use the XSORT method of gender selection and each couple gives birth to one baby. The XSORT method is designed to increase the likelihood that a baby will be a girl, but assume that the method has no effect, so the probability of a girl is 0.5.*

29. Gender Selection Assume that the groups consist of 36 couples.

a. Find the mean and standard deviation for the numbers of girls in groups of 36 births.

b. Use the range rule of thumb to find the values separating results that are significantly low or significantly high.

c. Is the result of 26 girls a result that is significantly high? What does it suggest about the effectiveness of the XSORT method?

30. Gender Selection Assume that the groups consist of 16 couples.

a. Find the mean and standard deviation for the numbers of girls in groups of 16 births.

b. Use the range rule of thumb to find the values separating results that are significantly low or significantly high.

c. Is the result of 11 girls a result that is significantly high? What does it suggest about the effectiveness of the XSORT method?

Significance with Range Rule of Thumb. *In Exercises 31 and 32, assume that hybridization experiments are conducted with peas having the property that for offspring, there is a 0.75 probability that a pea has green pods (as in one of Mendel's famous experiments).*

31. Hybrids Assume that offspring peas are randomly selected in groups of 10.

a. Find the mean and standard deviation for the numbers of peas with green pods in the groups of 10.

b. Use the range rule of thumb to find the values separating results that are significantly low or significantly high.

c. Is the result of 9 peas with green pods a result that is significantly high? Why or why not?

32. Hybrids Assume that offspring peas are randomly selected in groups of 16.

a. Find the mean and standard deviation for the numbers of peas with green pods in the groups of 16.

b. Use the range rule of thumb to find the values separating results that are significantly low or significantly high.

c. Is a result of 7 peas with green pods a result that is significantly low? Why or why not?

Composite Sampling.   *Exercises 33 and 34 involve the method of composite sampling, whereby a medical testing laboratory saves time and money by combining blood samples for tests so that only one test is conducted for several people. A combined sample tests positive if at least one person has the disease. If a combined sample tests positive, then individual blood tests are used to identify the individual with the disease or disorder.*

33. HIV It is estimated that in the United States, the proportion of people infected with the human immunodeficiency virus (HIV) is 0.00343. In tests for HIV, blood samples from 50 different people are combined. What is the probability that the combined sample tests positive for HIV? Is it unlikely for such a combined sample to test positive?

34. Workplace Drug Testing Workplace drug tests have an annual positive rate of 4.2% (based on data from Quest Diagnostics). Given that the rate is quite low, samples can be combined into groups of 100 and tested together. If the group fails, the individual samples can be retested to identify the particular workers who have positive test results. What is the probability that a combination of 100 samples yields a positive result? Based on the resulting probability, does it seem wise to combine 100 samples into one sample?

Acceptance Sampling.   *Exercises 35 and 36 involve the method of acceptance sampling. With acceptance sampling, a large shipment of items is accepted or rejected based on test results from a sample drawn from the shipment.*

35. Historical Use of Acceptance Sampling Methods of acceptance sampling were first used by the U.S. Army in World War II when batches of ammunition were accepted or rejected based on results from samples. A common World War II rifle was the M1, and it used 30 caliber ammunition, and an ammo can contains 500 rounds. Use this sampling plan: Randomly select and test 5 rounds from an ammo can, then accept the whole can if the number of defects is 0 or 1. If the true defect rate is 4%, what is the probability that an ammo can will be accepted? Based on the result, does it appear that there is a production problem with the ammo?

36. AAA Batteries AAA batteries are made by companies including Duracell, Energizer, Eveready, and Panasonic. When purchasing bulk orders of AAA batteries, a toy manufacturer uses this acceptance sampling plan: Randomly select 50 batteries and determine whether each is within specifications. The entire shipment is accepted if at most 2 batteries do not meet specifications. A shipment contains 2000 AAA batteries, and 2% of them do not meet specifications. What is the probability that this whole shipment will be accepted? Will almost all such shipments be accepted, or will many be rejected?

Ultimate Binomial Exercises!   *Exercises 37–40 involve finding binomial probabilities, finding parameters, and determining whether values are significantly high or low by using the range rule of thumb and probabilities.*

37. M&Ms Data Set 38 "Candies" in Appendix B includes data from 345 M&M candies, and 36 of them are brown. Mars, Inc. claims that 13% of its plain M&M candies are brown. For the following, assume that the claim of 13% is true, and assume that a sample consists of 345 M&Ms.

a. For the 345 M&Ms, use the range rule of thumb to identify the limits separating numbers of brown M&Ms that are significantly low and those that are significantly high. Based on the results, is the result of 36 brown M&Ms significantly low?

b. Find the probability of exactly 36 brown M&Ms.

c. Find the probability of 36 or fewer brown M&Ms.

d. Which probability is relevant for determining whether the result of 36 brown M&Ms is significantly low: the probability from part (b) or part (c)? Based on the relevant probability, is the result of 36 brown M&Ms significantly low?

e. What do the results suggest about the 13% claim by Mars, Inc.?

38. Politics The County Clerk in Essex, New Jersey, was accused of cheating by not using randomness in assigning the order in which candidates' names appeared on voting ballots. Among 41 different ballots, Democrats were assigned the desirable first line 40 times. Assume that Democrats and Republicans are assigned the first line using a method of random selection so that they are equally likely to get that first line.

a. Use the range rule of thumb to identify the limits separating values that are significantly low and those that are significantly high. Based on the results, is the result of 40 first lines for Democrats significantly high?

b. Find the probability of exactly 40 first lines for Democrats.

c. Find the probability of 40 or more first lines for Democrats.

d. Which probability is relevant for determining whether 40 first lines for Democrats is significantly high: the probability from part (b) or part (c)? Based on the relevant probability, is the result of 40 first lines for Democrats significantly high?

e. What do the results suggest about how the clerk met the requirement of using a random method to assign the order of candidates' names on voting ballots?

39. Perception and Reality In a presidential election, 611 randomly selected voters were surveyed, and 308 of them said that they voted for the winning candidate (based on data from ICR Survey Research Group). The actual percentage of votes for the winning candidate was 43%. Assume that 43% of voters actually did vote for the winning candidate, and assume that 611 voters are randomly selected.

a. Use the range rule of thumb to identify the limits separating values that are significantly low and those that are significantly high. Based on the results, is the 308 voters who said that they voted for the winner significantly high?

b. Find the probability of exactly 308 voters who actually voted for the winner.

c. Find the probability of 308 or more voters who actually voted for the winner.

d. Which probability is relevant for determining whether the value of 308 voters is significantly high: the probability from part (b) or part (c)? Based on the relevant probability, is the result of 308 voters who said that they voted for the winner significantly high?

e. What is an important observation about the survey results?

40. Hybrids One of Mendel's famous experiments with peas resulted in 580 offspring, and 152 of them were yellow peas. Mendel claimed that under the same conditions, 25% of offspring peas would be yellow. Assume that Mendel's claim of 25% is true, and assume that a sample consists of 580 offspring peas.

a. Use the range rule of thumb to identify the limits separating values that are significantly low and those that are significantly high. Based on the results, is the result of 152 yellow peas either significantly low or significantly high?

b. Find the probability of exactly 152 yellow peas.

c. Find the probability of 152 or more yellow peas.

d. Which probability is relevant for determining whether 152 peas is significantly high: the probability from part (b) or part (c)? Based on the relevant probability, is the result of 152 yellow peas significantly high?

e. What do the results suggest about Mendel's claim of 25%?

5-2 Beyond the Basics

41. Geometric Distribution If a procedure meets all the conditions of a binomial distribution except that the number of trials is not fixed, then the **geometric distribution** can be used. The probability of getting the first success on the xth trial is given by $P(x) = p(1 - p)^{x-1}$, where p is the probability of success on any one trial. Subjects are randomly selected for the National Health and Nutrition Examination Survey conducted by the National Center for Health Statistics, Centers for Disease Control and Prevention. The probability that someone is a universal donor (with group O and type Rh negative blood) is 0.06. Find the probability that the first subject to be a universal blood donor is the fifth person selected.

42. Multinomial Distribution The binomial distribution applies only to cases involving two types of outcomes, whereas the **multinomial distribution** involves more than two categories. Suppose we have three types of mutually exclusive outcomes denoted by A, B, and C. Let $P(A) = p_1$, $P(B) = p_2$, and $P(C) = p_3$. In n independent trials, the probability of x_1 outcomes of type A, x_2 outcomes of type B, and x_3 outcomes of type C is given by

$$\frac{n!}{(x_1)!(x_2)!(x_3)!} \cdot p_1^{x_1} \cdot p_2^{x_2} \cdot p_3^{x_3}$$

A roulette wheel in the Venetian casino in Las Vegas has 18 red slots, 18 black slots, and 2 green slots. If roulette is played 15 times, find the probability of getting 7 red outcomes, 6 black outcomes, and 2 green outcomes.

43. Hypergeometric Distribution If we sample from a small finite population without replacement, the binomial distribution should not be used because the events are not independent. If sampling is done without replacement and the outcomes belong to one of two types, we can use the **hypergeometric distribution**. If a population has A objects of one type (such as lottery numbers you selected), while the remaining B objects are of the other type (such as lottery numbers you didn't select), and if n objects are sampled without replacement (such as six drawn lottery numbers), then the probability of getting x objects of type A and $n - x$ objects of type B is

$$P(x) = \frac{A!}{(A - x)!x!} \cdot \frac{B!}{(B - n + x)!(n - x)!} \div \frac{(A + B)!}{(A + B - n)!n!}$$

In New Jersey's Pick 6 lottery game, a bettor selects six numbers from 1 to 49 (without repetition), and a winning six-number combination is later randomly selected. Find the probability of getting exactly four winning numbers with one ticket.

5-3 \ Poisson Probability Distributions

Key Concept In Section 5-1 we introduced general discrete probability distributions and in Section 5-2 we considered binomial probability distributions, which is one particular category of discrete probability distributions. In this section we introduce *Poisson probability distributions,* which are another category of discrete probability distributions.

The following definition states that Poisson distributions are used with occurrences of an event over a specified interval, and here are some applications:

- Number of automobile accidents in a day

- Number of patients arriving at an emergency room in one hour

- Number of Internet users logging onto a website in one day

- Number of Atlantic hurricanes in one year
- Number of speling errors on a page
- Number of machine failures in a month

Go Figure

53: Number of years before we run out of oil.

DEFINITION

A **Poisson probability distribution** is a discrete probability distribution that applies to occurrences of some event *over a specified interval.* The random variable x is the number of occurrences of the event in an interval. The interval can be time, distance, area, volume, or some similar unit. The probability of the event occurring x times over an interval is given by Formula 5-9.

FORMULA 5-9   Poisson Probability Distribution

$$P(x) = \frac{\mu^x \cdot e^{-\mu}}{x!}$$

where $e \approx 2.71828$

μ = mean number of occurrences of the event in the intervals

Requirements for the Poisson Probability Distribution

1. The random variable x is the number of occurrences of an event *in some interval.*
2. The occurrences must be *random.*
3. The occurrences must be *independent* of each other.
4. The occurrences must be *uniformly distributed* over the interval being used.

Parameters of the Poisson Probability Distribution

- The mean is μ.
- The standard deviation is $\sigma = \sqrt{\mu}$.

Properties of the Poisson Probability Distribution

1. A particular Poisson distribution is determined only by the mean μ.
2. A Poisson distribution has possible x values of 0, 1, 2, ... with no upper limit.

EXAMPLE 1   Atlantic Hurricanes

There have been 652 Atlantic hurricanes during the 118-year period starting in 1900. Assume that the Poisson distribution is a suitable model.

   a. Find μ, the mean number of hurricanes per year.

   b. Find the probability that in a randomly selected year, there are exactly 6 hurricanes. That is, find $P(6)$, where $P(x)$ is the probability of x Atlantic hurricanes in a year.   *continued*

c. In this 118-year period, there were actually 16 years with 6 Atlantic hurricanes. How does this actual result compare to the probability found in part (b)? Does the Poisson distribution appear to be a good model in this case?

SOLUTION

a. The Poisson distribution applies because we are dealing with the occurrences of an event (hurricanes) over some interval (a year). The mean number of hurricanes per year is

$$\mu = \frac{\text{number of hurricanes}}{\text{number of years}} = \frac{652}{118} = 5.5$$

b. Using Formula 5-9, the probability of $x = 6$ hurricanes in a year is as follows (with $x = 6$, $\mu = 5.5$, and $e = 2.71828$):

$$P(6) = \frac{\mu^x \cdot e^{-\mu}}{x!} = \frac{5.5^6 \cdot 2.71828^{-5.5}}{6!} = \frac{(27,680.64)(0.0040867866)}{720} = 0.157$$

The probability of exactly 6 hurricanes in a year is $P(6) = 0.157$.

c. The probability of $P(6) = 0.157$ from part (b) is the likelihood of getting 6 Atlantic hurricanes in 1 year. In 118 years, the expected number of years with 6 Atlantic hurricanes is $118 \times 0.157 = 18.5$ years. The expected number of years with 6 hurricanes is 18.5, which is reasonably close to the 16 years that actually had 6 hurricanes, so in this case, the Poisson model appears to work quite well.

▶ **YOUR TURN.** Do Exercise 5 "Hurricanes."

Poisson Distribution as Approximation to Binomial

The Poisson distribution is sometimes used to approximate the binomial distribution when n is large and p is small. One rule of thumb is to approximate the binomial distribution by using the Poisson distribution when the following two requirements are both satisfied.

Requirements for Using Poisson as an Approximation to Binomial

1. $n \geq 100$

2. $np \leq 10$

If both requirements are satisfied and we want to use the Poisson distribution as an approximation to the binomial distribution, we need a value for μ. That value can be calculated by using Formula 5-6 (from Section 5-2):

FORMULA 5-6   Mean for Poisson as an Approximation to Binomial

$$\mu = np$$

EXAMPLE 2 **Maine Pick 4**

In the Maine Pick 4 game, you pay 50¢ to select a sequence of four digits (0–9) with repetition allowed, such as 1377. If you play this game once every day, find the probability of winning at least once in a year with 365 days.

SOLUTION

The time interval is a day, and playing once each day results in $n = 365$ games. Because there is one winning set of numbers among the 10,000 that are possible (from 0000 to 9999), the probability of a win is $p = 1/10,000$. With $n = 365$ and $p = 1/10,000$, the conditions $n \geq 100$ and $np \leq 10$ are both satisfied, so we can use the Poisson distribution as an approximation to the binomial distribution. We first need the value of μ, which is found as follows:

$$\mu = np = 365 \cdot \frac{1}{10,000} = 0.0365$$

Having found the value of μ, we can proceed to find the probability for specific values of x. Because we want the probability that x is "at least 1," we will use the clever strategy of first finding $P(0)$, the probability of no wins in 365 days. The probability of at least one win can then be found by subtracting that result from 1. We find $P(0)$ by using $x = 0$, $\mu = 0.0365$, and $e = 2.71828$, as shown here:

$$P(0) = \frac{\mu^x \cdot e^{-\mu}}{x!} = \frac{0.0365^0 \cdot 2.71828^{-0.0365}}{0!} = \frac{1 \cdot 0.9642}{1} = 0.9642$$

Using the Poisson distribution as an approximation to the binomial distribution, we find that there is a 0.9642 probability of no wins, so the probability of at least one win is $1 - 0.9642 = 0.0358$. If we use the binomial distribution, we get a probability of 0.0358, so the Poisson distribution works quite well here.

 YOUR TURN. Do Exercise 17 "Mega Millions Lottery: Poisson Approximation to Binomial."

TECH CENTER

 Poisson Distributions

Access tech supplements, videos, and data sets at **www.TriolaStats.com**

Statdisk
1. Click **Analysis** in the top menu.
2. Select **Probability Distributions** from the dropdown menu and select **Poisson Distribution** from the submenu.
3. Enter the value of the mean and click **Evaluate.**

Minitab
1. Enter the values of x for which you want probabilities (such as 0, 1, 2, 3, 4, 5) in column C1.
2. Select **Calc** from the top menu.
3. Select **Probability Distributions** from the dropdown menu and **Poisson** from the submenu.
4. Select **Probability,** enter the mean, and select **C1** for *Input Column.*
5. Click **OK**.

StatCrunch
1. Click **Stat** in the top menu.
2. Select **Calculators** from the dropdown menu and **Poisson** from the submenu.
3. In the dialog box enter the value of the mean and the value of x. Select $=$ or the desired inequality for x.
4. Click **Compute.**

TI-83/84 Plus Calculator
1. Press **2ND** then **VARS** keys to access the *DISTR* (distributions) menu.
2. Select **poissonpdf** and press **ENTER**.
3. Enter the values for mean (μ) and x to complete the command **poissonpdf (μ, x).** Press **ENTER**.
Tip: Select **poissoncdf** in Step 2 for *cumulative* probability.

Excel
1. Enter the values of x for which you want probabilities (such as 0, 1, 2, 3, 4, 5) in column A.
2. Select cell **B1**, click **Insert Function f_x,** select the category **Statistical**, select the function **POISSON.DIST** and click **OK.**
3. Enter **A1** for X and then enter the value of the mean.
4. Enter **0** in the *Cumulative* box.
5. Click **OK** and the probability will appear in cell B1.
6. Copy B1 down the column to obtain the probability for each value of x listed in column A.
Tip: Enter **1** in Step 4 for the *cumulative* Poisson distribution.

R
R command: **dpois(x, μ).**
TIP: Use the R command **ppois(x, μ)** for *cumulative* probabilities.
A complete list of R statistical commands is available at TriolaStats.com

5-3 Basic Skills and Concepts

Statistical Literacy and Critical Thinking

1. Internet Traffic Data Set 27 "Internet Traffic" includes 9000 arrivals of Internet traffic at the Digital Equipment Corporation, and those 9000 arrivals occurred over a period of 19,130 thousandths of a minute. Let the random variable x represent the number of such Internet traffic arrivals in one thousandth of a minute. It appears that these Internet arrivals have a Poisson distribution. If we want to use Formula 5-9 to find the probability of exactly 2 arrivals in one thousandth of a minute, what are the values of μ, x, and e that would be used in that formula?

2. Internet Arrivals For the random variable x described in Exercise 1, what are the possible values of x? Is the value of $x = 4.8$ possible? Is x a discrete random variable or a continuous random variable?

3. Internet Traffic For the distribution described in Exercise 1, find the probability of exactly 2 arrivals in one thousandth of a minute.

4. Probability if 0 For the random variable x described in Exercise 1, use Formula 5-9 to evaluate $P(0)$. For *any* Poisson probability distribution, simplify Formula 5-9 for the case of $x = 0$.

Hurricanes.   *In Exercises 5–8, assume that the Poisson distribution applies; assume that the mean number of Atlantic hurricanes in the United States is 5.5 per year, as in Example 1; and proceed to find the indicated probability.*

5. Hurricanes

a. Find the probability that in a year, there will be 7 hurricanes.

b. In a 118-year period, how many years are expected to have 7 hurricanes?

c. How does the result from part (b) compare to the recent period of 118 years in which 14 years had 7 hurricanes? Does the Poisson distribution work well here?

6. Hurricanes

a. Find the probability that in a year, there will be no hurricanes.

b. In a 118-year period, how many years are expected to have no hurricanes?

c. How does the result from part (b) compare to the recent period of 118 years in which there were 2 years without any hurricanes? Does the Poisson distribution work well here?

7. Hurricanes

a. Find the probability that in a year, there will be 3 hurricanes.

b. In a 118-year period, how many years are expected to have 3 hurricanes?

c. How does the result from part (b) compare to the recent period of 118 years in which 17 years had 3 hurricanes? Does the Poisson distribution work well here?

8. Hurricanes

a. Find the probability that in a year, there will be 10 hurricanes.

b. In a 118-year period, how many years are expected to have 10 hurricanes?

c. How does the result from part (b) compare to the recent period of 118 years in which 4 years had 10 hurricanes? Does the Poisson distribution work well here?

In Exercises 9–16, use the Poisson distribution to find the indicated probabilities.

9. Births In a recent year (365 days), NYU-Langone Medical Center had 5942 births.

a. Find the mean number of births per day.

b. Find the probability that in a single day, there are 16 births.

c. Find the probability that in a single day, there are no births. Would 0 births in a single day be a significantly low number of births?

10. Murders In a recent year (365 days), there were 650 murders in Chicago. Find the mean number of murders per day, then use that result to find the probability that in a single day, there are no murders. Would 0 murders in a single day be a significantly low number of murders?

11. Radioactive Decay Radioactive atoms are unstable because they have too much energy. When they release their extra energy, they are said to decay. When studying cesium-137, a nuclear engineer found that over 365 days, 1,000,000 radioactive atoms decayed to 977,287 radioactive atoms; therefore 22,713 atoms decayed during 365 days.

a. Find the mean number of radioactive atoms that decayed in a day.

b. Find the probability that on a given day, exactly 50 radioactive atoms decayed.

12. Deaths from Horse Kicks A classical example of the Poisson distribution involves the number of deaths caused by horse kicks to men in the Prussian Army between 1875 and 1894. Data for 14 corps were combined for the 20-year period, and the 280 corps-years included a total of 196 deaths. After finding the mean number of deaths per corps-year, find the probability that a randomly selected corps-year has the following numbers of deaths: (**a**) 0, (**b**) 1, (**c**) 2, (**d**) 3, (**e**) 4. The actual results consisted of these frequencies: 0 deaths (in 144 corps-years); 1 death (in 91 corps-years); 2 deaths (in 32 corps-years); 3 deaths (in 11 corps-years); 4 deaths (in 2 corps-years). Compare the actual results to those expected by using the Poisson probabilities. Does the Poisson distribution serve as a good tool for predicting the actual results?

13. World War II Bombs In analyzing hits by V-1 buzz bombs in World War II, South London was partitioned into 576 regions, each with an area of 0.25 km^2. A total of 535 V-1 buzz bombs hit the combined area of 576 regions.

a. Find the probability that a randomly selected region had exactly 2 hits.

b. Among the 576 regions, find the expected number of regions with exactly 2 hits.

c. How does the result from part (b) compare to this actual result: There were 93 regions that had exactly 2 hits?

14. Disease Cluster Neuroblastoma, a rare form of cancer, occurs in 11 children in a million, so its probability is 0.000011. Four cases of neuroblastoma occurred in Oak Park, Illinois, which had 12,429 children.

a. Assuming that neuroblastoma occurs as usual, find the mean number of cases in groups of 12,429 children.

b. Using the unrounded mean from part (a), find the probability that the number of neuroblastoma cases in a group of 12,429 children is 0 or 1.

c. What is the probability of more than one case of neuroblastoma?

d. Does the cluster of four cases appear to be attributable to random chance? Why or why not?

15. Chocolate Chip Cookies In the production of chocolate chip cookies, we can consider each cookie to be the specified interval unit required for a Poisson distribution, and we can consider the variable x to be the number of chocolate chips in a cookie.

a. Refer to Data Set 39 "Chocolate Chip Cookies," and find the mean number of chocolate chips in the 34 Keebler cookies.

b. Assume that the Poisson distribution applies. Find the probability that a Keebler cookie will have 26 chocolate chips.

c. Find the expected number of Keebler cookies with 26 chocolate chips among 34 different Keebler cookies. Compare the result to the actual number of Keebler cookies with 26 chocolate chips.

16. Chocolate Chip Cookies Repeat Exercise 15 using 30 chocolate chips instead of 26 chocolate chips. In Data Set 39 "Chocolate Chip Cookies," six of the Keebler cookies have 30 chocolate chips.

5-3 Beyond the Basics

17. Mega Millions Lottery: Poisson Approximation to Binomial There is a 1/302,575,350 probability of winning the Mega Millions lottery jackpot with a single ticket. Assume that you purchase a single ticket in each of the next 5200 different Mega Millions games that are run over the next 50 years (with drawings twice each week). Find the probability of winning the jackpot with at least one of those tickets. Is there a good chance that you would win the jackpot at least once in 50 years? How many years of playing would be required to reach a 10% chance of winning the jackpot at least once?

Chapter Quick Quiz

1. What does the probability of $P(A) = 0+$ indicate? Does it indicate that it is impossible for event A to occur?

2. Is a probability distribution defined if the only possible values of a random variable are 0, 1, 2, and $P(0) = P(1) = P(2) = 0.5$?

3. Is a probability distribution defined if $P(x) = 0.2$, where the only possible values of x are 1, 2, 3, 4, 5?

4. Find the mean of the random variable x described in the preceding exercise.

5. Is the mean found in the preceding exercise a statistic or a parameter?

In Exercises 6–10, refer to the accompanying table, which describes the numbers of adults in groups of five who reported sleepwalking (based on data from "Prevalence and Comorbidity of Nocturnal Wandering In the U.S. Adult General Population," by Ohayon et al., **Neurology***, Vol. 78, No. 20).*

x	P(x)
0	0.172
1	0.363
2	0.306
3	0.129
4	0.027
5	0.002

6. Does the table describe a probability distribution?

7. Probability Find the probability that at least one of the subjects is a sleepwalker.

8. Mean Find the mean for the numbers of sleepwalkers in groups of five.

9. Standard Deviation The unrounded standard deviation is $\sigma = 1.019041635$ sleepwalkers. Find the rounded variance and include appropriate units.

10. Significant Events Is 4 a significantly high number of sleepwalkers in a group of 5 adults? Explain.

Review Exercises

In Exercises 1–5, assume that 4.2% of workers test positive when tested for illegal drugs (based on data from Quest Diagnostics). Assume that a group of ten workers is randomly selected.

1. Workplace Drug Testing Find the probability that exactly two of the ten workers test positive for illegal drugs.

2. Workplace Drug Testing Find the probability that at least one of the ten workers tests positive for illegal drugs.

3. Workplace Drug Testing Find the mean and standard deviation for the numbers of workers in groups of ten who test positive for illegal drugs.

4. Workplace Drug Testing If none of the ten workers tests positive for illegal drugs, is that a significantly low result?

5. Workplace Drug Testing If four of the ten workers test positive for illegal drugs, is that a significantly high result?

6. Acrophobia *USA Today* reported results from a survey in which subjects were asked if they are afraid of heights in tall buildings. The results are summarized in the accompanying table. Does this table describe a probability distribution? Why or why not?

Response	$P(x)$
Yes	0.46
No	0.54

7. Brand Recognition In a study of brand recognition of Sony, groups of four consumers are interviewed. If x is the number of people in the group who recognize the Sony brand name, then x can be 0, 1, 2, 3, or 4, and the corresponding probabilities are 0.0016, 0.0250, 0.1432, 0.3892, and 0.4096. Does the given information describe a probability distribution? Why or why not?

8. Family/Partner Groups of people aged 15–65 are randomly selected and arranged in groups of six. The random variable x is the number in the group who say that their family and/or partner contribute most to their happiness (based on a Coca-Cola survey). The accompanying table lists the values of x along with their corresponding probabilities. Does the table describe a probability distribution? If so, find the mean and standard deviation.

x	$P(x)$
0	0+
1	0.003
2	0.025
3	0.111
4	0.279
5	0.373
6	0.208

9. Detecting Fraud The Brooklyn District Attorney's office analyzed the leading (leftmost) digits of check amounts in order to identify fraud. The leading digit of 1 is expected to occur 30.1% of the time, according to "Benford's law," which applies in this case. Among 784 checks issued by a suspect company, there were none with amounts that had a leading digit of 1.

a. If there is a 30.1% chance that the leading digit of the check amount is 1, what is the expected number of checks among 784 that should have a leading digit of 1?

b. Assume that groups of 784 checks are randomly selected. Find the mean and standard deviation for the numbers of checks with amounts having a leading digit of 1.

c. Use the results from part (b) and the range rule of thumb to identify the values that are significantly low.

d. Given that the 784 actual check amounts had no leading digits of 1, is there very strong evidence that the suspect checks are very different from the expected results? Why or why not?

10. Poisson: Deaths Currently, an average of 7 residents of the village of Westport (population 760) die each year (based on data from the U.S. National Center for Health Statistics).

a. Find the mean number of deaths per day.

b. Find the probability that on a given day, there are no deaths.

c. Find the probability that on a given day, there is more than one death.

d. Based on the preceding results, should Westport have a contingency plan to handle more than one death per day? Why or why not?

Cumulative Review Exercises

1. Planets The planets of the solar system have the numbers of moons listed below in order from the sun. (Pluto is not included because it was uninvited from the solar system party in 2006.) Include appropriate units whenever relevant.

$$0 \quad 0 \quad 1 \quad 2 \quad 17 \quad 28 \quad 21 \quad 8$$

a. Find the mean.

b. Find the median.

continued

c. Find the mode.

d. Find the range.

e. Find the standard deviation.

f. Find the variance.

g. Use the range rule of thumb to identify the values separating significant values from those that are not significant.

h. Based on the result from part (g), do any of the planets have a number of moons that is significantly low or significantly high? Why or why not?

i. What is the level of measurement of the data: nominal, ordinal, interval, or ratio?

j. Are the data discrete or continuous?

2. Kentucky Pick 4 In the Kentucky Pick 4 lottery game, you can pay $1 for a "straight" bet in which you select four digits with repetition allowed. If you buy only one ticket and win, your prize is $2500.

a. If you buy one ticket, what is the probability of winning?

b. If you play this game once every day, find the mean number of wins in years with exactly 365 days.

c. If you play this game once every day, find the probability of no wins in 365 days.

d. Find the expected value for the purchase of one ticket.

3. Tennis Challenge In a recent U.S. Open tennis tournament, there were 945 challenges made by singles players, and 255 of them resulted in referee calls that were overturned. The accompanying table lists the results by gender.

	Challenge Upheld with Overturned Call	Challenge Rejected with No Change
Challenges by Men	160	398
Challenges by Women	95	292

a. If 1 of the 945 challenges is randomly selected, what is the probability that it resulted in an overturned call?

b. If one of the overturned calls is randomly selected, what is the probability that the challenge was made by a woman?

c. If two different challenges are randomly selected without replacement, find the probability that they both resulted in an overturned call.

d. If 1 of the 945 challenges is randomly selected, find the probability that it was made by a man or was upheld with an overturned call.

e. If one of the challenges is randomly selected, find the probability that it was made by a man, given that the challenge was upheld with an overturned call.

4. Salary Negotiations In a Jobvite survey, 2287 adult workers were randomly selected and asked about salary negotiations.

a. 29% of the respondents reported that they negotiated salary at their latest job. What is the number of respondents who reported that they negotiated salary?

b. Among those who negotiated salary, 84% received higher pay. How many received higher pay?

c. What percentage of the 2287 respondents received higher pay?

d. Is the value of 29% given in part (a) a parameter or a statistic?

5. Bar Graph Fox News broadcast a graph similar to the one shown here. The graph is intended to compare the number of people actually enrolled in a government health plan (left bar) and the goal for the number of enrollees (right bar). Does the graph depict the data correctly or is it somehow misleading? Explain.

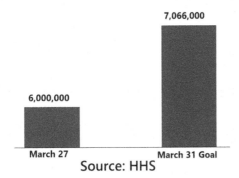

Source: HHS

6. Roulette A casino gambler plays roulette 50 times with a bet on the number 7 every time. To finish with a profit, at least 2 games must be won. For each game, $P(7) = 1/38$. For the 50 games, $P(\text{exactly 2 wins}) = 0.236$ and $P(2 \text{ or more wins}) = 0.380$. For the 50 games, is 2 wins a significantly high number? Why or why not? How do things look for this gambler?

7. Washing Hands Based on results from a Bradley Corporation poll, assume that 70% of adults always wash their hands after using a public restroom.

a. Find the probability that among 8 randomly selected adults, exactly 5 always wash their hands after using a public restroom.

b. Find the probability that among 8 randomly selected adults, at least 7 always wash their hands after using a public restroom.

c. For groups of 8 randomly selected adults, find the mean and standard deviation of the numbers in the groups who always wash their hands after using a public restroom.

d. If 8 adults are randomly selected and it is found that exactly 1 of them washes hands after using a public restroom, is that a significantly low number?

8. Happiness In a survey sponsored by Coca-Cola, subjects were asked what contributes most to their happiness, and the table summarizes their responses. Does the table represent a probability distribution? Explain.

x	P(x)
Family/partner	0.77
Friends	0.15
Other	0.08

Technology Project

Overbooking Flights Delta Airlines Flight 2673 from New York's JFK airport to San Francisco's SFO airport uses the Boeing 757-200 with 180 seats available for passengers. Delta can overbook by accepting more reservations than there are seats available. If the flight is not overbooked, the airline loses revenue from empty seats, but if too many seats are sold, the airline loses money from the compensation it must pay to the bumped passengers. Airlines calculate expected "no show" rates for each route and class of ticket, but for simplicity, assume that there is a 0.0995 probability that a passenger with a reservation will not show up for the flight (based on data from the IBM research paper "Passenger-Based Predictive Modeling of Airline No-Show

continued

Rates," by Lawrence, Hong, and Cherrier). Also assume that Delta Airlines accepts 200 reservations for the 180 seats that are available.

• Find the probability that when 200 reservations are accepted for Delta Airlines Flight 2673, there are more passengers showing up than there are seats available. Is the probability of overbooking small enough so that it does not happen very often, or does it seem too high so that changes must be made to make it lower?

• Use trial and error to find the maximum number of reservations that could be accepted so that the probability of having more passengers than seats is 0.05 or less.

Big (or Very Large) Data Project

Refer to Data Set 45 "Births in New York" from Appendix B.

a. Find the number of male births and find the number of female births. (Manual counting of those numbers is totally impractical given the sample size of $n = 465,506$.) Assuming that 0.512 of births are males (as is commonly believed), find the probability of getting a number of male births that is at least as extreme as the number of male births in the data set. What does the result suggest about the common belief that 0.512 of births are male births?

b. Construct a frequency distribution with the values of x consisting of the different lengths of stay paired with their corresponding frequencies. How many different values are there for lengths of stay?

c. Investigate whether the lengths of stay have a distribution that is approximately a Poisson distribution. Explain the approach used and state a conclusion.

FROM DATA TO DECISION

Critical Thinking: Using probability to test a claim

Consider a Kaspersky Lab survey of 2515 adult Internet users in the United States and Canada. Among those 2515 survey subjects, 46% said that they experienced at least one cybersecurity issue within the past five years. The cybersecurity issues include problems such as viruses, ransomware attacks, or malicious email. Here is a key question about this survey:

Do the survey data support a claim that fewer than half (or fewer than 50%) of adult Internet users have experienced cybersecurity issues within the past five years?

Clearly, 46% is less than 50%, but is 46% *significantly* less than 50%? Use the methods of this chapter to determine whether 46% is significantly less than 50% in this case. Address these questions:

a. Among the 2515 survey subjects, what is the actual number of them who said that they experienced at least one cybersecurity issue within the past five years?

b. Given the context of the Kaspersky Lab survey, is 46% significantly less than 50% in this case? Explain using relevant probabilities.

c. Based on the results from part (b), what should be concluded about the claim that fewer than half (or fewer than 50%) of adult Internet users have experienced cybersecurity issues within the past five years?

d. For this survey, would a result of 49.9% be significantly less than 50%?

e. For this survey, would a result of 10% be significantly less than 50%?

Cooperative Group Activities

1. In-class activity Win $1,000,000! The James Randi Educational Foundation offered a $1,000,000 prize to anyone who can show "under proper observing conditions, evidence of any paranormal, supernatural, or occult power or event." (That prize was discontinued in 2015.) Divide into groups of three. Select one person who will be tested for extrasensory perception (ESP) by trying to correctly identify a digit (0–9) randomly selected by another member of the group. Conduct at least 20 trials. Another group member should record the randomly selected digit, the digit guessed by the subject, and whether the guess was correct or wrong. Construct the table for the probability distribution of randomly generated digits, construct the relative frequency table for the random digits that were actually obtained, and construct a relative frequency table for the guesses that were made. After comparing the three tables, what do you conclude? What proportion of guesses is correct? Does it seem that the subject has the ability to select the correct digit significantly more often than would be expected by chance?

2. In-class activity See the preceding activity and *design an experiment* that would be effective in testing someone's claim that he or she has the ability to identify the color of a card selected from a standard deck of playing cards. Describe the experiment with great detail. Because the prize of $1,000,000 is at stake, we want to be careful to avoid the serious mistake of concluding that the person has a paranormal power when that power is not actually present. There will likely be some chance that the subject could make random guesses and be correct every time, so identify a probability that is reasonable for the event of the subject passing the test with random guesses. Be sure that the test is designed so that this probability is equal to or less than the probability value selected.

3. In-class activity Suppose we want to identify the probability distribution for the number of children in families with at least one child. For each student in the class, find the number of brothers and sisters and record the total number of children (including the student) in each family. Construct the relative frequency table for the result obtained. (The values of the random variable x will be 1, 2, 3, ...) What is wrong with using this relative frequency table as an estimate of the probability distribution for the number of children in randomly selected families?

4. Out-of-class activity The analysis of the last digits of data can sometimes reveal whether the data have been collected through actual measurements or reported by the subjects. Refer to an almanac or the Internet and find a collection of data (such as lengths of rivers in the world), and then analyze the distribution of last digits to determine whether the values were obtained through actual measurements.

5. Out-of-class activity In the past, leading (leftmost) digits of the amounts on checks have been analyzed for fraud. For checks not involving fraud, the leading digit of 1 is expected about 30.1% of the time. Obtain a random sample of actual check amounts and record the leading digits. Compare the actual number of checks with amounts that have a leading digit of 1 to the 30.1% rate expected. Do the actual checks conform to the expected rate, or is there a substantial discrepancy? Explain.

6. In-class activity Survey the class by asking this question: "Which man is named Bob and which man is named Tim?" Do the respondents appear to give results significantly different from what is expected with random guesses? (See "Who Do You Look Like? Evidence of Facial Stereotypes for Male Names," by Lea, Thomas, Lamkin, and Bell, *Psychonomic Bulletin & Review*, Vol. 14, Issue 5.)

6

NORMAL PROBABILITY DISTRIBUTIONS

CHAPTER PROBLEM — **So, You Want to Fly a U.S. Air Force Jet?**

Do you satisfy the U.S. Air Force requirement of having a height between 64 inches and 77 inches? What percentage of adult males satisfy this height requirement? What percentage of adult females satisfy this height requirement?

Ergonomics 101 *Ergonomics* is a discipline focused on the design of tools and equipment so that they can be used safely, comfortably, and efficiently. The design of civilian and military aircraft makes extensive use of ergonomics. Some

of the basic tools introduced in this chapter will enable us to solve many problems related to ergonomics, such as those involving the following requirements.

- The U.S. Air Force requires that its pilots must have heights between 64 inches and 77 inches. (This requirement was being changed at the time of this writing.)

- The U.S. Army requires that women must be between 58 in. and 80 in. tall.

- Section 4.4.2 of the Americans with Disabilities Act relates to height clearances with this statement: "Walks, halls, corridors, passageways, aisles, or other circulation spaces shall have 80 in. (2030 mm) minimum clear head room."

- The elevator in the San Francisco Airport rental car facility has a placard indicating a maximum load of 4000 lb or 27 passengers.

- A Disney requirement for someone wanting to be employed as the Tinkerbell character is that they must have a height between 58 inches and 62 inches.

- Radio City Music Hall Rockette dancers must be females with heights between 66 inches and 70.5 inches.

- The Bombardier Dash 8 aircraft can carry 37 passengers, and the fuel and baggage allow for a total passenger load of 6200 lb.

- When women were finally allowed to become pilots of fighter jets, engineers needed to redesign the ejection seats because they had been originally designed for men weighing between 140 lb and 211 lb.

Ergonomic problems often involve extremely important safety issues, and here are real cases that proved to be fatal:

- "We have an emergency for Air Midwest fifty-four eighty," said pilot Katie Leslie, just before her Beech plane crashed in Charlotte, North Carolina, resulting in the death of all 21 crew and passengers. Excessive total weight of the passengers was suspected as a factor that contributed to the crash.

- After 20 passengers perished when the *Ethan Allen* tour boat capsized on New York's Lake George, an investigation showed that although the number of passengers was below the maximum allowed, the boat should have been certified for a much smaller number of passengers.

- A water taxi sank in Baltimore's Inner Harbor, killing 5 of the 25 people on board. The boat was certified to carry 25 passengers, but their total weight exceeded the safe load of 3500 lb, so the number of passengers should have been limited to 20.

CHAPTER OBJECTIVES

Chapter 5 introduced *discrete* probability distributions, but in this chapter we introduce *continuous* probability distributions. Most of this chapter focuses on *normal distributions*, which are the most important distributions in the field of statistics. Here are the chapter objectives:

6-1   The Standard Normal Distribution

- Describe the characteristics of a standard normal distribution.

- Find the probability of some range of z scores in a standard normal distribution.

- Find z scores corresponding to regions under the curve representing a standard normal distribution.

6-2   Real Applications of Normal Distributions

- Develop the ability to describe a normal distribution (not necessarily a standard normal distribution).

- Find the probability of some range of values in a normal distribution.

- Find x scores corresponding to regions under the curve representing a normal distribution, and solve real problems using this skill.

6-3   Sampling Distributions and Estimators

- Develop the ability to describe a *sampling distribution of a statistic.*

- Determine whether a sample statistic serves as a good estimator of the corresponding population parameter.

6-4 The Central Limit Theorem

- Describe the central limit theorem.

- Apply the central limit theorem by finding the probability that a sample mean falls within some specified range of values.

- Identify conditions for which it is appropriate to use a normal distribution for the distribution of sample means.

6-5 Assessing Normality

- Develop the ability to examine histograms, outliers, and normal quantile plots to determine whether sample data appear to be from a population having a distribution that is approximately normal.

6-6 Normal as Approximation to Binomial (available at www.TriolaStats.com)

- Identify conditions for which it is appropriate to use a normal distribution as an approximation to a binomial probability distribution.

- Use the normal distribution for approximating probabilities for a binomial distribution.

6-1   The Standard Normal Distribution

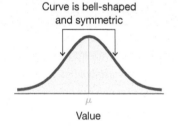

Curve is bell-shaped
and symmetric

μ

Value

FIGURE 6-1   The Normal Distribution

Key Concept In this section we present the *standard normal distribution*, which is a specific normal distribution having the following three properties:

1. Bell-shaped: The graph of the standard normal distribution is bell-shaped (as in Figure 6-1).

2. $\mu = 0$: The standard normal distribution has a mean equal to 0.

3. $\sigma = 1$: The standard normal distribution has a standard deviation equal to 1.

In this section we develop the skill to find areas (or probabilities or relative frequencies) corresponding to various regions under the graph of the standard normal distribution. In addition, we find z scores that correspond to areas under the graph. These skills become important in the next section as we study nonstandard normal distributions and the real and important applications that they involve.

Normal Distributions

There are infinitely many different normal distributions, depending on the values used for the mean and standard deviation. We begin with a brief introduction to this general family of normal distributions.

DEFINITION

If a continuous random variable has a distribution with a graph that can be described by the equation given as Formula 6-1 (shown on the next page), we say that it has a **normal distribution**. A normal distribution is bell-shaped and symmetric, as shown in Figure 6-1.

FORMULA 6-1

$$y = \frac{e^{-\frac{1}{2}\left(\frac{x-\mu}{\sigma}\right)^2}}{\sigma\sqrt{2\pi}}$$

Fortunately, we won't actually use Formula 6-1, but examining the right side of the equation reveals that any particular normal distribution is determined by two parameters: the population mean, μ, and population standard deviation, σ. (In Formula 6-1, x is a variable, $\pi = 3.14159\ldots$ and $e = 2.71828\ldots$.) Once specific values are selected for μ and σ, Formula 6-1 is an equation relating x and y, and we can graph that equation to get a result that will look like Figure 6-1. And that's about all we need to know about Formula 6-1!

Uniform Distributions

The major focus of this chapter is the concept of a normal probability distribution, but we begin with a *uniform distribution* so that we can see the following two very important properties:

1. The area under the graph of a continuous probability distribution is equal to 1.

2. There is a correspondence between area and probability, so *probabilities* can be found by identifying the corresponding *areas* in the graph using this formula for the area of a rectangle:

$$\text{Area} = \text{height} \times \text{width}$$

> **DEFINITION**
>
> A continuous random variable has a **uniform distribution** if its values are *equally* spread over the range of possible values. The graph of a uniform distribution results in a rectangular shape.

Density Curve The graph of any continuous probability distribution is called a **density curve,** and any density curve must satisfy the requirement that the total area under the curve is exactly 1. This requirement that the area must equal 1 simplifies probability problems, so the following statement is really important:

Because the total area under any density curve is equal to 1, there is a correspondence between *area* and *probability*.

EXAMPLE 1 **Waiting Times for Airport Security**

During certain time periods at JFK airport in New York City, passengers arriving at the security checkpoint have waiting times that are uniformly distributed between 0 minutes and 5 minutes, as illustrated in Figure 6-2 on the next page.

Refer to Figure 6-2 to see these properties:

- All of the different possible waiting times are *equally likely*.

- Waiting times can be *any* value between 0 min and 5 min, so it is possible to have a waiting time of 1.234567 min.

- By assigning the probability of 0.2 to the height of the vertical line in Figure 6-2, the *enclosed area is exactly 1*. (In general, we should make the height of the vertical line in a uniform distribution equal to 1/range.)

continued

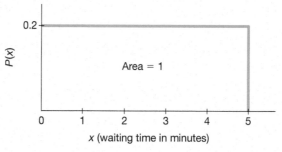

FIGURE 6-2   Uniform Distribution of Waiting Time

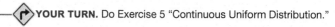

YOUR TURN. Do Exercise 5 "Continuous Uniform Distribution."

EXAMPLE 2   Waiting Times for Airport Security

Given the uniform distribution illustrated in Figure 6-2, find the probability that a randomly selected passenger has a waiting time of at least 2 minutes.

SOLUTION

The shaded area in Figure 6-3 represents waiting times of at least 2 minutes. Because the total area under the density curve is equal to 1, there is a correspondence between area and probability. We can easily find the desired *probability* by using *areas* as follows:

$$P(\text{wait time of at least 2 min}) = \text{height} \times \text{width of shaded area in Figure 6-3}$$
$$= 0.2 \times 3$$
$$= 0.6$$

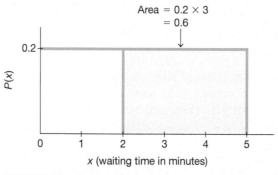

FIGURE 6-3   Using Area to Find Probability

INTERPRETATION

The probability of randomly selecting a passenger with a waiting time of at least 2 minutes is 0.6.

YOUR TURN. Do Exercise 7 "Continuous Uniform Distribution."

Standard Normal Distribution

The density curve of a uniform distribution is a horizontal straight line, so we can find the area of any rectangular region by applying this formula:

$$\text{Area} = \text{height} \times \text{width.}$$

Because the density curve of a normal distribution has a more complicated bell shape, as shown in Figure 6-1, it is more difficult to find areas. However, the basic principle is the same: *There is a correspondence between area and probability*. In Figure 6-4 we show that for a standard normal distribution, the area under the density curve is equal to 1. In Figure 6-4, we use "z Score" as a label for the horizontal axis, and this is common for the standard normal distribution, defined as follows.

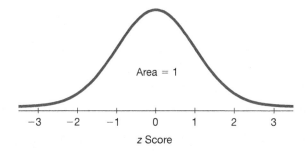

Area = 1

z Score

FIGURE 6-4   Standard Normal Distribution

DEFINITION

The **standard normal distribution** is a probability distribution with these properties:

- The distribution is a normal distribution, so it is bell-shaped as in Figure 6-4.
- The population parameter of the mean has the specific value of $\mu = 0$.
- The population parameter of the standard deviation has the specific value of $\sigma = 1$.
- The total area under its density curve is equal to 1 (as in Figure 6-4).

Finding Probabilities When Given z Scores

It is not easy to manually find areas in Figure 6-4, but we can find areas (or probabilities) for many different regions in Figure 6-4 by using technology, or we can also use Table A-2 (in Appendix A). Key features of the different methods are summarized in Table 6-1, which follows. (StatCrunch provides options for a cumulative left region, a cumulative right region, or the region between two boundaries.) Because calculators and software generally give more accurate results than Table A-2, we *strongly* recommend using technology. (When there are discrepancies, answers in Appendix D will generally include results based on technology as well as answers based on Table A-2.)

If using Table A-2, it is essential to understand these points:

1. Table A-2 is designed only for the *standard* normal distribution, which is a normal distribution with a mean of 0 and a standard deviation of 1.

2. Table A-2 is on two pages, with the left page for *negative z* scores and the right page for *positive z* scores.

3. Each value in the body of the table is a *cumulative area from the left* up to a vertical boundary above a specific *z* score.

4. When working with a graph, avoid confusion between *z* scores and areas.

   z score: *Distance* **along the horizontal scale of the standard normal distribution (corresponding to the number of standard deviations above or below the mean); refer to the leftmost column and top row of Table A-2.**

   Area: *Region* **under the curve; refer to the values in the** *body* **of Table A-2.**

5. The part of the *z* score denoting hundredths is found across the top row of Table A-2.

TABLE 6-1 Formats Used for Finding Normal Distribution Areas

Cumulative Area from the Left The following provide the *cumulative area from the left* up to a vertical line above a specific value of *z*: • **Table A-2** • **Statdisk** • **Minitab** • **Excel** • **StatCrunch**	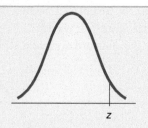 **Cumulative Left Region**
Area Between Two Boundaries The following provide the area bounded on the left and bounded on the right by vertical lines above specific values. • **TI-83/84 Plus calculator** • **StatCrunch**	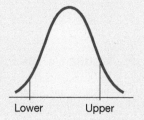 **Area Between Two Boundaries**

CAUTION When working with a normal distribution, be careful to avoid confusion between *z* scores and areas.

ROUND-OFF RULE FOR *z* SCORES Round *z* scores to two decimal places, such as 2.31. (Table A-2 includes *z* scores rounded to two decimal places.)

The following examples illustrate procedures that can be used with real and important applications introduced in the following sections.

EXAMPLE 3   **Bone Density Test**

A bone mineral density test can be helpful in identifying the presence or susceptibility to osteoporosis, a disease that causes bones to become more fragile and more likely to break. The result of a bone density test is commonly measured as a *z* score. The population of *z* scores is normally distributed with a mean of 0 and a standard deviation of 1, so these test results meet the requirements of a standard normal distribution, and the graph of the bone density test scores is as shown in Figure 6-5.

A randomly selected adult undergoes a bone density test. Find the probability that this person has a bone density test score less than 1.27.

SOLUTION

Note that the following are the *same* (because of the aforementioned correspondence between probability and area):

- *Probability* that the bone density test score is less than 1.27
- Shaded *area* shown in Figure 6-5

So we need to find the area in Figure 6-5 below $z = 1.27$. If using technology, see the Tech Center instructions included at the end of this section. If using Table A-2, begin with the *z* score of 1.27 by locating 1.2 in the left column; next find the value in the adjoining row of probabilities that is directly below 0.07, as shown in the accompanying excerpt. Table A-2 shows that there is an area of 0.8980 corresponding to $z = 1.27$. We want the area *below* 1.27, and Table A-2 gives the cumulative area from the left, so the desired area is 0.8980. Because of the correspondence between area and probability, we know that the probability of a z score below 1.27 is 0.8980.

INTERPRETATION

The *probability* that a randomly selected person has a bone density test result below 1.27 is 0.8980, shown as the shaded region in Figure 6-5. Another way to interpret this result is to conclude that 89.80% of people have bone density levels below 1.27.

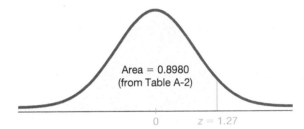

Area = 0.8980
(from Table A-2)

0        $z = 1.27$

FIGURE 6-5   Finding Area to the Left of $z = 1.27$

TABLE A-2 *(continued)* Cumulative Area from the LEFT

z	.00	.01	.02	.03	.04	.05	.06	.07	.08	.09
0.0	.5000	.5040	.5080	.5120	.5160	.5199	.5239	.5279	.5319	.5359
0.1	.5398	.5438	.5478	.5517	.5557	.5596	.5636	.5675	.5714	.5753
0.2	.5793	.5832	.5871	.5910	.5948	.5987	.6026	.6064	.6103	.6141
1.0	.8413	.8438	.8461	.8485	.8508	.8531	.8554	.8577	.8599	.8621
1.1	.8643	.8665	.8686	.8708	.8729	.8749	.8770	.8790	.8810	.8830
1.2	.8849	.8869	.8888	.8907	.8925	.8944	.8962	.8980	.8997	.9015
1.3	.9032	.9049	.9066	.9082	.9099	.9115	.9131	.9147	.9162	.9177
1.4	.9192	.9207	.9222	.9236	.9251	.9265	.9279	.9292	.9306	.9319

YOUR TURN. Do Exercise 9 "Standard Normal Distribution."

EXAMPLE 4   **Bone Density Test: Finding the Area to the *Right* of a Value**

Using the same bone density test from Example 3, find the probability that a randomly selected person has a result above −1.00. A value above −1.00 is considered to be in the "normal" range of bone density readings.

SOLUTION

We again find the desired *probability* by finding a corresponding *area*. We are looking for the area of the region to the right of $z = -1.00$ that is shaded in Figure 6-6 on the next page. The Statdisk display on the next page shows that the area to the right of $z = -1.00$ is 0.841345.

If we use Table A-2, we should know that it is designed to apply only to cumulative areas from the *left*. Referring to the page with *negative z* scores, we find that the cumulative area from the left up to $z = -1.00$ is 0.1587, as shown in Figure 6-6. Because the total area under the curve is 1, we can find the shaded area by

continued

subtracting 0.1587 from 1. The result is 0.8413. Even though Table A-2 is designed only for cumulative areas from the left, we can use it to find cumulative areas from the right, as shown in Figure 6-6.

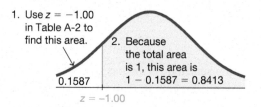

1. Use $z = -1.00$ in Table A-2 to find this area.

2. Because the total area is 1, this area is $1 - 0.1587 = 0.8413$

0.1587

$z = -1.00$

FIGURE 6-6   Finding the Area to the Right of $z = -1$

Statdisk

Normal Distribution	
Enter one value, then click Evaluate to find the other value:	Download Copy

z Value: [-1]

Cumulative area from the left: [   ]

[Evaluate]

```
z Value:      -1.00000
Prob Dens:     0.24197

Cumulative Probs
Left:          0.15866
Right:         0.84134
2 Tailed:      0.31731
Central:       0.68269
As Table A-2:  0.15866
```

INTERPRETATION

Because of the correspondence between probability and area, we conclude that the *probability* of randomly selecting someone with a bone density reading above -1 is 0.8413 (which is the *area* to the right of $z = -1.00$). We could also say that 84.13% of people have bone density levels above -1.00.

▶ **YOUR TURN.** Do Exercise 10 "Standard Normal Distribution."

Example 4 illustrates a way that Table A-2 can be used indirectly to find a cumulative area from the right. The following example illustrates another way that we can find an area indirectly by using Table A-2.

EXAMPLE 5 **Bone Density Test: Finding the Area *Between* Two Values**

A bone density test reading between -1.00 and -2.50 indicates that the subject has osteopenia, which is some bone loss. Find the probability that a randomly selected subject has a reading between -1.00 and -2.50.

SOLUTION

We are again dealing with normally distributed values having a mean of 0 and a standard deviation of 1. The values between -1.00 and -2.50 correspond to the shaded region in the third graph included in Figure 6-7. Table A-2 cannot be used to find that area directly, but we can use it to find the following:

- The area to the left of $z = -1.00$ is 0.1587.

- The area to the left of $z = -2.50$ is 0.0062.

- The area *between* $z = -2.50$ and $z = -1.00$ (the shaded area at the far right in Figure 6-7) is the difference between the areas found in the preceding two steps:

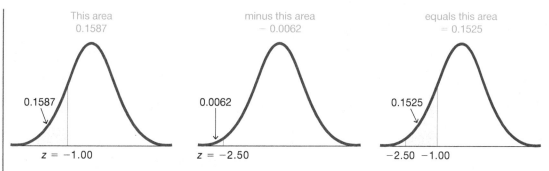

FIGURE 6-7   Finding the Area Between Two z Scores

INTERPRETATION

Using the correspondence between probability and area, we conclude that there is a probability of 0.1525 that a randomly selected subject has a bone density reading between −1.00 and −2.50. Another way to interpret this result is to state that 15.25% of people have osteopenia, with bone density readings between −1.00 and −2.50.

YOUR TURN. Do Exercise 11 "Standard Normal Distribution."

Example 5 can be generalized as the following rule:

The area corresponding to the region *between* two z scores can be found by finding the difference between the two areas found in Table A-2.

Figure 6-8 illustrates this general rule. The shaded region *B* can be found by calculating the *difference* between two areas found from Table A-2.

HINT Don't try to memorize a rule or formula for this case. Focus on *understanding* by using a graph. Draw a graph, shade the desired area, and then get creative to think of a way to find the desired area by working with cumulative areas from the left.

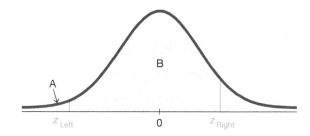

Shaded area B = (areas A and B combined) − (area A)

FIGURE 6-8   Finding the Area Between Two z Scores

Probabilities such as those in the preceding examples can also be expressed with the following notation.

Notation

$P(a < z < b)$ denotes the probability that the z score is between a and b.

$P(z > a)$ denotes the probability that the z score is greater than a.

$P(z < a)$ denotes the probability that the z score is less than a.

With this notation, $P(-2.50 < z < -1.00) = 0.1525$, states in symbols that the probability of a z score falling between −2.50 and −1.00 is 0.1525 (as in Example 5).

Finding z Scores from Known Areas

Examples 3, 4, and 5 all involved the standard normal distribution, and they were all examples with this same format: Given z scores, find areas (or probabilities). In many cases, we need a method for reversing the format: Given a known area (or probability), find the corresponding z score. In such cases, it is really important to avoid confusion between z scores and areas. Remember, z scores are *distances* along the horizontal scale, but areas (or probabilities) are regions under the density curve. (Table A-2 lists z-scores in the left column and across the top row, but areas are found in the *body* of the table.) We should also remember that z scores positioned in the left half of the curve are always negative. If we already know a probability and want to find the corresponding z score, we use the following procedure.

Procedure for Finding a z Score from a Known Area

1. Draw a bell-shaped curve and identify the region under the curve that corresponds to the given probability. If that region is not a cumulative region from the left, work instead with a known region that is a cumulative region from the left.

2. Use technology or Table A-2 to find the z score. With Table A-2, use the cumulative area from the left, locate the closest probability in the *body* of the table, and identify the corresponding z score.

Special Cases in Table A-2

z Score	Cumulative Area from the Left
1.645	0.9500
−1.645	0.0500
2.575	0.9950
−2.575	0.0050
Above 3.49	0.9999
Below −3.49	0.0001

Special Cases In the solution to Example 6 that follows, Table A-2 leads to a z score of 1.645, which is midway between 1.64 and 1.65. When using Table A-2, we can usually avoid interpolation by simply selecting the closest value. The accompanying table lists special cases that are often used in a wide variety of applications. (For one of those special cases, the value of z = 2.576 gives an area slightly closer to the area of 0.9950, but z = 2.575 has the advantage of being the value exactly midway between z = 2.57 and z = 2.58.) Except in these special cases, we can usually select the closest value in the table. (If a desired value is midway between two table values, select the larger value.) For z scores above 3.49, we can use 0.9999 as an approximation of the cumulative area from the left; for z scores below −3.49, we can use 0.0001 as an approximation of the cumulative area from the left.

EXAMPLE 6 **Bone Density Test: Finding a Test Score**

Use the same bone density test scores used in earlier examples. Those scores are normally distributed with a mean of 0 and a standard deviation of 1, so they meet the requirements of a standard normal distribution. Find the bone density score corresponding to P_{95}, the 95th percentile. That is, find the bone density score that separates the bottom 95% from the top 5%. See Figure 6-9.

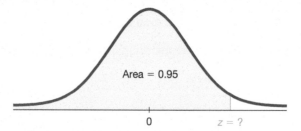

FIGURE 6-9 **Finding the 95th Percentile**

SOLUTION

Figure 6-9 shows the z score that is the 95th percentile, with 95% of the area (or 0.95) below it.

Technology: We could find the z score using technology. The accompanying Excel display shows that the z score with an area of 0.95 to its left is $z = 1.644853627$, or 1.645 when rounded.

Excel

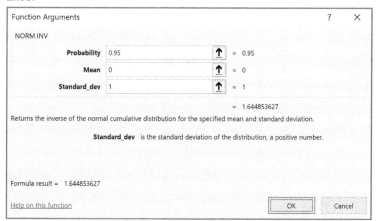

Table A-2: If using Table A-2, search for the area of 0.95 *in the body* of the table and then find the corresponding z score. In Table A-2 we find the areas of 0.9495 and 0.9505, but there's an asterisk with a special note indicating that 0.9500 corresponds to a z score of 1.645. We can now conclude that the z score in Figure 6-9 is 1.645, so the 95th percentile is $z = 1.645$.

INTERPRETATION

For bone density test scores, 95% of the scores are less than or equal to 1.645, and 5% of them are greater than or equal to 1.645.

> **YOUR TURN.** Do Exercise 37 "Finding Bone Density Scores."

EXAMPLE 7   **Bone Density Test**

Using the same bone density test described in Example 3, we have a standard normal distribution with a mean of 0 and a standard deviation of 1. Find the bone density test score that separates the bottom 2.5% and find the score that separates the top 2.5%.

SOLUTION

The required z scores are shown in Figure 6-10. Those z scores can be found using technology. If using Table A-2 to find the z score located to the left, we search the *body of the table* for an area of 0.025. The result is $z = -1.96$. To find the z score located to the right, we search *the body of* Table A-2 for an area of 0.975. (Remember that Table A-2 always gives cumulative areas from the *left*.) The result is $z = 1.96$. The values of $z = -1.96$ and $z = 1.96$ separate the bottom 2.5% and the top 2.5%, as shown in Figure 6-10.

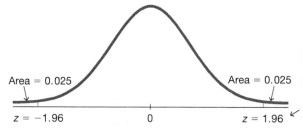

Area = 0.025   Area = 0.025

To find this z score, locate the cumulative area to the left in Table A-2. Locate 0.975 in the body of Table A-2.

$z = -1.96$ 0 $z = 1.96$

FIGURE 6-10   Finding z Scores

continued

INTERPRETATION

For the population of bone density test scores, 2.5% of the scores are equal to or less than -1.96 and 2.5% of the scores are equal to or greater than 1.96. Another interpretation is that 95% of all bone density test scores are between -1.96 and 1.96.

YOUR TURN. Do Exercise 39 "Finding Bone Density Scores."

Critical Values

DEFINITION

For the standard normal distribution, a **critical value** is a z score on the borderline separating those z scores that are *significantly low* or *significantly high*.

Common critical values are $z = -1.96$ and $z = 1.96$, and they are obtained as shown in Example 7. In Example 7, values of $z = -1.96$ or lower are significantly low because only 2.5% of the population have scores at or below -1.96, and the values at or above $z = 1.96$ are significantly high because only 2.5% of the population have scores at or above 1.96. Only 5% of all bone density scores are either -1.96 or lower or 1.96 or higher. Critical values will become extremely important in subsequent chapters. The following notation is used for critical z values found by using the standard normal distribution.

Notation

The expression z_α denotes the z score with an area of α to its right. (α is the Greek letter alpha.)

EXAMPLE 8 Finding the Critical Value z_α

Find the value of $z_{0.025}$. (Let $\alpha = 0.025$ in the expression z_α.)

SOLUTION

The notation of $z_{0.025}$ is used to represent the z score with an area of 0.025 to its *right*. Refer to Figure 6-10 and note that the value of $z = 1.96$ has an area of 0.025 to its right, so $z_{0.025} = 1.96$. Note that $z_{0.025}$ corresponds to a cumulative left area of 0.975.

YOUR TURN. Do Exercise 41 "Critical Values."

CAUTION When finding a value of z_α for a particular value of α, note that α is the area to the *right* of z_α, but Table A-2 and some technologies give cumulative areas to the *left* of a given z score. To find the value of z_α, resolve that conflict by using the value of $1 - \alpha$. For example, to find $z_{0.1}$, refer to the z score with an area of 0.9 to its left.

Examples 3 through 7 in this section are based on the real application of the bone density test, with scores that are normally distributed with a mean of 0 and standard deviation of 1, so that these scores have a standard normal distribution. Apart from the bone density test scores, it is rare to find such convenient parameters, because typical normal distributions have means different from 0 and standard deviations different from 1. In the next section we present methods for working with such normal distributions.

TECH CENTER

Finding z Scores/Areas (Standard Normal)

Access tech supplements, videos, and data sets at **www.TriolaStats.com**

Statdisk	Minitab	StatCrunch
1. Click **Analysis** in the top menu. 2. Select **Probability Distributions** from the dropdown menu and select **Normal Distribution** from the submenu. 3. Enter the desired z score or cumulative area from the left of the z score and click **Evaluate**.	1. Click **Calc** in the top menu. 2. Select **Probability Distributions** from the dropdown menu and select **Normal** from the submenu. **Finding Cumulative Area to the Left of a z Score** • Select **Cumulative probability**, enter mean of **0** and standard deviation of **1**. • Select **Input Constant**, enter the desired z score, and click **OK**. **Finding z Score from a Known Probability** • Select **Inverse cumulative probability**, enter mean of **0** and standard deviation of **1**. • Select **Input Constant**, enter the total area to the left of the z score, and click **OK**.	1. Click **Stat** in the top menu. 2. Select **Calculators** from the dropdown menu and **Normal** from the submenu. 3. In the calculator box enter mean of **0** and standard deviation of **1**. 4. Enter the desired z score (middle box) or known probability/area (rightmost box). Select the desired inequality. 5. Click **Compute**.

TI-83/84 Plus Calculator

Unlike most other technologies, the TI-83/84 Plus bases areas on the region between two z scores, rather than cumulative regions from the left.

Finding Area Between Two z Scores

1. Press **2ND** then **VARS** keys to access the *DISTR* (distributions) menu.
2. Select **normalcdf** and press **ENTER**.
3. Enter the desired lower z score and upper z score. Enter **0** for μ and **1** for σ to complete the command **normalcdf(lower z,upper z,μ,σ)**. Press **ENTER**.

TIP: If there is no lower z score, enter −99999999; if there is no upper z score, enter 99999999.

Finding z Score from a Known Probability

1. Press **2ND** then **VARS** keys to access the *DISTR* (distributions) menu.
2. Select **invNorm** and press **ENTER**.
3. Enter the area to the left or right of the z score, **0** for μ, and **1** for σ. For *Tail* select the tail where the area is located (*Left* or *Right*). The completed command is **InvNorm(area,0,1,TAIL)**. Press **ENTER**.

TIP: The TI-83 Plus only calculates area to the left of the z score. The completed command is **InvNorm(area,0,1)**.

Excel	R
Finding Cumulative Area to the Left of a z Score 1. Click **Insert Function f_x**, select the category **Statistical**, select the function **NORM.DIST**, and click **OK**. 2. For x enter the z score, enter **0** for *Mean,* enter **1** for *Standard_dev,* and enter **1** for *Cumulative*. 3. Click **OK**. **Finding z Score from a Known Probability** 1. Click **Insert Function f_x**, select the category **Statistical,** and select the function **NORM.INV**. 2. Enter the probability, enter **0** for *Mean,* and enter **1** for *Standard_dev*. 3. Click **OK**.	**R command not available at time of publication.** *R is rapidly evolving, and an updated list of statistical commands is available at TriolaStats.com*

6-1   Basic Skills and Concepts

Statistical Literacy and Critical Thinking

1. Normal Distribution What's wrong with the following statement? "Because the digits 0, 1, 2, . . . , 9 are the normal results from lottery drawings, such randomly selected numbers have a normal distribution."

2. Normal Distribution A normal distribution is informally described as a probability distribution that is "bell-shaped" when graphed. Draw a rough sketch of a curve having the bell shape that is characteristic of a normal distribution.

3. Standard Normal Distribution Identify the values of the mean and standard deviation for a normal distribution that is a *standard* normal distribution.

4. Notation What does the notation z_α indicate?

Continuous Uniform Distribution.   *In Exercises 5–8, refer to the continuous uniform distribution depicted in Figure 6-2 and described in Example 1. Assume that a passenger is randomly selected, and find the probability that the waiting time is within the given range.*

5. Greater than 3.00 minutes

6. Less than 4.00 minutes

7. Between 2 minutes and 3 minutes

8. Between 2.5 minutes and 4.5 minutes

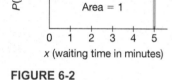

FIGURE 6-2

Standard Normal Distribution.   *In Exercises 9–12, find the area of the shaded region. The graph depicts the standard normal distribution of bone density scores with mean 0 and standard deviation 1.*

9.

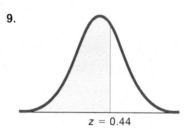

$z = 0.44$

10.

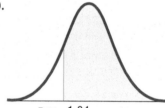

$z = -1.04$

11.

$z = -0.84$ $z = 1.28$

12.

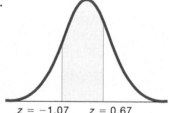

$z = -1.07$ $z = 0.67$

Standard Normal Distribution.   *In Exercises 13–16, find the indicated z score. The graph depicts the standard normal distribution of bone density scores with mean 0 and standard deviation 1.*

13.

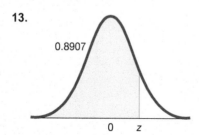

0.8907

0   z

14.

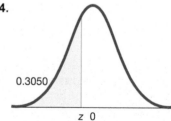

0.3050

z   0

15.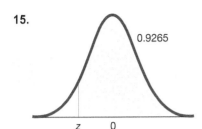

16.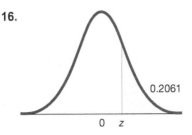

Standard Normal Distribution.   *In Exercises 17–36, assume that a randomly selected subject is given a bone density test. Those test scores are normally distributed with a mean of 0 and a standard deviation of 1. In each case, draw a graph, then find the probability of the given bone density test scores. If using technology instead of Table A-2, round answers to four decimal places.*

17. Less than -2.00

18. Less than -0.50

19. Less than 1.33

20. Less than 2.33

21. Greater than 1.00

22. Greater than 2.33

23. Greater than -1.75

24. Greater than -2.09

25. Between 1.50 and 2.00

26. Between 1.37 and 2.25

27. Between -1.22 and -2.36

28. Between -0.45 and -2.08

29. Between -1.55 and 1.55

30. Between -0.77 and 1.42

31. Between -2.00 and 3.50

32. Between -3.52 and 2.53

33. Greater than -3.77

34. Less than -3.93

35. Between -4.00 and 4.00

36. Between -3.67 and 4.25

Finding Bone Density Scores.   *In Exercises 37–40 assume that a randomly selected subject is given a bone density test. Bone density test scores are normally distributed with a mean of 0 and a standard deviation of 1. In each case, draw a graph, then find the bone density test score corresponding to the given information. Round results to two decimal places.*

37. Find P_{99}, the 99th percentile. This is the bone density score separating the bottom 99% from the top 1%.

38. Find P_{15}, the 15th percentile. This is the bone density score separating the bottom 15% from the top 85%.

39. If bone density scores in the bottom 1% and the top 1% are used as cutoff points for levels that are too low or too high, find the two readings that are cutoff values.

40. Find the bone density scores that are the quartiles Q_1, Q_2, and Q_3.

Critical Values.   *In Exercises 41–44, find the indicated critical value. Round results to two decimal places.*

41. $z_{0.25}$

42. $z_{0.90}$

43. $z_{0.02}$

44. $z_{0.05}$

Basis for the Range Rule of Thumb and the Empirical Rule.   *In Exercises 45–48, find the indicated area under the curve of the standard normal distribution; then convert it to a percentage and fill in the blank. The results form the basis for the range rule of thumb and the empirical rule introduced in Section 3-2.*

45. About _____% of the area is between $z = -1$ and $z = 1$ (or within 1 standard deviation of the mean).

46. About _____% of the area is between $z = -2$ and $z = 2$ (or within 2 standard deviations of the mean).

47. About _____% of the area is between $z = -3$ and $z = 3$ (or within 3 standard deviations of the mean).

48. About _____% of the area is between $z = -3.5$ and $z = 3.5$ (or within 3.5 standard deviations of the mean).

6-1 Beyond the Basics

49. Significance For bone density scores that are normally distributed with a mean of 0 and a standard deviation of 1, find the *percentage* of scores that are

a. *significantly high* (or at least 2 standard deviations above the mean).

b. *significantly low* (or at least 2 standard deviations below the mean).

c. *not significant* (or less than 2 standard deviations away from the mean).

50. Distributions In a continuous uniform distribution,

$$\mu = \frac{\text{minimum} + \text{maximum}}{2} \quad \text{and} \quad \sigma = \frac{\text{range}}{\sqrt{12}}$$

a. Find the mean and standard deviation for the distribution of the waiting times represented in Figure 6-2, which accompanies Exercises 5–8.

b. For a continuous uniform distribution with $\mu = 0$ and $\sigma = 1$, the minimum is $-\sqrt{3}$ and the maximum is $\sqrt{3}$. For this continuous uniform distribution, find the probability of randomly selecting a value between –1 and 1, and compare it to the value that would be obtained by incorrectly treating the distribution as a standard normal distribution. Does the distribution affect the results very much?

6-2 Real Applications of Normal Distributions

Key Concept Most of the preceding section dealt with the real-world application of bone density scores, which have a normal distribution with $\mu = 0$ and $\sigma = 1$. However, it is rare to find other real applications of a standard normal distribution. We now extend the methods of the previous section so that we can work with any *nonstandard normal distribution* (with a mean different from 0 and/or a standard deviation different from 1). The key is a simple conversion (Formula 6-2) that allows us to "standardize" any normal distribution so that x values can be transformed to z scores; then the methods of the preceding section can be used.

FORMULA 6-2

$$z = \frac{x - \mu}{\sigma} \quad (\text{round } z \text{ scores to 2 decimal places})$$

Figure 6-11 illustrates the conversion from a nonstandard to a standard normal distribution. The area in *any* normal distribution bounded by some score x (as in Figure 6-11a) is the *same* as the area bounded by the corresponding z score in the standard normal distribution (as in Figure 6-11b).

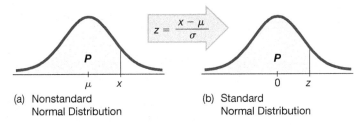

(a) Nonstandard
Normal Distribution

(b) Standard
Normal Distribution

FIGURE 6-11   Converting Distributions

Most statistics calculators and software do not require the use of Formula 6-2 to convert to z scores because probabilities can be found directly. However, if using Table A-2, we must first convert values to standard z scores.

When finding areas with a nonstandard normal distribution, use the following procedure.

Procedure for Finding Areas with a Nonstandard Normal Distribution

1. Sketch a normal curve, label the mean and any specific x values, and then *shade* the region representing the desired probability.

2. For each relevant value x that is a boundary for the shaded region, use Formula 6-2 to convert that value to the equivalent z score. (With many technologies, this step can be skipped.)

3. Use technology (software or a calculator) or Table A-2 to find the area of the shaded region. This area is the desired probability.

The following example illustrates the above procedure.

EXAMPLE 1   **What Proportion of Men Are Taller Than the 72 in. Height Requirement for Showerheads (According to Most Building Codes)?**

Heights of men are normally distributed with a mean of 68.6 in. and a standard deviation of 2.8 in. (based on Data Set 1 "Body Data" in Appendix B). Find the percentage of men who are taller than a showerhead positioned at 72 in. above the floor.

SOLUTION

Step 1: See Figure 6-12, which incorporates this information: Men have heights that are normally distributed with a mean of 68.6 in. and a standard deviation of 2.8 in. The shaded region represents the men who are taller than the showerhead height of 72 in.

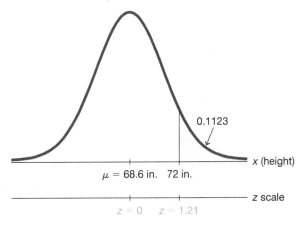

FIGURE 6-12   Heights of Men

continued

Step 2: We can convert the showerhead height of 72 in. to the z score of 1.21 by using Formula 6-2 as follows:

$$z = \frac{x - \mu}{\sigma} = \frac{72 - 68.6}{2.8} = 1.21 \ (\text{rounded to two decimal places})$$

Step 3: Technology: Technology can be used to find that the area to the right of 72 in. in Figure 6-12 is 0.1123 rounded. (With many technologies, Step 2 can be skipped. See technology instructions at the end of this section.) The result of 0.1123 from technology is more accurate than the result of 0.1131 found by using Table A-2.

Table A-2: Use Table A-2 to find that the cumulative area to the *left* of $z = 1.21$ is 0.8869. (Remember, Table A-2 is designed so that all areas are cumulative areas from the *left*.) Because the total area under the curve is 1, it follows that the shaded area in Figure 6-12 is $1 - 0.8869 = 0.1131$.

INTERPRETATION

The proportion of men taller than the showerhead height of 72 in. is 0.1123, or 11.23%. About 11% of men may find the design to be unsuitable. (*Note:* Some NBA teams have been known to intentionally use lower showerheads in the locker rooms of visiting basketball teams.)

 **YOUR TURN.** Do Exercise 13 "Pulse Rates."

CP EXAMPLE 2 Air Force Height Requirement

Until recently, the U.S. Air Force required that pilots have heights between 64 in. and 77 in. Heights of women are normally distributed with a mean of 63.7 in. and a standard deviation of 2.9 in. (based on Data Set 1 "Body Data" in Appendix B). What percentage of women meet that height requirement?

SOLUTION

Figure 6-13 shows the shaded region representing heights of women between 64 in. and 77 in.

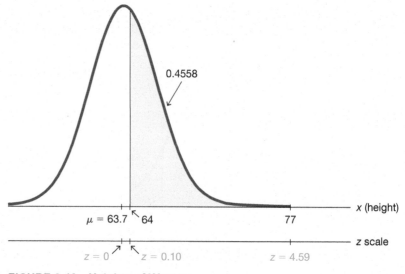

FIGURE 6-13 Heights of Women

Step 1: See Figure 6-13, which incorporates this information: Women have heights that are normally distributed with a mean of 63.7 in. and a standard deviation of 2.9 in. The shaded region represents the women with heights between 64 in. and 77 in.

Step 2: With some technologies, the shaded area in Figure 6-13 can be found directly and it is not necessary to convert the x scores of 64 in. and 77 in. to z scores. (See Step 3.)

If using Table A-2, we cannot find the shaded area directly, but we can find it indirectly by using the same procedures from Section 6-1, as follows: (1) Find the cumulative area from the left up to 77 in. (or $z = 4.59$); (2) find the cumulative area from the left up to 64 in. (or $z = 0.10$); (3) find the difference between those two areas. The heights of 77 in. and 64 in. are converted to z scores by using Formula 6-2 as follows:

$$\text{For } x = 77 \text{ in.: } z = \frac{x - \mu}{\sigma} = \frac{77 - 63.7}{2.9} = 4.59$$
$$(z = 4.59 \text{ yields an area of } 0.9999.)$$

$$\text{For } x = 64 \text{ in.: } z = \frac{x - \mu}{\sigma} = \frac{64 - 63.7}{2.9} = 0.10$$
$$(z = 0.10 \text{ yields an area of } 0.5398.)$$

Step 3: Technology: To use technology, refer to the Tech Center instructions on page 267. Technology will show that the shaded area in Figure 6-13 is 0.4588

Table A-2: Refer to Table A-2 with $z = 4.59$ and find that the cumulative area to the *left* of $z = 4.59$ is 0.9999. (Remember, Table A-2 is designed so that all areas are cumulative areas from the *left*.) Table A-2 also shows that $z = 0.10$ corresponds to an area of 0.5398. Because the areas of 0.9999 and 0.5398 are *cumulative areas from the left*, we find the shaded area in Figure 6-13 as follows:

$$\text{Shaded area in Figure 6–13} = 0.9999 - 0.5398 = 0.4601$$

There is a relatively small discrepancy between the area of 0.4588 found from technology and the area of 0.4601 found from Table A-2. The area obtained from technology is more accurate because it is based on unrounded z scores, whereas Table A-2 requires z scores rounded to two decimal places.

INTERPRETATION

Expressing the result as a percentage, we conclude that about 46% of women satisfy the requirement of having a height between 64 in. and 77 in. About 54% of women did not meet that requirement and they were not eligible to be pilots in the U.S. Air Force.

YOUR TURN. Do Exercise 15 "Pulse Rates."

Finding Values from Known Areas

Here are helpful hints for those cases in which the area (or probability or percentage) is known and we must find the relevant value(s):

1. Graphs are extremely helpful in visualizing, understanding, and successfully working with normal probability distributions, so they should always be used.

2. *Don't confuse z scores and areas.* Remember, z scores are *distances* along the horizontal scale, but areas are *regions* under the normal curve. Table A-2 lists z scores in the left columns and across the top row, but areas are found in the body of the table.

continued

3. *Choose the correct (right/left) side of the graph.* A value separating the *top* 10% from the others will be located on the right side of the graph, but a value separating the *bottom* 10% will be located on the left side of the graph.

4. A *z* score must be *negative* whenever it is located in the *left* half of the normal distribution.

5. Areas (or probabilities) are always between 0 and 1, and they are never negative.

Procedure for Finding Values from Known Areas or Probabilities

1. Sketch a normal distribution curve, write the given probability or percentage in the appropriate region of the graph, and identify the *x* value(s) being sought.

2. If using technology, refer to the Tech Center instructions at the end of this section. If using Table A-2, refer to the *body* of Table A-2 to find the area to the left of *x*, then identify the *z* score corresponding to that area.

3. If you know *z* and must convert to the equivalent *x* value, use Formula 6-2 by entering the values for μ, σ, and the *z* score found in Step 2, then solve for *x*. Based on Formula 6-2, we can solve for *x* as follows:

$$x = \mu + (z \cdot \sigma) \quad \text{(another form of Formula 6–2)}$$

$\uparrow$

(If *z* is located to the left of the mean, be sure that it is a negative number.)

4. Refer to the sketch of the curve to verify that the solution makes sense in the context of the graph and in the context of the problem.

The following example uses this procedure for finding a value from a known area.

EXAMPLE 3 **Designing a Front Door for a Home**

When designing equipment, one common criterion is to use a design that accommodates at least 95% of the population. What is the height of a door that would allow 95% of adults to walk through the doorway without bending or hitting their heads? Based on Data Set 1 "Body Data" in Appendix B, assume that heights of adults are normally distributed with a mean of 66.2 in. and a standard deviation of 3.8 in. How does the result compare to the door height of 80 in. required by the International Residential Code?

SOLUTION

Step 1: Figure 6-14 on the next page shows the normal distribution with the height *x* that we want to identify. The shaded area represents the shortest 95% of adults.

Step 2: Technology: Technology will provide the value of *x* in Figure 6-14. For example, see the Excel display on the next page showing that $x = 72.45044378$ in., or 72.5 in. when rounded.

Table A-2: If using Table A-2, search for an area of 0.9500 *in the body* of the table. (The area of 0.9500 shown in Figure 6-14 is a cumulative area from the left, and that is exactly the type of area listed in Table A-2.) The area of 0.9500 is between the Table A-2 areas of 0.9495 and 0.9505, but there is an asterisk and footnote indicating that an area of 0.9500 corresponds to $z = 1.645$.

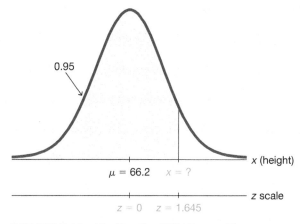

FIGURE 6-14   Finding the 95th Percentile

EXCEL

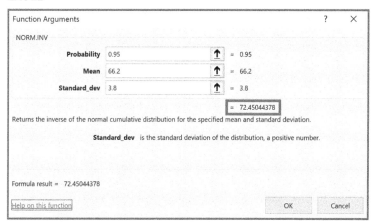

Step 3: With $z = 1.645$, $\mu = 66.2$ in., and $\sigma = 3.8$ in., we can solve for x by using Formula 6-2:

$$z = \frac{x - \mu}{\sigma} \quad \text{becomes} \quad 1.645 = \frac{x - 66.2}{3.8}$$

The result of $x = 72.451$ in. can be found directly with a little algebra, or that result can be found by using the following version of Formula 6-2:

$$x = \mu + (z \cdot \sigma) = 66.2 + (1.645 \cdot 3.8) = 72.451$$

Step 4: The solution of $x = 72.5$ in. (rounded) in Figure 6-14 is reasonable because it is greater than the mean of 66.2 in.

INTERPRETATION

A door height of 72.5 in. would allow 95% of adults to walk through without bending or hitting heads. The door height of 72.5 in. is well below the height of 80 in. required by the International Residential Code, so more than 95% of adults could walk through doors meeting this requirement without bending or hitting their heads.

YOUR TURN. Do Exercise 21 "Pulse Rates."

Significance

In Chapter 4 we saw that probabilities can be used to determine whether values are *significantly high* or *significantly low*. Chapter 4 referred to *x* successes among *n* trials, but we can adapt those criteria to apply to continuous variables as follows:

Significantly high: The value *x* is *significantly high* if $P(x \text{ or greater}) \le 0.05$.*

Significantly low: The value *x* is *significantly low* if $P(x \text{ or less}) \le 0.05$.*

*The value of 0.05 is not absolutely rigid, and other values such as 0.01 could be used instead.

EXAMPLE 4   Significantly Low Birth Weights

Use the preceding criteria to identify significantly low birth weights (grams) of males based on Data Set 6 "Births" in Appendix B. Assume that males have normally distributed birth weights with a mean of 3272.8 g and a standard deviation of 660.2 g.

SOLUTION

Step 1: We begin with the graph shown in Figure 6-15. We have entered the mean of 3272.8 and we have identified the *x* value separating the lowest 5% of male birth weights.

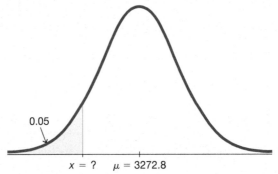

0.05

$x = ?$ $\mu = 3272.8$

FIGURE 6-15   Male Birth Weights

Step 2: Technology: To use technology, refer to the instructions at the end of this section. Technology will show that the value of *x* in Figure 6-15 is 2186.9 g.

Table A-2: If using Table A-2, we must work with cumulative areas from the left. For the value of *x*, the cumulative area from the left is 0.05, so search for an area of 0.05 *in the body* of the table to get $z = -1.645$ (identified by the asterisk between 0.0505 and 0.0495). Having found the *z* score, we now proceed to convert it to a birth weight.

Step 3: We now solve for *x* by using Formula 6-2 directly or by using the following version of Formula 6-2:

$$\text{Value of } x\text{: } x = \mu + (z \cdot \sigma) = 3272.8 + (-1.645 \cdot 660.2) = 2186.8 \text{ g}$$

Step 4: Referring to Figure 6-15, we see that the value of $x = 2186.9$ g (or 2186.8 g if using Table A-2) is reasonable because it is less than the mean of 3272.8 g.

INTERPRETATION

The birth weight of 2186.9 g is on the borderline that separates significantly low male birth weights from male birth weights that are not significantly low. (The World Health Organization uses 2500 g as the cutoff for low birth weights of males and females.) Babies with low birth weights are often given special treatments, such as care in the Neonatal Intensive Care Unit or the use of a temperature-controlled bed.

YOUR TURN. Do Exercise 23 "Significance."

TECH CENTER

Finding *x* Values/Areas

Access tech supplements, videos, and data sets at **www.TriolaStats.com**

Statdisk	Minitab	StatCrunch
1. Click **Analysis** in the top menu. 2. Select **Probability Distributions** from the dropdown menu and select **Normal Distribution** from the submenu. 3. Enter the desired *z* value or cumulative area from the left of the *z* score and click **Evaluate.** *TIP:* Statdisk does not work directly with nonstandard normal distributions, so use corresponding *z* scores.	1. Click **Calc** in the top menu. 2. Select **Probability Distributions** from the dropdown menu and select **Normal** from the submenu. **Finding Cumulative Area to the Left of an *x* Value** 3. Select **Cumulative probability,** enter the mean and standard deviation. 4. Select **Input constant,** enter the desired *x* value, and click **OK.** **Finding *x* Value from a Known Probability** 3. Select **Inverse cumulative probability,** enter the mean and standard deviation. 4. Select **Input constant,** enter the total area to the left of the *x* value, and click **OK.**	1. Click **Stat** in the top menu. 2. Select **Calculators** from the dropdown menu and **Normal** from the submenu. 3. In the calculator box enter the mean and standard deviation. 4. Enter the desired *x* value (middle box) or probability (rightmost box). 5. Click **Compute.**

TI-83/84 Plus Calculator

Unlike most other technologies, the TI-83/84 Plus bases areas on the region between two z scores, rather than cumulative regions from the left.

Finding Area Between Two *x* Values

1. Press **2ND** then **VARS** keys to access the *DISTR* (distributions) menu.
2. Select **normalcdf** and press **ENTER**.
3. Enter the desired *lower x* value and *upper x* value. Enter the mean (μ) and standard deviation (σ) to complete the command **normalcdf(lower x, upper x, μ, σ)**. Press **ENTER**.

TIP: If there is no lower *x* value, enter −99999999; if there is no upper *x* value, enter 99999999.

Finding *x* Value Corresponding to a Known Area

1. Press **2ND** then **VARS** keys to access the *DISTR* (distributions) menu.
2. Select **invNorm** and press **ENTER**.
3. Enter the *area* to the left or right of the *x* value, enter the mean (μ), and the standard deviation (σ). For *Tail* select the tail where the area is located (*Left* or *Right*) relative to the *x* value. The completed command is **InvNorm(area, μ, σ, TAIL)**. Press **ENTER**.

TIP: The TI-83 Plus only calculates area to the left of the *x* score. The completed command is **InvNorm(area, μ, σ)**.

Excel	R
Finding Cumulative Area to the Left of an *x* Value 1. Click **Insert Function *f_x*,** select the category **Statistical,** select the function **NORM.DIST,** and **click OK.** 2. For *x* enter the *x* value, enter *Mean,* enter *Standard_dev,* and enter **1** for *Cumulative.* 3. Click **OK.** **Finding *x* Value Corresponding to a Known Probability** 1. Click **Insert Function *f_x*,** select the category **Statistical,** select the function **NORM.INV,** and click **OK.** 2. Enter the probability or the area to the left of the desired *x* value, enter *Mean,* and enter *Standard_dev.* 3. Click **OK.**	**R command not available at time of publication.** *R is rapidly evolving, and an updated list of statistical commands is available at TriolaStats.com*

6-2   Basic Skills and Concepts

Statistical Literacy and Critical Thinking

1. Hershey Kisses Based on Data Set 38 "Candies" in Appendix B, weights of the chocolate in Hershey Kisses are normally distributed with a mean of 4.5338 g and a standard deviation of 0.1039 g.

a. What are the values of the mean and standard deviation after converting all weights of Hershey Kisses to z scores using $z = (x - \mu)/\sigma$?

b. The original weights are in grams. What are the units of the corresponding z scores?

2. Hershey Kisses Based on Data Set 38 "Candies" in Appendix B, weights of the chocolate in Hershey Kisses are normally distributed with a mean of 4.5338 g and a standard deviation of 0.1039 g.

a. For the bell-shaped graph of the normal distribution of weights of Hershey Kisses, what is the area under the curve?

b. What is the value of the median?

c. What is the value of the mode?

d. What is the value of the variance?

3. Normal Distributions Is the distribution described in the preceding exercise a standard normal distribution? Why or why not?

4. Mega Millions The Mega Millions lottery game requires that a number between 1 and 25 is randomly selected. What is the shape of the distribution of those selected numbers? Is it correct to say that because these selected numbers are the result of the normal selection procedure used for every drawing, the distribution of the selected numbers is a normal distribution?

IQ Scores.   *In Exercises 5–8, find the area of the shaded region. The graphs depict IQ scores of adults, and those scores are normally distributed with a mean of 100 and a standard deviation of 15 (as on the Wechsler IQ test).*

5.

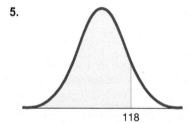

118

6.

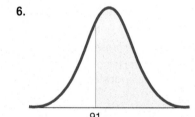

91

7.

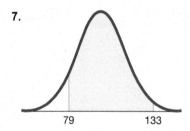

79   133

8.

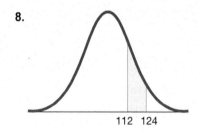

112 124

IQ Scores. *In Exercises 9–12, find the indicated IQ score and round to the nearest whole number. The graphs depict IQ scores of adults, and those scores are normally distributed with a mean of 100 and a standard deviation of 15 (as on the Wechsler IQ test).*

9.

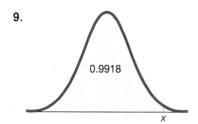

0.9918

10.

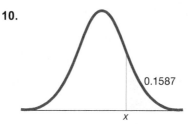

0.1587

11.

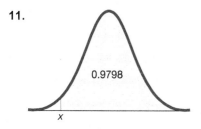

0.9798

12.

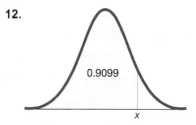

0.9099

Pulse Rates. *In Exercises 13–24, use the data in the table below for pulse rates of adult males and females (based on Data Set 1 "Body Data" in Appendix B). Hint: Draw a graph in each case.*

Pulse Rate (beats per minute)

	Mean	St. Dev.	Distribution
Males	69.6	11.3	Normal
Females	74.0	12.5	Normal

13. Find the probability that a male has a pulse rate less than 60 beats per minute.

14. Find the probability that a female has a pulse rate less than 60 beats per minute.

15. Find the probability that a female has a pulse rate greater than 80 beats per minute.

16. Find the probability that a male has a pulse rate greater than 80 beats per minute.

17. Find the probability that a female has a pulse rate between 70 beats per minute and 90 beats per minute.

18. Find the probability that a male has a pulse rate between 65 beats per minute and 85 beats per minute.

19. Find the probability that a male has a pulse rate between 70 beats per minute and 90 beats per minute.

20. Find the probability that a female has a pulse rate between 60 beats per minute and 70 beats per minute.

21. For males, find P_{90}, which is the pulse rate separating the bottom 90% from the top 10%.

22. For females, find the first quartile Q_1, which is the pulse rate separating the bottom 25% from the top 75%.

23. Significance Instead of using 0.05 for identifying significant values, use the criteria that a value x is *significantly high* if $P(x$ or greater$) \leq 0.01$ and a value is *significantly low* if $P(x$ or less$) \leq 0.01$. Find the pulse rates for males that separate significant pulse rates from those that are not significant. Using these criteria, is a male pulse rate of 90 beats per minute significantly high?

24. Significance Instead of using 0.05 for identifying significant values, use the criteria that a value x is *significantly high* if $P(x$ or greater$) \leq 0.025$ and a value is *significantly low* if $P(x$ or less$) \leq 0.025$. Find the female pulse rates separating significant values from those that are not significant. Using these criteria, is a female pulse rate of 48 beats per minute significantly low?

In Exercises 25–28, use these parameters (based on Data Set 1 "Body Data" in Appendix B):

- *Men's heights are normally distributed with mean 68.6 in. and standard deviation 2.8 in.*
- *Women's heights are normally distributed with mean 63.7 in. and standard deviation 2.9 in.*

25. Navy Pilots The U.S. Navy requires that fighter pilots have heights between 62 in. and 78 in.

a. Find the percentage of women meeting the height requirement. Are many women not qualified because they are too short or too tall?

b. If the Navy changes the height requirements so that all women are eligible except the shortest 3% and the tallest 3%, what are the new height requirements for women?

26. Air Force Pilots The U.S. Air Force required that pilots have heights between 64 in. and 77 in.

a. Find the percentage of men meeting the height requirement.

b. If the Air Force height requirements are changed to exclude only the tallest 2.5% of men and the shortest 2.5% of men, what are the new height requirements?

27. Mickey Mouse Disney World requires that people employed as a Mickey Mouse character must have a height between 56 in. and 62 in.

a. Find the percentage of men meeting the height requirement. What does the result suggest about the genders of the people who are employed as Mickey Mouse characters?

b. If the height requirements are changed to exclude the tallest 50% of men and the shortest 5% of men, what are the new height requirements?

28. Snow White Disney World requires that women employed as a Snow White character must have a height between 64 in. and 67 in.

a. Find the percentage of women meeting the height requirement.

b. If the height requirements are changed to exclude the shortest 40% of women and the tallest 5% of women, what are the new height requirements?

29. Designing Helmets Engineers must consider the circumferences of adult heads when designing motorcycle helmets. Adult head circumferences are normally distributed with a mean of 570.0 mm and a standard deviation of 18.3 mm (based on Data Set 3 "ANSUR II 2012"). Due to financial constraints, the helmets will be designed to fit all adults except those with head circumferences that are in the smallest 5% or largest 5%. Find the minimum and maximum head circumferences that the helmets will fit.

30. Designing a Desk A common design requirement is that an environment must fit the range of people who fall between the 5th percentile for women and the 95th percentile for men. In designing a desk, we must consider *sitting knee height*, which is the distance from the bottom of the feet to the top of the knee. Males have sitting knee heights that are normally distributed with a mean of 21.4 in. and a standard deviation of 1.2 in.; females have sitting knee heights that are normally distributed with a mean of 19.6 in. and a standard deviation of 1.1 in. (based on data from the Department of Transportation).

a. What is the minimum desk clearance height required to satisfy the requirement of fitting 95% of men? Why is the 95th percentile for women ignored in this case?

b. The author is writing this exercise at a desk with a clearance of 23.5 in. above the floor. What percentage of men fit this desk, and what percentage of women fit this desk? Does the desk appear to be made to fit almost everyone?

31. Aircraft Seat Width Engineers want to design seats in commercial aircraft so that they are wide enough to fit 99% of all adults. (Accommodating 100% of adults would require very wide seats that would be much too expensive.) Assume adults have hip widths that are normally distributed with a mean of 14.3 in. and a standard deviation of 0.9 in. (based on data from *Applied Ergonomics*). Find P_{99}. That is, find the hip width for adults that separates the smallest 99% from the largest 1%.

32. Freshman 15 The term "Freshman 15" refers to the claim that college students typically gain 15 lb during their freshman year at college. Assume that the amounts of weight that male college students gain during their freshman year are normally distributed with a mean of 2.6 lb and a standard deviation of 10.8 lb (based on Data Set 13 "Freshman 15"). Find the probability that a randomly selected male college student gains 15 lb or more during his freshman year. What does the result suggest about the claim of the "Freshman 15"?

33. Durations of Pregnancies The lengths of pregnancies are normally distributed with a mean of 268 days and a standard deviation of 15 days.

a. In a letter to "Dear Abby," a wife claimed to have given birth 308 days after a brief visit from her husband, who was working in another country. Find the probability of a pregnancy lasting 308 days or longer. What does the result suggest?

b. If we stipulate that a baby is *premature* if the duration of pregnancy is in the lowest 3%, find the duration that separates premature babies from those who are not premature. Premature babies often require special care, and this result could be helpful to hospital administrators in planning for that care.

34. Body Temperatures Based on the sample results in Data Set 5 "Body Temperatures" in Appendix B, assume that human body temperatures are normally distributed with a mean of 98.20°F and a standard deviation of 0.62°F.

a. According to emedicinehealth.com, a body temperature of 100.4°F or above is considered to be a fever. What percentage of normal and healthy persons would be considered to have a fever? Does this percentage suggest that a cutoff of 100.4°F is appropriate?

b. Physicians want to select a minimum temperature for requiring further medical tests. What should that temperature be, if we want only 2.0% of healthy people to exceed it? (Such a result is a *false positive*, meaning that the test result is positive, but the subject is not really sick.)

35. Designing Cars The sitting height of drivers must be considered in the design of a new car. The sitting height is measured from the seat to the top of the driver's head, and adults have sitting heights that are normally distributed with a mean of 35.4 in. and a standard deviation of 1.8 in. (based on Data Set 3 "ANSUR II 2012"). Engineers have provided plans that can accommodate adults with sitting heights up to 38.9 in., but taller adults cannot fit. Find the percentage of adults with sitting heights that fit this car. Based on the result, is the engineering design feasible?

36. Water Taxi Safety When a water taxi sank in Baltimore's Inner Harbor, an investigation revealed that the safe passenger load for the water taxi was 3500 lb. It was also noted that the mean weight of a passenger was assumed to be 140 lb. Assume a "worst-case" scenario in which all of the passengers are adult men. Assume that weights of men are normally distributed with a mean of 188.6 lb and a standard deviation of 38.9 lb (based on Data Set 1 "Body Data" in Appendix B).

a. If one man is randomly selected, find the probability that he weighs less than 174 lb (the new value suggested by the National Transportation and Safety Board).

b. With a load limit of 3500 lb, how many male passengers are allowed if we assume a mean weight of 140 lb?

c. With a load limit of 3500 lb, how many male passengers are allowed if we assume the updated mean weight of 188.6 lb?

d. Why is it necessary to periodically review and revise the number of passengers that are allowed to board?

6-2   Beyond the Basics

37. Curving Test Scores A professor gives a test and the scores are normally distributed with a mean of 60 and a standard deviation of 12. She plans to curve the scores.

a. If she curves by adding 15 to each grade, what is the new mean and standard deviation?

b. Is it fair to curve by adding 15 to each grade? Why or why not?

c. If the grades are curved so that grades of B are given to scores above the bottom 70% and below the top 10%, find the numerical limits for a grade of B.

d. Which method of curving the grades is fairer: adding 15 to each original score or using a scheme like the one given in part (c)? Explain.

38. Outliers For the purposes of constructing modified boxplots as described in Section 3-3, outliers are defined as data values that are above Q_3 by an amount greater than $1.5 \times$ IQR or below Q_1 by an amount greater than $1.5 \times$ IQR, where IQR is the interquartile range. Using this definition of outliers, find the probability that when a value is randomly selected from a normal distribution, it is an outlier.

6-3   Sampling Distributions and Estimators

Key Concept We now consider the concept of a *sampling distribution of a statistic.* Instead of working with values from the original population, we want to focus on the values of *statistics* (such as sample proportions or sample means) obtained from the population. Figure 6-16 shows the key points that we need to know, so try really, really hard to understand the story that Figure 6-16 tells.

A Statistics Story Among the population of all adults, exactly 70% do not feel comfortable in a self-driving vehicle (the author just knows this). In a TE Connectivity survey of 1000 adults, 69% said that they did not feel comfortable in a self-driving vehicle. Empowered by visions of multitudes of driverless cars, 50,000 people became so enthusiastic that they each conducted their own individual survey of 1000 randomly selected adults on the same topic. Each of these 50,000 newbie surveyors reported the percentage that they found, with results such as 68%, 72%, 70%. The author obtained each of the 50,000 sample percentages, he changed them to proportions, and then he constructed the histogram shown in Figure 6-17. Notice anything about the *shape* of the histogram? It's *normal* (unlike the 50,000 newbie surveyors). Notice anything about the mean of the sample proportions? They are centered about the value of 0.70, which happens to be the population proportion. Moral:

When samples of the same size are taken from the same population, the following two properties apply:

1. **Sample proportions tend to be normally distributed.**

2. **The mean of sample proportions is the same as the population mean.**

The implications of the preceding properties will be extensive in the chapters that follow. What a happy ending!

Proportions

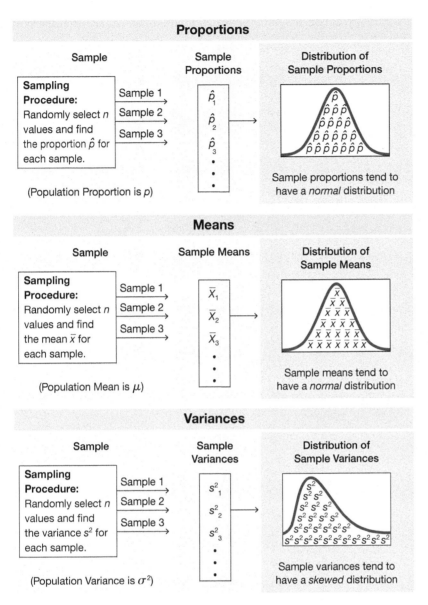

FIGURE 6-16   General Behavior of Sampling Distributions

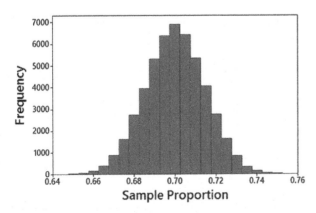

FIGURE 6-17   Histogram of 50,000 Sample Proportions

Let's formally define *sampling distribution,* the main character in the preceding statistics story.

> **DEFINITION**
>
> The **sampling distribution of a statistic** (such as a sample proportion or sample mean) is the distribution of all values of the statistic when all possible samples of the same size n are taken from the same population. (The sampling distribution of a statistic is typically represented as a probability distribution in the format of a probability histogram, formula, or table.)

Sampling Distribution of Sample Proportion

The preceding general definition of a sampling distribution of a statistic can now be restated for the specific case of a sample proportion:

> **DEFINITION**
>
> The **sampling distribution of the sample proportion** is the distribution of sample proportions (or the distribution of the variable $\hat{p}$), with all samples having the same sample size n taken from the same population. (The sampling distribution of the sample proportion is typically represented as a probability distribution in the format of a probability histogram, formula, or table.)

We need to distinguish between a population proportion p and a sample proportion, and the following notation is common and will be used throughout the remainder of this book, so it's very important.

Notation for Proportions

$x =$ number of successes

$n =$ sample size

$N =$ population size

$\hat{p} = x/n$ denotes the *sample proportion*

$p = x/N$ denotes the *population proportion*

HINT $\hat{p}$ is pronounced "p-hat." When symbols are used above a letter, as in $\bar{x}$ and $\hat{p}$, they represent *statistics*, not parameters.

Behavior of Sample Proportions

1. The distribution of sample proportions tends to approximate a normal distribution.

2. Sample proportions *target* the value of the population proportion in the sense that the mean of all of the sample proportions $\hat{p}$ is equal to the population proportion p; the expected value of the sample proportion is equal to the population proportion.

EXAMPLE 1   **Sampling Distribution of the Sample Proportion**

Consider repeating this process: Roll a die 5 times and find the proportion of *odd* numbers (1 or 3 or 5). What do we know about the behavior of all sample proportions that are generated as this process continues indefinitely?

SOLUTION

Figure 6-18 illustrates a process of rolling a die 5 times and finding the proportion of odd numbers. (Figure 6-18 shows results from repeating this process 10,000 times, but the true sampling distribution of the sample proportion involves repeating the process indefinitely.) Figure 6-18 shows that the sample proportions are approximately normally distributed. (Because the values of 1, 2, 3, 4, 5, 6 are all equally likely, the proportion of odd numbers in the population is 0.5, and Figure 6-18 shows that the sample proportions have a mean of 0.50.)

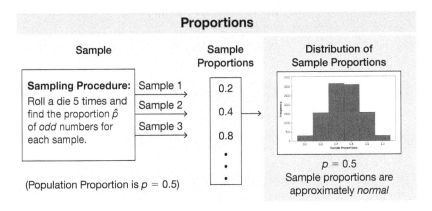

FIGURE 6-18   Sample Proportions from 10,000 Trials

YOUR TURN. Do Exercise 10 "Sampling Distribution of the Sample Proportion."

Go Figure

90%: Percentage of the world's data that have been generated in the past two years (according to *Science Daily*).

Sampling Distribution of the Sample Mean

We now consider sample means.

DEFINITION

The **sampling distribution of the sample mean** is the distribution of all possible sample means (or the distribution of the variable $\bar{x}$), with all samples having the same sample size *n* taken from the same population. (The sampling distribution of the sample mean is typically represented as a probability distribution in the format of a probability histogram, formula, or table.)

Behavior of Sample Means

1. The distribution of sample means tends to be a normal distribution. (This will be discussed further in the following section, but the distribution tends to become closer to a normal distribution as the sample size increases.)

2. The sample means *target* the value of the population mean. (That is, the mean of the sample means is the population mean. The expected value of the sample mean is equal to the population mean.)

EXAMPLE 2 Sampling Distribution of the Sample Mean

A friend of the author has three children with ages of 4, 5, and 9. Let's consider the population consisting of $\{4, 5, 9\}$. (We don't usually know all values in a population, and we don't usually work with such a small population, but it works well for the purposes of this example.) If two ages are randomly selected with replacement from the population $\{4, 5, 9\}$, identify the sampling distribution of the sample mean by creating a table representing the probability distribution of the sample mean. Do the values of the sample mean target the value of the population mean?

SOLUTION

If two values are randomly selected with replacement from the population $\{4, 5, 9\}$, the leftmost column of Table 6-2 lists the nine different possible samples. The second column lists the corresponding sample means. The nine samples are equally likely with a probability of 1/9. We saw in Section 5-1 that a probability distribution is a description that gives the probability for each value of a random variable, as in the second and third columns of Table 6-2. The second and third columns of Table 6-2 constitute a probability distribution for the random variable representing sample means, so the second and third columns represent the sampling distribution of the sample mean. In Table 6-2, some of the sample mean values are repeated, so we combined them in Table 6-3.

TABLE 6-2 Sampling Distribution of Mean

Sample	Sample Mean $\bar{x}$	Probability
4, 4	4.0	1/9
4, 5	4.5	1/9
4, 9	6.5	1/9
5, 4	4.5	1/9
5, 5	5.0	1/9
5, 9	7.0	1/9
9, 4	6.5	1/9
9, 5	7.0	1/9
9, 9	9.0	1/9

TABLE 6-3 Sampling Distribution of Mean (Condensed)

Sample Mean $\bar{x}$	Probability
4.0	1/9
4.5	2/9
5.0	1/9
6.5	2/9
7.0	2/9
9.0	1/9

INTERPRETATION

Because Table 6-3 lists the possible values of the sample mean along with their corresponding probabilities, Table 6-3 is an example of a sampling distribution of a sample mean.

The value of the mean of the population $\{4, 5, 9\}$ is $\mu = 6.0$. Using either Table 6-2 or 6-3, we could calculate the mean of the sample values and we get 6.0. Because the mean of the sample means (6.0) is equal to the mean of the population (6.0), we conclude that the values of the sample mean do *target* the value of the population mean. It's unfortunate that this sounds so much like doublespeak, but this illustrates that *the mean of the sample means is equal to the population mean μ.*

HINT Read the last sentence of the above paragraph a few times until it makes sense.

If we were to create a probability histogram from Table 6-2, it would not have the bell shape that is characteristic of a normal distribution, but that's because we are working with such small samples. If the population of $\{4, 5, 9\}$ were much larger and if we were selecting samples much larger than $n = 2$ as in this example, we would get a probability histogram that is much closer to being bell-shaped, indicating a normal distribution, as in Example 3.

▶ **YOUR TURN.** Do Exercise 11 "Sampling Distribution of the Sample Mean."

EXAMPLE 3 **Sampling Distribution of the Sample Mean**

Consider repeating this process: Roll a die 5 times to randomly select 5 values from the population $\{1, 2, 3, 4, 5, 6\}$, then find the mean $\bar{x}$ of the results. What do we know about the behavior of all sample means that are generated as this process continues indefinitely?

SOLUTION

Figure 6-19 illustrates a process of rolling a die 5 times and finding the mean of the results. Figure 6-19 shows results from repeating this process 10,000 times, but the true sampling distribution of the mean involves repeating the process indefinitely. Because the values of 1, 2, 3, 4, 5, 6 are all equally likely, the population has a mean of $\mu = 3.5$. The 10,000 sample means included in Figure 6-19 have a mean of 3.5. If the process is continued indefinitely, the mean of the sample means will be 3.5. Also, Figure 6-19 shows that the distribution of the sample means is approximately a normal distribution.

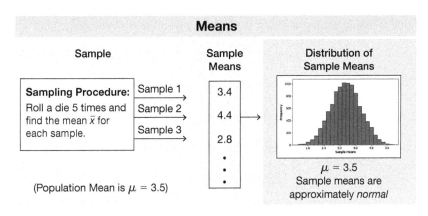

FIGURE 6-19 **Sample Means from 10,000 Trials**

Sampling Distribution of the Sample Variance

Let's now consider the sampling distribution of sample variances.

DEFINITION

The **sampling distribution of the sample variance** is the distribution of sample variances (the variable s^2), with all samples having the same sample size n taken from the same population. (The sampling distribution of the sample variance is typically represented as a probability distribution in the format of a table, probability histogram, or formula.)

> **CAUTION** When working with population standard deviations or variances, be sure to evaluate them correctly. In Section 3-2 we saw that the computations for *population* standard deviations or variances involve division by the population size N instead of $n - 1$, as shown here.

Population standard deviation: $\quad \sigma = \sqrt{\dfrac{\sum (x - \mu)^2}{N}}$

Population variance: $\quad \sigma^2 = \dfrac{\sum (x - \mu)^2}{N}$

Caution: Because the calculations are typically performed with software or calculators, be careful to correctly distinguish between the variance of a sample and the variance of a population.

Behavior of Sample Variances

1. The distribution of sample variances tends to be a distribution skewed to the right.

2. The sample variances *target* the value of the population variance. (That is, the mean of the sample variances is the population variance. The expected value of the sample variance is equal to the population variance.)

EXAMPLE 4 **Sampling Distribution of the Sample Variance**

Consider repeating this process: Roll a die 5 times and find the variance s^2 of the results. What do we know about the behavior of all sample variances that are generated as this process continues indefinitely?

SOLUTION

Figure 6-20 illustrates a process of rolling a die 5 times and finding the variance of the results. Figure 6-20 shows results from repeating this process 10,000 times, but the true sampling distribution of the sample variance involves repeating the process indefinitely. Because the values of 1, 2, 3, 4, 5, 6 are all equally likely, the population has a variance of $\sigma^2 = 2.9$, and the 10,000 sample variances included in Figure 6-20 have a mean of 2.9. If the process is continued indefinitely, the mean of the sample variances will be 2.9. Also, Figure 6-20 shows that the distribution of the sample variances is a skewed distribution, not a normal distribution with its characteristic bell shape.

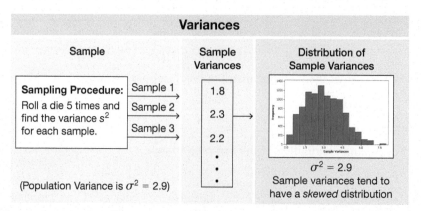

FIGURE 6-20 **Sample Variances from 10,000 Trials**

> **YOUR TURN.** Do Exercise 14 "Sampling Distribution of the Variance."

Estimators: Unbiased and Biased

The preceding examples show that sample proportions, means, and variances tend to *target* the corresponding population parameters. More formally, we say that sample proportions, means, and variances are *unbiased estimators*. See the following two definitions.

DEFINITIONS

An **estimator** is a statistic used to infer (or estimate) the value of a population parameter.

An **unbiased estimator** is a statistic that targets the value of the corresponding population parameter in the sense that the sampling distribution of the statistic has a mean that is equal to the corresponding population parameter.

Unbiased Estimators These statistics are *unbiased estimators*. That is, they each target the value of the corresponding population parameter (with a sampling distribution having a mean equal to the population parameter):

- Proportion $\hat{p}$
- Mean $\bar{x}$
- Variance s^2

Biased Estimators These statistics are *biased estimators*. That is, they do *not* target the value of the corresponding population parameter:

- Median
- Range
- Standard deviation s

   Important Note: The sample standard deviations do not target the population standard deviation σ, but the bias is relatively small in large samples, so **s is often used to estimate σ** even though s is a biased estimator of σ.

EXAMPLE 5   **Sampling Distribution of the Sample Range**

As in Example 2, consider samples of size $n = 2$ randomly selected from the population $\{4, 5, 9\}$.

   a. List the different possible samples along with the probability of each sample, then find the range for each sample.

   b. Describe the sampling distribution of the sample range in the format of a table summarizing the probability distribution.

   c. Based on the results, do the sample ranges target the population range, which is $9 - 4 = 5$?

   d. What do these results indicate about the sample range as an estimator of the population range?

SOLUTION

   a. In Table 6-4 on the next page we list the nine different possible samples of size $n = 2$ selected with replacement from the population $\{4, 5, 9\}$. The nine samples are equally likely, so each has probability $1/9$. Table 6-4 also shows the range for each of the nine samples.

continued

TABLE 6-4 Sampling Distribution of Range

Sample	Sample Range	Probability
4, 4	0	1/9
4, 5	1	1/9
4, 9	5	1/9
5, 4	1	1/9
5, 5	0	1/9
5, 9	4	1/9
9, 4	5	1/9
9, 5	4	1/9
9, 9	0	1/9

b. The last two columns of Table 6-4 list the values of the range along with the corresponding probabilities, so the last two columns constitute a table summarizing the probability distribution. Table 6-4 therefore describes the *sampling distribution* of the sample range.

c. The mean of the sample ranges in Table 6-4 is 20/9 or 2.2. The population of $\{4, 5, 9\}$ has a range of $9 - 4 = 5$. Because the mean of the sample ranges (2.2) is not equal to the population range (5), the sample ranges do *not* target the value of the population range.

d. Because the sample ranges do not target the population range, the sample range is a *biased estimator* of the population range.

INTERPRETATION

Because the sample range is a biased estimator of the population range, a sample range should generally not be used to estimate the value of the population range.

 **YOUR TURN.** Do Exercise 13 "Sampling Distribution of the Range."

Why Sample with Replacement? All of the examples in this section involved sampling *with replacement*. Sampling *without replacement* would have the very practical advantage of avoiding wasteful duplication whenever the same item is selected more than once. Many of the statistical procedures discussed in the following chapters are based on the assumption that sampling is conducted with replacement because of the following two very important reasons.

Reasons for Sampling with Replacement

1. When selecting a relatively small sample from a large population, it makes no significant difference whether we sample with replacement or without replacement.

2. Sampling with replacement results in *independent* events that are unaffected by previous outcomes, and independent events are easier to analyze and result in simpler calculations and formulas.

6-3 Basic Skills and Concepts

Statistical Literacy and Critical Thinking

1. Fatal Car Crashes There are about 15,000 car crashes each day in the United States, and the proportion of car crashes that are fatal is 0.00559 (based on data from the National Highway Traffic Safety Administration). Assume that each day, 1000 car crashes are randomly selected and the proportion of fatal car crashes is recorded.

a. What do you know about the mean of the sample proportions?

b. What do you know about the shape of the distribution of the sample proportions?

2. Sampling with Replacement The Pew Research Center conducts many different surveys in the United States each year.

a. Do you think that for each individual survey, the respondents are randomly selected with replacement or without replacement?

b. Give two reasons why statistical methods tend to be based on the assumption that sampling is conducted *with* replacement, instead of without replacement.

3. Unbiased Estimators Data Set 1 "Body Data" in Appendix B includes systolic blood pressure measurements from 147 adult females. If we compute the values of sample statistics from that sample, which of the following statistics are *unbiased* estimators of the corresponding population parameters: sample mean; sample median; sample range; sample variance; sample standard deviation; sample proportion?

4. Sampling Distribution Data Set 1 "Body Data" in Appendix B includes systolic blood pressure measurements from 147 adult females. If we explore this sample by constructing a histogram and finding the mean and standard deviation, do those results describe the sampling distribution of the mean? Why or why not?

5. Good Sample? An economist is investigating the incomes of college students. Because she lives in Maine, she obtains sample data from that state. Is the resulting mean income of college students a good estimator of the mean income of college students in the United States? Why or why not?

6. College Presidents There are about 4200 college presidents in the United States, and they have annual incomes with a distribution that is skewed instead of being normal. Many different samples of 40 college presidents are randomly selected, and the mean annual income is computed for each sample.

a. What is the approximate shape of the distribution of the sample means (uniform, normal, skewed, other)?

b. What value do the sample means target? That is, what is the mean of all such sample means?

In Exercises 7–10, use the same population of {4, 5, 9} that was used in Examples 2 and 5. As in Examples 2 and 5, assume that samples of size $n = 2$ are randomly selected with replacement.

7. Sampling Distribution of the Sample Variance

a. Find the value of the population variance σ^2.

b. Table 6-2 describes the sampling distribution of the sample mean. Construct a similar table representing the sampling distribution of the sample variance s^2. Then combine values of s^2 that are the same, as in Table 6-3 (*Hint:* See Example 2 on page 276 for Tables 6-2 and 6-3, which describe the sampling distribution of the sample mean.)

c. Find the mean of the sampling distribution of the sample variance.

d. Based on the preceding results, is the sample variance an unbiased estimator of the population variance? Why or why not?

8. Sampling Distribution of the Sample Standard Deviation For the following, round results to three decimal places.

a. Find the value of the population standard deviation σ.

b. Table 6-2 describes the sampling distribution of the sample mean. Construct a similar table representing the sampling distribution of the sample standard deviation s. Then combine values of s that are the same, as in Table 6-3 (*Hint:* See Example 2 on page 276 for Tables 6-2 and 6-3, which describe the sampling distribution of the sample mean.)

c. Find the mean of the sampling distribution of the sample standard deviation.

d. Based on the preceding results, is the sample standard deviation an unbiased estimator of the population standard deviation? Why or why not?

9. Sampling Distribution of the Sample Median

a. Find the value of the population median.

b. Table 6-2 describes the sampling distribution of the sample mean. Construct a similar table representing the sampling distribution of the sample median. Then combine values of the median that are the same, as in Table 6-3. (*Hint:* See Example 2 on page 276 for Tables 6-2 and 6-3, which describe the sampling distribution of the sample mean.)

c. Find the mean of the sampling distribution of the sample median.

d. Based on the preceding results, is the sample median an unbiased estimator of the population median? Why or why not?

10. Sampling Distribution of the Sample Proportion

a. For the population, find the proportion of odd numbers.

b. Table 6-2 describes the sampling distribution of the sample mean. Construct a similar table representing the sampling distribution of the sample proportion of odd numbers. Then combine values of the sample proportion that are the same, as in Table 6-3. (*Hint:* See Example 2 on page 276 for Tables 6-2 and 6-3, which describe the sampling distribution of the sample mean.)

c. Find the mean of the sampling distribution of the sample proportion of odd numbers.

d. Based on the preceding results, is the sample proportion an unbiased estimator of the population proportion? Why or why not?

In Exercises 11–14, use the population of {2, 3, 5, 9} of the lengths of hospital stay (days) of mothers who gave birth, found from Data Set 6 "Births" in Appendix B. Assume that random samples of size n = 2 are selected with replacement.

11. Sampling Distribution of the Sample Mean

a. After identifying the 16 different possible samples, find the mean of each sample, and then construct a table representing the sampling distribution of the sample mean. In the table, combine values of the sample mean that are the same. (*Hint:* See Table 6-3 in Example 2 on page 276.)

b. Compare the mean of the population {2, 3, 5, 9} to the mean of the sampling distribution of the sample mean.

c. Do the sample means target the value of the population mean? In general, do sample means make good estimators of population means? Why or why not?

12. Sampling Distribution of the Median Repeat Exercise 11 using medians instead of means.

13. Sampling Distribution of the Range Repeat Exercise 11 using ranges instead of means.

14. Sampling Distribution of the Variance Repeat Exercise 11 using variances instead of means.

15. Births: Sampling Distribution of Sample Proportion When two births are randomly selected, the sample space for genders is bb, bg, gb, and gg (where b = boy and g = girl). Assume that those four outcomes are equally likely. Construct a table that describes the sampling distribution of the sample proportion of girls from two births. Does the mean of the sample proportions equal the proportion of girls in two births? Does the result suggest that a sample proportion is an unbiased estimator of a population proportion?

16. Births: Sampling Distribution of Sample Proportion Repeat Exercise 15 using three births instead of two births.

17. MCAT The Medical College Admissions Test (MCAT) is used to help screen applicants to medical schools. Like many such tests, the MCAT uses multiple-choice questions with each question having five choices, one of which is correct. Assume that you must make random guesses for two such questions. Assume that both questions have correct answers of "a."

a. After listing the 25 different possible samples, find the proportion of correct answers in each sample, then construct a table that describes the sampling distribution of the sample proportions of correct responses.

b. Find the mean of the sampling distribution of the sample proportion.

c. Is the mean of the sampling distribution [from part (b)] equal to the population proportion of correct responses? Does the mean of the sampling distribution of proportions *always* equal the population proportion?

18. Hybridization A hybridization experiment begins with four peas having yellow pods and one pea having a green pod. Two of the peas are randomly selected *with replacement* from this population.

a. After identifying the 25 different possible samples, find the proportion of peas with yellow pods in each of them, then construct a table to describe the sampling distribution of the proportions of peas with yellow pods.

b. Find the mean of the sampling distribution.

c. Is the mean of the sampling distribution [from part (b)] equal to the population proportion of peas with yellow pods? Does the mean of the sampling distribution of proportions *always* equal the population proportion?

6-3 Beyond the Basics

19. Using a Formula to Describe a Sampling Distribution Exercise 15 "Births" requires the construction of a table that describes the sampling distribution of the proportions of girls from two births. Consider the formula shown here, and evaluate that formula using sample proportions (represented by *x*) of 0, 0.5, and 1. Based on the results, does the formula describe the sampling distribution? Why or why not?

$$P(x) = \frac{1}{2(2 - 2x)!(2x)!} \quad \text{where } x = 0, 0.5, 1$$

20. Mean Absolute Deviation Is the mean absolute deviation of a sample a good statistic for estimating the mean absolute deviation of the population? Why or why not? (*Hint:* See Example 5.)

6-4   The Central Limit Theorem

Key Concept In the preceding section we saw that the sampling distribution of sample means tends to be a normal distribution as the sample size increases. In this section we introduce and apply the *central limit theorem*. The central limit theorem allows us to use a normal distribution for some very meaningful and important applications.

Given any population with *any* distribution (uniform, skewed, whatever), the distribution of sample means $\bar{x}$ can be approximated by a normal distribution when the samples are large enough with $n > 30$. (There are some special cases of very non-normal distributions for which the requirement of $n > 30$ isn't quite enough, so the number 30 should be higher in those cases, but those cases are rare.)

CENTRAL LIMIT THEOREM

For all samples of the same size n with $n > 30$, the sampling distribution of $\bar{x}$ can be approximated by a normal distribution with mean μ and standard deviation $\sigma / \sqrt{n}$.

EXAMPLE 1 **Boston Commute Times**

Figures 6-21 and 6-22 illustrate the central limit theorem.

- **Original Data:** Figure 6-21 is a histogram of 1000 Boston commute times (minutes) from Data Set 31 "Commute Times" in Appendix B.

- **Sample Means:** Figure 6-22 is a histogram of 1000 *sample means*, where each of the 1000 samples includes 50 Boston commute times (randomly selected from Data Set 31 "Commute Times" in Appendix B).

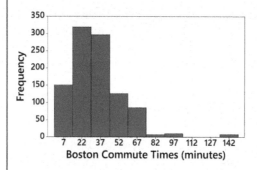

FIGURE 6-21 **Nonnormal Distribution: 1000 Boston Commute Times**

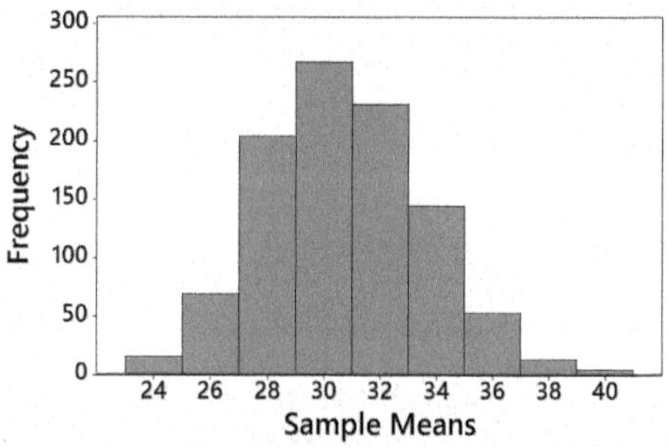

FIGURE 6-22 **Approximately Normal Distribution of 1000 Sample Means**

INTERPRETATION

The original Boston commute times depicted in Figure 6-21 have a skewed distribution, but when we collect samples and compute their means, those sample means tend to have a distribution that is *normal*, as in Figure 6-22.

A Universal Truth Example 1 and the central limit theorem are truly remarkable because they describe a rule of nature that works throughout the universe. If we could send a spaceship to a distant planet "in a galaxy far, far away," and if we collect samples of rocks (all of the same large sample size) and weigh them, the sample means would have a distribution that is approximately normal. Think about the significance of that!

The following key points form the foundation for estimating population parameters and hypothesis testing—topics discussed at length in the following chapters.

Central Limit Theorem and the Sampling Distribution of $\bar{x}$

Given

1. Population (with any distribution) has mean μ and standard deviation σ.

2. Simple random samples all of the same size n are selected from the population.

Practical Rules for Real Applications Involving a Sample Mean $\bar{x}$

Requirements: Population has a normal distribution *or* $n > 30$:

Mean of all values of $\bar{x}$: $\qquad\qquad \mu_{\bar{x}} = \mu$

Standard deviation of all values of $\bar{x}$: $\qquad \sigma_{\bar{x}} = \dfrac{\sigma}{\sqrt{n}}$

z score conversion of $\bar{x}$: $\qquad\qquad z = \dfrac{\bar{x} - \mu}{\dfrac{\sigma}{\sqrt{n}}}$

Original population is *not* normally distributed *and* $n \leq 30$: The distribution of $\bar{x}$ cannot be approximated well by a normal distribution, and the methods of this section do not apply. Use other methods, such as nonparametric methods (Chapter 13) or bootstrapping methods (Section 7-4).

Considerations for Practical Problem Solving

1. **Check Requirements:** When working with the mean from a sample, verify that the normal distribution can be used by confirming that the original population has a normal distribution or the sample size is $n > 30$.

2. **Individual Value or Mean from a Sample?** Determine whether you are using a normal distribution with a *single* value x or the mean $\bar{x}$ from a sample of n values. See the following.

   - Individual value: When working with an *individual* value from a normally distributed population, use the methods of Section 6-2 with $z = \dfrac{x - \mu}{\sigma}$.

   - Mean from a sample of values: When working with a mean for some *sample* of n values, be sure to use the value of $\sigma/\sqrt{n}$ for the standard deviation of the sample means, so use $z = \dfrac{\bar{x} - \mu}{\dfrac{\sigma}{\sqrt{n}}}$.

The following new notation is used for the mean and standard deviation of the distribution of $\bar{x}$.

NOTATION FOR THE SAMPLING DISTRIBUTION OF $\bar{x}$

If all possible simple random samples of size n are selected from a population with mean μ and standard deviation σ, the mean of all sample means is denoted by $\mu_{\bar{x}}$ and the standard deviation of all sample means is denoted by $\sigma_{\bar{x}}$.

Mean of all values of $\bar{x}$: $\qquad\qquad \mu_{\bar{x}} = \mu$

Standard deviation of all values of $\bar{x}$: $\qquad \sigma_{\bar{x}} = \dfrac{\sigma}{\sqrt{n}}$

Note: $\sigma_{\bar{x}}$ is called the *standard error of the mean* and is sometimes denoted as SEM.

Applying the Central Limit Theorem

Many practical problems can be solved with the central limit theorem. Example 2 is a good illustration of the central limit theorem because we can see the difference between working with an *individual* value in part (a) and working with the *mean* for a sample in part (b). Study Example 2 carefully to understand the fundamental difference between the procedures used in parts (a) and (b). In particular, note that when working with an *individual* value, we use $z = \dfrac{x - \mu}{\sigma}$, but when working with the mean $\bar{x}$ for a collection of *sample* values, we use $z = \dfrac{\bar{x} - \mu}{\sigma/\sqrt{n}}$.

EXAMPLE 2   Boeing 737 Airline Seats

American Airlines uses Boeing 737 jets with 126 seats in the main cabin. In an attempt to create more room, an engineer is considering a reduction of the seat width from 16.6 in. to 16.0. in. Adult males have hip widths that are normally distributed with a mean of 14.3 in. and a standard deviation of 0.9 in. (based on data from *Applied Ergonomics*).

   a. Find the probability that a randomly selected adult male has a hip width greater than the seat width of 16.0 in.

   b. Find the probability that 126 main cabin seats are all occupied by males with a mean hip width greater than the seat width of 16.0 in.

   c. For the design of the aircraft seats, which is more relevant: The result from part (a) or the result from part (b)? Why? What do the results suggest about the reduction of the seat width to 16.0 in.?

SOLUTION

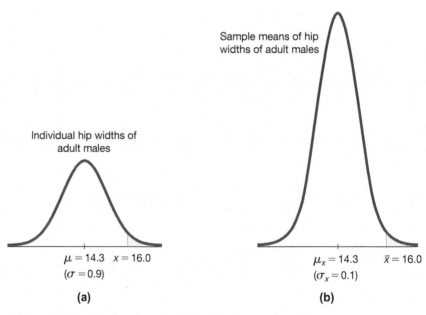

FIGURE 6-23   **Hip Widths of Adult Males**

a. **Approach Used for an Individual Value:** Use the methods presented in Section 6-2 because we are dealing with an *individual* value from a normally distributed population. We seek the area of the green-shaded region in Figure 6-23(a).

Technology: If using technology (as described at the end of Section 6-2), we find that the green-shaded area is 0.0295.

Table A-2: If using Table A-2, we convert the hip width of 16.0 in. to the corresponding z score of $z = 1.89$, as shown here:

$$z = \frac{x - \mu}{\sigma} = \frac{16.0 - 14.3}{0.9} = 1.89$$

We refer to Table A-2 to find that the cumulative area to the *left* of $z = 1.89$ is 0.9706, so the green-shaded area in Figure 6-23 is $1 - 0.9706 = 0.0294$. The result of 0.0295 from technology is more accurate.

b. **Approach Used for the Mean of Sample Values:** Because we are dealing with the *mean* of a sample of 126 males and not an individual male, use the central limit theorem.

REQUIREMENT CHECK FOR PART B   We can use the normal distribution if the original population is normally distributed or $n > 30$. The sample size is greater than 30, so samples of any size will yield means that are normally distributed. ☑

Because we are now dealing with a distribution of sample means, we must use the parameters $\mu_{\bar{x}}$ and $\sigma_{\bar{x}}$, which are evaluated as follows:

$$\mu_{\bar{x}} = \mu = 14.3$$

$$\sigma_{\bar{x}} = \frac{\sigma}{\sqrt{n}} = \frac{0.9}{\sqrt{126}} = 0.1$$

We want to find the green-shaded area shown in Figure 6-23(b). (*Note:* Figure 6-23(b) is not drawn to scale. If Figure 6-23(b) had been true to scale, the green-shaded area would not be visible and the normal curve would be much thinner and taller.)

Technology: If using technology, the green-shaded area in Figure 6-23(b) is 0+, which is a really small positive number.

Table A-2: If using Table A-2, we convert the value of $\bar{x} = 16.0$ to the corresponding z score of $z = 17.00$, as shown here:

$$z = \frac{\bar{x} - \mu_{\bar{x}}}{\sigma_{\bar{x}}} = \frac{16.0 - 14.3}{0.1} = 17.00$$

From Table A-2 we find that the cumulative area to the left of $z = 17$ is 0.9999, so the green-shaded area of Figure 6-23(b) is $1 - 0.9999 = 0.0001$. It is highly unlikely that the 126 adult males will have a mean hip width greater than 16.0 in.

INTERPRETATION

The result from part (a) is more relevant for the design of the aircraft seats. Individual seats will be occupied by individual passengers, not groups of passengers. The result from part (a) shows that with a 0.0295 probability, approximately 3% of adult males would have hip widths greater than the seat width. Although 3% appears to be small, that would result in several passengers on every flight that would somehow require a special accommodation, and that would likely lead to significant challenges for passengers and the flight crew. The reduction of the seat width to 16.0 in. does not appear to be feasible.

YOUR TURN. Do Exercise 5 "Using the Central Limit Theorem."

The Fuzzy Central Limit Theorem

In *The Cartoon Guide to Statistics*, by Gonick and Smith, the authors describe the Fuzzy Central Limit Theorem as follows: "Data that are influenced by many small and unrelated random effects are approximately normally distributed. This explains why the normal is everywhere: stock market fluctuations, student weights, yearly temperature averages, SAT scores: All are the result of many different effects." People's heights, for example, are the results of hereditary factors, environmental factors, nutrition, health care, geographic region, and other influences, which, when combined, produce normally distributed values.

Example 2 shows that we can use the same basic procedures from Section 6-2, but we must remember to correctly adjust the standard deviation when working with a *sample mean* instead of an individual sample value. The calculations used in Example 2 are exactly the type of calculations used by engineers when they design elevators, ski lifts, escalators, airplanes, boats, amusement park rides, and other devices that carry people.

Introduction to Hypothesis Testing

Carefully examine the conclusions that are reached in the next example illustrating the type of thinking that is the basis for the important procedure of hypothesis testing (formally introduced in Chapter 8). Example 3 uses the rare event rule for inferential statistics, first presented in Section 4-1:

Identifying Significant Results with Probabilities: The Rare Event Rule for Inferential Statistics

> **If, under a given assumption, the probability of a particular observed event is very small and the observed event occurs *significantly less than* or *significantly greater than* what we typically expect with that assumption, we conclude that the assumption is probably not correct.**

The following example illustrates the above rare event rule and it uses the author's all-time favorite data set. This example also illustrates the type of reasoning that is used for the important method of *hypothesis testing,* which is formally introduced in Chapter 8.

EXAMPLE 3 **Body Temperatures**

Assume that the population of human body temperatures has a mean of 98.6°F, as is commonly believed. Also assume that the population standard deviation is 0.62°F (based on Data Set 5 "Body Temperatures" in Appendix B). A sample of size $n = 106$ subjects was randomly selected and the mean body temperature of 98.2°F was obtained. If the mean body temperature is really 98.6°F, find the probability of getting a sample mean of 98.2°F or lower for a sample of size 106. Based on the result, is 98.2°F *significantly low*? What do these results suggest about the common belief that the mean body temperature is 98.6°F?

SOLUTION

We work under the assumption that the population of human body temperatures has a mean of 98.6°F. We weren't given the distribution of the population, but because the sample size $n = 106$ exceeds 30, we use the central limit theorem and conclude that the distribution of sample means is a normal distribution with these parameters:

$$\mu_{\bar{x}} = \mu = 98.6 \text{ (by assumption)}$$

$$\sigma_{\bar{x}} = \frac{\sigma}{\sqrt{n}} = \frac{0.62}{\sqrt{106}} = 0.0602197$$

Figure 6-24 shows the shaded area (see the tiny left tail of the graph) corresponding to the probability we seek. Having already found the parameters that apply to the distribution shown in Figure 6-24, we can now find the shaded area by using the same procedures developed in Section 6-2.

Technology: If we use technology to find the shaded area in Figure 6-24, we get 0.0000000000155, which can be expressed as 0+.

Table A-2: If we use Table A-2 to find the shaded area in Figure 6-24, we must first convert the sample mean of $\bar{x} = 98.2°F$ to the corresponding z score:

$$z = \frac{\bar{x} - \mu_{\bar{x}}}{\sigma_{\bar{x}}} = \frac{98.2 - 98.6}{0.0602197} = -6.64$$

Referring to Table A-2, we find that $z = -6.64$ is off the chart, but for values of z below -3.49, we use an area of 0.0001 for the cumulative left area up to $z = -3.49$. We therefore conclude that the shaded region in Figure 6-24 is 0.0001.

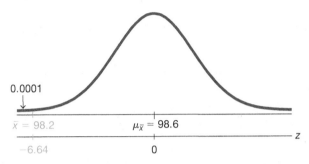

FIGURE 6-24   Means of Body Temperatures from Samples of Size $n = 106$

INTERPRETATION

The result shows that if the mean of our body temperatures is really 98.6°F, as we assumed, then there is an extremely small probability of getting a sample mean of 98.2°F or lower when 106 subjects are randomly selected. The sample mean of 98.2°F is *significantly low*. University of Maryland researchers did obtain such a sample mean, and after confirming that the sample is sound, there are two feasible explanations: (1) The population mean really is 98.6°F and their sample represents a chance event that is extremely rare; (2) the population mean is actually lower than the assumed value of 98.6°F and so their sample is typical. Because the probability is so low, it is more reasonable to conclude that the common belief of 98.6°F for the mean body temperature is a belief that is incorrect. Based on the sample data, we should reject the belief that the mean body temperature is 98.6°F.

YOUR TURN. Do Exercise 9 "Safe Loading of Elevators."

Not *Exactly,* but "At Least as Extreme"

In Example 3, we assumed that the mean body temperature is $\mu = 98.6°F$, and we determined that the probability of getting the sample mean of $\bar{x} = 98.2°F$ *or lower* is 0.0001, which suggests that the true mean body temperature is actually less than 98.6°F. In the context of Example 3, the sample mean of 98.2°F is *significantly low* not because the probability of *exactly* 98.2°F is low, but because the probability of 98.2°F *or lower* is small. (See Section 5-1 for the discussion of "Not *Exactly,* but At Least as Extreme.")

Correction for a Finite Population

In applying the central limit theorem, our use of $\sigma_{\bar{x}} = \sigma/\sqrt{n}$ assumes that the population has infinitely many members. When we sample with replacement, the population is effectively infinite. When sampling without replacement from a finite population, we may need to adjust $\sigma_{\bar{x}}$. Here is a common rule:

> **When sampling without replacement and the sample size n is greater than 5% of the finite population size N (that is, $n > 0.05N$), adjust the standard deviation of sample means $\sigma_{\bar{x}}$ by multiplying it by this *finite population correction factor*:**

$$\sqrt{\frac{N-n}{N-1}}$$

Except for Exercise 21 "Correcting for a Finite Population," the examples and exercises in this section assume that the finite population correction factor does *not* apply, because we are sampling with replacement, or the population is infinite, or the sample size doesn't exceed 5% of the population size.

6-4 Basic Skills and Concepts

Statistical Literacy and Critical Thinking

1. Requirements Medical researchers once conducted experiments to determine whether Lisinopril is a drug that is effective in lowering systolic blood pressure of patients. Patients in a treatment group had their systolic blood pressure measured after being treated with Lisinopril. Under what conditions can the mean systolic blood pressure of this sample be treated as a value that is from a population having a normal distribution?

2. Small Sample Weights of M&M plain candies are normally distributed. Twelve M&M plain candies are randomly selected and weighed, and then the mean of this sample is calculated. Is it correct to conclude that the resulting sample mean cannot be considered to be a value from a normally distributed population because the sample size of 12 is too small? Explain.

3. Notation In general, what do the symbols $\mu_{\bar{x}}$ and $\sigma_{\bar{x}}$ represent? What are the values of $\mu_{\bar{x}}$ and $\sigma_{\bar{x}}$ for samples of size 36 randomly selected from the population of IQ scores with population mean of 100 and standard deviation of 15?

4. Incomes of Statistics Students Annual incomes of statistics students are known to have a distribution that is skewed to the right instead of being normally distributed. Assume that we collect a random sample of annual incomes of 50 statistics students. Can the distribution of incomes in that sample be approximated by a normal distribution because the sample is large? Why or why not?

Using the Central Limit Theorem.   *In Exercises 5–8, assume that the amounts of weight that male college students gain during their freshman year are normally distributed with a mean of 1.2 kg and a standard deviation of 4.9 kg (based on Data Set 13 "Freshman 15" in Appendix B).*

5. a. If 1 male college student is randomly selected, find the probability that he has no weight gain during his freshman year. (That is, find the probability that during his freshman year, his weight gain is less than or equal to 0 kg.)

b. If 25 male college students are randomly selected, find the probability that their mean weight gain during their freshman year is less than or equal to 0 kg.

c. Why can the normal distribution be used in part (b), even though the sample size does not exceed 30?

6. a. If 1 male college student is randomly selected, find the probability that he gains at least 2.0 kg during his freshman year.

b. If 16 male college students are randomly selected, find the probability that their mean weight gain during their freshman year is at least 2.0 kg.

c. Why can the normal distribution be used in part (b), even though the sample size does not exceed 30?

7. a. If 1 male college student is randomly selected, find the probability that he gains between 0 kg and 3 kg during freshman year.

b. If 9 male college students are randomly selected, find the probability that their mean weight gain during freshman year is between 0 kg and 3 kg.

c. Why can the normal distribution be used in part (b), even though the sample size does not exceed 30?

8. a. If 1 male college student is randomly selected, find the probability that he gains between 0.5 kg and 2.5 kg during freshman year.

b. If 4 male college students are randomly selected, find the probability that their mean weight gain during freshman year is between 0.5 kg and 2.5 kg.

c. Why can the normal distribution be used in part (b), even though the sample size does not exceed 30?

Ergonomics. *Exercises 9–16 involve applications to* **ergonomics,** *as described in the* *Chapter Problem.*

9. Safe Loading of Elevators The elevator in the car rental building at San Francisco International Airport has a placard stating that the maximum capacity is "4000 lb—27 passengers." Because $4000/27 = 148$, this converts to a mean passenger weight of 148 lb when the elevator is full. We will assume a worst-case scenario in which the elevator is filled with 27 adult males. Based on Data Set 1 "Body Data" in Appendix B, assume that adult males have weights that are normally distributed with a mean of 189 lb and a standard deviation of 39 lb.

a. Find the probability that 1 randomly selected adult male has a weight greater than 148 lb.

b. Find the probability that a sample of 27 randomly selected adult males has a mean weight greater than 148 lb.

c. What do you conclude about the safety of this elevator?

10. Designing Manholes According to the website www.torchmate.com, "manhole covers must be a minimum of 22 in. in diameter, but can be as much as 60 in. in diameter." Assume that a manhole is constructed to have a circular opening with a diameter of 22 in. Men have shoulder widths that are normally distributed with a mean of 18.2 in. and a standard deviation of 1.0 in. (based on data from the National Health and Nutrition Examination Survey).

a. What percentage of men will fit into the manhole?

b. Assume that the Connecticut's Evergreen company employs 36 men who work in manholes. If 36 men are randomly selected, what is the probability that their mean shoulder width is less than 18.5 in.? Does this result suggest that money can be saved by making smaller manholes with a diameter of 18.5 in.? Why or why not?

11. Water Taxi Safety Passengers died when a water taxi sank in Baltimore's Inner Harbor. Men are typically heavier than women and children, so when loading a water taxi, assume a worst-case scenario in which all passengers are men. Assume that weights of men are normally distributed with a mean of 189 lb and a standard deviation of 39 lb (based on Data Set 1 "Body Data" in Appendix B). The water taxi that sank had a stated capacity of 25 passengers, and the boat was rated for a load limit of 3500 lb.

a. Given that the water taxi that sank was rated for a load limit of 3500 lb, what is the maximum mean weight of the passengers if the boat is filled to the stated capacity of 25 passengers?

b. If the water taxi is filled with 25 randomly selected men, what is the probability that their mean weight exceeds the value from part (a)?

c. After the water taxi sank, the weight assumptions were revised so that the new capacity became 20 passengers. If the water taxi is filled with 20 randomly selected men, what is the probability that their mean weight exceeds 175 lb, which is the maximum mean weight that does not cause the total load to exceed 3500 lb?

d. Is the new capacity of 20 passengers safe?

12. Loading a Tour Boat The Ethan Allen tour boat capsized and sank in Lake George, New York, and 20 of the 47 passengers drowned. Based on a 1960 assumption of a mean weight of 140 lb for passengers, the boat was rated to carry 50 passengers. After the boat sank, New York State changed the assumed mean weight from 140 lb to 174 lb.

a. Given that the boat was rated for 50 passengers with an assumed mean of 140 lb, the boat had a passenger load limit of 7000 lb. Assume that the boat is loaded with 50 male passengers, and assume that weights of men are normally distributed with a mean of 189 lb and a standard deviation of 39 lb (based on Data Set 1 "Body Data" in Appendix B). Find the probability that the boat is overloaded because the 50 male passengers have a mean weight greater than 140 lb.

b. The boat was later rated to carry only 14 passengers, and the load limit was changed to 2436 lb. If 14 passengers are all males, find the probability that the boat is overloaded because their mean weight is greater than 174 lb (so that their total weight is greater than the maximum capacity of 2436 lb). Do the new ratings appear to be safe when the boat is loaded with 14 male passengers?

13. Redesign of Ejection Seats When women were finally allowed to become pilots of fighter jets, engineers needed to redesign the ejection seats because they had been originally designed for men only. The ACES-II ejection seats were designed for men weighing between 140 lb and 211 lb. Weights of women are now normally distributed with a mean of 171 lb and a standard deviation of 46 lb (based on Data Set 1 "Body Data" in Appendix B).

a. If 1 woman is randomly selected, find the probability that her weight is between 140 lb and 211 lb.

b. If 25 different women are randomly selected, find the probability that their mean weight is between 140 lb and 211 lb.

c. When redesigning the fighter jet ejection seats to better accommodate women, which probability is more relevant: the result from part (a) or the result from part (b)? Why?

14. Loading Aircraft Before every flight, the pilot must verify that the total weight of the load is less than the maximum allowable load for the aircraft. The Bombardier Dash 8 aircraft can carry 37 passengers, and a flight has fuel and baggage that allows for a total passenger load of 6200 lb. The pilot sees that the plane is full and all passengers are men. The aircraft will be overloaded if the mean weight of the passengers is greater than $6200 \text{ lb}/37 = 167.6 \text{ lb}$. What is the probability that the aircraft is overloaded? Should the pilot take any action to correct for an overloaded aircraft? Assume that weights of men are normally distributed with a mean of 189 lb and a standard deviation of 39 lb (based on Data Set 1 "Body Data" in Appendix B).

15. Doorway Height The Boeing 757-200 ER airliner carries 200 passengers and has doors with a height of 72 in. Heights of men are normally distributed with a mean of 68.6 in. and a standard deviation of 2.8 in. (based on Data Set 1 "Body Data" in Appendix B).

a. If a male passenger is randomly selected, find the probability that he can fit through the doorway without bending.

b. If half of the 200 passengers are men, find the probability that the mean height of the 100 men is less than 72 in.

c. When considering the comfort and safety of passengers, which result is more relevant: the probability from part (a) or the probability from part (b)? Why?

d. When considering the comfort and safety of passengers, why are women ignored in this case?

16. Aircraft Cockpit The overhead panel in an aircraft cockpit typically includes controls for such features as landing lights, fuel booster pumps, and oxygen. It is important for pilots to be able to reach those overhead controls while sitting. Seated adult males have overhead grip reaches that are normally distributed with a mean of 51.6 in. and a standard deviation of 2.2 in.

a. If an aircraft is designed for pilots with an overhead grip reach of 53 in., what percentage of adult males would not be able to reach the overhead controls? Is that percentage too high?

b. If the cockpit is designed so that 95% of adult males would be able to reach the overhead controls, what is the overhead grip reach distance?

c. A small regional airline employs 40 male pilots. An engineer wants to design for an overhead grip reach that satisfies this criterion: There is a 0.95 probability that 40 randomly selected male pilots have a mean overhead grip reach that is greater than or equal to the designed overhead reach distance. What overhead grip reach distance satisfies that design? Why should this engineer be fired?

Hypothesis Testing. *In Exercises 17–20, apply the central limit theorem to test the given claim. (Hint: See Example 3.)*

17. Freshman 15 The term "Freshman 15" refers to the claim that college students gain 15 lb during their freshman year at college. Data Set 13 "Freshman 15" includes measurements from 67 college students from their freshman year, and they had weight gains with a mean of 2.6 lb and a standard deviation of 8.6 lb. Assume that the mean weight gain really is 15 lb and find the probability that a random sample of 67 college students would have a mean weight gain of 2.6 lb or less. What does the result suggest about the claim of the "Freshman 15"?

18. Adult Sleep Times (hours) of sleep for randomly selected adult subjects included in the National Health and Nutrition Examination Study are listed below. Here are the statistics for this sample: $n = 12$, $\bar{x} = 6.8$ hours, $s = 2.0$ hours. The times appear to be from a normally distributed population. A common recommendation is that adults should sleep between 7 hours and 9 hours each night. Assuming that the mean sleep time is 7 hours, find the probability of getting a sample of 12 adults with a mean of 6.8 hours or less. What does the result suggest about a claim that "the mean sleep time is less than 7 hours"?

4   8   4   4   8   6   9   7   7   10   7   8

19. Weight Watchers Diet When 40 people used the Weight Watchers diet for one year, their mean weight loss was 3.0 lb, and the standard deviation was 4.9 lb (based on data from "Comparison of the Atkins, Ornish, Weight Watchers, and Zone Diets for Weight Loss and Heart Disease Reduction," by Dansinger et al., *Journal of the American Medical Association*, Vol. 293, No. 1). Assuming that the diet has no effect so the true mean amount of lost weight is 0 lb, find the probability of getting a sample of 40 subjects with a mean weight loss of 3.0 lb or higher. Based on the result, is the mean weight loss of 3.0 lb *significantly high*? What do the results suggest about the effectiveness of the diet?

6-4 Beyond the Basics

20. Correcting for a Finite Population In a study of babies born with very low birth weights, 275 children were given IQ tests at age 8, and their scores approximated a normal distribution with $\mu = 95.5$ and $\sigma = 16.0$ (based on data from "Neurobehavioral Outcomes of School-age Children Born Extremely Low Birth Weight or Very Preterm," by Anderson et al., *Journal of the American Medical Association*, Vol. 289, No. 24). Fifty of those children are to be randomly selected without replacement for a follow-up study.

a. When considering the distribution of the mean IQ scores for samples of 50 children randomly selected from a population of 275 children, should $\sigma_{\bar{x}}$ be corrected by using the finite population correction factor? Why or why not? What is the value of $\sigma_{\bar{x}}$?

b. Find the probability that the mean IQ score of the follow-up sample is between 95 and 105.

Key Concept The following chapters include important statistical methods requiring that sample data are from a population having a distribution that is approximately *normal*. In this section we present these steps for determining whether sample data satisfy the requirement of a normal distribution:

1. Construct a histogram and determine whether it is roughly bell-shaped.

2. Construct a *normal quantile plot* and use the criteria given later in this section.

PART 1 Basic Concepts of Assessing Normality

When trying to determine whether a collection of data has a distribution that is approximately normal, we can visually inspect a histogram to see if it is approximately bell-shaped (as discussed in Section 2-2), and we can also use a *normal quantile plot* (discussed briefly in Section 2-2).

DEFINITION

A **normal quantile plot** (or **normal probability plot**) is a graph of points (x, y) where each x value is from the original set of sample data, and each y value is the corresponding z score that is expected from the standard normal distribution.

Procedure for Determining Whether It Is Reasonable to Assume That Sample Data Are from a Population Having a Normal Distribution

1. *Histogram:* Construct a histogram. If the histogram departs dramatically from a bell shape, conclude that the data do not have a normal distribution.

2. *Normal quantile plot:* If the histogram is basically symmetric, use technology to generate a *normal quantile plot.* Apply the following criteria to determine whether the distribution is normal. (These criteria can be used loosely for small samples, but they should be used more strictly for large samples.)

   Normal Distribution: The population distribution is normal if the pattern of the points is reasonably close to a straight line and the points do not show some systematic pattern that is not a straight-line pattern.

   Not a Normal Distribution: The population distribution is *not* normal if either or both of these two conditions applies:

   ■ The points do not lie reasonably close to a straight-line pattern.

   ■ The points show some *systematic pattern* that is not a straight-line pattern.

Advanced Methods: In addition to using histograms and normal quantile plots, there are other more advanced procedures for assessing normality, such as the Ryan-Joiner test (discussed briefly in Part 2 of this section). Other tests for normality include (insert drum roll here) the Shapiro-Wilk test, D'Agostino-Pearson test, chi-square goodness-of-fit test, Kolmogorov-Smirnov test, Lillefors corrected K-S test, Cramer-von Mises test, Anderson-Darling test, the Jarque-Bera test, and the Anscombe-Glynn kurtosis test.

Histograms and Normal Quantile Plots

In Part 2 of this section we describe the process of constructing a normal quantile plot, but for now we focus on *interpreting* a normal quantile plot. The following displays show histograms of data and the corresponding normal quantile plots.

Normal: The first case shows a histogram of IQ scores that is close to being bell-shaped, so the histogram suggests that the IQ scores are from a normal distribution. The corresponding normal quantile plot shows points that are reasonably close to a straight-line pattern, and the points do not show any other systematic pattern that is not a straight line. It is safe to assume that these IQ scores are from a population that has a normal distribution.

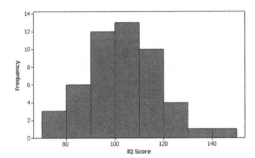 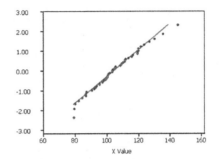

Uniform: The second case shows a histogram of data having a uniform (rectangular) distribution. The corresponding normal quantile plot suggests that the points are *not* normally distributed. Although the pattern of points is reasonably close to a straight-line pattern, *there is another systematic pattern that is not a straight-line pattern*. We conclude that these sample values are from a population having a distribution that is not normal.

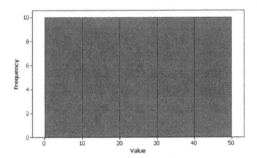 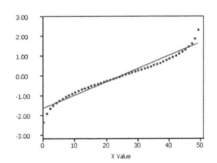

Skewed: The third case shows a histogram of the amounts of rainfall (in inches) in Boston for every Monday in one year. The shape of the histogram is skewed to the right, not bell-shaped. The corresponding normal quantile plot shows points that are not at all close to a straight-line pattern. These rainfall amounts are from a population having a distribution that is not normal.

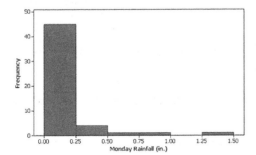 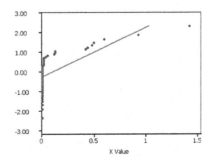

PART 2 Manual Construction of Normal Quantile Plots

The following is a relatively simple procedure for manually constructing a normal quantile plot, and it is the same procedure used by Statdisk and the TI-83/84 Plus calculator. Some statistical packages use various other approaches, but the interpretation of the graph is essentially the same.

Manual Construction of a Normal Quantile Plot

Step 1: First sort the data by arranging the values in order from lowest to highest.

Step 2: With a sample of size n, each value represents a proportion of $1/n$ of the sample. Using the known sample size n, find the values of $\frac{1}{2n}, \frac{3}{2n}, \frac{5}{2n}$, and so on, until you get n values. These values are the cumulative areas to the left of the corresponding sample values.

Step 3: Use the standard normal distribution (software or a calculator or Table A-2) to find the z scores corresponding to the cumulative left areas found in Step 2. (These are the z scores that are expected from a normally distributed sample.)

Step 4: Match the original sorted data values with their corresponding z scores found in Step 3, then plot the points (x, y), where each x is an original sample value and y is the corresponding z score.

Step 5: Examine the normal quantile plot and use the criteria given in Part 1. Conclude that the population has a normal distribution if the pattern of the points is reasonably close to a straight line and the points do not show some systematic pattern that is not a straight-line pattern.

EXAMPLE 1 Dallas Commute Times

Data set 31 "Commute Times" in Appendix B includes commute times (minutes) obtained from Dallas, Texas. Let's consider this sample of the first five commute times: 20, 16, 25, 10, 30. With only five sample values, a histogram will not be very helpful here. Instead, construct a normal quantile plot for these five values and determine whether they appear to be from a population that is normally distributed.

SOLUTION

The following steps correspond to those listed in the procedure above for constructing a normal quantile plot.

Step 1: First, sort the data by arranging them in order. We get 10, 16, 20, 25, 30.

Step 2: With a sample of size $n = 5$, each value represents a proportion of $1/5$ of the sample, so we proceed to identify the cumulative areas to the left of the corresponding sample values. The cumulative left areas, which are expressed in general as $\frac{1}{2n}, \frac{3}{2n}, \frac{5}{2n}$, and so on, become these specific areas for this example with $n = 5$: $\frac{1}{10}, \frac{3}{10}, \frac{5}{10}, \frac{7}{10}, \frac{9}{10}$. These cumulative left areas expressed in decimal form are 0.1, 0.3, 0.5, 0.7, and 0.9.

Step 3: We now use technology (or Table A-2) with the cumulative left areas of 0.1000, 0.3000, 0.5000, 0.7000, and 0.9000 to find these corresponding z scores: $-1.28, -0.52, 0, 0.52$, and 1.28. (For example, the z score of -1.28 has an area of 0.1000 to its left.)

Step 4: We now pair the original sorted Dallas commute times with their corresponding z scores. We get these (x, y) coordinates, which are plotted in the accompanying Statdisk display:

$$(10, -1.28), (16, -0.52), (20, 0), (25, 0.52), (30, 1.28)$$

Statdisk

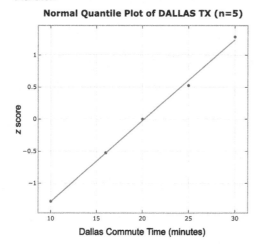

INTERPRETATION

We examine the normal quantile plot in the Statdisk display. The points do appear to lie reasonably close to the straight line, so we conclude that the sample of five commute times *does* appear to be from a normally distributed population.

YOUR TURN. Do Exercise 5 "Ages of Presidents."

Ryan-Joiner Test The Ryan-Joiner test is one of several formal tests of normality, each having its own advantages and disadvantages. Statdisk has a feature of **Normality Assessment** that displays a histogram, normal quantile plot, the number of potential outliers, and results from the Ryan-Joiner test.

EXAMPLE 2 **Dallas Commute Times**

Example 1 used only five of the Dallas commute times listed in Data Set 31 "Commute Times" in Appendix B. Shown in the accompanying display is the result obtained by using the Statdisk **Normality Assessment** feature with all 1000 Dallas commute times.

Statdisk

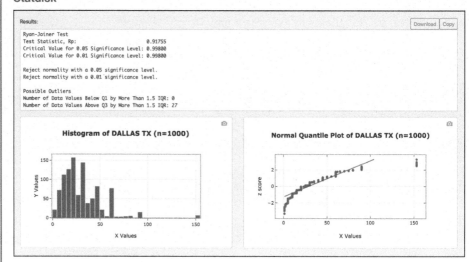

Let's use the display with the three criteria for assessing normality.

1. *Histogram:* We can see that the histogram is *skewed* to the right and is far from being bell-shaped.

2. *Normal quantile plot:* The points in the normal quantile plot are very far from a straight-line pattern. We conclude that the 1000 Dallas commute times do *not* appear to be from a population with a normal distribution.

YOUR TURN. Do Exercise 11 "Small World."

Outliers We should always be aware of the presence of any outliers, particularly because they can have very dramatic effects on results. Test for the effects of outliers by applying statistical methods with these outliers included and then a second time with outliers excluded. Outliers should be investigated because they may be the most important characteristics of the data and they may reveal critical information about the data. Discard outliers only if they are identified as being errors.

Data Transformations Many data sets have a distribution that is not normal, but we can *transform* the data so that the modified values have a normal distribution. One common transformation is to transform each value of x by taking its logarithm. (You can use natural logarithms or logarithms with base 10. If any original values are 0, take logarithms of values of $x + 1$). If the distribution of the logarithms of the values is a normal distribution, the distribution of the original values is called a **lognormal distribution**. (See Exercises 21 "Transformations" and 22 "Lognormal Distribution.") In addition to transformations with logarithms, there are other transformations, such as replacing each x value with $\sqrt{x}$, or $1/x$, or x^2. In addition to getting a required normal distribution when the original data values are not normally distributed, such transformations can be used to correct deficiencies, such as a requirement (found in later chapters) that different data sets have the same variance.

TECH CENTER

 ### Normal Quantile Plots

Access tech supplements, videos, and data sets at www.TriolaStats.com

Statdisk	Minitab	StatCrunch

Statdisk

1. Click **Data** in the top menu.
2. Select **Normal Quantile Plot** from the dropdown menu.
3. Select the desired data column and click **Plot**.

TIP: Select **Normality Assessment** in the dropdown menu under **Data** to obtain the normal quantile plot along with other results helpful in assessing normality.

Minitab

Minitab generates a probability plot that is similar to the normal quantile plot and can be interpreted using the same criteria given in this section.

Probability Plot

1. Click **Stat** in the top menu.
2. Select **Basic Statistics** from the dropdown menu and select **Normality Test** from the sub-menu.
3. Select the desired column in the *Variable* box and click **OK**.

Probability Plot with Boundaries

1. Click **Graph** in the top menu.
2. Select **Probability Plot** from the dropdown menu, select **Single**, and click **OK**.
3. Select the desired column in the *Graph variables* box and click **OK**.
4. If the points all lie within the boundaries, conclude that the data are normally distributed. If points are outside the boundaries, conclude that the data are not normally distributed.

StatCrunch

StatCrunch generates a QQ Plot that is similar to the normal quantile plot and can be interpreted using the same criteria given in this section.

1. Click **Graph** in the top menu.
2. Select **QQ Plot** in the dropdown menu.
3. Select the desired data column.
4. Click **Compute!**

TI-83/84 Plus Calculator

1. Open the **STAT PLOTS** menu by pressing **2ND**, **Y=**.
2. Press **ENTER** to access the Plot 1 settings screen as shown:
   a. Select **ON** and press **ENTER**.
   b. Select last graph type, press **ENTER**.
   c. Enter name of list containing data.
   d. For *Data Axis* select **X**.
3. Press **ZOOM** then **9** (ZoomStat) to generate the normal quantile plot.
4. Press **WINDOW** to customize graph and then press **GRAPH** to view the normal quantile plot.

```
NORMAL FLOAT AUTO REAL RADIAN MP
PRESS [<] OR [>] TO SELECT AN OPTION
Plot1 Plot2 Plot3
2a On Off
Type: ⬈ ⬊ ⬐ ⬑ ⬒ ⬓  2b
Data List:DALLS 2c
Data Axis:X Y 2d
Mark :□ + ·
Color: NAVY ◇
```

Excel

XLSTAT Add-In (Required)

1. Click on the **XLSTAT** tab in the Ribbon and then click **Describing Data**.
2. Select **Normality tests** from the dropdown menu.
3. Enter the desired data range in the *Data* box. If the first row of data contains a label, check the **Sample labels** box.
4. Click the **Charts** tab and confirm that the **Normal Q-Q plots** box is checked.
5. Click **OK** and scroll down the results to view the Normal Q-Q plot.

R

R command: **qqnorm(x)**

TIP: The R command **qqline(x)** can be used to add a reference line.

A complete list of R statistical commands is available at TriolaStats.com

6-5   Basic Skills and Concepts

Statistical Literacy and Critical Thinking

1. Satisfying Requirements Data Set 1 "Body Data" in Appendix B includes a sample of 147 pulse rates of randomly selected women. Does that sample satisfy the following requirement: (1) The sample appears to be from a normally distributed population; or (2) the sample has a size of $n > 30$?

2. Histogram and Normal Quantile Plot Pulse rates of women are normally distributed. If we construct a histogram and normal quantile plot using the same sample of 147 pulse rates described in the preceding exercise, describe the appearance of those two graphs.

3. Normal Quantile Plot After constructing a histogram of the ages of the 147 women included in Data Set 1 "Body Data" in Appendix B, you see that the histogram is far from being bell-shaped. What do you now know about the pattern of points in the normal quantile plot?

4. Assessing Normality The accompanying histogram is constructed from the pulse rates of the 153 men included in Data Set 1 "Body Data" in Appendix B. If you plan to conduct further statistical tests and there is a requirement of a normally distributed population, what do you conclude about the population distribution based on this histogram?

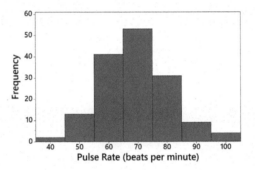

Interpreting Normal Quantile Plots.   *In Exercises 5–8, examine the normal quantile plot and determine whether the sample data appear to be from a population with a normal distribution.*

5. Ages of Presidents The normal quantile plot represents the ages of presidents of the United States at the times of their inaugurations. The data are from Data Set 22 "Presidents" in Appendix B.

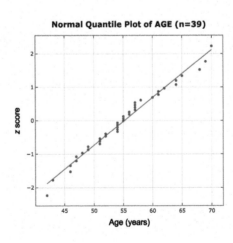

6. Diet Pepsi The normal quantile plot represents weights (pounds) of the contents of cans of Diet Pepsi (from Data Set 37 "Cola Weights and Volumes" in Appendix B).

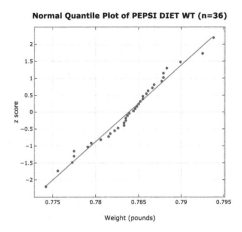

7. Dunkin' Donuts Service Times The normal quantile plot represents service times during the dinner hours at Dunkin' Donuts (from Data Set 36 "Fast Food" in Appendix B).

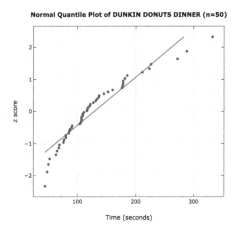

8. Tornadoes The normal quantile plot represents the distances (miles) that tornadoes traveled (from Data Set 25 "Tornadoes" in Appendix B).

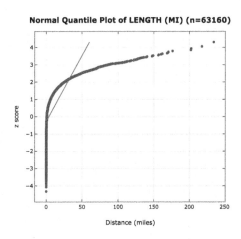

Determining Normality. *In Exercises 9–12, refer to the indicated sample data and determine whether they appear to be from a population with a normal distribution. Assume that this requirement is loose in the sense that the population distribution need not be exactly normal, but it must be a distribution that is roughly bell-shaped.*

9. M&Ms The weights (grams) of the red M&M plain candies, as listed in Data Set 38 "Candies" in Appendix B

10. Taxi Trips The distances (miles) traveled by New York City taxis transporting customers, as listed in Data Set 32 "Taxis" in Appendix B

11. Small World The waiting times (minutes) for the Disney World ride Small World at 5:00 PM, as listed in Data Set 33 "Disney World Wait Times" in Appendix B

12. Dunkin' Donuts The drive-through service times (seconds) of Dunkin' Donuts lunch customers, as listed in Data Set 36 "Fast Food" in Appendix B

Using Technology to Generate Normal Quantile Plots. *In Exercises 13–16, use the data from the indicated exercise in this section. Use software (such as Statdisk, Minitab, Excel, or StatCrunch) or a TI-83/84 Plus calculator to generate a normal quantile plot. Then determine whether the data come from a normally distributed population.*

13. Exercise 9 "M&Ms"   **14.** Exercise 10 "Taxi Trips"

15. Exercise 11 "Small World"   **16.** Exercise 12 "Dunkin' Donuts"

Constructing Normal Quantile Plots. *In Exercises 17–20, use the given data values to identify the corresponding z scores that are used for a normal quantile plot, then identify the coordinates of each point in the normal quantile plot. Construct the normal quantile plot, then determine whether the data appear to be from a population with a normal distribution.*

17. Body Temperatures A sample of body temperatures (°F) of women from Data Set 5 "Body Temperatures" in Appendix B: 98.7, 98.4, 98.0, 97.9, 98.2

18. Earthquake Depths A sample of depths (km) of earthquakes is obtained from Data Set 24 "Earthquakes" in Appendix B: 17.3, 7.0, 7.0, 7.0, 8.1, 6.8.

19. Brain Volumes A sample of human brain volumes (cm^3) is obtained from those listed in Data Set 12 "IQ and Brain Size" in Appendix B: 1027, 1029, 1034, 1070, 1079, 1079, 963, 1439.

20. Ages of Oscar-Winning Actresses A sample of the ages (years) of actresses who won Oscars, as listed in Data Set 21 "Oscar Winner Age" in Appendix B: 25, 24, 41, 30, 27, 35, 33, 29, 80

6-5 Beyond the Basics

21. Transformations The heights (in inches) of women listed in Data Set 1 "Body Data" in Appendix B have a distribution that is approximately normal, so it appears that those heights are from a normally distributed population.

a. If 2 inches is added to each height, are the new heights also normally distributed?

b. If each height is converted from inches to centimeters, are the heights in centimeters also normally distributed?

c. Are the logarithms of the normally distributed heights also normally distributed?

22. Lognormal Distribution The following are the values of net worth (in millions of dollars) of recent members of the executive branch of the U.S. government. Test these values for normality, then take the logarithm of each value and test for normality. What do you conclude?

1297   15.8   7.08   1.05   0.73   0.08   0.23   0.19

6-6 Normal as Approximation to Binomial (available at www.TriolaStats.com)

Because of our ability to use technology to find exact values of binomial probabilities, the use of a normal approximation to a binomial distribution has become largely obsolete, so this section is included on the website www.TriolaStats.com.

Here are two key points:

- Given probabilities p and q (where $q = 1 - p$) and sample size n, if the conditions $np \geq 5$ and $nq \geq 5$ are both satisfied, then probabilities from a binomial probability distribution can be approximated reasonably well by using a normal distribution having these parameters:

$$\mu = np$$
$$\sigma = \sqrt{npq}$$

- The binomial probability distribution is *discrete* (with whole numbers for the random variable x), but the normal approximation is *continuous*. To compensate, we use a "continuity correction" with each whole number x represented by the interval from $x - 0.5$ to $x + 0.5$.

Chapter Quick Quiz

Bone Density Test.   *In Exercises 1–4, assume that scores on a bone mineral density test are normally distributed with a mean of 0 and a standard deviation of 1.*

1. Bone Density Sketch a graph showing the shape of the distribution of bone density test scores.

2. Bone Density Find the bone density score that is the 90th percentile, which is the score separating the lowest 90% from the top 10%.

3. Bone Density For a randomly selected subject, find the probability of a bone density score greater than 1.55.

4. Bone Density For a randomly selected subject, find the probability of a bone density score between −1.00 and 2.00.

5. Notation

a. Identify the values of μ and σ for the standard normal distribution.

b. What do the symbols $\mu_{\bar{x}}$ and $\sigma_{\bar{x}}$ represent?

6. Salaries It is known that salaries of college professors have a distribution that is skewed. If we repeat the process of randomly selecting 50 college professors and find the mean of each sample, what is the distribution of these sample means?

Seat Designs.   *In Exercises 7–9, assume that when seated, adult males have back-to-knee lengths that are normally distributed with a mean of 23.5 in. and a standard deviation of 1.1 in. (based on anthropometric survey data from Gordon, Churchill, et al.). These data are used often in the design of different seats, including aircraft seats, train seats, theater seats, and classroom seats.*

7. Find the probability that a male has a back-to-knee length greater than 25.0 in.

8. Find the probability that a male has a back-to-knee length between 22.0 in. and 26.0 in.

9. Find the probability that nine males have back-to-knee lengths with a mean greater than 23.0 in.

10. *War and Peace* The accompanying normal quantile plot was constructed from the Flesch-Kincaid Grade Level scores for pages randomly selected from Leo Tolstoy's classic novel *War and Peace*. (Flesch-Kincaid Grade Level scores are measures of the U.S. grade level of education that the reader should have to understand the text.) What does the graph tell us about those scores?

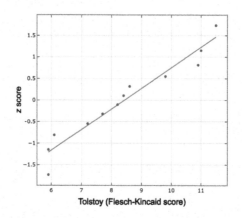

Review Exercises

1. Bone Density Test A bone mineral density test is used to identify a bone disease. The result of a bone density test is commonly measured as a z score, and the population of z scores is normally distributed with a mean of 0 and a standard deviation of 1.

a. For a randomly selected subject, find the probability of a bone density test score greater than -1.37.

b. For a randomly selected subject, find the probability of a bone density test score less than 2.34.

c. For a randomly selected subject, find the probability of a bone density test score between -0.67 and 1.29.

d. Find Q_1, the bone density test score separating the bottom 25% from the top 75%.

e. If the mean bone density test score is found for 9 randomly selected subjects, find the probability that the mean is greater than 0.23.

2. Unbiased Estimators

a. What is an unbiased estimator?

b. For the following statistics, identify those that are unbiased estimators: mean, median, range, variance, proportion.

c. Determine whether the following statement is true or false: "The sample standard deviation is a biased estimator, but the bias is relatively small in large samples, so s is often used to estimate σ."

3. Critical Values

a. Find the standard z score with a cumulative area to its left of 0.01.

b. Find the standard z score with a cumulative area to its right of 0.01.

c. Find the value of $z_{0.025}$.

4. Arm Circumferences Arm circumferences of adult men are normally distributed with a mean of 33.64 cm and a standard deviation of 4.14 cm (based on Data Set 1 "Body Data" in Appendix B). A sample of 25 men is randomly selected and the mean of the arm circumferences is obtained.

a. Describe the distribution of such sample means.

b. What is the mean of all such sample means?

c. What is the standard deviation of all such sample means?

5. Birth Weights Based on Data Set 6 "Births" in Appendix B, birth weights of girls are normally distributed with a mean of 3037.1 g and a standard deviation of 706.3 g.

a. For the bell-shaped graph, what is the area under the curve?

b. What is the value of the median?

c. What is the value of the mode?

d. What is the value of the variance?

6. Mensa Membership in Mensa requires a score in the top 2% on a standard intelligence test. The Wechsler IQ test is designed for a mean of 100 and a standard deviation of 15, and scores are normally distributed.

a. Find the minimum Wechsler IQ test score that satisfies the Mensa requirement.

b. If 4 randomly selected adults take the Wechsler IQ test, find the probability that their mean score is at least 131.

c. If 4 subjects take the Wechsler IQ test and they have a mean of 131 but the individual scores are lost, can we conclude that all 4 of them have scores of at least 131?

7. Tall Clubs The social organization Tall Clubs International has a requirement that women must be at least 70 in. tall. Assume that women have normally distributed heights with a mean of 63.7 in. and a standard deviation of 2.9 in. (based on Data Set 1 "Body Data" in Appendix B).

a. Find the percentage of women who satisfy the height requirement.

b. If the height requirement is to be changed so that the tallest 2.5% of women are eligible, what is the new height requirement?

In Exercises 8 and 9, assume that women have standing eye heights that are normally distributed with a mean of 59.7 in. and a standard deviation of 2.5 in. (based on anthropometric survey data from Gordon, Churchill, et al.).

8. Biometric Security In designing a security system based on eye (iris) recognition, we must consider the standing eye heights of women.

a. If an eye recognition security system is positioned at a height that is uncomfortable for women with standing eye heights less than 54 in., what percentage of women will find that height uncomfortable?

b. In positioning the eye recognition security system, we want it to be suitable for the lowest 95% of standing eye heights of women. What standing eye height of women separates the lowest 95% of standing eye heights from the highest 5%?

9. Significance Instead of using 0.05 for identifying significant values, use the criteria that a value x is *significantly high* if $P(x$ or greater$) \leq 0.01$ and a value is *significantly low* if $P(x$ or less$) \leq 0.01$. Find the standing eye heights of women that separate significant values from those that are not significant. Using these criteria, is a woman's standing eye height of 67 in. significantly high?

10. Assessing Normality Listed below are the recent salaries (in millions of dollars) of players on the LA Lakers professional basketball team. Do these salaries appear to come from a population that has a normal distribution? Why or why not?

35.6   14.4   12.0   9.0   7.5   5.8   4.4   3.5   2.4   1.8   1.7   1.7   1.5   1.5   1.0   0.1   0.1

Cumulative Review Exercises

In Exercises 1 and 2, use the following wait times (minutes) at 10:00 AM for the Tower of Terror ride at Disney World (from Data Set 33 "Disney World Wait Times" in Appendix B).

35   35   20   50   95   75   45   50   30   35   30   30

1. Tower of Terror Wait Times

a. Find the mean $\bar{x}$.

b. Find the median.

c. Find the standard deviation s.

d. Find the variance.

e. Convert the longest wait time to a z score.

f. Based on the result from part (e), is the longest wait time significantly high?

g. What level of measurement (nominal, ordinal, interval, ratio) describes this data set?

h. Are the wait times discrete data or continuous data?

2. Tower of Terror Wait Times

a. Find Q_1, Q_2, and Q_3.

b. Construct a boxplot.

c. Based on the boxplot from part (b), do the sample data appear to be from a normally distributed population?

d. The accompanying normal quantile plot is obtained by using all 50 wait times at 10:00 AM for the Tower of Terror ride at Disney World. Based on this normal quantile plot, do the sample data appear to be from a normally distributed population?

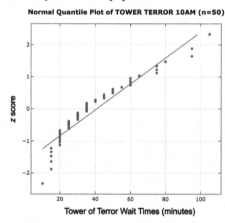

Normal Quantile Plot of TOWER TERROR 10AM (n=50)

Tower of Terror Wait Times (minutes)

3. Foot Lengths of Women

Assume that foot lengths of adult females are normally distributed with a mean of 246.3 mm and a standard deviation of 12.4 mm (based on Data Set 3 "ANSUR II 2012" in Appendix B).

a. Find the probability that a randomly selected adult female has a foot length less than 221.5 mm.

b. Find the probability that a randomly selected adult female has a foot length between 220 mm and 250 mm.

c. Find P_{95}.

d. Find the probability that 16 adult females have foot lengths with a mean greater than 250 mm.

e. Which is more helpful in planning for production of shoes for adult females: The result from part (c) or the result from part (d)? Why?

4. Blue Eyes Assume that 35% of us have blue eyes (based on a study by Dr. P. Soria at Indiana University).

a. Let B denote the event of selecting someone who has blue eyes. What does the event $\overline{B}$ denote?

b. Find the value of $P(B)$.

c. Find the probability of randomly selecting three different people and finding that all of them have blue eyes.

d. Find the probability that among 100 randomly selected people, at least 40 have blue eyes.

e. If 35% of us really do have blue eyes, is a result of 40 people with blue eyes among 100 randomly selected people a result that is significantly high?

5. Body Temperatures Listed below are body temperatures (°F) of adult males (based on Data Set 5 "Body Temperatures" in Appendix B).

97.6   98.2   99.6   98.7   99.4   98.2   980   98.6   98.6

a. Find the mean. Does the result seem reasonable?

b. Identify a characteristic of the data that is very notable.

c. Based on the result from part (b), what appears to be the mean body temperature of adult males?

Technology Project

Testing a Claim Using a Simulation Based on the Normal Distribution When 40 people used the Weight Watchers diet for one year, their mean weight loss was 3.0 lb and the standard deviation was 4.9 lb (based on data from "Comparison of the Atkins, Ornish, Weight Watchers, and Zone Diets for Weight Loss and Heart Disease Reduction," by Dansinger et al., *Journal of the American Medical Association*, Vol. 293, No. 1).

Make the following assumptions:

- The amounts of weight lost on the Weight Watchers diet are normally distributed.

- The diet has no effect, so the mean amount of weight lost is 0 lb.

- The standard deviation of amounts of lost weight is 4.9 lb.

- Samples of size $n = 40$ are randomly selected.

Use a technology capable of randomly generating values from a normal distribution with a desired sample size, mean, and standard deviation. Use the technology to randomly generate different samples with the preceding four assumptions. Find the mean of each generated sample.

a. Does it appear that the actual sample mean weight loss of 3.0 lb is significantly high? Explain.

b. Based on the values of the simulated sample means, what do you conclude about the effectiveness of the diet? Explain.

Big (or Very Large) Data Project

Refer to Data Set 45 "Births in New York" in Appendix B. Using the 465,506 birth weights (grams), test for normality. Do the histogram of the birth weights and the normal quantile plot of the birth weights suggest the same conclusion about normality?

FROM DATA TO DECISION

Critical Thinking: Designing a campus dormitory elevator

An Ohio college student died when he tried to escape from a dormitory elevator that was overloaded with 24 passengers. The elevator was rated for a maximum weight of 2500 pounds. Let's consider this elevator with an allowable weight of 2500 pounds. Let's also consider parameters for weights of adults, as shown in the accompanying table (based on Data Set 1 "Body Data" in Appendix B).

Weights of Adults

	Males	Females
μ	189 lb	171 lb
σ	39 lb	46 lb
Distribution	Normal	Normal

We could consider design features such as the type of music that could be played on the elevator. We could select songs such as "Imagine," or "Daydream Believer." Instead, we will focus on the critical design feature of weight.

a. First, elevators commonly have a 25% margin of error, so they can safely carry a load that is 25% greater than the stated load. What amount is 25% greater than 2500 pounds? Let's refer to this amount as "the maximum safe load" while the 2500 pound limit is the "placard maximum load."

b. Now we need to determine the maximum number of passengers that should be allowed. Should we base our calculations on the maximum safe load or the 2500 pound placard maximum load?

c. The weights given in the accompanying table are weights of adults not including clothing or textbooks. Add another 10 pounds for each student's clothing and textbooks. What is the maximum number of elevator passengers that should be allowed?

d. Do you think that weights of college students are different from weights of adults from the general population? If so, how? How would that affect the elevator design?

Cooperative Group Activities

1. In-class activity Each student states the last four digits of their Social Security number. For privacy concerns, those four digits can be given in any order. Construct a dotplot of the digits. What is the distribution of those digits? What value is the approximate center of the distribution? Then, each student calculates the mean of their four digits. Construct another dotplot for these means. What is the distribution of the means? What value is the approximate center of the distribution? Compare the variation in the original dotplot to the variation in the dotplot representing the sample means. What conclusions follow?

2. Out-of-class activity Use the Internet to find "Pick 4" lottery results for 50 different drawings. Find the 50 different means. Graph a histogram of the original 200 digits that were selected, and graph a histogram of the 50 sample means. What important principle do you observe?

3. In-class activity Divide into groups of three or four students and address these issues affecting the design of manhole covers.

• Which of the following is most relevant for determining whether a manhole cover diameter of 24 in. is large enough: weights of men, weights of women, heights of men, heights of women, hip widths of men, hip widths of women, shoulder widths of men, shoulder widths of women?

• Why are manhole covers usually round? (This was once a popular interview question asked of applicants at IBM, and there are at least three good answers. One good answer is sufficient here.)

4. Out-of-class activity Divide into groups of three or four students. In each group, develop an original procedure to illustrate the central limit theorem. The main objective is to show that when you randomly select samples from a population, the means of those samples tend to be *normally* distributed, regardless of the nature of the population distribution. For this illustration, begin with some population of values that does *not* have a normal distribution.

5. In-class activity Divide into groups of three or four students. Using a coin to simulate births, each individual group member should simulate 25 births and record the number of simulated girls. Combine all results from the group and record $n = $ total number of births and $x = $ number of girls. Given batches of n births, compute the mean and standard deviation for the number of girls. Is the simulated result unusual? Why or why not?

6. In-class activity Divide into groups of three or four students. Select a set of data from one of these data sets in Appendix B: 2, 3, 4, 6, 7, 8, 9, 10, 11, 13, 14, 15, 16, 17, 18, 19, 20, 23, 26, 27, 28, 29, 30, 34, 35, 39, 40, 41, 42, 43. (These are the data sets that were not used in examples or exercises in Section 6-5). Use the methods of Section 6-5 to construct a histogram and normal quantile plot, then determine whether the data set appears to come from a normally distributed population.

7. Out-of-class activity Divide into groups of three or four students and have each group collect an original data set of values at the interval or ratio level of measurement. Test for normality and provide reasons why the data set does or does not appear to be from a normally distributed population.

8. In-class activity Divide into groups of three or four students. In each group, develop an original procedure to illustrate that the median is a biased estimator.

9. In-class activity Divide into groups of three or four students. In each group, develop an original procedure to illustrate that the range is a biased estimator.

7

ESTIMATING PARAMETERS AND DETERMINING SAMPLE SIZES

CHAPTER PROBLEM — Surveys: The Window to Evolving Technologies

Importance of Surveys In our relatively new data-driven world, it is essential that we have the ability to analyze and understand the polls and surveys that play a critical role in guiding just about every facet of our lives. This chapter presents the tools for developing that ability. Listed below are some recent surveys that focus on evolving technologies, and it doesn't take much imagination to recognize that each of these surveys reveals results with serious implications.

- In a Pearson survey, 59% of Gen-Z respondents (ages 14–23) identified YouTube as a preferred learning tool (see Chapter 1 Problem). Good to know for college professors and textbook authors!

- In a National Center for Health Statistics survey of 16,113 subjects, 53.9% of them lived in homes with no landline phones. Good to know for those providing landline phone service and emergency responders.

- In a Mobile Banking Study of 2000 adults, 91% prefer using an app for banking instead of going to a physical bank. Good to know for bank officials.

- In a Sallie Mae survey of 950 undergraduate students, 53% take online courses. Good to know for college officials.

- In a Society for Human Resource Management survey of 3490 human resource professionals, 60% of employers offered telecommuting to employees. Good to know for business owners.

- Biometric Security: In a *USA Today* survey of 510 people, 53% said that we should replace passwords with biometric security, such as fingerprints. Good to know for computer, smartphone, and tablet manufacturers.

Because surveys are now so pervasive and extensive, and because they are often accepted without question, we should analyze them by considering issues such as the following:

- What method was used to select the survey subjects?

- How do we use sample results to estimate values of population parameters?

- How accurate are survey sample results likely to be?

- Typical media reports about surveys are missing an extremely important element of relevant information. What is usually missing?

- How do we correctly interpret survey results?

For example, the "biometric security" poll cited above is based on a *voluntary response sample* (described in Section 1-1), so its fundamental validity is very questionable. The other surveys all involve sound sampling methods, so with these surveys we can proceed to consider the other issues listed above.

CHAPTER OBJECTIVES

The preceding chapters focused on methods of *descriptive statistics*, but in this chapter we begin the study of methods of *inferential statistics.* The following are the major activities of inferential statistics, and this chapter introduces methods for the first activity of using sample data to estimate population parameters. Chapter 8 will introduce basic methods for testing claims (or hypotheses) about population parameters.

Major Activities of Inferential Statistics

1. Use sample data to *estimate values of population parameters* (such as a population proportion or population mean).

2. Use sample data to *test hypotheses* (or claims) made about population parameters.

Here are the chapter objectives:

7-1 Estimating a Population Proportion

- Construct a confidence interval estimate of a population proportion and interpret such confidence interval estimates.

- Identify the requirements necessary for the procedure that is used, and determine whether those requirements are satisfied.

- Develop the ability to determine the sample size necessary to estimate a population proportion.

7-2 Estimating a Population Mean

- Construct a confidence interval estimate of a population mean, and be able to interpret such confidence interval estimates.

- Determine the sample size necessary to estimate a population mean.

7-1 Estimating a Population Proportion

Key Concept This section presents methods for using a sample proportion to make an inference about the value of the corresponding population proportion. This section focuses on the population proportion p, but we can also work with probabilities or percentages. When working with percentages, we will perform calculations with the equivalent proportion value. Here are the three main concepts included in this section:

- **Point Estimate:** The sample proportion (denoted by $\hat{p}$) is the best *point estimate* (or single value estimate) of the population proportion p.

- **Confidence Interval:** We can use a sample proportion $\hat{p}$ to construct a *confidence interval* estimate of the true value of a population proportion p, and we should know how to construct and interpret such confidence intervals.

- **Sample Size:** We should know how to find the sample size necessary to estimate a population proportion p.

The concepts presented in this section are used in the following sections and chapters, so it is important to understand this section quite well. Below are the key notations that will be referenced.

Notation:

x = number of successes

n = sample size

N = population size

$\hat{p} = x/n$ denotes the *sample proportion*

$p = x/N$ denotes the *population proportion*

PART 1 Point Estimate, Confidence Interval, and Sample Size

Point Estimate

If we want to estimate a population proportion with a single value, the best estimate is the sample proportion $\hat{p}$. Because $\hat{p}$ consists of a single value that is equivalent to a point on a line, it is called a *point estimate*.

> **DEFINITION**
>
> A **point estimate** is a single value used to estimate a population parameter.

The sample proportion $\hat{p}$ is the best *point estimate* of the population proportion p.

Unbiased Estimator We use $\hat{p}$ as the point estimate of p because it is unbiased and it is the most consistent of the estimators that could be used. (An unbiased estimator is a statistic that targets the value of the corresponding population parameter in the sense that the sampling distribution of the statistic has a mean that is equal to the corresponding population parameter. The statistic $\hat{p}$ targets the population proportion p.) The sample proportion $\hat{p}$ is the most consistent estimator of p in the sense that the standard deviation of sample proportions tends to be smaller than the standard deviation of other unbiased estimators of p.

 EXAMPLE 1 **Online Courses**

The Chapter Problem included reference to a Sallie Mae survey of 950 undergraduate college students, and 53% of them said that they take online courses. Based on that result, find the best point estimate of the proportion of *all* undergraduate college students who take online courses.

SOLUTION

Because the sample proportion is the best point estimate of the population proportion, we conclude that the best point estimate of p is 0.53. (If using the sample results to estimate the *percentage* of all undergraduate college students who take online courses, the best point estimate is 53%.)

YOUR TURN. Find the point estimate in Exercise 13 "Tennis Challenges."

Confidence Interval

Why Do We Need Confidence Intervals? In Example 1 we saw that 0.53 is our *best* point estimate of the population proportion p, but we have no indication of how *good* that "best" estimate is. By giving us a range of values associated with a probability, a confidence interval gives us a much better sense of how good an estimate is.

> **DEFINITION**
>
> A **confidence interval** (or **interval estimate**) is a range (or an interval) of values used to estimate the true value of a population parameter. A confidence interval is sometimes abbreviated as CI.

Here's an example of a confidence interval illustrated later in Example 2:

> The 0.95 (or 95%) confidence interval estimate of a population proportion p is $0.499 < p < 0.562$.

Two key elements of a confidence interval are (1) the confidence level and the associated critical value, and (2) the margin of error. These key elements are described as follows.

Confidence Level

> **DEFINITION**
>
> The **confidence level** is the probability $1 - \alpha$ (such as 0.95, or 95%) that the confidence interval actually does contain the population parameter, assuming that the estimation process is repeated a large number of times. (The confidence level is also called the **degree of confidence,** or the **confidence coefficient.**)

Push Polling

Push polling is the practice of political campaigning under the guise of a poll. Its name is derived from its objective of pushing voters away from opposition candidates by asking loaded questions designed to discredit them. This survey question was used in one campaign: "Please tell me if you would be more likely or less likely to vote for Roy Romer if you knew that Governor Romer appoints a parole board which has granted early release to an average of four convicted felons per day every day since Romer took office." The National Council on Public Polls says that push polls are unethical. Reputable pollsters do not approve of push polling.

The following table shows the relationship between the confidence level and the corresponding value of α. The confidence level of 95% is the value used most often.

Most Common Confidence Levels	Corresponding Values of α
90% (or 0.90) confidence level:	$\alpha = 0.10$
95% (or 0.95) confidence level:	$\alpha = 0.05$
99% (or 0.99) confidence level:	$\alpha = 0.01$

Critical Value After selecting the confidence level, the associated critical value must be determined. The critical value, sample size, and sample proportion are used to evaluate the margin of error. We will use the following definition of *critical value*, which was first presented in Section 6-1, and this definition uses a z score from the standard normal distribution.

$\alpha/2$ $\alpha/2$

$z = 0$ $z_{\alpha/2}$

Found from
technology or
Table A-2

FIGURE 7-1   Critical Value $z_{\alpha/2}$ in the Standard Normal Distribution

> **DEFINITION**
>
> For the standard normal distribution, a **critical value** is a z score on the borderline separating those z scores that are *significantly low* or *significantly high*.

The number $z_{\alpha/2}$ separates an area of $\alpha/2$ in the right tail of the standard normal distribution. See Figure 7-2, showing that if $\alpha = 0.05$, then $z_{\alpha/2} = 1.96$ (as shown in Example 8 in Section 6-1).

Note that when finding the critical z score for a 95% confidence level, we use a cumulative left area of 0.9750 (*not* 0.95). See Figure 7-2 and think of it this way:

This is our confidence level:	The area in *both* tails is:	The area in the *right* tail is:	The cumulative area from the left, excluding the right tail, is:
95% $\rightarrow$	$\alpha = 0.05$ $\rightarrow$	$\alpha/2 = 0.025$ $\rightarrow$	$1 - 0.025 = 0.975$

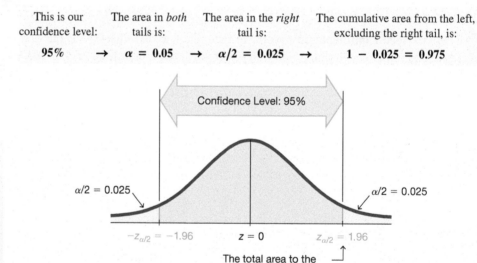

Confidence Level: 95%

$\alpha/2 = 0.025$ $\alpha/2 = 0.025$

$-z_{\alpha/2} = -1.96$ $z = 0$ $z_{\alpha/2} = 1.96$

The total area to the left of this boundary is 0.975.

FIGURE 7-2   Finding the Critical Value $z_{\alpha/2}$ for a 95% Confidence Level

The accompanying table lists the most commonly used critical values.

Confidence Level	α	Critical Value, $z_{\alpha/2}$
90%	0.10	1.645
95%	0.05	1.96
99%	0.01	2.575

Margin of Error We now formally define the *margin of error E* that we have all encountered so often in media reports.

> **DEFINITION**
>
> When using a sample statistic to estimate a population parameter, the **margin of error,** denoted by **E**, is the maximum likely amount of error (the amount by which the sample statistic misses the population parameter).

When using a sample proportion $\hat{p}$ to estimate a population proportion p, the difference between $\hat{p}$ and the actual value of p is an error, and the margin of error is the maximum likely amount of that error. The margin of error E can be found by multiplying the critical value and the estimated standard deviation of sample proportions, as shown in Formula 7-1. (This estimate of a standard deviation of a sampling distribution of proportions is called a **standard error** of the sample proportions.)

FORMULA 7-1   **MARGIN OF ERROR E FOR PROPORTIONS**

$$E = z_{\alpha/2}\underbrace{\sqrt{\frac{\hat{p}\hat{q}}{n}}}$$

Critical value   Estimated standard deviation of sample proportions

Wald Confidence Interval When constructing a confidence interval using the margin of error E given in Formula 7-1, the result is called a *Wald* confidence interval. Part 2 of this section will discuss other methods for constructing a confidence interval.

Interpreting a Confidence Interval

We must be careful to interpret confidence intervals correctly. There is a correct interpretation and many different and creative incorrect interpretations of the confidence interval $0.499 < p < 0.562$.

Correct:

"We are 95% confident that the interval from 0.499 to 0.562 actually does contain the true value of the population proportion p."
This is a short and acceptable way of saying that if we were to select many different random samples of size 950 and construct the corresponding confidence intervals, 95% of them would contain the population proportion p. In this correct interpretation, the confidence level of 95% refers to the *success rate of the process* used to estimate the population proportion.

Wrong:

"There is a 95% chance that the true value of p will fall between 0.499 and 0.562."
This is wrong because p is a population parameter with a fixed value; it is not a random variable with values that vary.

Wrong:

"95% of sample proportions will fall between 0.499 and 0.562."
This is wrong because the values of 0.499 and 0.562 result from one sample; they are not parameters describing the behavior of all samples.

Confidence Level: The Process Success Rate A confidence level of 95% tells us that the *process* we are using should, in the long run, result in confidence interval limits that contain the true population proportion 95% of the time. Suppose that the true

Shakespeare's Vocabulary

According to Bradley Efron and Ronald Thisted, Shakespeare's writings included 31,534 different words. They used probability theory to conclude that Shakespeare probably knew at least another 35,000 words that he didn't use in his writings. The problem of estimating the size of a population is an important problem often encountered in ecology studies, but the result given here is another interesting application. (See "Estimating the Number of Unseen Species: How Many Words Did Shakespeare Know?"; in *Biometrika,* Vol. 63, No. 3.)

proportion of undergraduate students who take online courses is actually $p = 0.50$. See Figure 7-3, which shows that 19 out of 20 (or 95%) different confidence intervals contain the assumed value of $p = 0.50$. Figure 7-3 is trying to tell this story: With a 95% confidence level, we expect about 19 out of 20 confidence intervals (or 95%) to contain the true value of p.

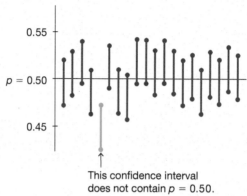

0.55

$p = 0.50$

0.45

This confidence interval
does not contain $p = 0.50$.

FIGURE 7-3   Confidence Intervals from 20 Different Samples

KEY ELEMENTS

Confidence Interval for Estimating a Population Proportion p

Objective

Construct a Wald confidence interval used to estimate a population proportion p.

Notation

$p = $ *population* proportion
$\hat{p} = $ *sample* proportion
$n = $ number of sample values

$E = $ margin of error
$z_{\alpha/2} = $ critical value: the z score separating an area of $\alpha/2$ in the right tail of the standard normal distribution

Requirements

1. The sample is a simple random sample.

2. The conditions for the binomial distribution are satisfied: There is a fixed number of trials, the trials are independent, there are two categories of outcomes, and the probabilities remain constant for each trial (as in Section 5-2).

3. There are at least 5 successes and at least 5 failures. (This requirement is a way to verify that $np \geq 5$ and $nq \geq 5$, so the normal distribution serves as a suitable approximation to the binomial distribution, which is the distribution of proportions.)

   DETOUR⟶ **(If this requirement is not satisfied, one alternative is to use the method of bootstrap resampling described in Section 7-4.)**

Confidence Interval Estimate of p and the Margin of Error

$$\hat{p} - E < p < \hat{p} + E \qquad \text{where the margin of error is} \qquad E = z_{\alpha/2}\sqrt{\frac{\hat{p}\hat{q}}{n}}$$

The confidence interval is often expressed in the following two equivalent formats:

$$\hat{p} \pm E \quad \text{or} \quad (\hat{p} - E, \hat{p} + E)$$

Round-Off Rule for Confidence Interval Estimates of p

Round the confidence interval limits for p to three significant digits.

Procedure for Constructing a Confidence Interval for p

1. Verify that the requirements in the preceding Key Elements box are satisfied.

2. Use technology or Table A-2 to find the critical value $z_{\alpha/2}$ that corresponds to the desired confidence level.

3. Evaluate the margin of error $E = z_{\alpha/2}\sqrt{\hat{p}\hat{q}/n}$.

4. Using the value of the calculated margin of error E and the value of the sample proportion $\hat{p}$, find the values of the *confidence interval limits* $\hat{p} - E$ and $\hat{p} + E$. Substitute those values in the general format for the confidence interval.

5. Round the resulting confidence interval limits to three significant digits.

CP ⊢ **EXAMPLE 2** **Constructing a Confidence Interval: Online Courses**

In the Chapter Problem, we noted that in a Sallie Mae survey of 950 undergraduate students, 53% take online courses. The sample results are $n = 950$ and $\hat{p} = 0.53$.

   a. Find the margin of error E that corresponds to a 95% confidence level.

   b. Find the 95% confidence interval estimate of the population proportion p.

   c. Based on the results, can we safely conclude that more than 50% of undergraduates take online courses?

   d. Assuming that you are an online reporter, write a brief statement that accurately describes the results, and include all of the relevant information.

SOLUTION

REQUIREMENT CHECK (1) The polling methods used by the Sallie Mae organization result in samples that can be considered to be simple random samples. (2) The conditions for a binomial experiment are satisfied because there is a fixed number of trials (950), the trials are independent (because the response from one undergraduate doesn't affect the probability of the response from another undergraduate), there are two categories of outcome (an undergraduate either takes online courses or does not), and the probability remains constant, because P(undergraduate takes online courses) is fixed for a given point in time. (3) With 53% of the 950 undergraduates taking online courses, the number taking online courses is 53% of 950, which is 504 (from 0.53×950). If 504 of the 950 undergraduates take online courses, the other 446 do not, so the number of "successes" (504) and the number of "failures" (446) are both at least 5, as required. The check of requirements has been successfully completed. ✅

Technology The confidence interval and margin of error can be easily found using technology. From the Statdisk display we can see the required entries on the left and the results displayed on the right. Like most technologies, Statdisk requires a value for the number of successes, so we find 53% of 950 and round the result of 503.5 to the whole number 504. The results show that the margin of error is $E = 0.03174$, and the confidence interval is $0.499 < p < 0.562$ (rounded). (The Wilson Score confidence interval included in the display will be discussed later in Part 2 of this section.)

Statdisk

Confidence Interval: Proportion One Sample	⧉ Show Sample Editor
Confidence Level: 0.95	Download Copy
Sample Size, n: 950	Margin of Error, E = 0.03174
Number of Successes, x: 504	95% Confidence Interval (using normal approx):
Evaluate	0.49879 < p < 0.56226
	Wilson Score Confidence Interval:
	0.49873 < p < 0.56208

continued

Bias in Internet Surveys?

Capitalizing on the widespread use of technology and social media, there is a growing trend to conduct surveys using only the Internet instead of using in-person interviews or phone calls to randomly selected subjects. Internet surveys are faster and much less expensive, and they provide important advantages in survey design and administration. But are Internet surveys biased because they use only subjects randomly selected from the 90% of the U.S. population that uses the Internet? The Pew Research Center studied this issue by comparing results from online polls to polls that included the offline population. It was found that the differences were generally quite small, but topics related to the Internet and technology resulted in much larger differences. We should be careful to consider consequences of bias with Internet surveys.

Manual Calculation Here is how to find the confidence interval with manual calculations:

a. The margin of error is found by using Formula 7-1 with $z_{\alpha/2} = 1.96$, $\hat{p} = 0.53, \hat{q} = 0.47$, and $n = 950$.

$$E = z_{\alpha/2} \sqrt{\frac{\hat{p}\hat{q}}{n}} = 1.96\sqrt{\frac{(0.53)(0.47)}{950}} = 0.0317381$$

b. Constructing the confidence interval is really easy now that we know that $\hat{p} = 0.53$ and $E = 0.0317381$. Simply substitute those values to obtain this result:

$$\hat{p} - E < p < \hat{p} + E$$

$$0.53 - 0.0317381 < p < 0.53 + 0.0317381$$

$$0.498 < p < 0.562 \quad (\text{rounded to three significant digits})$$

This same result could be expressed in the format of 0.53 ± 0.032 or (0.498, 0.562). If we want the 95% confidence interval for the true population *percentage,* we could express the result as $49.8\% < p < 56.2\%$.

Note that these expressions resulting from manual calculations differ slightly from the expression obtained using technology. The reason for the discrepancy is that the manual calculations are based on the critical value of $z_{0.025} = 1.96$, but technology uses the more accurate critical value of $z_{0.025} = 1.959963986$.

c. Based on the confidence interval obtained in part (b), we *cannot* safely conclude that more than 50% of undergraduates take online courses. Because the confidence interval ranges from 0.499 to 0.562, it is possible that the population percentage is below 50%.

d. Here is one statement that summarizes the results: 53% of undergraduates take online courses. That percentage is based on a Sallie Mae survey of 950 randomly selected undergraduates. In theory, in 95% of such polls, the percentage should differ by no more than 3.2 percentage points in either direction from the percentage that would be found by interviewing all undergraduates.

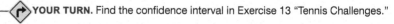 **YOUR TURN.** Find the confidence interval in Exercise 13 "Tennis Challenges."

Bootstrap Resampling for Constructing Confidence Intervals Section 7-4 describes the method of *bootstrap resampling* for constructing a confidence interval estimate of a population parameter. The basic approach is to use technology such as Statdisk to "resample" the sample data many times (such as 1000), then use the sorted list of 1000 results to find the confidence interval. If we repeat Example 2 using the bootstrap resampling method, here is a typical result: $0.498 < p < 0.561$. Because of the randomness used in the procedure, the resulting confidence interval may differ somewhat.

Analyzing Polls Example 2 deals with a typical poll. When analyzing results from polls, consider the following:

1. The sample should be a simple random sample, not an inappropriate sample (such as a voluntary response sample).

2. The confidence level should be provided. (It is often 95%, but media reports usually fail to identify the confidence level.)

3. The sample size should be provided. (It is often provided by the media, but not always.)

4. Except for relatively rare cases, the quality of the poll results depends on the sampling method and the size of the sample, but the size of the *population* is usually not a factor.

> **CAUTION** Never think that poll results are unreliable if the *sample size* is a small percentage of the *population size*. The population size is usually not a factor in determining the reliability of a poll.

Finding the Point Estimate and *E* from a Confidence Interval

Sometimes we want to better understand a confidence interval that might have been obtained from a journal article or technology. If we already know the confidence interval limits, the sample proportion (or the best point estimate) $\hat{p}$ and the margin of error *E* can be found as follows:

Point estimate of *p*:

$$\hat{p} = \frac{\text{(upper confidence interval limit)} + \text{(lower confidence interval limit)}}{2}$$

Margin of error:

$$E = \frac{\text{(upper confidence interval limit)} - \text{(lower confidence interval limit)}}{2}$$

EXAMPLE 3 **Finding the Sample Proportion and Margin of Error**

The article "High-Dose Nicotine Patch Therapy," by Dale, Hurt, et al. (*Journal of the American Medical Association,* Vol. 274, No. 17) includes this statement: "Of the 71 subjects, 70% were abstinent from smoking at 8 weeks (95% confidence interval [CI], 58% to 81%)." Use that statement to find the point estimate $\hat{p}$ and the margin of error *E*.

SOLUTION

We get the 95% confidence interval of $0.58 < p < 0.81$ from the given statement of "58% to 81%." The point estimate $\hat{p}$ is the value midway between the upper and lower confidence interval limits, so we get

$$\hat{p} = \frac{\text{(upper confidence limit)} + \text{(lower confidence limit)}}{2}$$

$$= \frac{0.81 + 0.58}{2} = 0.695$$

The margin of error can be found as follows:

$$E = \frac{\text{(upper confidence limit)} - \text{(lower confidence limit)}}{2}$$

$$= \frac{0.81 - 0.58}{2} = 0.115$$

Using Confidence Intervals for Hypothesis Tests

A confidence interval can be used to address some claim made about a population proportion. For example, if sample results consist of 70 heads in 100 tosses of a coin, the resulting 95% confidence interval of $0.610 < p < 0.790$ is evidence supporting the claim that the proportion of heads is *different from* 50% (because 0.50 is not contained within the confidence interval).

Author Testifying in Court

The author testified as an expert witness in New York State Supreme Court. He testified on behalf of a former student who lost an election apparently due to a misleading ballot format in one district. The author used a confidence interval as one item of evidence. When questioned about the confidence interval, the attorney opposing the former student argued that for my confidence interval, the 95% confidence level corresponded to a 5% error rate, and if you add that 5% to the margin of error of 3 percentage points, you get a total of 8%, which is far too high. That argument made no sense because the "5% error rate" and the "3 percentage point margin of error" are two totally different measures and it would be absurd to add them. In this case, lack of basic knowledge of statistics severely damaged the opposing attorney's arguments, and my former student won his case.

Determining Sample Size

When planning to collect sample data in order to estimate some population proportion p, we must first determine the *sample size*, which is the number of sample units that must be collected. If we solve the formula for the margin of error E (Formula 7-1) for the sample size n, we get Formula 7-2 below. Formula 7-2 requires $\hat{p}$ as an estimate of the population proportion p, but if no such estimate is known (as is often the case), we replace $\hat{p}$ by 0.5 and replace $\hat{q}$ by 0.5, with the result given in Formula 7-3. Replacing $\hat{p}$ and $\hat{q}$ with 0.5 results in the largest possible sample size, so we are sure that the sample size is adequate for estimating p.

KEY ELEMENTS

Finding the Sample Size Required to Estimate a Population Proportion

Objective

Determine how large the sample size n should be in order to estimate the population proportion p.

Notation

p = population proportion $\hat{p}$ = sample proportion

n = number of sample values E = desired margin of error

$z_{\alpha/2}$ = z score separating an area of $\alpha/2$ in the right tail of the standard normal distribution

Requirements

The sample must be a simple random sample of independent sample units.

When an estimate $\hat{p}$ is known: **Formula 7-2** $n = \dfrac{\left[z_{\alpha/2}\right]^2 \hat{p}\hat{q}}{E^2}$

When no estimate $\hat{p}$ is known: **Formula 7-3** $n = \dfrac{\left[z_{\alpha/2}\right]^2 0.25}{E^2}$

If a reasonable estimate of $\hat{p}$ can be made by using previous samples, a pilot study, or someone's expert knowledge, use Formula 7-2. If nothing is known about the value of $\hat{p}$, use Formula 7-3.

Round-Off Rule for Determining Sample Size

If the computed sample size n is not a whole number, round the value of n up to the next *larger* whole number, so the sample size is sufficient instead of being slightly insufficient. For example, round 708.135 to 709.

> **EXAMPLE 4** **What Percentage of Adults Make Online Purchases?**
>
> A 2016 Pew Research Center survey of 4787 randomly selected U.S. adults showed that 79% of the respondents shop online. If we want to conduct a new survey to determine whether that percentage has changed, how many adults must be surveyed in order to be 95% confident that the sample percentage is in error by no more than three percentage points?
>
> **a.** Assume that 79% of adults make online purchases (as in the earlier Pew survey).
>
> **b.** Assume that we have no prior information suggesting a possible value of the population proportion.

a. With a 95% confidence level, we have $\alpha = 0.05$, so $z_{\alpha/2} = 1.96$. Also, the margin of error is $E = 0.03$, which is the decimal equivalent of "three percentage points." The prior survey suggests that $\hat{p} = 0.79$, so $\hat{q} = 0.21$ (found from $\hat{q} = 1 - 0.79$). Because we have an estimated value of $\hat{p}$, we use Formula 7-2 as follows:

$$n = \frac{[z_{\alpha/2}]^2 \hat{p}\hat{q}}{E^2} = \frac{[1.96]^2 (0.79)(0.21)}{0.03^2}$$
$$= 708.135 = 709 \text{ (rounded up)}$$

We must obtain a simple random sample that includes at least 709 adults.

b. With no prior knowledge of $\hat{p}$ (or $\hat{q}$), we use Formula 7-3 as follows:

$$n = \frac{[z_{\alpha/2}]^2 \cdot 0.25}{E^2} = \frac{[1.96]^2 \cdot 0.25}{0.03^2}$$
$$= 1067.11 = 1068 \text{ (rounded up)}$$

We must obtain a simple random sample that includes at least 1068 adults.

INTERPRETATION

To be 95% confident that our sample percentage is within three percentage points of the true percentage for all adults, we should obtain a simple random sample of 1068 adults, assuming no prior knowledge. By comparing this result to the sample size of 709 found in part (a), we can see that if we have no knowledge of a prior study, a larger sample is required to achieve the same results as when the value of $\hat{p}$ can be estimated.

 YOUR TURN. Do Exercise 31 "Wiggle Your Ears."

CAUTION Try to avoid these three common errors when calculating sample size:

1. Don't make the mistake of using $E = 3$ as the margin of error corresponding to "three percentage points." If the margin of error is three percentage points, use $E = 0.03$.

2. Be sure to substitute the critical z score for $z_{\alpha/2}$. For example, when working with 95% confidence, be sure to replace $z_{\alpha/2}$ with 1.96. Don't make the mistake of replacing $z_{\alpha/2}$ with 0.95 or 0.05.

3. Be sure to round up to the next higher integer; don't round off using the usual round-off rules. Round 708.135 to 709.

Role of the Population Size N Formulas 7-2 and 7-3 are remarkable because they show that the sample size does not depend on the size (N) of the population; the sample size depends on the desired confidence level, the desired margin of error, and sometimes the known estimate of $\hat{p}$. (See Exercise 39 "Finite Population Correction Factor" for dealing with cases in which a relatively large sample is selected without replacement from a finite population, so the sample size n does depend on the population size N.)

PART 2 Better-Performing Confidence Intervals

Disadvantage of Wald Confidence Interval

Wald Coverage Probability Is Too Liberal A concept used to gauge the quality of a confidence interval is the *coverage probability*, defined as follows.

Curbstoning

The glossary for the Census defines *curbstoning* as "the practice by which a census enumerator fabricates a questionnaire for a residence without actually visiting it." Curbstoning occurs when a census enumerator sits on a curbstone (or anywhere else) and fills out survey forms by making up responses. Because data from curbstoning are not real, they can affect the validity of the Census. The extent of curbstoning has been investigated in several studies, and one study showed that about 4% of Census enumerators practiced curbstoning at least some of the time. The methods of Section 7-1 assume that the sample data have been collected in an appropriate way, so if much of the sample data have been obtained through curbstoning, then the resulting confidence interval estimates might be very flawed.

The *New York Times* reported on research showing that the margin of error in a typical survey is about twice as large as we might expect with our theoretical calculations. In a typical survey, we say that we have 95% confidence that the margin of error is *three* percentage points, but David Rothschild and Sharad Goel say that the real-world margin of error is about *six* percentage points. They base that conclusion on an analysis of 4221 surveys conducted late in election campaigns. They compared survey results to actual election results to identify the larger margin of error. Two explanations: (1) There is a discrepancy between those who are surveyed and those who actually vote; (2) There is a non-response error that occurs when the likelihood of responding to the survey is somehow related to how the survey questions are answered. They found that those who support a trailing candidate are less likely to respond to the survey. There is also bias created with the wording of survey questions. These are very real factors that could create a large discrepancy between a margin of error that we theoretically expect and the real-world margin of error that actually occurs.

> **DEFINITION**
>
> The **coverage probability** of a confidence interval estimate of the population proportion p is the actual proportion of such confidence intervals that contain the true population proportion.

If we select a specific confidence level, such as 0.95 (or 95%), we would like to get the *actual* coverage probability equal to our *desired* confidence level.

Disadvantage of the Wald Confidence Interval (described in Part 1):

> **Too "Liberal":** The coverage probability of a Wald confidence interval is usually *less than or equal to* the selected confidence level.

For example, if we select a 95% confidence level, we usually get 95% or *fewer* of confidence intervals containing the population proportion p. For this reason, the Wald confidence interval is rarely used in professional applications and professional journals.

Better-Performing Confidence Intervals

Important note about exercises: Except for some Beyond the Basics exercises, the exercises for this Section 7-1 are based on the method for constructing a Wald confidence interval as described in Part 1, not the confidence intervals described here. It is recommended that students learn the methods presented earlier, but recognize that there are better methods available, and they can be used with suitable technology.

Plus Four Method The *plus four confidence interval* performs better than the Wald confidence interval in the sense that its coverage probability is closer to the confidence level that is used.

> **Procedure for the Plus Four Method**
>
> 1. Add 2 to the number of successes x.
> 2. Add 2 to the number of failures (so the number of trials n is increased by 4).
> 3. Proceed to find the confidence interval using the same method described in Part 1.

The plus four confidence interval has coverage probabilities similar to those for the Wilson score confidence interval that follows.

Wilson Score Another confidence interval that performs better than the Wald CI is the *Wilson score confidence interval*. The upper and lower confidence interval limits are calculated using the following:

$$\frac{\hat{p} + \dfrac{z_{\alpha/2}^2}{2n} \pm z_{\alpha/2}\sqrt{\dfrac{\hat{p}\hat{q} + \dfrac{z_{\alpha/2}^2}{4n}}{n}}}{1 + \dfrac{z_{\alpha/2}^2}{n}}$$

The Wilson score confidence interval performs better than the Wald CI in the sense that the coverage probability is closer to the confidence level. Given its calculation complexity, it is easy to see why this superior Wilson score confidence interval is not used much in introductory statistics courses. The complexity of the above expression can be circumvented by using some technologies, such as Statdisk, that provide Wilson score confidence interval results.

Clopper-Pearson Method The Clopper-Pearson method is an "exact" method in the sense that it is based on the exact binomial distribution instead of an approximation of a distribution.

Disadvantage of the Clopper-Pearson Confidence Interval

> Too "Conservative": The coverage probability is usually *greater than or equal to* the selected confidence level.

Calculations with the Clopper-Pearson method are too messy to consider here.

Which Method Is Best? There are other methods for constructing confidence intervals that are not discussed here. There isn't universal agreement on which method is best for constructing a confidence interval estimate of *p*.

- The Wald confidence interval is best as a teaching tool for introducing students to confidence intervals.

- The plus four confidence interval is almost as easy as Wald and it performs better than Wald by having a coverage probability closer to the selected confidence level.

Again, note that except for some Beyond the Basic exercises, the exercises that follow are based on the Wald confidence interval given earlier, not the better-performing confidence intervals discussed here.

TECH CENTER

 ## Proportions: Confidence Intervals and Sample Size Determination
Access tech supplements, videos, and data sets at **www.TriolaStats.com**

Statdisk	Minitab
Confidence Interval	**Confidence Interval**
1. Click **Analysis** in the top menu.	1. Click **Stat** in the top menu.
2. Select **Confidence Intervals** from the dropdown menu and select **Proportion One Sample** from the submenu.	2. Select **Basic Statistics** from the dropdown menu and select **1 Proportion** from the submenu.
3. Enter the confidence level, sample size, and number of successes.	3. Select **Summarized data** in the dropdown window and enter the number of events (successes) and number of trials. Confirm *Perform hypothesis test* is not checked.
4. Click **Evaluate**.	4. Click the **Options** button and enter the desired confidence level. For *Alternative Hypothesis* select ≠ and for *Method* select **Normal approximation** for the methods of this section.
Sample Size Determination	5. Click **OK** twice.
1. Click **Analysis** in the top menu.	**Sample Size Determination**
2. Select **Sample Size Determination** from the dropdown menu and select **Estimate Proportion** from the submenu.	Minitab determines sample size using the binomial distribution (not normal distribution), so the results will differ from those found using the methods of this section.
3. Enter the confidence level, margin of error *E*, estimate of *p* if known, and population size if known.	1. Click **Stat** in the top menu.
4. Click **Evaluate**.	2. Select **Power and Sample Size** from the dropdown menu and select **Sample Size for Estimation** from the submenu.
	3. For *Parameter* select **Proportion (Binomial)** and enter an estimate of the proportion if known or enter **0.5** if not known.
	4. Select **Estimate sample sizes** from the dropdown menu and enter the margin of error for confidence intervals.
	5. Click the **Options** button to enter the confidence level and select a **two-sided** confidence interval.
	6. Click **OK** twice.

continued

TECH CENTER *continued*

 Proportions: Confidence Intervals and Sample Size Determination
Access tech supplements, videos, and data sets at **www.TriolaStats.com**

StatCrunch

Confidence Interval
1. Click **Stat** in the top menu.
2. Select **Proportion Stats** from the dropdown menu and select **One Sample—With Summary** from the submenu.
3. Enter the number of successes and number of observations.
4. Select **Confidence interval for p** and enter the confidence level. Select the **Standard-Wald** method.
5. Click **Compute!**

Sample Size Determination
Not available.

TI-83/84 Plus Calculator

Confidence Interval
1. Press **STAT**, then select **TESTS** in the top menu.
2. Select **1-PropZInt** in the menu and press **ENTER**.
3. Enter the number of successes x, number of observations n, and confidence level (*C-Level*).
4. Select **Calculate** and press **ENTER**.

Sample Size Determination
Not available.

Excel

XLSTAT Add-In (Required)
1. Click on the **XLSTAT** tab in the Ribbon and then click **Parametric tests.**
2. Select **Tests for one proportion** from the dropdown menu.
3. Under *Data format* select **Frequency** if you know the number of successes x or select **Proportion** if you know the sample proportion $\hat{p}$.
4. Enter the frequency or sample proportion, sample size, and **0.5** for *Test proportion*.
5. Check **z test** and uncheck **Continuity correction.**
6. Click the **Options** tab.
7. Under *Alternative hypothesis* select **≠ D**. Enter **0** for *Hypothesized difference* and enter the desired significance level (enter **5** for 95% confidence interval). Under *Variance (confidence interval)* select **Sample** and under *Confidence interval* select **Wald.**
8. Click **OK** to display the result under "confidence interval on the proportion (Wald)."

Sample Size Determination
Not available.

R

R command not available at time of publication.

R is rapidly evolving, and an updated list of statistical commands is available at TriolaStats.com.

7-1   Basic Skills and Concepts

Statistical Literacy and Critical Thinking

1. Poll Results in the Media *USA Today* provided results from a survey of 1144 Americans who were asked if they approve of Brett Kavanaugh as the choice for Supreme Court justice. 51% of the respondents said that they did approve, and the margin of error was given as plus or minus 3.5 percentage points. What important element of the survey was omitted?

2. Margin of Error For the poll described in Exercise 1, describe what is meant by the statement that "the margin of error was given as ± 3.5 percentage points."

3. Notation For the poll described in Exercise 1, what values do $\hat{p}$, $\hat{q}$, n, E, and p represent? If the confidence level is 95%, what is the value of α?

4. Confidence Levels Given specific sample data, such as the data given in Exercise 1, which confidence interval is wider: the 95% confidence interval or the 80% confidence interval? Why is it wider?

Finding Critical Values. *In Exercises 5–8, find the critical value $z_{\alpha/2}$ that corresponds to the given confidence level.*

5. 90%   **6.** 99%   **7.** 99.5%   **8.** 98%

Formats of Confidence Intervals. *In Exercises 9–12, express the confidence interval using the indicated format. (The confidence intervals are based on the proportions of red, orange, yellow, and blue M&Ms in Data Set 38 "Candies" in Appendix B.)*

9. Green M&Ms Express $0.116 < p < 0.192$ in the form of $\hat{p} \pm E$.

10. Orange M&Ms Express $0.193 < p < 0.283$ in the form of $\hat{p} \pm E$.

11. Yellow M&Ms Express the confidence interval $(0.0847, 0.153)$ in the form of $\hat{p} - E < p < \hat{p} + E$.

12. Blue M&Ms Express the confidence interval 0.255 ± 0.046 in the form of $\hat{p} - E < p < \hat{p} + E$.

Constructing and Interpreting Confidence Intervals. *In Exercises 13–16, use the given sample data and confidence level. In each case, (a) find the best point estimate of the population proportion p; (b) identify the value of the margin of error E; (c) construct the confidence interval; (d) write a statement that correctly interprets the confidence interval.*

13. Tennis Challenges In a recent U.S. Open tennis tournament, men playing singles matches used challenges on 240 calls made by the line judges. Among those challenges, 88 were found to be successful with the call overturned. Construct a 95% confidence interval for the proportion of successful challenges.

14. Eliquis The drug Eliquis (apixaban) is used to help prevent blood clots in certain patients. In clinical trials, among 5924 patients treated with Eliquis, 153 developed the adverse reaction of nausea (based on data from Bristol-Myers Squibb Co.). Construct a 99% confidence interval for the proportion of adverse reactions.

15. Survey Return Rate In a study of cell phone use and brain hemispheric dominance, an Internet survey was e-mailed to 5000 subjects randomly selected from an online group involved with ears. 717 surveys were returned. Construct a 90% confidence interval for the proportion of returned surveys.

16. Medical Malpractice In a study of 1228 randomly selected medical malpractice lawsuits, it was found that 856 of them were dropped or dismissed (based on data from the Physicians Insurers Association of America). Construct a 95% confidence interval for the proportion of medical malpractice lawsuits that are dropped or dismissed.

Critical Thinking. *In Exercises 17–28, use the data and confidence level to construct a confidence interval estimate of p, then address the given question.*

17. Births A random sample of 860 births in New York State included 426 boys. Construct a 95% confidence interval estimate of the proportion of boys in all births. It is believed that among all births, the proportion of boys is 0.512. Do these sample results provide strong evidence against that belief?

18. Mendelian Genetics One of Mendel's famous genetics experiments yielded 580 peas, with 428 of them green and 152 yellow.

a. Find a 99% confidence interval estimate of the *percentage* of green peas.

continued

b. Based on his theory of genetics, Mendel expected that 75% of the offspring peas would be green. Given that the percentage of offspring green peas is not 75%, do the results contradict Mendel's theory? Why or why not?

19. Tennis Challenges In a recent U. S. Open tennis tournament, women playing singles matches used challenges on 137 calls made by the line judges. Among those challenges, 33 were found to be successful with the call overturned.

a. Construct a 99% confidence interval for the *percentage* of successful challenges.

b. Compare the result from part (a) to this 99% confidence interval for the percentage of successful challenges made by the men playing singles matches: $28.7\% < p < 44.7\%$. Does it appear that either gender is more successful than the other?

20. OxyContin The drug OxyContin (oxycodone) is used to treat pain, but it is dangerous because it is addictive and can be lethal. In clinical trials, 227 subjects were treated with OxyContin and 52 of them developed nausea (based on data from Purdue Pharma L.P.).

a. Construct a 95% confidence interval estimate of the *percentage* of OxyContin users who develop nausea.

b. Compare the result from part (a) to this 95% confidence interval for 5 subjects who developed nausea among the 45 subjects given a placebo instead of OxyContin: $1.93\% < p < 20.3\%$. What do you conclude?

21. Touch Therapy When she was 9 years of age, Emily Rosa did a science fair experiment in which she tested professional touch therapists to see if they could sense her energy field. She flipped a coin to select either her right hand or her left hand, and then she asked the therapists to identify the selected hand by placing their hand just under Emily's hand without seeing it and without touching it. Among 280 trials, the touch therapists were correct 123 times (based on data in "A Close Look at Therapeutic Touch," *Journal of the American Medical Association,* Vol. 279, No. 13).

a. Given that Emily used a coin toss to select either her right hand or her left hand, what proportion of correct responses would be expected if the touch therapists made random guesses?

b. Using Emily's sample results, what is the best point estimate of the therapists success rate?

c. Using Emily's sample results, construct a 99% confidence interval estimate of the proportion of correct responses made by touch therapists.

d. What do the results suggest about the ability of touch therapists to select the correct hand by sensing an energy field?

22. Internet Use A random sample of 5005 adults in the United States includes 751 who do not use the Internet (based on three Pew Research Center polls). Construct a 95% confidence interval estimate of the *percentage* of U.S. adults who do not use the Internet. Based on the result, does it appear that the percentage of U.S. adults who do not use the Internet is different from 48%, which was the percentage in the year 2000?

23. Job Interviews In a Harris poll of 514 human resource professionals, 45.9% said that body piercings and tattoos were big personal grooming red flags.

a. Among the 514 human resource professionals who were surveyed, how many of them said that body piercings and tattoos were big personal grooming red flags?

b. Construct a 99% confidence interval estimate of the proportion of all human resource professionals believing that body piercings and tattoos are big personal grooming red flags.

c. Repeat part (b) using a confidence level of 80%.

d. Compare the confidence intervals from parts (b) and (c) and identify the interval that is wider. Why is it wider?

24. Job Interviews In a Harris poll of 514 human resource professionals, 90% said that the appearance of a job applicant is most important for a good first impression.

a. Among the 514 human resource professionals who were surveyed, how many of them said that the appearance of a job applicant is most important for a good first impression?

b. Construct a 99% confidence interval estimate of the proportion of all human resource professionals believing that the appearance of a job applicant is most important for a good first impression.

c. Repeat part (b) using a confidence level of 80%.

d. Compare the confidence intervals from parts (b) and (c) and identify the interval that is wider. Why is it wider?

25. Really Large Sample A Quest Diagnostics analysis of 10 million drug tests revealed that 4.2% of them tested positive for illegal drugs. Construct a 95% confidence interval estimate of the positive test rate, and construct a 99% confidence interval estimate of that rate. Comment on the results.

26. Gender Selection Before its clinical trials were discontinued, the Genetics & IVF Institute conducted a clinical trial of the XSORT method designed to increase the probability of conceiving a girl and, among the 945 babies born to parents using the XSORT method, there were 879 girls. The YSORT method was designed to increase the probability of conceiving a boy and, among the 291 babies born to parents using the YSORT method, there were 239 boys. Construct the two 95% confidence interval estimates of the percentages of success. Compare the results. What do you conclude?

27. Smoking Stopped In a program designed to help patients stop smoking, 198 patients were given *sustained* care, and 82.8% of them were no longer smoking after one month. Among 199 patients given *standard* care, 62.8% were no longer smoking after one month (based on data from "Sustained Care Intervention and Postdischarge Smoking Cessation Among Hospitalized Adults," by Rigotti et al., *Journal of the American Medical Association,* Vol. 312, No. 7). Construct the two 95% confidence interval estimates of the percentages of success. Compare the results. What do you conclude?

28. Measured Results vs. Reported Results The same study cited in the preceding exercise produced these results after six months for the 198 patients given sustained care: 25.8% were no longer smoking, and these results were biochemically confirmed, but 40.9% of these patients *reported* that they were no longer smoking. Construct the two 95% confidence intervals. Compare the results. What do you conclude?

Using Appendix B Data Sets. *In Exercises 29 and 30, use the indicated data set in Appendix B.*

 29. Heights of Presidents Refer to Data Set 22 "Presidents" in Appendix B. Treat the data as a sample and find the proportion of presidents who were taller than their opponents. Use that result to construct a 95% confidence interval estimate of the population percentage. Based on the result, does it appear that greater height is an advantage for presidential candidates? Why or why not?

 30. Green M&Ms Data Set 38 "Candies" in Appendix B includes data from 345 M&M plain candies, and 53 of them are green. The Mars candy company claims that 16% of its M&M plain candies are green. Use the sample data to construct a 95% confidence interval estimate of the percentage of green M&Ms. What do you conclude about the claim of 16%?

Determining Sample Size. *In Exercises 31–38, use the given data to find the minimum sample size required to estimate a population proportion or percentage.*

31. Wiggle Your Ears Find the sample size needed to estimate the percentage of adults who can wiggle their ears. Use a margin of error of 3 percentage points and use a confidence level of 99%.

continued

a. Assume that $\hat{p}$ and $\hat{q}$ are unknown.

b. Assume that 22% of adults can wiggle their ears (based on data from Soul Publishing).

32. Touch Your Nose With Your Tongue Find the sample size needed to estimate the percentage of adults who can touch their nose with their tongue. Use a margin of error of 2 percentage points and use a confidence level of 90%.

a. Assume that $\hat{p}$ and $\hat{q}$ are unknown.

b. Assume that a previous study showed that 10% of adults can touch their nose with their tongue (based on data from Onedio).

c. Does the use of the results from the previous study have much of an effect on the sample size?

33. E-Cigarettes A *New York Times* article reported that a survey conducted in 2014 included 36,000 adults, with 3.7% of them being regular users of e-cigarettes. Because e-cigarette use is relatively new, there is a need to obtain today's usage rate. How many adults must be surveyed now if we want a confidence level of 95% and a margin of error of 1.5 percentage points?

a. Assume that nothing is known about the rate of e-cigarette usage among adults.

b. Use the results from the 2014 survey.

c. Does the use of the result from the 2014 survey have much of an effect on the sample size?

34. Astrology A sociologist plans to conduct a survey to estimate the percentage of adults who believe in astrology. How many people must be surveyed if we want a confidence level of 99% and a margin of error of four percentage points?

a. Assume that nothing is known about the percentage to be estimated.

b. Use the information from a previous Harris survey in which 26% of respondents said that they believed in astrology.

35. Airline Seating You are the operations manager for American Airlines and you are considering a higher fare level for passengers in aisle seats. You want to estimate the percentage of passengers who now prefer aisle seats. How many randomly selected air passengers must you survey? Assume that you want to be 95% confident that the sample percentage is within 2.5 percentage points of the true population percentage.

a. Assume that nothing is known about the percentage of passengers who prefer aisle seats.

b. Assume that a prior survey suggests that about 38% of air passengers prefer an aisle seat (based on a 3M Privacy Filters survey).

36. Online Gambling Some states now allow online gambling. As a marketing manager for a casino, you need to determine the percentage of adults in those states who gamble online. How many adults must you survey in order to be 99% confident that your estimate is in error by no more than two percentage points?

a. Assume that nothing is known about the percentage of adults who gamble online.

b. Assume that 18% of all adults gamble online (based on 2017 data from a Gambling Commission study in Great Britain).

37. Smart Phone Apple is planning for the launch of a new and improved iPhone. The marketing team wants to know the worldwide percentage of consumers who intend to purchase the new model, so a survey is being planned. How many people must be surveyed in order to be 90% confident that the estimated percentage is within three percentage points of the true population percentage?

a. Assume that nothing is known about the worldwide percentage of consumers who intend to buy the new model.

b. Assume that 11% of consumers have a smartphone and plan to upgrade to a new model.

c. Given that the required sample size is relatively small, could you simply survey the people that you know?

38. Women Who Give Birth An epidemiologist plans to conduct a survey to estimate the percentage of women who give birth. How many women must be surveyed in order to be 99% confident that the estimated percentage is in error by no more than two percentage points?

a. Assume that nothing is known about the percentage to be estimated.

b. Assume that a prior study conducted by the U.S. Census Bureau showed that 82% of women give birth.

c. What is wrong with surveying randomly selected adult women?

7-1 Beyond the Basics

39. Finite Population Correction Factor For Formulas 7-2 and 7-3 we assume that the population is infinite or very large and that we are sampling with replacement. When we sample without replacement from a relatively small population with size N, we modify E to include the *finite population correction factor* shown here, and we can solve for n to obtain the result given here. Use this result to repeat part (b) of Exercise 38, assuming that we limit our population to a county with 2500 women who have completed the time during which they can give birth.

$$E = z_{\alpha/2}\sqrt{\frac{\hat{p}\hat{q}}{n}}\sqrt{\frac{N-n}{N-1}} \qquad n = \frac{N\hat{p}\hat{q}[z_{\alpha/2}]^2}{\hat{p}\hat{q}[z_{\alpha/2}]^2 + (N-1)E^2}$$

40. One-Sided Confidence Interval A one-sided claim about a population proportion is a claim that the proportion is less than (or greater than) some specific value. Such a claim can be formally addressed using a *one-sided confidence interval* for p, which can be expressed as $p < \hat{p} + E$ or $p > \hat{p} - E$, where the margin of error E is modified by replacing $z_{\alpha/2}$ with z_{α}. (Instead of dividing α between two tails of the standard normal distribution, put all of it in one tail.) The Chapter Problem refers to a Sallie Mae survey of 950 undergraduate students, and 53% of the survey subjects take online courses. Use that data to construct a one-sided 95% confidence interval that would be suitable for helping to determine whether the percentage of all undergraduates who take online courses is greater than 50%.

41. No Failures According to the *Rule of Three*, when we have a sample size n with $x = 0$ successes, we have 95% confidence that the true population proportion has an upper bound of $3/n$. (See "A Look at the Rule of Three," by Jovanovic and Levy, *American Statistician*, Vol. 51, No. 2.)

a. If n independent trials result in no successes, why can't we find confidence interval limits by using the methods described in this section?

b. In a study of failure rates of computer hard drives, 45 Toshiba model MD04ABA500V hard drives were tested and there were no failures. What is the 95% upper bound for the percentage of failures for the population of all such hard drives?

Estimating a Population Mean

Key Concept The main goal of this section is to present methods for using a sample mean $\bar{x}$ to make an inference about the value of the corresponding population mean μ. There are three main concepts included in this section:

- **Point Estimate:** The sample mean $\bar{x}$ is the best *point estimate* (or single value estimate) of the population mean μ.

- **Confidence Interval:** Use sample data to construct and interpret a *confidence interval* estimate of the true value of a population mean μ.

- **Sample Size:** Find the sample size necessary to estimate a population mean.

Estimating a Population Mean

It's rare that we want to estimate the unknown value of a population mean μ but we somehow know the value of the population standard deviation σ, so we now focus on the realistic situation in which σ is not known.

Point Estimate As discussed in Section 6-3, the sample mean $\bar{x}$ is an *unbiased estimator* of the population mean μ. Also, for many populations, sample means tend to vary less than other measures of center. For these reasons, the sample mean $\bar{x}$ is usually the best point estimate of the population mean μ.

> **The sample mean $\bar{x}$ is the best *point estimate* of the population mean μ.**

Because even the best point estimate gives us no indication of how accurate it is, we use a *confidence interval* (or *interval estimate*), which consists of a range (or an interval) of values instead of just a single value.

Confidence Interval The accompanying box includes the key elements for constructing a confidence interval estimate of a population mean μ in the common situation where σ is not known.

KEY ELEMENTS

Confidence Interval for Estimating a Population Mean with σ Not Known

Objective

Construct a confidence interval used to estimate a population mean.

Notation

μ = population mean n = number of sample values
$\bar{x}$ = sample mean E = margin of error
s = sample standard deviation

Requirements

1. The sample is a simple random sample.

2. Either or both of these conditions are satisfied: The population is normally distributed or $n > 30$.

DETOUR **If the second requirement is not satisfied, one alternative is to use the method of bootstrap resampling described in Section 7-4.**

Confidence Interval

Formats: $\bar{x} - E < \mu < \bar{x} + E$ or $\bar{x} \pm E$ or $(\bar{x} - E, \bar{x} + E)$

- **Margin of Error:** $E = t_{\alpha/2} \cdot \dfrac{s}{\sqrt{n}}$ (Use df = $n - 1$.)

- **Confidence Level:** The confidence interval is associated with a confidence level, such as 0.95 (or 95%), and α is the complement of the confidence level. For a 0.95 (or 95%) confidence level, $\alpha = 0.05$.

- **Critical Value:** $t_{\alpha/2}$ is the critical t value separating an area of $\alpha/2$ in the right tail of the Student t distribution.

- **Degrees of Freedom:** df = $n - 1$ is the number of degrees of freedom used when finding the critical value.

Round-Off Rule

1. *Original Data:* When using an *original set of data* values, round the confidence interval limits to one more decimal place than is used for the original set of data.

2. *Summary Statistics:* When using the *summary statistics* of n, $\bar{x}$, and s, round the confidence interval limits to the same number of decimal places used for the sample mean.

Requirement of "Normality or $n > 30$"

Normality Requirement with Large Samples ($n > 30$): It is common to consider the normality requirement to be satisfied if the sample is large ($n > 30$), because we know from the central limit theorem that for such large samples, the distribution of the sample means will tend to approximate a normal distribution. (For some population distributions that are extremely far from normal, the sample size might need to be much larger than 30.)

Normality Requirement with Small Samples ($n \leq 30$): With small samples, the method for finding a confidence interval estimate of μ is *robust* against a departure from normality, which means that the normality requirement is loose. The distribution need not be perfectly bell-shaped (it never is), but it should satisfy these conditions:

1. The distribution of the sample data should be somewhat close to being symmetric.

2. The distribution of the sample data should have one mode.

3. The sample data should not include any outliers.

Interpreting the Confidence Interval The confidence interval is associated with a **confidence level**, such as 0.95 (or 95%). When interpreting a confidence interval estimate of μ, know that the confidence level gives us the *success rate of the procedure* used to construct the confidence interval. For example, the 95% confidence interval estimate of 8.5901 g $< \mu <$ 9.0213 g can be interpreted as follows:

> **"We are 95% confident that the interval from 8.5901 g to 9.0213 g actually does contain the true value of μ."**

By "95% confident" we mean that if we were to select many different samples of the same size and construct the corresponding confidence intervals, in the long run, 95% of the confidence intervals should contain the value of μ.

Student t Distribution

In this section we use a *Student t distribution,* which is commonly referred to as a "t distribution." It was developed by William Gosset (1876–1937), who was a Guinness Brewery employee who needed a distribution that could be used with small samples. The brewery prohibited publication of research results, but Gosset got around this by publishing under the pseudonym "Student." (Strictly in the interest of better serving his readers, the author visited the Guinness Brewery and felt obligated to sample some of the product.) Here are some key points about the Student t distribution:

- **Student t Distribution** If a population has a normal distribution, then the distribution of

$$t = \frac{\bar{x} - \mu}{\frac{s}{\sqrt{n}}}$$

  is a **Student t distribution** for all samples of size n. A Student t distribution is commonly referred to as a t **distribution.**

- **Degrees of Freedom** Finding a critical value $t_{\alpha/2}$ requires a value for the **degrees of freedom** (or **df**). In general, the number of degrees of freedom for a collection of sample data is the number of sample values that can vary after certain restrictions have been imposed on all data values. (*Example:* If 10 test scores have the restriction that their mean is 80, then their sum must be 800, and we can freely assign values to the first 9 scores, but the 10th score would then be determined,

Estimating Wildlife Population Sizes

The National Forest Management Act protects endangered species, including the northern spotted owl, with the result that the forestry industry was not allowed to cut vast regions of trees in the Pacific Northwest. Biologists and statisticians were asked to analyze the problem, and they concluded that survival rates and population sizes were decreasing for the female owls, known to play an important role in species survival. Biologists and statisticians also studied salmon in the Snake and Columbia rivers in Washington State, and penguins in New Zealand. In the article "Sampling Wildlife Populations" (*Chance*, Vol. 9, No. 2), authors Bryan Manly and Lyman McDonald comment that in such studies, "biologists gain through the use of modeling skills that are the hallmark of good statistics. Statisticians gain by being introduced to the reality of problems by biologists who know what the crucial issues are."

so in this case there are 9 degrees of freedom.) For the methods of this section, the number of degrees of freedom is the sample size minus 1.

$$\text{Degrees of freedom} = n - 1$$

- **Finding Critical Value $t_{\alpha/2}$** A critical value $t_{\alpha/2}$ can be found using technology or Table A-3. Technology can be used with any number of degrees of freedom, but Table A-3 can be used for select numbers of degrees of freedom only. If using Table A-3 to find a critical value of $t_{\alpha/2}$, but the table does not include the exact number of degrees of freedom, you could use the closest value, or you could be conservative by using the next lower number of degrees of freedom found in the table, or you could interpolate.

- The Student t distribution is different for different sample sizes. (See Figure 7-4 for the cases $n = 3$ and $n = 12$.)

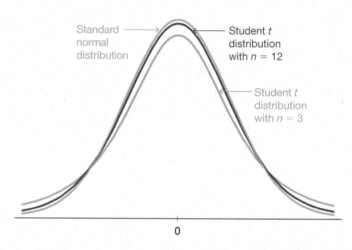

FIGURE 7-4   Student t Distributions for $n = 3$ and $n = 12$
The Student t distribution has the same general shape and symmetry as the standard normal distribution, but it has the greater variability that is expected with small samples.

- The Student t distribution has the same general symmetric bell shape as the standard normal distribution, but has more variability (with wider distributions), as we expect with small samples.

- The Student t distribution has a mean of $t = 0$ (just as the standard normal distribution has a mean of $z = 0$).

- The standard deviation of the Student t distribution varies with the sample size, but it is greater than 1 (unlike the standard normal distribution, which has $\sigma = 1$).

- As the sample size n gets larger, the Student t distribution gets closer to the standard normal distribution.

Procedure for Constructing a Confidence Interval for μ

Confidence intervals can be easily constructed with technology or they can be manually constructed by using the following procedure.

1. Verify that the two requirements are satisfied: The sample is a simple random sample and the population is normally distributed or $n > 30$.

2. With σ unknown (as is usually the case), use $n - 1$ degrees of freedom and use technology or a t distribution table (such as Table A-3) to find the critical value $t_{\alpha/2}$ that corresponds to the desired confidence level.

3. Evaluate the margin of error using $E = t_{\alpha/2} \cdot s/\sqrt{n}$.

4. Using the value of the calculated margin of error E and the value of the sample mean $\bar{x}$, substitute those values in one of the formats for the confidence interval:
$$\bar{x} - E < \mu < \bar{x} + E \quad \text{or} \quad \bar{x} \pm E \quad \text{or} \quad (\bar{x} - E, \bar{x} + E).$$

5. Round the resulting confidence interval limits as follows: With an *original set of data* values, round the confidence interval limits to one more decimal place than is used for the original set of data, but when using the *summary statistics* of n, $\bar{x}$, and s, round the confidence interval limits to the same number of decimal places used for the sample mean.

EXAMPLE 1 **Finding a Critical Value $t_{\alpha/2}$**

Find the critical value $t_{\alpha/2}$ corresponding to a 95% confidence level, given that the sample has size $n = 6$.

SOLUTION

Because $n = 6$, the number of degrees of freedom is $n - 1 = 5$. The 95% confidence level corresponds to $\alpha = 0.05$, so there is an area of 0.025 in each of the two tails of the t distribution, as shown in Figure 7-5.

Using Technology Technology can be used to find that for 5 degrees of freedom and an area of 0.025 in each tail, the critical value is $t_{\alpha/2} = t_{0.025} = 2.571$.

Using Table A-3 To find the critical value using Table A-3, use the column with 0.05 for the "Area in Two Tails" (or use the same column with 0.025 for the "Area in One Tail"). The number of degrees of freedom is df $= n - 1 = 5$. We get $t_{\alpha/2} = t_{0.025} = 2.571$.

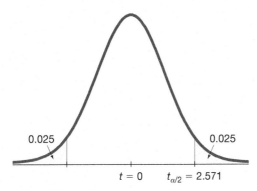

0.025   0.025

$t = 0$ $t_{\alpha/2} = 2.571$

FIGURE 7-5   Critical Value $t_{\alpha/2}$

▶ **YOUR TURN.** Find the critical value for Exercise 2 "Degrees of Freedom."

EXAMPLE 2 **Confidence Interval Using Peanut Butter Cups**

Listed below are weights (grams) of randomly selected Reese's Peanut Butter Cups Miniatures. They are from a package of 38 cups, and the package label states that the total weight is 12 oz, or 340.2 g. If the 38 cups have a total weight of 340.2 g, then the cups should have a mean weight of 340.2 g/38 = 8.953 g.

a. Use the listed sample data to find the point estimate of the mean weight of a Reese's Peanut Butter Cup Miniatures.

b. Use the listed sample data to construct a 95% confidence interval estimate of the mean weight of Reese's Peanut Butter Cup Miniatures.

continued

Based on the preceding results, does it seem that the packages are being filled so that the total package weight is 340.2 g as indicated by the label?

$$8.639 \quad 8.689 \quad 8.548 \quad 8.980 \quad 8.936 \quad 9.042$$

SOLUTION

a. The point estimate of the data is the sample mean $\bar{x}$, which is 8.8057 g.

b. REQUIREMENT CHECK Before constructing the 95% confidence interval, we must first verify that the requirements are satisfied. (1) The sample is a simple random sample. (2) Because the sample size is $n = 6$, the requirement that "the population is normally distributed or the sample size is greater than 30" can be satisfied only if the sample data appear to be from a normally distributed population, so we need to investigate normality. In the accompanying normal quantile plot, the points appear to fit a straight-line pattern, so the sample data appear to be from a normally distributed population. This second requirement is satisfied. ☑

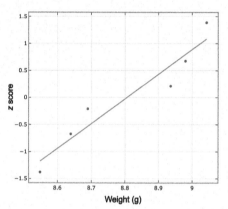

Using Technology Technology can be used to automatically construct the confidence interval. (See instructions near the end of this section.) Shown here is the StatCrunch display resulting from the six weights. The display shows the lower confidence interval limit (L. Limit) and the upper confidence interval limit (U. Limit). After rounding to four decimal places (one more than the original data), we can express the confidence interval as 8.5901 g $< \mu <$ 9.0213 g.

StatCrunch

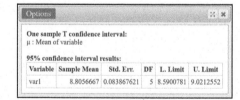

Manual Calculation First find the critical value $t_{0.025} = 2.571$ from Table A-3 using $n - 1 = 5$ degrees of freedom (as shown in Example 1). Find the standard deviation $s = 0.2054$ g from the original sample values. Now find the margin of error E:

$$E = t_{\alpha/2} \frac{s}{\sqrt{n}} = 2.571 \cdot \frac{0.2054}{\sqrt{6}} = 0.215589$$

With $\bar{x} = 8.8057$ g and $E = 0.215589$ g, we construct the confidence interval as follows:

$$\bar{x} - E < \mu < \bar{x} + E$$
$$8.8057 - 0.215589 < \mu < 8.8057 + 0.215589$$
$$8.5901 \text{ g} < \mu < 9.0213 \text{ g} \quad (\text{rounded to four decimal places})$$

INTERPRETATION

We are 95% confident that the limits of 8.5901 g and 9.0213 g actually do contain the value of the population mean μ. If we were to collect many different random samples of 6 Reese's Peanut Butter Cup Miniatures and find the mean weight of each sample, about 95% of the corresponding confidence intervals should contain the mean weight of all such peanut butter cups.

We noted earlier that the sample is from a bag of 38 cups and the bag is labeled as containing a total weight of 340.2 g, so the mean weight of a cup should be 340.2 g/38 = 8.953 g. The confidence interval limits do contain the desired mean of 8.953 g, so the package appears to have been filled with candy in an acceptable way. (It would have been better to obtain a simple random sample of six Reese's miniature peanut butter cups from six different bags from different regions of the country, but the author didn't have time for that—he needed to rotate his car tires.)

 **YOUR TURN.** Do Exercise 13 "Archeology."

Bootstrap Resampling for Constructing Confidence Intervals Section 7-4 describes the method of *bootstrap resampling* for constructing a confidence interval estimate of a population parameter. The basic approach is to use technology such as Statdisk to "resample" the sample data many times (such as 1000), then use the sorted list of 1000 results to find the confidence interval. If we repeat Example 2 using the bootstrap resampling method, here is a typical result: 8.6551 g $< \mu <$ 8.9468 g. Because of the randomness used in the procedure, the resulting confidence interval may differ somewhat.

EXAMPLE 3   Critical Thinking: Sales of Vinyl Records

Listed below are sales (millions) of vinyl LP units in the United States. The sales numbers are listed in order by year beginning with 1993.

a. Use the listed sample data to construct a 95% confidence interval estimate of the population mean.

b. Is the confidence interval method described in this section a good tool for gaining insight into the nature of the sample data?

c. Apart from the confidence interval, is there some other tool that would be better for gaining insight into the nature of the sample data? What is most notable about the sales numbers?

| 0.3 | 0.6 | 0.8 | 1.1 | 1.1 | 1.4 | 1.4 | 1.5 | 1.2 | 1.3 | 1.4 | 1.2 | 0.9 | 0.9 |
| 1.0 | 1.9 | 2.5 | 2.8 | 3.9 | 4.6 | 6.1 | 9.2 | 11.9 | 13.1 | 14.3 | 16.8 |

SOLUTION

a. Using the methods of this chapter, the 95% confidence interval is found to be 2.02 million $< \mu <$ 5.92 million.

continued

b. A check of the requirements will show that the sample is small ($n \leq 30$) and the data do not appear to be from a population having a normal distribution, so the requirements are not satisfied. The confidence interval is not a good tool for gaining insight into the nature of the data.

c. Because the sales numbers are listed in order by year, a time series graph should be helpful in revealing the nature of the data. The accompanying time series graph clearly shows this notable feature: There is a distinct pattern of increasing sales over recent years. This shows that the population is changing over time, but the confidence interval does not reveal that trend. This also shows that instead of blindly applying statistical methods, we should always *think* about what we are doing!

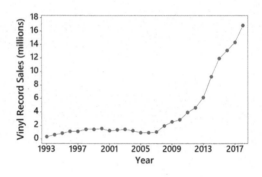

YOUR TURN. Do Exercise 19 "Mercury in Sushi."

Finding a Point Estimate and Margin of Error *E* from a Confidence Interval

Technology and journal articles often express a confidence interval in a format such as $(10.0, 30.0)$. The sample mean $\bar{x}$ is the value midway between those limits, and the margin of error E is one-half the difference between those limits (because the upper limit is $\bar{x} + E$ and the lower limit is $\bar{x} - E$, the distance separating them is $2E$).

$$\text{Point estimate of } \mu: \bar{x} = \frac{(\text{upper confidence limit}) + (\text{lower confidence limit})}{2}$$

$$\text{Margin of error: } E = \frac{(\text{upper confidence limit}) - (\text{lower confidence limit})}{2}$$

For example, the confidence interval $(10.0, 30.0)$ yields $\bar{x} = 20.0$ and $E = 10.0$.

Using Confidence Intervals to Describe, Explore, or Compare Data

In some cases, confidence intervals might be among the different tools used to describe, explore, or compare data sets, as in the following example.

EXAMPLE 4 Second-Hand Smoke

Figure 7-6 shows graphs of confidence interval estimates of the mean cotinine level in each of three samples: (1) people who smoke; (2) people who don't smoke but are exposed to tobacco smoke at home or work; (3) people who don't smoke and are not exposed to smoke. (These confidence intervals are based on *samples* of data taken from Data Set 15 "Passive and Active Smoke" in Appendix B.) Because cotinine is produced by the body when nicotine is absorbed, cotinine is a good indication of nicotine intake. Figure 7-6 helps us see the effects of second-hand smoke. In Figure 7-6, we see that the confidence interval for smokers does not overlap the other confidence intervals, so it appears that the mean cotinine level of smokers is different from that of the other two groups. The two nonsmoking groups have confidence intervals that do overlap, so it is possible that they have the same mean cotinine level. It is helpful to compare confidence intervals or their graphs, but such comparisons should not be used for making formal and final conclusions about equality of means. Chapters 9 and 12 introduce better methods for formal comparisons of means.

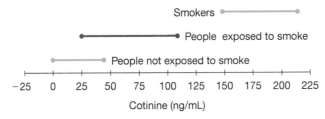

FIGURE 7-6   Comparing Confidence Intervals

▷ **YOUR TURN.** Do Exercise 30 "Second-Hand Smoke."

Go Figure

Gazillion: An extremely large number that doesn't have a specific value. It is now accepted as a valid word.

Estimating a Population Mean When σ Is Known

In the real world of professional statisticians and professional journals and reports, it is extremely rare that we want to estimate an unknown value of a population mean μ but we somehow know the value of the population standard deviation σ. If we somehow do know the value of σ, the confidence interval is constructed using the standard normal distribution instead of the Student t distribution, so the same procedure from "Estimating a Population Mean" provided earlier in this section can be used with this margin of error:

$$E = z_{\alpha/2} \cdot \frac{\sigma}{\sqrt{n}} \quad \text{(used with known } \sigma\text{)}$$

The requirements for using this margin of error are the same as those listed earlier for the t distribution: The sample should be a simple random sample and either $n > 30$ or the sample appears to be from a normally distributed population.

Choosing the Correct Distribution

When constructing a confidence interval estimate of the population mean μ, it is important to use the correct distribution. Table 7-1 summarizes the key points to consider.

TABLE 7-1 Choosing the Correct Distribution

Conditions	Method
σ not known and normally distributed population *or* σ not known and $n > 30$	Use Student t distribution with $$E = t_{\alpha/2}\frac{s}{\sqrt{n}}$$
σ known and normally distributed population *or* σ known and $n > 30$ (In reality, σ is rarely known.)	Use normal (z) distribution with $$E = z_{\alpha/2} \cdot \frac{\sigma}{\sqrt{n}}$$
Population is not normally distributed and $n \leq 30$.	Use the bootstrapping method (Section 7-4) or some other nonparametric method.

Determining Sample Size

If we want to collect a sample to be used for estimating a population mean μ, *how many* sample values do we need? When determining the sample size needed to estimate a population mean, we must have an estimated or known value of the population standard deviation σ, so that we can use Formula 7-4 shown in the Key Elements box on the next page.

Finding the Sample Size Required to Estimate a Population Mean

Objective

Determine the sample size n required to estimate the value of a population mean μ.

Notation

μ = population mean

σ = population standard deviation

$\bar{x}$ = sample mean

E = desired margin of error

$z_{\alpha/2}$ = z score separating an area of $\alpha/2$ in the right
tail of the standard normal distribution

Requirement

The sample must be a simple random sample.

Sample Size

The required sample size is found by using Formula 7-4.

$$\text{Formula 7-4} \qquad n = \left[\frac{z_{\alpha/2}\sigma}{E} \right]^2$$

Round-Off Rule

If the computed sample size n is not a whole number, round the value of n up to the next *larger* whole number.

Population Size Formula 7-4 does not depend on the size (N) of the population (except for cases in which a relatively large sample is selected without replacement from a finite population).

Rounding The sample size must be a whole number because it is the number of sample values that must be found, but Formula 7-4 usually gives a result that is not a whole number. The round-off rule is based on the principle that when rounding is necessary, the required sample size should be rounded *upward* so that it is at least adequately large instead of being slightly too small.

Dealing with Unknown σ When Finding Sample Size Formula 7-4 requires that we substitute a known value for the population standard deviation σ, but in reality, it is usually unknown. When determining a required sample size (not constructing a confidence interval), here are some ways that we can work around the problem of not knowing the value of σ:

1. **Range Rule of Thumb** Use the range rule of thumb (see Section 3-2) to estimate the standard deviation as follows: $\sigma \approx$ range$/4$, where the range is determined from sample data. (With a sample of 87 or more values randomly selected from a normally distributed population, range$/4$ will yield a value that is greater than or equal to σ at least 95% of the time.)

2. **Start and Improve** Start the sample collection process without knowing σ and, using the first several values, calculate the sample standard deviation s and use it in place of σ. The estimated value of σ can then be improved as more sample data are obtained, and the required sample size can be adjusted as you collect more sample data.

3. **Use Prior Results** Estimate the value of σ by using the results of some other earlier study. In addition, we can sometimes be creative in our use of other known results. For example, Wechsler IQ tests are designed so that the standard deviation is 15. Statistics students have IQ scores with a standard deviation less than 15, because they are a more homogeneous group than people randomly selected from the general population. We do not know the specific value of σ for statistics students, but we can be safe by using $\sigma = 15$. Using a value for σ that is larger than the true value will make the sample size larger than necessary, but using a value for σ that is too small would result in a sample size that is inadequate. *When determining the sample size n, any errors should always be conservative in the sense that they make the sample size too large instead of too small.*

Go Figure

Robocalls: In a recent year, there were 1517 robocalls made every second. There were 47,839,232,200 robocalls made in the year. 39.36% of the robocalls were scams.

EXAMPLE 5 **IQ Scores of Statistics Students**

Assume that we want to estimate the mean IQ score for the population of statistics students. How many statistics students must be randomly selected for IQ tests if we want 95% confidence that the sample mean is within 3 IQ points of the population mean?

SOLUTION

For a 95% confidence interval, we have $\alpha = 0.05$, so $z_{\alpha/2} = 1.96$. Because we want the sample mean to be within 3 IQ points of μ, the margin of error is $E = 3$. Also, we can assume that $\sigma = 15$ (see the discussion that immediately precedes this example). Using Formula 7-4, we get

$$n = \left[\frac{z_{\alpha/2}\sigma}{E}\right]^2 = \left[\frac{1.96 \cdot 15}{3}\right]^2 = 96.04 = 97 \quad \text{(rounded } up\text{)}$$

INTERPRETATION

Among the thousands of statistics students, we need to obtain a simple random sample of at least 97 of their IQ scores. With a simple random sample of only 97 statistics students, we will be 95% confident that the sample mean $\bar{x}$ is within 3 IQ points of the true population mean μ.

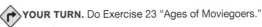 **YOUR TURN.** Do Exercise 23 "Ages of Moviegoers."

TECH CENTER

 Means: Confidence Intervals and Sample Size Determination
Access tech supplements, videos, and data sets at **www.TriolaStats.com**

Statdisk

Confidence Interval

1. Click **Analysis** in the top menu.
2. Select **Confidence Intervals** from the dropdown menu and select **Mean One Sample** from the submenu.
3. *Using Summary Statistics:* Select the **Use Summary Statistics** tab and enter the desired confidence level, sample size, sample mean, and sample standard deviation. *Using Sample Data:* Select the **Use Data** tab and select the desired data column.
4. Click **Evaluate**.

TIP: Statdisk will automatically choose between the normal and t distributions, depending on whether a value for the population standard deviation is entered.

Sample Size Determination

1. Click **Analysis** in the top menu.
2. Select **Sample Size Determination** from the dropdown menu and select **Estimate Mean** from the submenu.
3. Enter the confidence level, margin of error E, and population standard deviation. Also enter the known population size if you are sampling without replacement from a finite population.
4. Click **Evaluate**.

continued

TECH CENTER *continued*

 Means: Confidence Intervals and Sample Size Determination
Access tech supplements, videos, and data sets at **www.TriolaStats.com**

Minitab

Confidence Interval

1. Click **Stat** in the top menu.
2. Select **Basic Statistics** from the dropdown menu and select **1-Sample t** from the submenu.
3. *Using Summary Statistics:* Select **Summarized data** from the dropdown menu and enter the sample size, sample mean, and standard deviation.

   Using Sample Data: Select **One or more samples, each in a column** from the dropdown menu and select the desired data column(s).
4. Confirm *Perform hypothesis test* is not checked.
5. Click the **Options** button and enter the confidence level. For *Alternative Hypothesis* select ≠.
6. Click **OK** twice.

Sample Size Determination

1. Click **Stat** in the top menu.
2. Select **Power and Sample Size** from the dropdown menu and select **Sample Size for Estimation** from the submenu.
3. For *Parameter* select **Mean (Normal)** and enter the standard deviation.
4. Select **Estimate sample sizes** from the dropdown menu and enter the desired margin of error for confidence intervals.
5. Click the **Options** button to enter the confidence level and select a **two-sided** confidence interval.
6. Click **OK** twice.

StatCrunch

Confidence Interval

1. Click **Stat** in the top menu.
2. Select **T Stats** in the dropdown menu, then select **One Sample** from the submenu.
3. *Using Summary Statistics:* Select *With Summary* from the submenu and enter the sample mean, sample standard deviation, and sample size.

   Using Sample Data: Select *With Data* from the submenu and select the desired data column(s).
4. Select **Confidence interval for μ** and enter the desired confidence level.
5. Click **Compute!**

Sample Size Determination
Not available.

TI-83/84 Plus Calculator

Confidence Interval

1. Press **STAT**, then select **TESTS** in the top menu.
2. Select **TInterval** from the menu if σ is *not* known. (Choose **ZInterval** if σ is known.)
3. *Using Summary Statistics:* Select **stats**, press **ENTER**, and enter the values for sample mean $\bar{x}$, sample standard deviation Sx, and sample size n.

   Using Sample Data: Select **Data**, press **ENTER**, and enter the name of the list containing the sample data. *Freq* should be set to **1**.
4. Enter the desired confidence level, *C-Level*.
5. Select **Calculate** and press **ENTER**.

Sample Size Determination
Not available.

Excel

Confidence Interval

XLSTAT Add-In (Required)
Requires original sample data, does not work with summary data.

1. Click on the **XLSTAT** tab in the Ribbon and then click **Parametric tests.**
2. Select **One-sample t-test and z-test** from the dropdown menu.
3. Under *Data* enter the range of cells containing the sample data. For *Data format* select **One sample.** If the first row of data contains a label, also check the **Column labels** box.
4. Select **Student's t test.**
5. Click the **Options** tab.
6. Under *Alternative hypothesis* select ≠ **Theoretical mean.** Enter **0** for *Theoretical mean* and enter the desired significance level (enter **5** for 95% confidence interval).
7. Click **OK** to display the result under "confidence interval on the mean."

Sample Size Determination
Not available.

R

R command not available at time of publication.

R is rapidly evolving, and an updated list of statistical commands is available at TriolaStats.com.

7-2 Basic Skills and Concepts

Statistical Literacy and Critical Thinking

In Exercises 1–4, refer to the accompanying screen display that results from a simple random sample of times (minutes) between eruptions of the Old Faithful geyser. The confidence level of 95% was used.

1. Old Faithful Refer to the accompanying screen display.

a. Express the confidence interval in the format that uses the "less than" symbol. Round the confidence interval limits given that the original times are all rounded to one decimal place.

b. Identify the best point estimate of μ and the margin of error.

2. Degrees of Freedom

a. What is the number of degrees of freedom that should be used for finding the critical value $t_{\alpha/2}$?

b. Find the critical value $t_{\alpha/2}$ corresponding to a 95% confidence level.

c. Give a brief general description of the number of degrees of freedom.

3. Interpreting a Confidence Interval The results in the screen display are based on a 95% confidence level. Write a statement that correctly interprets the confidence interval.

4. Requirements

a. What are the requirements for using the methods of this section to construct a confidence interval estimate of a population mean?

b. What does it mean when we say that the confidence interval methods of this section are *robust* against departures from normality?

c. Does the sample used for the accompanying screen display satisfy the requirements for constructing a confidence interval estimate of the population mean μ? Explain.

In Exercises 5–8, (a) identify the critical value $t_{\alpha/2}$ used for finding the margin of error, (b) find the margin of error, (c) find the confidence interval estimate of μ, and (d) write a brief statement that interprets the confidence interval.

5. Birth Weights Here are summary statistics for randomly selected weights of newborn girls: $n = 36, \bar{x} = 3150.0$ g, $s = 695.5$ g (based on Data Set 6 "Births" in Appendix B). Use a confidence level of 95%.

6. Hershey Kisses Here are summary statistics for randomly selected weights of Hershey Kisses: $n = 32, \bar{x} = 4.5210$ g, $s = 0.1077$ g (based on a sample from Data Set 38 "Candies" in Appendix B). Use a confidence level of 99%.

7. Pepsi Weights Here are summary statistics for the weights of Pepsi in randomly selected cans: $n = 36, \bar{x} = 0.82410$ lb, $s = 0.00570$ lb (based on Data Set 37 "Cola Weights and Volumes" in Appendix B). Use a confidence level of 99%.

8. Airport Data Speeds Here are summary statistics for the phone data speeds of Verizon in different airports: $n = 38, \bar{x} = 18.86$ Mbps, $s = 15.66$ Mbps (based on a sample from Data Set 34 "Airport Data Speeds" in Appendix B). Use a confidence level of 95%.

Confidence Intervals.   *In Exercises 9–20, construct the confidence interval estimate of the mean.*

9. Mean Body Temperature Data Set 5 "Body Temperatures" in Appendix B includes a sample of 106 body temperatures having a mean of 98.20°F and a standard deviation of 0.62°F. Construct a 95% confidence interval estimate of the mean body temperature for the entire population. What does the result suggest about the common belief that 98.6°F is the mean body temperature?

TI-83/84 Plus

```
NORMAL FLOAT AUTO REAL RADIAN MP

        TInterval
(85.74,91.76)
x̄=88.75
Sx=8.897431411
n=36
```

10. Atkins Weight Loss Program In a test of weight loss programs, 40 adults used the Atkins weight loss program. After 12 months, their mean weight *loss* was found to be 2.1 lb, with a standard deviation of 4.8 lb. Construct a 90% confidence interval estimate of the mean weight loss for all such subjects. Does the Atkins program appear to be effective? Does it appear to be practical?

11. Insomnia Treatment A clinical trial was conducted to test the effectiveness of the drug zopiclone for treating insomnia in older subjects. Before treatment with zopiclone, 16 subjects had a mean wake time of 102.8 min. After treatment with zopiclone, the 16 subjects had a mean wake time of 98.9 min and a standard deviation of 42.3 min (based on data from "Cognitive Behavioral Therapy vs Zopiclone for Treatment of Chronic Primary Insomnia in Older Adults," by Sivertsen et al., *Journal of the American Medical Association*, Vol. 295, No. 24). Assume that the 16 sample values appear to be from a normally distributed population and construct a 98% confidence interval estimate of the mean wake time for a population with zopiclone treatments. What does the result suggest about the mean wake time of 102.8 min before the treatment? Does zopiclone appear to be effective?

12. Garlic for Reducing Cholesterol In a test of the effectiveness of garlic for lowering cholesterol, 49 subjects were treated with raw garlic. Cholesterol levels were measured before and after the treatment. The changes (before minus after) in their levels of LDL cholesterol (in mg/dL) had a mean of 0.4 and a standard deviation of 21.0 (based on data from "Effect of Raw Garlic vs Commercial Garlic Supplements on Plasma Lipid Concentrations in Adults with Moderate Hypercholesterolemia," by Gardner et al., *Archives of Internal Medicine*, Vol. 167). Construct a 98% confidence interval estimate of the mean net change in LDL cholesterol after the garlic treatment. What does the confidence interval suggest about the effectiveness of garlic in reducing LDL cholesterol?

13. Archeology Archeologists have studied sizes of Egyptian skulls in an attempt to determine whether breeding occurred between different cultures. Listed below are the widths (mm) of skulls from 150 A.D. (based on data from *Ancient Races of the Thebaid* by Thomson and Randall-Maciver). Construct a 99% confidence interval estimate of the mean skull width.

128   138   126   132   143   135   139   129

14. Minting Quarters Listed below are weights (grams) of quarters minted after 1964 (based on Data Set 40 "Coin Weights" in Appendix B). Construct a 95% confidence interval estimate of the mean weight of all quarters minted after 1964. Specifications require that the quarters have a weight of 5.670 g. What does the confidence interval suggest about that specification?

5.7790   5.5928   5.6486   5.6661   5.5491   5.7239   5.5591   5.5864   5.6872   5.6274

15. Los Angeles Commute Time Listed below are 15 Los Angeles commute times (based on a sample from Data Set 31 "Commute Times" in Appendix B). Construct a 99% confidence interval estimate of the population mean. Is the confidence interval a good estimate of the population mean?

5   25   45   5   5   40   25   8   50   5   5   30   15   25   50

16. Los Angeles Commute Time Repeat the preceding exercise using these 32 Los Angeles commute times:

5   25   45   5   5   40   25   8   50   5   5   30   15   25   50   18
25   45   75   60   40   25   8   50   10   10   30   15   25   50   20   30

17. Genes Samples of DNA are collected, and the four DNA bases of A, G, C, and T are coded as 1, 2, 3, and 4, respectively. The results are listed below. Construct a 95% confidence interval estimate of the mean. What is the practical use of the confidence interval?

2   2   1   4   3   3   3   3   4   1

18. Arsenic in Rice Listed below are amounts of arsenic (μg, or micrograms, per serving) in samples of brown rice from California (based on data from the Food and Drug Administration). Use a 90% confidence level. The Food and Drug Administration also measured amounts of arsenic in samples of brown rice from Arkansas. Can the confidence interval be used to describe arsenic levels in Arkansas?

5.4   5.6   8.4   7.3   4.5   7.5   1.5   5.5   9.1   8.7

19. Mercury in Sushi An FDA guideline is that the mercury in fish should be below 1 part per million (ppm). Listed below are the amounts of mercury (ppm) found in tuna sushi sampled at different stores in New York City. The study was sponsored by the *New York Times,* and the stores (in order) are D'Agostino, Eli's Manhattan, Fairway, Food Emporium, Gourmet Garage, Grace's Marketplace, and Whole Foods. Construct a 98% confidence interval estimate of the mean amount of mercury in the population. Does it appear that there is too much mercury in tuna sushi?

0.56   0.75   0.10   0.95   1.25   0.54   0.88

20. Caffeine in Soft Drinks Listed below are measured amounts of caffeine (mg per 12 oz of drink) obtained in one can from each of 20 brands (7UP, A&W Root Beer, Cherry Coke, . . . , TaB). Use a confidence level of 99%. Does the confidence interval give us good information about the population of all cans of the same 20 brands that are consumed? Does the sample appear to be from a normally distributed population? If not, how are the results affected?

0   0   34   34   34   45   41   51   55   36   47   41   0   0   53   54   38   0   41   47

Sample Size.   *In Exercises 21–29, find the sample size required to estimate the population mean.*

21. Mean IQ of Statistics Students The Wechsler IQ test is designed so that the mean is 100 and the standard deviation is 15 for the population of normal adults. Find the sample size necessary to estimate the mean IQ score of statistics students. We want to be 95% confident that our sample mean is within 3 IQ points of the true mean. The mean for this population is clearly greater than 100. The standard deviation for this population is less than 15 because it is a group with less variation than a group randomly selected from the general population; therefore, if we use $\sigma = 15$ we are being conservative by using a value that will make the sample size at least as large as necessary. Assume then that $\sigma = 15$ and determine the required sample size. Does the sample size appear to be practical?

22. Mean IQ of Data Scientists See the preceding exercise, in which we can assume that $\sigma = 15$ for the IQ scores. Data scientists are a group with IQ scores that vary less than the IQ scores of the general population. Find the sample size needed to estimate the mean IQ of data scientists, given that we want 98% confidence that the sample mean is within 2 IQ points of the population mean. Does the sample size appear to be practical?

23. Ages of Moviegoers Find the sample size needed to estimate the mean age of movie patrons, given that we want 98% confidence that the sample mean is within 1.5 years of the population mean. Assume that $\sigma = 19.6$ years, based on a previous report from the Motion Picture Association of America. Could the sample be obtained from one movie at one theater?

24. Lengths of Songs The manager for a radio station wants to estimate the mean length of all songs published after 1960. How many songs should be in the sample if we want 99% confidence that the sample mean is within 15 seconds of the population mean? Use the range rule of thumb to estimate σ, assuming that the shortest and longest songs are 1.5 minutes and 12 minutes long.

25. Mean Pulse Rate of Males Data Set 1 "Body Data" in Appendix B includes pulse rates of 153 randomly selected adult males, and those pulse rates vary from a low of 40 bpm to a high of 104 bpm. Find the minimum sample size required to estimate the mean pulse rate of adult males. Assume that we want 99% confidence that the sample mean is within 2 bpm of the population mean.

continued

a. Find the sample size using the range rule of thumb to estimate σ.

b. Assume that $\sigma = 11.3$ bpm, based on the value of $s = 11.3$ bpm for the sample of 153 male pulse rates.

c. Compare the results from parts (a) and (b). Which result is likely to be better?

26. Mean Pulse Rate of Females Data Set 1 "Body Data" in Appendix B includes pulse rates of 147 randomly selected adult females, and those pulse rates vary from a low of 36 bpm to a high of 104 bpm. Find the minimum sample size required to estimate the mean pulse rate of adult females. Assume that we want 99% confidence that the sample mean is within 2 bpm of the population mean.

a. Find the sample size using the range rule of thumb to estimate σ.

b. Assume that $\sigma = 12.5$ bpm, based on the value of $s = 12.5$ bpm for the sample of 147 female pulse rates.

c. Compare the results from parts (a) and (b). Which result is likely to be better?

27. Mean Grade-Point Average Assume that all grade-point averages are to be standardized on a scale between 0 and 4. How many grade-point averages must be obtained so that the sample mean is within 0.01 of the population mean? Assume that a 95% confidence level is desired. If we use the range rule of thumb, we can estimate σ to be range$/4 = (4 - 0)/4 = 1$. If conducting a telephone survey, does the sample size seem practical?

28. Mean Body Temperature Data Set 5 "Body Temperatures" in Appendix B includes 106 body temperatures of adults for Day 2 at 12 AM, and they vary from a low of 96.5°F to a high of 99.6°F. Find the minimum sample size required to estimate the mean body temperature of all adults. Assume that we want 98% confidence that the sample mean is within 0.1°F of the population mean.

a. Find the sample size using the range rule of thumb to estimate σ.

b. Assume that $\sigma = 0.62$°F, based on the value of $s = 0.62$°F for the sample of 106 body temperatures.

c. Compare the results from parts (a) and (b). Which result is likely to be better?

Appendix B Data Sets. *In Exercises 29–32, use the Appendix B data sets to construct the confidence interval estimates of the mean.*

 29. Pulse Rates Refer to Data Set 1 "Body Data" and construct a 95% confidence interval estimate of the mean pulse rate of adult females; then do the same for adult males. Compare the results.

 30. Second-Hand Smoke Refer to Data Set 15 "Passive and Active Smoke" and construct a 95% confidence interval estimates of the mean cotinine level in each of three samples: (1) people who smoke; (2) people who don't smoke but are exposed to tobacco smoke at home or work; (3) people who don't smoke and are not exposed to smoke. Measuring cotinine in people's blood is the most reliable way to determine exposure to nicotine. What do the confidence intervals suggest about the effects of smoking and second-hand smoke?

 31. New York Commute Time Refer to Data Set 31 "Commute Times" and use the 1000 New York commute times to construct a 95% confidence interval estimate of the population mean.

 32. Los Angeles Commute Time Repeat Exercise 15 using all of the 1000 Los Angeles commute times from Data Set 31 "Commute Times" to construct a 99% confidence interval estimate of μ.

7-2 Beyond the Basics

33. Ages of Prisoners The accompanying frequency distribution summarizes sample data consisting of ages of randomly selected inmates in federal prisons (based on data from the Federal Bureau of Prisons). Use the data to construct a 95% confidence interval estimate of the mean age of all inmates in federal prisons.

Age (years)	Number
16–25	13
26–35	61
36–45	66
46–55	36
56–65	14
Over 65	5

34. Finite Population Correction Factor If a simple random sample of size n is selected without replacement from a finite population of size N, and the sample size is more than 5% of the population size ($n > 0.05N$), better results can be obtained by using the finite population correction factor, which involves multiplying the margin of error E by $\sqrt{(N - n)/(N - 1)}$. Refer to the weights of the M&M candies in Data Set 38 "Candies" in Appendix B.

a. Use only the red M&Ms and treat that sample as a simple random sample from a very large population of M&Ms. Find the 95% confidence interval estimate of the mean weight of all M&Ms.

b. Use only the red M&Ms and treat that sample as a simple random sample selected from the population of the 345 M&Ms listed in the data set. Find the 95% confidence interval estimate of the mean weight of all 345 M&Ms. Compare the result to the actual mean of the population of all 345 M&Ms.

c. Compare the confidence intervals from parts (a) and (b).

7-3 Estimating a Population Standard Deviation or Variance

Key Concept This section presents methods for using a sample standard deviation s (or a sample variance s^2) to estimate the value of the corresponding population standard deviation σ (or population variance σ^2). Here are the main concepts included in this section:

- **Point Estimate:** The sample variance s^2 is the best *point estimate* (or single value estimate) of the population variance σ^2. The sample standard deviation s is commonly used as a point estimate of σ, even though it is a biased estimator, as described in Section 6-3.

- **Confidence Interval:** When constructing a *confidence interval* estimate of a population standard deviation (or population variance), we construct the confidence interval using the X^2 *distribution.* (The Greek letter X is pronounced "kigh.")

Chi-Square Distribution

Here are key points about the X^2 (chi-square or chi-squared) distribution:

- In a normally distributed population with variance σ^2, if we randomly select independent samples of size n and, for each sample, compute the sample variance s^2, the sample statistic $X^2 = (n - 1) s^2 / \sigma^2$ has a sampling distribution called the **chi-square distribution,** as shown in Formula 7-5.

FORMULA 7-5

$$X^2 = \frac{(n - 1)s^2}{\sigma^2}$$

- **Critical Values of** χ^2 We denote a right-tailed critical value by χ^2_R and we denote a left-tailed critical value by χ^2_L. Those critical values can be found by using technology or Table A-4, and they require that we first determine a value for the number of *degrees of freedom.*

- **Degrees of Freedom** For the methods of this section, the number of degrees of freedom is the sample size minus 1.

Degrees of freedom: df $= n - 1$

- The chi-square distribution is skewed to the right, unlike the normal and Student t distributions (see Figure 7-7).

- The values of chi-square can be zero or positive, but they cannot be negative, as shown in Figure 7-7.

- The chi-square distribution is different for each number of degrees of freedom, as illustrated in Figure 7-8. As the number of degrees of freedom increases, the chi-square distribution approaches a normal distribution.

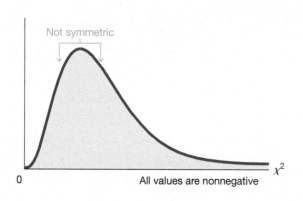

FIGURE 7-7   Chi-Square Distribution

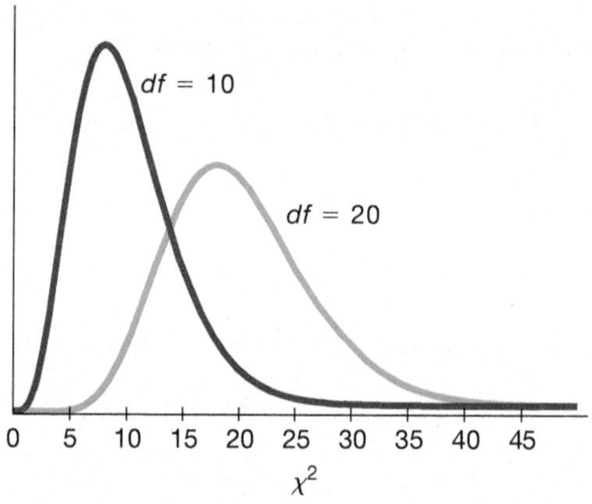

FIGURE 7-8   Chi-Square Distribution for df $= 10$ and df $= 20$

> **CAUTION** Because the chi-square distribution is not symmetric, a confidence interval estimate of σ^2 does not fit a format of $s^2 - E < \sigma^2 < s^2 + E$, so we must do separate calculations for the upper and lower confidence interval limits. Consequently, a confidence interval can be expressed in a format such as $7.6 < \sigma < 14.2$ or a format of $(7.6, 14.2)$, *but it cannot be expressed in a format of s $\pm$ E.*

If using Table A-4 for finding critical values, note the following design feature of that table:

> **In Table A-4, each critical value of χ^2 in the body of the table corresponds to an area given in the top row of the table, and each area in that top row is a *cumulative area to the right* of the critical value.**

> **CAUTION** Table A-2 for the standard normal distribution provides cumulative areas from the *left*, but Table A-4 for the chi-square distribution uses cumulative areas from the *right*.

EXAMPLE 1 Finding Critical Values of χ^2

A simple random sample of 22 pulse rates is obtained (as in Example 2, which follows). Construction of a confidence interval for the population standard deviation σ requires the left and right critical values of χ^2 corresponding to a confidence level of 95% and a sample size of $n = 22$. Find χ_L^2 (the critical value of χ^2 separating an area of 0.025 in the left tail), and find χ_R^2 (the critical value of χ^2 separating an area of 0.025 in the right tail).

SOLUTION

With a sample size of $n = 22$, the number of degrees of freedom is df $= n - 1 = 21$. See Figure 7-9.

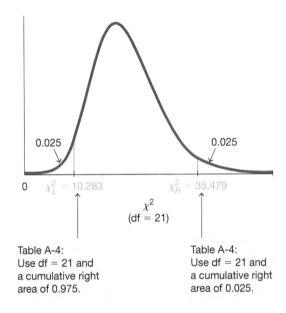

FIGURE 7-9   Finding Critical Values of χ^2

The critical value to the right ($\chi_R^2 = 35.479$) is obtained from Table A-4 in a straightforward manner by locating 21 in the degrees-of-freedom column at the left and 0.025 across the top row. The leftmost critical value of $\chi_L^2 = 10.283$ also corresponds to 21 in the degrees-of-freedom column, but we must locate 0.975 (or $1 - 0.025$) across the top row because the values in the top row are always *areas to the right* of the critical value. Refer to Figure 7-9 and see that the total area to the right of $\chi_L^2 = 10.283$ is 0.975.

YOUR TURN. Find the critical values in Exercise 5 "Nicotine in Menthol Cigarettes."

When obtaining critical values of χ^2 from Table A-4, if a number of degrees of freedom is not found in the table, you can be conservative by using the next lower number of degrees of freedom, or you can use the closest critical value in the table, or you can get an approximate result with interpolation. For numbers of degrees of freedom greater than 100, use the equation given in Exercise 23 "Finding Critical Values" on pages 354–355, or use a more extensive table, or use technology.

Although s^2 is the best point estimate of σ^2, there is no indication of how good it is, so we use a confidence interval that gives us a range of values associated with a confidence level.

KEY ELEMENTS

Confidence Interval for Estimating a Population Standard Deviation or Variance

Objective

Construct a confidence interval estimate of a population standard deviation or variance.

Notation

σ = population standard deviation

s = sample standard deviation

n = number of sample values

χ_L^2 = left-tailed critical value of χ^2

σ^2 = population variance

s^2 = sample variance

E = margin of error

χ_R^2 = right-tailed critical value of χ^2

Requirements

1. The sample is a simple random sample.

2. The population must have normally distributed values (even if the sample is large). The requirement of a normal distribution is much stricter here than in earlier sections, so large departures from normal distributions can result in large errors.

   [DETOUR] **(If this requirement is not satisfied, use the bootstrap method described in Section 7-4.)**

Confidence Interval Estimate of the Population Variance σ^2

$$\frac{(n-1)s^2}{\chi_R^2} < \sigma^2 < \frac{(n-1)s^2}{\chi_L^2}$$

Confidence Interval Estimate of the Population Standard Deviation σ

$$\sqrt{\frac{(n-1)s^2}{\chi_R^2}} < \sigma < \sqrt{\frac{(n-1)s^2}{\chi_L^2}}$$

Round-Off Rule

1. *Original Data:* When using the *original set of data* values, round the confidence interval limits to one more decimal place than is used for the original data.

2. *Summary Statistics:* When using the *summary statistics* (n, s), round the confidence interval limits to the same number of decimal places used for the sample standard deviation.

Procedure for Constructing a Confidence Interval for σ or σ^2

Confidence intervals can be easily constructed with technology or they can be constructed by using Table A-4 with the following procedure.

1. Verify that the two requirements are satisfied: The sample is a random sample from a normally distributed population.

2. Using $n - 1$ degrees of freedom, find the critical values χ_R^2 and χ_L^2 that correspond to the desired confidence level (as in Example 1).

3. To get a confidence interval estimate of σ^2, use the following:

$$\frac{(n-1)s^2}{\chi_R^2} < \sigma^2 < \frac{(n-1)s^2}{\chi_L^2}$$

4. To get a confidence interval estimate of σ, take the square root of each component of the above confidence interval.

5. Round the confidence interval limits using the round-off rule given in the preceding Key Elements box.

Using Confidence Intervals for Comparisons or Hypothesis Tests

Comparisons Confidence intervals can be used *informally* to compare the variation in different data sets, but *the overlapping of confidence intervals should not be used for making formal and final conclusions about equality of variances or standard deviations.*

EXAMPLE 2 **Confidence Interval Estimate of σ for Pulse Rates**

Listed below is a simple random sample of pulse rates (beats per minute or bpm) obtained from adult females (based on Data Set 1 "Body Data" in Appendix B). Construct a 95% confidence interval estimate of σ.

$$76 \quad 76 \quad 86 \quad 74 \quad 66 \quad 62 \quad 78 \quad 68 \quad 62 \quad 62 \quad 74$$
$$80 \quad 54 \quad 74 \quad 74 \quad 84 \quad 60 \quad 52 \quad 84 \quad 66 \quad 56 \quad 66$$

SOLUTION

REQUIREMENT CHECK

Step 1: Check requirements. (1) The sample is a simple random sample. (2) The accompanying normal quantile plot suggests that the sample is from a normally distributed population (because the points are close to a straight-line pattern). ✅

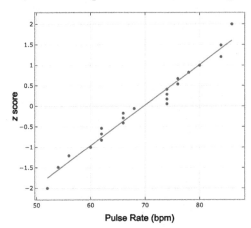

Step 2: Using Technology The confidence interval can be found using technology. The Statdisk display shows the confidence interval estimates of the population standard deviation σ and the population variance σ^2. Rounding the confidence interval limits to one decimal place, we get this 95% confidence interval estimate of σ: 7.6 bpm $< \sigma <$ 14.2 bpm.

Statdisk

```
Using data from column 1
95% Confidence Interval for the Standard Deviation:
7.63165 < SD < 14.17573

95% Confidence Interval for the Variance:
58.24214 < VAR < 200.95129
```

continued

Go Figure

1 minute and 41 seconds: The mean time it takes to talk to a human customer service representative when calling an 800 number at one of the top 100 Internet retailers.

Using Table A-4 If using Table A-4 , we first use the sample size of $n = 22$ to find degrees of freedom: df $= n - 1 = 21$. In Table A-4 , refer to the row corresponding to 21 degrees of freedom, and refer to the columns with areas of 0.975 and 0.025. (For a 95% confidence level, we divide $\alpha = 0.05$ equally between the two tails of the chi-square distribution, and we refer to the values of 0.975 and 0.025 across the top row of Table A-4 .) The critical values are $X_L^2 = 10.283$ and $X_R^2 = 35.479$ (as shown in Example 1).

Step 3: Using the critical values of $X_L^2 = 10.283$ and $X_R^2 = 35.479$, the sample standard deviation of $s = 9.91959$ and the sample size of $n = 22$, we construct the 95% confidence interval by evaluating the following:

$$\frac{(n-1)s^2}{X_R^2} < \sigma^2 < \frac{(n-1)s^2}{X_L^2}$$

$$\frac{(22-1)(9.91959)^2}{35.479} < \sigma^2 < \frac{(22-1)(0.91959)^2}{10.283}$$

Step 4: Evaluating the expression above results in $58.2419 < \sigma^2 < 200.9495$. Finding the square root of each part and rounding the result to one decimal place, we get this 95% confidence interval estimate of the population standard deviation σ: 7.6 bpm $< \sigma <$ 14.2 bpm.

INTERPRETATION

Based on this result, we have 95% confidence that the limits of 7.6 bpm and 14.2 bpm contain the true value of σ. The confidence interval can also be expressed as (7.6 bpm, 14.2 bpm), but *it cannot be expressed in a format of $s \pm E$.*

 YOUR TURN. Find the confidence interval in Exercise 5 "Nicotine in Menthol Cigarettes."

Bootstrap Resampling for Constructing Confidence Intervals Section 7-4 describes the method of *bootstrap resampling* for constructing a confidence interval estimate of a population parameter. A technology such as Statdisk can be used to "resample" the sample data many times (such as 1000), then use the sorted list of 1000 results to find the confidence interval. If we repeat Example 2 using the bootstrap resampling method, here is a typical result: 7.2 bpm $< \sigma <$ 11.5 bpm. Because of the randomness used in the procedure, the resulting confidence interval may differ somewhat.

Rationale for the Confidence Interval See Figure 7-9 on page 347 to make sense of this statement: If we select random samples of size n from a normally distributed population with variance σ^2, there is a probability of $1 - \alpha$ that the statistic $(n-1)s^2/\sigma^2$ will fall between the critical values of X_L^2 and X_R^2. It follows that there is a $1 - \alpha$ probability that both of the following are true:

$$\frac{(n-1)s^2}{\sigma^2} < X_R^2 \quad \text{and} \quad \frac{(n-1)s^2}{\sigma^2} > X_L^2$$

Multiply both of the preceding inequalities by σ^2, then divide each inequality by the appropriate critical value of X^2, so the two preceding inequalities can be expressed in these equivalent forms:

$$\frac{(n-1)s^2}{X_R^2} < \sigma^2 \quad \text{and} \quad \frac{(n-1)s^2}{X_L^2} > \sigma^2$$

The two preceding inequalities can be combined into one inequality to get the format of the confidence interval used in this section:

$$\frac{(n-1)s^2}{\chi_R^2} < \sigma^2 < \frac{(n-1)s^2}{\chi_L^2}$$

Determining Sample Size

The procedures for finding the sample size necessary to estimate σ are much more complex than the procedures given earlier for means and proportions. For normally distributed populations, Table 7-2 or the formula given in Exercise 24 "Finding Sample Size" on page 355 can be used.

Statdisk also provides sample sizes. With Statdisk, select **Analysis, Sample Size Determination,** and then **Estimate Standard Deviation.** Minitab, Excel, StatCrunch, and the TI-83/84 Plus calculator do not provide such sample sizes.

EXAMPLE 3 **Finding Sample Size for Estimating σ**

We want to estimate the standard deviation σ of all pulse rates of adult women. We want to be 99% confident that our estimate is within 5% of the true value of σ. How large should the sample be? Assume that the population is normally distributed.

SOLUTION

From Table 7-2, we can see that 99% confidence and an error of 5% for σ correspond to a sample of size 1336. We should obtain a simple random sample of 1336 pulse rates of adult women.

 YOUR TURN. Do Exercise 17 "IQ of Data Scientists."

TABLE 7-2 Finding Sample Size

σ	
To be 95% confident that s is within . . .	of the value of σ, the sample size n should be at least
1%	19,205
5%	768
10%	192
20%	48
30%	21
40%	12
50%	8
To be 99% confident that s is within . . .	of the value of σ, the sample size n should be at least
1%	33,218
5%	1,336
10%	336
20%	85
30%	38
40%	22
50%	14

TECH CENTER

 ## Confidence Interval Estimate for Standard Deviation or Variance
Access tech supplements, videos, and data sets at **www.TriolaStats.com**

Statdisk

Confidence Interval

1. Verify the distribution is normal using **Data—Normality Assessment.**
2. Click **Analysis** in the top menu.
3. Select **Confidence Intervals** from the dropdown menu and select **Standard Deviation One Sample** from the submenu.
4. *Using Summary Statistics:* Select the **Use Summary Statistics** tab and enter the desired confidence level, sample size, and sample standard deviation.

   Using Sample Data: Select the **Use Data** tab, enter the desired confidence level, and select the desired data column.
5. Click **Evaluate.**

Minitab

Confidence Interval

1. Click **Stat** in the top menu.
2. Select **Basic Statistics** from the dropdown menu and select **1 Variance** from the submenu.
3. *Using Summary Statistics:* Select **Sample standard deviation** or **Sample Variance** from the dropdown menu and enter sample size and sample standard deviation or sample variance.

   Using Sample Data: Select **One or more samples, each in a column** from the dropdown menu and select the desired data column(s).
4. Confirm *Perform hypothesis test* is not checked.
5. Click the **Options** button, enter the desired confidence level, and for *Alternative Hypothesis* select $\neq$.
6. Click **OK** twice. The results include a confidence interval for the standard deviation and a confidence interval for the variance.

Excel

Neither Excel nor XLSTAT has a function for generating a confidence interval estimate of standard deviation or variance.

continued

TECH CENTER *continued*

 Confidence Interval Estimate for Standard Deviation or Variance

Access tech supplements, videos, and data sets at **www.TriolaStats.com**

StatCrunch	TI-83/84 Plus Calculator	R
Confidence Interval 1. Click **Stat** in the top menu. 2. Select **Variance Stats** in the dropdown menu, then select **One Sample** from the submenu. 3. *Using Summary Statistics:* Select *With Summary* from the submenu and enter the sample variance and sample size. *Using Sample Data:* Select *With Data* from the submenu and select the desired data column(s). 4. Select **Confidence interval for σ^2** and enter the desired confidence level. 5. Click **Compute!**	1. Download and install the Michael Lloyd programs *S2INT* and *ZZINEWT* (available at www.TriolaStats.com) on your TI-83/84 Plus Calculator. 2. Press **PRGM**, select **S2INT** from the menu, and press **ENTER** twice. 3. Enter the sample variance Sx^2, sample size *n*, and confidence level *C-Level*. Press **ENTER** after each entry. 4. Wait for the σx^2 confidence interval to be displayed. (Be patient; it may take a while!). 5. Press **ENTER** to view the σx confidence interval.	**R command not available at time of publication.** *R is rapidly evolving, and an updated list of statistical commands is available at TriolaStats.com.*

7-3   Basic Skills and Concepts

Statistical Literacy and Critical Thinking

1. Margin of Error

a. Why does "margin of error" have no relevance for confidence interval estimates of σ or σ^2?

b. What is wrong with expressing the confidence interval of 7.6 bpm $< \sigma <$ 14.2 bpm (from Example 2) as 10.9 bpm $\pm$ 3.3 bpm?

2. Requirements

a. What are the requirements for constructing a confidence interval estimate of σ or σ^2?

b. How do the requirements from part (a) differ from the requirements for constructing a confidence interval estimate of μ?

c. In the California Daily 4 lottery, 4 numbers from 0 to 9 are randomly selected with replacement. Can the methods of this section be used to estimate σ for the numbers that are selected in this lottery? Why or why not?

3. Red Blood Cell Count Here is a 95% confidence interval estimate of σ obtained by using the red blood cell counts of adult females listed in Data Set 1 "Body Data" in Appendix B: 0.360 (million cells/μL) $< \sigma <$ 0.454 (million cells/μL). Identify the corresponding confidence interval estimate of σ^2 and include the appropriate units.

4. Critical Values A sample consists of 20 weights of McDonald's French fries. Find the critical values χ_L^2 and χ_R^2 used to construct a 95% confidence interval estimate of σ.

Finding Critical Values and Confidence Intervals. *In Exercises 5–8, use the given information to find the number of degrees of freedom, the critical values χ_L^2 and χ_R^2, and the confidence interval estimate of σ. The samples are from Appendix B and it is reasonable to assume that a simple random sample has been selected from a population with a normal distribution.*

5. Nicotine in Menthol Cigarettes 95% confidence; $n = 25$, $s = 0.24$ mg.

6. Weights of Dollar Coins 95% confidence; $n = 20$, $s = 0.04111$ g.

7. White Blood Counts of Women 99% confidence; $n = 147, s = 1.96$ (1000 cells/μL).

8. Heights of Men 99% confidence; $n = 153$, $s = 7.10$ cm.

Finding Confidence Intervals. *In Exercises 9–16, assume that each sample is a simple random sample obtained from a population with a normal distribution.*

9. Body Temperature Data Set 5 "Body Temperatures" in Appendix B includes a sample of 106 body temperatures having a mean of 98.20°F and a standard deviation of 0.62°F (for day 2 at 12 AM). Construct a 95% confidence interval estimate of the standard deviation of the body temperatures for the entire population.

10. Atkins Weight Loss Program In a test of weight loss programs, 40 adults used the Atkins weight loss program. After 12 months, their mean weight *loss* was found to be 2.1 lb, with a standard deviation of 4.8 lb. Construct a 90% confidence interval estimate of the standard deviation of the weight loss for all such subjects. Does the confidence interval give us information about the effectiveness of the diet?

11. Insomnia Treatment A clinical trial was conducted to test the effectiveness of the drug zopiclone for treating insomnia in older subjects. After treatment with zopiclone, 16 subjects had a mean wake time of 98.9 min and a standard deviation of 42.3 min (based on data from "Cognitive Behavioral Therapy vs Zopiclone for Treatment of Chronic Primary Insomnia in Older Adults," by Sivertsen et al., *Journal of the American Medical Association*, Vol. 295, No. 24). Assume that the 16 sample values appear to be from a normally distributed population and construct a 98% confidence interval estimate of the standard deviation of the wake times for a population with zopiclone treatments. Does the result indicate whether the treatment is effective?

12. Garlic for Reducing Cholesterol In a test of the effectiveness of garlic for lowering cholesterol, 49 subjects were treated with raw garlic. Cholesterol levels were measured before and after the treatment. The changes (before minus after) in their levels of LDL cholesterol (in mg/dL) had a mean of 0.4 and a standard deviation of 21.0 (based on data from "Effect of Raw Garlic vs Commercial Garlic Supplements on Plasma Lipid Concentrations in Adults with Moderate Hypercholesterolemia," by Gardner et al., *Archives of Internal Medicine*, Vol. 167). Construct a 98% confidence interval estimate of the standard deviation of the changes in LDL cholesterol after the garlic treatment. Does the result indicate whether the treatment is effective?

13. Heights of Female Soccer Players Listed below are the heights (in.) of players on the U.S. Women's National Soccer Team (at the time of this writing). Use those heights as a sample of the heights of all professional women soccer players to construct a 95% confidence interval estimate of σ. If we assume that the standard deviation of heights of the population of U.S. women is 2.9 in. (based on the data in Data Set 1 "Body Data"), what does the confidence interval suggest about this claim: The heights of women who are professional soccer players vary less than women in the general population?

67	67	70	61	67	69	69	66	69	66	64	68
68	71	72	67	69	65	66	64	67	67	67	

14. Mint Specs Listed below are weights (grams) from a simple random sample of pennies produced after 1983 (from Data Set 40 "Coin Weights" in Appendix B). Construct a 95% confidence interval estimate of σ for the population of such pennies. What does the confidence interval suggest about the U.S. Mint specifications that now require a standard deviation of 0.0230 g for weights of pennies?

2.5024	2.5298	2.4998	2.4823	2.5163	2.5222	2.4900	2.4907	2.5017

15. Professor Evaluation Scores Listed below are student evaluation scores of professors from Data Set 28 "Course Evaluations" in Appendix B. Construct a 95% confidence interval estimate of σ for each of the two data sets. Does there appear to be a difference in variation?

Female	4.4	3.4	4.8	2.9	4.4	4.9	3.5	3.7	3.4	4.8
Males	4.0	3.6	4.1	4.1	3.5	4.6	4.0	4.3	4.5	4.3

16. Comparing Waiting Lines

a. The values listed below are waiting times (in minutes) of customers at the Jefferson Valley Bank, where customers enter a single waiting line that feeds three teller windows. Construct a 95% confidence interval for the population standard deviation σ.

$$6.5 \quad 6.6 \quad 6.7 \quad 6.8 \quad 7.1 \quad 7.3 \quad 7.4 \quad 7.7 \quad 7.7 \quad 7.7$$

b. The values listed below are waiting times (in minutes) of customers at the Bank of Providence, where customers may enter any one of three different lines that have formed at three teller windows. Construct a 95% confidence interval for the population standard deviation σ.

$$4.2 \quad 5.4 \quad 5.8 \quad 6.2 \quad 6.7 \quad 7.7 \quad 7.7 \quad 8.5 \quad 9.3 \quad 10.0$$

c. Interpret the results found in parts (a) and (b). Do the confidence intervals suggest a difference in the variation among waiting times? Which arrangement seems better: the single-line system or the multiple-line system?

Determining Sample Size. *In Exercises 17–20, assume that each sample is a simple random sample obtained from a normally distributed population. Use Table 7-2 on page 351 to find the indicated sample size.*

17. IQ of Data Scientists
You want to estimate σ for the population of IQ scores of data scientists. Find the minimum sample size needed to be 99% confident that the sample standard deviation s is within 20% of σ. Is this sample size practical?

18. Blood Pressure
You want to estimate σ for the population of diastolic blood pressures of air traffic controllers in the United States. Find the minimum sample size needed to be 95% confident that the sample standard deviation s is within 1% of σ. Is this sample size practical?

19. Aspirin Tablets
You want to estimate σ for the population of weights of the aspirin in Bayer tablets. Find the minimum sample size needed to be 95% confident that the sample standard deviation s is within 10% of σ. Is this sample size practical?

20. Pulse Rates
You want to estimate σ for the population of pulse rates for the population of marathon runners. Find the minimum sample size needed to be 99% confident that the sample standard deviation s is within 50% of σ. Is this sample size practical?

Large Data Sets from Appendix B. *In Exercises 21 and 22, use the data set in Appendix B. Assume that each sample is a simple random sample obtained from a population with a normal distribution.*

 21. Comparing Waiting Lines Refer to Data Set 30 "Queues" in Appendix B. Construct separate 95% confidence interval estimates of σ using the two-line wait times and the single-line wait times. Do the results support the expectation that the single line has less variation? Do the wait times from both line configurations satisfy the requirements for confidence interval estimates of σ?

 22. Birth Weights Refer to Data Set 6 "Births" in Appendix B.

a. Use the 205 birth weights of girls to construct a 95% confidence interval estimate of the standard deviation of the population from which the sample was obtained.

b. Repeat part (a) using the 195 birth weights of boys.

c. Compare the results from part (a) and part (b).

7-3   Beyond the Basics

23. Finding Critical Values
In constructing confidence intervals for σ or σ^2, Table A-4 can be used to find the critical values χ_L^2 and χ_R^2 only for select values of n up to 101, so the number of degrees of freedom is 100 or smaller. For larger numbers of degrees of freedom, we can approximate χ_L^2 and χ_R^2 by using

$$\chi^2 = \frac{1}{2}\left[\pm z_{\alpha/2} + \sqrt{2k-1}\right]^2$$

where k is the number of degrees of freedom and $z_{\alpha/2}$ is the critical z score described in Section 7-1. Use this approximation to find the critical values χ_L^2 and χ_R^2 for Exercise 9 "Body Temperature," where the sample size is 106 and the confidence level is 95%. How do the results compare to the actual critical values of $\chi_L^2 = 78.536$ and $\chi_R^2 = 135.247$?

24. Finding Sample Size Instead of using Table 7-2 for determining the sample size required to estimate a population standard deviation σ, the following formula can also be used

$$n = \frac{1}{2}\left(\frac{z_{\alpha/2}}{d}\right)^2$$

where $z_{\alpha/2}$ corresponds to the confidence level and d is the decimal form of the percentage error. For example, to be 95% confident that s is within 15% of the value of σ, use $z_{\alpha/2} = 1.96$ and $d = 0.15$ to get a sample size of $n = 86$. Find the sample size required to estimate the standard deviation of IQ scores of data scientists, assuming that we want 98% confidence that s is within 5% of σ.

 # 7-4 Bootstrapping: Using Technology for Estimates

Key Concept The preceding sections presented methods for estimating population proportions, means, and standard deviations (or variances). All of those methods have certain requirements that limit the situations in which they can be used. When some of the requirements are not satisfied, we can often use the bootstrap method to estimate a parameter with a confidence interval. The bootstrap method typically requires the use of software such as Statdisk.

The bootstrap resampling method described in this section has these requirements:

1. **The sample must be collected in an appropriate way, such as a simple random sample.** (If the sample is not collected in an appropriate way, there's a good chance that *nothing* can be done to get a usable confidence interval estimate of a parameter.)

2. **When generating statistics using bootstrap resampling, the distribution of those statistics should be approximately symmetric.**

The preceding methods of this chapter also have these requirements:

- **CI for Proportion (Section 7-1):** There are at least 5 successes and at least 5 failures, or $np \geq 5$ and $nq \geq 5$.

- **CI for Mean (Section 7-2):** The population is normally distributed or $n > 30$.

- **CI for σ or σ^2 (Section 7-3):** The population must have normally distributed values, even if the sample is large.

When the above requirements are not satisfied, we should not use the methods presented in the preceding sections of this chapter, but we can use the bootstrap method instead. The bootstrap method does not require large samples. This method does not require the sample to be collected from a normal or any other particular distribution, and so the bootstrap method is called a **nonparametric** or **distribution-free method**; other nonparametric methods are included in Chapter 13.

DEFINITION

Given a simple random sample of size *n*, a **bootstrap sample** is another random sample of *n* values obtained *with replacement* from the original sample.

Without replacement, every sample would be identical to the original sample, so the proportions or means or standard deviations or variances would all be the same, and there would be no confidence "interval."

> **CAUTION** Note that a bootstrap sample involves sampling *with replacement*, so that when a sample value is selected, it is replaced before the next selection is made.

Advantage of Bootstrapping Bootstrap resampling gives us a reasonable estimate of how the point estimate of the parameter varies. With enough bootstrap samples, the resulting distribution of the sample statistic tends to be a reasonable approximation of the true distribution.

Disadvantage of Bootstrapping It should be noted that with this bootstrap method, many samples are generated, and those samples are then used to generate the statistic being used to estimate a parameter. The sampling distribution of those statistics is centered around the sample statistic of the original sample data, not the population parameter being estimated. If we have a sample with a point estimate that is a very poor estimate of the population parameter, the bootstrap method will not make that point estimate any better.

Limitation of Percentile Bootstrapping Confidence Interval The method of bootstrapping presented in this section involves resampling a data set then constructing a confidence interval by finding percentile values of the statistic being analyzed. The result is a confidence interval estimate of a parameter. This approach of constructing a confidence interval using percentile values is not ideal. There are more advanced methods, such as the bias-corrected BC bootstrap confidence interval, that yield better confidence intervals, but they are beyond the scope of this text.

EXAMPLE 1 Bootstrap Sample of Incomes

When the author collected annual incomes of current statistics students, he obtained these results (in thousands of dollars): 0, 2, 3, 7.

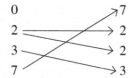

Original Sample   Bootstrap Sample

The sample of { 7, 2, 2, 3 } is one bootstrap sample obtained from the original sample. Other bootstrap samples may be different.

Incomes tend to have distributions that are skewed instead of being normal, so we should not use the methods of Section 7-2 with a small sample of incomes. This is a situation in which the bootstrap method comes to the rescue.

Why Is It Called "Bootstrap"? The term "bootstrap" is used because the data "pull themselves up by their own bootstraps" to generate new data sets. In days of yore, "pulling oneself up by one's bootstraps" meant that an impossible task was somehow accomplished, and the bootstrap method described in this section might seem impossible, but it works!

How Many? In the interest of providing manageable examples that don't occupy multiple pages each, the examples in this section involve very small data sets and no more than 20 bootstrap samples, but we should use at least 1000 bootstrap samples when we use bootstrap methods in serious applications. Professional statisticians commonly use 10,000 or more bootstrap samples.

Bootstrap Procedure for a Confidence Interval Estimate of a Parameter

1. Given a simple random sample of size n, obtain many (such as 1000 or more) bootstrap samples of the same size n.

2. For the parameter to be estimated, find the corresponding statistic for each of the bootstrap samples. (Example: For a confidence estimate of μ, find the *sample mean* $\bar{x}$ from each bootstrap sample.)

3. Sort the list of sample statistics from low to high.

4. Using the sorted list of the statistics, create the confidence interval by finding corresponding percentile values. Procedures for finding percentiles are given in Section 3-3. (Example: Using a list of sorted sample means, the 90% confidence interval limits are P_5 and P_{95}. The 90% confidence interval estimate of μ is $P_5 < \mu < P_{95}$, where P_5 and P_{95} are replaced with the actual percentile values calculated from the sample data.)

Limitations of the Following Examples For the purpose of illustrating the bootstrap procedure, Examples 2, 3, and 4 all involve very small samples with only 20 bootstrap samples. Consequently, the resulting confidence intervals include almost the entire range of sample values, and those confidence intervals are not very useful. Larger samples with 1000 or more bootstrap samples will provide much better results than those from Examples 2, 3, and 4.

Proportions

When working with proportions, it is very helpful to represent the data from the two categories by using 0's and 1's, as in the following example.

EXAMPLE 2 **Eye Color Survey: Bootstrap CI for Proportion**

In a survey, four randomly selected subjects were asked if they have brown eyes, and here are the results: 0, 0, 1, 0 (where 0 = no and 1 = yes). Use the bootstrap resampling procedure to construct a 90% confidence interval estimate of the population proportion p, the proportion of people with brown eyes in the population.

SOLUTION

REQUIREMENT CHECK The sample is a simple random sample. (There is no requirement of at least 5 successes and at least 5 failures or $np \geq 5$ and $nq \geq 5$. There is no requirement that the sample must be from a normally distributed population.) ☑
The four solution steps are on the next page:

continued

Step 1: In Table 7-3, we created 20 bootstrap samples from the original sample of 0, 0, 1, 0.

Step 2: Because we want a confidence interval estimate of the population proportion p, we want the sample proportion $\hat{p}$ for each of the 20 bootstrap samples, and those sample proportions are shown in the column to the right of the bootstrap samples.

Step 3: The column of data shown farthest to the right is a list of the 20 sample proportions arranged in order ("sorted") from lowest to highest.

Step 4: Because we want a confidence level of 90%, we want to find the percentiles P_5 and P_{95}. Recall that P_5 separates the lowest 5% of values, and P_{95} separates the top 5% of values. Using the methods from Section 3-3 for finding percentiles, we use the *sorted* list of bootstrap sample proportions to find that $P_5 = 0.00$ and $P_{95} = 0.75$. The 90% confidence interval estimate of the population proportion is $0.00 < p < 0.75$.

INTERPRETATION

The confidence interval of $0.00 < p < 0.75$ is quite wide. After all, every confidence interval for every proportion must fall between 0 and 1, so the 90% confidence interval of $0.00 < p < 0.75$ doesn't seem to be helpful, but it is based on only four sample values.

TABLE 7-3 Bootstrap Samples for p

Bootstrap Sample				$\hat{p}$	Sorted $\hat{p}$	
1	0	0	1	0.50	0.00	$\rightarrow P_5 = 0.00$
1	0	1	0	0.50	0.00	
0	1	1	1	0.75	0.00	
0	0	0	0	0.00	0.00	
0	1	0	0	0.25	0.25	
1	0	0	0	0.25	0.25	
0	1	0	1	0.50	0.25	
1	0	0	0	0.25	0.25	
0	0	0	0	0.00	0.25	
0	0	1	1	0.50	0.25	90% Confidence Interval:
0	0	0	1	0.25	0.25	$0.00 < p < 0.75$
0	0	1	0	0.25	0.25	
1	1	1	0	0.75	0.50	
0	0	0	0	0.00	0.50	
0	0	0	0	0.00	0.50	
0	1	1	0	0.50	0.50	
0	0	1	0	0.25	0.50	
1	0	0	0	0.25	0.75	
1	1	1	0	0.75	0.75	
0	0	0	1	0.25	0.75	$\rightarrow P_{95} = 0.75$

YOUR TURN. Do Exercise 5 "Online Buying."

HINT: Example 2 uses only 20 bootstrap samples, but effective use of the bootstrap method typically requires the use of software to generate 1000 or more bootstrap samples.

Means

In Section 7-2 we noted that when constructing a confidence interval estimate of a population mean, there is a requirement that the sample is from a normally distributed population or the sample size is greater than 30. The bootstrap method can be used when this requirement is not satisfied.

EXAMPLE 3 Incomes: Bootstrap CI for Mean

When the author collected a simple random sample of annual incomes of his statistics students, he obtained these results (in thousands of dollars): 0, 2, 3, 7. Use the bootstrap resampling procedure to construct a 90% confidence interval estimate of the mean annual income of the population of all of the author's statistics students.

SOLUTION

REQUIREMENT CHECK The sample is a simple random sample and there is no requirement that the sample must be from a normally distributed population. Because distributions of incomes are typically skewed instead of normal, we should not use the methods of Section 7-2 for finding the confidence interval, but the bootstrap method can be used. ☑

Step 1: In Table 7-4, we created 20 bootstrap samples (with replacement!) from the original sample of 0, 2, 3, 7. (Here we use only 20 bootstrap samples so we have a manageable example that doesn't occupy many pages of text, but we usually want at least 1000 bootstrap samples.)

Step 2: Because we want a confidence interval estimate of the population mean μ, we want the sample mean $\bar{x}$ for each of the 20 bootstrap samples, and those sample means are shown in the column to the right of the bootstrap samples.

Step 3: The column of data shown farthest to the right is a list of the 20 sample means arranged in order ("sorted") from lowest to highest.

Step 4: Because we want a confidence level of 90%, we want to find the percentiles P_5 and P_{95}. Recall that P_5 separates the lowest 5% of values, and P_{95} separates the top 5% of values. Using the methods from Section 3-3 for finding percentiles, we use the *sorted* list of bootstrap sample means to find that $P_5 = 1.75$ and $P_{95} = 4.875$. The 90% confidence interval estimate of the population mean is $1.75 < \mu < 4.875$, where the values are in thousands of dollars.

TABLE 7-4 Bootstrap Samples for μ

Bootstrap Sample				$\bar{x}$	Sorted $\bar{x}$
3	3	0	2	2.00	1.75
0	3	2	2	1.75	1.75
7	0	2	7	4.00	1.75
3	2	7	3	3.75	2.00
0	0	7	2	2.25	2.00
7	0	0	3	2.50	2.25
3	0	3	2	2.00	2.50
3	7	3	7	5.00	2.50
0	3	2	2	1.75	2.50
0	3	7	0	2.50	2.75
0	7	2	2	2.75	3.00
7	2	2	3	3.50	3.25
7	2	3	7	4.75	3.25
2	7	2	7	4.50	3.50
0	7	2	3	3.00	3.75
7	3	7	2	4.75	4.00
3	7	0	3	3.25	4.50
0	0	3	7	2.50	4.75
3	3	7	0	3.25	4.75
2	0	2	3	1.75	5.00

$\longrightarrow P_5 = 1.75$

90% Confidence Interval:
$1.75 < \mu < 4.875$

$\longrightarrow P_{95} = 4.875$

YOUR TURN. Do Exercise 7 "Freshman 15."

Standard Deviations

In Section 7-3 we noted that when constructing confidence interval estimates of population standard deviations or variances, there is a requirement that the sample must be from a population with normally distributed values. Even if the sample is large, this normality requirement is much stricter than the normality requirement used for estimating population means. Consequently, the bootstrap method becomes more important for confidence interval estimates of σ or σ^2.

EXAMPLE 4 Incomes: Bootstrap CI for Standard Deviation

Use these same incomes (thousands of dollars) from Example 3: 0, 2, 3, 7. Use the bootstrap resampling procedure to construct a 90% confidence interval estimate of the population standard deviation σ, the standard deviation of the annual incomes of the population of the author's statistics students.

SOLUTION

REQUIREMENT CHECK The same requirement check used in Example 3 applies here. ✓

The same basic procedure used in Example 3 is used here. Example 3 already includes 20 bootstrap samples, so here we find the *standard deviation* of each bootstrap sample, and then we sort them to get this sorted list of sample standard deviations:

1.26   1.26   1.26   1.41   1.41   2.22   2.31   2.38   2.63   2.63

2.87   2.87   2.89   2.94   2.99   3.30   3.32   3.32   3.32   3.56

The 90% confidence interval limits are found from this sorted list of standard deviations by finding P_5 and P_{95}. Using the methods from Section 3-3, we get $P_5 = 1.26$ and $P_{95} = 3.44$. The 90% confidence interval estimate of the population standard deviation σ is $1.26 < \sigma < 3.44$, where the values are in thousands of dollars.

YOUR TURN. Do part (b) of Exercise 8 "Cell Phone Radiation."

Again, know that for practical reasons, the examples of this section involved very small data sets and no more than 20 bootstrap samples, but use at least 1000 bootstrap samples. The use of 10,000 or more bootstrap samples is common.

TECH CENTER

Bootstrap Resampling
Access tech supplements, videos, and data sets at **www.TriolaStats.com**

Statdisk
1. Click **Resampling** in the top menu.
2. Select the desired type of randomization from the dropdown menu. Options include:
- **Bootstrap One Proportion**
- **Bootstrap Two Proportions**
- **Bootstrap One Mean**
- **Bootstrap Two Means**
- **Bootstrap Matched Pairs**
3. Enter the required inputs which include the confidence level and desired number of resamplings.
4. Click **Evaluate**.
5. The sorted results are listed in the Sample Editor.

Minitab
1. Click **Calc** in the top menu.
2. Select **Resampling** from the dropdown menu and select **Bootstrapping for 1-Sample Function** from the submenu.
3. For *Statistic*, select the desired parameter from the dropdown menu.
4. In the *Sample* box, enter the column containing the sample data.
5. In the *Number of Resamples* box, enter the desired number of resamples.
6. Click the **Options** button and enter the confidence level.
7. Click **OK** twice. The results will include the confidence interval.

StatCrunch
1. Click **Applets** in the top menu.
2. Select **Resampling – Bootstrap a statistic** in the dropdown menu.
3. *Using Summary Statistics:* Select **Proportion from summary** and enter the number of successes and number of observations.
Using Sample Data: Select **From data table**, select the column containing the sample data and select the desired statistic (e.g. *Mean*).
4. Click **Compute!** and the applet window will appear.
5. Click **1000 times** for 1000 resamplings. The confidence interval limits will be displayed.

TI-83/84 Plus Calculator
Not available.

Excel
XLSTAT Add-In (Required)
1. Click on the **XLSTAT** tab in the Ribbon and then click **Describing data.**
2. Select **Resampled statistics** from the dropdown menu.
3. Under *Quantitative Data* enter the range of cells containing the sample values. If the first row contains a label, check the **Sample labels** box.
4. Under *Method* select **Bootstrap.**
5. Enter the desired number of samples.
6. Click the **Outputs** tab and enter the confidence interval (%) of **95**; confirm **Standard bootstrap interval** is selected. Also select **Mean** and **Standard deviation** ($n-1$).
7. Click **OK.**

R
R command not available at time of publication.
R is rapidly evolving, and an updated list of statistical commands is available at TriolaStats.com.

7-4   Basic Skills and Concepts

Statistical Literacy and Critical Thinking

1. Bootstrap Requirements Listed below are sample times (seconds) that animated children's movies showed the use of tobacco (based on Data Set 20 "Alcohol and Tobacco in Movies" in Appendix B). If we plan to use the bootstrap method to construct a 95% confidence interval estimate of the population mean μ, what two requirements must be satisfied?

0   0   299   37   0   0   0   24   158   0   162   24   74   37   0

2. Bootstrap Sample For the sample data given in Exercise 1, what is a bootstrap sample?

3. How Many? The examples in this section all involved no more than 20 bootstrap samples. How many should be used in real applications?

4. Mean Assume that we want to use the sample data given in Exercise 1 with the bootstrap method to estimate the population mean. The mean of the values in Exercise 1 is 54.3 seconds, and the mean of all of the tobacco times in Data Set 20 "Alcohol and Tobacco in Movies" from Appendix B is 57.4 seconds. If we use 1000 bootstrap samples and find the corresponding 1000 means, do we expect that those 1000 means will target 54.3 seconds or 57.4 seconds? What does that result suggest about the bootstrap method in this case?

In Exercises 5–8, use the relatively small number of given bootstrap samples to construct the confidence interval.

5. Online Buying In a *Consumer Reports* Research Center survey, women were asked if they purchase books online, and responses included these: no, yes, no, no. Letting "yes" $= 1$ and letting "no" $= 0$, here are ten bootstrap samples for those responses: $\{0, 0, 0, 0\}$, $\{1, 0, 1, 0\}$, $\{1, 0, 1, 0\}$, $\{0, 0, 0, 0\}$, $\{0, 0, 0, 0\}$, $\{0, 1, 0, 0\}$, $\{0, 0, 0, 0\}$, $\{0, 0, 0, 0\}$, $\{0, 1, 0, 0\}$, $\{1, 1, 0, 0\}$. Using only the ten given bootstrap samples, construct a 90% confidence interval estimate of the proportion of women who said that they purchase books online.

6. Seating Choice In a 3M Privacy Filters poll, respondents were asked to identify their favorite seat when they fly, and the results include these responses: window, window, other, other. Letting "window" $= 1$ and letting "other" $= 0$, those four responses can be represented as $\{1, 1, 0, 0\}$. Here are ten bootstrap samples for those responses: $\{0, 0, 0, 0\}$, $\{0, 1, 0, 0\}$, $\{0, 1, 0, 1\}$, $\{0, 0, 1, 0\}$, $\{1, 1, 1, 0\}$, $\{0, 1, 1, 0\}$, $\{1, 0, 0, 1\}$, $\{0, 1, 1, 1\}$, $\{1, 0, 1, 0\}$, $\{1, 0, 0, 1\}$. Using only the ten given bootstrap samples, construct an 80% confidence interval estimate of the proportion of respondents who indicated their favorite seat is "window."

7. Freshman 15 Here is a sample of amounts of weight change (kg) of college students in their freshman year (from Data Set 13 "Freshman 15" in Appendix B): 11, 3, 0, -2, where -2 represents a *loss* of 2 kg and positive values represent weight gained. Here are ten bootstrap samples: $\{11, 11, 11, 0\}$, $\{11, -2, 0, 11\}$, $\{11, -2, 3, 0\}$, $\{3, -2, 0, 11\}$, $\{0, 0, 0, 3\}$, $\{3, -2, 3, -2\}$, $\{11, 3, -2, 0\}$, $\{-2, 3, -2, 3\}$, $\{-2, 0, -2, 3\}$, $\{3, 11, 11, 11\}$.

a. Using only the ten given bootstrap samples, construct an 80% confidence interval estimate of the mean weight change for the population.

b. Using only the ten given bootstrap samples, construct an 80% confidence interval estimate of the standard deviation of the weight changes for the population.

8. Cell Phone Radiation Here is a sample of measured radiation emissions (cW/kg) for cell phones (based on data from the Environmental Working Group): 38, 55, 86, 145. Here are ten bootstrap samples: $\{38, 145, 55, 86\}$, $\{86, 38, 145, 145\}$, $\{145, 86, 55, 55\}$, $\{55, 55, 55, 145\}$, $\{86, 86, 55, 55\}$, $\{38, 38, 86, 86\}$, $\{145, 38, 86, 55\}$, $\{55, 86, 86, 86\}$, $\{145, 86, 55, 86\}$, $\{38, 145, 86, 55\}$.

a. Using only the ten given bootstrap samples, construct an 80% confidence interval estimate of the population mean.

b. Using only the ten given bootstrap samples, construct an 80% confidence interval estimate of the population standard deviation.

In Exercises 9–24, use technology to create the large number of bootstrap samples.

9. Freshman 15 Repeat Exercise 7 "Freshman 15" using a confidence level of 90% for parts (a) and (b) and using 1000 bootstrap samples instead of the 10 that were given in Exercise 7.

10. Cell Phone Radiation Repeat Exercise 8 "Cell Phone Radiation" using a confidence level of 90% for parts (a) and (b) and using 1000 bootstrap samples instead of the 10 that were given in Exercise 8.

11. Archeology Archeologists have studied sizes of Egyptian skulls in an attempt to determine whether breeding occurred between different cultures. Listed below are the widths (mm) of skulls from 150 A.D. (based on data from *Ancient Races of the Thebaid* by Thomson and Randall-Maciver).

a. Use 1000 bootstrap samples to construct a 99% confidence interval estimate of the mean skull width.

b. How does the result compare to the confidence interval found in Exercise 13 in Section 7-2?

$$128 \quad 138 \quad 126 \quad 132 \quad 143 \quad 135 \quad 139 \quad 129$$

12. Minting Quarters Listed below are weights (grams) of quarters minted after 1964 (based on Data Set 40 "Coin Weights" in Appendix B).

a. Use 1000 bootstrap samples to construct a 95% confidence interval estimate of the mean weight of all quarters minted after 1964.

b. Specifications require that the quarters have a weight of 5.670 g. What does the confidence interval suggest about that specification?

c. How does the confidence interval compare to the result found in Exercise 14 in Section 7-2 on page 342?

$$5.7790 \quad 5.5928 \quad 5.6486 \quad 5.6661 \quad 5.5491 \quad 5.7239 \quad 5.5591 \quad 5.5864 \quad 5.6872 \quad 5.6274$$

13. Los Angeles Commute Time Listed below are 15 Los Angeles commute times (based on a sample from Data Set 31 "Commute Times" in Appendix B).

a. Use 1000 bootstrap samples to construct a 99% confidence interval estimate of the population mean.

b. Given that Exercise 15 in Section 7-2 used the same data for a 99% confidence interval based on use of the *t* distribution, and given that the data do not appear to be from a normally distributed population, which confidence interval is likely to be better: The confidence interval from part (a) or the confidence interval found in Exercise 15 in Section 7-2?

$$5 \quad 25 \quad 45 \quad 5 \quad 5 \quad 40 \quad 25 \quad 8 \quad 50 \quad 5 \quad 5 \quad 30 \quad 15 \quad 25 \quad 50$$

14. Los Angeles Commute Time Listed below are 32 Los Angeles commute times (based on a sample from Data Set 31 "Commute Times" in Appendix B).

a. Use 1000 bootstrap samples to construct a 99% confidence interval estimate of the population mean.

b. How does the result compare to the confidence interval found in Exercise 16 in Section 7-2?

$$5 \quad 25 \quad 45 \quad 5 \quad 5 \quad 40 \quad 25 \quad 8 \quad 50 \quad 5 \quad 5 \quad 30 \quad 15 \quad 25 \quad 50 \quad 18$$
$$25 \quad 45 \quad 75 \quad 60 \quad 40 \quad 25 \quad 8 \quad 50 \quad 10 \quad 10 \quad 30 \quad 15 \quad 25 \quad 50 \quad 20 \quad 30$$

15. Heights of Female Soccer Players Listed below are the heights (in.) of players on the U.S. Women's National Soccer Team (at the time of this writing). Use those heights as a sample of the heights of all professional women soccer players.

a. Use 1000 bootstrap samples to construct a 95% confidence interval estimate of σ.

b. How does the result compare to the confidence interval found in Exercise 13 in Section 7-3?

$$67 \quad 67 \quad 70 \quad 61 \quad 67 \quad 69 \quad 69 \quad 66 \quad 69 \quad 66 \quad 64 \quad 68$$
$$68 \quad 71 \quad 72 \quad 67 \quad 69 \quad 65 \quad 66 \quad 64 \quad 67 \quad 67 \quad 67$$

16. Mint Specs Listed below are weights (grams) from a simple random sample of pennies produced after 1983 (from Data Set 40 "Coin Weights" in Appendix B).

a. Use 1000 bootstrap samples to construct a 95% confidence interval estimate of σ.

b. How does the result compare to the confidence interval found in Exercise 14 in Section 7-3?

$$2.5024 \quad 2.5298 \quad 2.4998 \quad 2.4823 \quad 2.5163 \quad 2.5222 \quad 2.4900 \quad 2.4907 \quad 2.5017$$

17. Brain Volumes Use these measures of brain volumes (cm^3) from Data Set 12 "IQ and Brain Size" in Appendix B. Use the bootstrap method with 1000 bootstrap samples.

1005	963	1035	1027	1281	1272	1051	1079	1034	1070
1173	1079	1067	1104	1347	1439	1029	1100	1204	1160

a. Use 1000 bootstrap samples to construct a 90% confidence interval estimate of the population mean.

b. Use 1000 bootstrap samples to construct a 90% confidence interval estimate of the population standard deviation.

18. Caffeine in Soft Drinks Listed below are measured amounts of caffeine (mg per 12 oz of drink) obtained in one can from each of 20 brands (7UP, A&W Root Beer, Cherry Coke, . . . , TaB).

a. Use 1000 bootstrap samples to construct a 99% confidence interval estimate of the mean amount of caffeine in cans of soft drinks.

b. Given that Exercise 20 in Section 7-2 used the same data for a 99% confidence interval based on use of the t distribution, and given that the data do not appear to be from a normally distributed population, which confidence interval is likely to be better: The confidence interval from part (a) or the confidence interval found in Exercise 20 in Section 7-2?

c. How does the result compare to the confidence interval found in Exercise 20 in Section 7-2 on page 343?

0	0	34	34	34	45	41	51	55	36	47	41	0	0	53	54	38	0	41	47

19. Survey Return Rate In a study of cell phone use and brain hemispheric dominance, an Internet survey was e-mailed to 5000 subjects randomly selected from an online otological group (focused on ears), and 717 surveys were returned. Use the bootstrap method to construct a 90% confidence interval estimate of the proportion of returned surveys. Use 1000 bootstrap samples. How does the result compare to the confidence interval found in Exercise 15 "Survey Return Rate" from Section 7-1 on page 325?

20. Medical Malpractice In a study of 1228 randomly selected medical malpractice lawsuits, it was found that 856 of them were dropped or dismissed (based on data from the Physicians Insurers Association of America). Use the bootstrap method to construct a 95% confidence interval estimate of the proportion of lawsuits that are dropped or dismissed. Use 1000 bootstrap samples. How does the result compare to the confidence interval found in Exercise 16 "Medical Malpractice" from Section 7-1 on page 325?

21. Eliquis The drug Eliquis (apixaban) is used to help prevent blood clots in certain patients. In clinical trials, among 5924 patients treated with Eliquis, 153 developed the adverse reaction of nausea (based on data from Bristol-Myers Squibb Co.). Use the bootstrap method to construct a 99% confidence interval estimate of the proportion patients who experience nausea. Use 1000 bootstrap samples. How does the result compare to the confidence interval found in Exercise 14 "Eliquis" from Section 7-1 on page 325?

22. Job Interviews In a Harris poll of 514 human resource professionals, 463 said that the appearance of a job applicant is most important for a good first impression. Use 1000 bootstrap samples to construct a 99% confidence interval estimate of the proportion of all human resource professionals believing that the appearance of a job applicant is most important for a good first impression. How does the result compare to the confidence interval found in Exercise 24 part (b) in Section 7-1 on page 327?

23. Analysis of Last Digits Weights of respondents were recorded as part of the California Health Interview Survey. The last digits of weights from 50 randomly selected respondents are listed below.

5	0	1	0	2	0	5	0	5	0	3	8	5	0	5	0	5	6	0	0	0	0	0	0	8
5	5	0	4	5	0	0	4	0	0	0	0	0	8	0	9	5	3	0	5	0	0	0	5	8

continued

a. Use the bootstrap method with 1000 bootstrap samples to find a 95% confidence interval estimate of σ.

b. Find the 95% confidence interval estimate of σ found by using the methods of Section 7-3.

c. Compare the results. If the two confidence intervals are different, which one is better? Why?

24. Analysis of Last Digits Repeat Exercise 23 "Analysis of Last Digits" using the mean instead of the standard deviation. Compare the confidence interval to the one that would be found using the methods of Section 7-2.

7-4   Beyond the Basics

25. Effect of the Number of Bootstrap Samples Repeat Exercise 23 "Analysis of Last Digits" using 10,000 bootstrap samples instead of 1000. What happens?

26. Distribution Shapes Use the sample data given in Exercise 23 "Analysis of Last Digits."

a. Do the original sample values appear to be from a normally distributed population? Explain.

b. Do the 1000 bootstrap samples appear to have means that are from a normally distributed population? Explain.

c. Do the 1000 bootstrap samples appear to have standard deviations that are from a normally distributed population? Explain.

27. Confirming the Requirement of Symmetry Use the sample data listed in Exercise 1 to generate 1000 bootstrap samples, then find the mean in each of those samples. Construct a histogram of the 1000 bootstrap sample means. Does it appear to be approximately symmetric as required?

28. Estimating the Median Use the sample data listed in Exercise 1 "Bootstrap Requirements" to generate 1000 bootstrap samples, and find the median in each of those samples. After obtaining the 1000 sample medians, find the 95% confidence interval estimate of the population median by evaluating $P_{2.5}$ and $P_{97.5}$ from the sorted 1000 medians. Given that the sample times in Exercise 1 are from the 50 times in Data Set 20 "Alcohol and Tobacco in Movies" and those 50 times have a median of 5.5, how well did the bootstrap method work to create a "good" confidence interval?

Chapter Quick Quiz

1. Female Motorcycle Owners Here is a 95% confidence interval estimate of the percentage of motorcycle owners who are female: $17.5\% < p < 20.6\%$ (based on data from the Motorcycle Industry Council). What is the best point estimate of the percentage of motorcycle owners who are women?

2. Interpreting CI Write a brief statement that correctly interprets the confidence interval given in Exercise 1 "Female Motorcycle Owners."

3. Critical Value For the survey described in Exercise 1 "Female Motorcycle Owners," find the critical value that would be used for constructing a 99% confidence interval estimate of the population proportion.

4. Loose Change *USA Today* reported that 40% of people surveyed planned to use accumulated loose change for paying bills. The margin of error was given as ± 3.1 percentage points. Identify the confidence interval that corresponds to that information.

5. Sample Size for Proportion Find the sample size required to estimate the percentage of statistics students who take their statistics course online. Assume that we want 95% confidence that the proportion from the sample is within two percentage points of the true population percentage.

6. Sample Size for Mean Find the sample size required to estimate the mean IQ of airline pilots. Assume that we want 99% confidence that the mean from the sample is within two IQ points of the true population mean. Also assume that $\sigma = 15$.

7. Requirements A construction quality control analyst has collected a random sample of six concrete road barriers, and she plans to weigh each of them and construct a 95% confidence interval estimate of the mean weight of all such barriers. What requirements must be satisfied in order to construct the confidence interval with the method from Section 7-2 that uses the t distribution?

8. Degrees of Freedom In general, what does "degrees of freedom" refer to? For the sample data described in Exercise 7 "Requirements," find the number of degrees of freedom, assuming that you want to construct a confidence interval estimate of μ using the t distribution.

9. Critical Value Refer to Exercise 7 "Requirements" and assume that the requirements are satisfied. Find the critical value that would be used for constructing a 95% confidence interval estimate of μ using the t distribution.

10. Which Method? Refer to Exercise 7 "Requirements" and assume that sample of six weights appears to be from a population having a distribution that is substantially far from being normal. Should a 95% confidence interval estimate of σ be constructed using the χ^2 distribution? If not, what other method could be used to find a 95% confidence interval estimate of σ?

Review Exercises

1. Bachelor's Degree in Four Years In a study of government financial aid for college students, it becomes necessary to estimate the percentage of full-time college students who earn a bachelor's degree in four years or less. Find the sample size needed to estimate that percentage. Use a 0.1 margin of error, and use a confidence level of 95%.

a. Assume that nothing is known about the percentage to be estimated.

b. Assume that prior studies have shown that about 40% of full-time students earn bachelor's degrees in four years or less.

c. Does the added knowledge in part (b) have much of an effect on the sample size?

2. Bachelor's Degree The president of Brown University wants to estimate the mean time (years) it takes students to earn a bachelor's degree. How many students must be surveyed in order to be 95% confident that the estimate is within 0.2 year of the true population mean? Assume that the population standard deviation is $\sigma = 1.3$ years.

3. Voting Survey In a survey of 1002 people, 70% said that they voted in a recent presidential election (based on data from ICR Research Group). Voting records show that 61% of eligible voters actually did vote.

a. Among the 1002 people surveyed, what is the actual number of people who said that they voted?

b. Find a 95% confidence interval estimate of the percentage of people who say that they voted.

c. Fill in the blanks for this statement that a typical reporter might write: Based on a survey, _____ percent of those surveyed say that they voted in the presidential election, and the survey has a margin of error of _____.

d. Are the survey results consistent with the actual voter turnout of 61%? Why or why not?

4. Space Mountain Use the following wait times (minutes) for the Space Mountain ride at Disney World (from Data Set 33 "Disney World Wait Times" in Appendix B). Construct a 95% confidence interval estimate of the mean of all wait times. Write a brief statement that interprets that confidence interval.

$$40 \quad 35 \quad 40 \quad 40 \quad 25 \quad 80 \quad 50 \quad 30 \quad 35 \quad 40$$

5. Distributions Identify the distribution (normal, Student t, chi-square) that should be used in each of the following situations. If none of the three distributions can be used, what other method could be used?

continued

a. In constructing a confidence interval of μ, you have 75 sample values and they appear to be from a population with a skewed distribution. The population standard deviation is not known.

b. In constructing a confidence interval estimate of σ, you have 75 sample values and they appear to be from a population with a skewed distribution.

c. In constructing a confidence interval estimate of σ, you have 75 sample values and they appear to be from a population with a normal distribution.

d. In constructing a confidence interval estimate of p, you have 1200 survey respondents and 5% of them answered "yes" to the first question.

e. In constructing a confidence interval estimate of p, you have 20 survey respondents and 5% of them answered "yes" to the first question.

6. Flight Delays Listed below are arrival delays (minutes) of randomly selected American Airlines flights from New York (JFK) to Los Angeles (LAX). Negative numbers correspond to flights that arrived before the scheduled arrival time. Construct a 95% confidence interval estimate of the mean arrival delay time. How good is the on-time performance?

$$28 \quad 103 \quad 19 \quad -5 \quad -46 \quad 13 \quad -3 \quad 13$$

7. Flight Delays Use the data from the preceding exercise to construct a 95% confidence interval estimate of σ.

8. Bootstrap Repeat Exercise 7 using 1000 bootstrap samples.

9. Alcohol in Children's Movies Listed below is a simple random sample of times (seconds) that animated children's movies showed the use of alcohol (based on Data Set 20 "Alcohol and Tobacco in Movies" in Appendix B).

a. Are the requirements for constructing a 95% confidence interval estimate of the population mean μ satisfied? If so, construct that confidence interval.

b. Are the requirements for constructing a 95% confidence interval estimate of the population standard deviation σ satisfied? If so, construct that confidence interval.

$$39 \quad 0 \quad 0 \quad 0 \quad 28 \quad 0 \quad 74 \quad 0 \quad 0 \quad 0 \quad 5 \quad 0 \quad 72 \quad 73 \quad 0 \quad 13 \quad 38 \quad 46$$
$$0 \quad 7 \quad 0 \quad 3 \quad 123 \quad 76 \quad 0 \quad 0 \quad 414 \quad 34 \quad 0 \quad 0 \quad 0 \quad 39 \quad 142 \quad 0$$

10. Arm Circumferences Listed below are arm circumferences (cm) of randomly selected women (based on Data Set 1 "Body Data" from Appendix B). Also shown is the normal quantile plot of those measurements.

a. Are the requirements for constructing a 95% confidence interval estimate of the population mean μ satisfied? If so, construct that confidence interval.

b. Are the requirements for constructing a 95% confidence interval estimate of the population standard deviation σ satisfied? If so, construct that confidence interval.

$$33.5 \quad 26.6 \quad 36.5 \quad 29.9 \quad 32.0 \quad 29.0 \quad 29.0 \quad 23.7 \quad 35.1 \quad 25.2$$

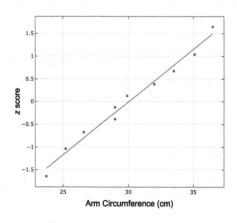

Cumulative Review Exercises

Cell Phone Radiation. *Listed below are amounts of cell phone radiation (W/kg) measured from randomly selected cell phones (based on data from the Federal Communications Commission). Use these values for Exercises 1–6.*

$$1.5 \quad 0.9 \quad 1.3 \quad 1.5 \quad 1.3 \quad 1.2 \quad 1.4 \quad 1.1 \quad 1.3 \quad 1.4 \quad 1.2$$

1. Statistics Find the mean, median, standard deviation, variance, and range. Are the results statistics or parameters?

2. Significance Use the results from Exercise 1 with the range rule of thumb to find amounts of radiation separating those that are significantly low and those that are significantly high. Is the lowest listed value significantly low?

3. Level of Measurement What is the level of measurement of these data (nominal, ordinal, interval, ratio)? Are the original unrounded amounts of radiation continuous data or discrete data?

4. Normality The accompanying graphs are a normal quantile plot and a histogram of the radiation amounts. What do these graphs suggest about the distribution of the population of cell phone radiation amounts?

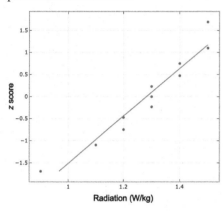 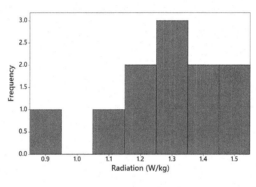

5. Confidence Interval Use the radiation amounts to construct a 95% confidence interval estimate of the population mean μ. Write a brief statement that interprets that confidence interval.

6. Sample Size Find the sample size necessary to estimate the mean amount of cell phone radiation. Assume that we want 95% confidence that the sample mean is in error by no more than 0.05 W/kg. Based on a larger sample than the one given for the preceding exercises, assume that all cell phones have a standard deviation of 0.29 W/kg.

7. Normal Distribution Using a larger data set than the one given for the preceding exercises, assume that cell phone radiation amounts are normally distributed with a mean of 1.17 W/kg and a standard deviation of 0.29 W/kg.

a. Find the probability that a randomly selected cell phone has a radiation amount that exceeds the U.S. standard of 1.6 W/kg or less.

b. Find the value of Q_3, the cell phone radiation amount that is the third quartile.

8. Controversial Song The song "Baby It's Cold Outside" generated much controversy because of its lyrics and tone. CBS New York conducted a survey by asking viewers to use the Internet to respond to a question asking whether that song was really too offensive to play. Among 1043 Internet users who chose to respond, 986 said that the song was not too offensive, and 57 of the respondents said that the song was too offensive.

a. Construct a 95% confidence interval estimate of the proportion of the population having the belief that the song is not too offensive.

continued

b. Based on the result from part (a), is it safe to say that the majority of the population does not feel that the song is too offensive.

c. What is wrong with this survey? Based on this survey, what do we really know about the population?

9. Flu Shots CVS Pharmacy sponsored a Harris survey of 2,020 adults, and 66% of them said that they plan to get a flu shot this year. Construct a 95% confidence interval estimate of the percentage of all adults who plan to get a flu shot this year. Is there anything about the survey that is questionable?

10. Tour de France Listed below are the average speeds (km/h) of winners of the Tour de France men's bicycle race. The speeds are listed in order by year, beginning with the year 2000.

a. Construct a 95% confidence interval estimate of the population mean.

b. Is a confidence interval the best tool for gaining insight into the data? Investigate the data using another tool that would be more helpful. What do you conclude?

| 39.56 | 40.02 | 39.93 | 40.94 | 40.55 | 41.65 | 40.78 | 38.98 | 40.50 | 40.31 |
| 39.59 | 39.79 | 39.88 | 40.54 | 40.69 | 39.64 | 39.62 | 41.00 | 40.21 | |

Technology Project

Chicago Commute Time Data Set 31 "Commute Times" from Appendix B includes 1000 commute times (minutes) in Chicago. Use the 1000 commute times for the following.

a. Find the mean and standard deviation.

b. Generate a histogram and normal quantile plot. Does it appear that the commute times are from a population having a normal distribution?

c. In obtaining a 95% confidence interval estimate of the commute times for the population of Chicago, are the requirements for using the t distribution satisfied? Explain.

d. Find the 95% confidence interval estimate of the population mean μ by using the t distribution.

e. Find the 95% confidence interval estimate of the population mean by using 1000 bootstrap samples.

f. Compare the results from parts (d) and (e). Which confidence interval is likely to be better? Given that the confidence intervals from parts (d) and (e) are obtained from dramatically different methods, do the two confidence intervals appear to be very different?

Big (or Very Large) Data Project

Refer to Data Set 45 "Births in New York" in Appendix B, which contains records from 465,506 births.

a. Use the birth weights (grams) of males to construct a 95% confidence interval estimate of the mean birth weight of all males.

b. Use the birth weights (grams) of females to construct a 95% confidence interval estimate of the mean birth weight of all females.

c. Compare the results from parts (a) and (b).

FROM DATA TO DECISION

Critical Thinking: What does the survey tell us?

Surveys have become an integral part of our lives. Because it is so important that every citizen has the ability to interpret survey results, surveys are the focus of this project. Use the following.

A Gallup poll of 3297 U.S. adults showed that 54% of the respondents said it is unlikely that they would use a self-driving car.

Analyzing the Data

1. Use the survey results to construct a 95% confidence interval estimate of the *percentage* of all U.S. adults who say they are unlikely to use self-driving cars.

2. Find the margin of error for this survey. How does it compare to this statement from Gallup: "For results based on the total sample of 3297 U.S. adults, the margin of sampling error is ± 2 percentage points at the 95% confidence level."?

3. Explain why or why not an online news website would be justified in publishing this claim: "Most U.S. adults say they are unlikely to use self-driving cars."

4. Assume that you are an online reporter. Write a description of the survey results for your website.

5. A common criticism of surveys is that they poll only a very small percentage of the population and therefore cannot be accurate. Given that a sample of size 3297 from a population of 256,338,241 adults is a sample that is only 0.001% of the population, is that sample size too small? Write a brief explanation of why the sample size of 3297 is or is not too small.

6. In reference to another survey, the president of a company wrote to the Associated Press about a nationwide survey of 1223 subjects. Here is what he wrote:

> When you or anyone else attempts to tell me and my associates that 1223 persons account for our opinions and tastes here in America, I get mad as hell! How dare you! When you or anyone else tells me that 1223 people represent America, it is astounding and unfair and should be outlawed.

The writer of that letter then proceeds to claim that because the sample size of 1223 people represents 120 million people, his single letter represents 98,000 (120 million divided by 1223) who share the same views. Do you agree or disagree with this claim? Write a response that either supports or refutes this claim.

Cooperative Group Activities

1. Out-of-class activity Collect sample data, and use the methods of this chapter to construct confidence interval estimates of population parameters. Here are some suggestions for parameters:

• Proportion of students at your college who can touch their nose with their tongue

• Proportion of students at your college who can raise one eyebrow without raising the other eyebrow

• Mean age of cars driven by statistics students and/or the mean age of cars driven by faculty

• Mean length of words in *New York Times* editorials and mean length of words in editorials found in your local newspaper

• Proportion of students at your college who can correctly identify the president, vice president, and secretary of state

• Proportion of students at your college who are over the age of 18 and are registered to vote

• Mean age of full-time students at your college

• Mean number of hours that students at your college study each week

• Proportion of student cars that are painted white

• Proportion of cars that are red

2. In-class activity Without using any measuring device, each student should draw a line believed to be 3 in. long and another line believed to be 3 cm long. Then use rulers to measure and record the lengths of the lines drawn. Find the means and standard deviations of the two sets of lengths. Use the sample data to construct a confidence interval for the length of the line estimated to be 3 in., and then do the same for the length of the line estimated to be 3 cm. Do the confidence interval limits actually contain the correct length? Compare the results. Do the estimates of the 3-in. line appear to be more accurate than those for the 3-cm line?

3. In-class activity Assume that a method of gender selection can affect the probability of a baby being a girl, so that the probability becomes 1/4. Each student should simulate 20 births by drawing 20 cards from a shuffled deck. (Which design better simulates reality: sampling the cards with replacement, or sampling the cards without replacement?) Consider the hearts to be girls and consider all other cards to be boys. After making 20 selections and recording the "genders" of the babies, construct a confidence interval estimate of the proportion of girls. Does the result appear to be effective in identifying the true value of the population proportion? (If decks of cards are not available, use some other way to simulate the births, such as using the random number generator on a calculator or using digits from phone numbers or Social Security numbers.)

4. Out-of-class activity Groups of three or four students should go to the library and collect a sample consisting of the ages of books (based on copyright dates). Plan and describe the sampling procedure, execute the sampling procedure, then use the results to construct a confidence interval estimate of the mean age of all books in the library.

5. In-class activity Each student should write an estimate of the age of the current president of the United States. All estimates should be collected, and the sample mean and standard deviation should be calculated. Then use the sample results to construct a confidence interval. Do the confidence interval limits contain the correct age of the president?

6. In-class activity A class project should be designed to conduct a test in which each student is given a taste of Coke and a taste of Pepsi. The student is then asked to identify which sample is Coke. After all of the results are collected, analyze the claim that the success rate is better than the rate that would be expected with random guesses.

7. In-class activity Each student should estimate the length of the classroom. The values should be based on visual estimates, with no actual measurements being taken. After the estimates have been collected, construct a confidence interval, then measure the length of the room. Does the confidence interval contain the actual length of the classroom? Is there a "collective wisdom," whereby the class mean is approximately equal to the actual room length?

8. In-class activity Divide into groups of three or four. Examine a sample of different issues of a current magazine and find the proportion of pages that include advertising. Based on the results, construct a 95% confidence interval estimate of the percentage of all such pages that have advertising. Compare results with other groups.

9. In-class activity Divide into groups of two. First find the sample size required to estimate the proportion of times that a coin turns up heads when tossed, assuming that you want 80% confidence that the sample proportion is within 0.08 of the true population proportion. Then toss a coin the required number of times and record your results. What percentage of such confidence intervals should actually contain the true value of the population proportion, which we know is $p = 0.5$? Verify this last result by comparing your confidence interval with the confidence intervals found in other groups.

10. Out-of-class activity Identify a topic of general interest and coordinate with all members of the class to conduct a survey. Instead of conducting a "scientific" survey using sound principles of random selection, use a convenience sample consisting of respondents who are readily available, such as friends, relatives, and other students. Analyze and interpret the results. Identify the population. Identify the shortcomings of using a convenience sample, and try to identify how a sample of subjects randomly selected from the population might be different.

11. Out-of-class activity Each student should find an article in a professional journal that includes a confidence interval of the type discussed in this chapter. Write a brief report describing the confidence interval and its role in the context of the article.

12. In-class activity Each student should first estimate the height of the current U.S. president in (a) feet; (b) meters. Combine all estimates to create a data set of estimates in feet and a second data set with estimates in meters. For each of the two data sets, (a) describe the distribution of estimates, (b) find the mean and standard deviation, and (c) construct a 95% confidence interval estimate of the mean of the population of all such estimates. Find the actual height of the president and compare it to the confidence interval estimates. Finally, identify the countries that are *not* on the metric system.

13. Out-of-class activity Working in groups of three or four students, each group should make observations and collect data to estimate the proportion of cars that fail to come to a complete stop at a particular stop sign. Use the sample data to construct a 95% confidence interval estimate of that proportion.

14. In-class activity Each student should estimate the current age of the person in the accompanying photograph. All of the estimates should be collected and a 95% confidence interval estimate should be found from the results. Does the 95% confidence interval estimate capture the true age of the person in the photograph?

8

HYPOTHESIS TESTING

CHAPTER PROBLEM **Cybersecurity: Do Most Internet Users Utilize Two-Factor Authentication to Protect Their Online Data?**

Cyberattacks and data breaches are now too common in our digital and networked world. Protecting data from cybercriminals becomes increasingly important as we continue to put more personal information online. One of the first lines of defense against hackers is account passwords, but passwords alone are vulnerable to hackers. A much more effective method of protecting online information is "two-factor authentication," which combines something you know

(such as a username and password) with something you have (your smartphone, fingerprint scan, face identification). Two-factor authentication is increasingly available on popular websites (e.g., Google, Apple, Amazon, Twitter) and should be used to protect accounts whenever available. In a recent Pew Research Center survey, 52% of Internet users ($n = 926$) reported that they utilize two-factor authentication with at least one online account. With this survey result, can we be justified in making this claim: "Most Internet users utilize two-factor authentication to protect their online data." (We interpret "most" to mean the majority, or more than half, or more than 50%.)

The claim about "most Internet users" is a claim that can be addressed by using the method of *hypothesis testing* that is presented in this chapter. We have the claim that $p > 0.5$, which is the symbolic form of the verbal claim that most (or the majority or more than half) of Internet users utilize two-factor authentication to protect their online data. This chapter will present the standard methods for testing such claims. It's important to note that the methods of hypothesis testing are not unique to statistics; methods of hypothesis testing are used in *many* different disciplines, including those with applications to health and medicine, business, and advertising. It would be a challenge to identify a discipline in which methods of hypothesis testing are not used. Consequently, the content of this chapter has broad application outside of the subject of statistics.

CHAPTER OBJECTIVES

Here are the chapter objectives:

8-1 Basics of Hypothesis Testing

- Develop the ability to identify the null and alternative hypotheses when given some claim about a population parameter (such as a proportion, mean, standard deviation, or variance).

- Develop the ability to calculate a test statistic, find critical values, calculate *P*-values, and state a final conclusion that addresses the original claim. Here are the components that should be included in the hypothesis test:

  - Statements of the null and alternative hypotheses expressed in symbolic form

  - Value of the test statistic

  - Selection of the sampling distribution to be used for the hypothesis test

  - Identification of a *P*-value and/or critical value(s)

  - Statement of one of these conclusions: *Reject* the null hypothesis, or *fail to reject* the null hypothesis

  - Statement of a final conclusion that uses simple and nontechnical terms to address the original claim

8-2 Testing a Claim About a Proportion

- Develop the ability to use sample data to conduct a formal hypothesis test of a claim about a population proportion. The procedure should include the components listed above with the objectives for Section 8-1.

8-3 Testing a Claim About a Mean

- Develop the ability to use sample data to conduct a formal hypothesis test of a claim made about a population mean. The procedure should include the same components listed above with the objectives for Section 8-1.

8-4 Testing a Claim About a Standard Deviation or Variance

- Develop the ability to use sample data to conduct a formal hypothesis test of a claim made about a population standard deviation or variance. The procedure should include the same components listed above with the objectives for Section 8-1.

8-5 Resampling: Using Technology for Hypothesis Testing

- Use the resampling methods of bootstrapping and randomization to test a claim about a population proportion, population mean, and population standard deviation or variance.

8-1   Basics of Hypothesis Testing

Key Concept In this section we present key components of a formal hypothesis test. The concepts in this section are general and apply to hypothesis tests involving proportions, means, or standard deviations or variances. In Part 1, we begin with the "big picture" to understand the basic underlying approach to hypothesis tests. Then we describe null and alternative hypotheses, significance level, types of tests (two-tailed, left-tailed, right-tailed), test statistic, *P*-value, critical values, and statements of conclusions. In Part 2 we describe types of errors (type I and type II). In Part 3 we describe the *power* of a hypothesis test.

PART 1   Basic Concepts of Hypothesis Testing

We begin with two very basic definitions.

> **DEFINITIONS**
>
> In statistics, a **hypothesis** is a claim or statement about a property of a population.
>
> A **hypothesis test** (or **test of significance**) is a procedure for testing a claim about a property of a population.

The "property of a population" referred to in the preceding definitions is often the value of a population parameter, so here are some examples of typical hypotheses (or claims):

- $p > 0.5$ "Most Internet users (more than half) utilize two-factor authentication to protect their online data."

- $\mu < 98.6°F$ "The mean body temperature of humans is less than 98.6°F."

- $\sigma = 15$ "The population of college students has IQ scores with a standard deviation equal to 15."

 EXAMPLE 1   **Most Internet Users Utilize Two-Factor Authentication to Protect Their Online Data**

Consider the claim from the Chapter Problem that "most Internet users utilize two-factor authentication to protect their online data." Using p to denote the proportion of Internet users who utilize two-factor authentication, the claim that "most" Internet users (or the "majority") is equivalent to the claim that the proportion is greater than half, or $p > 0.5$. The expression $p > 0.5$ is the symbolic form of the original claim.

(CP)—**The Big Picture** In the Chapter Problem, we have survey results showing that 52% of 926 Internet users utilize two-factor authentication to protect their online data. In Example 1, we have the claim that the population proportion p is such that $p > 0.5$.

> **Among 926 consumers, how many do we need to get a *significantly high* number who utilize two-factor authentication?**

- **Clearly *Not* Significantly High:** A result of 464 (or 50.1%) among 926 is just barely more than half, so 464 is clearly *not significantly high*.

- **Clearly Significantly High:** A result of 925 (or 99.9%) among 926 is clearly significantly high.

- **Unclear:** But what about a result such as 510 (or 55.1%) among 926? The formal method of hypothesis testing allows us to determine whether such a result is significantly high.

Using Technology It is easy to obtain hypothesis-testing results using technology. The accompanying screen displays show results from four different technologies, so *we can use computers or calculators to do all of the computational heavy lifting.* Examining the four screen displays, we see some common elements. They all display a "test statistic" of $z = 1.25$ (rounded), and they all include a "*P*-value" of 0.1059 or 0.106 (rounded). These two results of the test statistic and *P*-value are important, but *understanding* the hypothesis-testing procedure is far more important. Focus on *understanding* how the hypothesis-testing procedure works and learn the associated terminology. Only then will results from technology make sense.

Statdisk   **Minitab**

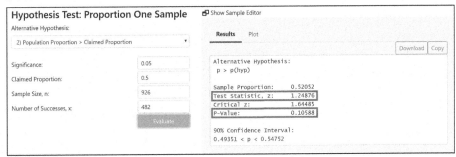

TI-83/84 Plus   **StatCrunch**

Significance Hypothesis tests are also called *tests of significance*. In Section 4-1 we used probabilities to determine when sample results are *significantly low* or *significantly high*. This chapter formalizes those concepts in a unified procedure that is used often throughout many different fields of application. Figure 8-1 on the next page summarizes the procedures used in two slightly different methods for conducting a formal hypothesis test. We will proceed to conduct a formal test of the claim from Example 1 that $p > 0.5$. In testing that claim, we will use the sample data from the survey cited in the Chapter Problem, with $n = 926$ and $\hat{p} = 0.52$.

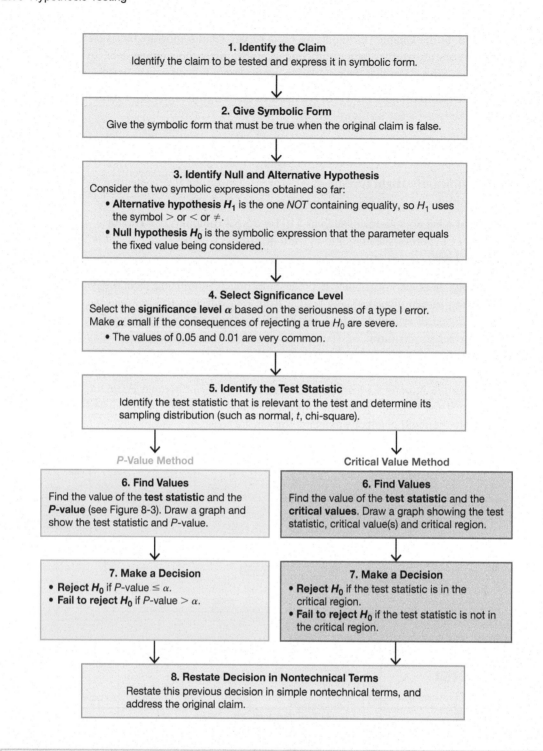

1. Identify the Claim
Identify the claim to be tested and express it in symbolic form.

2. Give Symbolic Form
Give the symbolic form that must be true when the original claim is false.

3. Identify Null and Alternative Hypothesis
Consider the two symbolic expressions obtained so far:
- **Alternative hypothesis H_1** is the one *NOT* containing equality, so H_1 uses the symbol $>$ or $<$ or $\neq$.
- **Null hypothesis H_0** is the symbolic expression that the parameter equals the fixed value being considered.

4. Select Significance Level
Select the **significance level** α based on the seriousness of a type I error. Make α small if the consequences of rejecting a true H_0 are severe.
- The values of 0.05 and 0.01 are very common.

5. Identify the Test Statistic
Identify the test statistic that is relevant to the test and determine its sampling distribution (such as normal, t, chi-square).

P-Value Method

6. Find Values
Find the value of the **test statistic** and the ***P*-value** (see Figure 8-3). Draw a graph and show the test statistic and *P*-value.

Critical Value Method

6. Find Values
Find the value of the **test statistic** and the **critical values**. Draw a graph showing the test statistic, critical value(s) and critical region.

7. Make a Decision
- **Reject H_0** if *P*-value $\leq \alpha$.
- **Fail to reject H_0** if *P*-value $> \alpha$.

7. Make a Decision
- **Reject H_0** if the test statistic is in the critical region.
- **Fail to reject H_0** if the test statistic is not in the critical region.

8. Restate Decision in Nontechnical Terms
Restate this previous decision in simple nontechnical terms, and address the original claim.

Confidence Interval Method

Construct a confidence interval with a confidence level selected as in Table 8-1.

Because a confidence interval estimate of a population parameter contains the likely values of that parameter, reject a claim that the population parameter has a value that is not included in the confidence interval.

Table 8-1 Confidence Level for Confidence Interval

		Two-Tailed Test	One-Tailed Test
Significance	0.01	99%	98%
Level for	0.05	95%	90%
Hypothesis	0.10	90%	80%
Test			

FIGURE 8-1 **Procedure for Hypothesis Tests**

Importance of Terminology This chapter introduces several terms that should be known *because they are the same terms used in many different fields, not just statistics.* For example, when learning the meaning of "null hypothesis" and "alternative hypothesis" and "*P*-value," you are learning terminology used in medicine, advertising, criminology, law, and many other disciplines. These terms are not unique to statistics.

Steps 1, 2, 3: Use the Original Claim to Create a Null Hypothesis H_0 and an Alternative Hypothesis H_1

The objective of Steps 1, 2, 3 is to identify the *null hypothesis* and *alternative hypothesis* so that the formal hypothesis test includes these standard components that are often used in many different disciplines. The null hypothesis includes the working assumption for the purposes of conducting the test.

DEFINITIONS

The **null hypothesis** (denoted by H_0) is a statement that the value of a population parameter (such as proportion, mean, or standard deviation) is *equal to* some claimed value.

The **alternative hypothesis** (denoted by H_1 or H_a or H_A) is a statement that the parameter has a value that somehow differs from the null hypothesis. For the methods of this chapter, the symbolic form of the alternative hypothesis must use one of these symbols: $<$, $>$, $\neq$.

HINT Think of the null hypothesis as a "working assumption" (that you may or may not believe).

The term *null* is used to indicate *no* change or no effect or no difference. We conduct the hypothesis test by assuming that the parameter is *equal to* some specified value so that we can work with a single distribution having a specific value.

Example: Here is an example of a null hypothesis involving a proportion:

$$H_0: p = 0.5$$

Example: Here are different examples of alternative hypotheses involving proportions:

$$H_1: p > 0.5 \quad H_1: p < 0.5 \quad H_1: p \neq 0.5$$

Given the claim from Example 1 that "most Internet users utilize two-factor authentication to protect their online data," we can apply Steps 1, 2, and 3 in Figure 8-1 as follows.

Step 1: Identify the claim to be tested and express it in symbolic form. Using p to denote the probability of selecting an Internet user utilizing two-factor authentication, the claim that "most Internet users utilize two-factor authentication" can be expressed in symbolic form as $p > 0.5$.

Step 2: Give the symbolic form that must be true when the original claim is false. If the original claim of $p > 0.5$ is false, then $p \leq 0.5$ must be true.

Step 3: This step is in two parts: Identify the alternative hypothesis H_1 and identify the null hypothesis H_0.

- Identify H_1: Using the two symbolic expressions $p > 0.5$ and $p \leq 0.5$, the alternative hypothesis H_1 is the one that does not contain equality. Of those two expressions, $p > 0.5$ does not contain equality, so we get

$$H_1: p > 0.5$$

continued

- Identify H_0: The null hypothesis H_0 is the symbolic expression that the parameter *equals* the fixed value being considered, so we get

$$H_0\text{: } p = 0.5$$

The first three steps yield the null and alternative hypotheses:

$$H_0\text{: } p = 0.5 \text{ (null hypothesis)}$$

$$H_1\text{: } p > 0.5 \text{ (alternative hypothesis)}$$

Note About Forming Your Own Claims (Hypotheses) If you are conducting a study and want to use a hypothesis test to *support* your claim, your claim must be worded so that it becomes the alternative hypothesis (and can be expressed using only the symbols $<$, $>$, or $\neq$). You can never support a claim that a parameter is *equal to* a specified value.

Step 4: Select the Significance Level α

> **DEFINITION**
>
> The **significance level** α for a hypothesis test is the probability value used as the cutoff for determining when the sample evidence constitutes *significant* evidence against the null hypothesis. By its nature, the significance level α is the probability of mistakenly rejecting the null hypothesis when it is true:
>
> **Significance level α = P(rejecting H_0 when H_0 is true)**

The significance level α is the same α introduced in Section 7-1, where we defined "critical value." Common choices for α are 0.05, 0.01, and 0.10; 0.05 is most common.

Step 5: Identify the Statistic Relevant to the Test and Determine Its Sampling Distribution (such as normal, t, or X^2)

Table 8-2 lists parameters along with the corresponding sampling distributions.

Example: The claim $p > 0.5$ is a claim about the population proportion p, so use the normal distribution, provided that the requirements are satisfied. (With $n = 926$, $p = 0.5$, and $q = 0.5$ from Example 1, $np \geq 5$ and $nq \geq 5$ are both true.)

TABLE 8-2 Parameters and Corresponding Test Statistics

Parameter	Sampling Distribution	Requirements	Test Statistic
Proportion p	Normal (z)	$np \geq 5$ and $nq \geq 5$	$z = \dfrac{\hat{p} - p}{\sqrt{\dfrac{pq}{n}}}$
Mean μ	t	σ not known and normally distributed population or σ not known and $n > 30$	$t = \dfrac{\bar{x} - \mu}{\dfrac{s}{\sqrt{n}}}$
Mean μ	Normal (z)	σ known and normally distributed population or σ known and $n > 30$	$z = \dfrac{\bar{x} - \mu}{\dfrac{\sigma}{\sqrt{n}}}$
St. dev. σ or variance σ^2	X^2	Strict requirement: normally distributed population	$X^2 = \dfrac{(n-1)s^2}{\sigma^2}$

Go Figure

140,000,000,000,000,000,000 miles: The distance you can see with your naked eye. What you see is light from 2.4 million years ago.

Step 6: Find the Value of the Test Statistic, Then Find Either the *P*-Value or the Critical Value(s)

The *test statistic* gives us a measure of the amount of the discrepancy between a sample statistic and the claimed value of the population parameter assumed in the null hypothesis. For proportions, the test statistic is a measure of the discrepancy between the sample proportion $\hat{p}$ and the claimed proportion p.

> **DEFINITION**
>
> The **test statistic** is a value used in making a decision about the null hypothesis. It is found by converting the sample statistic (such as $\hat{p}$, $\bar{x}$, or s) to a score (such as z, t, or χ^2) with the assumption that the null hypothesis is true.

In this chapter we use the test statistics listed in the last column of Table 8-2.

(CP)-*Example:* From Example 1 we have a claim made about the population proportion p, we have $n = 926$ and $\hat{p} = 0.52$. With the null hypothesis of H_0: $p = 0.5$, we are working with the assumption that $p = 0.5$, and it follows that $q = 1 - p = 0.5$. We can evaluate the test statistic as shown below (or technology can find the test statistic for us). The test statistic of $z = 1.25$ from each of the previous technology displays is more accurate than the result of $z = 1.22$ shown below. (If we replace 0.52 with $482/926 = 0.5205183585$, we get $z = 1.25$.)

$$z = \frac{\hat{p} - p}{\sqrt{\dfrac{pq}{n}}} = \frac{0.52 - 0.5}{\sqrt{\dfrac{(0.5)(0.5)}{926}}} = 1.22$$

Finding the *P*-value and/or critical value(s) requires that we first consider whether the hypothesis test is two-tailed, left-tailed, or right-tailed, which are described as follows.

Two-Tailed, Left-Tailed, Right-Tailed

> **DEFINITION**
>
> The **critical region** (or **rejection region**) is the area corresponding to all values of the test statistic that cause us to reject the null hypothesis.

Depending on the claim being tested, the critical region could be in the two extreme tails, it could be in the left tail, or it could be in the right tail.

- **Two-tailed test:** The critical region is in the two extreme regions (tails) under the curve (as in the top graph in Figure 8-2).

- **Left-tailed test:** The critical region is in the extreme left region (tail) under the curve (as in the middle graph in Figure 8-2).

- **Right-tailed test:** The critical region is in the extreme right region (tail) under the curve (as in the bottom graph in Figure 8-2).

HINT Look at the symbol used in the alternative hypothesis H_1.

- The symbol $>$ points to the right and the test is right-tailed.
- The symbol $<$ points to the left and the test is left-tailed.
- The symbol $\neq$ is used for a two-tailed test.

Example: With H_0: $p = 0.5$ and H_1: $p > 0.5$, we reject the null hypothesis and support the alternative hypothesis only if the sample proportion is greater than 0.5 by a significant amount, so the hypothesis test in this case is *right-tailed*.

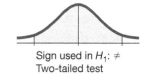

Sign used in H_1: $\neq$
Two-tailed test

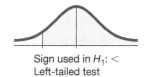

Sign used in H_1: $<$
Left-tailed test

Sign used in H_1: $>$
Right-tailed test

FIGURE 8-2 Critical Region in Two-Tailed, Left-Tailed, and Right-Tailed Tests

P-Value Method

With the **P-value method** of testing hypotheses, we make a decision by comparing the *P*-value to the significance level.

> **DEFINITION**
>
> In a hypothesis test, the **P-value** is the probability of getting a value of the test statistic that is *at least as extreme* as the test statistic obtained from the sample data, assuming that the null hypothesis is true.

> **CAUTION** Don't confuse the following notation:
>
> - *P*-value = probability of getting a test statistic at least as extreme as the one found from the sample data, assuming that the null hypothesis H_0 is true
> - p = population proportion
> - $\hat{p}$ = sample proportion

To find the *P*-value, first find the area beyond the test statistic, (using technology or Table A-2), then use the procedure given in Figure 8-3. That procedure can be summarized as follows:

- Critical region in left tail: *P*-value = area to the *left* of the test statistic
- Critical region in right tail: *P*-value = area to the *right* of the test statistic
- Critical region in two tails: *P*-value = *twice* the area in the tail beyond the test statistic

FIGURE 8-3
Finding *P*-Values

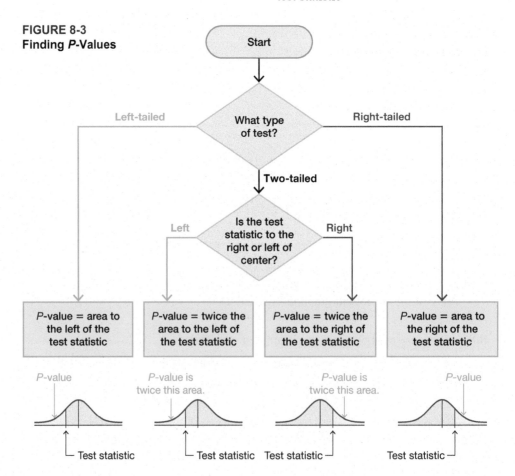

(CP)—*Example:* Using the data from the Chapter Problem, the test statistic is $z = 1.25$, and the area to the *right* of that test statistic is $1 - 0.8944 = 0.1056$ (using Table A-2), so a right-tailed test with test statistic $z = 1.25$ has a *P*-value $= 0.1056$. The *P*-value of 0.1056 differs slightly from the *P*-value of 0.1059 in the different technology displays shown earlier. The discrepancy between 0.1056 and 0.1059 is small, and it is due to the use of the rounded z scores in Table A-2. The *P*-value of 0.1059 from technology is more accurate.

P-Value and Hypothesis Testing Controversy

The standard method of testing hypotheses and the use of *P*-values have very widespread acceptance and use, but not everyone is convinced that these methods are sound. Editors of the *Journal of Basic and Applied Social Psychology* took a strong stand when they said that they would no longer publish articles that included *P*-values. They said that *P*-values are an excuse for lower-quality research and the *P*-value criterion is too easy to pass. In the past, *P*-values have been misinterpreted and misused, so a serious and important statistical analysis should not rely solely on *P*-value results. See Chapter 15 "Holistic Statistics" for a discussion of other aspects that should be considered. Some of those other aspects are included in this chapter.

Critical Value Method

With the **critical value method** (or traditional method) of testing hypotheses, we make a decision by comparing the test statistic to the critical value(s).

> **DEFINITION**
>
> In a hypothesis test, the **critical value(s)** separates the critical region (where we reject the null hypothesis) from the values of the test statistic that do not lead to rejection of the null hypothesis.

Critical values depend on the null hypothesis, the sampling distribution, and the significance level α.

(CP)—*Example:* The critical region in Figure 8-4 is shaded in green. Figure 8-4 shows that with a significance level of $\alpha = 0.05$, the critical value is $z = 1.645$.

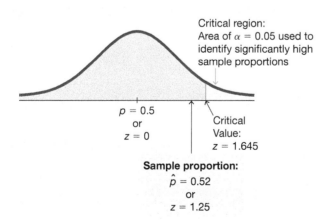

Critical region:
Area of $\alpha = 0.05$ used to identify significantly high sample proportions

$p = 0.5$
or
$z = 0$

Critical Value:
$z = 1.645$

Sample proportion:
$\hat{p} = 0.52$
or
$z = 1.25$

FIGURE 8-4   Critical Region, Critical Value, and Test Statistic

Journal Bans P-Values!

The *P*-value method of testing hypotheses has received widespread acceptance in the research community, but the editors of the journal *Basic and Applied Social Psychology* took a dramatic stance when they said that they would no longer publish articles that included *P*-values. In an editorial, David Trafimow and Michael Marks stated their belief that "the *P*-value bar is too easy to pass and sometimes serves as an excuse for lower quality research." David Trafimow stated that he did not know which statistical method should replace the use of *P*-values.

Many reactions to the *P*-value ban acknowledged that although *P*-values can be misused and misinterpreted, their use as a valuable research tool remains.

Step 7: Make a Decision to Either Reject H_0 or Fail to Reject H_0

Decision Criteria for the *P*-Value Method:

- If *P*-value $\leq \alpha$, reject H_0. ("If the *P* is low, the null must go.")
- If *P*-value $> \alpha$, fail to reject H_0.

CP—*Example:* With *P*-value = 0.106 (rounded) and significance level $\alpha = 0.05$, we have *P*-value $> \alpha$, so fail to reject H_0. Remember, the *P*-value is the probability of getting a sample result at least as extreme as the one obtained, so if the *P*-value is high (greater than α), the sample statistic is *not* significantly low or significantly high.

Decision Criteria for the Critical Value Method:

- If the test statistic is in the critical region, reject H_0.
- If the test statistic is not in the critical region, fail to reject H_0.

Example: With test statistic $z = 1.25$ and the critical region extending to the right from $z = 1.645$ (as shown in Figure 8-4), the test statistic does not fall within the critical region, so fail to reject H_0.

Step 8: Restate the Decision Using Simple and Nontechnical Terms

Without using technical terms not understood by most people, state a final conclusion that addresses the original claim with wording that can be understood by those without knowledge of statistical procedures.

CP—*Example:* There is not sufficient evidence to support the claim that "most Internet users utilize two-factor authentication to protect their online data."

Wording the Final Conclusion For help in wording the final conclusion, refer to Figure 8-5.

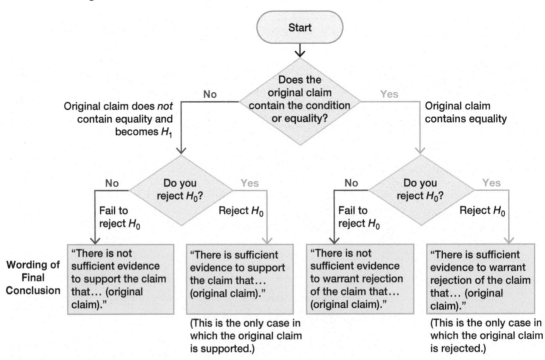

FIGURE 8-5   Hypothesis Tests: Wording of Final Conclusion

"Accept" Is Misleading We should say that we "fail to reject the null hypothesis" instead of saying that we "accept the null hypothesis." The term *accept* is misleading, because it implies incorrectly that the null hypothesis has been proved or is somehow being supported, but we can never prove a null hypothesis. The phrase *fail to reject* says more correctly that the available evidence isn't strong enough to warrant rejection of the null hypothesis.

Multiple Negatives Final conclusions can include as many as three negative terms. (*Example:* "There is *not* sufficient evidence to warrant *rejection* of the claim of *no* difference between 0.5 and the population proportion.") For such confusing conclusions, it is better to restate them to be understandable. Instead of saying that "there is not sufficient evidence to warrant rejection of the claim of no difference between 0.5 and the population proportion," a better statement would be this: "Until stronger evidence is obtained, continue to assume that the population proportion is equal to 0.5." It is important to effectively communicate the correct conclusion.

> **CAUTION** Never conclude a hypothesis test with a statement of "reject the null hypothesis" or "fail to reject the null hypothesis." Always make sense of the conclusion with a statement that uses simple nontechnical wording that addresses the original claim.

Confidence Intervals for Hypothesis Tests

In this section we have described the individual components used in a hypothesis test, but the following sections will combine those components in comprehensive procedures. We can test claims about population parameters by using the *P*-value method or the critical value method summarized in Figure 8-1, or we can use confidence intervals.

A confidence interval estimate of a population parameter contains the likely values of that parameter. If a confidence interval does not include a claimed value of a population parameter, reject that claim. For two-tailed hypothesis tests, construct a confidence interval with a confidence level of $1 - \alpha$, but for a one-tailed hypothesis test with significance level α, construct a confidence interval with a confidence level of $1 - 2\alpha$. (See Table 8-1 on page 376 for common cases.) After constructing the confidence interval, use this criterion:

> **A confidence interval estimate of a population parameter contains the likely values of that parameter. We should therefore reject a claim that the population parameter has a value that is not included in the confidence interval.**

Equivalent Methods

Caution: In some cases, a conclusion based on a confidence interval may be different from a conclusion based on a hypothesis test. The *P*-value method and critical value method are equivalent in the sense that they always lead to the same conclusion. The following table shows that for the methods included in this chapter, a confidence interval estimate of a proportion might lead to a conclusion different from that of a hypothesis test.

Parameter	Is a confidence interval *equivalent* to a hypothesis test in the sense that they always lead to the same conclusion?
Proportion	No
Mean	Yes
Standard deviation or variance	Yes

Aspirin Not Helpful for Geminis and Libras

Physician Richard Peto submitted an article to *Lancet*, a British medical journal. The article showed that patients had a better chance of surviving a heart attack if they were treated with aspirin within a few hours of their heart attacks. *Lancet* editors asked Peto to break down his results into subgroups to see if recovery worked better or worse for different groups, such as males or females. Peto believed that he was being asked to use too many subgroups, but the editors insisted. Peto then agreed, but he supported his objections by showing that when his patients were categorized by signs of the zodiac, aspirin was useless for Gemini and Libra heart attack patients, but aspirin is a lifesaver for those born under any other sign. This shows that when conducting multiple hypothesis tests with many different subgroups, there is a very large chance of getting some wrong results.

Resampling Methods (See Section 8-5) In addition to the *P*-value method, critical value method, and the use of confidence intervals, another approach for testing claims about population parameters is to use *resampling methods* that involve the use of technology to "resample" the original sample data many times. Section 8-5 is focused on these resampling methods:

- **Bootstrap** The bootstrap resampling method was introduced in Section 7-4, and it is used to construct a confidence interval that could be used to estimate a population parameter. The confidence interval can then be used to address the claim being tested.

- **Randomization** The *randomization* method involves resampling after the sample data have been modified to reflect the value of the population parameter that is assumed in the null hypothesis. The resamples help us to determine whether a sample statistic is consistent with the claimed value of a parameter or whether it contradicts the claimed value of a parameter.

PART 2   Type I and Type II Errors

When testing a null hypothesis, we arrive at a conclusion of rejecting it or failing to reject it. Our conclusions are sometimes correct and sometimes wrong (even if we apply all procedures correctly). With a hypothesis test, it is not simply a matter of being right or wrong. Different types of errors can have dramatically different consequences, and that is why we distinguish between type I errors and type II errors. For example, consider the dramatic difference between these two errors:

- Conclude that a new medicine is effective when in reality it is not effective.
- Conclude that a new medicine is not effective when in reality it is effective.

Table 8-3 includes two different types of errors and we distinguish between them by calling them type I and type II errors, as described here:

- **Type I error:** The mistake of rejecting the null hypothesis when it is actually true. The symbol α (alpha) is used to represent the probability of a type I error.

$$\alpha = P(\text{type I error}) = P(\text{rejecting } H_0 \text{ when } H_0 \text{ is true})$$

- **Type II error:** The mistake of failing to reject the null hypothesis when it is actually false. The symbol β (beta) is used to represent the probability of a type II error.

$$\beta = P(\text{type II error}) = P(\text{failing to reject } H_0 \text{ when } H_0 \text{ is false})$$

TABLE 8-3 Type I and Type II Errors

		True State of Nature	
		Null hypothesis is true	Null hypothesis is false
Preliminary Conclusion	Reject H_0	**Type I error:** Reject a true H_0. $P(\text{type I error}) = \alpha$	Correct decision ✓
	Fail to reject H_0	Correct decision ✓	**Type II error:** Fail to reject a false H_0. $P(\text{type II error}) = \beta$

MEMORY HINT FOR TYPE I AND TYPE II ERRORS Remember "routine for fun," and use the consonants from those words (**R**ou**TiN**e **F**o**R** **F**u**N**) to remember that a type I error is RTN: Reject True Null (hypothesis), and a type II error is FRFN: Fail to Reject a False Null (hypothesis).

HINT FOR DESCRIBING TYPE I AND TYPE II ERRORS Descriptions of a type I error and a type II error refer to the *null hypothesis* being true or false, but when wording a statement representing a type I error or a type II error, *be sure that the conclusion addresses the original claim* (which may or may not be the null hypothesis). See Example 2.

EXAMPLE 2 **Describing Type I and Type II Errors**

Consider the claim that a medical procedure designed to increase the likelihood of a baby girl is effective, so that the probability of a baby girl is $p > 0.5$. Given the following null and alternative hypotheses, write statements describing (a) a type I error, and (b) a type II error.

$H_0: p = 0.5$

$H_1: p > 0.5$ (original claim that will be addressed in the final conclusion)

SOLUTION

a. **Type I Error:** A type I error is the mistake of rejecting a true null hypothesis, so the following is a type I error: In reality $p = 0.5$, but sample evidence leads us to conclude that $p > 0.5$. (In this case, a type I error is to conclude that the medical procedure is effective when in reality it has no effect.)

b. **Type II Error:** A type II error is the mistake of failing to reject the null hypothesis when it is false, so the following is a type II error: In reality $p > 0.5$, but we fail to support that conclusion. (In this case, a type II error is to conclude that the medical procedure has no effect, when it really is effective in increasing the likelihood of a baby girl.)

YOUR TURN. Do Exercise 25 "Type I and Type II Errors."

Controlling Type I and Type II Errors Step 4 in our standard procedure for testing hypotheses is to select a significance level α (such as 0.05), which is the probability of a type I error. The values of α, β, and the sample size n are all related, so if you choose any two of them, the third is automatically determined (although β can't be determined until an alternative value of the population parameter has been specified along with α and n).

Good Practices

- Consider the seriousness of a type I error (with probability α) and also consider the seriousness of a type II error (with probability β).

- One common practice is to select the significance level α, then select a sample size that is practical, so the value of β is determined.

- If it's important to reduce the probability α (the probability of a Type I error) *and* the probability β (the probability of a Type II error), select α and β accordingly and then the required sample size n is automatically determined.

P-Hacking

Researchers often feel strong pressure to obtain meaningful results, such as a result that a potential drug is effective. When conducting an experiment, "P-hacking" is cheating to obtain such meaningful results. Some of the methods used to P-hack: Repeat the experiment many times, but include only those cases with a P-value less than 0.05; throw out any sample data that cause the P-value to exceed 0.05; discontinue sampling once a P-value less than 0.05 has been obtained. One effective way to prevent P-hacking is to use "preregistration," whereby a detailed research plan is prepared in advance and preregistered at an online registry, such as Open Science Framework.

PART 3 Power of a Hypothesis Test

We use β to denote the probability of failing to reject a false null hypothesis, so P(type II error) $= \beta$. It follows that $1 - \beta$ is the probability of rejecting a false null hypothesis, so $1 - \beta$ is a probability that is one measure of the effectiveness of a hypothesis test.

DEFINITION

The **power** of a hypothesis test is the probability $1 - \beta$ of rejecting a false null hypothesis. The value of the power is computed by using a particular significance level α and a *particular* value of the population parameter that is an alternative to the value assumed true in the null hypothesis.

Because determination of power requires a particular value that is an alternative to the value assumed in the null hypothesis, a hypothesis test can have many different values of power, depending on the particular values of the population parameter chosen as alternatives to the null hypothesis.

EXAMPLE 3 **Power of a Hypothesis Test**

Consider these preliminary results from the XSORT method of gender selection: There were 13 girls among the 14 babies born to couples using the XSORT method. If we want to test the claim that girls are more likely ($p > 0.5$) with the XSORT method, we have the following null and alternative hypotheses:

$$H_0: p = 0.5 \quad H_1: p > 0.5$$

Let's use a significance level of $\alpha = 0.05$. In addition to all of the given test components, finding power requires that we select a particular value of p that is an alternative to the value assumed in the null hypothesis $H_0: p = 0.5$. Find the values of power corresponding to these alternative values of p: 0.6, 0.7, 0.8, and 0.9.

SOLUTION

The values of power in the following table were found by using Minitab, and exact calculations are used instead of a normal approximation to the binomial distribution.

Specific Alternative Value of p	β	Power of Test $= 1 - \beta$
0.6	0.820	0.180
0.7	0.564	0.436
0.8	0.227	0.773
0.9	0.012	0.988

INTERPRETATION

On the basis of the power values listed above, we see that this hypothesis test has power of 0.180 (or 18.0%) of rejecting $H_0: p = 0.5$ when the population proportion p is actually 0.6. That is, if the true population proportion is actually equal to 0.6, there is an 18.0% chance of making the correct conclusion of rejecting the false null hypothesis that $p = 0.5$. That low power of 18.0% is not so good.

There is a 0.436 probability of rejecting $p = 0.5$ when the true value of p is actually 0.7. It makes sense that this test is more effective in rejecting the claim of $p = 0.5$ when the population proportion is actually 0.7 than when the population proportion is actually 0.6. (When identifying animals assumed to be horses, there's a better chance of rejecting an elephant as a horse—because of the greater difference—than rejecting a mule as a horse.) In general, increasing the difference between the assumed parameter value and the actual parameter value results in an increase in power, as shown in the table above.

——————————————— ▶ **YOUR TURN.** Do Exercise 30 "Calculating Power."

Because the calculations of power are quite complicated, the use of technology is strongly recommended. (In this section, only Exercises 29, 30, and 31 involve power.)

Power and the Design of Experiments

Just as 0.05 is a common choice for a significance level, a power of at least 0.80 is a common requirement for determining that a hypothesis test is effective. (Some statisticians argue that the power should be higher, such as 0.85 or 0.90.) When designing an experiment, we might consider how much of a difference between the claimed value of a parameter and its true value is an important amount of difference. If testing the effectiveness of the XSORT gender selection method, a change in the proportion of girls from 0.5 to 0.501 is not very important, whereas a change in the proportion of girls from 0.5 to 0.9 would be very important. Such magnitudes of differences affect power. When designing an experiment, a goal of having a power value of at least 0.80 can often be used to determine the minimum required sample size, as in the following example.

> **EXAMPLE 4** **Finding the Sample Size Required to Achieve 80% Power**

Here is a statement similar to one in an article from the *Journal of the American Medical Association:* "The trial design assumed that with a 0.05 significance level, 153 randomly selected subjects would be needed to achieve 80% power to detect a reduction in the coronary heart disease rate from 0.5 to 0.4." From that statement, we know the following:

- Before conducting the experiment, the researchers selected a significance level of 0.05 and a power of at least 0.80.

- The researchers decided that a reduction in the proportion of coronary heart disease from 0.5 to 0.4 is an important difference that they wanted to detect (by correctly rejecting the false null hypothesis).

- Using a significance level of 0.05, power of 0.80, and the alternative proportion of 0.4, technology such as Minitab is used to find that the required minimum sample size is 153.

The researchers can then proceed by obtaining a sample of at least 153 randomly selected subjects. Because of factors such as dropout rates, the researchers are likely to need somewhat more than 153 subjects. (See Exercise 31.)

——————————————— ▶ **YOUR TURN.** Do Exercise 31 "Finding Sample Size to Achieve Power."

8-1   Basic Skills and Concepts

Statistical Literacy and Critical Thinking

1. Mean Wait Time at Space Mountain A formal hypothesis test is to be conducted to test the claim that the wait times at the Space Mountain ride in Walt Disney World have a mean equal to 40 minutes.

a. What is the null hypothesis, and how is it denoted?

b. What is the alternative hypothesis, and how is it denoted?

c. What are the possible conclusions that can be made about the null hypothesis?

d. Is it possible to conclude that "there is sufficient evidence to support the claim that the mean wait time is equal to 40 minutes"?

2. Estimates vs. Hypothesis Tests Labels on cans of Dr. Pepper soda indicate that they contain 12 oz of the drink. We could collect samples of those cans and accurately measure the actual contents, then we could use methods of Section 7-2 for making an estimate of the mean amount of Dr. Pepper in cans, or we could use those measured amounts to test the claim that the cans contain a mean of 12 oz. What is the difference between estimating the mean and testing a hypothesis about the mean?

3. Interpreting _P_-value The Ericsson method is one of several methods claimed to increase the likelihood of a baby girl. In a clinical trial, results could be analyzed with a formal hypothesis test with the alternative hypothesis of $p > 0.5$, which corresponds to the claim that the method increases the likelihood of having a girl, so that the proportion of girls is greater than 0.5. If you have an interest in establishing the success of the method, which of the following _P_-values would you prefer as a result in your hypothesis test: 0.999, 0.5, 0.95, 0.05, 0.01, 0.001? Why?

4. Vitamin C vs. Lisinopril A bottle contains a label stating that it contains Spring Valley pills with 500 mg of vitamin C, and another bottle contains a label stating that it contains Merck pills with 40 mg of lisinopril that is used to treat high blood pressure. Identify which one of the following errors is most serious, explain why it is most serious, and characterize the error as being a type I error or a type II error.

  i. For lisinopril, fail to reject H_0: $\mu = 40$ mg when the mean is actually different from 40 mg.

  ii. For lisinopril, reject H_0: $\mu = 40$ mg when the mean is actually equal to 40 mg.

  iii. For vitamin C, fail to reject H_0: $\mu = 500$ mg when the mean is actually different from 500 mg.

  iv. For vitamin C, reject H_0: $\mu = 500$ mg when the mean is actually equal to 500 mg.

Identifying H_0 and H_1.   _In Exercises 5–8, do the following:_

a. Express the original claim in symbolic form.

b. Identify the null and alternative hypotheses.

5. Landline Phones _Claim:_ Fewer than 10% of homes have only a landline telephone and no wireless phone. _Sample data:_ A survey by the National Center for Health Statistics showed that among 16,113 homes, 5.8% had landline phones without wireless phones.

6. Light Year _Claim:_ Most adults know that a light year is a measure of distance. _Sample data:_ A Pew Research Center survey of 3278 adults showed that 72% knew that a light year is a measure of distance.

7. Systolic Blood Pressure _Claim:_ The mean systolic blood pressure of a healthy adult is less than 123 mm Hg. _Sample data:_ Data Set 1 "Body Data" in Appendix B shows that for 300 healthy adults, the mean systolic blood pressure level is 122.96 mm Hg and the standard deviation is 15.85 mm Hg.

8. Systolic Blood Pressure *Claim:* Healthy adults have systolic blood pressure levels with a standard deviation greater than 5 mm Hg. *Sample data:* Data Set 1 "Body Data" in Appendix B shows that for 300 healthy adults, the systolic blood pressure amounts have a standard deviation of 15.85 mm Hg.

Test Statistics. *In Exercises 9–12, refer to the exercise identified and find the value of the test statistic. (Refer to Table 8-2 on page 378 to select the correct expression for evaluating the test statistic.)*

9. Exercise 5 "Landline Phones"

10. Exercise 6 "Light Year"

11. Exercise 7 "Systolic Blood Pressure"

12. Exercise 8 "Systolic Blood Pressure"

Finding P-Values. *In Exercises 13–16, do the following:*

a. Identify the hypothesis test as being two-tailed, left-tailed, or right-tailed.

b. Find the *P*-value. (See Figure 8-3 on page 380.)

c. Using a significance level of $\alpha = 0.05$, should we reject H_0 or should we fail to reject H_0?

13. The test statistic of $z = -0.75$ is obtained when testing the claim that $p < 1/3$.

14. The test statistic of $z = 2.00$ is obtained when testing the claim that $p > 0.25$.

15. The test statistic of $z = 1.80$ is obtained when testing the claim that $p \neq 0.314$.

16. The test statistic of $z = -1.60$ is obtained when testing the claim that $p \neq 0.455$.

Finding Critical Values. *In Exercises 17–20, refer to the information in the given exercise and use a 0.05 significance level for the following.*

a. Find the critical value(s).

b. Should we reject H_0 or should we fail to reject H_0?

17. Exercise 13

18. Exercise 14

19. Exercise 15

20. Exercise 16

Final Conclusions. *In Exercises 21–24, use a significance level of $\alpha = 0.05$ and use the given information for the following:*

a. State a conclusion about the null hypothesis. (Reject H_0 or fail to reject H_0.)

b. Without using technical terms or symbols, state a final conclusion that addresses the original claim.

21. Original claim: More than 58% of adults would erase all of their personal information online if they could. The hypothesis test results in a *P*-value of 0.3257.

22. Original claim: More than 35% of air travelers would choose another airline to have access to inflight Wi-Fi. The hypothesis test results in a *P*-value of 0.00001.

23. Original claim: The mean pulse rate (in beats per minute) of adult males is 72 bpm. The hypothesis test results in a *P*-value of 0.0095.

24. Original claim: The standard deviation of pulse rates of adult males is more than 11 bpm. The hypothesis test results in a *P*-value of 0.3045.

Type I and Type II Errors.   *In Exercises 25–28, provide statements that identify the type I error and the type II error that correspond to the given claim. (Although conclusions are usually expressed in verbal form, the answers here can be expressed with statements that include symbolic expressions such as p = 0.1.)*

25. The proportion of people who write with their left hand is equal to 0.1.

26. The proportion of people who know that water boils at a lower temperature at high altitudes is equal to 0.34.

27. The proportion of drivers who make angry gestures is greater than 0.25.

28. The proportion of job interviews that result from online applications is less than 1/2.

8-1   Beyond the Basics

29. Interpreting Power Chantix (varenicline) tablets are used as an aid to help people stop smoking. In a clinical trial, 129 subjects were treated with Chantix twice a day for 12 weeks, and 16 subjects experienced abdominal pain (based on data from Pfizer, Inc.). If someone claims that more than 8% of Chantix users experience abdominal pain, that claim is supported with a hypothesis test conducted with a 0.05 significance level. Using 0.18 as an alternative value of p, the power of the test is 0.96. Interpret this value of the power of the test.

30. Calculating Power Consider a hypothesis test of the claim that the Ericsson method of gender selection is effective in increasing the likelihood of having a baby girl, so that the claim is $p > 0.5$. Assume that a significance level of $\alpha = 0.05$ is used, and the sample is a simple random sample of size $n = 64$.

a. Assuming that the true population proportion is 0.65, find the power of the test, which is the probability of rejecting the null hypothesis when it is false. (*Hint:* With a 0.05 significance level, the critical value is $z = 1.645$, so any test statistic in the right tail of the accompanying top graph is in the rejection region where the claim is supported. Find the sample proportion $\hat{p}$ in the top graph, and use it to find the power shown in the bottom graph.)

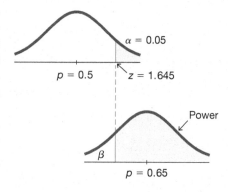

b. Explain why the green-shaded region of the bottom graph represents the power of the test.

31. Finding Sample Size to Achieve Power Researchers plan to conduct a test of a gender selection method. They plan to use the alternative hypothesis of $H_1: p > 0.5$ and a significance level of $\alpha = 0.05$. Find the sample size required to achieve at least 80% power in detecting an increase in p from 0.50 to 0.55. (This is a very difficult exercise. *Hint:* See Exercise 30.)

32. "At Least" and "At Most" Repeat Exercise 5 after changing the claim to this: "At most 10% of homes have only a landline telephone and no wireless phone." What do you conclude about this new claim of "at most 10%" if the null hypothesis is rejected? What do you conclude about this new claim of "at most 10%" if we fail to reject the null hypothesis?

8-2   Testing a Claim About a Proportion

Key Concept This section describes a complete hypothesis testing procedure for testing a claim made about a population proportion p. We illustrate hypothesis testing with these three methods: (1) the *P*-value method, (2) the critical value method, (3) the use of confidence intervals. In addition, Section 8-5 describes the alternative resampling methods of bootstrapping and randomization. The methods of this section can be used with claims about population proportions, probabilities, or the decimal equivalents of percentages.

There are different methods for testing a claim about a population proportion. Part 1 of this section is based on the use of a normal approximation to a binomial distribution, and this method serves well as an introduction to basic concepts, but it is not a method used by professional statisticians. Part 2 discusses other methods that might require the use of technology.

HINT: FINDING THE NUMBER OF SUCCESSES When using technology for hypothesis tests of proportions, we must usually enter the sample size n and the number of successes x, but in real applications the sample proportion $\hat{p}$ is often given instead of x. The number of successes x can be easily found by evaluating $x = n\hat{p}$. If 52% of 926 survey respondents answer "yes" to a question, the number who answered "yes" is $x = n \cdot \hat{p} = (926)(0.52) = 481.52$, which we must round to $x = 482$. (481.52 must be rounded to a whole number because it is a count of the number of people among 926, and also because technology typically requires entry of a whole number.)

Caution: When conducting hypothesis tests of claims about proportions, slightly different results can be obtained when calculating the test statistic using a given sample proportion instead of using a rounded value of x found by using $x = n\hat{p}$.

PART 1 Normal Approximation Method

The box on the next page includes the key elements used for testing a claim about a population proportion. The following procedure is based on the use of a normal distribution as an approximation to a binomial distribution. When obtaining sample proportions from samples that all have the same size n, and if n is large enough, the distribution of the sample proportions is approximately a normal distribution.

Equivalent Methods

When testing claims about proportions, the P-value method and the critical value method are equivalent to each other in the sense that they both lead to the same conclusion. However, the confidence interval method is not equivalent to them. (Both the P-value method and the critical value method use the same standard deviation based on the *claimed proportion p*, but the confidence interval method uses an estimated standard deviation based on the *sample proportion*.) So the confidence interval method could result in a different conclusion.

Recommendation: Use the P-value method or critical value method for *testing a claim* about a proportion (see Exercise 34), but use a confidence interval to *estimate* a population proportion.

Testing a Claim About a Population Proportion (Normal Approximation Method)

Objective

Conduct a formal hypothesis test of a claim about a population proportion p.

Notation

n = sample size or number of trials

$\hat{p} = \dfrac{x}{n}$ (*sample* proportion)

p = population proportion (p is the value used in the statement of the null hypothesis)

$q = 1 - p$

Requirements

1. The sample observations are a simple random sample.

2. The conditions for a *binomial distribution* are satisfied:

   - There is a fixed number of trials.

   - The trials are independent.

   - Each trial has two categories of "success" and "failure."

   - The probability of a success remains the same in all trials.

3. The conditions $np \geq 5$ and $nq \geq 5$ are both satisfied, so **the binomial distribution of sample proportions can be approximated by a normal distribution with** $\mu = np$ and $\sigma = \sqrt{npq}$ (as described in Section 6-6). Note that p used here is the *assumed* proportion used in the claim, not the sample proportion $\hat{p}$.

   DETOUR **(If this requirement is not satisfied, test the claim using a confidence interval obtained by using the resampling methods of bootstrapping, or use randomization described in Section 8-5, or use an exact method described in Part 2 of this section, or use the sign test described in Section 13-2.)**

Test Statistic for Testing a Claim About a Proportion

$$z = \frac{\hat{p} - p}{\sqrt{\dfrac{pq}{n}}}$$

P-values: *P*-values are automatically provided by technology. If technology is not available, use the standard normal distribution (Table A-2) and refer to Figure 8-3 on page 380.

Critical values: Use the standard normal distribution (Table A-2).

(CP) Claim: Most Internet Users Utilize Two-Factor Authentication to Protect Their Online Data

The Chapter Problem cited a Pew Research Center survey in which 926 Internet users were asked if they utilize two-factor authentication on at least one online account, and 52% of them responded with "yes." Use this result to test the claim that most Internet users utilize two-factor authentication to protect their online data.

REQUIREMENT CHECK We first check the three requirements.

1. The 926 consumers are randomly selected.

2. There is a fixed number (926) of independent trials with two categories (the respondent either utilizes two-factor authentication or does not).

3. The requirements $np \geq 5$ and $nq \geq 5$ are both satisfied with $n = 926$, $p = 0.5$, and $q = 0.5$. [The value of $p = 0.5$ comes from the claim. We get $np = (926)(0.5) = 463$ and we get $nq = (926)(0.5) = 463$, so both np and nq are greater than or equal to 5.]

The three requirements are satisfied. ✓

(CP) Solution: *P*-Value Method

Technology: Computer programs and calculators usually provide a *P*-value, so the *P*-value method is commonly used. See the accompanying TI-83/84 Plus calculator results showing the alternative hypothesis of "prop > 0.5," the test statistic of $z = 1.25$ (rounded), and the *P*-value of 0.1059 (rounded).

TI-83/84 Plus

Table A-2: If technology is not available, Figure 8-1 on page 376 in the preceding section lists the steps for using the *P*-value method. Using those steps from Figure 8-1, we can test the claim that most Internet users utilize two-factor authentication to protect their online data. We use the survey results of $n = 926$ and $\hat{p} = 0.52$.

Step 1: The original claim is that most Internet users utilize two-factor authentication to protect their online data. That claim can be expressed in symbolic form as $p > 0.5$.

Step 2: The opposite of the original claim is $p \leq 0.5$.

Step 3: Of the preceding two symbolic expressions, the expression $p > 0.5$ does not contain equality, so it becomes the alternative hypothesis. The null hypothesis is the statement that p equals the fixed value of 0.5. We can therefore express H_0 and H_1 as follows:

$$H_0: p = 0.5$$

$$H_1: p > 0.5 \text{ (original claim)}$$

Step 4: For the significance level, we select $\alpha = 0.05$, which is a very common choice.

Step 5: Because we are testing a claim about a population proportion p, the sample statistic $\hat{p}$ is relevant to this test. The sampling distribution of sample proportions $\hat{p}$ can be approximated by a normal distribution in this case.

Step 6: The test statistic $z = 1.25$ can be found by using technology or it can be calculated by using $\hat{p} = 482/926$, $n = 926$ (sample size), $p = 0.5$ (assumed in the null hypothesis), and $q = 1 - 0.5 = 0.5$. (482 is 52% of 926; see the hint on page 391.)

$$z = \frac{\hat{p} - p}{\sqrt{\dfrac{pq}{n}}} = \frac{\dfrac{482}{926} - 0.5}{\sqrt{\dfrac{(0.5)(0.5)}{926}}} = 1.25$$

The *P*-value can be found from technology or it can be found by using the following procedure, which is shown in Figure 8-3 on page 380.

Left-tailed test: *P*-value = area to left of test statistic z

Right-tailed test: *P*-value = area to right of test statistic z

Two-tailed test: *P*-value = *twice* the area of the extreme region bounded by the test statistic z

Because this hypothesis test is right-tailed with a test statistic of $z = 1.25$, the *P*-value is the area to the right of $z = 1.25$. Referring to Table A-2, we see that the cumulative area

Is 0.05 a Bad Choice?

The value of 0.05 is a very common choice for serving as the cutoff separating results considered to be significant from those that are not. Science writer John Timmer wrote in *Ars Technica* that some problems with conclusions in science are attributable to the fact that statistics is sometimes weak because of the common use of 0.05 for a significance level. He gives examples of particle physics and genetics experiments in which *P*-values must be much lower than 0.05. He cites a study by statistician Valen Johnson, who suggested that we should raise standards by requiring that experiments use a *P*-value of 0.005 or lower. We do know that the choice of 0.05 is largely arbitrary, and lowering the significance level will result in fewer conclusions of significance, along with fewer wrong conclusions.

to the *left* of $z = 1.25$ is 0.8944 (see Table A-2 row "1.2" and column ".05"), so the area to the right of that test statistic is $1 - 0.8944 = 0.1056$. We get P-value $= 0.1056$. Figure 8-6 shows the test statistic and P-value for this example. (If using technology, the P-value is 0.1059. This P-value is more accurate because it is found using an unrounded test statistic instead of the rounded value of $z = 1.25$.)

Step 7: Because the P-value of 0.1056 (or 0.1059 from technology) is greater than the significance level of $\alpha = 0.05$, we fail to reject the null hypothesis.

Step 8: Because we fail to reject H_0: $p = 0.5$, we *do not support* the alternative hypothesis of $p > 0.5$. Here is the conclusion: There is not sufficient sample evidence to support the claim that most Internet users utilize two-factor authentication to protect their online data.

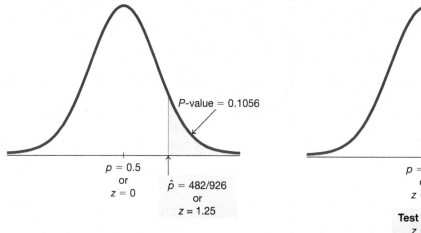

FIGURE 8-6   *P*-Value Method   FIGURE 8-7   Critical Value Method

ⓒⓟ Solution: Critical Value Method

The critical value method of testing hypotheses is summarized in Figure 8-1 on page 376. When using the critical value method with the claim given in Section 8-1 Example 1, "Most Internet users utilize two-factor authentication to protect their online data," Steps 1 through 5 are the same as in Steps 1 through 5 for the P-value method, as shown on the previous pages. We continue with Step 6 of the critical value method.

Step 6: The test statistic is computed to be $z = 1.25$, as shown for the preceding P-value method. With the critical value method, we now find the critical values (instead of the P-value). This is a right-tailed test, so the area of the critical region is an area of $\alpha = 0.05$ in the right tail. Referring to Table A-2 and applying the methods of Section 6-1, we find that the critical value is $z = 1.645$, which is at the boundary of the critical region, as shown in Figure 8-7.

Step 7: Because the test statistic does not fall within the critical region, we fail to reject the null hypothesis.

Step 8: Because we fail to reject H_0: $p = 0.5$, we conclude that there is not sufficient sample evidence to support the claim that most Internet users utilize two-factor authentication to protect their online data. (It is very important to use the correct wording for this final statement. See Figure 8-5 for help with wording this final conclusion.)

(CP) Solution: Confidence Interval Method

The claim given in Section 8-1 Example 1, "Most Internet users utilize two-factor authentication to protect their online data," can be tested with a 0.05 significance level by constructing a 90% confidence interval. (See Table 8-1 on page 376 to see why this right-tailed test with a 0.05 significance level corresponds to a 90% confidence interval.)

The 90% confidence interval estimate of the population proportion p is found using the sample data consisting of $n = 926$ and $x = 482$ (found from $\hat{p} = 0.52$). Using the methods of Section 7-1 we get this confidence interval:

$$0.494 < p < 0.548$$

This confidence interval shows us that it is likely that the true value of the population proportion p can be anywhere between 0.494 and 0.548, so it could be less than 0.5 and it could be equal to 0.5. Therefore, we can't conclude that $p > 0.5$ and we can't conclude that *most* Internet users utilize two-factor authentication. In this case, the conclusion is the same as with the P-value method and the critical value method, but that is not always the case. It is possible that a conclusion based on the confidence interval can be different from the conclusion based on the P-value method or critical value method.

(CP) Alternative Methods: Resampling Methods of Bootstrapping and Randomization

The claim given in the Chapter Problem, "Most Internet users utilize two-factor authentication to protect their online data," can be tested by using the resampling methods of bootstrapping and randomization. See Section 8-5 "Resampling: Using Technology for Hypothesis Testing."

Left-Tailed Test The preceding discussions in this section illustrated the method of hypothesis testing for a claim made about a proportion, and those preceding discussions are based on a right-tailed test. The following example illustrates a left-tailed test.

EXAMPLE 1   Fewer Than 30% of Adults Have Sleepwalked?

A study of sleepwalking or "nocturnal wandering" was described in *Neurology* magazine, and it included information that 29.2% of 19,136 American adults have sleepwalked. Would a reporter be justified in stating that "fewer than 30% of adults have sleepwalked"? Let's use a 0.05 significance level to test the claim that for the adult population, the proportion of those who have sleepwalked is less than 0.30.

SOLUTION

REQUIREMENT CHECK (1) The sample is a simple random sample. (2) There is a fixed number (19,136) of independent trials with two categories (a subject has sleepwalked or has not). (3) The requirements $np \geq 5$ and $nq \geq 5$ are both satisfied with $n = 19{,}136$ and $p = 0.30$. The three requirements are all satisfied. ✅

Step 1: The original claim is expressed in symbolic form as $p < 0.30$.

Step 2: The opposite of the original claim is $p \geq 0.30$.

Step 3: Because $p < 0.30$ does not contain equality, it becomes H_1. We get

$H_0: p = 0.30$ (null hypothesis)

$H_1: p < 0.30$ (alternative hypothesis and original claim)

continued

Step 4: The significance level is $\alpha = 0.05$.

Step 5: Because the claim involves the proportion p, the statistic relevant to this test is the sample proportion $\hat{p}$ and the sampling distribution of sample proportions can be approximated by the normal distribution.

Step 6: Technology If using technology, the test statistic and the P-value will be provided. See the accompanying results from StatCrunch showing that the test statistic is $z = -2.41$ (rounded) and the P-value $= 0.008$.

StatCrunch

Hypothesis test results:
p : Proportion of successes
H_0 : p = 0.3
H_A : p < 0.3

Proportion	Count	Total	Sample Prop.	Std. Err.	Z-Stat	P-value
p	5588	19136	0.29201505	0.0033127149	-2.4103945	0.008

Table A-2 If technology is not available, proceed as follows to conduct the hypothesis test using the P-value method summarized in Figure 8-1 on page 376.

The test statistic $z = -2.41$ is calculated as follows:

$$z = \frac{\hat{p} - p}{\sqrt{\dfrac{pq}{n}}} = \frac{0.292 - 0.30}{\sqrt{\dfrac{(0.30)(0.70)}{19{,}136}}} = -2.41$$

Refer to Figure 8-3 on page 380 for the procedure for finding the P-value. For this left-tailed test, the P-value is the area to the left of the test statistic. Using Table A-2, we see that the area to the left of $z = -2.41$ is 0.0080, so the P-value is 0.0080.

Step 7: Because the P-value of 0.0080 is less than or equal to the significance level of 0.05, we reject the null hypothesis.

INTERPRETATION

Because we reject the null hypothesis, we support the alternative hypothesis. We therefore conclude that there is sufficient evidence to support the claim that fewer than 30% of adults have sleepwalked.

YOUR TURN. Do Exercise 9 "Cursed Movie."

Critical Value Method If we were to repeat Example 1 using the critical value method of testing hypotheses, we would see that in Step 6 the critical value is $z = -1.645$, which can be found from technology or Table A-2. In Step 7 we would reject the null hypothesis because the test statistic of $z = -2.41$ would fall within the critical region bounded by $z = -1.645$. We would then reach the same conclusion given in Example 1.

Confidence Interval Method If we were to repeat Example 1 using the confidence interval method, we would use a 90% confidence level because we have a left-tailed test. (See Table 8-1.) We get this 90% confidence interval: $0.287 < p < 0.297$. Because the entire range of the confidence interval falls below 0.30, there is sufficient evidence to support the claim that fewer than 30% of adults have sleepwalked.

PART 2 Exact Methods for Testing Claims About a Population Proportion p

Instead of using the normal distribution as an *approximation* to the binomial distribution, we can get *exact* results by using the binomial probability distribution itself. Binomial probabilities are a real nuisance to calculate manually, but technology makes this approach quite simple. Also, this exact approach does not require that $np \geq 5$ and $nq \geq 5$, so we have a method that applies when that requirement is not satisfied. To test hypotheses using the exact method, find *P*-values as follows:

Exact Method Identify the sample size n, the number of successes x, and the claimed value of the population proportion p (used in the null hypothesis); then find the *P*-value by using technology for finding binomial probabilities as follows:

Left-tailed test: *P*-value $= P(x$ or fewer successes among n trials$)$

Right-tailed test: *P*-value $= P(x$ or more successes among n trials$)$

Two-tailed test: *P*-value $=$ twice the smaller of the preceding left-tailed and right-tailed values

Note: There is no universally accepted method for the two-tailed exact case, so this case can be treated with other different approaches, some of which are quite complex. For example, Minitab uses a "likelihood ratio test" that is different from the above approach that is commonly used.

EXAMPLE 2 Using the Exact Method

In Example 1 we have $n = 19{,}136$ subjects and 29.2% of them (or 5588) have sleepwalked. In Example 1 we used a hypothesis test to determine whether 29.2% is significantly less than 30% (or to determine whether 5588 is significantly low). Here, we can use the binomial probability distribution to find the probability of getting 5588 or fewer sleepwalkers when 19,136 subjects are randomly selected. Shown here is a portion of the Statdisk results obtained when finding binomial probabilities with $n = 19{,}136$ and $p = 0.30$. This Statdisk result shows that the probability of 5588 sleepwalkers or fewer is 0.0080286, which is the *P*-value. (This is the *P*-value because it is the probability of getting a result "at least as extreme" as the result of 5588 sleepwalkers that was obtained.) Given that the *P*-value is 0.0080286 and the significance level is 0.05, we reject the null hypothesis as we did in Example 1. We support the alternative hypothesis and we conclude that there is sufficient evidence to support the claim that fewer than 30% of adults have sleepwalked.

Statdisk

x	P(x)	P(x or fewer)	P(x or greater)
5588	0.0003421	0.0080286	0.9923135

YOUR TURN. Do Exercise 33 "Exact Method."

Improving the Exact Method A criticism of the exact method is that it is *too conservative* in the sense that the actual probability of a type I error is always less than or equal to α, and it could be much lower than α.

> **With the exact method, the *actual* probability of a type I error is less than or equal to α, which is the *desired* probability of a type I error.**

A **simple continuity correction** improves the conservative behavior of the exact method with an adjustment to the P-value that is obtained by subtracting from it the value that is one-half the binomial probability at the boundary, as shown below. (See Exercise 33 "Exact Method.") This method is easy to apply if technology is available for finding binomial probabilities.

Simple Continuity Correction to the Exact Method

Left-tailed test: $P\text{-value} = P(x \text{ or fewer}) - \dfrac{1}{2}P(\text{exactly } x)$

Right-tailed test: $P\text{-value} = P(x \text{ or more}) - \dfrac{1}{2}P(\text{exactly } x)$

Two-tailed test: $P\text{-value} = $ twice the smaller of the preceding left-tailed and right-tailed values

The above "simple continuity correction" is described in "Modifying the Exact Test for a Binomial Proportion and Comparisons with Other Approaches," by Alan Huston, *Journal of Applied Statistics,* Vol. 33, No. 7. For another improvement that uses weighted tail areas based on a measure of skewness, see the preceding article by Alan Huston.

TECH CENTER

Hypothesis Test: Proportion
Access tech supplements, videos, and data sets at **www.TriolaStats.com**

Statdisk	Minitab	StatCrunch
1. Click **Analysis** in the top menu. 2. Select **Hypothesis Testing** from the dropdown menu and select **Proportion One Sample** from the submenu. 3. Under *Alternative Hypothesis* select the format used for the alternative hypothesis, enter significance level, claimed proportion (from null hypothesis), sample size, and number of successes. 4. Click **Evaluate.**	1. Click **Stat** in the top menu. 2. Select **Basic Statistics** from the dropdown menu and select **1 Proportion** from the submenu. 3. Select **Summarized data** from the dropdown menu and enter number of events and number of trials (*n*). 4. Check the **Perform hypothesis test** box and enter the proportion used in the null hypothesis. 5. Click the **Options** button and enter the confidence level. (Enter 95.0 for a significance level of 0.05.) For *Alternative Hypothesis* select the format used for the alternative hypothesis. 6. For *Method* select **Normal approximation** to use the same method in this Section and click **OK** twice.	1. Click **Stat** in the top menu. 2. Select **Proportion Stats** from the dropdown menu, then select **One Sample—With Summary** from the submenu. 3. Enter the number of successes and number of observations (*n*). 4. Select **Hypothesis test for p** and for H_0 enter the claimed value of the population proportion (from the null hypothesis). For H_A select the format used for the alternative hypothesis. 5. Click **Compute!**

TECH CENTER

Hypothesis Test: Proportion

Access tech supplements, videos, and data sets at **www.TriolaStats.com**

TI-83/84 Plus Calculator	Excel	R
1. Press **STAT**, then select **TESTS** in the top menu. 2. Select **1-PropZTest** in the menu and press **ENTER**. 3. Enter the claimed population proportion p_0, number of successes x, and sample size n. For *prop* select the format used for the alternative hypothesis. 4. Select **Calculate** and press **ENTER**.	**XLSTAT Add-In (Required)** 1. Click on the **XLSTAT** tab in the Ribbon and then click **Parametric tests**. 2. Select **Tests for one proportion** from the dropdown menu. 3. Under *Data format* select **Frequency** if you know the number of successes x or select **Proportion** if you know the sample proportion $\hat{p}$. 4. Enter the frequency or sample proportion, sample size, and claimed value for the population proportion (*Test proportion*). 5. Check **z test** and uncheck **Continuity correction** for the methods of this section. 6. Click the **Options** tab. 7. Under *Alternative hypothesis* select the format used for the alternative hypothesis. For *Hypothesized difference* enter **0** and enter the desired significance level (enter **5** for a 0.05 significance level). Under *Variance (confidence interval)* select **Test proportion** and under *Confidence Interval* select **Wald**. 8. Click **OK** to display the result. The test statistic is labeled z *(Observed value)* and the *P*-value is below that. Critical values will also be displayed.	R command: **prop.test(x, n, p = NULL, alternative = c("two.sided", "less", "greater"), conf.level = 0.95, correct = FALSE)** *TIP:* To test the Chapter Problem claim: **prop.test (482, 926, 0.5, alternative = "greater", 0.95, correct = FALSE)** *A complete list of R statistical commands is available at TriolaStats.com*

8-2   Basic Skills and Concepts

Statistical Literacy and Critical Thinking

In Exercises 1–4, use the results from a Hankook Tire Gauge Index survey of a simple random sample of 1020 adults. Among the 1020 respondents, 86% rated themselves as above average drivers. We want to test the claim that more than 3/4 of adults rate themselves as above average drivers.

1. Number and Proportions

a. Identify the actual number of respondents who rated themselves as above average drivers.

b. Identify the sample proportion and use the symbol that represents it.

c. For the hypothesis test, identify the value used for the population proportion and use the symbol that represents it.

2. Null and Alternative Hypotheses and Test Statistic

a. Identify the null hypothesis and the alternative hypothesis.

b. Find the value of the test statistic.

3. Requirements Are the requirements of the hypothesis test all satisfied? Explain.

4. Equivalence, *P*-Value, and Significance Level

a. Regardless of the conclusion reached from the hypothesis test, is it possible that more than 3/4 of adults can be above average drivers?

b. If we use the same significance level to conduct the hypothesis test using the *P*-value method, the critical value method, and a confidence interval, which method is not always equivalent to the other two?

c. It was stated that we can easily remember how to interpret *P*-values with this: "If the *P* is low, the null must go." What does this mean?

d. Another memory trick sometimes used is this: "If the *P* is high, the null will fly." Given that a hypothesis test never results in a conclusion of proving or supporting a null hypothesis, how is this memory trick misleading?

e. Common significance levels are 0.01 and 0.05. Why would it be unwise to use a significance level with a number like 0.0483?

Using Technology.   In Exercises 5–8, identify the indicated values or interpret the given display. Use the normal distribution as an approximation to the binomial distribution, as described in Part 1 of this section. Use a 0.05 significance level and answer the following:

a. Is the test two-tailed, left-tailed, or right-tailed?

b. What is the test statistic?

c. What is the *P*-value?

d. What is the null hypothesis, and what do you conclude about it?

e. What is the final conclusion?

TI-83/84 Plus

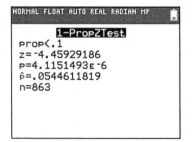

5. Adverse Reactions to Drug The drug Lipitor (atorvastatin) is used to treat high cholesterol. In a clinical trial of Lipitor, 47 of 863 treated subjects experienced headaches (based on data from Pfizer). The accompanying TI-83/84 Plus calculator display shows results from a test of the claim that fewer than 10% of treated subjects experience headaches.

6. Smartphone Protections In a Pew Research Center survey of 1040 smartphone owners, 28% of them said that they have no lock screen on their phones. The accompanying StatCrunch display results from testing the claim that more than 1/4 of smartphone owners have no lock screen on their phones.

StatCrunch

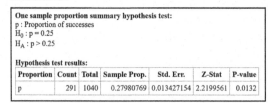

Minitab

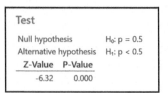

7. Online Selfie A Domain.ME survey of 1000 adults showed that 40% of the respondents searched for themselves online. The accompanying Minitab display results from a test of the claim that fewer than 50% of adults search for themselves online.

Statdisk

Sample proportion: 0.5294118
Test Statistic, z: 1.3284
Critical z: ±1.9600
P-Value: 0.1840

8. Biometric Security In a *USA Today* survey of 510 people, 53% said that we should replace passwords with biometric security, such as fingerprints. The accompanying Statdisk display results from a test of the claim that half of us say that we should replace passwords with biometric security.

Testing Claims About Proportions. *In Exercises 9–32, test the given claim. Identify the null hypothesis, alternative hypothesis, test statistic, P-value, or critical value(s), then state the conclusion about the null hypothesis, as well as the final conclusion that addresses the original claim. Use the P-value method unless your instructor specifies otherwise. Use the normal distribution as an approximation to the binomial distribution, as described in Part 1 of this section.*

9. Cursed Movie Released in 1956, the movie *The Conqueror* attracted considerable attention because many members of the cast and crew died from cancer supposedly resulting from exposure to radioactive fallout. The movie was shot a short distance from a site in Nevada where above-ground tests of atomic weapons were conducted. Among the 220 cast and crew members, 91 developed cancer. According to the National Cancer Institute, for that time period and for the age cohort, the incidence of cancer was about 40%. Use a 0.05 significance level to test the claim that the sample of cast and crew members is from a population in which the rate of cancer is greater than 40%. What do you conclude about the movie being a curse?

10. MythBusters The Discovery channel television show *MythBusters* conducted an experiment to study what happens when buttered toast is dropped on the floor. When 48 buttered slices of toast were dropped, 29 of them landed with the buttered side up and 19 landed with the buttered side down. Use a 0.05 significance level to test the claim that toast will land with the buttered side down 50% of the time. Write a conclusion that addresses the intent of the experiment.

11. Clothing Care Instructions For clothing, the accompanying symbol has been designated to indicate that the product should be dry-cleaned only. In a survey of 2005 Americans, 11% correctly knew what the symbol designated. Use a 0.01 significance level to test the claim that fewer than half of all Americans know what the symbol designates. What do these results suggest about this symbol?

12. M&Ms Data Set 38 "Candies" in Appendix B lists data from 345 M&Ms, and 25.5% of them are blue. The Mars candy company claims that the percentage of blue M&Ms is equal to 24%. Use a 0.05 significance level to test that claim. Should Mars take corrective action?

13. OxyContin The drug OxyContin (oxycodone) is used to treat pain, but it is dangerous because it is addictive and can be lethal. In clinical trials, 227 subjects were treated with OxyContin and 52 of them developed nausea (based on data from Purdue Pharma L.P.). Use a 0.05 significance level to test the claim that more than 20% of OxyContin users develop nausea. Does the rate of nausea appear to be too high?

14. Medical Malpractice In a study of 1228 randomly selected medical malpractice lawsuits, it was found that 856 of them were dropped or dismissed (based on data from the Physicians Insurers Association of America). Use a 0.01 significance level to test the claim that most medical malpractice lawsuits are dropped or dismissed. Should this be comforting to physicians?

15. News Media A Pew Research Center poll of 4581 Americans showed that 47% of the respondents prefer to watch the news rather than read or listen to it. Use those results with a 0.01 significance level to test the claim that fewer than half of Americans prefer to watch the news rather than read or listen to it.

16. Internet Use A random sample of 5005 adults in the United States includes 751 who do not use the Internet (based on three Pew Research Center polls). Use a 0.05 significance level to test the claim that the *percentage* of U.S. adults who do not use the Internet is now less than 48%, which was the percentage in the year 2000. If there appears to be a difference, is it dramatic?

17. Births A random sample of 860 births in New York State included 426 boys. Use a 0.05 significance level to test the claim that 51.2% of newborn babies are boys. Do the results support the belief that 51.2% of newborn babies are boys?

18. Mendelian Genetics When Mendel conducted his famous genetics experiments with peas, one sample of offspring consisted of 428 green peas and 152 yellow peas. Use a 0.01 significance level to test Mendel's claim that under the same circumstances, 25% of offspring peas will be yellow. What can we conclude about Mendel's claim?

19. Lie Detectors Trials in an experiment with a polygraph yield 98 results that include 24 cases of wrong results and 74 cases of correct results (based on data from experiments conducted by researchers Charles R. Honts of Boise State University and Gordon H. Barland of the Department of Defense Polygraph Institute). Use a 0.05 significance level to test the claim that such polygraph results are correct less than 80% of the time. Based on the results, should polygraph test results be prohibited as evidence in trials?

20. Tennis Instant Replay The Hawk-Eye electronic system is used in tennis for displaying an instant replay that shows whether a ball is in bounds or out of bounds so players can challenge calls made by referees. In a recent U.S. Open, singles players made 1569 challenges and 446 of them were successful, with the call overturned. Use a 0.01 significance level to test the claim that less than 30% of the challenges are successful. What do the results suggest about the ability of players to see calls better than referees?

21. Touch Therapy When she was 9 years of age, Emily Rosa did a science fair experiment in which she tested professional touch therapists to see if they could sense her energy field. She flipped a coin to select either her right hand or her left hand, and then she asked the therapists to identify the selected hand by placing their hand just under her hand without seeing it and without touching it. Among 280 trials, the touch therapists were correct 123 times (based on data in "A Close Look at Therapeutic Touch," *Journal of the American Medical Association*, Vol. 279, No. 13). Use a 0.10 significance level to test the claim that touch therapists use a method equivalent to random guesses. Do the results suggest that touch therapists are effective?

22. Online Friends A Pew Research Center poll of 1060 teens aged 13 to 17 showed that 57% of them have made new friends online. Use a 0.01 significance level to test the claim that half of all teens have made new friends online.

23. Road Rage In a survey of 2705 licensed drivers aged 16 and older, 33% of those respondents reported that they make angry gestures while driving (based on data from the Automobile Association of America). Use a 0.05 significance level to test the claim that among licensed drivers aged 16 and older, the percentage who make angry gestures while driving is equal to 35%. Does the conclusion change if the significance level is changed to 0.01?

24. Internet-Connected TV Penetration In a Leichtman Research Group survey of 1150 TV households, 74% of them had at least one Internet-connected TV device (e.g., Smart TV, stand-alone streaming device, connected video game console). A marketing executive wants to convey high penetration of Internet-connected TV devices, so he makes the claim that the percentage of all homes with at least one Internet-connected TV device is equal to 80%. Test that claim using a 0.05 significance level.

25. Super Bowl Wins Through the sample of the first 53 Super Bowls, 27 of them were won by teams in the National Football Conference (NFC). Use a 0.05 significance level to test the claim that NFC teams win the majority of Super Bowl games.

26. Supreme Court When Brett Kavanaugh was nominated to be a Supreme Court justice, a survey of 1144 Americans showed that 51% of them disapproved of Kavanaugh (based on a poll by the Washington Post and ABC News). *USA Today* published an article with this headline: "Majority of Americans Disapprove of Kavanaugh." Use a 0.05 significance level to test the claim made in that headline.

27. Overtime Rule in Football Before the overtime rule in the National Football League was changed in 2011, among 460 overtime games, 252 were won by the team that won the coin toss at the beginning of overtime. Using a 0.05 significance level, test the claim that the coin toss is fair in the sense that neither team has an advantage by winning it. Did the coin toss appear to be fair prior to the overtime rule change?

28. Postponing Death An interesting and popular hypothesis is that individuals can temporarily postpone death to survive a major holiday or important event such as a birthday. In a study, it was found that there were 6062 deaths in the week before Thanksgiving, and 5938 deaths the week after Thanksgiving (based on data from "Holidays, Birthdays, and Postponement of Cancer Death," by Young and Hade, *Journal of the American Medical Association,* Vol. 292, No. 24). If people can postpone death until after Thanksgiving, then the proportion of deaths in the week before should be less than 0.5. Use a 0.05 significance level to test the claim that the proportion of deaths in the week before Thanksgiving is less than 0.5. Based on the result, does there appear to be any indication that people can temporarily postpone death to survive the Thanksgiving holiday?

29. Belief in Ghosts In a Harris Interactive poll of 2250 adults, 42% of the respondents said that they believe in ghosts. Use a 0.01 significance level to test the claim that more than $1/3$ of adults believe in ghosts.

30. Smoking Stopped In a program designed to help patients stop smoking, 198 patients were given *sustained* care, and 82.8% of them were no longer smoking after one month (based on data from "Sustained Care Intervention and Postdischarge Smoking Cessation Among Hospitalized Adults," by Rigotti et al., *Journal of the American Medical Association,* Vol. 312, No. 7). Use a 0.01 significance level to test the claim that 80% of patients stop smoking when given sustained care. Does sustained care appear to be effective?

31. Bias in Jury Selection In the case of *Casteneda v. Partida,* it was found that during a period of 11 years in Hidalgo County, Texas, 870 people were selected for grand jury duty and 39% of them were Americans of Mexican ancestry. Among the people eligible for grand jury duty, 79.1% were Americans of Mexican ancestry. Use a 0.01 significance level to test the claim that the selection process is biased against Americans of Mexican ancestry. Does the jury selection system appear to be biased?

32. Legalization of Marijuana In 1969, only 12% of Americans were in favor of legalizing marijuana. A recent Pew Research Center poll of 1201 adults showed that 57% of them supported the legalization of marijuana. Use a 0.01 significance level to test the claim that the current rate of support is greater than the 12% level in 1969.

8-2 Beyond the Basics

33. Exact Method For each of the three different methods of hypothesis testing (identified in the left column), enter the *P*-values corresponding to the given alternative hypothesis and sample data. Use a 0.05 significance level. Note that the entries in the last column correspond to the Chapter Problem. How do the results agree with the large sample size?

	$H_1: p \neq 0.5$ $n = 10, x = 9$	$H_1: p \neq 0.4$ $n = 10, x = 9$	$H_1: p > 0.5$ $n = 926, x = 482$
Normal approximation			
Exact			
Exact with simple continuity correction			

34. Using Confidence Intervals to Test Hypotheses When analyzing the last digits of telephone numbers in Port Jefferson, it is found that among 1000 randomly selected digits, 119 are zeros. If the digits are randomly selected, the proportion of zeros should be 0.1.

a. Use the critical value method with a 0.05 significance level to test the claim that the proportion of zeros equals 0.1.

b. Use the *P*-value method with a 0.05 significance level to test the claim that the proportion of zeros equals 0.1.

continued

c. Use the sample data to construct a 95% confidence interval estimate of the proportion of zeros. What does the confidence interval suggest about the claim that the proportion of zeros equals 0.1?

d. Compare the results from the critical value method, the *P*-value method, and the confidence interval method. Do they all lead to the same conclusion?

35. Power For a hypothesis test with a specified significance level α, the probability of a type I error is α, whereas the probability β of a type II error depends on the particular value of p that is used as an alternative to the null hypothesis.

a. Using an alternative hypothesis of $p < 0.4$, using a sample size of $n = 50$, and assuming that the true value of p is 0.25, find the power of the test. See Exercise 30 "Calculating Power" in Section 8-1. [*Hint:* Use the values $p = 0.25$ and $pq/n = (0.25)(0.75)/50$.]

b. Find the value of β, the probability of making a type II error.

c. Given the conditions cited in part (a), find the power of the test. What does the power tell us about the effectiveness of the test?

36. Claim of "At Least" or "At Most"

How do the following results change?

a. Chapter Problem claim is changed to this: "*At least 50%* of Internet users utilize two-factor authentication to protect their online data."

b. Exercise 15 "News Media" claim is changed to this: "*At most half* of Americans prefer to watch the news rather than read or listen to it."

8-3   Testing a Claim About a Mean

Key Concept Testing a claim about a population mean is one of the most important methods presented in this book. This section deals with the very realistic and commonly used case in which the population standard deviation σ is not known. (There is a brief discussion of the procedure used when σ is known, which is very rare.)

Testing a Claim About μ with σ Not Known

In reality, it is very rare that we test a claim about an unknown value of a population mean μ but we somehow know the value of the population standard deviation σ. The realistic situation is that we test a claim about a population mean and the value of the population standard deviation σ is not known. When σ is not known, we estimate it with the sample standard deviation s. From the central limit theorem (Section 6-4), we know that the distribution of sample means $\bar{x}$ is approximately a normal distribution with mean $\mu_{\bar{x}} = \mu$ and standard deviation $\sigma_{\bar{x}} = \sigma/\sqrt{n}$, but if σ is unknown, we estimate it with $s/\sqrt{n}$, which is used in the test statistic for a "*t* test." This test statistic has a distribution called the Student *t* distribution. The requirements, test statistic, *P*-value, and critical values are summarized in the Key Elements box that follows.

Equivalent Methods

For the *t* test described in this section, the *P*-value method, the critical value method, and the confidence interval method are all equivalent in the sense that they all lead to the same conclusions.

Testing Claims About a Population Mean with σ Not Known

Objective

Use a formal hypothesis test to test a claim about a population mean μ.

Notation

n = sample size
s = *sample* standard deviation

$\bar{x}$ = *sample* mean
$\mu_{\bar{x}}$ = *population* mean (this value is taken from the claim and is used in the statement of the null hypothesis H_0)

Requirements

1. The sample is a simple random sample.

2. Either or both of these conditions are satisfied: The population is normally distributed or $n > 30$.

> **DETOUR** (If the second requirement is not satisfied, test the claim using a resampling method of bootstrapping or randomization described in Section 8-5, or use a nonparametric method such as the sign test (Section 13-2) or Wilcoxon signed-ranks test (Section 13-3).)

Test Statistic for Testing a Claim About a Mean

$$t = \frac{\bar{x} - \mu_{\bar{x}}}{\frac{s}{\sqrt{n}}}$$
(Round t to three decimal places, as in Table A-3.)

P-values: Use technology or use the Student t distribution (Table A-3) with degrees of freedom given by df $= n - 1$. (Figure 8-3 on page 380 summarizes the procedure for finding P-values.)

Critical values: Use the Student t distribution (Table A-3) with degrees of freedom given by df $= n - 1$. (When Table A-3 doesn't include the number of degrees of freedom, you could be conservative by using the next lower number of degrees of freedom found in the table, you could use the closest number of degrees of freedom in the table, or you could interpolate.)

Requirement of "Normality or $n > 30$"

Normality requirement with Large Samples ($n > 30$): It is common to consider the normality requirement to be satisfied if the sample is large ($n > 30$), because we know from the central limit theorem that for such large samples, the distribution of the sample means will tend to approximate a normal distribution. (For some population distributions that are extremely far from normal, the sample size might need to be much larger than 30.)

Normality requirement with Small Samples ($n \leq 30$): With small samples, the method for finding a confidence interval estimate of μ is *robust* against a departure from normality, which means that the normality requirement is loose. The distribution need not be perfectly bell-shaped (it never is), but it should satisfy these conditions:

1. The distribution of the sample data should be somewhat close to being symmetric.

2. The distribution of the sample data should have one mode.

3. The sample data should not include any outliers.

Go Figure

There are now 2.7 zettabytes (10^{21}) of data in our digital universe.

Important Properties of the Student *t* Distribution

Here is a brief review of important properties of the Student *t* distribution first presented in Section 7-2:

1. The Student *t* distribution is different for different sample sizes (see Figure 7-4 in Section 7-2).

2. The Student *t* distribution has the same general bell shape as the standard normal distribution; its wider shape reflects the greater variability that is expected when *s* is used to estimate σ.

3. The Student *t* distribution has a mean of $t = 0$ (just as the standard normal distribution has a mean of $z = 0$).

4. The standard deviation of the Student *t* distribution varies with the sample size and is greater than 1 (unlike the standard normal distribution, which has $\sigma = 1$).

5. As the sample size *n* gets larger, the Student *t* distribution gets closer to the standard normal distribution.

P-Value Method with Technology

If suitable technology is available, the *P*-value method of testing hypotheses is the way to go.

EXAMPLE 1 **Adult Sleep: *P*-Value Method with Technology**

The author obtained times of sleep for randomly selected adult subjects included in the National Health and Nutrition Examination Study, and those times (hours) are listed below. Here are the unrounded statistics for this sample: $n = 12$, $\bar{x} = 6.83333333$ hours, $s = 1.99240984$ hours. A common recommendation is that adults should sleep between 7 hours and 9 hours each night. Use the *P*-value method with a 0.05 significance level to test the claim that the mean amount of sleep for adults is less than 7 hours.

$$4 \quad 8 \quad 4 \quad 4 \quad 8 \quad 6 \quad 9 \quad 7 \quad 7 \quad 10 \quad 7 \quad 8$$

SOLUTION

REQUIREMENT CHECK (1) The sample is a simple random sample. (2) The second requirement is that "the population is normally distributed or $n > 30$." The sample size is $n = 12$, which does not exceed 30, so we must determine whether the sample data appear to be from a normally distributed population. The accompanying histogram and normal quantile plot, along with the apparent absence of outliers, indicate that the sample appears to be from a population with a distribution that is approximately normal. Both requirements are satisfied. ☑

Statdisk

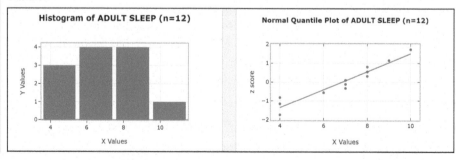

Here are the steps that follow the procedure summarized in Figure 8-1 on page 376.

Step 1: The claim that "the mean amount of adult sleep is less than 7 hours" becomes $\mu < 7$ hours when expressed in symbolic form.

Step 2: The alternative (in symbolic form) to the original claim is $\mu \geq 7$ hours.

Step 3: Because the statement $\mu < 7$ hours does not contain the condition of equality, it becomes the alternative hypothesis H_1. The null hypothesis H_0 is the statement that $\mu = 7$ hours.

$$H_0: \mu = 7 \text{ hours (null hypothesis)}$$

$$H_1: \mu < 7 \text{ hours (alternative hypothesis and original claim)}$$

Step 4: As specified in the statement of the problem, the significance level is $\alpha = 0.05$.

Step 5: Because the claim is made about the *population mean* μ, the sample statistic most relevant to this test is the *sample mean* $\bar{x}$, and we use the t distribution.

Step 6: The sample statistics of $n = 12, \bar{x} = 6.83333333$ hours, $s = 1.99240984$ hours are used to calculate the test statistic as follows, but technologies provide the test statistic of $t = -0.290$. In calculations such as the following, it is good to carry extra decimal places and not round.

$$t = \frac{\bar{x} - \mu_{\bar{x}}}{\frac{s}{\sqrt{n}}} = \frac{6.83333333 - 7}{\frac{1.99240984}{\sqrt{12}}} = -0.290$$

P-Value with Technology We could use technology to obtain the P-value. Shown below and on the next page are results from several technologies, and we can see that the P-value is 0.3887 (rounded). (SPSS shows a two-tailed P-value of 0.777, so it must be halved for this one-tailed test.)

Step 7: Because the P-value of 0.3887 is greater than the significance level of $\alpha = 0.05$, we fail to reject the null hypothesis.

INTERPRETATION

Step 8: Because we fail to reject the null hypothesis, we conclude that there is not sufficient evidence to support the claim that the mean amount of adult sleep is less than 7 hours.

 YOUR TURN. Do Exercise 13 "Systolic Blood Pressure."

continued

Go Figure

Mastercard alone receives about three Internet attack attempts every *second*.

TI-83/84 Plus

```
NORMAL FLOAT AUTO REAL RADIAN MP

          T-Test
μ<7
t=-.2897748534
p=.3886888459
x̄=6.833333333
Sx=1.99240984
n=12
```

Statdisk

```
t Test
Test Statistic, t: -0.28977
Critical t:        -1.79588
P-Value:            0.38869

90% Confidence interval:
5.80041 < μ < 7.86625
```

Excel (XLSTAT)

Difference	-0.1667
t (Observed value)	-0.2898
t (Critical value)	-1.7959
DF	11.0000
p-value (one-tailed)	0.3887
alpha	0.0500

Holistic Statistics

Instead of using only the *P*-value method of testing a claim about a population mean, it is wise to use *holistic statistics* with a variety of different approaches. Begin with an analysis of the sampling method, and explore the sample data looking for outliers, the nature of the distribution, and anything else notable about the data. In addition to the *t*-test described in this section, construct a confidence interval (Section 7-2), use the sign test (Section 13-2), Wilcoxon Signed-Ranks test (Section 13-3), use bootstrapping to obtain a confidence interval estimate of the population mean (Section 7-4), and use the resampling method of randomization (Section 8-5). This holistic approach is much more likely to provide us with clear understanding of the claim being tested. See Chapter 15.

Minitab

Descriptive Statistics

N	Mean	StDev	SE Mean	95% Upper Bound for μ
12	6.833	1.992	0.575	7.866

μ: mean of C10

Test

Null hypothesis H_0: μ = 7
Alternative hypothesis H_1: μ < 7

T-Value	P-Value
-0.29	0.389

JMP

Hypothesized Value	7
Actual Estimate	6.83333
DF	11
Std Dev	1.99241

t Test

Test Statistic	-0.2898
Prob > |t|	0.7774
Prob > t	0.6113
Prob < t	0.3887

StatCrunch

One sample T hypothesis test:
μ : Mean of variable
H_0 : μ = 7
H_A : μ < 7

Hypothesis test results:

Variable	Sample Mean	Std. Err.	DF	T-Stat	P-value
ADULT SLEEP	6.8333333	0.57515918	11	-0.28977485	0.3887

SPSS

	Test Value = 7				95% Confidence Interval of the Difference	
	t	df	Sig. (2-tailed)	Mean Difference	Lower	Upper
SLEEP	-.290	11	.777	-.16667	-1.4326	1.0993

Examine the technology displays to see that only two of them include critical values, but they all include *P*-values. This is a major reason why the *P*-value method of testing hypotheses has become so widely used in recent years.

P-Value Method Without Technology

If suitable technology is not available, we can use Table A-3 to identify a *range of values* containing the *P*-value. In using Table A-3, keep in mind that it is designed for positive values of *t* and right-tail areas only, but left-tail areas correspond to the same *t* values with negative signs.

EXAMPLE 2   Adult Sleep: *P*-Value Method Without Technology

Example 1 is a left-tailed test with a test statistic of $t = -0.290$ (rounded) and a sample size of $n = 12$, so the number of degrees of freedom is df $= n - 1 = 11$. Using the test statistic of $t = -0.290$ with Table A-3, examine the values of *t* in the row for df $= 11$ to see that 0.290 is less than all of the listed *t* values in the row, which indicates that the area in the left tail below the test statistic of $t = -0.290$ is greater than 0.10. In this case, Table A-3 allows us to conclude that *P*-value > 0.10, but technology provided the *P*-value of 0.3887. With the *P*-value > 0.10, the conclusions are the same as in Example 1.

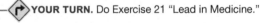 **YOUR TURN.** Do Exercise 21 "Lead in Medicine."

HINT Because using Table A-3 to find a range of values containing the *P*-value can be a bit tricky, the critical value method (see Example 3) might be easier than the *P*-value method if suitable technology is not available.

Critical Value Method

> **EXAMPLE 3** Adult Sleep: Critical Value Method
>
> Example 1 is a left-tailed test with test statistic $t = -0.290$ (rounded). The sample size is $n = 12$, so the number of degrees of freedom is df $= n - 1 = 11$. Given the significance level of $\alpha = 0.05$, refer to the row of Table A-3 corresponding to 11 degrees of freedom, and refer to the column identifying an "area in one tail" of 0.05 (the significance level). The intersection of the row and column yields the critical value of $t = 1.796$, but this test is left-tailed, so the actual critical value is $t = -1.796$. Figure 8-8 shows that the test statistic of $t = -0.290$ does not fall within the critical region bounded by the critical value $t = -1.796$, so we fail to reject the null hypothesis. The conclusions are the same as those given in Example 1.
>
>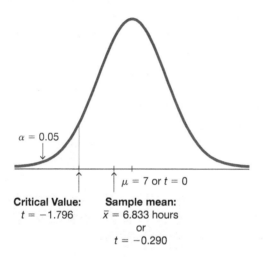
>
> $\alpha = 0.05$
>
> $\mu = 7$ or $t = 0$
>
> **Critical Value:**   **Sample mean:**
> $t = -1.796$ $\bar{x} = 6.833$ hours
>   or
> $t = -0.290$
>
> **FIGURE 8-8 t Test: Critical Value Method**

Confidence Interval Method

> **EXAMPLE 4** Adult Sleep: Confidence Interval Method
>
> Example 1 is a left-tailed test with significance level $\alpha = 0.05$, so we should use 90% as the confidence level (as indicated by Table 8-1 on page 376). For the sample data given in Example 1, here is the 90% confidence interval estimate of μ: 5.8 hours $< \mu <$ 7.9 hours. In testing the claim that $\mu < 7$ hours, we use H_0: $\mu = 7$ hours, but the assumed value of $\mu = 7$ hours is contained within the confidence interval limits, so the confidence interval is telling us that 7 hours could be the value of μ. We don't have sufficient evidence to reject H_0: $\mu = 7$ hours, so we fail to reject this null hypothesis and we get the same conclusions given in Example 1.

Alternative Methods Used When Population Is Not Normal and $n \leq 30$

The methods of this section include two requirements: (1) The sample is a simple random sample; (2) either the population is normally distributed or $n > 30$. If we have sample data that are not collected in an appropriate way, such as a voluntary response sample, it is likely that there is nothing that can be done to salvage the data, and the methods of this section should not be used. If the data are a simple random

Practical Significance

Merck conducted clinical trials of its sleep-aid drug Belsomra. Some key findings: (1) Subjects taking Belsomra fell asleep *six minutes* faster than those taking a placebo; (2) Belsomra subjects slept *16 minutes longer* than the placebo subjects; (3) the preceding two results were found to have statistical significance.

Merck proceeded to spend $96 million in one year for the promotion of Belsomra, and Merck expected to eventually have more Belsomra sales than Ambien and Lunesta, the current market leaders. Belsomra costs around $12 per pill and was met with negative reviews and poor sales given the high cost and potential side effects. Given the relatively small effects on sleep, it appears that Belsomra has statistical significance, but not practical significance.

sample but the second condition is violated, there are alternative methods that could be used, including these three alternative methods:

- **Bootstrap Resampling** Use the confidence interval method of testing hypotheses, but obtain the confidence interval using bootstrap resampling, introduced in Section 7-4. See Section 8-5 for more detail about using this resampling method.

- **Randomization** This method involves resampling (*with* replacement) after the sample data have been modified to reflect the value of the population parameter that is assumed in the null hypothesis. See Section 8-5 for more details about using this resampling method.

- **Sign Test** See Section 13-2.

- **Wilcoxon Signed-Ranks Test** See Section 13-3.

Two-Tailed Test

The preceding examples are based on the same left-tailed test. The following example illustrates a hypothesis test of a claim about a mean using a two-tailed test.

EXAMPLE 5   Is the Mean Body Temperature Really 98.6°F?

Data Set 5 "Body Temperatures" in Appendix B includes measured body temperatures with these statistics for 12 AM on day 2: $n = 106$, $\bar{x} = 98.20°F$, $s = 0.62°F$. (This is the author's favorite data set.) Use a 0.05 significance level to test the common belief that the population mean is 98.6°F.

SOLUTION

REQUIREMENT CHECK (1) With the study design used, we can treat the sample as a simple random sample. (2) The second requirement is that "the population is normally distributed or $n > 30$." The sample size is $n = 106$, so the second requirement is satisfied and there is no need to investigate the normality of the data. Both requirements are satisfied. ☑

Here are the steps that follow the procedure summarized in Figure 8-1.

Step 1: The claim that "the population mean is 98.6°F" becomes $\mu = 98.6°F$ when expressed in symbolic form.

Step 2: The alternative (in symbolic form) to the original claim is $\mu \neq 98.6°F$.

Step 3: Because the statement $\mu \neq 98.6°F$ does not contain the condition of equality, it becomes the alternative hypothesis H_1. The null hypothesis H_0 is the statement that $\mu = 98.6°F$.

$$H_0: \mu = 98.6°F \text{ (null hypothesis and original claim)}$$

$$H_1: \mu \neq 98.6°F \text{ (alternative hypothesis)}$$

Step 4: As specified in the statement of the problem, the significance level is $\alpha = 0.05$.

Step 5: Because the claim is made about the *population mean* μ, the sample statistic most relevant to this test is the *sample mean* $\bar{x}$. We use the t distribution because the relevant sample statistic is $\bar{x}$ and the requirements for using the t distribution are satisfied.

Step 6: The sample statistics are used to calculate the test statistic as follows, but technologies use unrounded values to provide the test statistic of $t = -6.61$.

$$t = \frac{\bar{x} - \mu_{\bar{x}}}{\frac{s}{\sqrt{n}}} = \frac{98.20 - 98.6}{\frac{0.62}{\sqrt{106}}} = -6.64$$

P-Value: The P-value is 0.0000 or 0+ (or "less than 0.01" if using Table A-3).

Critical Values: The critical values are ± 1.983 (or ± 1.984 if using Table A-3).

Confidence Interval: The 95% confidence interval is $98.08°F < \mu < 98.32°F$, which does not contain 98.6°F.

Step 7: All three approaches lead to the same conclusion: Reject H_0.

- **P-Value:** The P-value of 0.0000 is less than the significance level of $\alpha = 0.05$.

- **Critical Values:** The test statistic $t = -6.64$ falls in the critical region bounded by ± 1.983.

- **Confidence Interval:** The claimed mean of 98.6°F does not fall within the confidence interval of $98.08°F < \mu < 98.32°F$.

INTERPRETATION

Step 8: There is sufficient evidence to warrant *rejection* of the common belief that the population mean is 98.6°F.

YOUR TURN. Do Exercise 23 "Cell Phone Radiation."

Go Figure

Americans spend 37 billion hours in line each year.

Testing a Claim About μ When σ Is Known

In reality, it is very rare to test a claim about an unknown population mean while the population standard deviation is somehow known. For this case of known σ, the procedure is essentially the same as earlier in this section, the requirements are the same, but the test statistic, P-value, and critical values are as shown below.

> **CAUTION** In days of yore preceding the widespread availability of good technology, this "σ known" case was commonly used with this practice: If $n > 30$, treat the sample standard deviation s as if it were the known value of σ. Because we now have such great technology, we can use the t distribution instead of the normal distribution. Consequently, this "σ known" approach is now effectively obsolete.

KEY ELEMENTS

Testing a Claim About a Mean (When σ Is Known)

Requirements

(1) The sample is a simple random sample, (2) the population standard deviation σ is known, and (3) either or both of these conditions is satisfied: the sample is large $(n > 30)$ or the sample is from a normally distributed population.

Test Statistic

$$z = \frac{\bar{x} - \mu_{\bar{x}}}{\dfrac{\sigma}{\sqrt{n}}}$$

P-value: Provided by technology, or use the standard normal distribution (Table A-2) with the procedure in Figure 8-3 on page 380.

Critical values: Use the standard normal distribution (Table A-2).

TECH CENTER

 Hypothesis Test: Mean
Access tech supplements, videos, and data sets at **www.TriolaStats.com**

Statdisk

1. Click **Analysis** in the top menu.
2. Select **Hypothesis Testing** from the dropdown menu and select **Mean One Sample** from the submenu.
3. Select the desired format for the *Alternative Hypothesis*, enter the desired significance level and claimed mean (from the null hypothesis).
4. *Using Summary Statistics:* Select the **Use Summary Statistics** tab and enter the sample size, sample mean, and sample standard deviation.

   Using Sample Data: Select the **Use Data** tab and select the desired data column.
5. Click **Evaluate.**

Minitab

1. Click **Stat** in the top menu.
2. Select **Basic Statistics** from the dropdown menu and select **1-Sample t** from the submenu.
3. *Using Summary Statistics:* Select **Summarized data** from the dropdown menu and enter the sample size, sample mean, and sample standard deviation.

   Using Sample Data: Select **One or more samples, each in a column** from the dropdown menu and select the desired data column.
4. Check the **Perform hypothesis test** box and enter the mean used in the null hypothesis.
5. Click the **Options** button and enter the confidence level. (Enter 95.0 for a significance level of 0.05.) For *Alternative hypothesis* select the format used for the alternative hypothesis.
6. Click **OK** twice.

TIP: Another procedure is to click on **Assistant** in the top menu, then select **Hypothesis Tests** and **1-Sample t.** Complete the dialog box to get results, including *P*-value and other helpful information.

StatCrunch

1. Click **Stat** in the top menu.
2. Select **T Stats** from the dropdown menu, then select **One Sample** from the submenu.
3. *Using Summary Statistics:* Select **With Summary** from the submenu and enter the sample mean, sample standard deviation, and sample size.

   Using Sample Data: Select **With Data** from the submenu and select the desired data column.
4. Select **Hypothesis test for μ** and for H_0 enter the claimed value of the population mean (from the null hypothesis). For H_A select the format used for the alternative hypothesis.
5. Click **Compute!**

TI-83/84 Plus Calculator

1. Press **STAT**, then select **TESTS** in the top menu.
2. Select **T-Test** in the menu and press **ENTER**.
3. Enter the claimed value of the population mean μ_0.
4. *Using Summary Statistics:* Select **Stats**, press **ENTER** and enter the sample mean $\bar{x}$, sample standard deviation Sx, and sample size n.

   Using Sample Data: Select **Data**, press **ENTER**, and enter the name of the list containing the sample data. *Freq* should be set to **1**.
5. For μ select the format used for the alternative hypothesis.
6. Select **Calculate** and press **ENTER**.

Excel

XLSTAT Add-In (Required)
Requires original sample data; does not work with summary data.

1. Click on the **XLSTAT** tab in the Ribbon and then click **Parametric tests.**
2. Select **One-Sample t-test and z-test** from the dropdown menu.
3. Under *Data* enter the range of cells containing the sample data. For *Data format* select **One sample.** If the first row of data contains a label, also check the **Column labels** box.
4. Check the **Student's t test** box.
5. Click the **Options** tab.
6. Under *Alternative hypothesis* select the desired format ($\neq$ for two-tailed test, $<$ for left-tailed test, $>$ for right-tailed test).
7. For *Theoretical mean*, enter the claimed value of the population mean (from the null hypothesis). Enter the desired significance level (enter **5** for a significance level of 0.05).
8. Click **OK** to display the results. The test statistic is identified as *t(Observed value)* or *z(Observed value)*. The *P*-value and critical value(s) are also displayed.

R

R command:
t.test(x, alternative = c("two.sided", "less", "greater"), mu = 0, conf.level = 0.95)

TIP: For Example 1: **t.test(x, alternative = "less", mu = 7, conf.level = 0.95)**

A complete list of R statistical commands is available at TriolaStats.com

8-3   Basic Skills and Concepts

Statistical Literacy and Critical Thinking

1. Basketball Player Salaries Listed below are salaries (millions of dollars) of professional basketball players in a recent year. What requirements must be satisfied to test the claim that the salaries are from a population with a mean greater than 5 million dollars? Are those requirements satisfied?

1   1   2   2   2   2   2   2   4   4   6   7   9   12   36

2. df If we are using the sample data from Exercise 1 for a t test of the claim that the population mean is greater than \$5 million, what does df denote, and what is its value?

3. t Test Exercise 2 refers to a t test. What is a t test? Why is the letter t used? What is unrealistic about the z test method described at the end of this section?

4. Test Statistic and Critical Value The statistics for the sample data in Exercise 1 are $n = 15$, $\bar{x} = 6.133333$, and $s = 8.862978$, where the units are millions of dollars. Find the test statistic and critical value(s) for a test of the claim that the salaries are from a population with a mean greater than 5 million dollars. Assume that a 0.05 significance level is used.

Finding P-values.   *In Exercises 5–8, either use technology to find the P-value or use Table A-3 to find a range of values for the P-value. Based on the result, what is the final conclusion?*

5. Weights of Quarters The claim is that weights (grams) of quarters made after 1964 have a mean equal to 5.670 g as required by mint specifications. The sample size is $n = 40$ and the test statistic is $t = -3.135$.

6. Weights of Pennies The claim is that weights (grams) of pennies made after 1983 have a mean equal to 2.500 g as required by mint specifications. The sample size is $n = 37$ and the test statistic is $t = -0.331$.

7. Cotinine in Smokers The claim is that smokers have a mean cotinine level greater than the level of 2.84 ng/mL found for nonsmokers. (Cotinine is used as a biomarker for exposure to nicotine.) The sample size is $n = 902$ and the test statistic is $t = 56.319$.

8. Body Temperatures The claim is that for 8 AM body temperatures of males, the mean is less than 98.6°F. The sample size is $n = 33$ and the test statistic is $t = -4.411$.

Technology.   *In Exercises 9–12, test the given claim by using the display provided from technology. Use a 0.05 significance level. Identify the null and alternative hypotheses, test statistic, P-value (or range of P-values), or critical value(s), and state the final conclusion that addresses the original claim.*

9. Peanut Butter Cups Data Set 38 "Candies" includes weights of Reese's peanut butter cups. The accompanying Statdisk display results from using all 38 weights to test the claim that the sample is from a population with a mean equal to 8.953 g.

10. Taxi Times Data Set 32 "Taxis" in Appendix B includes times (minutes) of taxi cab rides in New York City. Using the first 36 times to test the claim that the mean of all such times is less than 15 minutes, the accompanying Minitab display is obtained.

11. Tower of Terror Data Set 33 "Disney World Wait Times" includes wait times (minutes) for the Tower of Terror ride at 5:00 PM. Using the first 40 times to test the claim that the mean of all such wait times is more than 30 minutes, the accompanying Excel display is obtained.

Statdisk

```
t Test
Test Statistic, t:  -3.42304
Critical t:         ±2.02619
P-Value:            0.00153
```

Minitab

Test		
Null hypothesis	H_0: $\mu = 15$	
Alternative hypothesis	H_1: $\mu < 15$	
T-Value	P-Value	
-1.61	0.058	

Excel (XLSTAT)

Difference	3
t (Observed value)	0.940
t (Critical value)	1.685
DF	39
p-value (one-tailed)	0.177
alpha	0.05

JMP

Hypothesized Value	300
Actual Estimate	221.03
DF	32
Std Dev	124.053
t Test	
Test Statistic	-3.6569
Prob > |t|	0.0009*
Prob > t	0.9995
Prob < t	0.0005*

12. Service Times Data Set 30 "Queues" in Appendix B includes service times (seconds) of cars being serviced at a Delaware inspection center. Using the first 33 times to test the claim that the mean of all such times is less than 5 minutes or 300 seconds, the accompanying display is obtained.

Testing Hypotheses. *In Exercises 13–24, assume that a simple random sample has been selected and test the given claim. Unless specified by your instructor, use either the P-value method or the critical value method for testing hypotheses. Identify the null and alternative hypotheses, test statistic, P-value (or range of P-values), or critical value(s), and state the final conclusion that addresses the original claim.*

13. Systolic Blood Pressure Systolic blood pressure levels above 120 mm Hg are considered to be high. For the 300 systolic blood pressure levels listed in Data Set 1 "Body Data" from Appendix B, the mean is 122.96000 mm Hg and the standard deviation is 15.85169 mm Hg. Use a 0.01 significance level to test the claim that the sample is from a population with a mean greater than 120 mm Hg.

14. Diastolic Blood Pressure Diastolic blood pressure levels of 60 mm Hg or lower are considered to be too low. For the 300 diastolic blood pressure levels listed in Data Set 1 "Body Data" from Appendix B, the mean is 70.75333 mm Hg and the standard deviation is 11.61618 mm Hg. Use a 0.01 significance level to test the claim that the sample is from a population with a mean greater than 60 mm Hg.

15. IQ and Lead Exposure Standard IQ tests are designed to yield a population mean of 100. Data Set 11 "IQ and Lead" in Appendix B includes IQ scores of 21 children with high exposure to lead. For this group, the IQ scores have a mean of 86.90476 and a standard deviation of 8.988352. Use a 0.05 significance level to test the claim that this sample is from a population with mean IQ equal to 100. Do the results prove that exposure to lead has an adverse effect on IQ scores of children?

16. Taxi Fares For the first 40 taxi fares (dollars) listed in Data Set 32 "Taxis" from Appendix B, the mean is \$12.035 and the standard deviation is \$8.361. Use a 0.05 significance level to test the claim that the mean cost of a taxicab ride in New York City is less than \$15.00.

17. Is the Diet Practical? When 40 people used the Weight Watchers diet for one year, their mean weight loss was 3.0 lb and the standard deviation was 4.9 lb (based on data from "Comparison of the Atkins, Ornish, Weight Watchers, and Zone Diets for Weight Loss and Heart Disease Reduction," by Dansinger et al., *Journal of the American Medical Association*, Vol. 293, No. 1). Use a 0.01 significance level to test the claim that the mean weight loss is greater than 0. Based on these results, does the diet appear to have statistical significance? Does the diet appear to have practical significance?

18. How Many English Words? A simple random sample of 10 pages from *Merriam-Webster's Collegiate Dictionary* is obtained. The numbers of words defined on those pages are found, with these results: $n = 10, \bar{x} = 53.3$ words, $s = 15.7$ words. Given that this dictionary has 1459 pages with defined words, the claim that there are more than 70,000 defined words is equivalent to the claim that the mean number of words per page is greater than 48.0 words. Assume a normally distributed population. Use a 0.01 significance level to test the claim that the mean number of words per page is greater than 48.0 words. What does the result suggest about the claim that there are more than 70,000 defined words?

19. Cans of Coke Data Set 37 "Cola Weights and Volumes" in Appendix B includes volumes (ounces) of a sample of cans of regular Coke. The summary statistics are $n = 36, \bar{x} = 12.19$ oz, $s = 0.11$ oz. Use a 0.05 significance level to test the claim that cans of Coke have a mean volume of 12.00 ounces. Does it appear that consumers are being cheated?

20. Insomnia Treatment A clinical trial was conducted to test the effectiveness of the drug zopiclone for treating insomnia in older subjects. Before treatment with zopiclone, 16 subjects had a mean wake time of 102.8 min. After treatment with zopiclone, the 16 subjects had a mean wake time of 98.9 min and a standard deviation of 42.3 min (based on data from "Cognitive Behavioral Therapy vs Zopiclone for Treatment of Chronic Primary Insomnia in Older Adults," by Sivertsen et al., *Journal of the American Medical Association,* Vol. 295, No. 24). Assume that the 16 sample values appear to be from a normally distributed population, and test the claim that after treatment with zopiclone, subjects have a mean wake time of less than 102.8 min. Does zopiclone appear to be effective?

21. Lead in Medicine Listed below are the lead concentrations (in $\mu g/g$) measured in different Ayurveda medicines. Ayurveda is a traditional medical system commonly used in India. The lead concentrations listed here are from medicines manufactured in the United States (based on data from "Lead, Mercury, and Arsenic in US and Indian Manufactured Ayurvedic Medicines Sold via the Internet," by Saper et al., *Journal of the American Medical Association,* Vol. 300, No. 8). Use a 0.05 significance level to test the claim that the mean lead concentration for all such medicines is less than 14 $\mu g/g$.

3.0   6.5   6.0   5.5   20.5   7.5   12.0   20.5   11.5   17.5

22. Got a Minute? Students of the author estimated the length of one minute without reference to a watch or clock, and the times (seconds) are listed below. Use a 0.05 significance level to test the claim that these times are from a population with a mean equal to 60 seconds. Does it appear that students are reasonably good at estimating one minute?

69   81   39   65   42   21   60   63   66   48   64   70   96   91   65

23. Cell Phone Radiation Listed below are the measured radiation levels (in W/kg) corresponding to these cell phones: iPhone X, iPhone 7, Google Pixel, Samsung Galaxy S8, OnePlus 5, Motorola VE465, LG G3, and HTC Desire 310. The data are from the Federal Communications Commission. The Federal Communications Commission (FCC) has a standard that a cell phone radiation level must be 1.6 W/kg or less. Use a 0.01 significance level to test the claim that the sample is from a population of cell phones with a mean amount of radiation that is less than the FCC standard of 1.6 W/kg.

0.97   1.38   0.93   1.52   1.37   1.09   0.48   0.65

24. Dollar Coins Listed below are weights (grams) of dollar coins from Data Set 40 "Coin Weights" in Appendix B. Use a 0.01 significance level to test the claim that the sample is from a population with a mean equal to 8.1 grams, which is the weight specified by the mint. What is a reasonable explanation for the result?

8.1008   8.1072   8.0271   8.0813   8.0241   8.0510   7.9817   8.0954   8.0658   8.1238
8.1281   8.0307   8.0719   8.0345   8.0775   8.1384   8.1041   8.0894   8.0538   8.0342

Large Data Sets from Appendix B. *In Exercises 25–28, use the data set from Appendix B to test the given claim. Use the P-value method unless your instructor specifies otherwise.*

25. Los Angeles Commute Time Use the 1000 Los Angeles Commute times listed in Data Set 31 "Commute Times" to test the claim that the mean Los Angeles commute time is less than 35 minutes. Use a 0.01 significance level. Compare the sample mean to the claimed mean of 35 minutes. Is the difference between those two values statistically significant? Does the difference between those two values appear to have practical significance?

26. Taxi Fares Repeat Exercise 16 using all 703 of the New York City taxi fares listed in Data Set 32 "Taxis" from Appendix B.

27. Arm Span Use the arm span distances (mm) of the 4082 males listed in Data Set 3 "ANSUR II 2012" in Appendix B to test the claim that the sample is from a population with a mean less than 1818 mm. Use a 0.01 significance level. Compare the sample mean to the claimed mean of 1818 mm. Is the difference between those two values statistically significant? Does the difference between those two values appear to have practical significance?

28. Army Height Based on the results of the 1988 survey of U.S. Army personnel, the mean height of males is 1755.8 mm. Use the heights (mm) of the 4082 males listed in Data Set 3 "ANSUR II 2012" in Appendix B to test the claim that this sample collected in 2012 is from a population with a mean greater than 1755.8 mm. Use a 0.05 significance level. Does it appear that male army personnel were taller in 2012 than in 1988?

8-3   Beyond the Basics

29. Large Sample and a Small Difference It has been said that with really large samples, even very small differences between the sample mean and the claimed population mean can appear to be significant, but in reality they are not significant. Test this statement using the claim that the mean IQ score of adults is 100, given the following sample data: $n = 1,000,000$, $\bar{x} = 100.05$, $s = 15$. Based on this sample, is the difference between $\bar{x} = 100.05$ and the claimed mean of 100 statistically significant? Does that difference have practical significance?

30. Interpreting Power For the sample data in Exercise 23 "Cell Phone Radiation," the hypothesis test has power of 0.9127 of supporting the claim that $\mu < 1.6$ W/kg when the actual population mean is 1.0 W/kg. Interpret this value of the power, then identify the value of β and interpret that value. (For the t test in this section, a "noncentrality parameter" makes calculations of power much more complicated than the process described in Section 8-1, so software is recommended for power calculations.)

31. Finding Critical t Values When finding critical values, we often need significance levels other than those available in Table A-3. Some computer programs approximate critical t values by calculating $t = \sqrt{df \cdot (e^{A^2/df} - 1)}$ where $df = n - 1$, $e = 2.718$, $A = z(8 \cdot df + 3)/(8 \cdot df + 1)$, and z is the critical z score. Use this approximation to find the critical t score for Exercise 28 "Army Height," using a significance level of 0.05. Compare the results to the critical t score of 1.645 found from technology. Does this approximation appear to work reasonably well?

32. Hypothesis Test with Known σ

a. How do the results from Example 1 in this section change if σ is known to be 1.99240984 g? Does the knowledge of σ have much of an effect on the results of this hypothesis test?

b. In general, can knowledge of σ have much of an effect on the results of a hypothesis test of a claim about a population mean μ?

8-4   Testing a Claim About a Standard Deviation or Variance

Key Concept An important goal of business and industry is to improve quality of goods and/or services by reducing variation. A hypothesis test can be used to confirm that an improvement has occurred by confirming that a relevant standard deviation has been lowered. This section presents methods for conducting a formal hypothesis test of a claim made about a population standard deviation σ or population variance σ^2. The methods of this section use the chi-square distribution that was first introduced in Section 7-3. The assumptions, test statistic, P-value, and critical values are summarized as follows.

KEY ELEMENTS

Testing Claims About σ or σ^2

Objective

Conduct a hypothesis test of a claim made about a population standard deviation σ or population variance σ^2.

Notation

$n = $ sample size
$s = $ *sample* standard deviation
$\sigma = $ *population* standard deviation

$s^2 = $ *sample* variance
$\sigma^2 = $ *population* variance

Requirements

1. The sample is a simple random sample.

2. There is a fairly strict requirement that the population has a normal distribution.

📳 **(If the second requirement is not satisfied, one alternative is to use the confidence interval method of testing hypotheses, but obtain the confidence interval using the bootstrap resampling method described in Section 8-5.)**

Test Statistic

$$\chi^2 = \frac{(n-1)s^2}{\sigma^2} \text{ (round to three decimal places, as in Table A-4)}$$

P-values: Use technology or Table A-4 with degrees of freedom: df $= n - 1$. See "Hint: *P*-Value in Two-Tailed Tests" that follows.
Critical values: Use Table A-4 with degrees of freedom df $= n - 1$.

CAUTION The χ^2 (chi-square) test of this section is not *robust* against a departure from normality, meaning that the test does not work well if the population has a distribution that is far from normal. The condition of a normally distributed population is therefore a much stricter requirement when testing claims about σ or σ^2 than when testing claims about a population mean μ.

Equivalent Methods

When testing claims about σ or σ^2, the *P*-value method, the critical value method, and the confidence interval method will always lead to the same conclusion.

Properties of the Chi-Square Distribution

The chi-square distribution was introduced in Section 7-3, where we noted the following important properties.

1. All values of χ^2 are nonnegative, and the distribution is not symmetric (see Figure 8-9).

2. There is a different χ^2 distribution for each number of degrees of freedom (see Figure 8-10).

3. The critical values are found in Table A-4 using

$$\textbf{degrees of freedom } = n - 1$$

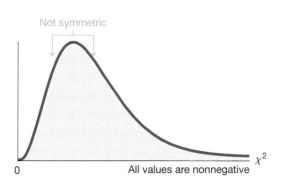

FIGURE 8-9   Properties of the Chi-Square Distribution

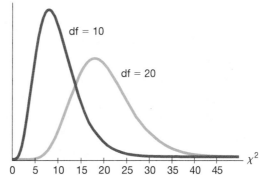

FIGURE 8-10   Chi-Square Distribution for df = 10 and df = 20

Here is an important note if using Table A-4 for finding critical values:

In Table A-4, each critical value of χ^2 in the body of the table corresponds to an area given in the top row of the table, and each area in that top row is a *cumulative area to the right* of the critical value.

> **CAUTION** Table A-4 for the chi-square distribution uses cumulative areas from the *right* (unlike Table A-2 for the standard normal distribution, which provides cumulative areas from the *left*.) See Example 1 in Section 7-3.

EXAMPLE 1   Minting Quarters

U.S. Mint specifications require that quarters manufactured after 1964 have weights with a mean of 5.670 g and a standard deviation of 0.062 g. Listed below are weights (grams) of a simple random sample of quarters made with a new minting process designed to reduce the standard deviation so that weights of quarters are more consistent. Use a 0.05 significance level to test the claim that these weights are from a population with a standard deviation that is less than 0.062 g.

5.7424	5.7328	5.7268	5.5938	5.6342	5.6839	5.6651	5.6925
5.6803	5.6245	5.7985	5.7180	5.7299	5.6582	5.7360	5.6546
5.7222	5.6619	5.7041	5.6528	5.6210	5.6613	5.6484	5.6502

SOLUTION

REQUIREMENT CHECK (1) The sample is a simple random sample. (2) In checking for normality, we see that the sample has no outliers, the accompanying normal quantile plot shows points that are reasonably close to a straight-line pattern, and there is no other pattern that is not a straight line. Both requirements are satisfied. ☑

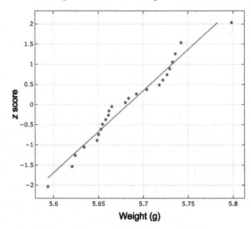

Technology Technology capable of conducting this test will typically display the *P*-value. Statdisk can be used as described at the end of this section, and the result will be as shown in the accompanying display. The display shows that the test statistic is $\chi^2 = 13.795$ (rounded) and the *P*-value is 0.0674.

Statdisk

Test Statistic, ChiSq:	13.79508
Critical ChiSq:	13.09050
P-Value:	0.06741

Step 1: The claim that "the standard deviation is less than 0.062 g" is expressed in symbolic form as $\sigma < 0.062$ g.

Step 2: If the original claim is false, then $\sigma \geq 0.062$ g.

Step 3: The expression $\sigma < 0.062$ g does not contain equality, so it becomes the alternative hypothesis. The null hypothesis is the statement that $\sigma = 0.062$ g.

$$H_0: \sigma = 0.062 \text{ g} \quad H_1: \sigma < 0.062 \text{ g}$$

Step 4: The significance level is $\alpha = 0.05$.

Step 5: Because the claim is made about σ, we use the χ^2 (chi-square) distribution.

Step 6: The Statdisk display shows the test statistic of $\chi^2 = 13.795$ (rounded) and it shows that the P-value is 0.0674.

Step 7: Because the P-value is greater than the significance level of $\alpha = 0.05$, we fail to reject H_0.

> **INTERPRETATION**
>
> **Step 8:** There is not sufficient evidence to support the claim that the listed weights are from a population with a standard deviation that is less than 0.062 g. There isn't enough evidence to show that the new minting procedure is achieving the goal of reducing the variation of weights of quarters.

 **YOUR TURN.** Do Exercise 7 "Body Temperature."

Critical Value Method

Technology typically provides a P-value, so the P-value method is used. If technology is not available, the P-value method of testing hypotheses is a bit challenging because Table A-4 allows us to find only a range of values for the P-value. Instead, we could use the critical value method. Steps 1 through 5 in Example 1 would be the same. In Step 6, the test statistic is calculated by using $\sigma = 0.062$ g (as assumed in the null hypothesis in Example 1), $n = 24$, and $s = 0.0480164$ g, which is the unrounded standard deviation computed from the original list of 24 weights. We get this test statistic:

$$\chi^2 = \frac{(n-1)s^2}{\sigma^2} = \frac{(24-1)(0.0480164)^2}{0.062^2} = 13.795$$

The critical value of $\chi^2 = 13.091$ is found from Table A-4, and it corresponds to 23 degrees of freedom and an "area to the right" of 0.95 (based on the significance level of 0.05 for a left-tailed test). See Figure 8-11. In Step 7 we fail to reject the null hypothesis because the test statistic of $\chi^2 = 13.795$ does not fall in the critical region, as shown in Figure 8-11. We conclude that there is not sufficient evidence to support the claim that the listed weights are from a population with a standard deviation that is less than 0.062 g.

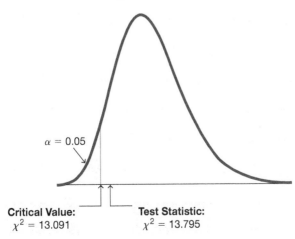

FIGURE 8-11   Testing the Claim That $\sigma < 0.062$ g

Confidence Interval Method

As stated earlier, when testing claims about σ or σ^2, the P-value method, the critical value method, and the confidence interval method are all equivalent in the sense that they will always lead to the same conclusion. See Example 2.

EXAMPLE 2   **Minting Quarters: Confidence Interval Method**

Repeat the hypothesis test in Example 1 by constructing a suitable confidence interval.

SOLUTION

First, we should be careful to select the correct confidence level. Because the hypothesis test is left-tailed and the significance level is 0.05, we should use a confidence level of 90%, or 0.90. (See Table 8-1 on page 376 for help in selecting the correct confidence level.)

Using the methods described in Section 7-3, we can use the sample data listed in Example 1 to construct a 90% confidence interval estimate of σ. We use $n = 24$, $s = 0.0480164$ g, $\chi_L^2 = 13.091$, and $\chi_R^2 = 35.172$. (The critical values χ_L^2 and χ_R^2 are found in Table A-4. Use the row with df $= n - 1 = 23$. The 0.90 confidence level corresponds to $\alpha = 0.10$ and we divide that area of 0.10 equally between the two tails so that the areas to the *right* of the critical values are 0.95 and 0.05. Refer to Table A-4 and use the columns with areas of 0.95 and 0.05 and use the 23rd row.)

$$\sqrt{\frac{(n-1)s^2}{\chi_R^2}} < \sigma < \sqrt{\frac{(n-1)s^2}{\chi_L^2}}$$

$$\sqrt{\frac{(24-1)(0.0480164)^2}{35.172}} < \sigma < \sqrt{\frac{(24-1)(0.0480164)^2}{13.091}}$$

$$0.03883 \text{ g} < \sigma < 0.06365 \text{ g}$$

With this confidence interval, we cannot support the claim that $\sigma < 0.062$ g because the value of 0.062 g is contained within the confidence interval. The confidence interval is telling us that σ can be any value between 0.03883 g and 0.06365 g; the confidence interval is *not* telling us that σ is less than 0.062 g. We reach the same conclusion found with the P-value method and the critical value method.

FINDING P-VALUES IN TWO-TAILED TESTS Because the χ^2 distribution is not symmetric, P-values in two-tailed tests are extremely difficult to find. A common procedure is to approximate P-values in two-tailed hypothesis tests by doubling the tail areas, as we have done in the preceding sections of this chapter. Because the χ^2 distribution becomes more symmetric for larger sample sizes, such approximations get better for larger sample sizes. Doubling the tail areas is the procedure used by Minitab, XLSTAT, Statdisk, and StatCrunch. (SPSS and JMP don't do hypothesis tests for a claim about the standard deviation or variance.) For two-tailed tests, we always have the option of using the critical value method of testing hypotheses of claims about σ or σ^2.

Alternative Method Used When Population Is Not Normal

The methods of this section include two requirements: (1) The sample is a simple random sample; (2) the population is normally distributed. If sample data are not collected in a random manner, the methods of this section do not apply. If the sample appears to be from a population not having a normal distribution, we could use the confidence interval method of testing hypotheses, but obtain the confidence interval using bootstrap resampling, as described in Section 8-5. We could also use the resampling method of *randomization*. See Exercise 13 in Section 8-5.

TECH CENTER

Hypothesis Test: Standard Deviation or Variance
Access tech supplements, videos, and data sets at **www.TriolaStats.com**

Statdisk
1. Click **Analysis** in the top menu.
2. Select **Hypothesis Testing** from the dropdown menu and select **Standard Deviation One Sample** from the submenu.
3. Select the desired format for the *Alternative Hypothesis,* then enter the desired significance level and claimed standard deviation (from the null hypothesis).
4. *Using Summary Statistics:* Select the **Use Summary Statistics** tab and enter the sample size and sample standard deviation.
Using sample data: Select the **Use Data** tab and select the desired data column.
5. Click **Evaluate.**

Minitab
1. Click **Stat** in the top menu.
2. Select **Basic Statistics** from the dropdown menu and select **1 Variance** from the submenu.
3. *Using Summary Statistics:* Select **Sample standard deviation** (or **variance**) from the dropdown menu and enter the sample size and sample standard deviation (or variance).
Using Sample Data: Select **One or more samples, each in a column** from the dropdown menu and select the desired data column.
4. Check the **Perform hypothesis test** box and enter the standard deviation (or variance) used in the null hypothesis.
5. Click the **Options** button and enter the confidence level. (Enter 95.0 for a significance level of 0.05.) For *Alternative hypothesis* select the format used for the alternative hypothesis.
6. Click **OK** twice.
TIP: Another procedure is to click on **Assistant** in the top menu, then select **Hypothesis Tests** and **1-Sample Standard Deviation.** Complete the dialog box to get results, including *P*-value and other helpful information.

StatCrunch
1. Click **Stat** in the top menu.
2. Select **Variance Stats** from the dropdown menu, then select **One Sample** from the submenu.
3. *Using Summary Statistics:* Select **With Summary** from the submenu and enter the sample variance and sample size.
Using Sample Data: Select **With Data** from the submenu and select the desired data column.
4. Select **Hypothesis test for** σ^2 and for H_0 enter the claimed value of the population variance. For H_A select the format used for the alternative hypothesis.
5. Click **Compute!**

TI-83/84 Plus Calculator
1. Download and install the Michael Lloyd programs *S2TEST* and *ZZINEWT* (available at www.TriolaStats.com) on your TI-83/84 Plus Calculator.
2. Press the **PRGM** button, then select **S2TEST** from the menu and press **ENTER** twice.
3. Enter the population variance σx^2, sample variance Sx^2, and sample size *n*. Press **ENTER** after each entry.
4. For SIGMA^2 select the desired format for the alternative hypothesis ($\neq$ for two-tailed test, $<$ for left-tailed test, $>$ for right-tailed test).
5. Press **ENTER** and the test statistic and the *P*-value will be provided.

continued

TECH CENTER *continued*

Hypothesis Test: Standard Deviation or Variance
Access tech supplements, videos, and data sets at **www.TriolaStats.com/ES13**

Excel

XLSTAT Add-In (Required)
Requires original sample data; does not work with summary data.

1. Click on the **XLSTAT** tab in the Ribbon and then click **Parametric tests.**

2. Select **One-sample variance test** from the dropdown menu.

3. Under *Data* enter the range of cells containing the sample data. For *Data format* select **One column per sample.** If the first row of data contains a label, also check the **Column labels** box.

4. For *Range,* enter a cell location such as D5 where the results will be displayed.

5. Click the **Options** tab.

6. Under *Alternative hypothesis* select the desired format ($\neq$ for two-tailed test, $<$ for left-tailed test, $>$ for right-tailed test).

7. For *Theoretical variance,* enter the claimed value of the population variance. Enter the desired significance level (enter **5** for a significance level of 0.05).

8. Click **OK** to display the results. The test statistic is identified as Chi-square (Observed value). The *P*-value is also displayed.

TIP: The above procedure is based on testing a claim about a population *variance;* to test a claim about a population standard deviation, use the same procedure and enter σ^2 for the *Theoretical Variance.*

R

R command not available at time of publication.

R is rapidly evolving, and an updated list of statistical commands is available at TriolaStats.com.

8-4 Basic Skills and Concepts

Statistical Literacy and Critical Thinking

1. Minting Dollar Coins Assume that the U.S. Mint manufactures dollar coins so that the standard deviation is 0.04000 g (based on Data Set 40 "Coin Weights" in Appendix B). Listed below are weights (grams) of dollar coins manufactured with a new process designed to decrease the standard deviation so that it is less than 0.04000 g. This sample has these summary statistics: $n = 16$, $\bar{x} = 8.06576$ g, $s = 0.02176$ g. If we want to use a 0.05 significance level to test the claim that the sample is from a population with a standard deviation less than 0.04000 g, what requirements must be satisfied? How does the normality requirement for a hypothesis test of a claim about a standard deviation differ from the normality requirement for a hypothesis test of a claim about a mean?

8.0652	8.0548	8.0754	8.0545	8.0334	8.0126	8.0758	8.0517
8.0730	8.1084	8.0678	8.0808	8.0680	8.0818	8.0684	8.0806

2. Minting Dollar Coins Use the data and the claim given in Exercise 1 to identify the null and alternative hypotheses and the test statistic. What is the sampling distribution of the test statistic?

3. Minting Dollar Coins For the sample data from Exercise 1, we get a *P*-value of 0.0041 when testing the claim that $\sigma < 0.04000$ g.

a. What should we conclude about the null hypothesis?

b. What should we conclude about the original claim?

c. What do these results suggest about the new minting process?

4. Minting Dollar Coins: Confidence Interval If we use the data given in Exercise 1, we get this 90% confidence interval estimate of the standard deviation of weights with the new minting process: 0.01686 g $< \sigma < 0.03128$ g. What does this confidence interval tell us about the new filling process?

Testing Claims About Variation. *In Exercises 5–16, test the given claim. Identify the null hypothesis, alternative hypothesis, test statistic, P-value, or critical value(s), then state the conclusion about the null hypothesis, as well as the final conclusion that addresses the original claim. Assume that a simple random sample is selected from a normally distributed population.*

5. Pulse Rates of Men A simple random sample of 153 men results in a standard deviation of 11.3 beats per minute (based on Data Set 1 "Body Data" in Appendix B). The normal range of pulse rates of adults is typically given as 60 to 100 beats per minute. If the range rule of thumb is applied to that normal range, the result is a standard deviation of 10 beats per minute. Use the sample results with a 0.05 significance level to test the claim that pulse rates of men have a standard deviation equal to 10 beats per minute; see the accompanying StatCrunch display for this test. What do the results indicate about the effectiveness of using the range rule of thumb with the "normal range" from 60 to 100 beats per minute for estimating σ in this case?

One sample variance hypothesis test:
σ^2 : Variance of variable
$H_0 : \sigma^2 = 100$
$H_A : \sigma^2 \neq 100$

Hypothesis test results:

Variable	Sample Var.	DF	Chi-Square Stat	P-value
PULSE	128.40282	152	195.17229	0.0208

6. Pulse Rates of Women Repeat the preceding exercise using the pulse rates of women listed in Data Set 1 "Body Data" in Appendix B. For the sample of pulse rates of women, $n = 147$ and $s = 12.5$. See the accompanying JMP display that results from using the original list of pulse rates instead of the summary statistics. (*Hint:* The bottom three rows of the display provide P-values for a two-tailed test, a left-tailed test, and a right-tailed test, respectively.) What do the results indicate about the effectiveness of using the range rule of thumb with the "normal range" from 60 to 100 beats per minute for estimating σ in this case?

◿ Test Standard Deviation

Hypothesized Value	10
Actual Estimate	12.5436
DF	146
Test	ChiSquare
Test Statistic	229.7176
Min PValue	<.0001*
Prob < ChiSq	1.0000
Prob > ChiSq	<.0001*

7. Body Temperature Example 5 in Section 8-3 involved a test of the claim that humans have body temperatures with a mean equal to 98.6°F. The sample of 106 body temperatures has a standard deviation of 0.62°F. The conclusion in that example would change if the sample standard deviation s were 2.08°F or greater. Use a 0.01 significance level to test the claim that the sample of 106 body temperatures is from a population with a standard deviation less than 2.08°F. What does the result tell us about the validity of the hypothesis test in Example 5 in Section 8-3?

8. Birth Weights A simple random sample of birth weights of 30 girls has a standard deviation of 829.5 g. Use a 0.01 significance level to test the claim that birth weights of girls have the same standard deviation as birth weights of boys, which is 660.2 g (based on Data Set 6 "Births" in Appendix B).

9. M&Ms Plain M&M candies are fairly consistent in their sizes, but Data Set 38 "Candies" shows that their weights do vary. Here are the statistics for the weights of a sample of the M&M candies listed in that data set: $n = 20$, $\bar{x} = 0.8724$ g, $s = 0.0337$ g. If it is a goal to manufacture M&Ms so that they have weights with a standard deviation less than 0.0400 g, does the sample of M&Ms appear to satisfy that goal? Use a significance level of 0.01.

10. Minting of Pennies Data Set 40 "Coin Weights" lists weights (grams) of pennies minted after 1983. Here are the statistics for those weights: $n = 37$, $\bar{x} = 2.49910$ g, $s = 0.01648$ g. Use a 0.05 significance level to test the claim that the sample is from a population of pennies with weights having a standard deviation greater than 0.01000 g.

11. Taxi Times Assume that Friday morning taxi-cab rides have times with a standard deviation of $\sigma = 9.9$ minutes (based on Data Set 32 "Taxis" in Appendix B). A cab driver records times of rides during a Friday afternoon time period and obtains these statistics: $n = 12$, $\bar{x} = 19.3$ minutes, $s = 13.2$ minutes. Use a 0.05 significance level to test the claim that these Friday afternoon times have greater variation than the Friday morning times.

12. Spoken Words Couples were recruited for a study of how many words people speak in a day. A random sample of 56 males resulted in a mean of 16,576 words and a standard deviation of 7871 words. Use a 0.01 significance level to test the claim that males have a standard deviation that is greater than the standard deviation of 7460 words for females (based on Data Set 14 "Word Counts").

13. Aircraft Altimeters The Skytek Avionics company uses a new production method to manufacture aircraft altimeters. A simple random sample of new altimeters resulted in the errors listed below. Use a 0.05 level of significance to test the claim that the new production method has errors with a standard deviation greater than 32.2 ft, which was the standard deviation for the old production method. If it appears that the standard deviation is greater, does the new production method appear to be better or worse than the old method? Should the company take any action?

$$-42 \quad 78 \quad -22 \quad -72 \quad -45 \quad 15 \quad 17 \quad 51 \quad -5 \quad -53 \quad -9 \quad -109$$

14. Bank Lines The Jefferson Valley Bank once had a separate customer waiting line at each teller window, but it now has a single waiting line that feeds the teller windows as vacancies occur. The standard deviation of customer waiting times with the old multiple-line configuration was 1.8 min. Listed below is a simple random sample of waiting times (minutes) with the single waiting line. Use a 0.05 significance level to test the claim that with a single waiting line, the waiting times have a standard deviation less than 1.8 min. What improvement occurred when banks changed from multiple waiting lines to a single waiting line?

$$6.5 \quad 6.6 \quad 6.7 \quad 6.8 \quad 7.1 \quad 7.3 \quad 7.4 \quad 7.7 \quad 7.7 \quad 7.7$$

15. Weights of Peanut Butter Cups Listed below are weights (grams) of randomly selected Reese's Peanut Butter Cup Miniatures. Use the listed sample data to test the claim that the sample is from a population having weights with a standard deviation equal to 0.2000 g. Use a significance level of $\alpha = 0.05$.

$$8.639 \quad 8.689 \quad 8.548 \quad 8.980 \quad 8.936 \quad 9.042$$

16. Mint Specs Listed below are weights (grams) from a simple random sample of post-1983 pennies (from Data Set 40 "Coin Weights" in Appendix B). U.S. Mint specifications now require a standard deviation of 0.0230 g for weights of pennies. Use a 0.01 significance level to test the claim that pennies are manufactured so that their weights have a standard deviation equal to 0.0230 g. Does the Mint specification appear to be met?

$$2.5024 \quad 2.5298 \quad 2.4998 \quad 2.4823 \quad 2.5163 \quad 2.5222 \quad 2.4900 \quad 2.4907 \quad 2.5017$$

Large Data Sets from Appendix B. *In Exercises 17 and 18, use the data set from Appendix B to test the given claim. Identify the null hypothesis, alternative hypothesis, test statistic, P-value, or critical value(s), then state the conclusion about the null hypothesis, as well as the final conclusion that addresses the original claim.*

17. Los Angeles Commute Time Use the 1000 Los Angeles commute times listed in Data Set 31 "Commute Times" to test the claim that the sample is from a population with a standard deviation equal to 20 minutes. Use a 0.01 significance level. Also determine whether the distribution of the 1000 Los Angeles commute times satisfies the requirements of this hypothesis test.

18. Height Based on the results of the 1988 survey of U.S. Army personnel, the standard deviation of heights of males is 66.8 mm. Use the heights (mm) of the 4082 males listed in Data Set 3 "ANSUR II 2012" in Appendix B to test the claim that this sample collected in 2012 is from a population with a standard deviation different from 66.8 mm. Use a 0.05 significance level. Also determine whether the distribution of the 4082 heights satisfies the requirements of this hypothesis test.

8-4   Beyond the Basics

19. Finding Critical Values of χ^2 For large numbers of degrees of freedom, we can approximate critical values of χ^2 as follows:

$$\chi^2 = \frac{1}{2}(z + \sqrt{2k - 1})^2$$

Here k is the number of degrees of freedom and z is the critical value(s) found from technology or Table A-2. In Exercise 12 "Spoken Words" we have df $= 55$, so Table A-4 does not list an exact critical value. If we want to approximate a critical value of χ^2 in the right-tailed hypothesis test with $\alpha = 0.01$ and a sample size of 56, we let $k = 55$ with $z = 2.33$ (or the more accurate value of $z = 2.326348$ found from technology). Use this approximation to estimate the critical value of χ^2 for Exercise 12. How close is it to the critical value of $\chi^2 = 82.292$ obtained by using Statdisk and Minitab?

20. Finding Critical Values of χ^2 Repeat Exercise 19 using this approximation (with k and z as described in Exercise 19):

$$\chi^2 = k\left(1 - \frac{2}{9k} + z\sqrt{\frac{2}{9k}}\right)^3$$

8-5   Resampling: Using Technology for Hypothesis Testing

Key Concept The preceding sections of this chapter included three methods for testing claims about a population proportion, population mean and population standard deviation or variance. Those methods have certain requirements that limit the situations in which they can be used. When some of the requirements are not satisfied, we can often use *resampling methods* that involve the use of technology to "resample" the original sample data many times. Even when requirements are satisfied, resampling methods can be used along with other methods to provide an additional perspective and insight into the data. It is wise to use "holistic statistics" by applying two or more different methods. Resampling methods can serve as a good "second opinion."

Usefulness of Resampling Methods

Resampling methods have the following advantages:

1. There is no requirement about the underlying distribution of data. There is no requirement that the data must be from a normally distributed population.

2. There is no requirement of a minimum sample size.

Most of the methods used in the preceding sections of this chapter cannot be used with small samples selected from populations not having normal distributions, but resampling methods can be used instead. See the Technology Project near the end of this chapter for a small sample randomly selected from a population with a distribution that is far from normal.

In this section we include these resampling methods:

- **Bootstrap** The bootstrap resampling method is used to construct a confidence interval that could be used to test a claim about a population parameter. See Section 7-4 for more detail on bootstrap resampling.

- **Randomization** Randomization, which is used for hypothesis testing, is another method of resampling. While bootstrapping generates resamples of the same original data, randomization requires that the sample data be modified to agree with the assumption used in the null hypothesis.

The bootstrap resampling method was first introduced in Section 7-4. We now introduce the *randomization* method of resampling. Randomization applies to tests of claims about a population proportion, population mean, or population standard deviation.

Randomization

DEFINITION

Randomization is a method of hypothesis testing that involves resampling (*with* replacement) after the sample data have been modified to conform to the value of the population parameter that is assumed in the null hypothesis.

Resample with Replacement? When using randomization for a hypothesis test of a claim about one proportion, mean, or standard deviation, resampling from one sample without replacement would result in the same generated sample every time, which is not useful. Instead, when working with one sample, we resample *with replacement*.

POOR TERMINOLOGY Because we have already used the terms of "random" and "randomness" to describe sampling methods in Chapter 1, it is poor terminology to use "randomization" for a method of resampling, but that is the term now in use. Another term for a randomization test is a "permutation test," but that is also poor terminology because combinations are used instead of permutations. A good term for randomization would be "resampling for hypothesis tests," but apparently that is not snappy enough.

The following example illustrates randomization with one sample.

EXAMPLE 1 **Randomization Method**

Assume that we want to use randomization to test the claim that the mean service time (minutes) at Mario's Pizza food truck is equal to 6.5 minutes. That claim results in the following hypotheses

$$H_0: \mu = 6.5 \text{ minutes}$$

$$H_1: \mu \neq 6.5 \text{ minutes}$$

Shown on the next page in the leftmost column is this sample of five wait times (minutes): 2, 3, 6, 8, 11. Because this sample has a mean of $\bar{x} = 6.0$ minutes but the hypothesis test is conducted with the assumption that $\mu = 6.5$ minutes, we modify the original data set by adding 0.5 minute to each value so that the mean becomes $\bar{x} = 6.5$ minutes as assumed. We then resample the modified data, and one such resampling is shown on the next page in the rightmost column.

Original Data (minutes) $\bar{x} = 6.0$	Modified Data (minutes) $\bar{x} = 6.5$	Resample #1 (Resample Modified Data *With* Replacement) $\bar{x}_1 = 7.1$
2	2.5	3.5
3	3.5	3.5
6	6.5	8.5
8	8.5	8.5
11	11.5	11.5

If we proceed to obtain many (such as 1000) resamples and find the sample mean for each of them, we can use the 1000 sample means to determine whether the original sample mean of $\bar{x} = 6.0$ minutes can easily occur with a population having a mean of $\mu = 6.5$ minutes, or whether such a sample mean is very unlikely, suggesting that the population mean is *not* 6.5 minutes. This is the key question:

> **Do the resamples provide means suggesting that the original sample mean is *significantly* different from the claimed mean?**

SOLUTION

The following procedure is based on 1000 resamples. While any number of resamples could be used instead, 1000 is a recommended minimum. The steps in the following procedure are vastly simplified by using technology. See the Tech Center at the end of this section.

Step 1: Find the difference d between the claimed mean (from the null hypothesis) and the sample mean.

Example: The null hypothesis H_0: $\mu = 6.5$ minutes shows that the claimed mean is 6.5 minutes. The sample mean is $\bar{x} = 6.0$ minutes. The difference is $d = 6.5 - 6.0 = 0.5$.

Step 2: Modify the Sample Data to Conform to the Null Hypothesis.

Example: Add $d = 0.5$ to each sample value so that the modified sample has a mean equal to the claimed mean of 6.5 minutes.

Step 3: Resample with replacement 1000 times or more. Find the Value of the Sample Mean for Each Resampling.

Example: Use technology to resample the *modified* data set 1000 times (or more). (You *really* need technology for this step.)

Step 4: Find the number of sample means (found in Step 3) that are "at least as extreme" as the mean of the original sample.

Example: The author used randomization to find that there were 743 samples with means at least as extreme as $\bar{x} = 6.0$ from the original sample. For more details about the correct interpretation of "at least as extreme," see the comments following this example.

Step 5: Divide the value from Step 4 by the number of randomizations to get the estimated P-value.

Example: P-value is estimated to be $743/1000 = 0.743$.

INTERPRETATION

Using a significance level of 0.05, we fail to reject the null hypothesis of H_0: $\mu = 6.5$ because the P-value of 0.743 is greater than the significance level of 0.05. Using the randomization method, we find that there is not sufficient evidence to warrant rejection of the claim that the mean service time is equal to 6.5 minutes.

▷**YOUR TURN.** Do Exercise 9 "Lead in Medicine."

> **HINT** Technologies such as Statdisk will automatically execute the steps listed in the preceding example, so enter and use the *original* unmodified data. There is no need to manually perform the calculations illustrated in the preceding example.

Criteria for "At Least As Extreme" The following criteria for "at least as extreme" are based on means, but proportions or standard deviations could also be addressed using these same criteria.

In the following, $\bar{x}$ is the original sample mean found from the unmodified original sample, and μ is the value of the population mean assumed in the null hypothesis. "Values" refers to the sample mean for each resampling.

- **Left-tailed test:** Values at least as extreme as the original sample mean $\bar{x}$ are sample means that are less than or equal to $\bar{x}$.

- **Right-tailed test:** Values at least as extreme as $\bar{x}$ are sample means that are greater than or equal to $\bar{x}$.

- **Two-tailed test:** Find the difference d between $\bar{x}$ and μ (the claimed value of the population parameter used in the null hypothesis), and express d as a positive value. That is, $d = |\bar{x} - \mu|$. Using that difference d, values at least as extreme as $\bar{x}$ are those that are . . .

$$\text{less than or equal to } (\mu - d)$$

$$\text{or greater than or equal to } (\mu + d)$$

In Example 1 we have a sample with $\bar{x} = 6.0$ and we have a two-tailed hypothesis test in which we assume that $\mu = 6.5$. For Example 1, $d = |6.0 - 6.5| = 0.5$. The value of $\mu - d$ is $6.5 - 0.5 = 6.0$; the value of $\mu + d$ is $6.5 + 0.5 = 7.0$. So values that are *at least as extreme* as $\bar{x}$ are those that are

$$\text{less than or equal to } 6.0$$

$$\text{or greater than or equal to } 7.0$$

How Many Randomizations? It would be wise to repeat the randomization at least 1000 times. Professional statisticians commonly resample 10,000 or more times. It is obviously impractical to resample that many times using any manual procedure, so the use of software such as Statdisk is very strongly recommended.

Testing a Claim About a Proportion Section 8-2 presents methods for testing a claim made about a population proportion. Example 2 shows how resampling can be used to test such claims.

CP **EXAMPLE 2** **Resampling to Test a Claim About a Proportion**

The claim given in the Chapter Problem, "Most Internet users utilize two-factor authentication to protect their online data," can be tested by using the resampling methods of bootstrapping (introduced in Section 7-4) and randomization.

Bootstrapping The confidence interval obtained from the bootstrap resampling method can be used to determine the likely values of the population proportion p, and that can be used to form a conclusion about the claim being tested.

Example: Using bootstrap resampling to find the 90% confidence interval limits for the Chapter Problem ($n = 926$; $x = 482$) yields the result of approximately $0.495 < p < 0.548$. Because of the random nature of this process, your resulting confidence interval might be somewhat different. The confidence interval of $0.495 < p < 0.548$ shows that it is likely that the true value of the population proportion p can be anywhere between $0.495 < p < 0.548$, so it could be less than or equal to 0.5 and we can't conclude that $p > 0.5$. We can't support the conclusion that *most* Internet users utilize two-factor authentication to protect their online data.

Randomization Modify the original sample data to have the same value of the proportion claimed in the null hypothesis. (Use a column of 0s and 1s, where the proportion of 1s is the proportion claimed in the null hypothesis.) Next, resample with replacement to determine the likelihood of getting a sample proportion at least as extreme as the one obtained.

Example: In this example, we use technology to modify the original sample data ($n = 926; x = 482$) to have a sample proportion of 0.5 (as defined by the null hypothesis) and then generate 1000 resampled data sets using this modified data set. A typical result is that among these 1000 resampled data sets, there are 114 sample proportions that are at least 0.52, so there appears to be about a 0.114 chance of getting a sample proportion of 0.52 or greater. It appears that the sample proportion of 0.52 can easily occur with a population proportion of 0.5. That is, the sample proportion of 0.52 does not appear to be significantly high, so there is not sufficient evidence to support the claim that $p > 0.5$. There is not sufficient sample evidence to support the claim that most Internet users utilize two-factor authentication to protect their online data.

 **YOUR TURN.** Do Exercise 5 "Cursed Movie."

Testing a Claim About a Mean Section 8-3 presents methods for testing a claim made about a population mean. Example 3 illustrates the use of resampling for testing such claims.

EXAMPLE 3 **Adult Sleep: Resampling Methods**

The first example in Section 8-3 included the following sample data consisting of hours slept in one night for randomly selected adults. That example specified that a 0.05 significance level be used to test the claim that the mean amount of sleep for adults is less than 7 hours. This claim can be tested by using the resampling methods of bootstrapping and randomization.

4   8   4   4   8   6   9   7   7   10   7   8

Bootstrapping The confidence interval obtained from the bootstrap resampling method can be used to determine the likely values of the population mean μ, and that can be used to form a conclusion about the claim being tested.

Example: Using technology for bootstrapping to find the 90% confidence interval limits for this example, we get a confidence interval of approximately 5.9 hours $< \mu <$ 7.8 hours, which is quite close to the confidence interval of 5.8 hours $< \mu <$ 7.9 hours obtained using the methods of Section 8-3. The confidence interval shows that there is not sufficient evidence to support the conclusion that the population mean μ is less than 7 hours.

Randomization Modify the sample data to have the same mean claimed in the null hypothesis, then resample with replacement to determine the likelihood of getting a sample mean at least as extreme as the one obtained.

continued

Example: In this example, we use technology to modify the original sample ($n = 12$, $\bar{x} = 6.83333333$ hours) to have a sample mean of 7.0 hours, and then generate 1000 resampled data sets using this modified data set. A typical result is that among 1000 resampled data sets, there are 377 sample means that are at 6.83333333 or lower, so there appears to be about a 0.377 chance of getting a sample mean of 6.83333333 or lower. It appears that the sample mean of 6.83333333 can easily occur with a population mean of 7.0. The sample mean of 6.83333333 does not appear to be significantly low, so there is not sufficient evidence to support the claim that $\mu < 7$ hours. There is not sufficient sample evidence to support the claim that the mean amount of sleep for adults is less than 7 hours.

> **YOUR TURN.** Do Exercise 11 "Cell Phone Radiation."

Testing a Claim About a Standard Deviation or Variance Section 8-4 presents methods for testing a claim made about a population standard deviation or variance. Example 4 shows how resampling can be used to test such claims.

EXAMPLE 4 **Minting Quarters: Bootstrap Resampling Method**

The first example in Section 8-4 included the following sample data consisting of weights of randomly selected quarters. That example specified that a 0.05 significance level be used to test the claim that these weights are from a population with a standard deviation that is less than 0.062 g. This claim can be tested by using the resampling method of bootstrapping.

5.7424	5.7328	5.7268	5.5938	5.6342	5.6839	5.6651	5.6925
5.6803	5.6245	5.7985	5.7180	5.7299	5.6582	5.7360	5.6546
5.7222	5.6619	5.7041	5.6528	5.6210	5.6613	5.6484	5.6502

Bootstrapping The confidence interval obtained from the bootstrap resampling method can be used to determine the likely values of the population standard deviation or variance, and that can be used to form a conclusion about the claim being tested.

Example: Using technology with bootstrapping to obtain the 90% confidence interval using the bootstrap resampling method (from Section 7-4), we get this approximate confidence interval: 0.03374 g $< \sigma < 0.05851$ g. Because of the randomness used, this confidence interval might differ somewhat. In testing the claim that "the standard deviation is less than 0.062 g," we see that the assumed value of $\sigma = 0.062$ g is not contained within the confidence interval and all values of the confidence interval are less than 0.062 g, so we support the claim that the sample weights are from a population with a standard deviation less than 0.062 g. This conclusion is different than the one reached in Example 2 in Section 8-4.

Randomization As of this writing, there is no statistical software that does randomization for a standard deviation or variance. See Exercise 13 for an approach used by the author.

TECH CENTER

Randomization – One Sample (See Section 7-4 for "Bootstrap Resampling" Tech Center)

Access tech supplements, videos, and data sets at **www.TriolaStats.com**

Statdisk	Minitab	StatCrunch

Statdisk

1. Click **Resampling** in the top menu.
2. Select the desired type of randomization from the dropdown menu. Options include:
   - **Randomization One Proportion**
   - **Randomization One Mean**
3. Enter the required inputs which include the claimed value of population mean or proportion and desired number of resamplings.
4. Click **Evaluate**.

Minitab

1. Click **Calc** in the top menu.
2. Select **Resampling** from dropdown menu.
3. Select the desired type of randomization from the dropdown menu. Options include:
   - **Randomization Test for 1-Sample Mean**
   - **Randomization Test for 1-Sample Proportion**
4. Enter the required inputs which include the hypothesized mean or proportion and the desired number of resamplings.
5. Click the **Options** button and select the format of the alternative hypothesis.
6. Click **OK** twice.

StatCrunch

1. Modify the sample data to conform to the null hypothesis (See Examples 1 & 2 for procedure). Enter the modified data in a column such as *var3*.
2. Click **Stat** in the top menu.
3. Select **Resample** in the dropdown menu and **Statistic** in the submenu.
4. Select the column that contains the modified sample data, such as *var3*.
5. For *Statistic* enter **mean(var3)**.
6. For the *Resampling method* select **Bootstrap – with replacement**. For the *Type of resample* select **Univariate – resample columns at different rows**.
7. For Number of resamples, enter the desired number of resamples, such as **1000**.
8. For *Other options* select **Store resampled statistics in data table**.
9. Click **Compute!**
10. A column of means (or proportions) will be generated. Sort the column and find the number of the resampled values that are at least as extreme as the original sample mean (or proportion).

TI-83/84 Plus Calculator	Excel	R

TI-83/84 Plus Calculator

Not available.

Excel

XLSTAT Add-In

1. Modify the sample data to conform to the null hypothesis (See Examples 1 & 2 for procedure). Enter the modified data in a column such as *C*.
2. Click the **XLSTAT** tab in the Ribbon and then click **Describing data**.
3. Select **Resampled statistics** from dropdown menu.
4. For *Quantitative data*, enter the cell range for the modified sample data.
5. For *Method*, select **Bootstrap** and enter the desired number of resamples, such as **1000**.
6. Click the **Outputs** tab and confirm **Mean** and **Standard deviation (n-1)** are selected under *Quantitative data*. Also check the **Resampled statistics** box.
7. Click **OK**.
8. Results include a list of the resampled statistics. Sort this list and find the number of the resampled values that are at least as extreme as the original sample mean (or proportion).

R

R command not available at time of publication.

R is rapidly evolving, and an updated list of statistical commands is available at TriolaStats.com.

8-5   Basic Skills and Concepts

Statistical Literacy and Critical Thinking

1. Resampling

a. In general, what does it mean to "resample" the following data set consisting of wait times (minutes) of customers waiting in line for the Space Mountain ride at Walt Disney World: 50, 25, 75, 35, 50?

b. When resampling from the data set given in part (a), is it done with replacement or without replacement? Why?

c. When testing a claim about a proportion or mean or standard deviation, what is an important advantage of using a resampling method instead of the parametric method described in the preceding sections of this chapter?

2. Bootstrapping and Randomization When dealing with one sample of individual data values, what is the fundamental difference between the resampling methods of bootstrapping and randomization?

3. At Least As Extreme A random sample of 860 births in New York State included 426 boys, and that sample is to be used for a test of the common belief that the proportion of male births in the population is equal to 0.512.

a. In testing the common belief that the proportion of male babies is equal to 0.512, identify the values of $\hat{p}$ and p.

b. For random samples of size 860, what sample proportions of male births are *at least as extreme* as the sample proportion of 426/860?

c. In using the method of randomization with 1000 resamples, it is found that 310 of them have sample proportions that are at least as extreme as 426/860. What should be concluded about the claim that the proportion of male births is equal to 0.512?

4. At Least As Extreme

a. Data Set 5 "Body Temperatures" includes a column of 38 body temperatures with a mean of 98.13°F, and that sample is to be used to test the claim that the population has a mean body temperature equal to 98.6°F. For random samples of 38 body temperatures, what sample means are *at least as extreme* as the sample mean of 98.13°F?

b. In using the method of randomization with 1000 resamples, it is found that none of the resampled data sets have sample means that are at least as extreme as 98.13°F. What should be concluded about the claim that the population has a mean body temperature equal to 98.6°F?

Randomization: Testing a Claim About a Proportion. *In Exercises 5–8, use the randomization procedure for the indicated exercise.*

5. Section 8-2, Exercise 9 "Cursed Movie"

6. Section 8-2, Exercise 10 "MythBusters"

7. Section 8-2, Exercise 11 "Clothing Care Instructions"

8. Section 8-2, Exercise 12 "M&Ms"

Randomization: Testing a Claim About a Mean. *In Exercises 9–12, use the randomization procedure for the indicated exercise.*

9. Section 8-3, Exercise 21 "Lead in Medicine"

10. Section 8-3, Exercise 22 "Got a Minute?"

11. Section 8-3, Exercise 23 "Cell Phone Radiation"

12. Section 8-3, Exercise 24 "Dollar Coins"

8-5   Beyond the Basics

13. Randomization with Standard Deviation When dealing with a single list of sample data, hypothesis testing with randomization requires that we modify the original sample data to conform to the assumption used for the null hypothesis. When testing a claim about σ with sample data having standard deviation s, we can multiply each sample data value by σ/s so that the sample has a standard deviation of σ as required. We can then resample the modified data set to find the number of resamples having standard deviations that are at least as extreme as the value of s from the original sample. Apply this method to repeat Example 4 using randomization. How do the results using randomization compare to those obtained from Example 1 in Section 8-4? What does that comparison suggest about the effectiveness of randomness in this case?

14. Randomization Data Set The solution to Exercise 9 included the count of 53 as the number of resamplings with a mean of 11.05 $\mu g/g$ or less. Repeat Exercise 9 many more times (such as 100) and record the counts of the numbers of resamplings with a mean of 11.05 $\mu g/g$ or less. Explore this new data set and identify the mean, standard deviation, range, minimum, maximum, nature of the distribution, and identify any outliers. Comment on the results.

Chapter Quick Quiz

1. Discarded Plastic Data Set 42 "Garbage Weight" includes weights (pounds) of discarded plastic from 62 different households. Those 62 weights have a mean of 1.911 pounds and a standard deviation of 1.065 pounds. We want to use a 0.05 level of significance to test the claim that this sample is from a population with a mean less than 2.000 pounds. Identify the null hypothesis and alternative hypothesis.

2. Discarded Plastic Find the test statistic used for the hypothesis test described in Exercise 1.

3. Discarded Plastic

a. What distribution is used for the hypothesis test described in Exercise 1?

b. For the hypothesis test described in Exercise 1, is it necessary to determine whether the 62 weights appear to be from a population having a normal distribution? Why or why not?

4. Discarded Plastic The P-value for the hypothesis test described in Exercise 1 is 0.2565.

a. What should be concluded about the null hypothesis?

b. What is the final conclusion that addresses the original claim?

5. Streaming Devices A Leichtman Research Group survey of 1150 TV households showed that 49% of them had at least one stand-alone streaming device. We want to use these results with a 0.01 significance level to test the claim that for the population of all homes, more than 45% have streaming devices. Identify the null hypothesis and alternative hypothesis.

6. Streaming Devices Find the test statistic used for the hypothesis test described in Exercise 5.

7. Streaming Devices The P-value for the hypothesis test described in Exercise 5 is 0.0029.

a. What should be concluded about the null hypothesis?

b. What is the final conclusion that addresses the original claim?

8. Distributions Using the methods of this chapter, identify the distribution that should be used for testing a claim about the given population parameter, assuming that the requirements are satisfied.

a. Mean

b. Proportion

c. Standard deviation

9. True or False Determine whether the given statements are true or false.

a. In hypothesis testing, it is *never* valid to form a conclusion of supporting the null hypothesis.

b. The conclusion of "fail to reject the null hypothesis" has exactly the same meaning as "accept the null hypothesis."

c. If correct methods of hypothesis testing are used with a large simple random sample that satisfies the test requirements, the conclusion will always be true.

d. When conducting a hypothesis test about the claimed proportion of adults who have current driving licenses, the problems with a convenience sample can be overcome by using a larger sample size.

e. When repeating the same hypothesis test with different random samples of the same size, the conclusions will all be the same.

10. Robust Explain what is meant by the statements that the t test for a claim about μ is robust, but the χ^2 test for a claim about σ is not robust.

Review Exercises

1. Job Search A Gallup poll of 195,600 employees showed that 51% of them were actively searching for new jobs. Use a 0.01 significance level to test the claim that the majority of employees are searching for new jobs.

2. Tour de France Listed below are the mean speeds (km/h) of recent winners of the Tour de France bicycle race. Use these speeds with a 0.05 significance level to test the claim that these recent mean winning speeds are not significantly different from the 27.2 km/h mean winning speed from the first few Tour de France races in the early 20th century.

> 40.3 39.6 40.0 39.9 40.9 40.6 41.7 40.8 39.0 40.5
> 40.3 39.6 39.8 39.9 40.5 40.7 39.6 39.6 41.0 40.2

3. Red Blood Cell Count A simple random sample of 40 adult males is obtained, and the red blood cell count (in cells per microliter) is measured for each of them, with these results: $n = 40$, $\bar{x} = 4.932$ million cells per microliter, $s = 0.504$ million cells per microliter (from Data Set 1 "Body Data" in Appendix B). Use a 0.01 significance level to test the claim that the sample is from a population with a mean less than 5.4 million cells per microliter, which is often used as the upper limit of the range of normal values. Does the result suggest that each of the 40 males has a red blood cell count below 5.4 million cells per microliter?

4. Perception and Reality In a presidential election, 308 out of 611 voters surveyed said that they voted for the candidate who won (based on data from ICR Survey Research Group). Use a 0.05 significance level to test the claim that among all voters, the percentage who believe that they voted for the winning candidate is equal to 43%, which is the actual percentage of votes for the winning candidate. What does the result suggest about voter perceptions?

5. Type I Error and Type II Error

a. In general, what is a type I error? In general, what is a type II error?

b. For the hypothesis test in Exercise 4 "Perception and Reality," write a statement that would be a type I error, and write another statement that would be a type II error.

6. True/False Determine whether the given statements are true or false.

a. In a hypothesis test, a very high P-value indicates strong support of the alternative hypothesis.

b. The Student t distribution can be used to test a claim about a population mean whenever the sample data are randomly selected from a normally distributed population.

c. When using a X^2 distribution to test a claim about a population standard deviation, there is a very loose requirement that the sample data are from a population having a normal distribution.

d. When testing a claim about a population proportion, the normal distribution can be used regardless of the sample size.

e. In a test of the claim that $\sigma = 15$ for the population of IQ scores of current statistics students, we find that the rightmost critical value is $X_R^2 = 83.298$, so the leftmost critical value is $X_L^2 = -83.298$.

Cumulative Review Exercises

1. Lightning Deaths Listed below are the numbers of deaths from lightning strikes in the United States each year for a sequence of recent and consecutive years. Find the values of the indicated statistics.

   46   51   44   51   43   32   38   48   45   27   34   29   26   28   23   26   28   40   16   20

a. Mean   **b.** Median   **c.** Standard deviation   **d.** Variance   **e.** Range

f. What important feature of the data is not revealed from an examination of the statistics, and what tool would be helpful in revealing it? What does a quick examination of the data reveal?

2. Lightning Deaths Refer to the sample data in Cumulative Review Exercise 1.

a. What is the level of measurement of the data (nominal, ordinal, interval, ratio)?

b. Are the values discrete or continuous?

c. Are the data categorical or quantitative?

d. Is the sample a simple random sample?

3. Confidence Interval for Lightning Deaths

a. Use the sample values given in Cumulative Review Exercise 1 to construct a 99% confidence interval estimate of the population mean. Assume that the population has a normal distribution.

b. Write a brief statement that interprets the confidence interval.

c. Is the confidence interval estimate of μ good for predicting the number of lightning deaths 10 years into the future? Why or why not?

4. Hypothesis Test for Lightning Deaths Refer to the sample data given in Cumulative Review Exercise 1 and consider those data to be a random sample of annual lightning deaths from recent years. Use those data with a 0.01 significance level to test the claim that the mean number of annual lightning deaths is less than the mean of 72.6 deaths from the 1980s. If the mean is now lower than in the past, identify one of the several factors that could explain the decline.

5. Lightning Deaths The accompanying bar chart shows the numbers of lightning strike deaths broken down by gender for a recent period of eleven years. What is wrong with the graph?

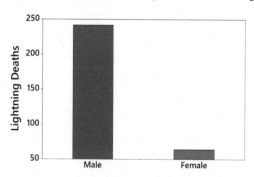

6. Lightning Deaths The graph in Cumulative Review Exercise 5 was created by using data consisting of 242 male deaths from lightning strikes and 64 female deaths from lightning strikes. Assume that these data are randomly selected lightning deaths and proceed to test the claim that the proportion of male deaths is greater than $1/2$. Use a 0.01 significance level. Any explanation for the result?

7. Lightning Deaths The graph in Cumulative Review Exercise 5 was created by using data consisting of 242 male deaths from lightning strikes and 64 female deaths from lightning strikes. Assume that these data are randomly selected lightning deaths and proceed to construct a 95% confidence interval estimate of the proportion of males among all lightning deaths. Based on the result, does it seem feasible that males and females have equal chances of being killed by lightning?

8. Lightning Deaths Based on the results given in Cumulative Review Exercise 6, assume that for a randomly selected lightning death, there is a 0.8 probability that the victim is a male.

a. Find the probability that three random people killed by lightning strikes are all males.

b. Find the probability that three random people killed by lightning strikes are all females.

c. Find the probability that among three people killed by lightning strikes, at least one is a male.

d. If five people killed by lightning strikes are randomly selected, find the probability that exactly three of them are males.

e. A study involves random selection of different groups of 50 people killed by lightning strikes. For those groups, find the mean and standard deviation for the numbers of male victims.

f. For the same groups described in part (e), would 46 be a significantly high number of males in a group? Explain.

Technology Project

Bootstrapping and Robustness Consider the probability distribution defined by the formula $P(x) = \dfrac{3x^2}{1000}$ where x can be any value between 0 and 10 inclusive (not just integers). The graph of this probability distribution on the next page shows that its shape is very far from the bell shape of a normal distribution. This probability distribution has parameters $\mu = 7.5$ and $\sigma = 1.93649$. Listed below is a simple random sample of values from this distribution, and the normal quantile plot for this sample is shown. Given the very non-normal shape of the distribution, it is not surprising to see the normal quantile plot with points that are far from a straight-line pattern, confirming that the sample does not appear to be from a normally distributed population.

| 8.69 | 2.03 | 9.09 | 7.15 | 9.05 | 9.40 | 6.30 | 7.89 | 7.98 | 7.67 |
| 7.77 | 7.17 | 8.86 | 8.29 | 9.21 | 7.80 | 7.70 | 8.12 | 9.11 | 7.64 |

$P(x) = \dfrac{3x^2}{1000}$ defined on [0, 10]

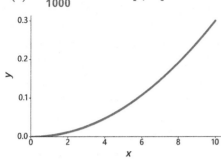

Normal Quantile Plot of 20 Sample Values

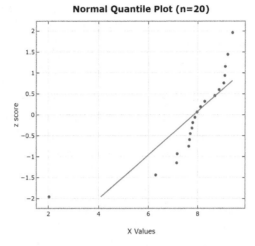

a. Mean Test the claim that the 20 given sample values are from a population having a mean equal to 7.5, which is the known population mean. Because the sample is not from a normally distributed population and because $n = 20$ does not satisfy the requirement of $n > 30$, we should not use the methods of Section 8-3. Instead, test the claim by using (a) the confidence interval method based on a bootstrap sample of size 1000 (see Section 7-4), and (b) the randomization method. Use a 0.05 significance level. What do the resampling methods of bootstrapping and randomization suggest about the claim that the sample is from a population with a mean of 7.5?

b. Standard Deviation Test the claim that the 20 sample values are from a population with a standard deviation equal to 1.93649, which is the known population standard deviation. Use the confidence interval method based on a bootstrap sample of size 1000. (See Section 7-4.) Use a 0.05 significance level. Does the bootstrap confidence interval contain the known population standard deviation of 1.93649? Is the bootstrap method effective for this test? What happens if we conduct the test by throwing all caution to the wind and constructing the 95% confidence interval by using the χ^2 distribution as described in Section 7-3?

Big (or Very Large) Data Project

Refer to Data Set 45 "Births in New York" in Appendix B. Use all 465,506 birth weights to test the claim that babies have a mean birth weight less than 3255 grams. Use a 0.05 significance level.

FROM DATA TO DECISION

Critical Thinking: Did the Official Cheat?

A county clerk in Essex County, New Jersey, had the responsibility of selecting the order in which candidates' names appeared on election ballots. Being placed first on the ballot is generally recognized as an advantage. The clerk was supposed to use random selection for those ballot placements. Here are the clerk's results:

Democrats were selected first in 40 of 41 ballots.

Republicans claimed that instead of using randomness, the clerk cheated by using a method that favored Democrats.

Analyzing the Results

a. In testing the claim made by the Republicans, choose between a significance level of 0.01 or 0.05. Consider the seriousness of the two types of errors. Explain your choice.

b. Analyze the result of Democrats getting the top line in 40 of 41 ballots. Describe the method used and the conclusions reached.

c. Assume that you are preparing an argument that will be presented in court. Is there strong evidence to support the claim that the clerk cheated? This is serious stuff, so write a thorough description of your analysis.

Cooperative Group Activities

1. In-class activity The "psychic staring effect": Can you sense when someone is staring at you? Pair off students and conduct an experiment to test this effect. For each pair of students, one student is the subject being stared at, and the other is the student who does (or does not) stare and cannot be seen by the subject. Each pair of students should conduct ten trials in which some of the trials involve staring and the others do not. In each trial, the subject must identify whether staring is occurring. Select the trials using random selection, such as tossing a coin to determine when staring is used. Combine all of the results and use them to test the claim that the proportion of correct responses by the subjects is $p = 0.5$, which corresponds to random guesses. What do you conclude about the psychic staring effect?

2. Out-of-class activity The author was told that 1962 pennies are biased in this sense: When they are made to stand on the edge and the table is bumped, heads will occur 80% of the time. Obtaining a sample of 1962 pennies may be challenging, so groups of three or four students may use a sample of any pennies to test that claim. What do you conclude?

3. Out-of-class activity Exercise 10 in Section 8-2 deals with results from the *MythBusters* television show in which buttered toast was dropped. The goal was to determine whether dropped buttered toast lands with the buttered side down at a rate significantly different from 50%. In groups of three or four, replicate the *MythBusters* experiment by creating your own experiment to test the claim that buttered toast lands with the buttered side down at a rate significantly different from 50%.

4. Out-of-class activity How do you draw the letter X? Working in groups of three or four, randomly select subjects and ask them to draw the letter X. Observe how the X is drawn, and record whether it is drawn by starting at the top left side and drawing \, then starting at the top right side and drawing /. Test the claim that the majority of people draw the X as described here.

5. Out-of-class activity Here is the breakdown of the most common car colors from PPG Industries: 23% are white, 18% are black, 16% are gray, 15% are silver, and 10% are red. After selecting one of the given colors, groups of three or four students should go to the college parking lot and randomly select cars to test the claim that the percentage for the chosen color is as claimed.

6. Out-of-class activity In the United States, 40% of us have brown eyes, according to Dr. P. Sorita Soni at Indiana University. Groups of three or four students should randomly select people and identify the color of their eyes. The claim that 40% of us have brown eyes can then be tested.

7. In-class activity Without using any measuring device, each student should draw a line believed to be 3 in. long and another line believed to be 3 cm long. Then use rulers to measure and record the lengths of the lines drawn. Find the means and standard deviations of the two sets of lengths. Test the claim that the lines estimated to be 3 in. have a mean length that is equal to 3 in. Test the claim that the lines estimated to be 3 cm have a mean length that is equal to 3 cm. Compare the results. Do the estimates of the 3-in. line appear to be more accurate than those for the 3-cm line? What do these results suggest?

8. In-class activity Assume that a method of gender selection can affect the probability of a baby being a girl so that the probability becomes $1/4$. Each student should simulate 20 births by drawing 20 cards from a shuffled deck. Replace each card after it has been drawn, then reshuffle. Consider the hearts to be girls and consider all other cards to be boys. After making 20 selections and recording the "genders" of the babies, use a 0.10 significance level to test the claim that the proportion of girls is equal to $1/4$. How many students are expected to get results leading to the wrong conclusion that the proportion is not $1/4$? How does that relate to the probability of a type I error? Does this procedure appear to be effective in identifying the effectiveness of the gender selection method? (If decks of cards are not available, use some other way to simulate the births, such as using the random number generator on a calculator or using digits from phone numbers or Social Security numbers.)

9. Out-of-class activity Groups of three or four students should go to the library and collect a sample consisting of the ages of books (based on copyright dates). Plan and describe the sampling plan, execute the sampling procedure, and then use the results to test the claim that the mean age of books in the library is greater than 20 years.

10. In-class activity Each student should write an estimate of the age of the current president of the United States. All estimates should be collected, and the sample mean and standard deviation should be calculated. Then test the hypothesis that the mean of all such estimates is equal to the actual current age of the president.

11. In-class activity A class project should be designed to conduct a test in which each student is given a taste of Coke and a taste of Pepsi. The student is then asked to identify which sample is Coke. After all of the results are collected, test the claim that the success rate is better than the rate that would be expected with random guesses.

12. In-class activity Each student should estimate the length of the classroom. The values should be based on visual estimates, with no actual measurements being taken. After the estimates have been collected, measure the length of the room, then test the claim that the sample mean is equal to the actual length of the classroom. Is there a "collective wisdom," whereby the class mean is approximately equal to the actual room length?

13. Out-of-class activity Using one wristwatch that is reasonably accurate, set the time to be exact. Visit www.time.gov to set the exact time. If you cannot set the time to the nearest second, record the error for the watch you are using. Now compare the time on this watch to the time on other watches that have not been set to the exact time. Record the errors with negative signs for watches that are ahead of the actual time and positive signs for those watches that are behind the actual time. Use the data to test the claim that the mean error of all wristwatches is equal to 0. Do we collectively run on time, or are we early or late? Also test the claim that the standard deviation of errors is less than 1 min. What are the practical implications of a standard deviation that is excessively large?

14. In-class activity In a group of three or four people, conduct an extrasensory perception (ESP) experiment by selecting one of the group members as the subject. Draw a circle on one small piece of paper and draw a square on another sheet of the same size. Repeat this experiment 20 times: Randomly select the circle or the square and place it in the subject's hand behind his or her back so that it cannot be seen, then ask the subject to identify the shape (without seeing it); record whether the response is correct. Test the claim that the subject has ESP because the proportion of correct responses is significantly greater than 0.5.

15. In-class activity After dividing into groups of between 10 and 20 people, each group member should record the number of heartbeats in a minute. After calculating the sample mean and standard deviation, each group should proceed to test the claim that the mean is greater than 48 beats per minute, which is the author's result. (When people exercise, they tend to have lower pulse rates, and the author runs 5 miles a few times each week. What a guy!)

16. Out-of-class activity In groups of three or four, collect data to determine whether subjects have a Facebook page, then combine the results and test the claim that more than 3/4 of students have a Facebook page.

17. Out-of-class activity Each student should find an article in a professional journal that includes a hypothesis test of the type discussed in this chapter. Write a brief report describing the hypothesis test and its role in the context of the article.

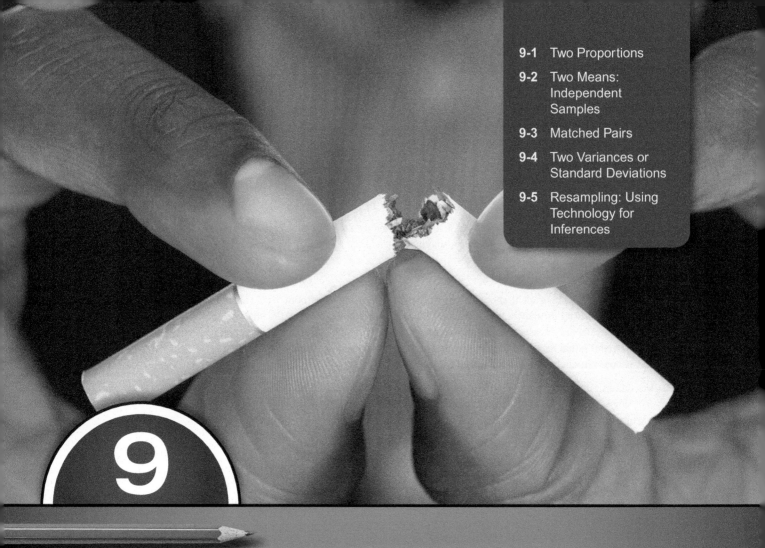

9

INFERENCES FROM TWO SAMPLES

CHAPTER PROBLEM   **To Stop Smoking, Which is Better: E-Cigarettes or Nicotine Replacement?**

Researchers conducted a trial in which 884 smokers were randomly placed in one of two different groups for smoking cessation treatment with either e-cigarettes or nicotine replacement (nicotine patch, nicotine gum, etc.). Table 9-1 shows the results obtained 52 weeks after the treatment (based on "A Randomized Trial of E-Cigarettes versus Nicotine-Replacement Therapy," by Hajek, et al., *New England Journal of Medicine*).

From Table 9-1 we can see that the success rates are 18.0% for the e-cigarette group and 9.9% for the nicotine replacement group. Clearly, 18.0% is higher than 9.9%, but is the difference statistically significant? This chapter will introduce methods for answering such questions. In this case, the answer will reveal whether the e-cigarette is a more effective smoking cessation aid than the nicotine replacement treatment.

TABLE 9-1 Results of Smoking Cessation Trials

	E-Cigarettes	Nicotine Replacement
Not smoking after 52 weeks	79	44
Number of subjects	438	446

In addition to using the data in Table 9-1 to evaluate the effectiveness of e-cigarettes as an aid to stop smoking, we must also consider other factors such as health and behavioral risks. E-cigarettes can contain harmful ingredients, cause addiction, harm the respiratory system, and may impair brain development. While e-cigarettes may be used as an aid to stop smoking, the use of e-cigarettes should never be considered a healthy behavior.

CHAPTER OBJECTIVES

Inferential statistics involves forming conclusions (or inferences) about a population parameter. Two major activities of inferential statistics are estimating values of population parameters using confidence intervals (as in Chapter 7) and testing claims made about population parameters (as in Chapter 8). Chapters 7 and 8 both involved methods for dealing with a sample from *one* population, and this chapter extends those methods to situations involving *two* populations. Here are the chapter objectives:

9-1 Two Proportions

- Conduct a formal hypothesis test of a claim made about two population proportions.

- Construct a confidence interval estimate of the difference between two population proportions.

9-2 Two Means: Independent Samples

- Distinguish between a situation involving two independent samples and a situation involving two samples that are not independent.

- Conduct a formal hypothesis test of a claim made about two means from independent populations.

- Construct a confidence interval estimate of the difference between two population means.

9-3 Matched Pairs

- Identify sample data consisting of matched pairs.

- Conduct a formal hypothesis test of a claim made about the mean of the differences between matched pairs.

- Construct a confidence interval estimate of the mean difference between matched pairs.

9-4 Two Variances or Standard Deviations

- Develop the ability to conduct a formal hypothesis test of a claim made about two population variances or standard deviations.

9-5 Resampling: Using Technology for Inferences

- Use the resampling methods of bootstrapping and randomization for inferences about two proportions, two means from independent populations, two means from matched pairs, or two population standard deviations or variances.

9-1 Two Proportions

Key Concept In this section we present methods for (1) testing a claim made about two population proportions and (2) constructing a confidence interval estimate of the difference between two population proportions. The methods of this section can also be used with probabilities or the decimal equivalents of percentages.

KEY ELEMENTS

Inferences About Two Proportions

Objectives

1. **Hypothesis Test:** Conduct a hypothesis test of a claim about two population proportions.

2. **Confidence Interval:** Construct a confidence interval estimate of the difference between two population proportions.

Notation for Two Proportions

For population 1 we let

$p_1 = $ *population* proportion

$n_1 = $ size of the first sample

$x_1 = $ number of successes in the first sample

$\hat{p}_1 = \dfrac{x_1}{n_1}$ (*sample* proportion)

$\hat{q}_1 = 1 - \hat{p}_1$ (complement of $\hat{p}_1$)

The corresponding notations p_2, n_2, x_2, $\hat{p}_2$, and $\hat{q}_2$ apply to population 2.

Pooled Sample Proportion

The **pooled sample proportion** is denoted by $\bar{p}$ and it combines the two sample proportions into one proportion, as shown here:

$$\bar{p} = \frac{x_1 + x_2}{n_1 + n_2}$$
$$\bar{q} = 1 - \bar{p}$$

Requirements

1. The sample proportions are from two simple random samples.

2. The two samples are *independent*. (Samples are *independent* if the sample values selected from one population are not related to or somehow naturally paired or matched with the sample values from the other population.)

3. For each of the two samples, there are at least 5 successes and at least 5 failures. (That is, $n\hat{p} \geq 5$ and $n\hat{q} \geq 5$ for each of the two samples).

DETOUR **(If the third requirement is not satisfied, alternatives include the resampling methods of bootstrapping or randomization described in Section 9-5, or Fisher's exact test described in Section 11-2.)**

Test Statistic for Two Proportions (with H_0: $p_1 = p_2$)

$$z = \frac{(\hat{p}_1 - \hat{p}_2) - (p_1 - p_2)}{\sqrt{\dfrac{\bar{p}\bar{q}}{n_1} + \dfrac{\bar{p}\bar{q}}{n_2}}}$$ where $p_1 - p_2 = 0$ (assumed in the null hypothesis)

Where $\bar{p} = \dfrac{x_1 + x_2}{n_1 + n_2}$ (*pooled* sample proportion)   and $\bar{q} = 1 - \bar{p}$

P-Value: P-values are automatically provided by technology. If technology is not available, use Table A-2 (standard normal distribution) and find the P-value using the procedure given in Figure 8-3 on page 380.

Critical Values: Use Table A-2. (Based on the significance level α, find critical values by using the same procedures introduced in Section 8-1.)

Confidence Interval Estimate of $p_1 - p_2$

The confidence interval estimate of the difference $p_1 - p_2$ is

$$(\hat{p}_1 - \hat{p}_2) - E < (p_1 - p_2) < (\hat{p}_1 - \hat{p}_2) + E$$

where the margin of error E is given by $E = z_{\alpha/2}\sqrt{\dfrac{\hat{p}_1\hat{q}_1}{n_1} + \dfrac{\hat{p}_2\hat{q}_2}{n_2}}.$

Rounding: Round the confidence interval limits to three significant digits.

Equivalent Methods

When testing a claim about two population proportions:

- The P-value method and the critical value method are equivalent.

- The confidence interval method is *not* equivalent to the P-value method or the critical value method.

Recommendation: If you want to *test a claim* about two population proportions, use the P-value method or critical value method; if you want to *estimate* the difference between two population proportions, use the confidence interval method.

Hypothesis Tests

For tests of hypotheses made about two population proportions, we consider only tests having a null hypothesis of $p_1 = p_2$ (so the null hypothesis is $H_0\colon p_1 = p_2$). With the assumption that $p_1 = p_2$, the estimates of $\hat{p}_1$ and $\hat{p}_2$ are combined to provide the best estimate of the common value of $\hat{p}_1$ and $\hat{p}_2$, and that combined value is the pooled sample proportion $\bar{p}$ given in the preceding Key Elements box. The following example will help clarify the roles of x_1, n_1, $\hat{p}_1$, $\bar{p}$, and so on. Note that with the assumption of equal population proportions, the best estimate of the common population proportion is obtained by pooling both samples into one big sample, so that $\bar{p}$ is the estimator of the common population proportion.

P-Value Method

  EXAMPLE 1 **Is There a Difference Between Success Rates of E-Cigarettes and Nicotine Replacement for Smokers Who Try to Stop Smoking?**

Table 9-1 in the Chapter Problem includes these two sample proportions of success for the e-cigarette treatment group and the nicotine replacement treatment group.

Proportion of Success (not smoking after 52 weeks)

E-Cigarette Group: $\hat{p}_1 = 79/438 = 0.180$

Nicotine Replacement Group: $\hat{p}_2 = 44/446 = 0.099$

Use a 0.05 significance level and the P-value method to test the claim that there is no difference in success rates between the two treatment groups.

continued

SOLUTION

REQUIREMENT CHECK We first verify that the three necessary requirements are satisfied. (1) The description of the selection of study subjects and the random assignment to groups confirms that the two samples can be treated as simple random samples for the purposes of this analysis. (2) The two samples are independent because subjects in the samples are not matched or paired in any way. (3) Consider a "success" to be a smoker who is not smoking after 52 weeks. For the e-cigarette group, the number of successes is 79 and the number of failures is $438 - 79 = 359$, so they are both at least 5. For the nicotine replacement group, the number of successes is 44 and the number of failures $446 - 44 = 402$, so they are both at least 5. The requirements are satisfied. ☑

The following steps are from the *P*-value method of testing hypotheses, which is summarized in Figure 8-1 on page 376.

Step 1: The claim of no significance difference between the two treatment groups can be expressed as $p_1 = p_2$.

Step 2: If $p_1 = p_2$ is false, then $p_1 \neq p_2$.

Step 3: Because the claim of $p_1 \neq p_2$ does not contain equality, it becomes the alternative hypothesis. The null hypothesis is the statement of equality, so we have

$$H_0: p_1 = p_2 \quad H_1: p_1 \neq p_2$$

Step 4: The significance level was specified as $\alpha = 0.05$, so we use $\alpha = 0.05$. (Who are we to argue?)

Step 5: Using Technology Steps 5 and 6 can be skipped when using technology; see the accompanying Statdisk display showing the test statistic and *P*-value.

Statdisk

```
Alternative Hypothesis:    p1 not = p2

Pooled Proportion:     0.13914
Test Statistic, z:     3.50965
Critical z:            ±1.95996
P-Value:               0.00045

95% Confidence Interval:
0.03630 < p1-p2 < 0.12712
```

Manual Calculation If not using technology, we use the normal distribution (with the test statistic given in the Key Elements box) as an approximation to the binomial distribution. We estimate the common value of p_1 and p_2 with the pooled sample estimate $\bar{p}$ calculated as shown below, with extra decimal places used to minimize rounding errors in later calculations.

$$\bar{p} = \frac{x_1 + x_2}{n_1 + n_2} = \frac{79 + 44}{438 + 446} = 0.13914027$$

With $\bar{p} = 0.13914027$, it follows that $\bar{q} = 1 - 0.13914027 = 0.86085973$.

Step 6: Because we assume in the null hypothesis that $p_1 = p_2$, the value of $p_1 - p_2$ is 0 in the following calculation of the test statistic:

$$z = \frac{(\hat{p}_1 - \hat{p}_2) - (p_1 - p_2)}{\sqrt{\frac{\bar{p}\,\bar{q}}{n_1} + \frac{\bar{p}\,\bar{q}}{n_2}}}$$

$$= \frac{\left(\frac{79}{438} - \frac{44}{446}\right) - 0}{\sqrt{\frac{(0.13914027)(0.86085973)}{438} + \frac{(0.13914027)(0.86085973)}{446}}}$$

$$= 3.51$$

This is a two-tailed test, so the P-value is twice the area to the right of the test statistic $z = 3.51$ as shown in Figure 8-3 on page 380. Refer to Table A-2 and find that the area to the right of $z = 3.51$ is 0.0001, so the P-value is $2(0.0001) = 0.0002$. Technology provides a more accurate P-value of 0.00045 (as shown in the preceding Statdisk display). The test statistic and P-value are shown in Figure 9-1(a).

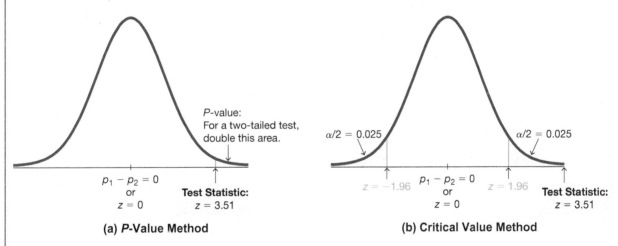

(a) **P-Value Method**   (b) **Critical Value Method**

FIGURE 9-1 Hypothesis Test with Two Proportions

Step 7: Because the P-value of 0.00045 is less than the significance level of $\alpha = 0.05$, we reject the null hypothesis of $p_1 = p_2$. ("If the P is *low*, the null must go.")

INTERPRETATION

We must address the original claim that there is no difference in success rates between the two treatment groups. Because we reject the null hypothesis, we conclude that there is sufficient evidence to warrant rejection of the claim that $p_1 = p_2$. It appears that there is a significant difference between success rates in the two treatment groups.

But wait, we're not done. Based on this hypothesis test, it appears that the e-cigarette treatment is better than the nicotine replacement treatment. We can verify that with a right-tailed test of $p_1 > p_2$, the test statistic is the same $z = 3.51$ and the P-value will be 0.00022 (the P-value is 0.00045 for the two-tailed test, and it is 0.00022 for the right-tailed test). However, even the e-cigarette treatment has a success rate of only 18.0%, indicating that smokers using this treatment have less than a 20% chance of success in their attempt to stop smoking. The e-cigarette treatment might be *better*, but it is not that effective.

▶ **YOUR TURN.** Do Part (a) of Exercise 7 "Buttered Toast Drop Test."

Polio Experiment

In 1954 an experiment was conducted to test the effectiveness of the Salk vaccine as protection against the devastating effects of polio. Approximately 200,000 children were injected with an ineffective salt solution, and 200,000 other children were injected with the vaccine. The experiment was "double blind" because the children being injected didn't know whether they were given the real vaccine or the placebo, and the doctors giving the injections and evaluating the results didn't know either. Only 33 of the 200,000 vaccinated children later developed paralytic polio, whereas 115 of the 200,000 injected with the salt solution later developed paralytic polio. Statistical analysis of these and other results led to the conclusion that the Salk vaccine was indeed effective against paralytic polio.

Critical Value Method

The critical value method of testing hypotheses (see Figure 8-1 on page 376) can also be used for Example 1. In Step 6, instead of finding the P-value, find the critical values. With a significance level of $\alpha = 0.05$ in a two-tailed test based on the normal distribution, we refer to Table A-2 and find that an area of $\alpha = 0.05$ divided equally between the two tails corresponds to the critical values of $z = \pm 1.96$. In Figure 9-1(b) on the preceding page we can see that the test statistic of $z = 3.51$ falls within the critical region beyond the critical value of 1.96. We again reject the null hypothesis. The conclusions are the same as in Example 1.

Confidence Intervals

Using the format given in the preceding Key Elements box, we can construct a confidence interval estimate of the difference between population proportions $(p_1 - p_2)$. If a confidence interval estimate of $p_1 - p_2$ does not include 0, we have evidence suggesting that p_1 and p_2 have different values. The confidence interval uses a standard deviation based on estimated values of the population proportions, whereas a hypothesis test uses a standard deviation based on the *assumption* that the two population proportions are equal. Consequently, a conclusion based on a confidence interval might be different from a conclusion based on a hypothesis test. See the caution that follows Example 2.

CP — **EXAMPLE 2**   **Confidence Interval for Claim About Two Treatment Groups**

Use the sample data given in Example 1 to construct a 95% confidence interval estimate of the difference between the two population proportions. What does the result suggest about the claim that there is no difference in success rates between the two treatment groups?

SOLUTION

REQUIREMENT CHECK   We are using the same data from Example 1, and the same requirement check applies here, so the requirements are satisfied. ✓

The confidence interval can be found using technology; see the preceding Statdisk display. If not using technology, proceed as follows.

With a 95% confidence level, $z_{\alpha/2} = 1.96$ (from Table A-2). We first calculate the value of the margin of error E as shown here.

$$E = z_{\alpha/2}\sqrt{\frac{\hat{p}_1\hat{q}_1}{n_1} + \frac{\hat{p}_2\hat{q}_2}{n_2}} = 1.96\sqrt{\frac{\left(\frac{79}{438}\right)\left(\frac{359}{438}\right)}{438} + \frac{\left(\frac{44}{446}\right)\left(\frac{402}{446}\right)}{446}}$$

$$= 0.04541521$$

With $\hat{p}_1 = 79/438 = 0.18036530$ and $\hat{p}_2 = 44/446 = 0.09865471$, we get $\hat{p}_1 - \hat{p}_2 = 0.08171059$. With $\hat{p}_1 - \hat{p}_2 = 0.08171059$ and $E = 0.04541521$, the confidence interval is evaluated as follows, with the confidence interval limits rounded to three significant digits.

$$(\hat{p}_1 - \hat{p}_2) - E < p_1 - p_2 < (\hat{p}_1 - \hat{p}_2) + E$$

$$0.08171059 - 0.04541521 < p_1 - p_2 < 0.08171059 + 0.04541521$$

$$0.0363 < p_1 - p_2 < 0.127$$

See the preceding Statdisk display in Example 1 showing that after rounding, we get the same confidence interval obtained here.

INTERPRETATION

The confidence interval limits do not contain 0, suggesting that it is very unlikely that $\hat{p}_1 - \hat{p}_2 = 0$, so there is a significant difference between the two proportions. We should therefore reject the null hypothesis of $\hat{p}_1 = \hat{p}_2$. It appears that the e-cigarette and nicotine replacement treatment groups have different success rates.

YOUR TURN. Do Part (b) of Exercise 7 "Buttered Toast Drop Test."

CAUTION Use of One Confidence Interval Don't test for equality of two population proportions by determining whether there is an overlap between two individual confidence interval estimates of the two individual population proportions. When compared to the confidence interval estimate of $p_1 - p_2$, the analysis of overlap between two individual confidence intervals is more conservative (by rejecting equality less often), and it has less power (because it is less likely to reject $p_1 - p_2$ when in reality $p_1 \neq p_2$). See Exercise 25 "Overlap of Confidence Intervals."

CP〉**Alternative Methods: Resampling Methods of Bootstrapping and Randomization**

The claim that there is no difference in success rates between the E-cigarette group and nicotine replacement group can be tested by using the resampling methods of bootstrapping and randomization. See Section 9-5 "Resampling: Using Technology for Inferences."

Rationale: Why Do the Procedures of This Section Work?

Hypothesis Tests With $n_1\hat{p}_1 \geq 5$ and $n_1\hat{q}_1 \geq 5$, the distribution of $\hat{p}_1$ can be approximated by a normal distribution with mean p_1, standard deviation $\sqrt{p_1 q_1 / n_1}$, and variance $p_1 q_1 / n_1$ (based on Sections 6-6 and 7-1). This also applies to the second sample. The distributions of $\hat{p}_1$ and $\hat{p}_2$ are each approximated by a normal distribution, so the difference $\hat{p}_1 - \hat{p}_2$ will also be approximated by a normal distribution with mean $p_1 - p_2$ and variance

$$\sigma^2_{(\hat{p}_1 - \hat{p}_2)} = \sigma^2_{\hat{p}_1} + \sigma^2_{\hat{p}_2} = \frac{p_1 q_1}{n_1} + \frac{p_2 q_2}{n_2}$$

(The result above is based on this property: The variance of the *differences* between two independent random variables is the *sum* of their individual variances.)

The pooled estimate of the common value of p_1 and p_2 is $\bar{p} = (x_1 + x_2)/(n_1 + n_2)$. If we replace p_1 and p_2 by $\bar{p}$ and replace q_1 and q_2 by $\bar{q} = 1 - \bar{p}$, the variance above leads to the following standard deviation:

$$\sigma_{(\hat{p}_1 - \hat{p}_2)} = \sqrt{\frac{\bar{p}\bar{q}}{n_1} + \frac{\bar{p}\bar{q}}{n_2}}$$

We now know that the distribution of $\hat{p}_1 - \hat{p}_2$ is approximately normal, with mean $p_1 - p_2$ and standard deviation as shown above, so the z test statistic has the form given in the Key Elements box near the beginning of this section.

Confidence Interval The form of the confidence interval requires an expression for the variance different from the one given above. When constructing a confidence

interval estimate of the difference between two proportions, we don't assume that the two proportions are equal, and we estimate the standard deviation as

$$\sqrt{\frac{\hat{p}_1 \hat{q}_1}{n_1} + \frac{\hat{p}_2 \hat{q}_2}{n_2}}$$

In the test statistic

$$z = \frac{(\hat{p}_1 - \hat{p}_2) - (p_1 - p_2)}{\sqrt{\dfrac{\hat{p}_1 \hat{q}_1}{n_1} + \dfrac{\hat{p}_2 \hat{q}_2}{n_2}}}$$

use the positive and negative values of z (for two tails) and solve for $p_1 - p_2$. The results are the limits of the confidence interval given in the Key Elements box near the beginning of this section.

TECH CENTER

Inferences with Two Proportions

Access tech supplements, videos, and data sets at **www.TriolaStats.com**

Statdisk

Hypothesis Testing

1. Click **Analysis** in the top menu.
2. Select **Hypothesis Testing** from the dropdown menu and **Proportion Two Samples** from the submenu.
3. Select the desired format for *Alternative Hypothesis* and enter the significance level. For both samples, enter sample size and number of successes.
4. Click **Evaluate**.

Confidence Intervals

1. Click **Analysis** in the top menu.
2. Select **Confidence Intervals** from the dropdown menu and **Proportion Two Samples** from the submenu.
3. Enter the desired confidence level. For both samples, enter sample size and number of successes.
4. Click **Evaluate**.

Minitab

1. Click **Stat** in the top menu.
2. Select **Basic Statistics** from the dropdown menu and select **2 Proportions** from the submenu.
3. Select **Summarized data** from the dropdown menu and enter the number of events and number of trials for both samples.
4. Click the **Options** button and enter the confidence level. If testing a hypothesis, enter **0** for *Hypothesized difference* and select the desired format for *the Alternative hypothesis*.
5. For *Test method* select **Use the pooled estimate of the proportion**.
6. Click **OK** twice.

TIP: Another procedure is to click on **Assistant** in the top menu, then select **Hypothesis Tests** and **2-Sample % Defective**. Complete the dialog box to get results, including *P*-value and other helpful information.

StatCrunch

1. Click **Stat** in the top menu.
2. Select **Proportion Stats** from the dropdown menu, then select **Two Sample—With Summary** from the submenu.
3. Enter the number of successes and number of observations for both samples.
4. *Hypothesis Testing*: Select **Hypothesis test for p_1-p_2**. Enter **0** for the hypothesized difference (H_0) and select the desired format for the alternative hypothesis (H_A).

   Confidence Intervals: Select **Confidence interval for p_1-p_2** and enter the confidence level.
5. Click **Compute!**

TI-83/84 Plus Calculator

Hypothesis Testing:

1. Press **STAT**, then select **TESTS** in the top menu.
2. Select **2-PropZTest** in the menu and press **ENTER**.
3. Enter the number of successes *(x)* and number of observations *(n)* for both samples. Select the desired format for the alternative hypothesis *(p1)*.
4. Select **Calculate** and press **ENTER**.

Confidence Intervals:

1. Press **STAT**, then select **TESTS** in the top menu.
2. Select **2-PropZInt** in the menu and press **ENTER**.
3. Enter the number of successes *(x)* and number of observations *(n)* for both samples. Enter the desired confidence level *(C-Level)*.
4. Select **Calculate** and press **ENTER**.

TECH CENTER *continued*

Inferences with Two Proportions
Access tech supplements, videos, and data sets at **www.TriolaStats.com**

Excel

XLSTAT Add-In (Required)

1. Click on the **XLSTAT** tab in the Ribbon and then click **Parametric tests.**
2. Select **Tests for two proportions** from the dropdown menu.
3. Under *Data Format* select **Frequencies** if you know the number of successes *x* or select **Proportions** if you know the sample proportion $\hat{p}$.
4. Enter the frequency or sample proportion and sample size for both samples.
5. Check **z test,** uncheck **Continuity Correction,** and uncheck **Monte Carlo method.**
6. Click the **Options** tab.
7. *Hypothesis Testing:*

   Under *Alternative hypothesis* select the desired format (≠ for two-tailed test, < for left-tailed test, > for right-tailed test). *For Hypothesized difference* enter **0.** Enter the desired significance level (enter **5** for 0.05 significance level). Under *Variance* select **pq(1/n1 + 1/n2).**

   Confidence Intervals:

   Under *Alternative hypothesis* select ≠ **D** for a two-tailed test. *For Hypothesized difference* enter **0.** Enter the desired significance level (enter **5** for a 95% confidence level). Under *Variance* select **p1q1/n1 + p2q2/n2.**
8. Click **OK** to display the results that include the test statistic labeled *z(Observed value)*, *P*-value, and confidence interval.

R

R command:
prop.test(x, y, alternative = c("two.sided", "less", "greater"), conf.level = 0.95, correct = FALSE)

where *x* is a vector of successes in group 1 and 2 and *y* is a vector of the sample sizes of group 1 and 2.

TIP: The results include the χ^2 (X-squared) statistic. The *z*-statistic can be found by taking the square root of the χ^2 statistic.

TIP: For Example 1: prop.test(x, y, alternative="two. sided", conf.level=0.95, correct=FALSE); where x=c(79,44) and y=c(438,446).

A complete list of R statistical commands is available at TriolaStats.com

9-1 Basic Skills and Concepts

Statistical Literacy and Critical Thinking

1. Salk Vaccine: Verifying Requirements In the largest clinical trial ever conducted, 401,974 children were randomly assigned to two groups. The treatment group consisted of 201,229 children given the Salk vaccine for polio, and 33 of those children developed polio. The other 200,745 children were given a placebo, and 115 of those children developed polio. If we want to use the methods of this section to test the claim that the rate of polio is less for children given the Salk vaccine, are the requirements for a hypothesis test satisfied? Explain.

2. Notation For the sample data given in Exercise 1, consider the Salk vaccine treatment group to be the first sample. Identify the values of $n_1, \hat{p}_1, \hat{q}_1, n_2, \hat{p}_2, \hat{q}_2, \bar{p}$, and $\bar{q}$. Round all values so that they have six significant digits.

3. Hypotheses and Conclusions Refer to the hypothesis test described in Exercise 1.

a. Identify the null hypothesis and the alternative hypothesis.

b. If the *P*-value for the test is reported as "less than 0.001," what should we conclude about the original claim?

4. Using Confidence Intervals

a. In general, when dealing with inferences about two population proportions, which two of the following are equivalent: confidence interval method; *P*-value method; critical value method?

b. If we want to use a 0.05 significance level to test the claim that $p_1 < p_2$ using a confidence interval, what confidence level should we use for that confidence interval?

c. If we test the claim in part (b) using the sample data in Exercise 1, we get this confidence interval: $-0.000508 < p_1 - p_2 < -0.000309$. What does this confidence interval suggest about the claim?

Statdisk

```
Pooled proportion: 0.35
Test Statistic, z: 12.8231
Critical z: 2.3264
P-Value: 0.0000

98% Confidence interval:
0.4762035 < p1-p2 < 0.6404632
```

StatCrunch

Difference	0.1949
z (Observed value)	3.1226
z (Critical value)	2.3263
p-value (one-tailed)	0.0009
alpha	0.01

Interpreting Displays.   *In Exercises 5 and 6, use the results from the given displays.*

5. Testing Laboratory Gloves
The *New York Times* published an article about a study in which Professor Denise Korniewicz and other Johns Hopkins researchers subjected laboratory gloves to stress. Among 240 vinyl gloves, 63% leaked viruses. Among 240 latex gloves, 7% leaked viruses. See the accompanying display of the Statdisk results. Using a 0.01 significance level, test the claim that vinyl gloves have a greater virus leak rate than latex gloves.

6. Treating Carpal Tunnel Syndrome
Carpal tunnel syndrome is a common wrist complaint resulting from a compressed nerve, and it is often the result of extended use of repetitive wrist movements, such as those associated with the use of a keyboard. In a randomized controlled trial, 73 patients were treated with surgery and 67 were found to have successful treatments. Among 83 patients treated with splints, 60 were found to have successful treatments (based on data from "Splinting vs Surgery in the Treatment of Carpal Tunnel Syndrome," by Gerritsen et al., *Journal of the American Medical Association,* Vol. 288, No. 10). Use the accompanying StatCrunch display with a 0.01 significance level to test the claim that the success rate is better with surgery.

Testing Claims About Proportions.   *In Exercises 7–22, test the given claim. Identify the null hypothesis, alternative hypothesis, test statistic, P-value or critical value(s), then state the conclusion about the null hypothesis, as well as the final conclusion that addresses the original claim.*

7. Buttered Toast Drop Test
The Discovery TV show *MythBusters* conducted an experiment in which they tested the common belief that dropped buttered toast tends to fall with the buttered side down. Here are the results of that experiment: Among 48 slices of buttered toast that were dropped, 19 landed with the buttered side down. Among 48 slices of toast that were not buttered but were marked with an X on one side, 22 landed with the X side down. Use a 0.05 significance level to test the claim that when dropped, buttered toast and toast marked with an X have the same proportion that land with the buttered/X side down.

a. Test the claim using a hypothesis test.

b. Test the claim by constructing an appropriate confidence interval.

8. Tennis Challenges
Since the Hawk-Eye instant replay system for tennis was introduced at the U.S. Open in 2006, men's singles players challenged 6036 referee calls, with the result that 1757 were successfully overturned. Women's singles players challenged 3327 referee calls, with the result that 887 were successfully overturned. Use a 0.05 significance level to test the claim that men and women singles players have equal success in challenging calls.

a. Test the claim using a hypothesis test.

b. Test the claim by constructing an appropriate confidence interval.

c. Based on the results, does it appear that men and women have equal success in challenging calls?

9. Cell Phones and Handedness
A study was conducted to investigate the association between cell phone use and hemispheric brain dominance. Among 216 subjects who prefer to use their left ear for cell phones, 166 were right-handed. Among 452 subjects who prefer to use their right ear for cell phones, 436 were right-handed (based on data from "Hemispheric

Dominance and Cell Phone Use," by Seidman et al., *JAMA Otolaryngology—Head & Neck Surgery,* Vol. 139, No. 5). We want to use a 0.01 significance level to test the claim that the rate of right-handedness for those who prefer to use their left ear for cell phones is less than the rate of right-handedness for those who prefer to use their right ear for cell phones. (Try not to get too confused here.)

a. Test the claim using a hypothesis test.

b. Test the claim by constructing an appropriate confidence interval.

10. Denomination Effect A trial was conducted with 75 women in China given a 100-yuan bill, while another 75 women in China were given 100 yuan in the form of smaller bills (a 50-yuan bill plus two 20-yuan bills plus two 5-yuan bills). Among those given the single bill, 60 spent some or all of the money. Among those given the smaller bills, 68 spent some or all of the money (based on data from "The Denomination Effect," by Raghubir and Srivastava, *Journal of Consumer Research,* Vol. 36). We want to use a 0.05 significance level to test the claim that when given a single large bill, a smaller proportion of women in China spend some or all of the money when compared to the proportion of women in China given the same amount in smaller bills.

a. Test the claim using a hypothesis test.

b. Test the claim by constructing an appropriate confidence interval.

c. If the significance level is changed to 0.01, does the conclusion change?

11. Dreaming in Black and White A study was conducted to determine the proportion of people who dream in black and white instead of color. Among 306 people over the age of 55, 68 dream in black and white, and among 298 people under the age of 25, 13 dream in black and white (based on data from "Do We Dream in Color?" by Eva Murzyn, *Consciousness and Cognition,* Vol. 17, No. 4). We want to use a 0.01 significance level to test the claim that the proportion of people over 55 who dream in black and white is greater than the proportion of those under 25.

a. Test the claim using a hypothesis test.

b. Test the claim by constructing an appropriate confidence interval.

c. An explanation given for the results is that those over the age of 55 grew up exposed to media that was mostly displayed in black and white. Can the results from parts (a) and (b) be used to verify that explanation?

12. Clinical Trials of OxyContin OxyContin (oxycodone) is a drug used to treat pain, but it is well known for its addictiveness and danger. In a clinical trial, among subjects treated with OxyContin, 52 developed nausea and 175 did not develop nausea. Among other subjects given placebos, 5 developed nausea and 40 did not develop nausea (based on data from Purdue Pharma L.P.). Use a 0.05 significance level to test for a difference between the rates of nausea for those treated with OxyContin and those given a placebo.

a. Use a hypothesis test.

b. Use an appropriate confidence interval.

c. Does nausea appear to be an adverse reaction resulting from OxyContin?

13. Are Seat Belts Effective? A simple random sample of front-seat occupants involved in car crashes is obtained. Among 2823 occupants not wearing seat belts, 31 were killed. Among 7765 occupants wearing seat belts, 16 were killed (based on data from "Who Wants Airbags?" by Meyer and Finney, *Chance,* Vol. 18, No. 2). We want to use a 0.05 significance level to test the claim that seat belts are effective in reducing fatalities.

a. Test the claim using a hypothesis test.

b. Test the claim by constructing an appropriate confidence interval.

c. What does the result suggest about the effectiveness of seat belts?

14. Cigarette Pack Warnings A study was conducted to find the effects of cigarette pack warnings that consisted of text or pictures. Among 1078 smokers given cigarette packs with text warnings, 366 tried to quit smoking. Among 1071 smokers given cigarette packs with warning pictures, 428 tried to quit smoking. (Results are based on data from "Effect of Pictorial Cigarette Pack Warnings on Changes in Smoking Behavior," by Brewer et al., *Journal of the American Medical Association*.) Use a 0.01 significance level to test the claim that the proportion of smokers who tried to quit in the text warning group is less than the proportion in the picture warning group.

a. Test the claim using a hypothesis test.

b. Test the claim by constructing an appropriate confidence interval.

15. Can Dogs Detect Malaria? A study was conducted to determine whether dogs could detect malaria from socks worn by malaria patients and socks worn by patients without malaria. Among 175 socks worn by malaria patients, the dogs made correct identifications 123 times. Among 145 socks worn by patients without malaria, the dogs made correct identifications 131 times (based on data presented at an annual meeting of the American Society of Tropical Medicine, by principal investigator Steve Lindsay). Use a 0.05 significance level to test the claim of no difference between the two rates of correct responses.

a. Test the claim using a hypothesis test.

b. Test the claim by constructing an appropriate confidence interval.

c. What do the results suggest about the use of dogs to detect malaria?

16. Bednets to Reduce Malaria In a randomized controlled trial in Kenya, insecticide-treated bednets were tested as a way to reduce malaria. Among 343 infants using bednets, 15 developed malaria. Among 294 infants not using bednets, 27 developed malaria (based on data from "Sustainability of Reductions in Malaria Transmission and Infant Mortality in Western Kenya with Use of Insecticide-Treated Bednets," by Lindblade et al., *Journal of the American Medical Association,* Vol. 291, No. 21). We want to use a 0.01 significance level to test the claim that the incidence of malaria is lower for infants using bednets.

a. Test the claim using a hypothesis test.

b. Test the claim by constructing an appropriate confidence interval.

c. Based on the results, do the bednets appear to be effective?

17. Car License Plates The author collected the data in the table below by randomly selecting cars in Connecticut and New York. Use a 0.05 significance level to test the claim that Connecticut and New York have the same proportion of cars with rear license plates only.

a. Test the claim using a hypothesis test.

b. Test the claim by constructing an appropriate confidence interval.

	Connecticut	New York
Cars with rear license plate only	239	9
Cars with front and rear license plates	1810	541
Total	**2049**	**550**

18. Car and Truck License Plate Laws Among 2049 Connecticut passenger cars, 239 had only rear license plates. Among 334 Connecticut trucks, 45 had only rear license plates (based on samples collected by the author). A reasonable hypothesis is that passenger car owners violate license plate laws at a higher rate than owners of commercial trucks. Use a 0.05 significance level to test that hypothesis.

a. Test the claim using a hypothesis test.

b. Test the claim by constructing an appropriate confidence interval.

19. Blue Eyes and Gender Professors collected data consisting of eye color and gender of statistics students. Among 1107 female students, 370 had blue eyes. Among 919 male students, 359 had blue eyes (based on data from "Does Eye Color Depend on Gender? It Might Depend on Who or How You Ask," by Froelich and Stephenson, *Journal of Statistics Education*, Vol. 21, No. 2). Use a 0.01 significance level to test the claim that the proportions of blue eyes are the same for females and males.

a. Test the claim using a hypothesis test.

b. Test the claim by constructing an appropriate confidence interval.

c. What is the type of sampling used? Is it likely that the sample is biased?

20. Brown Eyes and Gender Professors collected data consisting of eye color and gender of statistics students. Among 1107 female students, 352 had brown eyes. Among 919 male students, 290 had brown eyes (based on data from "Does Eye Color Depend on Gender? It Might Depend on Who or How You Ask," by Froelich and Stephenson, *Journal of Statistics Education*, Vol. 21, No. 2). Use a 0.01 significance level to test the claim that the proportions of brown eyes are the same for females and males.

a. Test the claim using a hypothesis test.

b. Test the claim by constructing an appropriate confidence interval.

c. What is the type of sampling used? Is it likely that the sample is biased?

21. Lefties In a random sample of males, it was found that 23 write with their left hands and 217 do not. In a random sample of females, it was found that 65 write with their left hands and 455 do not (based on data from "The Left-Handed: Their Sinister History," by Elaine Fowler Costas, Education Resources Information Center, Paper 399519). We want to use a 0.01 significance level to test the claim that the rate of left-handedness among males is less than that among females.

a. Test the claim using a hypothesis test.

b. Test the claim by constructing an appropriate confidence interval.

c. Based on the results, is the rate of left-handedness among males less than the rate of left-handedness among females?

22. Ground vs. Helicopter for Serious Injuries A study investigated rates of fatalities among patients with serious traumatic injuries. Among 61,909 patients transported by helicopter, 7813 died. Among 161,566 patients transported by ground services, 17,775 died (based on data from "Association Between Helicopter vs. Ground Emergency Medical Services and Survival for Adults With Major Trauma," by Galvagno et al., *Journal of the American Medical Association*, Vol. 307, No. 15). Use a 0.01 significance level to test the claim that the rate of fatalities is higher for patients transported by helicopter.

a. Test the claim using a hypothesis test.

b. Test the claim by constructing an appropriate confidence interval.

c. Considering the test results and the actual sample rates, is one mode of transportation better than the other? Are there other important factors to consider?

9-1 Beyond the Basics

23. Determining Sample Size The sample size needed to estimate the difference between two population proportions to within a margin of error E with a confidence level of $1 - \alpha$ can be found by using the following expression:

$$E = z_{\alpha/2}\sqrt{\frac{p_1 q_1}{n_1} + \frac{p_2 q_2}{n_2}}$$

continued

Replace n_1 and n_2 by n in the preceding formula (assuming that both samples have the same size) and replace each of p_1, q_1, p_2, and q_2 by 0.5 (because their values are not known). Solving for n results in this expression:

$$n = \frac{z_{\alpha/2}^2}{2E^2}$$

Use this expression to find the size of each sample if you want to estimate the difference between the proportions of men and women who shop online. Assume that you want 95% confidence that your error is no more than 0.02.

24. Yawning and Fisher's Exact Test In one segment of the TV series *MythBusters*, an experiment was conducted to test the common belief that people are more likely to yawn when they see others yawning. In one group, 34 subjects were exposed to yawning, and 10 of them yawned. In another group, 16 subjects were not exposed to yawning, and 4 of them yawned. We want to test the belief that people are more likely to yawn when they are exposed to yawning.

a. Why can't we test the claim using the methods of this section?

b. If we ignore the requirements and use the methods of this section, what is the *P*-value? How does it compare to the *P*-value of 0.5128 that would be obtained by using Fisher's exact test?

c. Comment on the conclusion of the *MythBusters* segment that yawning is contagious.

25. Overlap of Confidence Intervals In the article "On Judging the Significance of Differences by Examining the Overlap Between Confidence Intervals," by Schenker and Gentleman (*American Statistician*, Vol. 55, No. 3), the authors consider sample data in this statement: "Independent simple random samples, each of size 200, have been drawn, and 112 people in the first sample have the attribute, whereas 88 people in the second sample have the attribute."

a. Use the methods of this section to construct a 95% confidence interval estimate of the difference $p_1 - p_2$. What does the result suggest about the equality of p_1 and p_2?

b. Use the methods of Section 7-1 to construct individual 95% confidence interval estimates for each of the two population proportions. After comparing the overlap between the two confidence intervals, what do you conclude about the equality of p_1 and p_2?

c. Use a 0.05 significance level to test the claim that the two population proportions are equal. What do you conclude?

d. Based on the preceding results, what should you conclude about the equality of p_1 and p_2? Which of the three preceding methods is least effective in testing for the equality of p_1 and p_2?

26. Equivalence of Hypothesis Test and Confidence Interval Two different simple random samples are drawn from two different populations. The first sample consists of 20 people with 10 having a common attribute. The second sample consists of 2000 people with 1404 of them having the same common attribute. Compare the results from a hypothesis test of $p_1 = p_2$ (with a 0.05 significance level) and a 95% confidence interval estimate of $p_1 - p_2$.

27. Large Data Sets Use a 0.01 significance level to test the claim that the proportion of males in the sample in Data Set 2 "ANSUR I 1988" is the same as the proportion of males in the sample in Data Set 3 "ANSUR II 2012."

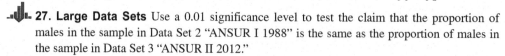

9-2 Two Means: Independent Samples

Key Concept This section presents methods for using sample data from two independent samples to (1) test hypotheses made about two population means or to (2) construct confidence interval estimates of the difference between two population means. In Part 1 we discuss situations in which the standard deviations of the two populations are unknown and are not assumed to be equal. In Part 2 we briefly discuss two other situations: (1) The two population standard deviations are unknown but are assumed to be equal; (2) the unrealistic case in which two population standard deviations are both known.

PART 1 Independent Samples: σ_1 and σ_2 Unknown and Not Assumed Equal

This section involves two *independent* samples, and the following section deals with samples that are *dependent* because they consist of matched pairs. It is important to know the difference between independent samples and dependent samples.

DEFINITIONS

Two samples are **independent** if the sample values from one population are not related to or somehow naturally paired or matched with the sample values from the other population.

Two samples are **dependent** (or consist of **matched pairs**) if the sample values are somehow matched, where the matching is based on some inherent relationship. (That is, each pair of sample values consists of two measurements from the same subject—such as before/after data—or each pair of sample values consists of matched pairs—such as husband/wife data—where the matching is based on some meaningful relationship.) *Caution*: "Dependence" does not require a direct cause/effect relationship.

HINT If the two samples have different sample sizes with no missing data, they must be independent. If the two samples have the same sample size, the samples may or may not be independent.

Here is an example of independent samples and another example of dependent samples consisting of matched pairs:

- *Independent Samples:* **Heights of Men and Women** Data Set 1 "Body Data" in Appendix B includes the following heights (cm) of samples of men and women, and the two samples are not matched according to some inherent relationship. They are actually two independent samples that just happen to be listed in a way that might cause us to incorrectly think that they are matched.

| Heights (cm) of Men | 172 | 154 | 156 | 158 | 169 |
| Heights (cm) of Women | 186 | 161 | 179 | 167 | 179 |

- *Dependent Samples:* **Heights of Husbands and Wives** Students of the author collected data consisting of the heights (cm) of husbands and the heights (cm) of their wives. Five of those pairs of heights are listed below. These two samples are dependent, because the height of each husband is *matched* with the height of his wife.

| Height (cm) of Husband | 175 | 180 | 173 | 176 | 178 |
| Height (cm) of Wife | 160 | 165 | 163 | 162 | 166 |

For inferences about means from two independent populations, the following box summarizes key elements of a hypothesis test and a confidence interval estimate of the difference between the population means.

Inferences About Two Means: Independent Samples

Objectives

1. **Hypothesis Test:** Conduct a hypothesis test of a claim about two independent population means.

2. **Confidence Interval:** Construct a confidence interval estimate of the difference between two independent population means.

Notation

For population 1 we let

$\mu_1 = population$ mean $\bar{x}_1 = sample$ mean

$\sigma_1 = population$ standard deviation $s_1 = sample$ standard deviation

$n_1 = $ size of the first sample

The corresponding notations μ_2, σ_2, $\bar{x}_2$, s_2, and n_2, apply to population 2.

Requirements

1. The values of σ_1 and σ_2 are unknown and we do not assume that they are equal.

2. The two samples are *independent.*

3. Both samples are *simple random samples.*

4. Either or both of these conditions are satisfied: The two sample sizes are both *large* (with $n_1 > 30$ and $n_2 > 30$) or both samples come from populations having normal distributions. (The methods used here are *robust* against departures from normality, so for small samples, the normality requirement is loose in the sense that the procedures perform well as long as there are no outliers and departures from normality are not too extreme.)

DETOUR **(If the third requirement is not satisfied, alternatives for hypothesis tests include the resampling methods of bootstrapping and randomization described in Section 9-5, or the Wilcoxon rank-sum test described in Section 13-4.)**

Hypothesis Test Statistic for Two Means: Independent Samples (with H_0: $\mu_1 = \mu_2$)

$$t = \frac{(\bar{x}_1 - \bar{x}_2) - (\mu_1 - \mu_2)}{\sqrt{\dfrac{s_1^2}{n_1} + \dfrac{s_2^2}{n_2}}} \quad \left(\text{where } \mu_1 - \mu_2 \text{ is often assumed to be } 0\right)$$

Degrees of Freedom When finding critical values or P-values, use the following for determining the number of degrees of freedom, denoted by df. (Although these two methods typically result in different numbers of degrees of freedom, the conclusion of a hypothesis test is rarely affected by the choice.)

1. Use this simple and conservative estimate:

$$\textbf{df} = \textbf{smaller of } n_1 - 1 \textbf{ and } n_2 - 1$$

2. Technologies typically use the more accurate but more difficult estimate given in Formula 9-1.

FORMULA 9-1

$$\text{df} = \frac{(A + B)^2}{\dfrac{A^2}{n_1 - 1} + \dfrac{B^2}{n_2 - 1}}$$

$$\text{where} \quad A = \frac{s_1^2}{n_1} \quad \text{and} \quad B = \frac{s_2^2}{n_2}$$

Note: Answers in Appendix D include technology answers based on Formula 9-1 along with "Table" answers based on using Table A-3 with the simple estimate of df given in option 1 at the left.

P-Values: P-values are automatically provided by technology. If technology is not available, refer to the t distribution in Table A-3. Use the procedure summarized in Figure 8-3 on page 380.

Critical Values: Refer to the t distribution in Table A-3.

Confidence Interval Estimate of $\mu_1 - \mu_2$: Independent Samples

The confidence interval estimate of the difference $\mu_1 - \mu_2$ is

$$(\bar{x}_1 - \bar{x}_2) - E < (\mu_1 - \mu_2) < (\bar{x}_1 - \bar{x}_2) + E$$

where

$$E = t_{\alpha/2}\sqrt{\frac{s_1^2}{n_1} + \frac{s_2^2}{n_2}}$$

and the number of degrees of freedom df is as described for hypothesis tests. (In this book, we use df = smaller of $n_1 - 1$ and $n_2 - 1$.)

Equivalent Methods

The P-value method of hypothesis testing, the critical value method of hypothesis testing, and confidence intervals all use the same distribution and standard error, so they are all equivalent in the sense that they result in the same conclusions.

P-Value Method

| EXAMPLE 1 | Are People Getting Taller? |

Listed below are heights (mm) of randomly selected U.S. Army male personnel measured in 1988 (from Data Set 2 "ANSUR I 1988") and different heights (mm) of randomly selected U.S. Army male personnel measured in 2012 (from Data Set 3 "ANSUR II 2012"). Use a 0.05 significance level to test the claim that the mean height of the 1988 population is less than the mean height of the 2012 population.

ANSUR I 1988	1698	1727	1734	1684	1667	1680	1785	1885
	1841	1702	1738	1732				
ANSUR II 2012	1810	1850	1777	1811	1780	1733	1814	1861
	1709	1740	1694	1766	1748	1794	1780	

SOLUTION

REQUIREMENT CHECK (1) The values of the two population standard deviations are not known and we are not making an assumption that they are equal. (2) The two samples are independent because the measurements are from different people, and they are not matched or paired in any way. (3) The samples are simple random samples. (4) Both samples are small (30 or fewer), so we need to determine whether both samples come from populations having normal distributions. Normal quantile plots of the two samples suggest that the samples are from populations having distributions that are not far from normal. The requirements are all satisfied. ☑

Using the P-value method summarized in Figure 8-1 on page 376, we can test the claim as follows.

Step 1: The claim that "the mean height of the 1988 population is less than the mean height of the 2012 population" can be expressed as $\mu_1 < \mu_2$.

Step 2: If the original claim is false, then $\mu_1 \geq \mu_2$.

Step 3: The alternative hypothesis is the expression not containing equality, and the null hypothesis is an expression of equality, so we have

$$H_0: \mu_1 = \mu_2 \quad H_1: \mu_1 < \mu_2$$

We now proceed with the assumption that $\mu_1 = \mu_2$, or $\mu_1 - \mu_2 = 0$.

continued

Step 4: The significance level is $\alpha = 0.05$.

Step 5: Using Technology Steps 5 and 6 can be skipped when using technology; see the accompanying Statdisk display showing the test statistic and P-value.

Statdisk

```
Test Statistic, t: -1.67937
Critical t:        -1.72744
P-Value:            0.05457

Degrees of Freedom:  19.37038

90% Confidence Interval:
-77.86539 < µ1-µ2 < 1.09872
```

Manual Calculation If not using technology, we use the t distribution with the test statistic given in the Key Elements box.

Step 6: The test statistic is calculated using these statistics (with extra decimal places) obtained from the listed sample data:

$$\text{ANSUR I 1988: } n = 12, \bar{x} = 1739.417 \text{ mm}, s = 66.6012 \text{ mm}$$

$$\text{ANSUR II 2012: } n = 15, \bar{x} = 1777.8 \text{ mm}, s = 47.86618 \text{ mm}$$

$$t = \frac{(\bar{x}_1 - \bar{x}_2) - (\mu_1 - \mu_2)}{\sqrt{\dfrac{s_1^2}{n_1} + \dfrac{s_2^2}{n_2}}} = \frac{(1739.417 - 1777.8) - 0}{\sqrt{\dfrac{66.6012^2}{12} + \dfrac{47.86618^2}{15}}} = -1.679$$

P-Value With test statistic $t = -1.679$, we refer to Table A-3 (t distribution). The number of degrees of freedom is the smaller of $n_1 - 1$ and $n_2 - 1$, or the smaller of $(12 - 1)$ and $(15 - 1)$, which is 11. With df $= 11$ and a left-tailed test, Table A-3 indicates that the P-value is greater than 0.05 (and less than 0.10). Technology will provide the P-value of 0.0546 when using the original data or unrounded sample statistics.

Step 7: Because the P-value is greater than the significance level of 0.05, we fail to reject the null hypothesis. ("If the P is *low*, the null must go." Here, the P-value is not low, so it doesn't go.)

INTERPRETATION

Step 8: There is not sufficient evidence to support the claim that the mean height of the 1988 male population is less than the mean height of the 2012 male population.

Are people getting taller? Maybe, maybe not, but the given data do not provide enough evidence to support that claim. The sample mean from 1988 is 1739.4 mm and the sample mean from 2012 is 1777.8 mm, so the 2012 sample mean is larger. Perhaps a larger sample might provide sufficient evidence to support the claim. Also, the sample data are from U.S. male Army personnel, and this sample might be from a population that is different from the general population.

YOUR TURN. Do Part (a) of Exercise 5 "Better Tips by Giving Candy."

Critical Value Method

If technology is not available, the critical value method of testing a claim about two means is generally easier than the P-value method. Example 1 can be solved using the critical value method. When finding critical values in Table A-3, we use df $=$ smaller of $n_1 - 1$ and $n_2 - 1$ as a relatively easy way to avoid using the really messy calculation required with Formula 9-1. In Example 1 with sample sizes of $n_1 = 12$ and $n_2 = 15$, the number of degrees of freedom is 11, which is the smaller of 11 and 14. In Table A-3 with df $= 11$ and $\alpha = 0.05$ in the left tail, we get a critical value of $t = -1.796$. (Table A-3 gives us $t = 1.796$, but we must make it negative because this is a left-tailed test.) Technology can be used to find the more accurate critical value of $t = -1.727$ (as shown in the preceding Statdisk display). Figure 9-2 shows the more accurate critical value of $t = -1.727$. Figure 9-2 shows that the test statistic does not fall within the critical region, so we fail to reject the null hypothesis, as we did in Example 1.

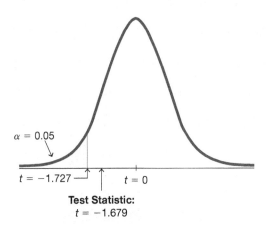

$\alpha = 0.05$

$t = -1.727$ $t = 0$

Test Statistic:
$t = -1.679$

FIGURE 9-2   **Hypothesis Test of Means from Two Independent Populations**

Confidence Intervals

EXAMPLE 2   **Confidence Interval Estimate of Difference Between 1988 Heights and 2012 Heights**

Repeat Example 1 by constructing a confidence interval estimate of the difference between the mean height in 1988 and the mean height in 2012.

SOLUTION

First, we must be careful to use the appropriate confidence level. The test in Example 1 is left-tailed with a 0.05 significance level, so we should construct the confidence interval using a confidence level of 90%. (See Table 8-1 on page 376, which shows that for a significance level of 0.05 in a one-tailed test, we should use a 90% confidence interval.)

REQUIREMENT CHECK Because we are using the same data from Example 1, the same requirement check applies here, so the requirements are satisfied. ✅

Technology Technology can be used to find this 90% confidence interval estimate of the difference between the two populations: -77.9 mm $< \mu_1 - \mu_2 < 1.1$ mm (as shown in the Statdisk display included with Example 1).

Manual Calculations For manual calculations, we must first find the value of the margin of error E. In Table A-3 with df $= 11$ and $\alpha = 0.05$ in one tail, we get the critical value of $t = 1.796$. (Technology can be used to find the more accurate critical value of $t = 1.727$.) We use the critical value of $t = 1.796$ and the sample statistics $n_1 = 12$, $s_1 = 66.6012$ mm, $n_2 = 15$, and $s_2 = 47.86618$ mm to evaluate the margin of error as follows.

$$E = t_{\alpha/2}\sqrt{\frac{s_1^2}{n_1} + \frac{s_2^2}{n_2}} = 1.796\sqrt{\frac{66.6012^2}{12} + \frac{47.86618^2}{15}} = 41.049035$$

continued

Super Bowls

Students were invited to a Super Bowl game, and half of them were given large 4-liter snack bowls while the other half were given smaller 2-liter bowls. Those using the large bowls consumed 56% more than those using the smaller bowls. (See "Super Bowls: Serving Bowl Size and Food Consumption," by Wansink and Cheney, *Journal of the American Medical Association,* Vol. 293, No. 14.)

A separate study showed that there is "a significant increase in fatal motor vehicle crashes during the hours following the Super Bowl telecast in the United States." Researchers analyzed 20,377 deaths on 27 Super Bowl Sundays and 54 other Sundays used as controls. They found a 41% increase in fatalities after Super Bowl games. (See "Do Fatal Crashes Increase Following a Super Bowl Telecast?" by Redelmeier and Stewart, *Chance,* Vol. 18, No. 1.)

Using $E = 41.049035$, $\bar{x}_1 = 1739.417$, and $\bar{x}_2 = 1777.8$, we can now use simple substitution to find the confidence interval as shown here:

$$(\bar{x}_1 - \bar{x}_2) - E < \mu_1 - \mu_2 < (\bar{x}_1 - \bar{x}_2) + E$$
$$-79.4 \text{ mm} < \mu_1 - \mu_2 < 2.7 \text{ mm}$$

The confidence interval limits of $(-77.9 \text{ mm}, 1.1 \text{ mm})$ found from technology are more accurate, but we can see that the manual calculations give us a result that is reasonably good, even though we used a simplified method for finding the number of degrees of freedom (instead of getting more accurate results by using Formula 9-1 to compute the number of degrees of freedom).

INTERPRETATION

We are 90% confident that the confidence interval actually does contain the difference between the mean height in 1988 and the mean height in 2012. Because the confidence interval does contain 0, it suggests that there is not a significant difference between the mean height in 1988 and the mean height in 2012.

 YOUR TURN. Do Part (b) of Exercise 5 "Better Tips by Giving Candy."

Alternative Methods: Resampling Methods of Bootstrapping and Randomization

The claim that the mean height of U.S. Army male personnel in 1988 is less than the mean height of this population in 2012 can be tested by using the resampling methods of bootstrapping and randomization. See Section 9-5 "Resampling: Using Technology for Inferences."

PART 2 Alternative Methods

Part 1 of this section dealt with situations in which the two population standard deviations are unknown and are not assumed to be equal. In Part 2 we address two other situations:

1. The two population standard deviations are unknown but are assumed to be equal.

2. The two population standard deviations are both known.

Alternative Method: Assume That $\sigma_1 = \sigma_2$ and *Pool* the Sample Variances

Even when the specific values of σ_1 and σ_2 are not known, if it can be assumed that they have the *same* value, the sample variances s_1^2 and s_2^2 can be *pooled* to obtain an estimate of the common population variance σ^2. The **pooled estimate of σ^2** is denoted by s_p^2 and is a weighted average of s_1^2 and s_2^2, which is used in the test statistic for this case:

$$\textbf{Test Statistic} \quad t = \frac{(\bar{x}_1 - \bar{x}_2) - (\mu_1 - \mu_2)}{\sqrt{\dfrac{s_p^2}{n_1} + \dfrac{s_p^2}{n_2}}}$$

where $\quad s_p^2 = \dfrac{(n_1 - 1)s_1^2 + (n_2 - 1)s_2^2}{(n_1 - 1) + (n_2 - 1)} \quad$ (pooled sample variance)

and the number of degrees of freedom is df $= n_1 + n_2 - 2$.

The requirements for this case are the same as in Part 1, except the first requirement is that σ_1 and σ_2 are not known but they are assumed to be equal. Confidence intervals are found by evaluating $(\bar{x}_1 - \bar{x}_2) - E < \mu_1 - \mu_2 < (\bar{x}_1 - \bar{x}_2) + E$ with the following margin of error E.

Margin of Error for Confidence Interval $\quad E = t_{\alpha/2}\sqrt{\dfrac{s_p^2}{n_1} + \dfrac{s_p^2}{n_2}}$

where s_p^2 is as given in the test statistic above, and df $= n_1 + n_2 - 2$.

When Should We Assume That $\sigma_1 = \sigma_2$? If we use randomness to assign subjects to treatment and placebo groups, we know that the samples are drawn from the same population. So if we conduct a hypothesis test assuming that two population means are equal, it is reasonable to assume that the samples are from populations with the same standard deviations (but we should still check that assumption).

Advantage of Pooling Sample Variances The advantage of this alternative method of pooling sample variances is that the number of degrees of freedom is a little higher, so hypothesis tests have more power and confidence intervals are a little narrower.

Alternative Method Used When σ_1 and σ_2 Are Known

In reality, the population standard deviations σ_1 and σ_2 are almost never known, but if they are somehow known, the test statistic and confidence interval are based on the normal distribution instead of the t distribution. The requirements are the same as those given in Part 1, except for the first requirement that σ_1 and σ_2 are known. Critical values and P-values are found using technology or Table A-2, and the test statistic for this case is as follows:

Test Statistic $\quad z = \dfrac{(\bar{x}_1 - \bar{x}_2) - (\mu_1 - \mu_2)}{\sqrt{\dfrac{\sigma_1^2}{n_1} + \dfrac{\sigma_2^2}{n_2}}}$

Confidence intervals are found by evaluating $(\bar{x}_1 - \bar{x}_2) - E < \mu_1 - \mu_2 < (\bar{x}_1 - \bar{x}_2) + E$, where:

Margin of Error for Confidence Interval $\quad E = z_{\alpha/2}\sqrt{\dfrac{\sigma_1^2}{n_1} + \dfrac{\sigma_2^2}{n_2}}$

What if One Standard Deviation Is Known and the Other Is Unknown? If σ_1 is known but σ_2 is unknown, use the procedures in Part 1 of this section with these changes: Replace s_1 with the known value of σ_1 and use the number of degrees of freedom found from the expression below. (See "The Two-Sample t Test with One Variance Unknown," by Maity and Sherman, *The American Statistician,* Vol. 60, No. 2.)

$$\text{df} = \frac{\left(\dfrac{\sigma_1^2}{n_1} + \dfrac{s_2^2}{n_2}\right)^2}{\dfrac{\left(s_2^2/n_2\right)^2}{n_2 - 1}}$$

Recommended Strategy for Two Independent Means

Here is the recommended strategy for the methods of this section:

> **Assume that σ_1 and σ_2 are unknown, do *not* assume that $\sigma_1 = \sigma_2$, and use the test statistic and confidence interval given in Part 1 of this section.**

Using Statistics to Identify Thieves

Methods of statistics can be used to determine that an employee is stealing, and they can also be used to estimate the amount stolen. For comparable time periods, samples of sales have means that are significantly different. The mean sale amount decreases significantly. There is a significant increase in "no sale" register openings. There is a significant decrease in the ratio of cash receipts to checks. (See "How to Catch a Thief," by Manly and Thomson, *Chance,* Vol. 11, No. 4.)

TECH CENTER

Inferences with Two Means: Independent Samples
Access tech supplements, videos, and data sets at **www.TriolaStats.com**

Statdisk

Hypothesis Testing
1. Click **Analysis** in the top menu.
2. Select **Hypothesis Testing** from the dropdown menu and **Mean Two Independent Samples** from the submenu.
3. Select the desired format for *Alternative Hypothesis* and enter the significance level. For both samples enter the sample statistics, or click the **Use Data** tab to use columns of data.
4. Under *Method of Analysis* select **Unequal variances: No Pool.**
5. Click **Evaluate.**

Confidence Intervals
1. Click **Analysis** in the top menu.
2. Select **Confidence Intervals** from the dropdown menu and **Mean Two Independent Samples** from the submenu.
3. Enter the desired confidence level. For both samples enter the sample statistics, or click the **Use Data** tab to use columns of data.
4. Under *Method of Analysis* select **Unequal variances: No Pool.**
5. Click **Evaluate.**

Minitab

1. Click **Stat** in the top menu.
2. Select **Basic Statistics** from the dropdown menu and select **2-sample t** from the submenu.
3. *Using Summary Statistics:* Select **Summarized data** from the dropdown menu and enter the sample size, sample mean, and sample standard deviation for each sample.

   Using Sample Data: Select **Each sample is in its own column** from the dropdown menu and select the desired data columns.
4. Click the **Options** button and enter the confidence level. Enter **0** for *Hypothesized difference* and select the desired format for the *Alternative hypothesis*.
5. Leave **Assume equal variances** unchecked. Check this box only if you want to assume the populations have equal variances—this is not recommended.
6. Click **OK** twice.

Tip: Another procedure is to click on **Assistant** in the top menu, select **Hypothesis Tests** and **2-Sample t.** Complete the dialog box to get results, including *P*-value and other helpful information.

StatCrunch

1. Click **Stat** in the top menu.
2. Select **T Stats** from the dropdown menu, then select **Two Sample** from the submenu.
3. *Using Summary Statistics:* Select **With Summary** from the submenu and enter the sample mean, sample standard deviation, and sample size for each sample.

   Using Sample Data: Select **With Data** from the submenu and select the desired data column for each sample.
4. Leave **Pool variances** unchecked. Check this box only if you want to assume the populations have equal variances—this is not recommended.
5. *Hypothesis Testing:* Select **Hypothesis test for $\mu_1 - \mu_2$.** For hypothesized difference (H_0) enter **0** and select the desired format for the alternative hypothesis (H_A).

   Confidence Intervals: Select **Confidence interval for $\mu_1 - \mu_2$** and enter the confidence level.
6. Click **Compute!**

TI-83/84 Plus Calculator

Hypothesis Testing:
1. Press **STAT**, then select **TESTS** in the top menu.
2. Select **2-SampTTest** in the menu and press **ENTER**.
3. Select **Data** if you have sample data in lists or **Stats** if you have summary statistics. Press **ENTER** and enter the list names (leave *Freq* = **1**) or summary statistics.
4. For μ_1 select the desired format for the alternative hypothesis.
5. For pooled select **No.** Select *Yes* only if the population variances are believed to be equal.
6. Select **Calculate** and press **ENTER**.

Confidence Intervals:
1. Press **STAT**, then select **TESTS** in the top menu.
2. Select **2-SampTInt** in the menu and press **ENTER**.
3. Select **Data** if you have sample data in lists or **Stats** if you have summary statistics. Press **ENTER** and enter the list names (leave *Freq* = **1**) or summary statistics.
4. For *C-Level* enter the desired confidence level.
5. For pooled select **No.** Select *Yes* only if the population variances are believed to be equal.
6. Select **Calculate** and press **ENTER**.

TECH CENTER *continued*

Inferences with Two Means: Independent Samples
Access tech supplements, videos, and data sets at **www.TriolaStats.com**

Excel

Hypothesis Test

XLSTAT Add-In

Requires original sample data; does not work with summary data.

1. Click on the **XLSTAT** tab in the Ribbon and then click **Parametric tests.**
2. Select **Two-sample t-test and z-test** from the dropdown menu.
3. For *Data format* select **One column per sample.** Under *Sample 1 & 2* enter the range of cells containing the sample data.
4. Select **Student's t test.**
5. If the first row of data contains a label, check the **Column labels** box.
6. Click the **Options** tab.
7. Under *Alternative hypothesis* select the desired format (≠ for two-tailed test, < for left-tailed test, > for right-tailed test). Enter **0** for *Hypothesized difference (D)* and enter the desired significance level (enter **5** for 0.05 significance level). Select **Asymptotic p-value.**
8. Uncheck the **Assume equality** box and uncheck the **Cochran-Cox** box. Uncheck the **Use an *F*-test** box.
9. Click **OK** to display the test statistic (labeled *t Observed value*) and *P*-value.

Excel (Data Analysis Add-In)

1. Click on **Data** in the ribbon, then click on the **Data Analysis** tab.
2. Select **t-Test: Two-Sample Assuming Unequal Variances** and click **OK.**
3. Enter the data range for each variable in the *Variable Range* boxes. If the first row contains a label, check the **Labels** box.
4. Enter **0** for *Hypothesized Mean Difference.*
5. Enter the desired significance level in the *Alpha* box and click **OK.** The test statistic is labeled *t Stat* and *P*-value is labeled *P*.

Confidence Interval

XLSTAT Add-In (Required)

Requires original sample data; does not work with summary data.

1-5. Follow above Steps 1–5 for **Hypothesis Test** using XLSTAT Add-In.
6. Click the **Options** tab.
7. Under *Alternative hypothesis* select the two-tailed option ≠ . Enter **0** for *Hypothesized difference (D)* and enter the desired significance level (enter **5** for 95% confidence level). Select **Asymptotic p-value.**
8. Uncheck the **Assume equality** box and uncheck the **Cochran-Cox box.** Uncheck the **Use an *F*-test** box.
9. Click **OK** to display the confidence interval.

R

R command: **t.test(x, y, alternative = c("two.sided", "less", "greater"), paired = FALSE, conf.level = 0.95)**

where *x* is a vector of group 1 sample data and *y* is a vector of group 2 sample data.

TIP: For Example 1: **t.test(x, y, alternative = "less", paired = FALSE, conf.level = 0.90)**

A complete list of R statistical commands is available at TriolaStats.com

9-2 Basic Skills and Concepts

Statistical Literacy and Critical Thinking

1. Independent Samples Which of the following involve independent samples?

a. Data Set 4 "Measured and Reported" includes measured heights matched with the heights that were reported when the subjects were asked for those values.

b. Data Set 6 "Births" includes birth weights of a sample of baby boys and a sample of baby girls.

c. Data Set 1 "Body Data" includes a sample of pulse rates of 147 women and a sample of pulse rates of 153 men.

2. Pulse Rates of Women and Men Using the samples of women and men included in Data Set 1 "Body Data," we get this 95% confidence interval estimate of the difference between the population mean of pulse rates (bpm) of women and the population mean of pulse rates (bpm) of men: 1.7 bpm $< \mu_1 - \mu_2 <$ 7.2 bpm. In this confidence interval, women correspond to population 1 and men correspond to population 2.

a. What does the confidence interval suggest about equality of the mean pulse rate of women and the mean pulse rate of men?

b. Write a brief statement that interprets the confidence interval.

c. Express the confidence interval with measures from men being population 1 and measures from women being population 2.

3. Hypothesis Tests and Confidence Intervals for Pulse Rates

a. Exercise 2 includes a confidence interval. If you use the *P*-value method or the critical value method from Part 1 of this section to test the claim that women and men have the same mean pulse rates, will the hypothesis tests and the confidence interval result in the same conclusion?

b. In general, if you conduct a hypothesis test using the methods of Part 1 of this section, will the *P*-value method, the critical value method, and the confidence interval method result in the same conclusion?

c. Assume that you want to use a 0.01 significance level to test the claim that the mean pulse rate of women is *greater* than the mean pulse rate of men. What *confidence level* should be used if you want to test that claim using a confidence interval?

4. Degrees of Freedom For Example 1 on page 457, we used df = smaller of $n_1 - 1$ and $n_2 - 1$, we got df = 11, and the corresponding critical value is $t = -1.796$ (found from Table A-4). If we calculate df using Formula 9-1, we get df = 19.370, and the corresponding critical value is $t = -1.727$. How is using the critical value of $t = -1.796$ "more conservative" than using the critical value of $t = -1.727$?

In Exercises 5–20, assume that the two samples are independent simple random samples selected from normally distributed populations, and do not assume that the population standard deviations are equal. (Note: Answers in Appendix D include technology answers based on Formula 9-1 along with "Table" answers based on Table A-3 with df equal to the smaller of $n_1 - 1$ and $n_2 - 1$.)

5. Better Tips by Giving Candy An experiment was conducted to determine whether giving candy to dining parties resulted in greater tips. The mean tip percentages and standard deviations are given below along with the sample sizes (based on data from "Sweetening the Till: The Use of Candy to Increase Restaurant Tipping," by Strohmetz et al., *Journal of Applied Social Psychology*, Vol. 32, No. 2).

a. Use a 0.05 significance level to test the claim that giving candy does result in greater tips.

b. Construct the confidence interval suitable for testing the claim in part (a).

No Candy:	$n = 20, \bar{x} = 18.95, s = 1.50$
Two candies:	$n = 20, \bar{x} = 21.62, s = 2.51$

6. Readability of Font On a Computer Screen The statistics shown below were obtained from a standard test of readability of fonts on a computer screen (based on data from "Reading on the Computer Screen: Does Font Type Have Effects on Web Text Readability?" by Ali et al., *International Education Studies*, Vol. 6, No. 3). Reading speed and accuracy were combined into a readability performance score (x), where a higher score represents better font readability.

a. Use a 0.05 significance level to test the claim that there is no significant difference in readability between Roman and Arial fonts.

b. Construct the confidence interval suitable for testing the claim in part (a).

Roman:	$n = 24, \bar{x} = 66.25, s = 12.96$
Arial:	$n = 24, \bar{x} = 65.62, s = 9.93$

7. Hand Cleansing An experiment was conducted to determine whether there is a difference between washing hands with antiseptic soap and rubbing hands with an alcohol based solution. Hand bacteria counts were measured in colony forming units (cfu) with the results summarized below (based on data from "Efficacy of Handrubbing With Alcohol Based Solution versus Standard Handwashing with Antiseptic Soap," by Girou et al., *British Medical Journal*).

a. Use a 0.01 significance level to test the claim that rubbing with alcohol results in a lower bacteria count.

b. Construct the confidence interval suitable for testing the claim in part (a).

c. Does the conclusion change if the significance level is changed to 0.05?

Washing With Soap:	$n = 55, \bar{x} = 69, s = 106$
Rubbing With Alcohol:	$n = 59, \bar{x} = 35, s = 59$

8. Birth Weights Listed below are birth weight statistics from Data Set 6 "Births" in Appendix B.

a. Use a 0.01 significance level to test the claim that at birth, girls have a lower mean weight than boys.

b. Construct the confidence interval suitable for testing the claim in part (a).

Girls:	$n = 205, \bar{x} = 3037.1$ g, $s = 706.3$ g
Boys:	$n = 195, \bar{x} = 3272.8$ g, $s = 660.2$ g

9. Color and Cognition Researchers from the University of British Columbia conducted a study to investigate the effects of color on cognitive tasks. Words were displayed on a computer screen with background colors of red and blue. Results from scores on a test of word recall are given below. Higher scores correspond to greater word recall.

a. Use a 0.05 significance level to test the claim that the samples are from populations with the same mean.

b. Construct a confidence interval appropriate for the hypothesis test in part (a). What is it about the confidence interval that causes us to reach the same conclusion from part (a)?

c. Does the background color appear to have an effect on word recall scores? If so, which color appears to be associated with higher word memory recall scores?

Red Background	$n = 35, \bar{x} = 15.89, s = 5.90$
Blue Background	$n = 36, \bar{x} = 12.31, s = 5.48$

10. Color and Creativity Researchers from the University of British Columbia conducted trials to investigate the effects of color on creativity. Subjects with a red background were asked to think of creative uses for a brick; other subjects with a blue background were given the same task. Responses were scored by a panel of judges and results from scores of creativity are given below. Higher scores correspond to more creativity. The researchers make the claim that "blue enhances performance on a creative task."

a. Use a 0.01 significance level to test the claim that blue enhances performance on a creative task.

b. Construct the confidence interval appropriate for the hypothesis test in part (a). What is it about the confidence interval that causes us to reach the same conclusion from part (a)?

Red Background:	$n = 35, \bar{x} = 3.39, s = 0.97$
Blue Background:	$n = 36, \bar{x} = 3.97, s = 0.63$

11. Magnet Treatment of Pain People spend around $5 billion annually for the purchase of magnets used to treat a wide variety of pains. Researchers conducted a study to determine whether magnets are effective in treating back pain. Pain was measured using the visual analog scale, and the results given below are among the results obtained in the study (based on data from "Bipolar Permanent Magnets for the Treatment of Chronic Lower Back Pain: A Pilot Study," by Collacott, Zimmerman, White, and Rindone, *Journal of the American Medical Association,* Vol. 283, No. 10). Higher scores correspond to greater pain levels.

a. Use a 0.05 significance level to test the claim that those treated with magnets have a greater mean reduction in pain than those given a sham treatment (similar to a placebo).

b. Construct the confidence interval appropriate for the hypothesis test in part (a).

c. Does it appear that magnets are effective in treating back pain? Is it valid to argue that magnets might appear to be effective if the sample sizes are larger?

Reduction in Pain Level After Magnet Treatment: $n = 20, \bar{x} = 0.49, s = 0.96$

Reduction in Pain Level After Sham Treatment: $n = 20, \bar{x} = 0.44, s = 1.4$

12. Second-Hand Smoke Samples from Data Set 15 "Passive and Active Smoke" in Appendix B include cotinine levels measured in a group of nonsmokers exposed to tobacco smoke ($n = 40, \bar{x} = 60.58$ ng/mL, $s = 138.08$ ng/mL) and a group of nonsmokers not exposed to tobacco smoke ($n = 40, \bar{x} = 16.35$ ng/mL, $s = 62.53$ ng/mL). Cotinine is a metabolite of nicotine, meaning that when nicotine is absorbed by the body, cotinine is produced.

a. Use a 0.05 significance level to test the claim that nonsmokers exposed to tobacco smoke have a higher mean cotinine level than nonsmokers not exposed to tobacco smoke.

b. Construct the confidence interval appropriate for the hypothesis test in part (a).

c. What do you conclude about the effects of second-hand smoke?

13. Bicycle Commuting A researcher used two different bicycles to commute to work. One bicycle was steel and weighed 30.0 lb; the other was carbon and weighed 20.9 lb. The commuting times (minutes) were recorded with the results shown below (based on data from "Bicycle Weights and Commuting Time," by Jeremy Groves, *British Medical Journal*).

a. Use a 0.05 significance level to test the claim that the mean commuting time with the heavier bicycle is the same as the mean commuting time with the lighter bicycle.

b. Construct the confidence interval suitable for testing the claim in part (a).

Heavier Bicycle:	$n = 30, \bar{x} = 107.8$ min, $s = 4.9$ min
Lighter Bicycle:	$n = 26, \bar{x} = 108.4$ min, $s = 6.3$ min

14. IQ and Lead Exposure Data Set 11 "IQ and Lead" in Appendix B lists full IQ scores for a random sample of subjects with low lead levels in their blood and another random sample of subjects with high lead levels in their blood. The statistics are summarized below.

a. Use a 0.05 significance level to test the claim that the mean IQ score of people with low blood lead levels is higher than the mean IQ score of people with high blood lead levels.

b. Construct a confidence interval appropriate for the hypothesis test in part (a).

c. Does exposure to lead appear to have an effect on IQ scores?

$$\text{Low Blood Lead Level:} \quad n = 78, \bar{x} = 92.88462, s = 15.34451$$
$$\text{High Blood Lead Level:} \quad n = 21, \bar{x} = 86.90476, s = 8.988352$$

15. Are Quarters Now Lighter? Weights of quarters are carefully considered in the design of the vending machines that we have all come to know and love. Data Set 40 "Coin Weights" in Appendix B includes weights of a sample of pre-1964 quarters ($n = 40, \bar{x} = 6.19267$ g, $s = 0.08700$ g) and weights of a sample of post-1964 quarters ($n = 40, \bar{x} = 5.63930$ g, $s = 0.06194$ g).

a. Use a 0.05 significance level to test the claim that pre-1964 quarters have a mean weight that is greater than the mean weight of post-1964 quarters.

b. Construct a confidence interval appropriate for the hypothesis test in part (a).

c. Do post-1964 quarters appear to weigh less than before 1964? If so, why aren't vending machines affected very much by the difference?

16. Bad Stuff in Children's Movies Data Set 20 "Alcohol and Tobacco in Movies" in Appendix B includes lengths of times (seconds) of tobacco use shown in animated children's movies. For the Disney movies, $n = 33, \bar{x} = 61.6$ sec, $s = 118.8$ sec. For the other movies, $n = 17, \bar{x} = 49.3$ sec, $s = 69.3$ sec. The sorted times for the non-Disney movies are listed below.

a. Use a 0.05 significance level to test the claim that Disney animated children's movies and other animated children's movies have the same mean time showing tobacco use.

b. Construct a confidence interval appropriate for the hypothesis test in part (a).

c. Conduct a quick visual inspection of the listed times for the non-Disney movies and comment on the normality requirement. How does the normality of the 17 non-Disney times affect the results?

$$0 \quad 0 \quad 0 \quad 0 \quad 0 \quad 0 \quad 1 \quad 5 \quad 6 \quad 17 \quad 24 \quad 55 \quad 91 \quad 117 \quad 155 \quad 162 \quad 205$$

17. Are Weights Changing Over Time? Listed below are weights (kg) of randomly selected U.S. Army male personnel measured in 1988 (from Data Set 2 "ANSUR I 1988") and different weights (kg) of randomly selected U.S. Army male personnel measured in 2012 (from Data Set 3 "ANSUR II 2012").

a. Use a 0.05 significance level to test the claim that the mean weight of the 1988 population is less than the mean weight of the 2012 population.

b. Construct a confidence interval appropriate for the hypothesis test in part (a).

ANSUR I 1988	76.9	85.2	97.9	69.4	71.2	77.7	78.2	75.6	84.4	72.0	60.6	83.0
ANSUR II 2012	79.2	91.5	96.5	67.5	107.3	79.3	78.2	88.2	71.5	94.7	66.5	87.9
	67.5	88.4	69.5									

18. Queues Listed on the next page are waiting times (seconds) of observed cars at a Delaware inspection station. The data from two waiting lines are real observations, and the data from the single waiting line are modeled from those real observations. These data are from Data Set 30 "Queues" in Appendix B. The data were collected by the author.

continued

a. Use a 0.01 significance level to test the claim that cars in two queues have a mean waiting time equal to that of cars in a single queue.

b. Construct the confidence interval suitable for testing the claim in part (a).

Two Lines	64	216	86	340	200	630	333	329	915	553
	597	865	1090	663	518	566	268	350	95	100
	163	101								
One Line	64	157	142	279	253	476	478	474	402	722
	761	692	837	903	734	606	268	310	129	133
	122	129	233	461	482	518	509	580		

19. Regular Coke and Diet Coke Listed below are weights (lb) of samples of the contents of cans of regular Coke and Diet Coke (from Data Set 37 "Cola Weights and Volumes" in Appendix B).

a. Use a 0.01 significance level to test the claim that the contents of cans of regular Coke have weights with a mean that is greater than the mean for Diet Coke.

b. Construct the confidence interval appropriate for the hypothesis test in part (a).

c. Can you explain why cans of regular Coke would weigh more than cans of Diet Coke?

Regular	0.8192	0.8150	0.8163	0.8211	0.8181	0.8247	0.8062	0.8128
	0.8172	0.8110	0.8251	0.8264				
Diet	0.7773	0.7758	0.7896	0.7868	0.7844	0.7861	0.7806	0.7830
	0.7852	0.7879	0.7881	0.7826	0.7923	0.7852	0.7872	0.7813

20. Blanking Out on Tests Many students have had the unpleasant experience of panicking on a test because the first question was exceptionally difficult. The arrangement of test items was studied for its effect on anxiety. The following scores are measures of "debilitating test anxiety," which most of us call panic or blanking out (based on data from "Item Arrangement, Cognitive Entry Characteristics, Sex and Test Anxiety as Predictors of Achievement in Examination Performance," by Klimko, *Journal of Experimental Education,* Vol. 52, No. 4.) Is there sufficient evidence to support the claim that the two populations of scores have different means? Is there sufficient evidence to support the claim that the arrangement of the test items has an effect on the score? Is the conclusion affected by whether the significance level is 0.05 or 0.01?

Questions Arranged from Easy to Difficult				
24.64	39.29	16.32	32.83	28.02
33.31	20.60	21.13	26.69	28.90
26.43	24.23	7.10	32.86	21.06
28.89	28.71	31.73	30.02	21.96
25.49	38.81	27.85	30.29	30.72

Questions Arranged from Difficult to Easy			
33.62	34.02	26.63	30.26
35.91	26.68	29.49	35.32
27.24	32.34	29.34	33.53
27.62	42.91	30.20	32.54

Larger Data Sets. *In Exercises 21–24, use the indicated Data Sets in Appendix B. The complete data sets can be found at www.TriolaStats.com. Assume that the two samples are independent simple random samples selected from normally distributed populations. Do not assume that the population standard deviations are equal.*

21. Are We Getting Heavier? Exercise 17 used weights of small samples of males from Data Set 2 "ANSUR I 1988" and from Data Set 3 "ANSUR II 2012." Repeat Exercise 17 using the 1774 weights of males from the ANSUR I 1988 data set and the 4082 weights of males from the ANSUR II 2012 data set.

22. Are We Getting Taller? Example 1 used heights of small samples of males from Data Set 2 "ANSUR I 1988" and from Data Set 3 "ANSUR II 2012." Repeat Example 1 using the 1774 heights of males from the ANSUR I 1988 data set and the 4082 heights of males from the ANSUR II 2012 data set. Do the larger samples provide sufficient evidence to suggest that people are getting taller?

23. Do Men Talk Less Than Women? Refer to Data Set 14 "Word Counts" and use the measured word counts from men in the third column ("M2") and the measured word counts from women in the fourth column ("F2"). Use a 0.05 significance level to test the claim that men talk less than women.

24. Queues Repeat Exercise 18 using all of the *waiting times* from the two line configuration and the single line configuration in Data Set 30 "Queues" in Appendix B.

9-2 Beyond the Basics

25. Pooling Repeat Exercise 14 "IQ and Lead Exposure" by assuming that the two population standard deviations are equal, so $\sigma_1 = \sigma_2$. Use the appropriate method from Part 2 of this section. Does pooling the standard deviations yield results showing greater significance?

26. Degrees of Freedom In Exercise 20 "Blanking Out on Tests," using the "smaller of $n_1 - 1$ and $n_2 - 1$" for the number of degrees of freedom results in df $= 15$. Find the number of degrees of freedom using Formula 9-1. In general, how are hypothesis tests and confidence intervals affected by using Formula 9-1 instead of the "smaller of $n_1 - 1$ and $n_2 - 1$"?

27. No Variation in a Sample An experiment was conducted to test the effects of alcohol. Researchers measured the breath alcohol levels for a treatment group of people who drank ethanol and another group given a placebo. The results are given below (based on data from "Effects of Alcohol Intoxication on Risk Taking, Strategy, and Error Rate in Visuomotor Performance," by Streufert et al., *Journal of Applied Psychology*, Vol. 77, No. 4). Use a 0.05 significance level to test the claim that the two sample groups come from populations with the same mean.

$$\text{Treatment Group:} \quad n_1 = 22, \bar{x}_1 = 0.049, s_1 = 0.015$$
$$\text{Placebo Group:} \quad n_2 = 22, \bar{x}_2 = 0.000, s_2 = 0.000$$

9-3 Matched Pairs

Key Concept This section presents methods for testing hypotheses and constructing confidence intervals involving the mean of the differences of the values from two populations that consist of matched pairs. The pairs must be matched according to some relationship, such as these:

- Before/after measurements from the same subjects
- IQ scores of husbands and wives
- Measured and reported weights from a sample of subjects

Good Experimental Design

Many experiments have been conducted to test the effectiveness of drug treatments in lowering blood pressure. When designing such experiments to test the effectiveness of a treatment, there are different approaches that could be taken, such as these:

1. Measure the blood pressure of each subject before and after the treatment, then analyze the "before – after" differences.

continued

2. For the entire sample of subjects, find the mean blood pressure before the treatment and then find the mean after the treatment.

3. Obtain a random sample of subjects and use randomness to separate them into one sample given the treatment and another sample given a placebo.

An advantage of using the matched pairs from the first approach is that we reduce the extraneous variation, which could easily occur with different independent samples. The strategy for designing an experiment can be generalized by the following principle of good design:

> **When designing an experiment or planning an observational study, using matched pairs is generally better than using two independent samples.**

Déjà Vu All Over Again The methods of hypothesis testing in this section are the *same methods* for testing a claim about a population mean (Section 8-3), except that here we use the *differences* from the matched pairs of sample data.

There are no exact procedures for dealing with matched pairs, but the following approximation methods are commonly used.

KEY ELEMENTS

Inferences About Differences from Matched Pairs

Objectives

1. **Hypothesis Test:** Use the differences from matched pairs to test a claim about the mean of the population of all such differences.

2. **Confidence Interval:** Use the differences from matched pairs to construct a confidence interval estimate of the mean of the population of all such differences.

Notation for Matched Pairs

d = individual difference between the two values in a single matched pair

μ_d = mean value of the differences d for the *population* of all matched pairs of data

$\bar{d}$ = mean value of the differences d for the paired *sample* data

s_d = standard deviation of the differences d for the paired *sample* data

n = number of *pairs* of sample data

Requirements

1. The sample data are matched pairs.

2. The matched pairs are a simple random sample.

3. Either or both of these conditions are satisfied: The number of pairs of sample data is large ($n > 30$) or the pairs of values have differences that are from a population having a distribution that is approximately normal.

These methods are *robust* against departures for normality, so the normality requirement is loose.

[DETOUR] **(If the third requirement is not satisfied, alternatives include the resampling methods of bootstrapping and randomization as described in Section 9-5, or the Sign test as described in Section 13-2.)**

Test Statistic for Matched Pairs (with H_0: $\mu_d = 0$)

$$t = \frac{\bar{d} - \mu_d}{\frac{s_d}{\sqrt{n}}}$$

P-Values: P-values are automatically provided by technology or the t distribution in Table A-3 can be used. Use the procedure given in Figure 8-3 on page 380.

Critical Values: Use Table A-3 (t distribution). For degrees of freedom, use df $= n - 1$.

Confidence Intervals for Matched Pairs

$$\bar{d} - E < \mu_d < \bar{d} + E$$

where $E = t_{\alpha/2}\dfrac{s_d}{\sqrt{n}}$ (Degrees of freedom: df $= n - 1$.)

Procedures for Inferences with Matched Pairs

1. Verify that the sample data consist of matched pairs, and verify that the requirements in the preceding Key Elements box are satisfied.

2. Find the difference d for each pair of sample values. (*Caution:* Be sure to subtract in a consistent manner, such as "before – after").

3. Find the value of $\bar{d}$ (mean of the differences) and s_d (standard deviation of the differences).

4. For hypothesis tests and confidence intervals, use the same t test procedures used for a single population mean (described in Section 8-3).

Equivalent Methods

Because the hypothesis test and confidence interval in this section use the same distribution and standard error, they are *equivalent* in the sense that they result in the same conclusions. Consequently, a null hypothesis that the mean difference equals 0 can be tested by determining whether the confidence interval includes 0.

EXAMPLE 1   **Are People Honest About their Weight?**

It is a common belief that if you *ask* someone how much they weigh, you tend to get a number that is somewhat lower than the number that you would get by using a scale to actually weigh them. Listed below are measured and reported weights (lb) of random male subjects (from Data Set 4 "Measured and Reported" in Appendix B). Use a 0.05 significance level to test the claim that for males, the measured weights tend to be higher than the reported weights.

TABLE 9-2 Measured and Reported Weights (lb)

Subject	1	2	3	4	5	6	7	8
Measured Weight (lb)	152.6	149.3	174.8	119.5	194.9	180.3	215.4	239.6
Reported Weight (lb)	150	148	170	119	185	180	224	239

SOLUTION

REQUIREMENT CHECK   We address the three requirements listed earlier in the Key Elements box. (1) The data are matched pairs because each pair of values is from the same subject. (2) The pairs of data are randomly selected. We will consider the data to be a simple random sample. (3) Because the number of pairs of data is $n = 8$, which is not large, we should check for normality of the differences and we should check for outliers. There are no outliers, and a normal quantile plot shows that the points approximate a straight-line pattern with no other pattern, so the differences satisfy the loose requirement of being from a normally distributed population. All requirements are satisfied. ☑

continued

Matched Pairs

In the late 1950s, Procter & Gamble introduced Crest toothpaste as the first such product with fluoride. To test the effectiveness of Crest in reducing cavities, researchers conducted experiments with several sets of twins. One of the twins in each set was given Crest with fluoride, while the other twin continued to use ordinary toothpaste without fluoride. It was believed that each pair of twins would have similar eating, brushing, and genetic characteristics. Results showed that the twins who used Crest had significantly fewer cavities than those who did not. This use of twins as matched pairs samples allowed the researchers to control many of the different variables affecting cavities.

We will follow the same method of hypothesis testing that we used for testing a claim about a mean (see Figure 8-1 on page 376), but we use *differences* instead of the original raw sample data.

Step 1: The claim that the measured weights tend to be higher than the reported weights can be expressed as $\mu_d > 0$ lb.

Step 2: If the original claim is not true, we have $\mu_d \leq 0$ lb.

Step 3: The null hypothesis must express equality and the alternative hypothesis cannot include equality, so we have

$$H_0: \mu_d = 0 \text{ lb} \quad H_1: \mu_d > 0 \text{ lb (original claim)}$$

Step 4: The significance level is $\alpha = 0.05$.

Step 5: Using Technology Steps 5 and 6 can be done with technology. Shown here is the Excel (XLSTAT) display for this hypothesis test, and it shows the test statistic is $t = 0.778$ ("observed value") and the *P*-value is 0.231.

Excel (XLSTAT)

Difference	1.425
t (Observed value)	0.778
t (Critical value)	1.895
DF	7
p-value (one-tailed)	0.231
alpha	0.05

Manual Calculation If not using technology, we use the Student *t* distribution with the *differences*.

Step 6: Manual Calculations From Table 9-2 we get these "measured – reported" differences: 2.6, 1.3, 4.8, 0.5, 9.9, 0.3, −8.6, 0.6. We use this list of differences to find these unrounded sample statistics: $n = 8$, $\bar{d} = 1.425$ lb, $s_d = 5.181216$ lb. Using these sample statistics and the assumption from the null hypothesis that $\mu_d = 0$ lb, we can now find the value of the test statistic as shown below.

$$t = \frac{\bar{d} - \mu_d}{\frac{s_d}{\sqrt{n}}} = \frac{1.425 - 0}{\frac{5.181216}{\sqrt{8}}} = 0.778$$

P-Value Method Because we are using a *t* distribution, we refer to Table A-3 for the row with df $= 7$ and we see that the test statistic $t = 0.778$ corresponds to an "Area in One Tail" that is greater than 0.10, so *P*-value > 0.10. (The preceding XLSTAT display shows that *P*-value $= 0.231$.)

Critical Value Method Refer to Table A-3 to find the critical value of $t = 1.895$ as follows: Use the column for 0.05 (Area in One Tail), and use the row with degrees of freedom of $n - 1 = 7$. We get the critical value of $t = 1.895$. See Figure 9-3(b).

Step 7: If we use the *P*-value method, we fail to reject H_0 because the *P*-value of 0.231 is greater than the significance level of 0.05. If we use the critical value method, we fail to reject H_0 because the test statistic of $t = 0.778$ does not fall in the critical region.

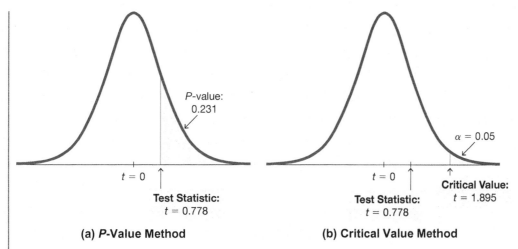

(a) P-Value Method   **(b) Critical Value Method**

FIGURE 9-3 Hypothesis Test with Matched Pairs

INTERPRETATION

We conclude that there is not sufficient evidence to support $\mu_d > 0$ lb. There is not sufficient evidence to support the claim that for males, the measured weights tend to be higher than the reported weights. Based on the very small sample, it appears that males do not tend to report weights that are much lower than their actual weights. It is possible that a much larger sample would lead to a different conclusion.

 **YOUR TURN.** Do Part (a) of Exercise 5 "Measured and Reported Weights."

EXAMPLE 2 Confidence Interval for Estimating the Mean of the Differences Between Measured Weights and Reported Weights of Males

Using the same sample data in Table 9-2, construct a 90% confidence interval estimate of μ_d, which is the mean of the differences between measured weights and reported weights of males. By using a confidence level of 90%, we get a result that could be used for the hypothesis test in Example 1. (Because the hypothesis test is one-tailed with a significance level of $\alpha = 0.05$, the confidence level should be 90%. See Table 8-1 on page 376.)

SOLUTION

REQUIREMENT CHECK   The solution for Example 1 includes verification that the requirements are satisfied. ✓

Some technologies such as Statdisk, Minitab, XLSTAT, and the TI-83/84 Plus calculator will provide the confidence interval when asked politely.

To manually find the confidence interval, use these sample statistics found in Example 1: $n = 8$, $\bar{d} = 1.425$ lb, $s_d = 5.181216$ lb and use the critical value of $t = 1.895$ (also found in Example 1). We first calculate the value of the margin of error E.

$$E = t_{\alpha/2}\frac{s_d}{\sqrt{n}} = 1.895 \cdot \frac{5.181216}{\sqrt{8}} = 3.4713301$$

We now find the confidence interval.

$$\bar{d} - E < \mu_d < \bar{d} + E$$
$$1.425 - 3.4713301 < \mu_d < 1.425 + 3.4713301$$
$$-2.05 \text{ lb} < \mu_d < 4.90 \text{ lb}$$

continued

Gender Gap in Drug Testing

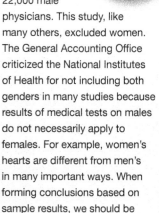

A study of the relationship between heart attacks and doses of aspirin involved 22,000 male physicians. This study, like many others, excluded women. The General Accounting Office criticized the National Institutes of Health for not including both genders in many studies because results of medical tests on males do not necessarily apply to females. For example, women's hearts are different from men's in many important ways. When forming conclusions based on sample results, we should be wary of an inference that extends to a population larger than the one from which the sample was drawn.

> **INTERPRETATION**
>
> We have 90% confidence that the limits of -2.05 lb and 4.90 lb contain the true value of the mean of the "measured – reported" differences. In the long run, 90% of such samples will lead to confidence interval limits that actually do contain the true population mean of those differences. See that the confidence interval includes the value of 0 lb, so it is very possible that the mean of the differences is equal to 0 lb, indicating that there is no significant difference between measured weights and reported weights. Remember, this conclusion is based on the very small sample included in Table 9-2.

 YOUR TURN. Do Part (b) of Exercise 5 "Measured and Reported Weights."

Alternative Methods: Resampling Methods of Bootstrapping and Randomization

The claim that the measured weights of males tend to be higher than the reported weights can be tested by using the resampling methods of bootstrapping and randomization. See Section 9-5 "Resampling: Using Technology for Inferences."

TECH CENTER

 ### Inferences with Two Means: Matched Pairs
Access tech supplements, videos, and data sets at www.TriolaStats.com

Statdisk
Requires *paired sample data* entered in columns.
Hypothesis Testing
1. Click **Analysis** in the top menu.
2. Select **Hypothesis Testing** from the dropdown menu and **Mean Matched Pairs** from the submenu.
3. Select the desired format for *Alternative Hypothesis*, enter the significance level, and select the data columns to compare.
4. Click **Evaluate**.
Confidence Intervals
1. Click **Analysis** in the top menu.
2. Select **Confidence Intervals** from the dropdown menu and **Mean Matched Pairs** from the submenu.
3. Enter the desired confidence level and select the data columns to compare.
4. Click **Evaluate**.

Minitab
Requires *paired sample data* entered in columns.
1. Click **Stat** in the top menu.
2. Select **Basic Statistics** from the dropdown menu and select **Paired t** from the submenu.
3. Select **Each sample is in a column** from the dropdown menu and select the desired data columns.
4. Click the **Options** button and enter the confidence level. Enter **0** for the *Hypothesized difference* and select the desired format for the *Alternative hypothesis*.
5. Click **OK** twice.

StatCrunch
Requires *paired sample data* entered in columns.
1. Click **Stat** in the top menu.
2. Select **T Stats** from the dropdown menu, then select **Paired** from the submenu.
3. Select the columns containing paired sample data.
4. *Hypothesis Testing:* Select **Hypothesis test for $\mu_D = \mu_1 - \mu_2$**. For hypothesized difference (H_0) enter **0** and select the desired format for the alternative hypothesis (H_A).
Confidence Intervals: Select **Confidence interval for $\mu_D = \mu_1 - \mu_2$** and enter the confidence level.
5. Click **Compute!**

TECH CENTER *continued*

Inferences with Two Means: Matched Pairs
Access tech supplements, videos, and data sets at **www.TriolaStats.com**

TI-83/84 Plus Calculator

Caution: Do not use the menu item **2-SampTTest** because it applies only to *independent samples*.

1. Enter the data for the first variable in list *L1* and the data for the second variable in list *L2*.
2. Create a list of differences and store the list in *L3* by entering **L1** ⊖ **L2** 〔STO〕 **L3** 〔ENTER〕.
3. Press 〔STAT〕, then select **TESTS** in the top menu.

Hypothesis Testing

1. Choose **T-Test** and press 〔ENTER〕.
2. Select **Data** and press 〔ENTER〕.
3. For μ_0 enter **0**.
4. For *List* enter **L3** (leave *Freq* = **1**).
5. For μ select the desired format for the alternative hypothesis.
6. Select **Calculate** and press 〔ENTER〕.

Confidence Interval

1. Choose **TInterval** and press 〔ENTER〕.
2. Select **Data**, press 〔ENTER〕, and enter **L3** for list name (leave *Freq* = **1**).
3. Enter the desired confidence level *C-Level*.
4. Select **Calculate** and press 〔ENTER〕.

TIP: The list name *L1* (and *L2 . . . L6*) can be quickly entered by pressing 〔2ND〕 ①.

Excel

Requires *paired sample data* entered in columns.

Hypothesis Test

XLSTAT Add-In

1. Click on the **XLSTAT** tab in the Ribbon and then click **Parametric tests.**
2. Select **Two-sample t-test and z-test** from the dropdown menu.
3. For *Data format* select **Paired samples.** Under *Sample 1 & 2,* enter the range of cells containing the paired sample data.
4. Select **Student's t test.**
5. If the first row of data contains a label, check the **Column labels** box.
6. Click the **Options** tab.
7. Under *Alternative hypothesis* select the desired format (≠ for two-tailed test, < for left-tailed test, > for right-tailed test). Enter **0** for *Hypothesized difference (D)* and enter the desired significance level (enter **5** for 0.05 significance level). Select **Asymptotic p-value.**
8. Click **OK** to display the test statistic (labeled *t Observed value*) and *P*-value.

Excel (Data Analysis Add-In)

1. Click on **Data** in the ribbon, then click on the **Data Analysis** tab.
2. Select **t-Test: Paired Two Sample for Means** and click **OK.**
3. Enter the data range for each variable in the *Variable Range* boxes. If the first row contains a label, check the **Labels** box.
4. Enter **0** for *Hypothesized Mean Difference.*
5. Enter the desired significance level in the *Alpha* box.
6. Click **OK.** The results include the test statistic (labeled *t Stat*), *P*-values for a one-tail and two-tail test, and critical values for one-tail and two-tail test.

Confidence Interval

XLSTAT Add-In (Required)

1–5. Follow above Steps 1–5 for **Hypothesis Test** using the XLSTAT Add-In.
6. Click the **Options** tab.
7. Under *Alternative hypothesis* select the two-tailed option ≠. Enter **0** for *Hypothesized difference (D) and* enter the desired significance level (enter **5** for 95% confidence level). Select **Asymptotic p-value.**
8. Click **OK** to display the confidence interval.

continued

TECH CENTER *continued*

Inferences with Two Means: Matched Pairs
Access tech supplements, videos, and data sets at **www.TriolaStats.com**

R

R command: **t.test(x, y, alternative = c("two.sided", "less", "greater"), paired = TRUE, conf.level = 0.95)**

where *x* and *y* are each vectors of matched pairs of sample data.

TIP: For Example 1: **t.test(x, y, alternative = "greater", paired = TRUE, conf.level = 0.95)**

A complete list of R statistical commands is available at TriolaStats.com

9-3 Basic Skills and Concepts

Statistical Literacy and Critical Thinking

1. Is Friday the 13th Unlucky? Listed below are numbers of hospital admissions in one region due to traffic accidents on different Fridays falling on the 6th day of a month and the following 13th day of the month (based on data from "Is Friday the 13th Bad for Your Health," by Scanlon et al., *British Medical Journal*, Vol. 307). Assume that we want to use a 0.05 significance level to test the claim that the data support the claim that fewer hospital admissions due to traffic accidents occur on Friday the 6th than on the following Friday the 13th. Identify the null hypothesis and alternative hypothesis.

Friday 6th	9	6	11	11	3	5
Friday 13th	13	12	14	10	4	12

2. Friday the 13th Refer to the sample data from Exercise 1.

a. Find the differences d, then find the values of $\bar{d}$ and s_d.

b. In general, what does μ_d represent?

3. Confidence Interval Assume that we want to use the sample data in Exercise 1 for constructing a confidence interval to be used for testing the given claim.

a. What is the confidence level that should be used for the confidence interval?

b. What is the critical t value that should be used for finding the margin of error E?

c. If the resulting confidence interval is -5.8 admissions $< \mu_d < -0.9$ admissions, what do you conclude?

4. True or False For the methods of this section, determine whether the following statements are true or false.

a. When testing a claim with matched pairs of data, hypothesis tests using the P-value method, critical value method, and confidence interval method will all result in the same conclusion.

b. If a simple random sample of 50 matched pairs of data yields differences with a distribution that is far from normal, then the methods of this section should not be used.

c. The methods of this section can be used with pulse rates of 100 randomly selected adult women and 100 randomly selected adult men.

d. If using the methods of this section to test a claim that $\mu_d \neq 0$ and it is found that the 95% confidence interval does not include 0, then the P-value must be 0.05 or less.

e. If the methods of this section are used with pulse rates of 100 subjects before and after exercise, the sample size is $n = 200$.

In Exercises 5–16, use the listed paired sample data, and assume that the samples are simple random samples and that the differences have a distribution that is approximately normal.

5. Measured and Reported Weights Listed below are measured and reported weights (lb) of random female subjects (from Data Set 4 "Measured and Reported" in Appendix B).

a. Use a 0.05 significance level to test the claim that for females, the measured weights tend to be higher than the reported weights.

b. Construct the confidence interval that could be used for the hypothesis test described in part (a). What feature of the confidence interval leads to the same conclusion reached in part (a)?

Measured	147.3	268.7	213.4	201.3	107.1	172.0	187.4	132.5	122.1	151.9
Reported	142	267	210	204	107	176	187	135	122	150

6. Do Men Talk Less than Women? Listed below are word counts of males and females in couple relationships (from Data Set 14 "Word Counts" in Appendix B).

a. Use a 0.05 significance level to test the claim that men talk less than women.

b. Construct the confidence interval that could be used for the hypothesis test described in part (a). What feature of the confidence interval leads to the same conclusion reached in part (a)?

Men	13,560	18,876	13,825	9274	20,547	17,190
Women	21,261	12,964	33,789	8709	10,508	11,909

7. The Freshman 15 The "Freshman 15" refers to the belief that college students gain 15 lb (or 6.8 kg) during their freshman year. Listed below are weights (kg) of randomly selected male college freshmen (from Data Set 13 "Freshman 15" in Appendix B). The weights were measured in September and later in April.

a. Use a 0.01 significance level to test the claim that for the population of freshman male college students, the weights in September are less than the weights in the following April.

b. Construct the confidence interval that could be used for the hypothesis test described in part (a). What feature of the confidence interval leads to the same conclusion reached in part (a)?

c. What do you conclude about the Freshman 15 belief?

September	67	68	87	81	60	70	68	68	80
April	67	68	88	82	61	71	69	69	82

8. QWERTY vs Dvorak Currently, keyboards have the keys configured in an arrangement referred to as "QWERTY" because of the placement of those particular letters on the second row from the top. Supposedly, that configuration was designed to slightly slow typing so that keys would not jam in typewriters commonly used in days of yore. The Dvorak keyboard configuration is claimed to be more efficient by arranging keys according to frequency of use. Listed below are difficulty ratings of typing different words on each of the two keyboards (based on data collected by the author). The data are paired according to the same word used on both keyboards, and higher numbers correspond to words that are more difficult to type.

a. Use a 0.01 significance level to test the claim that word difficulty scores are higher with the QWERTY keyboard.

b. Construct the confidence interval that could be used for the hypothesis test described in part (a). What feature of the confidence interval leads to the same conclusion reached in part (a)?

QWERTY	5	6	6	8	10	7	2	2	10	5	8	2	5	4	2
Dvorak	3	3	1	3	5	4	2	0	5	1	4	0	3	5	0

9. Audiometry Listed below are results from subjects tested for hearing in the right ear and left ear (based on data from the National Center for Health Statistics). Values are in decibels Hearing Level (db HL) which represent the quietest sound level subjects can hear at a specific frequency.

a. Use a 0.05 significance level to test the claim that the population of such differences has a mean equal to 0.

b. Construct the confidence interval that could be used for the hypothesis test described in part (a). What feature of the confidence interval leads to the same conclusion reached in part (a)?

Right Ear	5	10	5	5	40	10	45	15	30	5	20	5
Left Ear	5	10	15	5	25	5	35	10	15	10	25	10

10. Vision Test Listed below are results from subjects tested for visual acuity in the right eye and left eye (based on data from the National Center for Health Statistics). Lower values represent better vision.

a. Use a 0.05 significance level to test the claim that the population of such differences has a mean equal to 0.

b. Construct the confidence interval that could be used for the hypothesis test described in part (a). What feature of the confidence interval leads to the same conclusion reached in part (a)?

Right Eye	30	25	20	20	25	50	20	20	25	25
Left Eye	20	25	25	20	25	40	20	20	20	30

11. Oscars Listed below are ages of actresses and actors when they won Academy Awards for their performances (from Data Set 21 "Oscar Winner Age" in Appendix B). Each pair of ages is from the same year.

a. Use a 0.05 significance level to test the claim that Oscar-winning actresses tend to be younger than Oscar-winning actors.

b. Construct the confidence interval that could be used for the hypothesis test described in part (a). What feature of the confidence interval leads to the same conclusion reached in part (a)?

Actress (years)	28	28	31	29	35	26	26	41	30	34
Actor (years)	62	37	36	38	29	34	51	39	37	42

12. Heights of Presidents A popular theory is that presidential candidates have an advantage if they are taller than their main opponents. Listed are heights (cm) of presidents along with the heights of their main opponents (from Data Set 22 "Presidents" in Appendix B).

a. Use the sample data with a 0.05 significance level to test the claim that for the population of heights of presidents and their main opponents, the differences have a mean greater than 0 cm.

b. Construct the confidence interval that could be used for the hypothesis test described in part (a). What feature of the confidence interval leads to the same conclusion reached in part (a)?

Height (cm) of President	185	178	175	183	193	173
Height (cm) of Main Opponent	171	180	173	175	188	178

13. Heights of Mothers and Daughters Listed below are heights (in.) of mothers and their first daughters. The data are from a journal kept by Francis Galton. (See Data Set 10 "Family Heights" in Appendix B.) Use a 0.05 significance level to test the claim that there is no difference in heights between mothers and their first daughters.

Height of Mother	68.0	60.0	61.0	63.5	69.0	64.0	69.0	64.0	63.5	66.0
Height of Daughter	68.5	60.0	63.5	67.5	68.0	65.5	69.0	68.0	64.5	63.0

14. Heights of Fathers and Sons Listed below are heights (in.) of fathers and their first sons. The data are from a journal kept by Francis Galton. (See Data Set 10 "Family Heights" in Appendix B.) Use a 0.05 significance level to test the claim that there is no difference in heights between fathers and their first sons.

Height of Father	72.0	66.0	69.0	70.0	70.0	70.0	70.0	75.0	68.2	65.0
Height of Son	73.0	68.0	68.0	71.0	70.0	70.0	71.0	71.0	70.0	63.0

15. Hypnotism for Reducing Pain A study was conducted to investigate the effectiveness of hypnotism in reducing pain. Results for randomly selected subjects are given in the accompanying table (based on "An Analysis of Factors That Contribute to the Efficacy of Hypnotic Analgesia," by Price and Barber, *Journal of Abnormal Psychology,* Vol. 96, No. 1). The values are before and after hypnosis; the measurements are in centimeters on a pain scale. Higher values correspond to greater levels of pain. Construct a 95% confidence interval for the mean of the "before/after" differences. Does hypnotism appear to be effective in reducing pain?

Subject	A	B	C	D	E	F	G	H
Before	6.6	6.5	9.0	10.3	11.3	8.1	6.3	11.6
After	6.8	2.4	7.4	8.5	8.1	6.1	3.4	2.0

16. Gosset Data Listed below are paired data from W. S. Gosset, who introduced us to the famous *t* distribution. The values are hours of sleep gained or lost by 10 patients after each of two different sleep treatments (based on data from "Probable Error of the Mean," by W. S. Gosset, *Biometrica,* Vol. 6).

a. Use a 0.01 significance level to test the claim that both sleep treatments have the same effect.

b. Construct the confidence interval that could be used for the hypothesis test described in part (a). What feature of the confidence interval leads to the same conclusion reached in part (a)?

Dextro	0.7	−1.6	−0.2	−1.2	−1.0	3.4	3.7	0.8	0.0	2.0
Laevo	1.9	0.8	1.1	0.1	−0.1	4.4	5.5	1.6	4.6	3.4

Larger Data Sets.   *In Exercises 17–24, use the indicated Data Sets from Appendix B. The complete data sets can be found at www.TriolaStats.com. Assume that the paired sample data are simple random samples and the differences have a distribution that is approximately normal.*

17. Measured and Reported Weights Repeat Exercise 5 using all of the 2971 measured and reported weights (lb) of females listed in Data Set 4 "Measured and Reported" in Appendix B. Did the larger data set have much of an effect on the results?

18. Measured and Reported Weights Repeat Example 1 using all of the 2784 measured and reported weights of males listed in Data Set 4 "Measured and Reported" in Appendix B. Did the larger data set have much of an effect on the results?

19. Oscars Repeat Exercise 11 "Oscars" using all of the sample data from Data Set 21 "Oscar Winner Age" in Appendix B. Note that the pairs of data consist of ages that are matched according to the year in which the Oscars were won. Again use a significance level of 0.05.

20. Heights of Presidents Repeat Exercise 12 "Heights of Presidents" using all of the sample data from Data Set 22 "Presidents" in Appendix B.

21. Height and Arm Span Supposedly, a person's height is approximately equal to their arm span. Refer the Data Set 3 "ANSUR II 2012" and use the heights and arm spans (cm) of the 4082 males. Use a 0.05 significance level to test the claim that for males, their height is the same as their arm span.

22. Do Men Talk Less than Women? Repeat Exercise 6 "Do Men Talk Less than Women" using all of the data in the first two columns of Data Set 14 "Word Counts" in Appendix B.

23. Heights of Mothers and Daughters Repeat Exercise 13 "Heights of Mothers and Daughters" using all of the heights of mothers and daughters listed in Data Set 10 "Family Heights" in Appendix B.

24. Heights of Fathers and Sons Repeat Exercise 14 "Heights of Fathers and Sons" using all of the heights of fathers and sons listed in Data Set 10 "Family Heights" in Appendix B.

9-3 Beyond the Basics

25. Heights of Fathers and Sons

a. Repeat Exercise 14 using a confidence interval constructed with the methods of this section.

b. Repeat Exercise 14 using a confidence interval constructed by using the bootstrap method described in Section 7-4.

c. Compare the results from parts (a) and (b).

9-4 Two Variances or Standard Deviations

Key Concept In this section we present the F test for testing claims made about two population variances (or standard deviations). The F test (named for statistician Sir Ronald Fisher) uses the F distribution introduced in this section. The F test requires that both populations have normal distributions. Instead of being robust, this test is *very* sensitive to departures from normal distributions, so the normality requirement is quite strict. Part 1 describes the F test procedure for conducting a hypothesis test, and Part 2 gives a brief description of two alternative methods for comparing variation in two samples.

PART 1 F Test with Two Variances or Standard Deviations

The following Key Elements box includes elements of a hypothesis test of a claim about two population variances or two population standard deviations. The procedure is based on using the two sample variances, but the *same procedure* is used for claims made about two population standard deviations.

The actual F test could be two-tailed, left-tailed, or right-tailed, but we can make computations much easier by stipulating that the larger of the two sample variances is denoted by s_1^2. It follows that the smaller sample variance is denoted as s_2^2. This stipulation of denoting the larger sample variance by s_1^2 allows us to avoid the somewhat messy problem of finding a critical value of F for the left tail.

Hypothesis Test with Two Variances or Standard Deviations

Objective

Conduct a hypothesis test of a claim about two population variances or standard deviations. (Any claim made about two population standard deviations can be restated with an equivalent claim about two population variances, so the same procedure is used for two population standard deviations or two population variances.)

Notation

$s_1^2 = $ *larger* of the two sample variances
$n_1 = $ size of the sample with the *larger* variance
$\sigma_1^2 = $ variance of the population from which the sample with the *larger* variance was drawn

The symbols s_2^2, n_2, and σ_2^2 are used for the other sample and population.

Requirements

1. The two populations are *independent.*

2. The two samples are simple random samples.

3. Each of the two populations must be *normally distributed,* regardless of their sample sizes. This F test is *not robust* against departures from normality,

so it performs poorly if one or both of the populations have a distribution that is not normal. The requirement of normal distributions is quite strict for this F test.

DETOUR **(If the third requirement is not satisfied, alternative methods include the *count five* method, the Levene-Brown-Forsythe test, and resampling methods.)**

Test Statistic for Hypothesis Tests with Two Variances (with H_0: $\sigma_1^2 = \sigma_2^2$)

$F = \dfrac{s_1^2}{s_2^2}$ (where s_1^2 is the *larger* of the two sample variances)

P-Values: *P*-values are automatically provided by technology. If technology is not available, use the computed value of the F test statistic with Table A-5 to find a range for the *P*-value.

Critical Values: Use Table A-5 to find critical F values that are determined by the following:

1. The significance level α (Table A-5 includes critical values for $\alpha = 0.025$ and $\alpha = 0.05$.)

2. **Numerator degrees of freedom $= n_1 - 1$** (determines *column* of Table A-5)

3. **Denominator degrees of freedom $= n_2 - 1$** (determines *row* of Table A-5) For significance level $\alpha = 0.05$, refer to Table A-5 and use the right-tail

area of 0.025 or 0.05, depending on the type of test, as shown below:

- *Two-tailed test:* Use Table A-5 with 0.025 in the right tail. (The significance level of 0.05 is divided between the two tails, so the area in the right tail is 0.025.)

- *One-tailed test:* Use Table A-5 with $\alpha = 0.05$ in the right tail.

Find the critical F value for the right tail: Because we are stipulating that the larger sample variance is s_1^2, all one-tailed tests will be right-tailed and all two-tailed tests will require that we find only the critical value located to the right. (We have no need to find the critical value at the left tail, which is not very difficult. See Exercise 19 "Finding Lower Critical F Values.")

Explore the Data! Because the F test requirement of normal distributions is quite strict, be sure to examine the distributions of the two samples using histograms and normal quantile plots, and confirm that there are no outliers. (See "Assessing Normality" in Section 6-5.)

F Distribution

For two normally distributed populations with equal variances $(\sigma_1^2 = \sigma_2^2)$, the sampling distribution of the test statistic $F = s_1^2/s_2^2$ is the **F distribution** shown in Figure 9-4 (provided that we have not yet imposed the stipulation that the larger sample variance is s_1^2). If you repeat the process of selecting samples from two normally distributed populations with equal variances, the distribution of the ratio s_1^2/s_2^2 is the *F* distribution.

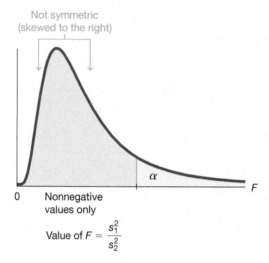

FIGURE 9-4 *F* Distribution

There is a different *F* distribution for each different pair of degrees of freedom for the numerator and denominator.

See Figure 9-4 and note these properties of the *F* distribution:

- The *F* distribution is not symmetric.
- Values of the *F* distribution cannot be negative.
- The exact shape of the *F* distribution depends on the two different degrees of freedom.

Interpreting the Value of the *F* Test Statistic

If the two populations have equal variances, then the ratio s_1^2/s_2^2 will tend to be close to 1. Because we are stipulating that s_1^2 is the larger sample variance, the ratio s_1^2/s_2^2 will be a *large* number whenever s_1^2 and s_2^2 are far apart in value. Consequently, a value of *F* near 1 will be evidence in favor of $\sigma_1^2 = \sigma_2^2$, but a large value of *F* will be evidence against $\sigma_1^2 = \sigma_2^2$.

Large **values of *F* are evidence *against* $\sigma_1^2 = \sigma_2^2$.**

EXAMPLE 1 Weights of Male Army Personnel

Listed below are weights (kg) of randomly selected male U.S. Army personnel from Data Set 2 "ANSUR I 1988" and Data Set 3 "ANSUR II 2012." Use a 0.05 significance level to test the claim that the variation among weights did not change from the ANSUR I study in 1988 to the ANSUR II study in 2012.

| ANSUR I 1988 | 63.0 | 88.9 | 71.1 | 83.6 | 84.2 | 76.3 | 69.5 | 74.4 | 81.4 | 72.0 | 85.5 | 111.1 |
| ANSUR II 2012 | 90.8 | 86.1 | 101.1 | 76.9 | 63.0 | 98.4 | 83.5 | 65.1 | 111.5 | 78.0 | | |

REQUIREMENT CHECK (1) The two populations are independent of each other. The two samples are not matched in any way. (2) Given the design for the study, we assume that the two samples can be treated as simple random samples. (3) A normal quantile plot of each set of sample weights shows that both samples appear to be from populations with a normal distribution. The requirements are satisfied. ☑

Here are the statistics for the above data sets:

- ANSUR I 1988: $n = 12$, $s = 12.4194$ kg
- ANSUR II 2012: $n = 10$, $s = 15.5306$ kg

Because we stipulate that in this section the larger variance is denoted by s_1^2, we switch the above two data sets and we let $s_1^2 = 15.5306^2$ and $n_1 = 10$. By default, $s_2^2 = 12.4194^2$ and $n_2 = 12$.

Step 1: The claim that the variation did not change from ANSUR I 1988 to ANSUR II 2012 can be expressed symbolically as $\sigma_1^2 = \sigma_2^2$ or as $\sigma_1 = \sigma_2$. We will use $\sigma_1 = \sigma_2$.

Step 2: If the original claim is false, then $\sigma_1 \neq \sigma_2$.

Step 3: Because the null hypothesis is the statement of equality and because the alternative hypothesis cannot contain equality, we have

$$H_0: \sigma_1 = \sigma_2 \quad \text{(original claim)} \qquad H_1: \sigma_1 \neq \sigma_2$$

Step 4: The significance level is $\alpha = 0.05$.

Step 5: Using Technology Steps 5 and 6 can be skipped using technology. See the accompanying StatCrunch display showing that the test statistic is $F = 1.5637842$ and the P-value is 0.4779.

StatCrunch

Hypothesis test results:

Ratio	Num. DF	Den. DF	Sample Ratio	F-Stat	P-value
$\sigma_1{}^2/\sigma_2{}^2$	9	11	1.5637842	1.5637842	0.4779

Manual Calculations If technology is not available, first note that because this test involves two population variances, we use the F distribution.

Step 6: The test statistic is

$$F = \frac{s_1^2}{s_2^2} = \frac{15.5306^2}{12.4194^2} = 1.5638$$

P-Value Method Due to the format of Table A-5, the P-value method is a bit tricky without technology, but here we go. For a two-tailed test with significance level 0.05, there is an area of 0.025 in the right tail, so we use the two pages for the F distribution (Table A-5) with "0.025 in the right tail." The degrees of freedom are found as follows:

- Numerator degrees of freedom $= n_1 - 1 = 10 - 1 = 9$
- Denominator degrees of freedom $= n_2 - 1 = 12 - 1 = 11$

With numerator degrees of freedom $= 9$ and denominator degrees of freedom $= 11$, we find that the critical value of F is 3.5879. The test statistic of $F = 1.5638$ is not greater than the critical value, so we know that the area to the right of the test statistic is more than 0.025, and it follows that for this two-tailed test, P-value > 0.05.

continued

Critical Value Method As with the *P*-value method, we find that the critical value is 3.5879. The test statistic $F = 1.5638$ is not greater than the critical value, so the test statistic does not fall in the critical region. See Figure 9-5.

Step 7: Figure 9-5 shows that the test statistic $F = 1.5638$ does not fall within the critical region, so we fail to reject the null hypothesis of equal variances. There is not sufficient evidence to warrant rejection of the claim of equal standard deviations.

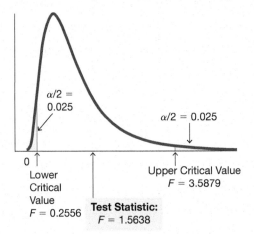

FIGURE 9-5 *F*-Test of Equal Standard Deviations

INTERPRETATION

Step 8: There is not sufficient evidence to warrant rejection of the claim that the two standard deviations are equal. It appears that the variation among weights of male U.S. Army personnel did not change from 1988 to 2012.

YOUR TURN. Do Exercise 5 "Minting of Quarters."

Caution: Part 2 of Section 9-2 includes methods for testing claims about two population means, and one of those methods has a requirement that $\sigma_1 = \sigma_2$. Using the *F* test is *not* recommended as a way to decide whether this requirement is met. For Section 9-2, using the *F* test runs the risk of using differences that are too small to have an effect on the *t* test for two independent samples. That approach is often described as being analogous to sending someone out to sea in a rowboat (the preliminary *F* test) to determine whether the sea is safe for an ocean liner (the *t* test).

PART 2 Alternative Methods

Part 1 of this section presents the *F* test for testing claims made about the standard deviations (or variances) of two independent populations. Because that test is so sensitive to departures from normality, we now briefly describe alternative methods that are not so sensitive to departures from normality.

Count Five

The *count five* method is a relatively simple alternative to the *F* test, and it does not require normally distributed populations. (See "A Quick, Compact, Two-Sample Dispersion Test: Count Five," by McGrath and Yeh, *American Statistician,* Vol. 59, No. 1.) If the two sample sizes are equal, and if one sample has at least five of the largest mean absolute deviations (MAD), then we conclude that its population has a larger variance. See Exercise 17 "Count Five Test" for the specific procedure.

Levene-Brown-Forsythe Test

The *Levene-Brown-Forsythe test* (or modified Levene's test) is another alternative to the *F* test, and it is much more robust against departures from normality. This test begins with a transformation of each set of sample values. Within the first sample, replace each *x* value with $|x - \text{median}|$, and apply the same transformation to the second sample. Using the transformed values, conduct a *t* test of equality of means for independent samples, as described in Part 1 of Section 9-2. Because the transformed values are now deviations, the *t* test for equality of means is actually a test comparing variation in the two samples. See Exercise 18 "Levene-Brown-Forsythe Test."

There are other alternatives to the *F* test, as well as adjustments that improve the performance of the *F* test. See "Fixing the *F* Test for Equal Variances," by Shoemaker, *American Statistician,* Vol. 57, No. 2.

Go Figure

Every minute there are more than 350,000 tweets, 212 million e-mails, and 16 million text messages.

TECH CENTER

Inferences from Two Standard Deviations

Access tech supplements, videos, and data sets at **www.TriolaStats.com**

Statdisk

1. Click **Analysis** in the top menu.
2. Select **Hypothesis Testing** from the dropdown menu and **Standard Deviation Two Samples** from the submenu.
3. *Using Summary Statistics:* Select the **Use Summary Statistics** tab and enter the sample size and sample standard deviation for each sample.

   Using Sample Data: Select the **Use Data** tab and select the desired data columns.
4. Select the desired format for *Alternative Hypothesis* and enter the significance level.
5. Click **Evaluate.**

Minitab

1. Click **Stat** in the top menu.
2. Select **Basic Statistics** from the dropdown menu and select **2 Variances** from the submenu.
3. *Using Summary Statistics:* Select **Sample variances** or **Sample standard deviations** from the dropdown menu and enter the sample sizes and sample variances or standard deviations.

   Using sample data: Select **Each sample is in its own column** from the dropdown menu and select the desired data columns.
4. Click the **Options** button and select the desired ratio. Enter the desired confidence level and enter **1** for *Hypothesized ratio.* Select the desired format for *the Alternative hypothesis.*
5. Check the box labeled **Use test and confidence intervals based on normal distribution.**
6. Click **OK** twice.

TIP: Another procedure is to click on **Assistant** in the top menu, then select **Hypothesis Tests** and **2-Sample Standard Deviation.** Complete the dialog box to get results, including *P*-value and other helpful information.

StatCrunch

1. Click **Stat** in the top menu.
2. Select **Variance Stats** from the dropdown menu, then select **Two Sample** from the submenu.
3. *Using Summary Statistics:* Select **With Summary** from the submenu and enter the sample variances and sample sizes.

   Using Sample Data: Select **With Data** from the submenu and select the desired data column for each sample.
4. Select **Hypothesis test for σ_1^2/σ_2^2.** Enter **1** for the hypothesized ratio (H_0) and select the desired format for the alternative hypothesis (H_A).
5. Click **Compute!**

TI-83/84 Plus Calculator

1. Press **STAT**, then select **TESTS** in the top menu.
2. Select **2-SampFTest** in the menu and press **ENTER**.
3. Select **Data** if you have sample data in lists or **Stats** if you have summary statistics. Press **ENTER** and enter the list names (leave *Freq* = **1**) or summary statistics.
4. For σ_1 select the desired format for the alternative hypothesis.
5. Select **Calculate** and press **ENTER**.

continued

TECH CENTER *continued*

 Inferences from Two Standard Deviations
Access tech supplements, videos, and data sets at **www.TriolaStats.com**

Excel

XLSTAT Add-In
Requires original sample data, does not work with summary data.
1. Click on the **XLSTAT** tab in the Ribbon and then click **Parametric tests.**
2. Select **Two-sample comparison of variances** from the dropdown menu.
3. Under *Sample 1 & 2* enter the range of cells containing the sample data. For *Data format* select **One column per sample.** If the first row of data contains a label, also check the **Column labels** box.
4. Select **Fisher's F-test.**
5. Click the **Options** tab.
6. Under *Alternative hypothesis* select the desired format ($\neq$ for two-tailed test, $<$ for left-tailed test, $>$ for right-tailed test). Enter the *Hypothesized ratio* (usually **1**) and enter the desired significance level (enter **5** for 0.05 significance level). Select **Asymptotic p-value.**
7. Click **OK** to display the test statistic (labeled *F Observed value*) and *P*-value.

Excel (Data Analysis Add-In)
1. Click on **Data** in the ribbon, then click on the **Data Analysis** tab.
2. Select **F-Test Two-Sample for Variances** and click **OK.**
3. Enter the data range for each variable in the *Variable Range* boxes. If the first row contains a label, check the **Labels** box.
4. Enter the desired significance level in the *Alpha* box and click **OK.** The results include the *F* test statistic, *P*-value for a one-tail test, and critical value for a one-tail test.

TIP: For a two-tailed test make two adjustments: (1) Enter the value that is half the significance level (Step 4) and (2) double the *P*-value given in the results.

R

R command not available at time of publication.

R is rapidly evolving, and an updated list of statistical commands is available at TriolaStats.com.

9-4   Basic Skills and Concepts

Statistical Literacy and Critical Thinking

1. *F* Test Statistic

a. If s_1^2 represents the larger of two sample variances, can the *F* test statistic ever be less than 1?

b. Can the *F* test statistic ever be a negative number?

c. If testing the claim that $\sigma_1^2 \neq \sigma_2^2$, what do we know about the two samples if the test statistic *F* is very close to 1?

d. Is the *F* distribution symmetric, skewed left, or skewed right?

2. *F* Test Using sample data from Data Set 2 "ANSUR I 1988" and Data Set 3 "ANSUR II 2012" for a test of the claim that heights of female U.S. Army personnel in 1988 and 2012 have different amounts of variation, we find that $s = 63.6$ cm for 1988 and $s = 64.2$ cm for 2012.

a. Find the values of s_1^2 and s_2^2 and express them with appropriate units of measure.

b. Identify the null and alternative hypotheses.

c. Find the value of the *F* test statistic and round it to four decimal places.

d. The *P*-value for this test is 0.6695. What do you conclude about the stated claim?

3. Test for Normality For the hypothesis test described in Exercise 2, the sample sizes are $n_1 = 2208$ and $n_2 = 1986$. When using the F test with these data, is it correct to reason that there is no need to check for normality because both samples have sizes that are greater than 30?

4. Robust What does it mean when we say that the F test described in this section is *not robust* against departures from normality?

In Exercises 5–16, test the given claim.

5. Minting of Quarters Before 1964, quarters were 90% silver and 10% copper. After 1964, quarters were made with a copper-nickel alloy. Using the data from Data Set 40 "Coin Weights" we get the statistics shown below. Use a 0.05 significance level to test the claim that the variation of weights before 1964 is greater than the variation of weights after 1964. If that claim is supported, what is an advantage of the change?

Before 1964:	$n = 40$, $s = 0.086995$ g
After 1964:	$n = 40$, $s = 0.061937$ g

6. Minting of Pennies Before 1983, pennies were 97% copper and 3% zinc, but after 1983 they are 3% copper and 97% zinc. Using the data from Data Set 40 "Coin Weights" we get the statistics shown below. Use a 0.05 significance level to test the claim that the variation of weights before 1983 is greater than the variation of weights after 1983. If that claim is supported, what is an advantage of the change?

Before 1983:	$n = 35$, $s = 0.03910$ g
After 1983:	$n = 37$, $s = 0.01648$ g

7. Color and Creativity Researchers from the University of British Columbia conducted trials to investigate the effects of color on creativity. Subjects with a red background were asked to think of creative uses for a brick; other subjects with a blue background were given the same task. Responses were scored by a panel of judges and results from scores of creativity are given below. Use a 0.05 significance level to test the claim that creative task scores have the same variation with a red background and a blue background.

Red Background:	$n = 35$, $\bar{x} = 3.39$, $s = 0.97$
Blue Background:	$n = 36$, $\bar{x} = 3.97$, $s = 0.63$

8. Color and Recall Researchers from the University of British Columbia conducted trials to investigate the effects of color on the accuracy of recall. Subjects were given tasks consisting of words displayed on a computer screen with background colors of red and blue. The subjects studied 36 words for 2 minutes, and then they were asked to recall as many of the words as they could after waiting 20 minutes. Results from scores on the word recall test are given below. Use a 0.05 significance level to test the claim that variation of scores is the same with the red background and blue background.

Accuracy Scores

Red Background:	$n = 35$, $\bar{x} = 15.89$, $s = 5.90$
Blue Background:	$n = 36$, $\bar{x} = 12.31$, $s = 5.48$

9. Testing Effects of Alcohol Researchers conducted an experiment to test the effects of alcohol. Errors were recorded in a test of visual and motor skills for a treatment group of 22 people who drank ethanol and another group of 22 people given a placebo. The errors for the treatment group have a standard deviation of 2.20, and the errors for the placebo group have a standard deviation of 0.72 (based on data from "Effects of Alcohol Intoxication on Risk Taking, Strategy, and Error Rate in Visuomotor Performance," by Streufert et al., *Journal of Applied Psychology,* Vol. 77, No. 4). Use a 0.05 significance level to test the claim that both groups have the same amount of variation among the errors.

10. Second-Hand Smoke Samples from Data Set 15 "Passive and Active Smoke" include cotinine levels measured in a group of smokers ($n = 40, \bar{x} = 172.48$ ng/mL, $s = 119.50$ ng/mL) and a group of nonsmokers not exposed to tobacco smoke ($n = 40, \bar{x} = 16.35$ ng/mL, $s = 62.53$ ng/mL). Cotinine is a metabolite of nicotine, meaning that when nicotine is absorbed by the body, cotinine is produced.

a. Use a 0.05 significance level to test the claim that the variation of cotinine in smokers is greater than the variation of cotinine in nonsmokers not exposed to tobacco smoke.

b. The 40 cotinine measurements from the nonsmoking group consist of these values (all in ng/mL): 1, 1, 90, 244, 309, and 35 other values that are all 0. Does this sample appear to be from a normally distributed population? If not, how are the results from part (a) affected?

11. Bicycle Commuting A researcher used two different bicycles to commute to work. One bicycle was carbon and weighed 20.9 lb; the other bicycle was steel and weighed 30.0 lb. The commuting times (minutes) were recorded with the results shown below (based on data from "Bicycle Weights and Commuting Time," by Jeremy Groves, *British Medical Journal*). Use a 0.05 significance level to test the claim that commuting times with the lighter bicycle have more variation than commuting times with the heavier bicycle.

Lighter Bicycle:	$n = 26, \bar{x} = 108.4$ min, $s = 6.3$ min
Heavier Bicycle:	$n = 30, \bar{x} = 107.8$ min, $s = 4.9$ min

12. Birth Weights Listed below are birth weight statistics from Data Set 6 "Births" in Appendix B. Use a 0.05 significance level to test the claim that at birth, weights of girls have more variation than weights of boys.

Girls:	$n = 205, \bar{x} = 3037.1$ g, $s = 706.3$ g
Boys:	$n = 195, \bar{x} = 3272.8$ g, $s = 660.2$ g

13. Female and Male Pulse Rates Listed below are pulse rates of randomly selected subjects from Data Set 1 "Body Data." Use a 0.05 significance level to test the claim that the variation among pulse rates of females is greater than the variation among males.

Female	56	54	72	70	80	72	62	96	72	60	98	72
Male	76	78	78	84	74	72	60	70	66			

14. Weights of Female Army Personnel Listed below are weights (kg) of randomly selected female U.S. Army personnel from Data Set 2 "ANSUR I 1988" and Data Set 3 "ANSUR II 2012." Use a 0.05 significance level to test the claim that the variation among weights did not change from the ANSUR I study in 1988 to the ANSUR II study in 2012.

ANSUR I 1988:	70.1	65.6	62.2	59.6	57.3	67.7	59.2	57.3	57.0	66.2	68.4	51.5
ANSUR II 2012:	71.2	72.2	61.0	81.7	79.9	60.2	58.4	60.1	83.4	97.3		

15. IQ and Lead Exposure Data Set 11 "IQ and Lead" in Appendix B lists full IQ scores for a random sample of subjects with medium lead levels in their blood and another random sample of subjects with high lead levels in their blood. Those IQ scores are listed below. Use a 0.05 significance level to test the claim that IQ scores of subjects with medium lead levels vary more than IQ scores of subjects with high lead levels.

Medium:	72	90	92	71	86	79	83	114	100	93	91	98
	91	46	85	82	97	91	92	77	111	78		
High:	82	93	85	75	85	80	101	89	80	94	88	
	104	88	88	83	104	96	76	80	79	75		

16. Blanking Out on Tests Many students have had the unpleasant experience of panicking on a test because the first question was exceptionally difficult. The arrangement of test items was studied for its effect on anxiety. The following scores are measures of "debilitating test anxiety," which most of us call panic or blanking out (based on data from "Item Arrangement, Cognitive Entry Characteristics, Sex and Test Anxiety as Predictors of Achievement in Examination Performance," by Klimko, *Journal of Experimental Education,* Vol. 52, No. 4.) Using a 0.05 significance level, test the claim that the two populations of scores have different amounts of variation.

Questions Arranged from Easy to Difficult				
24.64	39.29	16.32	32.83	28.02
33.31	20.60	21.13	26.69	28.90
26.43	24.23	7.10	32.86	21.06
28.89	28.71	31.73	30.02	21.96
25.49	38.81	27.85	30.29	30.72

Questions Arranged from Difficult to Easy			
33.62	34.02	26.63	30.26
35.91	26.68	29.49	35.32
27.24	32.34	29.34	33.53
27.62	42.91	30.20	32.54

9-4 Beyond the Basics

17. Count Five Test for Comparing Variation in Two Populations Repeat Exercise 16 "Blanking Out on Tests," but instead of using the F test, use the following procedure for the "count five" test of equal variations (which is not as complicated as it might appear).

a. For each value x in the first sample, find the absolute deviation $|x - \bar{x}|$, then sort the absolute deviation values. Do the same for the second sample.

b. Let c_1 be the count of the number of absolute deviation values in the first sample that are greater than the largest absolute deviation value in the other sample. Also, let c_2 be the count of the number of absolute deviation values in the second sample that are greater than the largest absolute deviation value in the other sample. (One of these counts will always be zero.)

c. If the sample sizes are equal $(n_1 = n_2)$, use a critical value of 5. If $n_1 \neq n_2$, calculate the critical value shown below.

$$\frac{\log(\alpha/2)}{\log\left(\dfrac{n_1}{n_1 + n_2}\right)}$$

d. If $c_1 \geq$ critical value, then conclude that $\sigma_1^2 > \sigma_2^2$. If $c_2 \geq$ critical value, then conclude that $\sigma_2^2 > \sigma_1^2$. Otherwise, fail to reject the null hypothesis of $\sigma_1^2 = \sigma_2^2$.

18. Levene-Brown-Forsythe Test Repeat Exercise 16 "Blanking Out on Tests" using the Levene-Brown-Forsythe test.

19. Finding Lower Critical *F* Values For hypothesis tests that are two-tailed, the methods of Part 1 require that we need to find only the upper critical value. Let's denote the upper critical value by F_R, where the subscript indicates the critical value for the right tail. The lower critical value F_L (for the left tail) can be found as follows: (1) Interchange the degrees of freedom used for finding F_R, then (2) using the degrees of freedom found in Step 1, find the F value from Table A-5; (3) take the reciprocal of the F value found in Step 2, and the result is F_L. Find the critical values F_L and F_R for Exercise 16 "Blanking Out on Tests."

9-5 Resampling: Using Technology for Inferences

Key Concept The preceding sections of this chapter included methods for testing claims about two proportions, two independent means, means of differences from matched pairs, and two standard deviations (or variances). Those methods have certain requirements that limit the situations in which they can be used. When some of the requirements are not satisfied, we can often use resampling methods of bootstrapping or randomization. Even when requirements are satisfied, resampling methods can be used in addition to other methods to provide an additional perspective and insight into the data. These methods typically require the use of software such as Statdisk (www.statdisk.com).

For this section, here are key differences between bootstrap resampling and randomization:

- **Bootstrap: Construct a *confidence interval* by resampling *with* replacement.**
- **Randomization: *Test a claim* by resampling *without* replacement.**

Bootstrapping with Two Samples

The basic concept of bootstrap resampling with one sample was introduced in Section 7-4. The procedure for Bootstrapping with two samples is similar but requires some additional steps based on the claims being tested. These steps are summarized in this section and are also illustrated with examples.

Randomization with Two Samples

Randomization for one sample was introduced in Section 8-5, and we now introduce the *randomization* method for two samples.

> **DEFINITION**
>
> **Randomization** of sample data from two samples occurs when we randomly reassign the data to the two samples *without replacement*.

The following example is designed to illustrate this central concept of randomization with two samples:

> **If there is no difference between two groups, any individual sample value is just as likely to be in one group as in the other group.**

How Many Times to Resample? It would be wise to repeat a resampling at least 1000 times. Professional statisticians commonly resample 10,000 or more times. It is obviously impractical to resample that many times using any manual procedure, so the use of software such as Statdisk is very strongly recommended.

EXAMPLE 1 Randomization with Two Samples

Illustrated below is a randomization of income data (thousands of dollars) from two samples of college students arranged according to gender. *See that the data have been randomly reallocated between the two samples, and the random selections were made without replacement. Also note that the original sample sizes of 3 and 4 are the same in the randomization.*

Usefulness of Randomization: Assume that we are testing the null hypothesis that salaries are independent of gender so that there is no difference between the two sample means, so that $H_0: \mu_1 = \mu_2$ and $H_1: \mu_1 \neq \mu_2$:

- The original data show a difference between means of -4.0.
- The randomization shown below yields a difference of -1.1.
- We can repeat the randomization 1000 times to determine whether the difference of -4.0 is *significant* in the sense that it rarely occurs, or whether the difference is not significant because it occurs often.

Original Data Two Independent Samples ($k)				Combined Two Samples ($k)		Randomization Combined Samples Reallocated ($k)		
Male	**Female**					**Male**	**Female**	
2	5			2		2	3	
3	6			3		6	5	
7	9			7		9	7	
	12			5			12	
				6				
Difference in means (*d*):				9		**Difference in means:**		
4.0 − 8.0 = −4.0				12		5.7 − 6.8 = −1.1		

Here are two important observations about the preceding reallocation of data from the two samples:

1. See that the reallocation of data to the male group and female group reflects a null hypothesis that there is no difference between the two groups. The resampling therefore yields a distribution of differences between means that is based on the null hypothesis, so it makes sense to use the resulting distribution for hypothesis tests about the mean difference.

2. See that the reallocation of data to the male group and female group destroys the individual characteristics of the original two data sets (such as means, standard deviations, distributions). As a result, the distribution of differences between means is worthless for obtaining a confidence interval that is an estimate of the difference between the two group means.

SOLUTION

Randomization Procedure for Estimating the *P*-Value

Randomization is used to estimate a *P*-value that can be used to form a conclusion about the null hypothesis $H_0: \mu_1 = \mu_2$. The following procedure for estimating a *P*-value is based on 1000 repetitions, but any large number of repetitions could be used instead. The steps in the following procedure are vastly simplified by using technology.

Step 1: Find the difference *d* between the means of the original two samples.

Example: The difference between means for male and female income samples is $d = 4.0 - 8.0 = -4.0$.

Step 2: Repeat Randomization (Reallocation) Procedure 1000 times or more.

Example: The randomization (reallocation) is completed 1000 times, with the male/female income sample data randomly reallocated (without replacement) between the two samples.

continued

Step 3: Find the difference between the means for each randomization sample, then sort these means in ascending order.

Example: The difference between the male/female means for each of the 1000 randomization samples is calculated and sorted.

Step 4: Find the number of randomization sample mean differences (found in Step 3) that are "at least as extreme" as $d = -4.0$ found in Step 1.

To determine the number of differences that are "at least as extreme" as -4.0, find the number of differences less than or equal to -4 and greater than or equal to 4.

Example: Among 1000 resamplings, there are 89 with sample mean differences of -4 or lower, and there are 90 sample differences greater than or equal to 4.

Step 5: Add the two values from Step 4 and divide by the number of randomizations (from Step 2) to get the estimated *P*-value.

Example: P-Value is estimated to be $(89 + 90)/1000$, or 0.179.

> **INTERPRETATION**
>
> Using a significance level of 0.05, we fail to reject the null hypotheses of $H_0: \mu_1 = \mu_2$ because the estimated *P*-value of 0.179 is greater than the significance level of 0.05. Using the randomization method, we find that there is not sufficient evidence to warrant rejection of the claim that the mean income of males is different from the mean income of females.

YOUR TURN. Do Exercise 9 "Are Weights Changing Over Time?"

Two Proportions Section 9-1 presents methods for making inferences about two population proportions. The following example illustrates how resampling can be used to construct confidence intervals and test hypotheses.

CP **EXAMPLE 2** Resampling to Test a Claim About Two Proportions

The first example in Section 9-1 included the following sample data. That example specified a 0.05 significance level for testing the claim that there is no difference in success rates between the two smoking cessation treatment groups.

Proportion of Success (not smoking after 52 weeks)

E-Cigarette Group: $\hat{p}_1 = 79/438 = 0.180$

Nicotine Replacement Group: $\hat{p}_2 = 44/446 = 0.099$

The above two samples have this difference between the proportions:

$$\hat{p}_1 - \hat{p}_2 = 0.180 - 0.099 = 0.081$$

Bootstrapping The procedure for bootstrap resampling with two samples involves creating a bootstrap sample for the first sample by sampling *with* replacement, then doing the same for the second sample. Next, find the difference between the two *unsorted* bootstrap sample means. Repeat many times to get a large list of differences, then sort those differences and find $P_{2.5}$ and $P_{97.5}$, which are the confidence interval limits of a 95% confidence interval estimate of the difference between the two population proportions.

Example: Using the bootstrap procedure with the sample proportions of 79/438 and 44/446, a typical result is this 95% confidence interval: $0.0363 < p_1 - p_2 < 0.123$.

This confidence interval is very close to the one previously obtained in Section 9-1. Again, because the confidence interval does not include 0, it appears that the e-cigarette and nicotine replacement treatment groups have *different* success rates. Also, the confidence interval gives us an estimate of the size of the difference.

Randomization The randomization method for two sample proportions involves combining both sets of sample data (for proportions, use 0's and 1's), and then randomly selecting samples without replacement using the same sample sizes as the original samples.

Example: The difference between the two sample proportions is $79/438 - 44/446 = 0.08171059$. If we use the randomization procedure with those two sample proportions and if we use technology to get 1000 simulated differences, a typical result is that the difference of 0.08171059 or more will never occur, and the difference of -0.08171059 or below will never occur. That is, a difference "at least as extreme" as 0.08171059 will not occur. Consequently, there is a very small chance of getting a difference at least as extreme as 0.08171059. This is similar to the results of the P-value method in Section 9-1 (P-value $= 0.00045$). Because the original samples *do* have a difference of 0.08171059, we conclude that this difference is significant, so that there appears to be a significant difference between the two samples. It appears that the e-cigarette and nicotine replacement treatment groups have *different* success rates.

Two Means: Independent Samples Section 9-2 presents methods for using sample data from two independent samples to make inferences about two population means. The following example illustrates the use of resampling with means from two independent samples.

EXAMPLE 3 **Resampling to Test a Claim About Two Means: Independent Samples**

Example 1 in Section 9-2 includes the following heights (mm) of randomly selected U.S. Army male personnel measured in 1988 (from Data Set 2 "ANSUR I 1988") and different heights (mm) of randomly selected U.S. Army male personnel measured in 2012 (from Data Set 3 "ANSUR II 2012"). That example specified a 0.05 significance level for testing the claim that the mean height of the 1988 population is less than the mean height of the 2012 population.

ANSUR I 1988:	1698	1727	1734	1684	1667	1680	1785	1885
	1841	1702	1738	1732				
ANSUR II 2012:	1810	1850	1777	1811	1780	1733	1814	1861
	1709	1740	1694	1766	1748	1794	1780	

The above two data sets have this difference between their means:

$$\bar{x}_1 - \bar{x}_2 = 1739.4 - 1777.8 = -38.4$$

Bootstrapping The procedure for bootstrap resampling involves creating a bootstrap sample for the first sample by sampling *with* replacement, then doing the same for the second sample. Next, find the difference between the two bootstrap sample means. Repeat many times to get a large list of differences, then sort those differences and find $P_{2.5}$ and $P_{97.5}$, which are the limits of a 95% confidence interval estimate of the difference between the two population means.

continued

Example: A 90% confidence interval is required for this left-tailed case, so we create a large list of differences (1000 resamples) and then find the confidence interval limits of $P_{0.05}$ and $P_{0.95}$. A typical result is a 90% confidence interval: -74.1 mm $< \mu_1 - \mu_2 < 0.683$ mm. This result is similar to the confidence interval found in Example 2 in Section 9-2. Because the confidence interval does include 0, it appears that there is not a significant difference between the mean height in 1988 and the mean height in 2012. (*Note:* Repeating this bootstrap procedure several times will easily lead to confidence interval limits that do *not* include 0, so it could easily appear that there *is* a significant difference between the mean height in 1988 and the mean height in 2012. The *P*-value of 0.0546 from the *t*-test from Example 1 in Section 9-2 also confirms that the sample data are close to the borderline between supporting and failing to support the claim that the mean height of the 1988 population is less than the mean height of the 2012 population. In this case, the sample data do not provide *compelling* evidence in favor or against that claim.)

Randomization As previously described, the randomization procedure involves combining both sets of sample data, then randomly selecting samples without replacement using the same sample sizes as the original samples. Find the difference in sample means, and then repeat many times to determine whether the original difference rarely occurs or commonly occurs.

Example: Using the sample data, we get $\bar{x}_1 - \bar{x}_2 = 1739.4 - 1777.8 = -38.4$ mm. If we use the randomization procedure described in Example 1 with the two sets of sample data to generate 1000 simulated differences, a typical result is that the difference of -38.4 mm or below will occur 51 times (for a proportion of 0.051). This is quite close to the *P*-value of 0.0546 from Example 1 in Section 9-2. As in Example 1, we conclude that there is not sufficient evidence to support the claim that the mean height of the 1988 male population is less than the mean height of the 2012 male population. (*Note:* As in the preceding bootstrapping example, the sample data are close to the borderline between supporting and failing to support the claim that the mean height of the 1988 population is less than the mean height of the 2012 population. The sample data do not provide *compelling* evidence in favor or against that claim.)

YOUR TURN. Do Exercise 11 "Regular Coke and Diet Coke."

HINT For the randomization in Example 3, it was found that there were 51 differences of -38.4 mm or below. Instead of getting a result of 51 each time, repeating that randomization process will result in counts typically ranging from about 35 to 65. In such cases, answers in Appendix B include the statement that "results vary." Know that such results can vary by somewhat substantial amounts.

Matched Pairs Section 9-3 presents methods for making inferences about matched pairs. The following example illustrates the use of resampling with matched pairs.

EXAMPLE 4 **Resampling with Matched Pairs**

Examples 1 and 2 in Section 9-3 use the following eight measured and reported weights to test the claim that for males, the measured weights tend to be higher than the reported weights. Use a 0.05 significance level.

TABLE 9-2 Measured and Reported Weights (lb)

Subject	1	2	3	4	5	6	7	8
Measured Weight (lb)	152.6	149.3	174.8	119.5	194.9	180.3	215.4	239.6
Reported Weight (lb)	150	148	170	119	185	180	224	239

Bootstrapping For the bootstrap resampling procedure with matched pairs, first find the differences d between the matched pairs of data, and then use the same bootstrapping procedure described in Section 7-4 for one mean.

Example: The matched pairs of data have these "measured – reported" differences: 2.6, 1.3, 4.8, 0.5, 9.9, 0.3, −8.6, 0.6. A 90% confidence interval is required, so we find the confidence interval limits of $P_{0.05}$ and $P_{0.95}$. A typical result is the confidence interval: -1.46 lb $< \mu_d < 4.08$ lb. This confidence interval is reasonably close to the confidence interval obtained in Section 9-3. Because the confidence interval does include 0, it appears that there is no significant difference between measured weights and reported weights.

Randomization For the randomization procedure for matched pairs, we are assuming in the null hypothesis that $\mu_d = 0$, so each pair of values can occur in any order. We therefore randomly select the order for each pair of values, then find the difference d, then find the mean $\overline{d}$. We repeat that procedure many times, such as 1000, and we proceed to find the number of $\overline{d}$ values that are at least as extreme as the original value of $\overline{d}$ found from the original sample values.

Example: Using the sample data, we get $\overline{d} = 1.425$ lb. We use the randomization procedure to find the likelihood of getting a value $\overline{d} \geq 1.425$ (or at least as extreme as the value of 1.425 that was obtained) for this *right-tailed* test. Here is a typical result: With 1000 resamples, the mean of 1.425 or greater occurs 222 times so its likelihood is about 0.222. This is similar to the P-value $= 0.231$ found in Section 9-3. This shows that $\overline{d} = 1.425$ is not rare and can easily occur by chance, so it appears that there is no significant difference between measured weights and reported weights.

 **YOUR TURN.** Do Exercise 13 "Measured and Reported Weights."

Two Variances or Standard Deviations Section 9-4 presents methods for making inferences about two population variances (or standard deviations). For our resampling methods involving two variances or standard deviations, we will use these same two stipulations:

1. Let the first sample be the one with the larger standard deviation (or variance).

2. Use the test statistic format of $F = s_1^2 / s_2^2$.

EXAMPLE 5 **Resampling With Two Variances or Standard Deviations**

Example 1 in Section 9-4 tested the claim that the variation among male U.S. Army personnel weights did not change from the ANSUR I study in 1988 to the ANSUR II study in 2012, and that example used a 0.05 significance level. Here are the data used in that example after the two samples have been switched so that the first sample has the larger standard deviation.

ANSUR II 2012	90.8	86.1	101.1	76.9	63.0	98.4	83.5	65.1	111.5	78.0	
ANSUR I 1988	63.0	88.9	71.1	83.6	84.2	76.3	69.5	74.4	81.4	72.0	85.5	111.1

continued

Bootstrap Resampling with Two Standard Deviations or Two Variances The bootstrap method can be applied as follows: (1) Generate separate bootstrap samples from each of the two sets of sample data; (2) obtain the standard deviation from each of the bootstrap samples; (3) Using the two lists of *unsorted* standard deviations, divide the first list by the second list to obtain a list of ratios of the type s_1/s_2; (4) sort those ratios; (5) find the percentile values (such as $P_{2.5}$ and $P_{97.5}$) from the sorted list of ratios. If the confidence interval includes the ratio of 1 (indicating that $\sigma_1 = \sigma_2$), that is evidence that there is not a significant difference between σ_1 and σ_2. If the confidence interval does not include 1, that suggests that there is a significant difference between σ_1 and σ_2.

As of this writing, it is rare to find statistics software that does bootstrapping with two standard deviations or variances, but we can apply the bootstrap method using any software capable of bootstrapping one sample and generating standard deviations or variances. Statdisk, Minitab, and StatCrunch generate such bootstrap samples, and they can be used for the above procedure.

Example: Using the above procedure with the samples, a typical result is this 95% confidence interval: $0.67 < \sigma_1/\sigma_2 < 2.72$. Because the confidence interval does include the ratio of 1, conclude that there is not sufficient evidence to warrant rejection of the claim that the two standard deviations (or variances) are equal. It appears that the variation among weights of male U.S. Army personnel did not change from 1988 to 2012.

Randomization with Two Standard Deviations or Two Variances Randomization would first require that the two samples be combined into one big sample, random samples of the same sizes are then drawn without replacement, and the ratio s_1^2/s_2^2 is found. That process is repeated many times (such as 1000). We can then find the number of ratios s_1^2/s_2^2 that are at least as extreme as the ratio s_1^2/s_2^2 found from the original two samples. We can then determine whether the two variances (or standard deviations) are significantly different.

As of this writing, it is rare to find statistics software that does randomization with two standard deviations or variances.

TECH CENTER

Bootstrapping and Randomization – Two Samples
Access tech supplements, videos, and data sets at **www.TriolaStats.com**

Statdisk	Minitab	StatCrunch
1. Click **Resampling** in the top menu. 2. Select the desired type of bootstrapping or randomization from the dropdown menu. Options include: – **Bootstrap Two Proportions** – **Bootstrap Two Means** – **Randomization Two Proportions** – **Randomization Two Means** – **Randomization Matched Pairs** 3. Enter the required inputs which includes the desired number of resamplings. 4. Click **Evaluate**.	1. Click **Calc** in the top menu. 2. Select **Resampling** from dropdown menu. 3. Select the desired resampling function from the submenu: – **Bootstrapping for 2-Sample Means** – **Randomization Test for 2-Sample Means** 4. Enter the required inputs which includes the desired number of resamplings. 5. Click the **Options** button. For *randomization*, select the format of the alternative hypothesis. For *bootstrapping*, enter the desired confidence level. 6. Click **OK** twice. *TIP:* If bootstrapping and/or randomization is desired for two *proportions*, enter two columns of 0's and 1's that represent the two sample proportions, then proceed to use the bootstrapping and randomization functions for two means.	1. Click **Applets** in the top menu. 2. Select **Resampling** in the dropdown menu and select the desired randomization from the submenu. Options include: – **Randomization test for two proportions** – **Randomization test for two means** 3. Enter the required *Sample 1* and *Sample 2* data. 4. Click **Compute!** and the applet window will appear. 5. Click **1000 times** for 1000 resamplings. The results will be displayed. StatCrunch does not currently have a function for bootstrapping two proportions or two means.

TECH CENTER *continued*

Bootstrapping and Randomization – Two Samples
Access tech supplements, videos, and data sets at **www.TriolaStats.com**

TI-83/84 Plus Calculator	Excel	R
Not available.	Not available.	**R command not available at time of publication.** *R is rapidly evolving, and an updated list of statistical commands is available at TriolaStats.com.*

9-5 Basic Skills and Concepts

Statistical Literacy and Critical Thinking

1. Bootstrapping and Randomization When resampling data from two independent samples, what is the fundamental difference between bootstrapping and randomization?

2. Sampling Methods A student obtains a sample of responses to the question "Do you plan to take or have you taken a statistics course?" A second student obtains a sample of responses to the same question. The first student surveys only males at the same college, and the second student surveys only females at the same college. What is wrong with the samples? Can randomization be used to overcome the flaws of those samples?

3. Randomization with Commute Times Given the two samples of commute times (minutes) shown here, which of the following are randomizations of them?

Boston:	5	10	25	30	45
New York:	10	20	60		

a. Boston: 10 10 60. New York: 5 20 25 30 45.

b. Boston: 10 10 60 20 25. New York: 5 30 45.

c. Boston: 5 10 25 25 60. New York: 5 30 30 60.

d. Boston: 10 10 60. New York: 5 20 25 30 45.

e. Boston: 10 10 10 10 10. New York: 60 60 60.

4. Randomization vs *t* Test Two samples of commute times from Boston and New York are randomly selected and it is found that the samples sizes are $n_1 = 8$ and $n_2 = 12$ and each of the two samples appears to be from a population with a distribution that is dramatically far from normal. Which method is more likely to yield better results for testing $\mu_1 \neq \mu_2$: Hypothesis test using the *t* distribution (as in Section 9-2) or the resampling method?

Two Proportions. *In Exercises 5–8, use (a) randomization and (b) bootstrapping for the indicated exercise from Section 9-1. Compare the results to those obtained in the original exercise.*

5. Exercise 7 in Section 9-1 "Buttered Toast Drop"

6. Exercise 8 in Section 9-1 "Tennis Challenges"

7. Exercise 9 in Section 9-1 "Cell Phones and Handedness"

8. Exercise 10 in Section 9-1 "Denomination Effect"

Two Means. *In Exercises 9–12, use (a) randomization and (b) bootstrapping for the indicated exercise from Section 9-2. Compare the results to those obtained in the original exercise.*

9. **Exercise 17 in Section 9-2 "Are Weights Changing Over Time?"**

10. **Exercise 18 in Section 9-2 "Queues"**

11. **Exercise 19 in Section 9-2 "Regular Coke and Diet Coke"**

12. **Exercise 20 in Section 9-2 "Blanking Out on Tests"** (use randomization only.)

Matched Pairs. *In Exercises 13–16, use (a) randomization and (b) bootstrapping for the indicated exercise from Section 9-3. Compare the results to those obtained in the original exercise.*

13. **Exercise 5 in Section 9-3 "Measured and Reported Weights"**

14. **Exercise 6 in Section 9-3 "Do Men Talk Less than Women?"**

15. **Exercise 7 in Section 9-3 "The Freshman 15"**

16. **Exercise 8 in Section 9-3 "QWERTY vs Dvorak"**

9-5 Beyond the Basics

17. **Effect of the Number of Bootstrap Samples** Use the weights (lb) of regular Coke and diet Coke from Data Set 37 "Cola Weights and Volumes." Use resampling to find a 95% confidence interval estimate of the difference between the two population means. Use 1000 bootstrap samples, then use 10,000 resamples. Does the larger number of resamples have much of an effect on the results?

18. **Bootstrapping with Two Standard Deviations** Use the weights (lb) of regular Coke and diet Coke from Data Set 37 "Cola Weights and Volumes." Use bootstrap resamples to construct a 95% confidence interval estimate of the ratio of the two variances. What does the confidence interval suggest about the variation in the two populations?

Chapter Quick Quiz

1. **Identifying Hypotheses** In a randomized clinical trial of adults with an acute sore throat, 288 were treated with the drug dexamethasone and 102 of them experienced complete resolution; 277 were treated with a placebo and 75 of them experienced complete resolution (based on data from "Effect of Oral Dexamethasone Without Immediate Antibiotics vs Placebo on Acute Sore Throat in Adults," by Hayward et al., *Journal of the American Medical Association*). Identify the null and alternative hypotheses corresponding to the claim that patients treated with dexamethasone and patients given a placebo have the same rate of complete resolution.

2. **Test Values** Find the values of $\hat{p}_1$, $\hat{p}_2$, and the pooled proportion $\bar{p}$ obtained when testing the claim given in Exercise 1.

3. **P-Value** The test statistic of $z = 2.14$ is obtained when using the data from Exercise 1 and testing the claim that patients treated with dexamethasone and patients given a placebo have the same rate of complete resolution.

a. Find the *P*-value for the test.

b. If a significance level of 0.05 is used to test the claim, what should be concluded?

4. Confidence Interval When using the given sample results and the claim given in Exercise 1, the 95% confidence interval of $(0.00732, 0.159)$ is obtained.

a. Express the confidence interval in the format of an inequality that uses the symbol $<$.

b. What feature of the confidence interval is a basis for deciding whether there is a significant difference between the success rate in the treatment group and the success rate in the placebo group?

5. Coke and Diet Coke Data Set 37 "Cola Weights and Volumes" in Appendix B includes the weights (in pounds) of cola for a sample of cans of regular Coke ($n = 36$, $\bar{x} = 0.81682$ lb, $s = 0.00751$ lb) and the weights of cola for a sample of cans of Diet Coke ($n = 36$, $\bar{x} = 0.78479$ lb, $s = 0.00439$ lb).

a. Are the two samples independent or are they dependent? Explain.

b. If we want to test the claim that the weights of regular Coke and the weights of Diet Coke have the same mean, what is the value of the test statistic?

6. Variation Find the value of the test statistic used for testing the claim that the two samples from Exercise 5 are from populations having the same variation.

7. Body Temperatures Listed below are body temperatures from six different subjects measured at two different times in a day (from Data Set 5 "Body Temperatures" in Appendix B).

a. Are the two sets of data independent or dependent? Explain.

b. Identify the null and alternative hypotheses for using the sample data to test the claim that the differences between 8 AM temperatures and 12 AM temperatures are from a population with a mean equal to 0°F.

Temperature (°F) at 8 AM	98.2	97.4	97.8	98.4	97.6	96.2
Temperature (°F) at 12 AM	98.0	98.2	98.0	98.0	97.0	97.2

8. Body Temperatures Technology is used to test the claim that for the sample data from Exercise 7, the differences between 8 AM temperatures and 12 AM temperatures are from a population with a mean equal to 0°F. Technology provides this 95% confidence interval: $-0.82°F < \mu_d < 0.55°F$. What does this confidence interval suggest about the data?

9. True? Determine whether the following statement is true: When random samples of 250 men and 250 women are obtained and we want to test the claim that men and women have the same mean SAT scores, there is no need to confirm that the samples are from populations with normal distributions.

10. True? When we collect random samples to test the claim that the proportion of female statistics professors is equal to the proportion of female physics professors, there is a requirement that $np \geq 30$ and $nq \geq 30$.

Review Exercises

1. Denomination Effect In the article "The Denomination Effect" by Priya Raghubir and Joydeep Srivastava, *Journal of Consumer Research,* Vol. 36, researchers reported results from studies conducted to determine whether people have different spending characteristics when they have larger bills, such as a $20 bill, instead of smaller bills, such as twenty $1 bills. In one trial, 89 undergraduate business students from two different colleges were randomly assigned to two different groups. In the "dollar bill" group, 46 subjects were given dollar bills; the "quarter" group consisted of 43 subjects given quarters. All subjects from both groups were given a choice of keeping the money or buying gum or mints. The article includes the claim that "money in a large denomination is less likely to be spent relative to an equivalent amount in smaller denominations." Test that claim using a 0.05 significance level with the following sample data from the study.

	Group 1 Subjects Given $1 Bill	Group 2 Subjects Given 4 Quarters
Spent the money	$x_1 = 12$	$x_2 = 27$
Subjects in group	$n_1 = 46$	$n_2 = 43$

2. Denomination Effect Construct the confidence interval that could be used to test the claim in Exercise 1. What feature of the confidence interval leads to the same conclusion from Exercise 1?

3. Forecast and Actual Temperatures Listed below are actual temperatures (°F) along with the temperatures that were forecast five days earlier (data collected by the author). Use a 0.05 significance level to test the claim that differences between actual temperatures and temperatures forecast five days earlier are from a population with a mean of 0°F.

Actual Temperature (°F)	80	77	81	85	73	73	80	72	83	81
Temperature (°F) Forecast Five Days Earlier	80	80	79	80	79	82	76	73	77	83

4. Forecast and Actual Temperatures Construct the confidence interval that could be used to test the claim in Exercise 3. What feature of the confidence interval leads to the same conclusion from Exercise 3? Based on these results, does it appear that weather forecasters are doing a good job?

5. Smoking Cessation Programs Among 198 smokers who underwent a "sustained care" program, 51 were no longer smoking after six months. Among 199 smokers who underwent a "standard care" program, 30 were no longer smoking after six months (based on data from "Sustained Care Intervention and Postdischarge Smoking Cessation Among Hospitalized Adults," by Rigotti et al., *Journal of the American Medical Association*, Vol. 312, No. 7). We want to use a 0.01 significance level to test the claim that the rate of success for smoking cessation is greater with the sustained care program. Test the claim using a hypothesis test.

6. Smoking Cessation Programs

a. Construct the confidence interval that could be used to test the claim in Exercise 5. What feature of the confidence interval leads to the same conclusion from Exercise 5?

b. Does the difference between the success rate of the sustained care program and the standard care program appear to have practical significance?

c. Does the more successful program appear to have practical significance?

7. Seat Belts A study of seat belt use involved children who were hospitalized after motor vehicle crashes. For a group of 123 children who were wearing seat belts, the number of days in intensive care units (ICU) has a mean of 0.83 and a standard deviation of 1.77. For a group of 290 children who were not wearing seat belts, the number of days spent in ICUs has a mean of 1.39 and a standard deviation of 3.06 (based on data from "Morbidity Among Pediatric Motor Vehicle Crash Victims: The Effectiveness of Seat Belts," by Osberg and Di Scala, *American Journal of Public Health*, Vol. 82, No. 3). Use a 0.05 significance level to test the claim that children wearing seat belts have a lower mean length of time in an ICU than the mean for children not wearing seat belts.

8. Seat Belts Construct the confidence interval that could be used to test the claim in Exercise 7. What feature of the confidence interval leads to the same conclusion from Exercise 7?

9. Waist Circumferences Listed below are waist circumferences (mm) of randomly selected U.S. Army male personnel measured in 1988 (from Data Set 2 "ANSUR I 1988") and waist circumferences (mm) of different randomly selected U.S. Army male personnel measured in 2012 (from Data Set 3 "ANSUR II 2012"). Use a 0.05 significance level to test the claim that the differences between the pairs of data are from a population with a mean of 0 mm, indicating that there is no change. What is seriously wrong with this question?

Waist (1988)	808	852	729	841	825	903	874	935
Waist (2012)	787	938	933	986	946	748	934	802

10. Variation of Hospital Times Use the sample data given in Exercise 7 "Seat Belts" and test the claim that for children hospitalized after motor vehicle crashes, the numbers of days in intensive care units for those wearing seat belts and for those not wearing seat belts have the same variation. Use a 0.05 significance level.

Cumulative Review Exercises

In Exercises 1–10, based on the nature of the given data, do the following:

a. Pose a key question that is relevant to the given data.

b. Identify a procedure or tool from this chapter or the preceding chapters to address the key question from part (a).

c. Analyze the data and state a conclusion.

1. Video Games The graph below shows percentages of people aged 18–29 who say that they play video games often or sometimes (based on data from Pew Research Center).

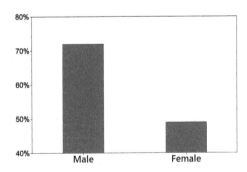

2. Video Games In a survey of subjects aged 18–29, subjects were asked if they play video games often or sometimes. Among 984 females, 49% answered "yes" (based on data from a Pew Research Center survey).

3. Video Games In a survey of subjects aged 18–29, subjects were asked if they play video games often or sometimes. Among 1017 males, 72% answered "yes." Among 984 females, 49% answered "yes" (based on data from a Pew Research Center survey).

4. IQ Scores of Twins Listed below are IQ scores of twins listed in Data Set 12 "IQ and Brain Size" in Appendix B. The data are pairs of IQ scores from ten different families.

First Born	96	87	101	103	127	101	93	94	97	113
Second Born	89	87	103	96	126	96	88	85	114	124

5. CD Sales Listed below are amounts of CD sales in billions of dollars (based on data from the Recording Industry Association of America). The amounts are listed in order by year beginning with the year 1999.

12.8	13.2	12.9	12.0	11.2	11.4	10.5	9.4	7.5	5.5
4.3	3.4	3.1	2.3	2.1	1.8	1.4	1.1	1.1	0.9

6. Eyewitness Accuracy of Police An experiment tested eyewitness memory of police one week after a non-stressful interrogation of a cooperative suspect and one week after a stressful interrogation of an uncooperative and belligerent suspect. The numbers of details recalled one week after the incident were recorded, and the summary statistics are given below (based on data from "Eyewitness Memory of Police Trainees for Realistic Role Plays," by Yuille et al., *Journal of Applied Psychology*, Vol. 79, No. 6). Higher values for x represent better memory recall.

Non-stressful interrogation: $n = 40, \bar{x} = 53.3, s = 11.6$

Stressful interrogation: $n = 40, \bar{x} = 45.4, s = 13.2$

7. Deaths from Risk Factors Here are estimated numbers of global deaths for common risk factors in a recent year: alcohol (2.3 million), drug use (0.5 million), total pollution (9.2 million), road accidents (1.4 million), tobacco smoking (7.2 million), malnutrition (1.4 million), war and murder (0.4 million).

8. Heights of Supermodels Adult women from the general population have a mean height of 162 cm. Listed below are the heights (cm) for the simple random sample of female supermodels Lima, Bundchen, Ambrosio, Ebanks, Iman, Rubik, Kurkova, Kerr, Kroes, Swanepoel, Prinsloo, Hosk, Kloss, Robinson, Heatherton, and Refaeli.

178 177 176 174 175 178 175 178 178 177 180 176 180 178 180 176

9. Daily 4 Lottery Numbers The table below summarizes results from 250 drawings for the California Daily 4 lottery game.

Number Selected	0	1	2	3	4	5	6	7	8	9
Frequency	101	90	115	105	92	102	82	114	86	113

10. Manatees Listed below are numbers of registered pleasure boats in Florida (tens of thousands) and the numbers of manatee fatalities from encounters with boats in Florida for each of several recent years.

Pleasure Boats	99	99	97	95	90	90	87	90	90
Manatee Fatalities	92	73	90	97	83	88	81	73	68

Technology Project

Queues Listed on the next page are ten pairs of waiting line times (sec) from Data Set 30 "Queues" in Appendix B. The first row lists actual wait times of drivers in two lines at a Delaware vehicle inspection station, and the second row lists modeled times for the same drivers assuming that they used a single common waiting line for the same two inspection stations.

a. Do the differences appear to satisfy the requirement of being from a normally distributed population or $n > 30$?

b. Use a 95% confidence level and use the methods of this chapter to construct a confidence interval for testing the claim that there is no difference in wait times between the two-line configuration and the single-line configuration.

c. Use a 95% confidence level and use the bootstrap method to construct a confidence interval for testing the claim that there is no difference in wait times between the two-line configuration and the single-line configuration.

d. Repeat Part (a) using all 85 of the two-line wait times and single-line wait times listed in Data Set 30 "Queues" from Appendix B.

e. Repeat Part (b) using all 85 of the two-line wait times and single-line wait times listed in Data Set 30 "Queues" from Appendix B.

f. Repeat Part (c) using all 85 of the two-line wait times and single-line wait times listed in Data Set 30 "Queues" from Appendix B.

g. What do you conclude?

Two Lines	113	225	270	393	506	574	675	579	351	347
Single Line	113	225	270	390	504	574	610	455	482	346

Big (or Very Large) Data Project

Refer to Data Set 45 "Births in New York." Separate the 465,506 birth weights (grams) into two samples according to gender. Use a 0.05 significance level to test the claim that males have a mean birth weight that is greater than the mean birth weight of females.

FROM DATA TO DECISION

What Is the Effect of the NFL Overtime Rule Change?

The National Football League (NFL) changed the overtime rules in 2012. Before 2012, games tied at the end of regulation play continued with a coin toss to determine which team would receive the ball, then "sudden death" was put into place so that the first team that scored won the game. Beginning in 2012, that rule was modified so that if a team scored with a field goal, the opposing team would get possession of the ball in an attempt to either tie or win. The goal was to make the overtime rules more fair. Listed in the table below (from the Chapter 5 Problem) are results for games played before and after the overtime rule change in 2012. (The data for the games after 2012 are current up to the time of this writing.) The table does not include games that ended in a tie after the overtime period ended.

TABLE 5-1 NFL Games Decided in Overtime

	Before 2012	Since 2012
Team Won Overtime Coin Toss and Won Game	252	67
Team Won Overtime Coin Toss and Lost Game	208	54

Analysis

1. Is there a significant difference between win rates by overtime coin toss winners before 2012 and after 2012?

2. Was the overtime rule change effective in improving the fairness of the game by eliminating the advantage that the coin toss could give?

3. Was the pre-2012 win rate by coin toss winners significantly better than 50%, so that the rule change was really necessary?

4. Is the post-2012 game win rate by coin toss winners significantly better than 50%?

5. Bottom line: Did the 2012 overtime rule change accomplish anything, or was it a waste of time and effort?

Cooperative Group Activities

1. Out-of-class activity Exercise 7 in Section 9-1 included data from a *MythBusters* episode involving a drop test of buttered toast and toast that was marked with an X on one side (but not buttered). Construct your own experiment to replicate the one televised on *MythBusters*. What do you conclude about the results?

2. Out-of-class activity Working in groups of three or four students, each group should make observations and collect data to determine whether there is a cost difference between genders for a particular product or service, such as prices of haircuts or the cost of dry cleaning men's and women's pants or shirts.

3. Out-of-class activity Pedometers are used to count the number of steps that a person walks. Those steps are often converted to distances, often by calibrating the pedometer. High school and college running tracks are typically either 400 meters in length or 440 yards in length. Use such a track with a known length and conduct an experiment to test the accuracy of a pedometer. Some pedometers are inexpensive, such as less than $1. Others, such as a Fitbit, are much more expensive. Also, there are free smartphone apps that can function as pedometers.

4. Out-of-class activity Exercise 17 in Section 9-1 is based on observations of cars with only rear license plates in states with laws that require both front and rear license plates. Work together in groups of three or four and collect data in your state. Use a hypothesis test to test the claim that in your state, the proportion of cars with only rear license plates is the same as the proportion of 239/2049 from Connecticut. (Connecticut students can compare the proportion they get to the proportion of 239/2049 obtained by the author.)

5. Out-of-class activity Survey couples and record the number of credit cards each person has. Analyze the paired data to determine whether the males in couple relationships have more credit cards than the females. Try to identify reasons for any discrepancy.

6. Out-of-class activity Measure and record the height of the male and the height of the female from each of several different couples. Estimate the mean of the differences. Compare the result to the difference between the mean height of men and the mean height of women included in Data Set 1 "Body Data" in Appendix B. Do the results suggest that height is a factor when people select couple partners?

7. Out-of-class activity Are estimates influenced by anchoring numbers? Refer to the related Chapter 3 Cooperative Group Activity on page 140. In Chapter 3 we noted that, according to author John Rubin, when people must estimate a value, their estimate is often "anchored" to (or influenced by) a preceding number. In that Chapter 3 activity, some subjects were asked to quickly estimate the value of $8 \times 7 \times 6 \times 5 \times 4 \times 3 \times 2 \times 1$, and others were asked to quickly estimate the value of $1 \times 2 \times 3 \times 4 \times 5 \times 6 \times 7 \times 8$. In Chapter 3, we could compare the two sets of results by using statistics (such as the mean) and graphs (such as boxplots). The methods of this chapter now allow us to compare the results with a formal hypothesis test. Specifically, collect your own sample data and test the claim that when we begin with larger numbers (as in $8 \times 7 \times 6$), our estimates tend to be larger.

8. In-class activity Divide into groups according to gender, with about 10 or 12 students in each group. Each group member should record his or her pulse rate by counting the number of heartbeats in 1 minute, then the group statistics $(n, \bar{x}, s)$ should be calculated. The groups should test the null hypothesis of no difference between their mean pulse rate and the mean of the pulse rates for the population from which subjects of the same gender were selected for Data Set 1 "Body Data" in Appendix B.

9. Out-of-class activity Randomly select a sample of male students and a sample of female students and ask each selected person a yes/no question, such as whether they support a death penalty for people convicted of murder, or whether they believe that the federal government should fund stem cell research. Record the response, the gender of the respondent, and the gender of the person asking the question. Use a formal hypothesis test to determine whether there is a difference between the proportions of *yes* responses from males and females. Also, determine whether the responses appear to be influenced by the gender of the interviewer.

10. Out-of-class activity Construct a short survey of just a few questions, including a question asking the subject to report his or her height. After the subject has completed the survey, measure the subject's height (without shoes) using an accurate measuring system. Record the gender, reported height, and measured height of each subject. Do male subjects appear to exaggerate their heights? Do female subjects appear to exaggerate their heights? Do the errors for males appear to have the same mean as the errors for females?

11. In-class activity Without using any measuring device, ask each student to draw a line believed to be 3 in. long and another line believed to be 3 cm long. Then use rulers to measure and record the lengths of the lines drawn. Record the errors along with the genders of the students making the estimates. Test the claim that when estimating the length of a 3-in. line, the mean error from males is equal to the mean error from females. Also, do the results show that we have a better understanding of the British system of measurement (inches) than the SI system (centimeters)?

12. Out-of-class activity Obtain simple random samples of cars in the student and faculty parking lots, and test the claim that students and faculty have the same proportions of foreign cars.

13. Out-of-class activity Obtain sample data to test the claim that in the college library, science books have a mean age that is less than the mean age of fiction novels.

14. Out-of-class activity Conduct experiments and collect data to test the claim that there are no differences in taste between ordinary tap water and different brands of bottled water.

15. Out-of-class activity Collect sample data and test the claim that people who exercise tend to have pulse rates that are lower than those who do not exercise.

16. Out-of-class activity Collect sample data and test the claim that the proportion of female students who smoke is equal to the proportion of male students who smoke.

17. Out-of-class activity Collect sample data to test the claim that women carry more pocket change than men.

10

CORRELATION AND REGRESSION

CHAPTER PROBLEM

Are Powerball Ticket Lines Longer When the Jackpot is Higher?

Table 10-1 lists paired data consisting of amounts of Power-ball lottery jackpots (millions of dollars) and numbers of lottery tickets sold (millions). Many of us have seen that ticket lines for lotteries often grow large when the jackpot is high. Is that just anecdotal evidence, or are there data to support the theory that more lottery tickets are sold when the jackpot is higher? We will analyze the data in Table 10-1 to address questions such as these:

- Is there a *correlation* between lottery jackpot amounts and numbers of tickets sold?

- If there is a correlation between lottery jackpot amounts and numbers of tickets sold, can we describe it with an equation so that we can predict the numbers of tickets sold when given the lottery jackpot amount?

- Will increasing the lottery jackpot cause an increase in sales of lottery tickets?

506

TABLE 10-1 Powerball Tickets Sold and Jackpot Amounts

Jackpot	334	127	300	227	202	180	164	145	255
Tickets	54	16	41	27	23	18	18	16	26

When considering the first two of the preceding questions, it is important to recognize that a correlation between two variables does not necessarily imply that one of the variables is the *cause* of the other. One of the most memorable quotes from introductory statistics courses is that "correlation does not imply causality." Maybe increasing a lottery jackpot will cause an increase in sales of lottery tickets, but there is no way that we can make that conclusion based on a statistical analysis.

The last of the preceding questions involves at least as much common sense as statistical knowledge. Like every topic in statistics, common sense or critical thinking proves to be an indispensable tool.

CHAPTER OBJECTIVES

A major focus of this chapter is to analyze *paired* sample data. In Section 9-3 we considered sample data consisting of matched pairs, but the goal in Section 9-3 was to make inferences about the *mean of the differences* from the matched pairs. In this chapter we again consider paired sample data, but the objective is fundamentally different from that of Section 9-3. In this chapter we present methods for determining whether there is a *correlation,* or association, between two variables. For linear correlations, we can identify an equation of a straight line that best fits the data, and we can use that equation to predict the value of one variable given the value of the other variable. Here are the chapter objectives:

10-1 Correlation

- Use paired data to find the value of the linear correlation coefficient *r*.

- Determine whether there is sufficient evidence to support a conclusion that there is a linear correlation between two variables.

- Use the resampling method of randomization to test a null hypothesis of no correlation.

10-2 Regression

- Use paired sample data to find the equation of the regression line.

- Find the best predicted value of a variable given some value of the other variable.

10-3 Prediction Intervals and Variation

- Use paired sample data to determine the value of the coefficient of determination r^2, and to interpret that value.

- Use a given value of one variable to find a prediction interval for the other variable.

10-4 Multiple Regression

- Interpret results from technology to determine whether a multiple regression equation is suitable for making predictions.

- Compare results from different combinations of predictor variables and identify the combination that results in the best multiple regression equation.

10-5 Nonlinear Regression

- Use paired data to identify the linear, quadratic, logarithmic, exponential, and power models.

- Determine which model best fits the paired data.

10-1 | Correlation

Key Concept In Part 1 we introduce the *linear correlation coefficient r*, which is a number that measures how well paired sample data fit a straight-line pattern when graphed. We use the sample of paired data (sometimes called **bivariate data**) to find the value of r (usually using technology), and then we use that value to decide whether there is a linear correlation between the two variables. In this section we consider only *linear* relationships, which means that when graphed in a scatterplot, the points approximate a *straight-line* pattern. In Part 2, we discuss methods for conducting a formal hypothesis test that can be used to decide whether there is a linear correlation between all population values for the two variables. Finally, in Part 3 we discuss a method of randomization whereby we resample many times to test the null hypothesis of no correlation.

PART 1 | Basic Concepts of Correlation

We begin with the basic definition of *correlation,* a term commonly used in the context of an association between two variables.

> **DEFINITIONS**
>
> A **correlation** exists between two variables when the values of one variable are somehow associated with the values of the other variable.
>
> A **linear correlation** exists between two variables when there is a correlation and the plotted points of paired data result in a pattern that can be approximated by a straight line.

Table 10-1, for example, includes paired sample data consisting of lottery jackpot amounts and numbers of tickets sold for nine different Powerball lotteries. We will determine whether there is a linear correlation between the variable x (jackpot amount) and the variable y (number of tickets sold). Instead of blindly jumping into the calculation of the linear correlation coefficient r, it is wise to first *explore* the data.

Explore!

Because it is always wise to explore sample data before applying a formal statistical procedure, we should use a scatterplot to graph the paired data in Table 10-1 and observe if there is a distinct pattern in the plotted points. (Scatterplots were first introduced in Section 2-4.) The scatterplot is shown in Figure 10-1 and there does appear to be a distinct pattern of increasing Powerball ticket sales corresponding to increasing jackpot amounts. There do not appear to be any outliers, which are data points that are far away from the other data points.

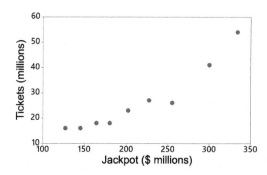

FIGURE 10-1   Scatterplot from Table 10-1

Interpreting Scatterplots

Figure 10-2 shows four scatterplots with different characteristics.

■ Figure 10-2(a): Distinct straight-line, or linear, pattern. We say that there is a *positive* linear correlation between x and y, since as the x values increase, the corresponding y values also increase.

■ Figure 10-2(b): Distinct straight-line, or linear pattern. We say that there is a *negative* linear correlation between x and y, since as the x values increase, the corresponding y values decrease.

■ Figure 10-2(c): No distinct pattern, which suggests that there is no correlation between x and y.

■ Figure 10-2(d): Distinct pattern suggesting a correlation between x and y, but the pattern is not that of a straight line.

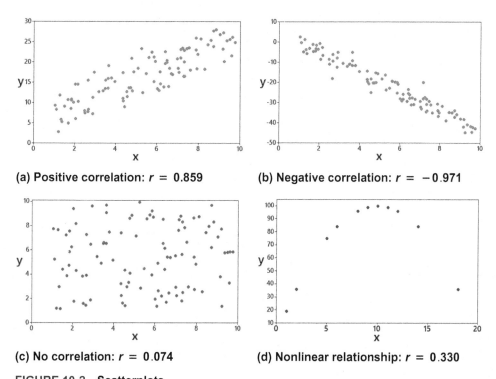

(a) Positive correlation: $r = 0.859$

(b) Negative correlation: $r = -0.971$

(c) No correlation: $r = 0.074$

(d) Nonlinear relationship: $r = 0.330$

FIGURE 10-2   Scatterplots

Measure the Strength of the Linear Correlation with r

Because conclusions based on visual examinations of scatterplots are largely subjective, we need more objective measures. We use the linear correlation coefficient r, which is a number that measures the strength of the linear association between the two variables.

DEFINITION

The **linear correlation coefficient** r measures the strength of the linear correlation between the paired quantitative x values and y values in a *sample*. The linear correlation coefficient r is computed by using Formula 10-1 or Formula 10-2, included in the following Key Elements box. [The linear correlation coefficient is sometimes referred to as the **Pearson product moment correlation coefficient** in honor of Karl Pearson (1857–1936), who originally developed it.]

Because the linear correlation coefficient r is calculated using sample data, it is a sample statistic used to measure the strength of the linear correlation between x and y. If we had every pair of x and y values from an entire population, the result of Formula 10-1 or Formula 10-2 would be a population parameter, represented by ρ (Greek letter rho).

KEY ELEMENTS

Calculating and Interpreting the Linear Correlation Coefficient r

Objective

Determine whether there is a linear correlation between two variables.

Notation for the Linear Correlation Coefficient

n	number of *pairs* of sample data.
Σ	denotes addition of the items indicated.
Σx	sum of all x values.
Σx^2	indicates that each x value should be squared and then those squares added.
$(\Sigma x)^2$	indicates that the x values should be added and the total then squared. Avoid confusing Σx^2 and $(\Sigma x)^2$.
Σxy	indicates that each x value should first be multiplied by its corresponding y value. After obtaining all such products, find their sum.
r	linear correlation coefficient for *sample* data.
ρ	linear correlation coefficient for a *population* of paired data.

Requirements

Given any collection of sample paired quantitative data, the linear correlation coefficient r can always be computed, but the following requirements should be satisfied when using the sample paired data to make a conclusion about linear correlation in the corresponding population of paired data.

1. The sample of paired (x, y) data is a simple random sample of quantitative data. (It is important that the sample data have not been collected using some inappropriate method, such as using a voluntary response sample.)

2. Visual examination of the scatterplot must confirm that the points approximate a straight-line pattern.*

3. Because results can be strongly affected by the presence of outliers, any outliers must be removed if they are known to be errors. The effects of any other outliers should be considered by calculating r with and without the outliers included.*

*Note: Requirements 2 and 3 above are simplified attempts at checking this formal requirement: The pairs of (x, y) data must have a **bivariate normal distribution.** Normal distributions are discussed in Chapter 6, but this assumption basically requires that for any fixed value of x, the corresponding values of y have a distribution that is approximately normal, and for any fixed value of y, the values of x have a distribution that is approximately normal. This requirement is usually difficult to check, so for now, we will use Requirements 2 and 3 as listed above.

DETOUR **Alternatives** If the first requirement is violated and the data have been collected using an inappropriate method, it is likely that nothing can be done to conduct a reasonable analysis of correlation. If other requirements are violated, possible alternatives include using rank correlation (Section 13-6) or a randomization test, which is discussed later in Part 3 of this section.

Formulas for Calculating *r*

FORMULA 10-1

$$r = \frac{n(\Sigma xy) - (\Sigma x)(\Sigma y)}{\sqrt{n(\Sigma x^2) - (\Sigma x)^2}\sqrt{n(\Sigma y^2) - (\Sigma y)^2}} \quad \text{(Good format for calculations)}$$

FORMULA 10-2

$$r = \frac{\Sigma(z_x z_y)}{n - 1} \quad \text{(Good format for understanding)}$$

where z_x denotes the z score for an individual sample value x and z_y is the z score for the corresponding sample value y.

Rounding the Linear Correlation Coefficient *r*

Round the linear correlation coefficient r to three decimal places so that its value can be directly compared to critical values in Table A-6.

Interpreting the Linear Correlation Coefficient *r*

- **Using P-Value from Technology to Interpret r:** Use the P-value and significance level α as follows:

  P-value $\leq \alpha$: Supports the claim of a linear correlation.

  P-value $> \alpha$: Does not support the claim of a linear correlation.

- **Using Table A-6 to Interpret r:** Consider critical values from Table A-6 or technology as being both positive and negative, draw a graph similar to Figure 10-3 shown below and used in Example 4 on page 516, and then use the following decision criteria:

  Correlation If the computed linear correlation coefficient r lies in the left tail at or below the leftmost critical value or if it lies in the right tail at or above the rightmost critical value (that is, $|r| \geq$ critical value), conclude that there is sufficient evidence to support the claim of a linear correlation.

  No Correlation If the computed linear correlation coefficient lies *between* the two critical values (that is, $|r| <$ critical value), conclude that there is not sufficient evidence to support the claim of a linear correlation.

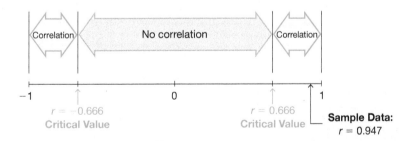

FIGURE 10-3   Critical *r* Values and the Computed *r* Value

CAUTION Remember, the methods of this section apply to a *linear* correlation. If you conclude that there does not appear to be a linear correlation, it is possible that there might be some other association that is not linear, as in Figure 10-2(d). Always generate a scatterplot to see relationships that might not be linear.

Properties of the Linear Correlation Coefficient *r*

1. The value of *r* is always between −1 and 1 inclusive. That is, $-1 \leq r \leq 1$.

2. If all values of either variable are converted to a different scale, the value of *r* does not change.

3. The value of *r* is not affected by the choice of *x* or *y*. Interchange all *x* values and *y* values, and the value of *r* will not change.

4. *r* measures the strength of a *linear* relationship. It is not designed to measure the strength of a relationship that is not linear [as in Figure 10-2(d)].

5. *r* is very sensitive to outliers in the sense that a single outlier could dramatically affect its value.

Calculating the Linear Correlation Coefficient *r*

The following three examples illustrate three different methods for finding the value of the linear correlation coefficient *r*, but you need to use only one method. *The use of technology (as in Example 1) is strongly recommended.* If manual calculations are absolutely necessary, Formula 10-1 is recommended (as in Example 2). If a better understanding of *r* is desired, Formula 10-2 is recommended (as in Example 3).

CP ▶ **EXAMPLE 1** Finding *r* Using Technology

Use technology to find the value of the linear correlation coefficient *r* for the Powerball jackpot amounts and numbers of tickets listed in Table 10-1.

TABLE 10-1 Powerball Tickets Sold and Jackpot Amounts

Jackpot	334	127	300	227	202	180	164	145	255
Tickets	54	16	41	27	23	18	18	16	26

SOLUTION

The value of *r* will be automatically calculated with software or a calculator. See the accompanying technology displays showing that $r = 0.947$ (rounded to three decimal places).

Statdisk

```
Correlation Results:
Correlation Coeff, r:  0.94735
Critical r:            ±0.66638
P-Value (two-tailed):  0.00010
```

Minitab

```
Correlations
                  Jackpot
Tickets            0.947
```

StatCrunch

```
Sample size: 9
R (correlation coefficient) = 0.94734912
R-sq = 0.89747036
Estimate of error standard deviation: 4.4372227
```

XLSTAT

Variables	Jackpot	Tickets
Jackpot	1	0.947
Tickets	0.947	1

TI-83/84 Plus

```
NORMAL FLOAT AUTO REAL RADIAN MP

        LinRegTTest
y=a+bx
β≠0 and ρ≠0
↑df=7
  a=-10.87168641
  b=0.1741702056
  s=4.437222696
  r²=0.8974703628
  r=0.947349124
```

JMP

Summary Statistics				
	Value	Lower 95%	Upper 95%	Signif. Prob
Correlation	0.947349	0.763736	0.989145	0.0001*
Covariance	865.8194			
Count	9			

SPSS

Correlations

		Jackpot	Tickets
Jackpot	Pearson Correlation	1	.947**
	Sig. (2-tailed)		.000
	N	9	9
Tickets	Pearson Correlation	.947**	1
	Sig. (2-tailed)	.000	
	N	9	9

**. Correlation is significant at the 0.01 level (2-tailed).

▶ **YOUR TURN.** Do Exercise 13 "Powerball Jackpots and Tickets Sold."

CP ▶ **EXAMPLE 2** Finding *r* Using Formula 10-1

Use Formula 10-1 to find the value of the linear correlation coefficient *r* for the Powerball jackpot amounts and numbers of tickets listed in Table 10-1.

SOLUTION

Using Formula 10-1, the value of *r* is calculated as shown below. Here, the variable *x* is used for the jackpot amount, and the variable *y* is used for the numbers of lottery tickets. Because there are 9 pairs of data, $n = 9$, and the other required values are computed in Table 10-2.

TABLE 10-2 Calculating *r* with Formula 10-1

x (Jackpot)	y (Tickets)	x^2	y^2	xy
334	54	111,556	2916	18,036
127	16	16,129	256	2032
300	41	90,000	1681	12,300
227	27	51,529	729	6129
202	23	40,804	529	4646
180	18	32,400	324	3240
164	18	26,896	324	2952
145	16	21,025	256	2320
255	26	65,025	676	6630
$\Sigma x = 1934$	$\Sigma y = 239$	$\Sigma x^2 = 455,364$	$\Sigma y^2 = 7691$	$\Sigma xy = 58,285$

Using Formula 10-1 with the paired data from Table 10-1, *r* is calculated as follows:

$$r = \frac{n\Sigma xy - (\Sigma x)(\Sigma y)}{\sqrt{n(\Sigma x^2) - (\Sigma x)^2}\sqrt{n(\Sigma y^2) - (\Sigma y)^2}}$$

$$= \frac{9(58,285) - (1934)(239)}{\sqrt{9(455,364) - (1934)^2}\sqrt{9(7691) - (239)^2}}$$

$$= \frac{62,339}{\sqrt{357,920}\sqrt{12,098}} = 0.947$$

▶ **YOUR TURN.** Do Exercise 13 "Powerball Jackpots and Tickets Sold."

Speeding Out-of-Towners Ticketed More?

Are police more likely to issue a ticket to a speeding driver who is out-of-town than to a local driver? George Mason University researchers Michael Makowsky and Thomas Stratmann addressed this question by examining more than 60,000 warnings and tickets issued by Massachusetts police in one year. They found that out-of-town drivers from Massachusetts were 10% more likely to be ticketed than local drivers, and the 10% figure rose to 20% for out-of-state drivers. They also found a statistical association between a town's finances and speeding tickets. When compared to local drivers, out-of-town drivers had a 37% greater chance of being ticketed when speeding in a town in which voters had rejected a proposition to raise taxes more than the 2.5% amount allowed by the state levy limit.

CP)─ **EXAMPLE 3** Finding *r* Using Formula 10-2

Use Formula 10-2 to find the value of the linear correlation coefficient *r* for the Powerball jackpot amounts and numbers of tickets listed in Table 10-1.

SOLUTION

If manual calculations are absolutely necessary, Formula 10-1 is much easier than Formula 10-2, but Formula 10-2 has the advantage of making it easier to *understand* how *r* works. (See the *rationale* for *r* discussed later in this section.) As in Example 2, the variable *x* is used for the jackpot amount, and the variable *y* is used for the numbers of lottery tickets sold. In Formula 10-2, each sample value is replaced by its corresponding *z* score. For example, using unrounded numbers, the jackpots have a mean of $\bar{x} = 214.8889$ and a standard deviation of $s_x = 70.5061$, so the first *x* value of 334 is converted to a *z* score of 1.6894, as shown here:

$$z_x = \frac{x - \bar{x}}{s_x} = \frac{334 - 214.8889}{70.5061} = 1.6894$$

Table 10-3 lists the *z* scores for all of the jackpot amounts (see the third column) and the *z* scores for all of the numbers of tickets (see the fourth column). The last column of Table 10-3 lists the products $z_x \cdot z_y$.

TABLE 10-3 Calculating *r* with Formula 10-2

x (Jackpot)	*y* (Tickets)	z_x	z_y	$z_x \cdot z_y$
334	54	1.6894	2.1172	3.57680
127	16	−1.2465	−0.8143	1.01502
300	41	1.2071	1.1143	1.34507
227	27	0.1718	0.0343	0.00589
202	23	−0.1828	−0.2743	0.05014
180	18	−0.4948	−0.6600	0.32657
164	18	−0.7218	−0.6600	0.47639
145	16	−0.9912	−0.8143	0.80713
255	26	0.5689	−0.0429	−0.02441
				$\Sigma z_x \cdot z_y = 7.57862$

Using $\Sigma (z_x \cdot z_y) = 7.57862$ from Table 10-3, the value of *r* is calculated by using Formula 10-2, as shown below.

$$r = \frac{\Sigma (z_x \cdot z_y)}{n - 1} = \frac{7.57862}{9 - 1} = 0.947$$

▶**YOUR TURN.** Do Exercise 13 "Powerball Jackpots and Tickets Sold."

Is There a Linear Correlation?

We know from the preceding three examples that the value of the linear correlation coefficient is $r = 0.947$ for the data in Table 10-1. We now proceed to interpret the meaning of $r = 0.947$ from the nine pairs of data listed in Table 10-1, and our goal in this section is to decide whether there appears to be a linear correlation between lottery jackpot amounts and numbers of tickets sold. Using the criteria given in the preceding Key Elements box, we can base our interpretation on a *P*-value or a critical value from Table A-6. (See the criteria for "Interpreting the Linear Correlation Coefficient *r*" given in the preceding Key Elements box on page 511.)

(CP) **EXAMPLE 4** Is There a Linear Correlation?

Using the value of $r = 0.947$ for the nine pairs of data in Table 10-1 and using a significance level of 0.05, is there sufficient evidence to support a claim that there is a linear correlation between Powerball jackpot amounts and numbers of tickets sold?

SOLUTION

REQUIREMENT CHECK The data are a simple random sample, so the first requirement is satisfied. The second requirement of a scatterplot showing a straight-line pattern is satisfied. See the scatterplot in Figure 10-1 on page 509. The scatterplot of Figure 10-1 also shows that the third requirement of no outliers is satisfied. ☑

We can base our conclusion about correlation on either the P-value obtained from technology or the critical value found in Table A-6. (See the criteria for "Interpreting the Linear Correlation Coefficient r" given in the preceding Key Elements box.)

■ **Using P-Value from Technology to Interpret r:** Use the P-value and significance level α as follows:

P-value $\leq \alpha$: Supports the claim of a linear correlation.

P-value $> \alpha$: Does not support the claim of a linear correlation.

The Statdisk display shows that the P-value is 0.0001. Because that P-value is less than or equal to the significance level of 0.05, we conclude that *there is sufficient evidence to support the conclusion that there is a linear correlation between Powerball lottery jackpot amounts and numbers of tickets sold.*

Statdisk

```
Correlation Results:
Correlation Coeff, r:   0.94735
Critical r:             ±0.66638
P-Value (two-tailed):   0.00010
```

■ **Using Table A-6 to Interpret r:** Consider critical values from Table A-6 as being both positive and negative, and draw a graph similar to Figure 10-3 on the next page. For the 9 pairs of data in Table 10-1, Table A-6 yields a critical value of $r = 0.666$; technology yields a critical value of $r = 0.666$. We can now compare the computed value of $r = 0.947$ to the critical values of $r = \pm 0.666$, as shown in Figure 10-3.

Correlation If the computed linear correlation coefficient r lies in the left or right tail region at or beyond the critical value for that tail, conclude that there is sufficient evidence to support the claim of a linear correlation.

No Correlation If the computed linear correlation coefficient lies between the two critical values, conclude that there is not sufficient evidence to support the claim of a linear correlation.

Because Figure 10-3 shows that the computed value of $r = 0.947$ lies beyond the upper critical value, we conclude that *there is sufficient evidence to support the claim of a linear correlation between Powerball jackpot amounts and numbers of lottery tickets sold.*

continued

Teacher Evaluations Correlate with Grades

Student evaluations of faculty are often used to measure teaching effectiveness. Many studies reveal a correlation, with higher student grades being associated with higher faculty evaluations. One study at Duke University involved student evaluations collected before and after final grades were assigned. The study showed that "grade expectations or received grades caused a change in the way students perceived their teacher and the quality of instruction." It was noted that with student evaluations, "the incentives for faculty to manipulate their grading policies in order to enhance their evaluations increase." It was concluded that "the ultimate consequence of such manipulations is the degradation of the quality of education in the United States." (See "Teacher Course Evaluations and Student Grades: An Academic Tango," by Valen Johnson, *Chance*, Vol. 15, No. 3.)

Go Figure

300,000: The average number of items in a home in America.

It appears that there is a linear correlation between lottery jackpot amounts and numbers of tickets sold. It appears that higher jackpots correspond to more tickets sold. In addition to the numbers, common sense and critical thinking also support this finding.

Although we have found a linear correlation, we should not conclude that one of the variables is a *cause* of the other. It is reasonable to believe that larger jackpots *cause* higher ticket sales, but that belief is not justified by the statistical analysis. Correlation does not imply causation.

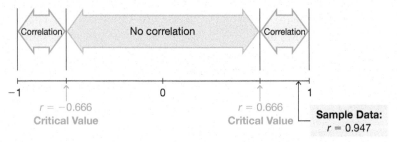

FIGURE 10-3 Critical *r* Values and the Computed *r* Value

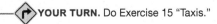
YOUR TURN. Do Exercise 15 "Taxis."

EXAMPLE 5 Spurious Correlation

Table 10-4 lists paired data consisting of per capita consumption of margarine (pounds) in the United States and the divorce rate in Maine (divorces per 1000 people in Maine). Each pair of data is from a different year. The data are from the U.S. Census Bureau and the U.S. Department of Agriculture. Is there a linear correlation? What do you conclude?

TABLE 10-4 U.S. Margarine Consumption and Divorces in Maine

Margarine	8.2	7.0	6.5	5.3	5.2	4.0	4.6	4.5	4.2	3.7
Divorces	5.0	4.7	4.6	4.4	4.3	4.1	4.2	4.2	4.2	4.1

SOLUTION

Here are the key points about the data in Table 10-4:

- The requirements appear to be satisfied.
- A scatterplot shows a very clear pattern of points that is close to a straight-line pattern, and there are no outliers.
- The linear correlation coefficient r is equal to 0.993.
- The P-value is 0.000.
- The critical values are $r = \pm 0.632$ (assuming a 0.05 significance level).

Based on these results, we should support a claim that there is a linear correlation between margarine consumption and the divorce rate in Maine. But, come on! Common sense strongly suggests that there is no real association between those two variables. It would be totally ridiculous to argue that one of the variables is the cause of the other. Statistics is so much more than blindly running data through formulas and procedures—it requires *critical thinking*!

YOUR TURN. Do Exercise 25 "Car Sales and the Super Bowl."

DEFINITION

A **spurious correlation** is a correlation that doesn't have an actual association, as in Example 5.

Spurious correlations will become more common with the increased use of big data, and they are more likely to occur with time-series data that have similar trends.

Interpreting *r*: Explained Variation

If we conclude that there is a linear correlation between x and y, we can find a linear equation that expresses y in terms of x, and that equation can be used to predict values of y for given values of x. In Section 10-2 we will describe a procedure for finding such equations and show how to predict values of y when given values of x. But a predicted value of y will not necessarily be the exact result that occurs because in addition to x, there are other factors affecting y, such as random variation and other characteristics not included in the study. In Section 10-3 we will present a rationale and more details about this principle:

The value of r^2 is the proportion of the variation in y that is explained by the linear relationship between x and y.

CP **EXAMPLE 6** **Explained Variation**

Using the 9 pairs of data from Table 10-1 included with the Chapter Problem, we get a linear correlation coefficient of $r = 0.947$. What proportion of the variation in the numbers of tickets sold can be explained by the variation in jackpot amounts?

SOLUTION

With $r = 0.947$, we get $r^2 = 0.897$.

INTERPRETATION

We conclude that 0.897 (or about 90%) of the variation in the numbers of tickets sold can be explained by the linear relationship between jackpot amounts and numbers of tickets sold. This implies that about 10% of the variation in the numbers of tickets sold cannot be explained by the linear correlation between the two variables.

Interpreting *r* with Causation: Don't Go There!

In Example 4 we concluded that there is sufficient evidence to support the claim of a linear correlation between lottery jackpot amounts and numbers of tickets sold. We should *not* make any conclusion that includes a statement about a cause-effect relationship between the two variables. We should not conclude that an increase in the jackpot amount will cause ticket sales to increase. See the first of the following common errors, and know this:

Correlation does not imply causality!

Common Errors Involving Correlation

Here are three of the most common errors made in interpreting results involving correlation:

1. *Assuming that correlation implies causality.* One classic example involves paired data consisting of the stork population in Oldenburg, Germany and the number of human births. For the years of 1930 to 1936, the data suggested a linear correlation. *Bulletin:* Storks do not actually cause births, and births do not cause storks. Both variables were affected by another variable lurking in the background. (A **lurking variable** is one that affects the variables being studied but is not included in the study.) Here, an increasing human population resulted in more births and increased construction of thatched roofs that attracted storks!

2. *Using data based on averages.* Averages suppress individual variation and may inflate the correlation coefficient. One study produced a 0.4 linear correlation coefficient for paired data relating income and education among individuals, but the linear correlation coefficient became 0.7 when regional averages were used.

3. *Ignoring the possibility of a nonlinear relationship.* If there is no linear correlation, there might be some other correlation that is not linear, as in Figure 10-2(d).

PART 2 Formal Hypothesis Test

Hypotheses If conducting a formal hypothesis test to determine whether there is a significant linear correlation between two variables, use the following null and alternative hypotheses that use ρ to represent the linear correlation coefficient of the population:

$$\textbf{Null Hypothesis} \qquad H_0: \rho = 0 \ (\text{No correlation})$$
$$\textbf{Alternative Hypothesis} \quad H_1: \rho \neq 0 \ (\text{Correlation})$$

Test Statistic The same methods of Part 1 can be used with the test statistic r, or the t test statistic can be found using the following:

$$\textbf{Test Statistic } t = \frac{r}{\sqrt{\dfrac{1 - r^2}{n - 2}}} \quad (\text{with } n - 2 \text{ degrees of freedom})$$

If the above t test statistic is used, P-values and critical values can be found using technology or Table A-3 as described in earlier chapters. See the following example.

CP EXAMPLE 7 Hypothesis Test Using the *P*-Value from the *t* Test

Use the paired data from Table 10-1 on page 507 to conduct a formal hypothesis test of the claim that there is a linear correlation between lottery jackpot amounts and numbers of tickets sold. Use a 0.05 significance level with the P-value method of testing hypotheses.

SOLUTION

REQUIREMENT CHECK In Example 4 we noted that the requirements appear to be satisfied. ✅

To claim that there is a linear correlation is to claim that the population linear correlation coefficient ρ is different from 0. We therefore have the following hypotheses:

$$H_0: \rho = 0 \quad (\text{There is no linear correlation.})$$
$$H_1: \rho \neq 0 \quad (\text{There is a linear correlation.})$$

The linear correlation coefficient is $r = 0.947$ and $n = 9$ (because there are 9 pairs of sample data), so the test statistic is

$$t = \frac{r}{\sqrt{\dfrac{1 - r^2}{n - 2}}} = \frac{0.947}{\sqrt{\dfrac{1 - 0.947^2}{9 - 2}}} = 7.800$$

With $n - 2 = 7$ degrees of freedom, Table A-3 shows that the test statistic of $t = 7.800$ yields a P-value that is less than 0.01. Technologies show that the P-value is 0.000 when rounded. Because the P-value of 0.000 is less than the significance level of 0.05, we reject H_0. ("If the P is low, the null must go." Yup, the P-value of 0.000 is low.)

INTERPRETATION

This formal hypothesis test results in the same conclusion as Example 4. It appears that there is a linear correlation between lottery jackpots amounts and numbers of tickets sold. It appears that higher jackpots correspond to more tickets sold.

YOUR TURN. Do Exercise 17 "Taxis."

One-Tailed Tests The examples and exercises in this section generally involve two-tailed tests, but one-tailed tests can occur with a claim of a positive linear correlation or a claim of a negative linear correlation. In such cases, the hypotheses will be as shown here.

Claim of Negative Correlation (Left-Tailed Test)	Claim of Positive Correlation (Right-Tailed Test)
$H_0: \rho = 0$	$H_0: \rho = 0$
$H_1: \rho < 0$	$H_1: \rho > 0$

For these one-tailed tests, the P-value method can be used as in earlier chapters.

Rationale for Methods of This Section We have presented Formulas 10-1 and 10-2 for calculating r and have illustrated their use. Those formulas are given below along with some other formulas that are "equivalent," in the sense that they all produce the same values.

FORMULA 10-1 $r = \dfrac{n\Sigma xy - (\Sigma x)(\Sigma y)}{\sqrt{n(\Sigma x^2) - (\Sigma x)^2}\sqrt{n(\Sigma y^2) - (\Sigma y)^2}}$

FORMULA 10-2 $r = \dfrac{\Sigma(z_x z_y)}{n - 1}$

$$r = \frac{\Sigma(x - \bar{x})(y - \bar{y})}{(n - 1)s_x s_y} \qquad r = \frac{\Sigma\left[\dfrac{(x - \bar{x})(y - \bar{y})}{s_x \quad s_y}\right]}{n - 1}$$

$$r = \frac{s_{xy}}{\sqrt{s_{xx}}\sqrt{s_{yy}}}$$

We will use Formula 10-2 to help us understand the reasoning that underlies the development of the linear correlation coefficient. Because Formula 10-2 uses z scores, the value of $\Sigma(z_x z_y)$ does not depend on the scale that is used for the x and y values. Figure 10-4 shows the scatterplot of the paired data from Table 10-1 after the original

jackpot/ticket data values have been converted to z scores. Figure 10-4 is essentially the same scatterplot as Figure 10-1, except that Figure 10-4 uses different scales. The red lines in Figure 10-4 form the same coordinate axes that we have all come to know and love from earlier mathematics courses. Those red lines partition Figure 10-4 into four quadrants.

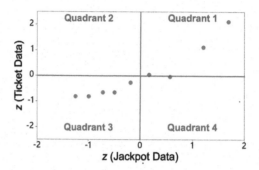

FIGURE 10-4   Scatterplot of z Scores from the Data in Table 10-1

If the points of the scatterplot approximate an uphill line (as in Figure 10-4), individual values of the product $z_x \cdot z_y$ tend to be positive (because most of the points are found in the first and third quadrants, where the values of z_x and z_y are either both positive or both negative), so $\Sigma(z_x z_y)$ tends to be positive. If the points of the scatterplot approximate a downhill line, most of the points are in the second and fourth quadrants, where z_x and z_y are opposite in sign, so $\Sigma(z_x z_y)$ tends to be negative. Points that follow no linear pattern tend to be scattered among the four quadrants, so the value of $\Sigma(z_x z_y)$ tends to be close to 0.

Using $\Sigma(z_x z_y)$ as a measure of how the points are configured among the four quadrants, we get the following:

- **Positive Correlation:** A large positive value of $\Sigma(z_x z_y)$ suggests that the points are predominantly in the first and third quadrants (corresponding to a positive linear correlation).

- **Negative Correlation:** A large negative value of $\Sigma(z_x z_y)$ suggests that the points are predominantly in the second and fourth quadrants (corresponding to a negative linear correlation).

- **No Correlation:** A value of $\Sigma(z_x z_y)$ near 0 suggests that the points are scattered among the four quadrants (with no linear correlation).

We divide $\Sigma(z_x z_y)$ by $n - 1$ to get an average instead of a statistic that becomes larger simply because there are more data values. (The reasons for dividing by $n - 1$ instead of n are essentially the same reasons that relate to the standard deviation.) The end result is Formula 10-2, which can be algebraically manipulated into any of the other expressions for r.

PART 3   Randomization Test

When listing the requirements for an analysis of correlation, we noted that alternatives to the method presented in Part 1 are to use rank correlation (Section 13-6) or the resampling method of randomization. The randomization method is based on the principle that when assuming a null hypothesis of no correlation, we can resample by holding the x data values fixed while randomly shuffling the order of the y data values. We do the shuffling without replacement, so we are working with a randomization test that can be used to test the assumption (null hypothesis) of no correlation.

Shown below is Table 10-1 from the Chapter Problem, followed by two resamplings in which the ticket data are shuffled in a random order. Such shuffles are based on the null hypothesis of no correlation, and if we calculate the linear correlation coefficient r for each new shuffle, we get a list of r values that can be used to determine whether the actual $r = 0.947$ from the original data in Table 10-1 is *significant* in the sense that it is not likely to occur by chance when there really is no correlation.

TABLE 10-1 Lottery Tickets Sold and Jackpot Amounts

Jackpot	334	127	300	227	202	180	164	145	255
Tickets	54	16	41	27	23	18	18	16	26

Random shuffling of ticket data:

Tickets	16	54	16	26	18	27	41	23	18

Another random shuffling of ticket data:

Tickets	18	16	54	27	41	23	18	16	26

Using the paired data in Table 10-1, we can use technology to create 1000 samples using the preceding method of shuffling. Here is one result from technology: Among the 1000 values of r created by shuffling the ticket values as described above, none of them are at least as extreme as the value of $r = 0.947$ found from the original data in Table 10-1. Because a result of $r = 0.947$ never occurred among 1000 samples, it appears that the likelihood of such an extreme value is around 0.000. This shows that a value such as $r = 0.947$ is significant in the sense that it is not likely to occur by chance. This suggests that there *is* a correlation between the jackpot amounts and the numbers of tickets sold.

TECH CENTER

Correlation
Access tech supplements, videos, and data sets at **www.TriolaStats.com**

Statdisk	Minitab	StatCrunch
1. Click **Analysis** in the top menu. 2. Select **Correlation and Regression** from the dropdown menu. 3. Enter the desired significance level and select the columns to be evaluated. 4. Click **Evaluate**. 5. Click **Scatterplot** to obtain a scatterplot with the regression line included.	1. Click **Stat** in the top menu. 2. Select **Basic Statistics** from the dropdown menu and select **Correlation** from the submenu. 3. Select the columns to be evaluated under *Variables*. 4. Click the **Options** button, select **Pearson correlation** for *Method* and enter the desired confidence level. 5. Click **OK** twice. **Scatterplot** 1. Click **Stat** in the top menu. 2. Select **Regression—Fitted Line Plot** from the dropdown menu. 3. Select the desired columns for the *y* variable and *x* variable. 4. Select **Linear** under *Type of Regression Model* and click **OK**. *TIP:* Another procedure is to click on **Assistant** in the top menu, then select **Regression** and **Simple Regression**. Complete the dialog box to get results.	1. Click **Stat** in the top menu. 2. Select **Regression** from the dropdown menu, then select **Simple Linear** from the submenu. 3. Select the columns to be used for the *x* variable and *y* variable. 4. Click **Compute!** 5. Click the arrow at the bottom of the results window to view the scatterplot.

continued

TECH CENTER *continued*

Correlation

Access tech supplements, videos, and data sets at **www.TriolaStats.com**

TI-83/84 Plus Calculator

1. Press **STAT**, then select **TESTS** in the top menu.
2. Select **LinRegTTest** in the menu and press **ENTER**.
3. Enter the list names for the *x* and *y* variables. Enter **1** for *Freq* and for β & ρ select $\neq$ **0** to test the null hypothesis of no correlation.
4. Select **Calculate** and press **ENTER**.

Scatterplot
1. Open the **STAT PLOTS** menu by pressing **2ND**, **Y=**.
2. Press **ENTER** to access the Plot 1 settings screen as shown:
   a. Select **ON** and press **ENTER**.
   b. Select first chart option (scatterplot), then press **ENTER**.
   c. Enter names of lists containing data for the *x* and *y* variables.
3. Press **ZOOM** then **9** (ZoomStat) to generate the scatterplot.

Excel

XLSTAT Add-In
1. Click on the **XLSTAT** tab in the Ribbon and then click **Modeling data.**
2. Select **Linear regression** from the dropdown menu.
3. Enter the range of cells containing the *Y/Dependent variable* data and *X/Explanatory variable* data. Check the **Quantitative** box under *X/Explanatory variable.* If the first data row includes a label, check the **Variable labels** box.
4. Click the **Outputs** tab and ensure **Correlations** and **Analysis of variance** are both checked.
5. Click **OK,** and the linear correlation coefficient, *P*-value, a scatterplot, and hypothesis test results will be displayed. The linear coefficient *r* is found in the *Correlation matrix* and the *P*-value is found in the *Analysis of Variance* table under *Pr > F.*

Excel
1. Click **Insert Function** f_x, select the category **Statistical,** and select the function **CORREL.** Click **OK.**
2. For *Array1* enter the data range for the independent *x* variable. For *Array2* enter the data range for the dependent *y* variable.
3. Click **OK** for the linear correlation coefficient *r*.

Scatterplot (Excel)
1. Select the data range.
2. Click the **Insert** tab in the Ribbon.
3. In the *Charts* section of the top menu select the **Scatter** chart type.
4. Right click on the chart to customize.

R

R commands:

Correlation: **cor(x,y)**

Scatterplot: **plot(x,y)**

Add Regression Line to Scatterplot: **abline(lm(y~x))**

A complete list of R statistical commands is available at TriolaStats.com

10-1   Basic Skills and Concepts

Statistical Literacy and Critical Thinking

1. Notation The author conducted an experiment in which the height of each student was measured in centimeters and those heights were matched with the same students' scores on the first statistics test.

a. For this sample of paired data, what does r represent, and what does ρ represent?

b. Without doing any research or calculations, estimate the value of r.

c. Does r change if the heights are converted from centimeters to inches?

2. Interpreting r For the same two variables described in Exercise 1, if we find that $r = 0$, does that indicate that there is no association between those two variables?

3. Global Warming If we find that there is a linear correlation between the concentration of carbon dioxide (CO_2) in our atmosphere and the global mean temperature, does that indicate that changes in CO_2 cause changes in the global mean temperature? Why or why not?

4. Scatterplots Match these values of r with the five scatterplots shown below: 0.268, 0.992, -1, 0.746, and 1.

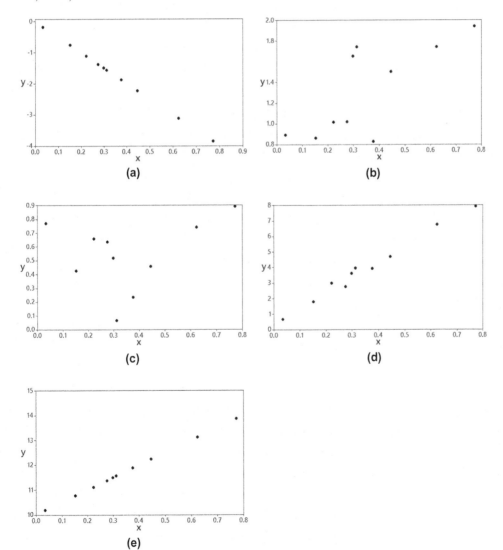

Interpreting r.   In Exercises 5–8, use a significance level of α = 0.05 and refer to the accompanying displays.

5. Bear Weight and Chest Size Fifty-four wild bears were anesthetized, and then their weights and chest sizes were measured and listed in Data Set 18 "Bear Measurements" in Appendix B; results are shown in the accompanying Statdisk display. Is there sufficient evidence to support the claim that there is a linear correlation between the weights of bears and their chest sizes? When measuring an anesthetized bear, is it easier to measure chest size than weight? If so, does it appear that a measured chest size can be used to predict the weight?

Correlation Results:
Correlation coeff,   r: 0.963141
Critical r: ±0.2680855
P-value (two-tailed): 0.000

6. Bear Length and Weight The lengths (inches) and weights (pounds) of 54 bears are obtained from Data Set 18 "Bear Measurements" in Appendix B, and results are shown in the accompanying XLSTAT display. Is there sufficient evidence to support the claim that there is a linear correlation between length and weight?

XLSTAT

Variables	LENGTH	WEIGHT
LENGTH	1	0.864
WEIGHT	0.864	1

7. Word Counts of Men and Women The first two columns of Data Set 14 "Word Counts" in Appendix B list the 56 pairs of numbers of words spoken in a day by men and women in couple relationships. StatCrunch results are shown in the accompanying display. Is there sufficient evidence to support the claim that there is a linear correlation between the numbers of words spoken in a day by men and women in couple relationships?

StatCrunch

Simple linear regression results:
Dependent Variable: Women
Independent Variable: Men
Women = 13438.929 + 0.30189898 Men
Sample size: 56
R (correlation coefficient) = 0.31856705
R-sq = 0.10148496
Estimate of error standard deviation: 7136.1559

8. Heights of Mothers and Daughters Data Set 10 "Family Heights" in Appendix B includes heights (inches) of mothers and their first daughters. Using the first 10 pairs of those heights results in the TI-83/84 Plus results shown here. Is there sufficient evidence to support the claim that there is a linear correlation between heights of mothers and heights of their first daughters?

TI-83/84 Plus

9. Outlier Refer to the accompanying Minitab-generated scatterplot.

a. Examine the pattern of all 10 points and subjectively determine whether there appears to be a correlation between x and y.

b. After identifying the 10 pairs of coordinates corresponding to the 10 points, find the value of the correlation coefficient r and determine whether there is a linear correlation.

c. Now remove the point with coordinates $(10, 10)$ and repeat parts (a) and (b).

d. What do you conclude about the possible effect from a single pair of values?

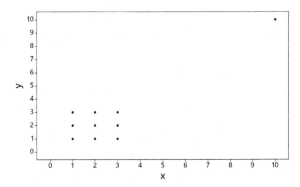

10. Clusters Refer to the Minitab-generated scatterplot. The four points in the lower left corner are measurements from women, and the four points in the upper right corner are from men.

a. Examine the pattern of the four points in the lower left corner (from women) only, and subjectively determine whether there appears to be a correlation between x and y for women.

b. Examine the pattern of the four points in the upper right corner (from men) only, and subjectively determine whether there appears to be a correlation between x and y for men.

c. Find the linear correlation coefficient using only the four points in the lower left corner (for women). Will the four points in the upper right corner (for men) have the same linear correlation coefficient?

d. Find the value of the linear correlation coefficient using all eight points. What does that value suggest about the relationship between x and y?

e. Based on the preceding results, what do you conclude? Should the data from women and the data from men be considered together, or do they appear to represent two different and distinct populations that should be analyzed separately?

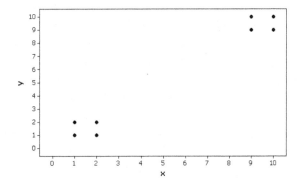

Explore!   *Exercises 11 and 12 provide two data sets from "Graphs in Statistical Analysis," by F. J. Anscombe, the American Statistician, Vol. 27. For each exercise,*

a. Construct a scatterplot.

b. Find the value of the linear correlation coefficient r, then determine whether there is sufficient evidence to support the claim of a linear correlation between the two variables.

c. Identify the feature of the data that would be missed if part (b) was completed without constructing the scatterplot.

11.

x	10	8	13	9	11	14	6	4	12	7	5
y	9.14	8.14	8.74	8.77	9.26	8.10	6.13	3.10	9.13	7.26	4.74

12.

x	10	8	13	9	11	14	6	4	12	7	5
y	7.46	6.77	12.74	7.11	7.81	8.84	6.08	5.39	8.15	6.42	5.73

Testing for a Linear Correlation.   *In Exercises 13–28, construct a scatterplot, and find the value of the linear correlation coefficient r. Also find the P-value or the critical values of r from Table A-6. Use a significance level of $\alpha = 0.05$. Determine whether there is sufficient evidence to support a claim of a linear correlation between the two variables. (Save your work because the same data sets will be used in Section 10-2 exercises.)*

13. Powerball Jackpots and Tickets Sold Listed below are the same data from Table 10-1 in the Chapter Problem, but an additional pair of values has been added in the last column. Is there sufficient evidence to conclude that there is a linear correlation between lottery jackpot amounts and numbers of tickets sold? Comment on the effect of the added pair of values in the last column. Compare the results to those obtained in Example 4 on pages 515 and 516.

Jackpot	334	127	300	227	202	180	164	145	255	400
Tickets	54	16	41	27	23	18	18	16	26	17

14. Powerball Jackpots and Tickets Sold Listed below are the same data from Table 10-1 in the Chapter Problem, but an additional pair of values has been added from actual Powerball results. Is there sufficient evidence to conclude that there is a linear correlation between lottery jackpots and numbers of tickets sold? Comment on the effect of the added pair of values in the last column. Compare the results to those obtained in Example 4.

Jackpot	334	127	300	227	202	180	164	145	255	625
Tickets	54	16	41	27	23	18	18	16	26	90

15. Taxis The table below includes data from New York City taxi rides (from Data Set 32 "Taxis" in Appendix B). The distances are in miles, the times are in minutes, the fares are in dollars, and the tips are in dollars. Is there sufficient evidence to support the claim that there is a linear correlation between the time of the ride and the tip amount? Does it appear that riders base their tips on the time of the ride?

Distance	0.68	2.47	8.51	12.71	1.65	1.02	1.32	0.49
Time	6.00	18.00	31.00	27.00	11.00	8.00	8.00	2.00
Fare	6.30	14.30	31.75	36.80	9.80	7.80	7.80	4.80
Tip	1.89	4.29	2.98	0.00	1.96	2.34	0.00	0.00

16. Taxis Using the data from Exercise 15, is there sufficient evidence to support the claim that there is a linear correlation between the distance of the ride and the tip amount? Does it appear that riders base their tips on the distance of the ride?

17. Taxis Using the data from Exercise 15, is there sufficient evidence to support the claim that there is a linear correlation between the distance of the ride and the fare (cost of the ride)?

18. Taxis Using the data from Exercise 15, is there sufficient evidence to support the claim that there is a linear correlation between the time of the ride and the fare (cost of the ride)?

19. Oscars Listed below are ages of recent Oscar winners matched by the years in which the awards were won (from Data Set 21 "Oscar Winner Age" in Appendix B). Is there sufficient evidence to conclude that there is a linear correlation between the ages of Best Actresses and Best Actors? Should we expect that there would be a correlation?

Best Actor	32	33	45	29	62	22	44	54	26	28	60	45
Best Actress	50	48	60	50	39	55	44	33	41	41	59	37

20. POTUS Media periodically discuss the issue of heights of winning presidential candidates and heights of their main opponents. Listed below are those heights (cm) from several recent presidential elections (from Data Set 22 "Presidents" in Appendix B). Is there sufficient evidence to conclude that there is a linear correlation between heights of winning presidential candidates and heights of their main opponents? Should there be such a correlation?

President	192	182	177	185	188	188	183	188	191
Opponent	180	180	183	177	173	188	185	175	169

21. Prices of Pizza and Subway Rides The "pizza connection" is the principle that the price of a slice of pizza in New York City is always about the same as the subway fare. Use the pizza and subway cost data in the table below to determine whether there is a linear correlation between these two items.

Year	1960	1973	1986	1995	2002	2003	2009	2013	2015	2019
Pizza Cost	0.15	0.35	1.00	1.25	1.75	2.00	2.25	2.30	2.75	3.00
Subway Fare	0.15	0.35	1.00	1.35	1.50	2.00	2.25	2.50	2.75	2.75
CPI	29.6	44.4	109.6	152.4	180.0	184.0	214.5	233.0	237.0	252.2

22. Subway and the CPI Use subway fare/CPI data from the preceding exercise to determine whether there is a significant linear correlation between the subway fare and the CPI (Consumer Price Index).

23. CSI Statistics Police crime scene investigators sometimes measure footprints at crime scenes so that they can learn something about criminals. Listed below are foot lengths (mm) and heights (mm) of males (from Data Set 3 "ANSUR II 2012" in Appendix B). Is there sufficient evidence to conclude that there is a linear correlation between foot lengths and heights of males? Based on these results, does it appear that police can use a footprint length to estimate the height of a male?

Foot Length	282	278	253	259	279	258	274	262
Height	1785	1771	1676	1646	1859	1710	1789	1737

24. Crickets and Temperature A classic application of correlation involves the association between the temperature and the number of times a cricket chirps in a minute. Listed below are the numbers of chirps in 1 min and the corresponding temperatures in °F (based on data from *The Song of Insects,* by George W. Pierce, Harvard University Press). Is there sufficient evidence to conclude that there is a linear correlation between the number of chirps in 1 min and the temperature?

Chirps in 1 min	882	1188	1104	864	1200	1032	960	900
Temperature (°F)	69.7	93.3	84.3	76.3	88.6	82.6	71.6	79.6

25. Car Sales and the Super Bowl Listed below are annual data for various years. The data are the numbers of cars sold (thousands) and the numbers of points scored in the Super Bowl. Is there sufficient evidence to conclude that there is a linear correlation between those two variables? Would it be reasonable to expect a correlation?

Car Sales	8175	8213	8518	8991	8635	8527	8272	8142
Super Bowl Points	61	69	43	75	44	56	55	53

26. Cheese and Engineering Listed below are annual data for various years. The data are weights (pounds) of per capita consumption of mozzarella cheese and the numbers of civil engineering PhD degrees awarded (based on data from the U.S. Department of Agriculture and the National Science Foundation). Is there sufficient evidence to conclude that there is a linear correlation between the two variables? Do the results suggest that consumption of mozzarella cheese causes people to earn PhD degrees in civil engineering?

Cheese Consumption	9.3	9.7	9.7	9.7	9.9	10.2	10.5	11.0	10.6	10.6
Civil Engineering PhDs	480	501	540	552	547	622	655	701	712	708

27. Lemons and Car Crashes Listed below are annual data for various years. The data are weights (metric tons) of lemons imported from Mexico and U.S. car crash fatality rates per 100,000 population [based on data from "The Trouble with QSAR (or How I Learned to Stop Worrying and Embrace Fallacy)," by Stephen Johnson, *Journal of Chemical Information and Modeling*, Vol. 48, No. 1]. Is there sufficient evidence to conclude that there is a linear correlation between weights of lemon imports from Mexico and U.S. car fatality rates? Do the results suggest that imported lemons cause car fatalities?

Lemon Imports	230	265	358	480	530
Crash Fatality Rate	15.9	15.7	15.4	15.3	14.9

28. Weighing Seals with a Camera Listed below are the overhead widths (cm) of seals measured from photographs and the weights (kg) of the seals (based on "Mass Estimation of Weddell Seals Using Techniques of Photogrammetry," by R. Garrott of Montana State University). The purpose of the study was to determine if weights of seals could be determined from overhead photographs. Is there sufficient evidence to conclude that there is a linear correlation between overhead widths of seals from photographs and the weights of the seals?

Overhead Width	7.2	7.4	9.8	9.4	8.8	8.4
Weight	116	154	245	202	200	191

Appendix B Data Sets. *In Exercises 29–32, use the data from Appendix B to construct a scatterplot, find the value of the linear correlation coefficient r, and find either the P-value or the critical values of r from Table A-6 using a significance level of α = 0.05. Determine whether there is sufficient evidence to support the claim of a linear correlation between the two variables.*

29. Taxis Repeat Exercise 15 using all of the time/tip data from the 703 taxi rides listed in Data Set 32 "Taxis" from Appendix B. Compare the results to those found in Exercise 15.

30. Taxis Repeat Exercise 16 using all of the distance/tip data from the 703 taxi rides listed in Data Set 32 "Taxis" from Appendix B. Compare the results to those found in Exercise 16.

31. Taxis Repeat Exercise 17 using all of the distance/fare data from the 703 taxi rides listed in Data Set 32 "Taxis" from Appendix B. Compare the results to those found in Exercise 17.

32. Taxis Repeat Exercise 18 using all of the time/fare data from the 703 taxi rides listed in Data Set 32 "Taxis" from Appendix B. Compare the results to those found in Exercise 18.

10-1 Beyond the Basics

Randomization. *For Exercises 33–36, repeat the indicated exercise using the resampling method of randomization.*

33. Powerball Jackpots and Tickets Sold Exercise 13

34. Powerball Jackpots and Tickets Sold Exercise 14

35. Taxis Exercise 15

36. Taxis Exercise 16

37. Finding Critical *r* Values Table A-6 lists critical values of *r* for selected values of *n* and α. More generally, critical *r* values can be found by using the formula

$$r = \frac{t}{\sqrt{t^2 + n - 2}}$$

where the *t* value is found from the table of critical *t* values (Table A-3) assuming a two-tailed case with $n - 2$ degrees of freedom. Use the formula for *r* given here and in Table A-3 (with $n - 2$ degrees of freedom) to find the critical *r* values corresponding to $H_1: \rho \neq 0$, $\alpha = 0.05$, and $n = 703$ as in Exercises 29–32.

10-2 Regression

Key Concept This section presents methods for finding the equation of the straight line that best fits the points in a scatterplot of paired sample data. That best-fitting straight line is called the *regression line,* and its equation is called the *regression equation.* We can use the regression equation to make predictions for the value of one of the variables, given some specific value of the other variable. In Part 2 of this section we discuss marginal change, influential points, and residual plots as tools for analyzing correlation and regression results.

PART 1 Basic Concepts of Regression

In some cases, two variables are related in a *deterministic* way, meaning that given a value for one variable, the value of the other variable is exactly determined without any error, as in the equation $y = 2.54x$ for converting a distance *x* from inches to centimeters. Such equations are considered in algebra courses, but statistics courses focus on *probabilistic* models, which are equations with a variable that is not determined completely by the other variable. For example, the height of a child cannot be determined completely by the height of the father and/or mother. Sir Francis Galton (1822–1911) studied the phenomenon of heredity and showed that when tall or short couples have children, the heights of those children tend to *regress,* or revert to the more typical mean height for people of the same gender. We continue to use Galton's "regression" terminology, even though our data do not involve the same height phenomena studied by Galton.

> **DEFINITIONS**
>
> Given a collection of paired sample data, the **regression line** (or *line of best fit,* or *least-squares line*) is the straight line that "best" fits the scatterplot of the data. (The specific criterion for the "best-fitting" straight line is the "least-squares" property described later.)
>
> The **regression equation**
>
> $$\hat{y} = b_0 + b_1 x$$
>
> algebraically describes the regression line. The regression equation expresses a relationship between *x* (called the **explanatory variable,** or **predictor variable,** or **independent variable**) and $\hat{y}$ (called the **response variable** or **dependent variable**).

The preceding definition shows that in statistics, the typical equation of a straight line $y = mx + b$ is expressed in the form $\hat{y} = b_0 + b_1 x$, where b_0 is the *y*-intercept and b_1 is the slope. The values of the slope b_1 and *y*-intercept b_0 can be easily found by using any one of the many computer programs and calculators designed to provide those values, as illustrated in Example 1. The values of b_1 and b_0 can also be found with manual calculations, as shown in Example 2.

Finding the Equation of the Regression Line

Objective

Find the equation of a regression line.

Notation for the Equation of a Regression Line

	Sample Statistic	Population Parameter
y-intercept of regression line	b_0	β_0
Slope of regression line	b_1	β_1
Equation of the regression line	$\hat{y} = b_0 + b_1 x$	$y = \beta_0 + \beta_1 x$

Requirements

1. The sample of paired (x, y) data is a *random* sample of quantitative data.

2. Visual examination of the scatterplot shows that the points approximate a straight-line pattern.*

3. Outliers can have a strong effect on the regression equation, so remove any outliers if they are known to be errors. Consider the effects of any outliers that are not known errors. In particular, consider the effects of any outliers that dramatically affect the regression line.*

Note: Requirements 2 and 3 above are simplified attempts at checking these formal requirements for regression analysis:

- For each fixed value of x, the corresponding values of y have a normal distribution.

- For the different fixed values of x, the distributions of the corresponding y-values all have the same standard deviation. (This is violated if part of the scatterplot shows points very close to the regression line while another portion of the scatterplot shows points that are much farther away from the regression line. See the discussion of residual plots in Part 2 of this section.)

- For the different fixed values of x, the distributions of the corresponding y values have means that lie along the same straight line.

The methods of this section are not seriously affected if departures from normal distributions and equal standard deviations are not too extreme.

Formulas for Finding the Slope b_1 and y-Intercept b_0 in the Regression Equation $\hat{y} = b_0 + b_1 x$

FORMULA 10-3   **Slope:** $b_1 = r \dfrac{s_y}{s_x}$ where r is the linear correlation coefficient, s_y is the standard deviation of the y values, and s_x is the standard deviation of the x values.

FORMULA 10-4   **y-intercept:** $b_0 = \bar{y} - b_1 \bar{x}$

The slope b_1 and y-intercept b_0 can also be found using the following formulas that are useful for manual calculations or writing computer programs:

$$b_1 = \frac{n(\Sigma xy) - (\Sigma x)(\Sigma y)}{n(\Sigma x^2) - (\Sigma x)^2} \qquad b_0 = \frac{(\Sigma y)(\Sigma x^2) - (\Sigma x)(\Sigma xy)}{n(\Sigma x^2) - (\Sigma x)^2}$$

Rounding the Slope b_1 and the y-Intercept b_0

Round b_1 and b_0 to three significant digits. It's difficult to provide a simple universal rule for rounding values of b_1 and b_0, but this rule will work for most situations in this book. (Depending on how you round, this book's answers to examples and exercises may be slightly different from your answers.)

(CP) EXAMPLE 1 Using Technology to Find the Regression Equation

Table 10-1 from the Chapter Problem is reproduced here. (Jackpot amounts are in millions of dollars and numbers of tickets sold are in millions.) Use technology to find the equation of the regression line in which the explanatory variable (or *x* variable) is the amount of the lottery jackpot and the response variable (or *y* variable) is the corresponding number of lottery tickets sold.

TABLE 10-1 Lottery Tickets Sold and Jackpot Amounts

Jackpot	334	127	300	227	202	180	164	145	255
Tickets	54	16	41	27	23	18	18	16	26

SOLUTION

REQUIREMENT CHECK (1) The data are a simple random sample. (2) The scatterplot in Figure 10-1 on page 509 shows that the pattern of points is reasonably close to a straight-line pattern. (3) The scatterplot also shows that there are no outliers. The requirements are satisfied. ☑

Technology The use of technology is recommended for finding the equation of a regression line. Shown below are the results from different technologies. Minitab and XLSTAT provide the actual equation; the other technologies list the values of the *y*-intercept and the slope. All of these technologies show that the regression equation can be expressed as $\hat{y} = -10.9 + 0.174x$, where $\hat{y}$ is the predicted number of tickets sold and *x* is the amount of the jackpot.

Statdisk

```
Regression Results:
Y= b0 + b1x:
Y Intercept, b0:      -10.87169
Slope, b1:             0.17417
```

Excel (XLSTAT)

```
Equation of the model (Tickets):

Tickets = -10.87169+0.17417*Jackpot
```

Minitab

```
Regression Equation

Tickets  =  -10.87 + 0.1742 Jackpot
```

TI-83/84 Plus

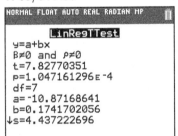

```
NORMAL FLOAT AUTO REAL RADIAN MP

        LinRegTTest
y=a+bx
β≠0 and ρ≠0
t=7.82770351
p=1.047161296ᴇ-4
df=7
a=-10.87168641
b=0.1741702056
↓s=4.437222696
```

SPSS

Model		Unstandardized Coefficients		Standardized Coefficients		
		B	Std. Error	Beta	t	Sig.
1	(Constant)	-10.872	5.005		-2.172	.066
	Jackpot	.174	.022	.947	7.828	.000

JMP

Parameter Estimates

Term	Estimate	Std Error	t Ratio	Prob>|t|
Intercept	-10.87169	5.004925	-2.17	0.0664
Column 1	0.1741702	0.02225	7.83	0.0001*

StatCrunch

Simple linear regression results:
Dependent Variable: Tickets
Independent Variable: Jackpot
Tickets = -10.871686 + 0.17417021 Jackpot

We should know that the regression equation is an *estimate* of the true regression equation for the population of paired data. This estimate is based on one particular set of sample data, but another sample drawn from the same population would probably lead to a slightly different equation.

 YOUR TURN. Do Exercise 13 "Powerball Jackpots and Tickets Sold."

(CP)—**EXAMPLE 2**   Using Manual Calculations to Find the
Regression Equation

Use the sample data in Table 10-1 (shown in Example 1). Use Formulas 10-3 and
10-4 to find the equation of the regression line in which the explanatory variable (or
x variable) is the jackpot amount and the response variable (or *y* variable) is the corresponding number of tickets sold.

SOLUTION

REQUIREMENT CHECK   The requirements are verified in Example 1. ✅
We begin by finding the slope b_1 using Formula 10-3 as follows (with extra digits included for greater accuracy). Remember, *r* is the linear correlation coefficient,
s_y is the standard deviation of the sample *y* values, and s_x is the standard deviation of
the sample *x* values.

$$b_1 = r\frac{s_y}{s_x} = 0.947349 \cdot \frac{12.96255}{70.50611} = 0.174170$$

After finding the slope b_1, we can now use Formula 10-4 to find the *y*-intercept as
follows:

$$b_0 = \bar{y} - b_1\bar{x} = 26.55556 - (0.174170)(214.88889) = -10.87164$$

After rounding, the slope is $b_1 = 0.174$ and the *y*-intercept is $b_0 = -10.9$. We
can now express the regression equation as $\hat{y} = -10.9 + 0.174x$, where $\hat{y}$ is the
predicted number of tickets sold and *x* is the amount of the jackpot.

↪**YOUR TURN.** Do Exercise 13 "Powerball Jackpots and Tickets Sold."

(CP)—**EXAMPLE 3**   Graphing the Regression Line

Graph the regression equation $\hat{y} = -10.9 + 0.174x$ (found in Examples 1 and 2)
on the scatterplot of the jackpot/tickets data from Table 10-1 and examine the graph
to subjectively determine how well the regression line fits the data.

SOLUTION

Shown below is the Minitab display of the scatterplot with the graph of the
regression line included. We can see that the regression line fits the points reasonably well.

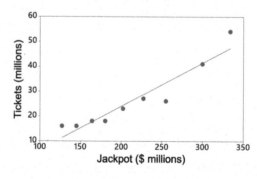

Making Predictions

Regression equations are often useful for *predicting* the value of one variable, given some specific value of the other variable. When making predictions, we should consider the following:

1. **Bad Model:** If the regression equation does not appear to be useful for making predictions, *don't* use the regression equation for making predictions. For bad models, the best predicted value of a variable is simply its sample mean. However, the sample mean is not a *good* predicted value because it is the predicted value for *any* value of the other variable.

2. **Good Model:** Use the regression equation for predictions only if the graph of the regression line on the scatterplot confirms that the regression line fits the points reasonably well.

3. **Correlation:** Use the regression equation for predictions only if the linear correlation coefficient r indicates that there is a linear correlation between the two variables (as described in Section 10-1).

4. **Scope:** Use the regression line for predictions only if the data do not go much beyond the scope of the available sample data. (Predicting too far beyond the scope of the available sample data is called *extrapolation*, and it could result in bad predictions.)

Figure 10-5 summarizes a strategy for predicting values of a variable y when given some value of x. Figure 10-5 shows that if the regression equation is a good model, then we substitute the value of x into the regression equation to find the predicted value of y. However, if the regression equation is not a good model, the best predicted value of y is simply $\bar{y}$, the mean of the y values. (But if $\bar{y}$ is the best predicted value, it isn't very good because it is the predicted value of y for *any* value of x.) Remember, this strategy applies to *linear* patterns of points in a scatterplot. If the scatterplot shows a pattern that is nonlinear (not a straight-line) pattern, other methods apply.

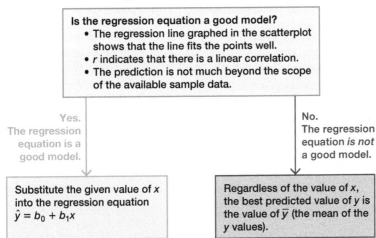

Strategy for Predicting Values of *y*

Is the regression equation a good model?
- The regression line graphed in the scatterplot shows that the line fits the points well.
- r indicates that there is a linear correlation.
- The prediction is not much beyond the scope of the available sample data.

Yes.
The regression equation is a good model.

No.
The regression equation *is not* a good model.

Substitute the given value of x into the regression equation
$\hat{y} = b_0 + b_1 x$

Regardless of the value of x, the best predicted value of y is the value of $\bar{y}$ (the mean of the y values).

FIGURE 10-5   Recommended Strategy for Predicting Values of *y*

CP | **EXAMPLE 4** Making Predictions

a. Use the jackpot/tickets data from Table 10-1 on page 507 to predict the number of lottery tickets sold when the jackpot is $625 million. How close is the predicted value to the actual value of 90 million tickets that were actually sold when the Powerball lottery had a jackpot of $625 million?

b. Predict the IQ score of an adult who is exactly 175 cm tall.

SOLUTION

a. Good Model: Use the Regression Equation for Predictions. The regression line fits the points well, as shown in Example 3. Also, there is a linear correlation between Powerball jackpot amounts and numbers of tickets sold, as shown in Section 10-1. Because the regression equation $\hat{y} = -10.9 + 0.174x$ is a good model, substitute $x = 625$ into the regression equation to get a predicted value of 97.9 million tickets sold. The actual number of tickets sold was 90 million, so the predicted value of 97.9 million tickets is pretty good.

b. Bad Model: Use $\bar{y}$ for predictions. There is no correlation between height and IQ score, so we know that a regression equation is not a good model. Therefore, the best predicted IQ score value is the mean IQ score, which is 100.

INTERPRETATION

Note that in part (a), the paired data result in a *good* regression model, so the predicted number of tickets sold is found by substituting the value of $x = 625$ into the regression equation. However, in part (b) there is no correlation between height and IQ, so the best predicted IQ score is the mean IQ score of $\bar{y} = 100$.

Key point: Use the regression equation for predictions only if it is a good model. If the regression equation is not a good model, use $\bar{y}$ for the predicted value of y.

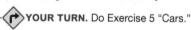
YOUR TURN. Do Exercise 5 "Cars."

PART 2 Beyond the Basics of Regression

In Part 2 we consider the concept of marginal change, which is helpful in interpreting a regression equation; then we consider the effects of outliers and special points called *influential points*. We also consider residual plots.

Interpreting the Regression Equation: Marginal Change

We can use the regression equation to see the effect on one variable when the other variable changes by some specific amount.

DEFINITION

In working with two variables related by a regression equation, the **marginal change** in a variable is the amount that it changes when the other variable changes by exactly one unit. The slope b_1 in the regression equation represents the marginal change in y that occurs when x changes by one unit.

Let's consider the nine pairs of jackpot/ticket data included in Table 10-1 from the Chapter Problem. Those nine pairs of data result in this regression equation: $\hat{y} = -10.9 + 0.174x$ (as shown in Examples 1 and 2). The slope of 0.174 tells us that if we increase the jackpot x by 1 (million dollars), the predicted number of tickets sold will increase by 0.174 million (or 174,000 tickets). That is, for every additional 1 million dollars added to the jackpot amount, we expect the ticket sales to increase by 174,000 tickets. This realization has led lottery officials to adjust their rules to make winning more difficult so that jackpots will grow considerably larger and drive greater lottery ticket sales.

Outliers and Influential Points

A correlation/regression analysis of bivariate (paired) data should include an investigation of *outliers* and *influential points,* defined as follows.

> **DEFINITIONS**
>
> In a scatterplot, an **outlier** is a point lying far away from the other data points.
>
> Paired sample data may include one or more **influential points,** which are points that strongly affect the graph of the regression line.

To determine whether a point is an outlier, examine the scatterplot to see if the point is far away from the others. Here's how to determine whether a point is an influential point: First graph the regression line resulting from the data with the point included, then graph the regression line resulting from the data with the point excluded. If the regression line changes by a considerable amount, the point is influential.

CP- **EXAMPLE 5** **Influential Point**

Consider the nine pairs of jackpot/ticket data from Table 10-1 in the Chapter Problem. The scatterplot located to the left below shows the regression line. If we include the additional pair of $x = 980$ and $y = 12$, we get the regression line shown to the right below. The additional point $(980, 12)$ is an influential point because the graph of the regression line did change considerably in the right graph. Compare the two graphs to see clearly that the addition of this one pair of values has a very dramatic effect on the regression line, so that additional point is an influential point. The additional point is also an outlier because it is far from the other points.

**Original Jackpot/Ticket
Data from Table 10-1**

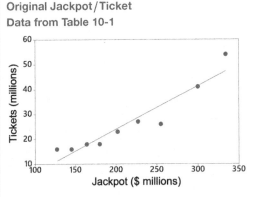

**Jackpot/Ticket Data with
Additional Point: (980, 12)**

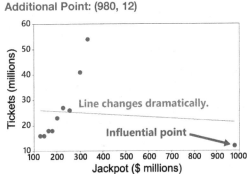

Residuals and the Least-Squares Property

We stated that the regression equation represents the straight line that "best" fits the data. The criterion to determine the line that is better than all others is based on the vertical distances between the original data points and the regression line. Such distances are called *residuals*.

> **DEFINITION**
>
> For a pair of sample x and y values, the **residual** is the difference between the *observed* sample value of y and the y value that is *predicted* by using the regression equation. That is,
>
> $$\text{Residual} = \text{observed } y - \text{predicted } y = y - \hat{y}$$

So far, this definition hasn't yet won any prizes for simplicity, but you can easily understand residuals by referring to Figure 10-6, which corresponds to the paired sample data shown in the margin. In Figure 10-6, the residuals are represented by the dashed lines. The paired data are plotted as red points in Figure 10-6.

x	8	12	20	24
y	4	24	8	32

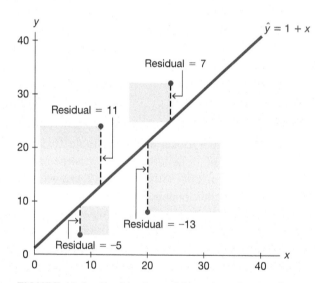

FIGURE 10-6   Residuals and Squares of Residuals

Consider the sample point with coordinates of $(8, 4)$ plotted in Figure 10-6. We get the following:

- **Observed value:** For $x = 8$, the corresponding *observed* value is $y = 4$.
- **Predicted value:** If we substitute $x = 8$ into the regression equation of $\hat{y} = 1 + x$, we get the *predicted* value $\hat{y} = 9$.
- **Residual:** The difference between the observed value and predicted value is the residual, so the residual is $y - \hat{y} = 4 - 9 = -5$.

The regression equation represents the line that "best" fits the points according to the following least-squares property.

DEFINITION

A straight line satisfies the **least-squares property** if the sum of the squares of the residuals is the smallest sum possible.

From Figure 10-6, we see that the residuals are $-5, 11, -13$, and 7, so the sum of their squares is

$$(-5)^2 + 11^2 + (-13)^2 + 7^2 = 364$$

We can visualize the least-squares property by referring to Figure 10-6, where the squares of the residuals are represented by the shaded square areas. The sum of the shaded square areas is 364, which is the smallest sum possible. Use any other straight line, and the shaded squares will combine to produce an area larger than the combined shaded area of 364.

Fortunately, we need not deal directly with the least-squares property when we want to find the equation of the regression line. Calculus has been used to build the least-squares property into Formulas 10-3 and 10-4. Because the derivations of these formulas require calculus, we don't include the derivations in this text.

Residual Plots

In this section and the preceding section we listed simplified requirements for the effective analyses of correlation and regression results. We noted that we should always begin with a scatterplot, and we should verify that the pattern of points is approximately a straight-line pattern. We should also consider outliers. A *residual plot* can be another helpful tool for analyzing correlation and regression results and for checking the requirements necessary for making inferences about correlation and regression.

DEFINITION

A **residual plot** is a scatterplot of the (x, y) values after each of the y-coordinate values has been replaced by the residual value $y - \hat{y}$ (where $\hat{y}$ denotes the predicted value of y). That is, a residual plot is a graph of the points $(x, y - \hat{y})$.

To construct a residual plot, draw a horizontal reference line through the residual value of 0, then plot the paired values of $(x, y - \hat{y})$. Because the manual construction of residual plots can be tedious, the use of technology is strongly recommended.

Usefulness of a Residual Plot

- A residual plot helps us determine whether the regression line is a good model of the sample data.

- A residual plot helps us to check the requirement that for different values of x, the corresponding y values all have the same standard deviation.

continued

Criteria for Residual Plot

- The residual plot should not have any obvious pattern (not even a straight-line pattern). (This lack of a pattern confirms that a scatterplot of the sample data is a straight-line pattern instead of some other pattern.)

- The residual plot should not become much wider (or thinner) when viewed from left to right. (This confirms the requirement that for the different fixed values of x, the distributions of the corresponding y values all have the same standard deviation.)

CP — **EXAMPLE 6** **Residual Plot**

The jackpot/ticket data from Table 10-1 are used to obtain the accompanying Statdisk-generated residual plot, which is a plot of the $(x, y - \hat{y})$ values. See that this residual plot satisfies the preceding two general criteria for residual plots.

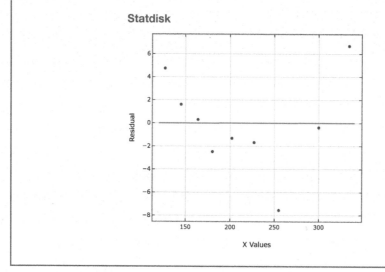

See the three residual plots below. The leftmost residual plot suggests that the regression equation is a good model. The middle residual plot shows a distinct pattern, suggesting that the sample data do not follow a straight-line pattern as required. The rightmost residual plot becomes thicker, which suggests that the requirement of equal standard deviations is violated.

Residual Plot Suggesting That the Regression Equation Is a Good Model

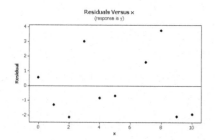

Residual Plot with an Obvious Pattern, Suggesting That the Regression Equation Is Not a Good Model

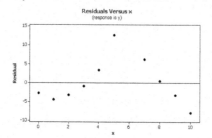

Residual Plot That Becomes Wider, Suggesting That the Regression Equation Is Not a Good Model

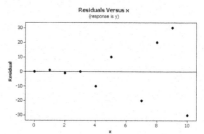

TECH CENTER

Regression

Access tech supplements, videos, and data sets at **www.TriolaStats.com**

Statdisk

1. Click **Analysis** in the top menu.
2. Select **Correlation and Regression** from the dropdown menu.
3. Enter the desired significance level and select the columns to be evaluated.
4. Click **Evaluate.**
5. Click **Scatterplot** to obtain a scatterplot with the regression line.

Minitab

1. Click **Stat** in the top menu.
2. Select **Regression** from the dropdown menu and select **Regression—Fit Regression Model** from the submenu.
3. Under *Responses* select the column that contains the dependent *y* values. Under *Continuous predictors* select the column that contains the independent *x* values.
4. Click **OK.** The regression equation is included in the results.

Scatterplot

1. Click **Stat** in the top menu.
2. Select **Regression—Fitted Line Plot** from the dropdown menu.
3. Select the desired columns for the *y* variable and *x* variable.
4. Select **Linear** under *Type of Regression Model* and click **OK.**

TIP: Another procedure is to click on **Assistant** in the top menu, then select **Regression,** and **Simple Regression.** Complete the dialog box to get results, including the regression equation.

StatCrunch

1. Click **Stat** in the top menu.
2. Select **Regression** from the dropdown menu, then select **Simple Linear** from the submenu.
3. Select the columns to be used for the *x* variable and *y* variable.
4. Click **Compute!**
5. Click the arrow at the bottom of the results window to view the scatterplot with regression line.

TI-83/84 Plus Calculator

1. Press **STAT**, then select **TESTS** in the top menu.
2. Select **LinRegTTest** in the menu and press **ENTER**.
3. Enter the list names for the *x* and *y* variables. Enter **1** for *Freq* and for β & ρ select $\neq$ **0** to test the null hypothesis of no correlation.
4. Select **Calculate** and press **ENTER** to view results, which include the *y*-intercept (a) and slope (b) of the regression equation.

Excel

XLSTAT Add-In

1. Click on the **XLSTAT** tab in the Ribbon and then click **Modeling data.**
2. Select **Linear regression** from the dropdown menu.
3. Enter the range of cells containing the *Y/Dependent variable* data and *X/Explanatory variable* data. Check the **Quantitative** box under *X/Explanatory variable*. If the first data row includes a label, check the **Variable labels** box.
4. Click the **Outputs** tab and ensure **Correlations** and **Analysis of variance** and **Prediction and residuals** are checked.
5. Click **OK,** and the equation of the regression line will be displayed in the results.

Excel (Data Analysis Add-In)

1. Click on the **Data** tab in the Ribbon and then click the **Data Analysis** tab.
2. Select **Regression** under *Analysis Tools* and click **OK.**
3. For *Input Y Range* enter the data range for the dependent *y* variable. For *Input X Range* enter the data range for the independent *x* variable.
4. Check the **Labels** box if the first row contains a label.
5. Check the **Line Fit Plots** box and **Residuals Plots** box and click **OK** to display the results. In the *Coefficients* table, the slope is labeled *X Variable* (or data label) and the *y*-intercept is labeled *Intercept.*

TIP: The displayed graph will include a scatterplot of the original sample points along with the points that would be predicted by the regression equation. You can obtain the regression line by connecting the "predicted *y*" points.

R

R commands:

Regression results (*y* intercept and slope): **lm($y \sim x$)**

Additional regression details: **summary(lm($y \sim x$))**

A complete list of R statistical commands is available at TriolaStats.com

10-2   Basic Skills and Concepts

Statistical Literacy and Critical Thinking

1. Notation Using the weights (lb) and highway fuel consumption amounts (mi/gal) of the 48 cars listed in Data Set 35 "Car Data" of Appendix B, we get this regression equation: $\hat{y} = 58.9 - 0.00749x$, where x represents weight.

a. What does the symbol $\hat{y}$ represent?

b. What are the specific values of the slope and y-intercept of the regression line?

c. What is the predictor variable?

d. Assuming that there is a significant linear correlation between weight and highway fuel consumption, what is the best predicted value of highway fuel consumption of a car that weighs 3000 lb?

2. Notation What is the difference between the regression equation $\hat{y} = b_0 + b_1 x$ and the regression equation $y = \beta_0 + \beta_1 x$?

3. Best-Fit Line

a. What is a residual?

b. In what sense is the regression line the straight line that "best" fits the points in a scatterplot?

4. Correlation and Slope What is the relationship between the linear correlation coefficient r and the slope b_1 of a regression line?

Making Predictions.   *In Exercises 5–8, let the predictor variable x be the first variable given. Use the given data to find the regression equation and the best predicted value of the response variable. Be sure to follow the prediction procedure summarized in Figure 10-5 on page 533. Use a 0.05 significance level.*

5. Cars For the 12 small cars included in Data Set 35 "Car Data" from Appendix B, the weights of the cars (x) are paired with the highway fuel consumption (y). The 12 paired values yield $\bar{x} = 2817.7$ lb, $\bar{y} = 37.3$ mi/gal, $r = -0.395$, P-value $= 0.203$, and the regression equation is $\hat{y} = 53.7 - 0.00580x$. Find the best predicted value of the highway fuel consumption for a small car that weighs 2500 lb.

6. Bear Measurements Head widths (in.) and weights (lb) were measured for 20 randomly selected bears (from Data Set 18 "Bear Measurements" in Appendix B). The 20 pairs of measurements yield $\bar{x} = 6.9$ in., $\bar{y} = 214.3$ lb, $r = 0.879$, P-value $= 0.000$, and $\hat{y} = -212 + 61.9x$. Find the best predicted weight of a bear given that the bear has a head width of 6.5 in.

7. Height and Weight Heights (cm) and weights (kg) are measured for 100 randomly selected adult males (from Data Set 1 "Body Data" in Appendix B). The 100 paired measurements yield $\bar{x} = 173.79$ cm, $\bar{y} = 85.93$ kg, $r = 0.418$, P-value $= 0.000$, and $\hat{y} = -106 + 1.10x$. Find the best predicted weight given an adult male who is 180 cm tall.

8. Cigarette Tar and Nicotine For 25 king-size cigarettes listed in Data Set 16 "Cigarette Contents" in Appendix B, the amount (x) of tar (mg) and the amount (y) of nicotine (mg) are listed for each cigarette. The 25 paired amounts yield $\bar{x} = 21.1$ mg, $\bar{y} = 1.26$ mg, $r = 0.245$, P-value $= 0.237$, and the regression equation is $\hat{y} = 0.883 + 0.0177x$. Find the best predicted amount of nicotine for a cigarette with 10 mg of tar.

Finding the Equation of the Regression Line.   *In Exercises 9 and 10, use the given data to find the equation of the regression line. Examine the scatterplot and identify a characteristic of the data that is ignored by the regression line.*

9.

x	10	8	13	9	11	14	6	4	12	7	5
y	9.14	8.14	8.74	8.77	9.26	8.10	6.13	3.10	9.13	7.26	4.74

10.

x	10	8	13	9	11	14	6	4	12	7	5
y	7.46	6.77	12.74	7.11	7.81	8.84	6.08	5.39	8.15	6.42	5.73

11. Effects of an Outlier Refer to the Minitab-generated scatterplot given in Exercise 9 of Section 10-1 on page 525.

a. Using the pairs of values for all 10 points, find the equation of the regression line.

b. After removing the point with coordinates $(10, 10)$, use the pairs of values for the remaining 9 points and find the equation of the regression line.

c. Compare the results from parts (a) and (b).

12. Effects of Clusters Refer to the Minitab-generated scatterplot given in Exercise 10 of Section 10-1 on page 525.

a. Using the pairs of values for all 8 points, find the equation of the regression line.

b. Using only the pairs of values for the 4 points in the lower left corner, find the equation of the regression line.

c. Using only the pairs of values for the 4 points in the upper right corner, find the equation of the regression line.

d. Compare the results from parts (a), (b), and (c).

Regression and Predictions. *Exercises 13–28 use the same data sets as Exercises 13–28 in Section 10-1.*

(a) Find the regression equation, letting the first variable be the predictor (x) variable.

(b) Find the indicated predicted value by following the prediction procedure summarized in Figure 10-5 on page 533.

13. Powerball Jackpots and Tickets Sold Listed below are the same data from Table 10-1 in the Chapter Problem, but an additional pair of values has been added in the last column. (Jackpot amounts are in millions of dollars, ticket sales are in millions.) Find the best predicted number of tickets sold when the jackpot was actually 625 million dollars. How does the result compare to the value of 90 million tickets that were actually sold?

Jackpot	334	127	300	227	202	180	164	145	255	400
Tickets	54	16	41	27	23	18	18	16	26	17

14. Powerball Jackpots and Tickets Sold Listed below are the same data from Table 10-1 in the Chapter Problem, but an additional pair of values has been added from actual Powerball results. (Jackpot amounts are in millions of dollars, ticket sales are in millions.) Find the best predicted number of tickets sold when the jackpot was actually 345 million dollars. How does the result compare to the value of 55 million tickets that were actually sold?

Jackpot	334	127	300	227	202	180	164	145	255	625
Tickets	54	16	41	27	23	18	18	16	26	90

15. Taxis Use the time/tip data from the table below, which includes data from New York City taxi rides (from Data Set 32 "Taxis" in Appendix B). (The distances are in miles, the times are in minutes, the fares are in dollars, and the tips are in dollars.) Find the best predicted tip for a ride that takes 20 minutes. How does the result compare to the actual tip amount of $4.55?

Distance	0.68	2.47	8.51	12.71	1.65	1.02	1.32	0.49
Time	6.00	18.00	31.00	27.00	11.00	8.00	8.00	2.00
Fare	6.30	14.30	31.75	36.80	9.80	7.80	7.80	4.80
Tip	1.89	4.29	2.98	0.00	1.96	2.34	0.00	0.00

16. Taxis Use the distance/tip data from Exercise 15. Find the best predicted tip for a ride that is 3.10 miles. How does the result compare to the actual tip of $4.55?

17. Taxis Use the distance/fare data from Exercise 15 and find the best predicted fare amount for a distance of 3.10 miles. How does the result compare to the actual fare of $15.30?

18. Taxis Use the time/fare data from Exercise 15 and find the best predicted fare amount for a time of 20 minutes. How does the result compare to the actual fare of $15.30?

19. Oscars Listed below are ages of recent Oscar winners matched by the years in which the awards were won (from Data Set 21 "Oscar Winner Age" in Appendix B). Find the best predicted age of an Oscar-winning actress given that the Oscar winner for best actor is 59 years of age. How does the result compare to the actual actress age of 60 years?

Best Actor	32	33	45	29	62	22	44	54	26	28	60	45
Best Actress	50	48	60	50	39	55	44	33	41	41	59	37

20. POTUS Listed below are the heights (cm) of winning presidential candidates and their main opponents from several recent presidential elections (from Data Set 22 "Presidents" in Appendix B). Find the best predicted height of an opponent given that the president had a height of 191 cm. How close is the result to the actual opponent height of 169 cm?

President	192	182	177	185	188	188	183	188	191
Opponent	180	180	183	177	173	188	185	175	169

21. Prices of Pizza and Subway Rides In the table below, use the pizza cost and the subway fare. (Pizza cost is in dollars per slice, subway fare and CPI are in dollars.) What is the best predicted subway fare when pizza costs $4.00 per slice?

Year	1960	1973	1986	1995	2002	2003	2009	2013	2015	2019
Pizza Cost	0.15	0.35	1.00	1.25	1.75	2.00	2.25	2.30	2.75	3.00
Subway Fare	0.15	0.35	1.00	1.35	1.50	2.00	2.25	2.50	2.75	2.75
CPI	29.6	44.4	109.6	152.4	180.0	184.0	214.5	233.0	237.0	252.2

22. Subway and the CPI Use the subway/CPI data from the preceding exercise. What is the best predicted value of the CPI when the subway fare is $3.00?

23. CSI Statistics Listed below are foot lengths (mm) and heights (mm) of males (from Data Set 3 "ANSUR II 2012" in Appendix B). Find the best predicted height of a male with a foot length of 273 mm. How does the result compare to the actual height of 1776 mm?

Foot Length	282	278	253	259	279	258	274	262
Height	1785	1771	1676	1646	1859	1710	1789	1737

24. Crickets and Temperature Find the best predicted temperature at a time when a cricket chirps 3000 times in 1 minute. What is wrong with this predicted temperature?

Chirps in 1 min	882	1188	1104	864	1200	1032	960	900
Temperature (°F)	69.7	93.3	84.3	76.3	88.6	82.6	71.6	79.6

25. Cars Sales and the Super Bowl Listed below are the annual numbers of cars sold (thousands) and the numbers of points scored in the Super Bowl that same year. What is the best predicted number of Super Bowl points in a year with sales of 8423 thousand cars? How close is the predicted number to the actual result of 37 points?

Car Sales	8175	8213	8518	8991	8635	8527	8272	8142
Super Bowl Points	61	69	43	75	44	56	55	53

26. Cheese and Engineering Listed below are weights (pounds) of per capita consumption of mozzarella cheese and the numbers of civil engineering PhD degrees awarded in various years (based on data from the U.S. Department of Agriculture and the National Science Foundation). What is the best predicted number of civil engineering PhD degrees awarded in a year when per capita cheese consumption is 12.0 pounds? Is that prediction likely to be accurate?

Cheese Consumption	9.3	9.7	9.7	9.7	9.9	10.2	10.5	11.0	10.6	10.6
Civil Engineering PhDs	480	501	540	552	547	622	655	701	712	708

27. Lemons and Car Crashes Listed below are annual data for weights (metric tons) of lemons imported from Mexico and U.S. car crash fatalities per 100,000 population. Using these data, find the best predicted crash fatality rate for a year in which there are 500 metric tons of lemon imports. Is the prediction worthwhile?

Lemon Imports	230	265	358	480	530
Crash Fatality Rate	15.9	15.7	15.4	15.3	14.9

28. Weighing Seals with a Camera Listed below are the overhead widths (cm) of seals measured from photographs and weights (kg) of the seals. Using the listed data, find the best predicted weight of a seal if the overhead width measured from a photograph is 2 cm. Can the prediction be correct? If not, what is wrong?

Overhead Width	7.2	7.4	9.8	9.4	8.8	8.4
Weight	116	154	245	202	200	191

Large Data Sets. *Exercises 29–32 use the same Appendix B data sets as Exercises 29–32 in Section 10-1. In each case, find the regression equation, letting the first variable be the predictor (x) variable. Find the indicated predicted values following the prediction procedure summarized in Figure 10-5 on page 533.*

 29. Taxis Repeat Exercise 15 using all of the time/tip data from the 703 taxi rides listed in Data Set 32 "Taxis" from Appendix B.

 30. Taxis Repeat Exercise 16 using all of the distance/tip data from the 703 taxi rides listed in Data Set 32 "Taxis" from Appendix B.

 31. Taxis Repeat Exercise 17 using all of the distance/fare data from the 703 taxi rides listed in Data Set 32 "Taxis" from Appendix B.

 32. Taxis Repeat Exercise 18 using all of the time/fare data from the 703 taxi rides listed in Data Set 32 "Taxis" from Appendix B.

10-2 Beyond the Basics

33. Least-Squares Property According to the least-squares property, the regression line minimizes the sum of the squares of the residuals. Refer to the jackpot/tickets data in Table 10-1 on page 507 and use the regression equation $\hat{y} = -10.9 + 0.174x$ that was found in Examples 1 and 2 of this section.

a. Identify the nine residuals.

b. Find the sum of the squares of the residuals.

c. Show that the equation $\hat{y} = -10.0 + 0.200x$ results in a larger sum of squares of residuals.

10-3 Prediction Intervals and Variation

Key Concept In Section 10-2 we presented a method for using a regression equation to find a predicted value of *y*, but it would be great to have a way of determining the *accuracy* of such predictions. In this section we introduce the *prediction interval,* which is an interval estimate of a predicted value of *y*. See the following definitions for the distinction between *confidence interval* and *prediction interval*.

> **DEFINITIONS**
>
> A **prediction interval** is a range of values used to estimate a *variable* (such as a predicted value of *y* in a regression equation).
>
> A **confidence interval** is a range of values used to estimate a population *parameter* (such as *p* or μ or σ).

In Example 4(a) from the preceding section, we showed that when using the 9 pairs of jackpot/tickets data from Table 10-1, the regression equation is $\hat{y} = -10.9 + 0.174x$, and for a jackpot of $x = 625$ million dollars, the predicted value of *y* is 97.9 million tickets (which is found by substituting $x = 625$ in the regression equation). For $x = 625$, the "best" predicted value of *y* is 97.9, but we have no sense of the accuracy of that estimate, so we need an interval estimate. A prediction interval estimate of a predicted value $\hat{y}$ can be found using the components in the following Key Elements box. Given the nature of the calculations, the use of technology is strongly recommended. Minitab and StatCrunch can be used to automatically generate 95% prediction intervals.

KEY ELEMENTS

Prediction Intervals

Objective

Find a prediction interval, which is an interval estimate of a predicted value of *y*.

Requirement

For each fixed value of *x*, the corresponding sample values of *y* are normally distributed about the regression line, and those normal distributions have the same variance.

Formulas for Creating a Prediction Interval

Given a fixed and known value x_0, the prediction interval for an individual *y* value is

$$\hat{y} - E < y < \hat{y} + E$$

where the margin of error is

$$E = t_{\alpha/2} s_e \sqrt{1 + \frac{1}{n} + \frac{n(x_0 - \bar{x})^2}{n(\Sigma x^2) - (\Sigma x)^2}}$$

and x_0 is a given value of *x*, $t_{\alpha/2}$ has $n - 2$ degrees of freedom, and s_e is the **standard error of estimate** found from Formula 10-5 or Formula 10-6. (The standard error of estimate s_e is a measure of variation of the residuals, which are the differences between the observed sample *y* values and the predicted values $\hat{y}$ that are found from the regression equation.)

FORMULA 10-5 $$s_e = \sqrt{\frac{\Sigma(y - \hat{y})^2}{n - 2}}$$

FORMULA 10-6 $$s_e = \sqrt{\frac{\Sigma y^2 - b_0\Sigma y - b_1\Sigma xy}{n - 2}}$$ (This is an equivalent form of Formula 10-5 that is good for manual calculations or writing computer programs.)

CP — **EXAMPLE 1** **Powerball Jackpots and Ticket Sales: Finding a Prediction Interval**

For the paired jackpot/tickets data in Table 10-1 from the Chapter Problem, we found that there is sufficient evidence to support the claim of a linear correlation between those two variables, and we found that the regression equation is $\hat{y} = -10.9 + 0.174x$. We also found that if the jackpot amount is $x = 625$ million dollars, the predicted number of tickets sold is 97.9 million (or 98.0 million if using calculations with more decimal places). Use the jackpot amount of 625 million dollars to construct a 95% prediction interval for the number of tickets.

SOLUTION

The accompanying StatCrunch and Minitab displays provide the 95% prediction interval, which is 73.7 million tickets $< y <$ 122 million tickets when rounded.

StatCrunch

Predicted values:

X value	Pred. Y	s.e.(Pred. y)	95% C.I. for mean	95% P.I. for new
625	97.984692	9.2442639	(76.125482, 119.8439)	(73.737738, 122.23165)

Minitab

Prediction

Fit	SE Fit	95% CI	95% PI
97.9847	9.24426	(76.1255, 119.844)	(73.7377, 122.232)

The same 95% prediction interval could be manually calculated using these components:

$x_0 = 625$ (given)

$s_e = 4.437223$ (provided by many technologies, including Statdisk, Minitab, Excel, StatCrunch, and the TI-83/84 Plus calculator)

$\hat{y} = 97.9$ (predicted value of y found by substituting $x = 625$ into the regression equation)

$t_{\alpha/2} = 2.365$ (from Table A-3 with df $= n - 2 = 7$ and an area of 0.05 in two tails)

$n = 9, \bar{x} = 214.8889, \Sigma x = 1934, \Sigma x^2 = 455{,}364$

continued

INTERPRETATION

The 95% prediction interval is **73.7 million tickets** $<$ **y** $<$ **122 million tickets** (which does contain the value of 90 million tickets that were actually sold in this particular lottery). This means that if we select some particular lottery with a jackpot of 625 million dollars ($x = 625$), we have 95% confidence that the limits of

73.7 million tickets and 122 million tickets

contain the actual ticket sales in millions. That is a wide range of values. The prediction interval would be much narrower and our estimated number of tickets would be much better if the margin of error E was not so large (due to the small sample size and the large difference between the outlier jackpot of $x = 625$ million dollars and $\bar{x} = 214.8889$ million dollars).

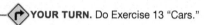 **YOUR TURN.** Do Exercise 13 "Cars."

Explained and Unexplained Variation

Assume that we have a sample of paired data having the following properties shown in Figure 10-7:

- There is sufficient evidence to support the claim of a linear correlation between x and y.
- The equation of the regression line is $\hat{y} = 3 + 2x$.
- The mean of the y values is given by $\bar{y} = 9$.
- One of the pairs of sample data is $x = 5$ and $y = 19$.
- The point $(5, 13)$ is one of the points on the regression line, because substituting $x = 5$ into the regression equation of $\hat{y} = 3 + 2x$ yields $\hat{y} = 13$.

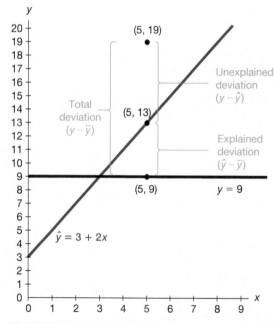

FIGURE 10-7 Total, Explained, and Unexplained Deviation

Figure 10-7 shows that the point (5, 13) lies on the regression line, but the point (5, 19) from the original data set does not lie on the regression line. If we completely ignore correlation and regression concepts and want to predict a value of y given a value of x and a collection of paired (x, y) data, our best guess would be the mean $\bar{y} = 9$. But in this case there is a linear correlation between x and y, so a better way to predict the value of y when $x = 5$ is to substitute $x = 5$ into the regression equation to get $\hat{y} = 13$. We can *explain* the discrepancy between $\bar{y} = 9$ and $\hat{y} = 13$ by noting that there is a linear relationship best described by the regression line. Consequently, when $x = 5$, the predicted value of y is 13, not the mean value of 9. For $x = 5$, the predicted value of y is 13, but the observed sample value of y is actually 19. The discrepancy between $\hat{y} = 13$ and $y = 19$ cannot be explained by the regression line, and it is called a *residual* or *unexplained deviation,* which can be expressed in the general format of $y - \hat{y}$.

As in Section 3-2, where we defined the standard deviation, we again consider a *deviation* to be a difference between a value and the mean. (In this case, the mean is $\bar{y} = 9$.) Examine Figure 10-7 carefully and note these specific deviations from $\bar{y} = 9$:

$$\textit{Total deviation } (\text{from } \bar{y} = 9) \text{ of the point } (5, 19) = y - \bar{y} = 19 - 9 = 10$$

$$\textit{Explained deviation } (\text{from } \bar{y} = 9) \text{ of the point } (5, 19) = \hat{y} - \bar{y} = 13 - 9 = 4$$

$$\textit{Unexplained deviation } (\text{from } \bar{y} = 9) \text{ of the point } (5, 19) = y - \hat{y} = 19 - 13 = 6$$

These deviations from the mean are generalized and formally defined as follows.

DEFINITIONS

Assume that we have a collection of paired data containing the sample point (x, y), that $\hat{y}$ is the predicted value of y (obtained by using the regression equation), and that the mean of the sample y values is $\bar{y}$.

The **total deviation** of (x, y) is the vertical distance $y - \bar{y}$, which is the distance between the point (x, y) and the horizontal line passing through the sample mean $\bar{y}$.

The **explained deviation** is the vertical distance $\hat{y} - \bar{y}$, which is the distance between the predicted y value and the horizontal line passing through the sample mean $\bar{y}$.

The **unexplained deviation** is the vertical distance $y - \hat{y}$, which is the vertical distance between the point (x, y) and the regression line. (The distance $y - \hat{y}$ is also called a *residual,* as defined in Section 10-2.)

In Figure 10-7 we can see the following relationship for an individual point (x, y):

$$(\text{total deviation}) = (\text{explained deviation}) + (\text{unexplained deviation})$$
$$(y - \bar{y}) \quad = \quad (\hat{y} - \bar{y}) \quad + \quad (y - \hat{y})$$

The expression above involves deviations away from the mean, and it applies to any one particular point (x, y). If we sum the squares of deviations using all points (x, y), we get amounts of *variation.* The same relationship applies to the sums of squares shown in Formula 10-7, even though the expression above is not algebraically equivalent to Formula 10-7. In Formula 10-7, the **total variation** is the sum of the squares of the total deviation values, the **explained variation** is the sum of the squares of the explained deviation values, and the **unexplained variation** is the sum of the squares of the unexplained deviation values.

FORMULA 10-7

$$(\text{total variation}) = (\text{explained variation}) + (\text{unexplained variation})$$
$$\Sigma(y - \bar{y})^2 = \Sigma(\hat{y} - \bar{y})^2 + \Sigma(y - \hat{y})^2$$

Coefficient of Determination

In Section 10-1 we saw that the linear correlation coefficient r can be used to find the proportion of the total variation in y that can be explained by the linear correlation. This statement was made in Section 10-1:

> **The value of r^2 is the proportion of the variation in y that is explained by the linear relationship between x and y.**

This statement about the explained variation is formalized with the following definition.

DEFINITION

The **coefficient of determination** is the proportion of the variation in y that is explained by the regression line. It is computed as

$$r^2 = \frac{\text{explained variation}}{\text{total variation}}$$

We can compute r^2 by using the formula given in the preceding definition (along with Formula 10-7), or we can simply square the linear correlation coefficient r. Go with squaring r.

CP **EXAMPLE 2** Jackpot/Tickets Data: Finding the Coefficient of Determination

If we use the nine pairs of jackpot/tickets data from Table 10-1, we find that the linear correlation coefficient is $r = 0.947$. Find the coefficient of determination. Also, find the percentage of the total variation in y (tickets) that can be explained by the linear correlation between the jackpot amount and number of tickets sold.

SOLUTION

With $r = 0.947$ the coefficient of determination is $r^2 = 0.897$.

INTERPRETATION

Because r^2 is the proportion of total variation that can be explained, we conclude that 89.7% of the total variation in tickets sold can be explained by the amount of the jackpot, and the other 10.3% cannot be explained by the jackpot. The other 10.3% might be explained by some other factors and/or random variation.

YOUR TURN. Do Exercise 5 "Times of Taxi Rides and Tips."

TECH CENTER

 Prediction Intervals

Access tech supplements, videos, and data sets at **www.TriolaStats.com**

Statdisk	Minitab	StatCrunch
Statdisk provides the intercept and slope of the regression equation, the standard error of estimate (labeled "Standard Error"), and the coefficient of determination. These results are helpful in finding a prediction interval, but the actual prediction interval is not provided. 1. Click **Analysis** in the top menu. 2. Select **Correlation and Regression** from the dropdown menu. 3. Enter the desired significance level and select the two columns to be evaluated. 4. Click **Evaluate.**	1. Complete the Minitab Regression procedure from Section 10-2 to get the regression equation. Minitab will automatically use this equation in this procedure. 2. Click **Stat** in the top menu. 3. Select **Regression** from the dropdown menu and select **Regression—Predict** from the submenu. 4. Select **Enter individual values** from the dropdown menu. 5. Enter the desired value(s) for the *x* variable. 6. Click the **Options** button and change the confidence level to the desired value. 7. Click **OK** twice.	1. Click **Stat** in the top menu. 2. Select **Regression** from the dropdown menu, then select **Simple Linear** from the submenu. 3. Select the columns to be used for the *x* variable and *y* variable. 4. For *Prediction of Y* enter the desired *x* value(s) and significance level. 5. Click **Compute!**

TI-83/84 Plus Calculator

TI-83/84 Plus results include the intercept (a) and slope of the regression equation (b), the standard error of estimate (s), and the coefficient of determination (r^2). These results are helpful in finding a prediction interval, but the actual prediction interval is not provided.

1. Press **STAT**, then select **TESTS** in the top menu.
2. Select **LinRegTTest** in the menu and press **ENTER**.
3. Enter the list names for the *x* and *y* variables. Enter **1** for *Freq* and for β & ρ select $\neq$ **0** to test the null hypothesis of no correlation.
4. Select **Calculate** and press **ENTER** to view results.

Excel

XLSTAT Add-In

1. Enter the sample data in columns of the worksheet.
2. Enter the desired value(s) for *x* to be used for the prediction interval in a column.
3. Click on the **XLSTAT** tab in the Ribbon and then click **Modeling data.**
4. Select **Linear regression** from the dropdown menu.
5. Enter the range of cells containing the *Y/Dependent variable* data and *X/Explanatory variable* data. Check the **Quantitative** box under *X/Explanatory variable*. If the first data row includes a label, check the **Variable labels** box.
6. Click the **Options** tab and enter the desired confidence interval, such as **95.**
7. Click the **Prediction** tab.
8. Check the **Prediction** box and in the *Quantitative* box enter the cell range containing the desired value(s) of *x* from Step 2. The first cell in the range must contain a value, not a label.
9. Click **OK.** The prediction interval(s) are in the *Predictions for the new observations* table.

Excel (Data Analysis Add-In)
Excel provides the intercept and slope of the regression equation, the standard error of estimate s_e (labeled "Standard Error"), and the coefficient of determination (labeled "R Square"). These results are helpful in finding a prediction interval, but the actual prediction interval is not provided.

1. Click on the **Data** tab in the Ribbon and then click the **Data Analysis** tab.
2. Select **Regression** under *Analysis Tools* and click **OK.**
3. For *Input Y Range* enter the data range for the dependent *y* variable. For *Input X Range* enter the data range for the independent *x* variable.
4. Check the **Labels** box if the first row contains a label.
5. Click **OK** to display the results.

R

R command:

predict(lm(y~x), interval = "confidence", conf.level = 0.95)

TIP: Results provided for each value of x and in same order that x values occur in data set.

A complete list of R statistical commands is available at TriolaStats.com

10-3 Basic Skills and Concepts

Statistical Literacy and Critical Thinking

1. s_e Notation Using Data Set 1 "Body Data" in Appendix B, if we let the predictor variable x represent heights of males and let the response variable y represent weights of males, the sample of 153 heights and weights results in $s_e = 16.27555$ cm. In your own words, describe what that value of s_e represents.

2. Prediction Interval Using the heights and weights described in Exercise 1, a height of 180 cm is used to find that the predicted weight is 91.3 kg, and the 95% prediction interval is (59.0 kg, 123.6 kg). Write a statement that interprets that prediction interval. What is the major advantage of using a prediction interval instead of simply using the predicted weight of 91.3 kg? Why is the terminology of *prediction interval* used instead of *confidence interval*?

3. Coefficient of Determination Using the heights and weights described in Exercise 1, the linear correlation coefficient r is 0.394. Find the value of the coefficient of determination. What practical information does the coefficient of determination provide?

4. Standard Error of Estimate A random sample of 118 different female statistics students is obtained and their weights are measured in kilograms and in pounds. Using the 118 paired weights (weight in kg, weight in lb), what is the value of s_e? For a female statistics student who weighs 100 lb, the predicted weight in kilograms is 45.4 kg. What is the 95% prediction interval?

Interpreting the Coefficient of Determination. *In Exercises 5–8, use the value of the linear correlation coefficient r to find the coefficient of determination and the percentage of the total variation that can be explained by the linear relationship between the two variables.*

5. Times of Taxi Rides and Tips $r = 0.298$ (x = time in minutes, y = amount of tip in dollars)

6. Distances of Taxi Rides and Tips $r = -0.114$ (x = distance in miles, y = amount of tip in dollars)

7. Distances of Taxi Rides and Fares $r = 0.986$ (x = distance in miles, y = fare in dollars)

8. Times of Taxi Rides and Fares $r = 0.953$ (x = time in minutes, y = fare in dollars)

Interpreting a Computer Display. *In Exercises 9–12, refer to the display obtained by using the paired data consisting of weights (pounds) and highway fuel consumption amounts (mi/gal) of the large cars included in Data Set 35 "Car Data" in Appendix B. Along with the paired weights and fuel consumption amounts, StatCrunch was also given the value of 4000 pounds to be used for predicting highway fuel consumption.*

StatCrunch

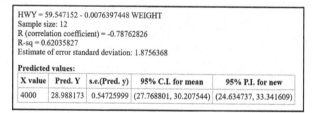

X value	Pred. Y	s.e.(Pred. y)	95% C.I. for mean	95% P.I. for new
4000	28.988173	0.54725999	(27.768801, 30.207544)	(24.634737, 33.341609)

9. Testing for Correlation Use the information provided in the display to determine the value of the linear correlation coefficient. Is there sufficient evidence to support a claim of a linear correlation between weights of large cars and the highway fuel consumption amounts?

10. Identifying Total Variation What percentage of the total variation in highway fuel consumption can be explained by the linear correlation between weight and highway fuel consumption?

11. Predicting Highway Fuel Consumption Using a car weight of $x = 4000$ (pounds), what is the single value that is the best predicted amount of highway fuel consumption?

12. Finding a Prediction Interval For a car weighing 4000 pounds $(x = 4000)$, identify the 95% prediction interval estimate of the highway fuel consumption. Write a statement interpreting that interval.

Finding a Prediction Interval. *In Exercises 13–16, use the following paired data consisting of weights of large cars (pounds) and highway fuel consumption (mi/gal) from Data Set 35 "Car Data" in Appendix B. (These are the same data used in Exercises 9-12.) Let x represent the weight of the car and let y represent the corresponding highway fuel consumption. Use the given weight and the given confidence level to construct a prediction interval estimate of highway fuel consumption.*

Weight	3608	3962	4253	4006	3754	3859	3874	4674	4321	4346	3891	3957
Highway	32	27	25	31	28	30	30	24	27	26	33	31

13. Cars Use $x = 3500$ pounds with a 95% confidence level.

14. Cars Use $x = 4200$ pounds with a 99% confidence level.

15. Cars Use $x = 3800$ pounds with a 99% confidence level.

16. Cars Use $x = 3750$ pounds with a 95% confidence level.

Variation and Prediction Intervals. *In Exercises 17–20, find the (a) explained variation, (b) unexplained variation, and (c) indicated prediction interval. In each case, there is sufficient evidence to support a claim of a linear correlation, so it is reasonable to use the regression equation when making predictions.*

17. Altitude and Temperature Listed below are altitudes (thousands of feet) and outside air temperatures (°F) recorded by the author during Delta Flight 1053 from New Orleans to Atlanta. For the prediction interval, use a 95% confidence level with the altitude of 6327 ft (or 6.327 thousand feet).

Altitude (thousands of feet)	3	10	14	22	28	31	33
Temperature (°F)	57	37	24	−5	−30	−41	−54

18. Town Courts Listed below are amounts of court income and salaries paid to the town justices (based on data from the *Poughkeepsie Journal*). All amounts are in thousands of dollars, and all of the towns are in Dutchess County, New York. For the prediction interval, use a 99% confidence level with a court income of $800,000.

Court Income	65	404	1567	1131	272	252	111	154	32
Justice Salary	30	44	92	56	46	61	25	26	18

19. Crickets and Temperature The table below lists numbers of cricket chirps in 1 minute and the temperature in °F. For the prediction interval, use 1000 chirps in 1 minute and use a 90% confidence level.

Chirps in 1 min	882	1188	1104	864	1200	1032	960	900
Temperature (°F)	69.7	93.3	84.3	76.3	88.6	82.6	71.6	79.6

20. Weighing Seals with a Camera The table below lists overhead widths (cm) of seals measured from photographs and the weights (kg) of the seals (based on "Mass Estimation of Weddell Seals Using Techniques of Photogrammetry," by R. Garrott of Montana State University). For the prediction interval, use a 99% confidence level with an overhead width of 9.0 cm.

Overhead Width	7.2	7.4	9.8	9.4	8.8	8.4
Weight	116	154	245	202	200	191

10-3 Beyond the Basics

21. Confidence Interval for Mean Predicted Value Example 1 in this section illustrated the procedure for finding a prediction interval for an *individual* value of y. When using a specific value x_0 for predicting the *mean* of all values of y, the confidence interval is as follows:

$$\hat{y} - E < \bar{y} < \hat{y} + E$$

where

$$E = t_{\alpha/2} \cdot s_e \sqrt{\frac{1}{n} + \frac{n(x_0 - \bar{x})^2}{n(\Sigma x^2) - (\Sigma x)^2}}$$

The critical value $t_{\alpha/2}$ is found with $n - 2$ degrees of freedom. Using the 9 pairs of jackpot/tickets data from Table 10-1 on page 507, find a 95% confidence interval estimate of the mean number of tickets sold when the jackpot is 625 million dollars.

10-4 Multiple Regression

Key Concept So far in this chapter we have discussed the linear correlation between *two* variables, but this section presents methods for analyzing a linear relationship with *more than two* variables. We focus on these two key elements: (1) finding the multiple regression equation, and (2) using the value of adjusted R^2 and the P-value as measures of how well the multiple regression equation fits the sample data. Because the required calculations are so difficult, manual calculations are impractical and a threat to mental health, so this section emphasizes the use and interpretation of results from technology.

PART 1 Basic Concepts of a Multiple Regression Equation

As in the preceding sections of this chapter, we will consider *linear* relationships only. The following *multiple regression equation* describes linear relationships involving more than two variables.

> **DEFINITION**
>
> A **multiple regression equation** expresses a linear relationship between a response variable y and two or more predictor variables $(x_1, x_2, \ldots, x_k)$. The general form of a multiple regression equation obtained from sample data is
>
> $$\hat{y} = b_0 + b_1 x_1 + b_2 x_2 + \cdots + b_k x_k$$

The following Key Elements box includes the key components of this section. For notation, see that the coefficients $b_0, b_1, b_2, \ldots, b_k$ are sample *statistics* used to estimate the corresponding population parameters $\beta_0, \beta_1, \beta_2, \ldots, \beta_k$. Also, note that the multiple regression equation is a natural extension of the format $\hat{y} = b_0 + b_1 x_1$ used in Section 10-2 for regression equations with a single independent variable x_1. In Section 10-2, it would have been reasonable to question why we didn't use the more common and familiar format of $y = mx + b$, and we can now see that using $\hat{y} = b_0 + b_1 x_1$ allows us to easily extend that format to include additional predictor variables.

Finding a Multiple Regression Equation

Objective

Use sample matched data from three or more variables to find a multiple regression equation that is useful for predicting values of the response variable y.

Notation

$\hat{y} = b_0 + b_1 x_1 + b_2 x_2 + \cdots + b_k x_k$ (multiple regression equation found from *sample* data)

$y = \beta_0 + \beta_1 x_1 + \beta_2 x_2 + \cdots + \beta_k x_k$ (multiple regression equation for the *population* of data)

$\hat{y}$ = predicted value of y (computed using the multiple regression equation)

k = number of *predictor* variables (also called *independent variables* or x variables)

n = sample size (number of values for any one of the variables)

Requirements

For any specific set of x values, the regression equation is associated with a random error often denoted by ε. We assume that such errors are normally distributed with a mean of 0 and a standard deviation of σ and that the random errors are independent.

Procedure for Finding a Multiple Regression Equation

Manual calculations are not practical, so technology must be used. (See the "Tech Center" instructions at the end of this section.)

In 1886, Francis Galton was among the first to study genetics using the methods of regression we are now considering. He wrote the article "Regression Towards Mediocrity in Hereditary Stature," claiming that heights of offspring regress or revert back toward a mean. Although we continue to use the term "regression," current applications extend far beyond those involving heights.

EXAMPLE 1   Predicting Weight

Data Set 1 "Body Data" in Appendix B includes heights (cm), waist circumferences (cm), and weights (kg) from a sample of 153 males. Find the multiple regression equation in which the response variable (y) is the weight of a male and the predictor variables are height (x_1) and waist circumference (x_2).

SOLUTION

Using Statdisk with the sample data in Data Set 1, we obtain the results shown in the display on the top of the next page. The coefficients b_0, b_1, and b_2 are used in the multiple regression equation:

$$\hat{y} = -149 + 0.769 x_1 + 1.01 x_2$$

or

$$\text{Weight} = -149 + 0.769\,\text{Height} + 1.01\,\text{Waist}$$

The obvious advantage of the second format above is that it is easier to keep track of the roles that the variables play.

continued

Statdisk

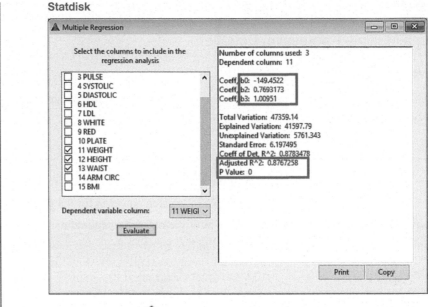

<figure>
Multiple Regression

Select the columns to include in the regression analysis

☐ 3 PULSE
☐ 4 SYSTOLIC
☐ 5 DIASTOLIC
☐ 6 HDL
☐ 7 LDL
☐ 8 WHITE
☐ 9 RED
☐ 10 PLATE
☑ 11 WEIGHT
☑ 12 HEIGHT
☑ 13 WAIST
☐ 14 ARM CIRC
☐ 15 BMI

Dependent variable column: [11 WEIGI ∨]

[Evaluate]

Number of columns used: 3
Dependent column: 11

Coeff. b0: -149.4522
Coeff. b2: 0.7693173
Coeff. b3: 1.00951

Total Variation: 47359.14
Explained Variation: 41597.79
Unexplained Variation: 5761.343
Standard Error: 6.197495
Coeff of Det, R^2: 0.8783478
Adjusted R^2: 0.8767258
P Value: 0

[Print] [Copy]
</figure>

▶ **YOUR TURN.** Do Exercise 13 "Predicting Car Fuel Consumption."

If a multiple regression equation fits the sample data well, it can be used for predictions. For example, if we determine that the multiple regression equation in Example 1 is suitable for predictions, we can use the height and waist circumference of a male to predict his weight. But how do we determine whether the multiple regression equation fits the sample data well? Two very helpful tools are the values of adjusted R^2 and the P-value.

R^2 and Adjusted R^2

R^2 denotes the **multiple coefficient of determination**, which is a measure of how well the multiple regression equation fits the sample data. A perfect fit would result in $R^2 = 1$, and a very good fit results in a value near 1. A very poor fit results in a value of R^2 close to 0. The value of $R^2 = 0.878$ ("Coeff of Det, R^2") in the Statdisk display for Example 1 indicates that 87.8% of the variation in weights of males can be explained by their heights and waist circumferences. However, the multiple coefficient of determination R^2 has a serious flaw: As more variables are included, R^2 increases. (R^2 could remain the same, but it usually increases.) The largest R^2 is obtained by simply including *all* of the available variables, but the best multiple regression equation does not necessarily use all of the available variables. Because of that flaw, it is better to use the *adjusted coefficient of determination,* which is R^2 adjusted for the number of variables and the sample size.

> **DEFINITION**
>
> The **adjusted coefficient of determination** is the multiple coefficient of determination R^2 modified to account for the number of variables and the sample size. It is calculated by using Formula 10-8.

FORMULA 10-8

$$\text{Adjusted } R^2 = 1 - \frac{(n - 1)}{[n - (k + 1)]}(1 - R^2)$$

where

$$n = \text{sample size}$$
$$k = \text{number of predictor } (x) \text{ variables}$$

   The preceding Statdisk display shows the adjusted coefficient of determination as "Adjusted R^2" = 0.877 (rounded). If we use Formula 10-8 with $R^2 = 0.8783478$, $n = 153$, and $k = 2$, we get adjusted $R^2 = 0.877$ (rounded). When comparing this multiple regression equation to others, it is better to use the adjusted R^2 of 0.877. When considering the adjusted R^2 of 0.877 by itself, we see that it is fairly high (close to 1), suggesting that the regression equation is a good fit with the sample data.

P-Value

The *P*-value is a measure of the overall significance of the multiple regression equation. The displayed *P*-value of 0 (rounded) is small, indicating that the multiple regression equation has good overall significance and is usable for predictions. We can predict weights of males based on their heights and waist circumferences. Like the adjusted R^2, this *P*-value is a good measure of how well the equation fits the sample data. The *P*-value results from a test of the null hypothesis that $\beta_1 = \beta_2 = 0$. Rejection of $\beta_1 = \beta_2 = 0$ implies that at least one of β_1 and β_2 is not 0, indicating that this regression equation is effective in predicting weights of males. A complete analysis of results might include other important elements, such as the significance of the individual coefficients, but we are keeping things simple (!) by limiting our discussion to the three key components—multiple regression equation, adjusted R^2, and *P*-value.

Finding the Best Multiple Regression Equation

When trying to find the best multiple regression equation, we should not necessarily include all of the available predictor variables. Finding the best multiple regression equation requires abundant use of judgment and common sense, and there is no exact and automatic procedure that can be used to find the best multiple regression equation. *Determination of the best multiple regression equation is often quite difficult and is beyond the scope of this section,* but the following guidelines are helpful.

Guidelines for Finding the Best Multiple Regression Equation

1. *Use common sense and practical considerations to include or exclude variables.* For example, when trying to find a good multiple regression equation for predicting the height of a daughter, we should exclude the height of the physician who delivered the daughter, because that height is obviously irrelevant.

2. *Consider the P-value.* Select an equation having overall significance, as determined by a low *P*-value found in the technology results display.

3. *Consider equations with high values of adjusted R^2, and try to include only a few variables.* Instead of including almost every available variable, try to include relatively few predictor (x) variables. Use these guidelines:

   - Select an equation having a value of adjusted R^2 with this property: If an additional predictor variable is included, the value of adjusted R^2 does not increase very much.

   - For a particular number of predictor (x) variables, select the equation with the largest value of adjusted R^2.

   - In excluding predictor (x) variables that don't have much of an effect on the response (y) variable, it might be helpful to find the linear correlation coefficient r for each pair of variables being considered. If two predictor values have a very high linear correlation coefficient (called *multicollinearity*), there is no need to include them both, and we should exclude the variable with the lower value of adjusted R^2.

The following example illustrates that common sense and *critical thinking* are essential tools for effective use of methods of statistics.

EXAMPLE 2   **Predicting Height from Footprint Evidence**

Data Set 9 "Foot and Height" in Appendix B includes the age, foot length, shoe print length, shoe size, and height for each of 40 different subjects. Using those sample data, find the regression equation that is best for predicting height. Is the "best" regression equation a *good* equation for predicting height?

SOLUTION

Using the response variable of height and possible predictor variables of age, foot length, shoe print length, and shoe size, there are 15 different possible combinations of predictor variables. Table 10-5 includes key results from five of those combinations. Blind and thoughtless application of regression methods would suggest that the best regression equation uses all four of the predictor variables, because that combination yields the highest adjusted R^2 value of 0.7585. However, given the objective of using evidence to estimate the height of a suspect, we use *critical thinking* as follows.

1. Delete the variable of age, because criminals rarely leave evidence identifying their ages.

2. Delete the variable of shoe size, because it is really a rounded form of foot length.

3. For the remaining variables of foot length and shoe print length, use only foot length because its adjusted R^2 value of 0.7014 is greater than 0.6520 for shoe print length, and it is not very much less than the adjusted R^2 value of 0.7484 for both foot length and shoe print length. In this case, it is better to use one predictor variable instead of two.

4. Although it appears that the use of the single variable of foot length is best, we also note that criminals usually wear shoes, so shoe print lengths are more likely to be found than foot lengths.

TABLE 10-5 Select Key Results from Data Set 9 "Foot and Height" in Appendix B

Predictor Variables	Adjusted R^2	P-Value	
Age	0.1772	0.004	← **Not best:** Adjusted R^2 is far less than 0.7014 for Foot Length.
Foot Length	**0.7014**	**0.000**	← **Best:** High adjusted R^2 and lowest P-value.
Shoe Print Length	0.6520	0.000	← **Not best:** Adjusted R^2 is less than 0.7014 for Foot Length.
Foot Length/Shoe Print Length	0.7484	0.000	← **Not best:** The adjusted R^2 value is not very much higher than 0.7014 for the single variable of Foot Length.
Age/Foot Length/ Shoe Print Length/ Shoe Size	0.7585	0.000	← **Not best:** There are other cases using fewer variables with adjusted R^2 that are not too much smaller.

INTERPRETATION

Blind use of regression methods suggests that when estimating the height of a subject, we should use all of the available data by including all four predictor variables of age, foot length, shoe print length, and shoe size, but practical considerations suggest that it is best to use the single predictor variable of foot length. So the best regression equation appears to be: Height = 64.1 + 4.29 (Foot Length).

However, given that criminals usually wear shoes, it is best to use the single predictor variable of shoe print length, so the best practical regression equation appears to be this: Height $= 80.9 + 3.22$ (Shoe Print Length). The P-value of 0.000 suggests that the regression equation yields a good model for estimating height.

Because the results of this example are based on sample data from only 40 subjects, estimates of heights will not be very accurate. As is usually the case, better results could be obtained by using larger samples.

YOUR TURN. Do Exercise 13 "Predicting Car Fuel Consumption."

Tests of Regression Coefficients The preceding guidelines for finding the best multiple regression equation are based on the adjusted R^2 and the P-value, but we could also conduct individual hypothesis tests based on values of the regression coefficients. Consider the regression coefficient of β_1. A test of the null hypothesis $\beta_1 = 0$ can tell us whether the corresponding predictor variable should be included in the regression equation. Rejection of $\beta_1 = 0$ suggests that β_1 has a nonzero value and is therefore helpful for predicting the value of the response variable. Procedures for such tests are described in Exercise 17.

Predictions With Multiple Regression

When we discussed regression in Section 10-2, we listed (on page 533) four points to consider when using regression equations to make predictions. These same points should be considered when using multiple regression equations.

PART 2 Dummy Variables and Logistic Regression

So far in this chapter, all variables have represented continuous data, but many situations involve a variable with only *two* possible qualitative values (such as male/female or dead/alive or cured/not cured). To obtain regression equations that include such variables, we must somehow assign numbers to the two different categories. A common procedure is to represent the two possible values by 0 and 1, where 0 represents a "failure" and 1 represents a "success." For disease outcomes, 1 is often used to represent the event of the disease or death, and 0 is used to represent the nonevent.

> **DEFINITION**
>
> A **dummy variable** is a variable having only the values of 0 and 1 that are used to represent the two different categories of a qualitative variable.

A dummy variable is sometimes called a *dichotomous variable*. The word "dummy" is used because the variable does not actually have any quantitative value, but we use it as a substitute to represent the different categories of the qualitative variable.

Dummy Variable as a Predictor Variable

Procedures of regression analysis differ dramatically, depending on whether the dummy variable is a predictor (x) variable or the response (y) variable. If we include a dummy variable as another *predictor* (x) variable, we can use the same methods of Part 1 in this section, as illustrated in Example 3.

Icing the Kicker

Just as a kicker in football is about to attempt a field goal, it is a common strategy for the opposing coach to call a time-out to "ice" the kicker. The theory is that the kicker has time to think and become nervous and less confident, but does the practice actually work? In "The Cold-Foot Effect" by Scott M. Berry in *Chance* magazine, the author wrote about his statistical analysis of results from two National Football League (NFL) seasons. He uses a logistic regression model with variables such as wind, clouds, precipitation, temperature, the pressure of making the kick, and whether a time-out was called prior to the kick. He writes that "the conclusion from the model is that icing the kicker works—it is likely icing the kicker reduces the probability of a successful kick."

EXAMPLE 3   Using a Dummy Variable as a Predictor Variable

Table 10-6 is adapted from Data Set 10 "Family Heights" in Appendix B and it is in a more convenient format for this example. Use the dummy variable of sex (coded as 0 = female, 1 = male). Given that a father is 69 in. tall and a mother is 63 in. tall, find the multiple regression equation and use it to predict the height of (a) a daughter and (b) a son.

TABLE 10-6 Heights (inches) of Fathers, Mothers, and Their Children

Height of Father	Height of Mother	Height of Child	Sex of Child (1 = Male)
66.5	62.5	70.0	1
70.0	64.0	68.0	1
67.0	65.0	69.7	1
68.7	70.5	71.0	1
69.5	66.0	71.0	1
70.0	65.0	73.0	1
69.0	66.0	70.0	1
68.5	67.0	73.0	1
65.5	60.0	68.0	1
69.5	66.5	70.5	1
70.5	63.0	64.5	0
71.0	65.0	62.0	0
70.5	62.0	60.0	0
66.0	66.0	67.0	0
68.0	61.0	63.5	0
68.0	63.0	63.0	0
71.0	62.0	64.5	0
65.5	63.0	63.5	0
64.0	60.0	60.0	0
71.0	63.0	63.5	0

SOLUTION

Using the methods of multiple regression from Part 1 of this section and computer software, we get this regression equation:

$$\text{Height of child} = 36.5 - 0.0336\,(\text{Height of father})$$
$$+ 0.461\,(\text{Height of mother}) + 6.14\,(\text{Sex})$$

where the value of the dummy variable of sex is either 0 for a daughter or 1 for a son.

   a. To find the predicted height of a *daughter*, we substitute 0 for the sex variable, and we also substitute 69 in. for the father's height and 63 in. for the mother's height. The result is a predicted height of 63.2 in. for a daughter.

   b. To find the predicted height of a *son*, we substitute 1 for the sex variable, and we also substitute 69 in. for the father's height and 63 in. for the mother's height. The result is a predicted height of 69.4 in. for a son.

The coefficient of 6.14 in the regression equation shows that when given the height of a father and the height of a mother, a son will have a predicted height that is 6.14 in. more than the height of a daughter.

 YOUR TURN. Do Exercise 19 "Dummy Variable."

Logistic Regression In Example 3, we could use the same methods of Part 1 in this section because the dummy variable of sex is a *predictor* variable. However, if the dummy variable is the response (y) variable, we cannot use the methods in Part 1 of this section, and we should use a different method known as **logistic regression.** This section does not include detailed procedures for using logistic regression, but many books are devoted to this topic. Example 4 briefly illustrates the method of logistic regression.

EXAMPLE 4 **Logistic Regression**

Let a sample data set consist of the heights (cm) and arm circumferences (cm) of women and men as listed in Data Set 1 "Body Data" in Appendix B. Let the *response y* variable represent gender (0 = female, 1 = male). Using the gender values of y and the combined list of corresponding heights and arm circumferences, logistic regression could be used to obtain this model:

$$\ln\left(\frac{p}{1-p}\right) = -40.6 + 0.242(\text{HT}) + 0.000129(\text{ArmCirc})$$

In the expression above, p is the probability of a male, so $p = 1$ indicates that the subject is definitely a male, and $p = 0$ indicates that the subject is definitely not a male (so the subject is a female). [To solve for p, substitute values for height and arm circumference to get a value v, then $p = e^v/(1 + e^v)$.] See the following two sets of results.

- If we use the model above and substitute a height of 183 cm (or 72.0 in.) and an arm circumference of 33 cm (or 13.0 in.), we can solve for p to get $p = 0.976$, indicating that such a person has a 97.6% chance of being a male.

- In contrast, a smaller person with a height of 150 cm (or 59.1 in.) and an arm circumference of 20 cm (or 7.9 in.) results in a probability of $p = 0.0134$, indicating that such a small person is very unlikely to be a male.

TECH CENTER

Multiple Regression
Access tech supplements, videos, and data sets at **www.TriolaStats.com**

Statdisk	Minitab	StatCrunch
1. Click **Analysis** in the top menu.	1. Click **Stat** in the top menu.	1. Click **Stat** in the top menu.
2. Select **Multiple Regression** from the dropdown menu.	2. Select **Regression** from the dropdown menu and select **Regression—Fit Regression Model** from the submenu.	2. Select **Regression** from the dropdown menu, then select **Multiple Linear** from the submenu.
3. Select the columns to be included in the regression analysis. For *Dependent variable column,* select the column to be used for the dependent *y* variable.	3. Under *Responses* select the column that contains the dependent *y* values. Under *Continuous predictors* select the columns that contain the variables you want included as predictor *x* variables.	3. Select the column to be used for the *y* variable and columns to be used for the *x* variable.
4. Click **Evaluate**.	4. Click **OK**. The regression equation is included in the results.	4. Click **Compute!**

continued

TECH CENTER *continued*

Multiple Regression

Access tech supplements, videos, and data sets at **www.TriolaStats.com**

TI-83/84 Plus Calculator

Requires program *A2MULREG* (available at TriolaStats.com)

1. Data must be entered as columns in *Matrix D*, with the first column containing values of the dependent *y* variable:
   Manually enter data: Press **2ND** then **x⁻¹** to get to the *MATRIX* menu, select **EDIT** from the top menu, select **[D]**, and press **ENTER**. Enter the number of rows and columns needed, press **ENTER**, and proceed to enter the sample values.

   Using existing lists: Lists can be combined and stored in *Matrix D*. Press **2ND** then **x⁻¹** to get to the *MATRIX* menu, select **MATH** from the top menu, and select the item **List → matr**. Enter the list names (the first list must contain values for the dependent *y* variable), followed by the matrix name **[D]**, all separated by **,** .
   Important: The matrix name must be entered by pressing **2ND** then **x⁻¹**, selecting **[D]**, and pressing **ENTER**. The following is a summary of the commands used to create a matrix from three lists (L1, L2, L3):
   List → matr(L1, L2, L3, [D]).

2. Press **PRGM**, select *A2MULREG*, press **ENTER** three times, select **MULT REGRESSION**, and press **ENTER**.

3. Enter the number of independent *x* variables, then enter the column number of each independent *x* variable. Press **ENTER** after each entry.

4. The results will be displayed, including *P*-value and adjusted R^2. Press **ENTER** to view additional results, including values used in the multiple regression equation.

5. Press **ENTER** to select the **QUIT** option.

TIP: The list name *L1* (and *L2 . . . L6*) can be quickly entered by pressing **2ND** **1**.

Excel

XLSTAT Add-In

1. Click on the **XLSTAT** tab in the Ribbon and then click **Modeling data.**
2. Select **Linear regression** from the dropdown menu.
3. Enter the range of cells containing the *Y/Dependent variable* data and *X/Explanatory variable* data (multiple columns). Check the **Quantitative** box under *X/Explanatory variable.* If the first data row includes a label, check the **Variable labels** box.
4. Click the **Outputs** tab and ensure **Correlations** and **Analysis of variance** are both checked.
5. Click **OK,** and the equation of the multiple regression line will be displayed in the results.

Excel (Data Analysis Add-In)

1. Click on the **Data** tab in the Ribbon and then click the **Data Analysis** tab. Select **Regression** under *Analysis Tools.*
2. For *Input Y Range* enter the data range for the dependent *y* variable. For *Input X Range* enter the data range for the independent *x* variables. *The x variable data must be located in adjacent columns.*
3. Check the **Labels** box if the first row contains a label.
4. Click **OK** to display the results.

R

R commands:

Regression results (*y* intercept and slope):
lm(y~x+z)

Additional regression details:
summary(lm(y~x+z))

Predictions of *y*: **predict(lm(y~x+z), interval = "confidence", conf.level = 0.95)**

Where *y* is the dependent variable.

TIP: Additional independent variables can be added to the above formulas as needed.

A complete list of R statistical commands is available at TriolaStats.com

10-4   Basic Skills and Concepts

Statistical Literacy and Critical Thinking

1. Response and Predictor Variables Using all of the Tour de France bicycle race results up to a recent year, we get this multiple regression equation: Speed = 29.2 − 0.00260 Distance + 0.540 Stages + 0.0570 Finishers, where Speed is the mean speed of the winner (km/h), Distance is the length of the race (km), Stages is the number of stages in the race, and Finishers is the number of bicyclists who finished the race. Identify the response and predictor variables.

2. Best Multiple Regression Equation For the multiple regression equation given in Exercise 1, the P-value is 0.000 and the adjusted R^2 value is 0.894. If we were to include an additional predictor variable of the number of bicyclists who entered the race, the P-value is 0.000 and the adjusted R^2 is again 0.894. Is it correct to reason that we should include the number of bicyclists who entered the race because the adjusted R^2 remains the same but the multiple regression equation gives us more information because it includes another variable? Explain.

3. Adjusted Coefficient of Determination For Exercise 2, why is it better to use values of adjusted R^2 instead of simply using values of R^2?

4. Interpreting R^2 For the multiple regression equation given in Exercise 1, we get $R^2 = 0.897$. What does that value tell us?

Interpreting a Computer Display.   In Exercises 5–8, we want to consider the correlation between heights of fathers and mothers and the heights of their sons. Refer to the StatCrunch display and answer the given questions or identify the indicated items. The display is based on Data Set 10 "Family Heights" in Appendix B. (The response y variable represents heights of sons.)

Parameter estimates:

Parameter	Estimate	Std. Err.	Alternative	DF	T-Stat	P-value
Intercept	17.966577	6.4779134	≠ 0	131	2.7735131	0.0064
Father	0.50354896	0.067077219	≠ 0	131	7.507004	<0.0001
Mother	0.27714316	0.078318967	≠ 0	131	3.5386467	0.0006

Analysis of variance table for multiple regression model:

Source	DF	SS	MS	F-stat	P-value
Model	2	320.94662	160.47331	37.637221	<0.0001
Error	131	558.54293	4.2636865		
Total	133	879.48955			

Summary of fit:
Root MSE: 2.0648696
R-squared: 0.3649
R-squared (adjusted): 0.3552

5. Height of Son Identify the multiple regression equation that expresses the height of a son in terms of the height of his father and mother.

6. Height of Son Identify the following:

a. The P-value corresponding to the overall significance of the multiple regression equation

b. The value of the multiple coefficient of determination R^2

c. The adjusted value of R^2

7. Height of Son Should the multiple regression equation be used for predicting the height of a son based on the height of his father and mother? Why or why not?

8. Height of Son A son will be born to a father who is 70 in. tall and a mother who is 60 in. tall. Use the multiple regression equation to predict the height of the son. Is the result likely to be a good predicted value? Why or why not?

Garbage: Finding the Best Multiple Regression Equation. *In Exercises 9–12, refer to the accompanying table, which was obtained by using the data from 62 households listed in Data Set 42 "Garbage Weight" in Appendix B. The response (y) variable is PLAS (weight of discarded plastic in pounds). The predictor (x) variables are METAL (weight of discarded metals in pounds), PAPER (weight of discarded paper in pounds), and GLASS (weight of discarded glass in pounds).*

Predictor (x) Variables	P-Value	R^2	Adjusted R^2	Regression Equation
METAL/PAPER/GLASS	0.000	0.563	0.540	PLAS = −0.170 + 0.290 METAL + 0.122 PAPER + 0.0777 GLASS
METAL/PAPER	0.000	0.514	0.498	PLAS = 0.00394 + 0.344 METAL + 0.121 PAPER
PAPER/GLASS	0.000	0.499	0.482	PLAS = 0.0647 + 0.157 PAPER + 0.0967 GLASS
METAL/GLASS	0.000	0.392	0.371	PLAS = 0.469 + 0.519 METAL + 0.0774 GLASS
METAL	0.000	0.344	0.333	PLAS = 0.641 + 0.573 METAL
PAPER	0.000	0.421	0.411	PLAS = 0.348 + 0.166 PAPER
GLASS	0.005	0.126	0.111	PLAS = 1.46 + 0.121 GLASS

9. If only one predictor (x) variable is used to predict the weight of discarded plastic, which single variable is best? Why?

10. If exactly two predictor (x) variables are to be used to predict the weight of discarded plastic, which two variables should be chosen? Why?

11. Which regression equation is best for predicting weight of discarded plastic? Why?

12. A household discards 3.00 lb of metal, 10.25 lb of paper, and 9.35 lb of glass. What is the best predicted value for the weight of discarded plastic? Is that predicted value likely to be a good estimate? Is that predicted value likely to be very accurate?

Appendix B Data Sets. *In Exercises 13–16, refer to the indicated data set in Appendix B and use technology to obtain results.*

13. Predicting Car Fuel Consumption Refer to Data Set 35 "Car Data" in Appendix B and use the weight, engine displacement, and highway fuel consumption (HWY) of all 48 cars. Find the best regression equation for predicting the highway fuel consumption. Why is it best? Is the best regression equation a good regression equation for predicting the highway fuel consumption? Why or why not?

14. Predicting Height Refer to Data Set 3 "ANSUR II 2012" in Appendix B and use the variables of Height, Foot_Length, and ArmSpan for all 6068 subjects. Find the best regression equation for predicting Height. Why is it best? Is the best regression equation a good regression equation for predicting Height? Why or why not?

15. Predicting IQ Score Refer to Data Set 12 "IQ and Brain Size" in Appendix B and find the best regression equation with IQ score as the response (y) variable. Use predictor variables of brain volume and/or body weight. Why is this equation best? Based on these results, can we predict someone's IQ score if we know their brain volume and body weight? Based on these results, does it appear that people with larger brains have higher IQ scores?

16. Full IQ Score Refer to Data Set 11 "IQ and Lead" in Appendix B and find the best regression equation with IQ FULL (full IQ score) as the response (y) variable. Use predictor variables of IQ VERB (verbal IQ score) and IQ PERF (performance IQ score). Why is this equation best? Based on these results, can we predict someone's full IQ score if we know their verbal IQ score and their performance IQ score? Is such a prediction likely to be very accurate?

10-4   Beyond the Basics

17. Testing Hypotheses About Regression Coefficients If the coefficient β_1 has a non-zero value, then it is helpful in predicting the value of the response variable. If $\beta_1 = 0$, it is not helpful in predicting the value of the response variable and can be eliminated from the regression equation. To test the claim that $\beta_1 = 0$ use the test statistic $t = (b_1 - 0)/s_{b_1}$. Critical values or P-values can be found using the t distribution with $n - (k + 1)$ degrees of freedom, where k is the number of predictor (x) variables and n is the number of observations in the sample. The standard error s_{b_1} is often provided by software. For example, see the accompanying StatCrunch display for Example 1, which shows that $s_{b_1} = 0.071141412$ (found in the column with the heading of "Std. Err." and the row corresponding to the first predictor variable of height). Use the sample data in Data Set 1 "Body Data" and the StatCrunch display to test the claim that $\beta_1 = 0$. Also test the claim that $\beta_2 = 0$. What do the results imply about the regression equation?

Parameter estimates:

Parameter ♦	Estimate ♦	Std. Err. ♦	Alternative ♦	DF ♦	T-Stat ♦	P-value ♦
Intercept	-149.45217	12.523494	≠ 0	150	-11.933743	<0.0001
Height	0.76931731	0.071141412	≠ 0	150	10.813917	<0.0001
Waist	1.0095102	0.033812346	≠ 0	150	29.856261	<0.0001

18. Confidence Intervals for a Regression Coefficients A confidence interval for the regression coefficient β_1 is expressed as

$$b_1 - E < \beta_1 < b_1 + E$$

where

$$E = t_{\alpha/2} s_{b_1}$$

The critical t score is found using $n - (k + 1)$ degrees of freedom, where k, n, and s_{b_1} are described in Exercise 17. Using the sample data from Example 1, $n = 153$ and $k = 2$, so df $= 150$ and the critical t scores are ± 1.976 for a 95% confidence level. Use the sample data for Example 1, the Statdisk display in Example 1 on page 554, and the StatCrunch display in Exercise 17 to construct 95% confidence interval estimates of β_1 (the coefficient for the variable representing height) and β_2 (the coefficient for the variable representing waist circumference). Does either confidence interval include 0, suggesting that the variable be eliminated from the regression equation?

19. Dummy Variable Refer to Data Set 18 "Bear Measurements" in Appendix B and use the sex, age, and weight of the bears. For sex, let 0 represent female and let 1 represent male. Letting the response (y) variable represent weight, use the variable of age and the dummy variable of sex to find the multiple regression equation. Use the equation to find the predicted weight of a bear with the characteristics given below. Does sex appear to have much of an effect on the weight of a bear?

a. Female bear that is 20 years of age

b. Male bear that is 20 years of age

10-5   Nonlinear Regression

Key Concept The preceding sections of this chapter deal with *linear* relationships only, but not all in the world is linear. This section is a brief introduction to methods for finding some *nonlinear* functions that fit sample data. We focus on the use of technology because the required calculations are quite complex.

Shown below are five basic generic models considered in this section. Each of the five models is given with a generic formula along with an example of a specific function and its graph.

Linear: $y = a + bx$
Example: $y = 1 + 2x$

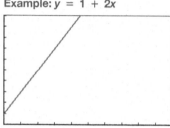

Logarithmic: $y = a + b \ln x$
Example: $y = 1 + 2 \ln x$

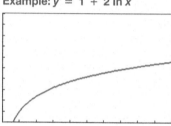

Power: $y = ax^b$
Example: $y = 3x^{2.5}$

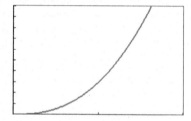

Quadratic: $y = ax^2 + bx + c$
Example: $y = x^2 - 8x + 18$

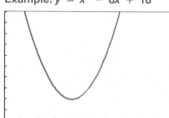

Exponential: $y = ab^x$
Example: $y = 2^x$

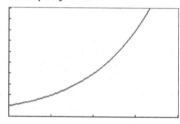

Here are three basic rules for identifying a good mathematical model:

1. ***Look for a pattern in the graph.*** Construct a graph, compare it to those shown here, and identify the model that appears to be most similar.

2. ***Compare values of R^2.*** For each model being considered, use technology to find the value of the coefficient of determination R^2. Choose functions that result in larger values of R^2, because such larger values correspond to functions that better fit the observed sample data.

   - Don't place much importance on small differences, such as the difference between $R^2 = 0.984$ and $R^2 = 0.989$.

   - Unlike in Section 10-4, we don't need to use values of adjusted R^2. Because the examples of this section all involve a single predictor variable, it makes sense to compare values of R^2.

   - In addition to R^2, another measure used to assess the quality of a model is the sum of squares of the residuals. See Exercise 18 "Sum of Squares Criterion."

3. ***Think.*** Use common sense. Don't use a model that leads to predicted values that are unrealistic. Use the model to calculate future values, past values, and values for missing data, and then determine whether the results are realistic and make sense. Don't go too far beyond the scope of the available sample data.

EXAMPLE 1 Finding the Best Population Model

Table 10-7 lists the population of the United States for different 20-year intervals. Find a mathematical model for the population size, then predict the size of the U.S. population in the year 2040.

TABLE 10-7 Population (in millions) of the United States

Year	1800	1820	1840	1860	1880	1900	1920	1940	1960	1980	2000	2020
Coded Year	1	2	3	4	5	6	7	8	9	10	11	12
Population	5	10	17	31	50	76	106	132	179	227	281	335

SOLUTION

First, we "code" the year values by using 1, 2, 3, . . . , instead of 1800, 1820, 1840, ... The reason for this coding is to use values of x that are much smaller and much less likely to cause computational difficulties.

1. *Look for a pattern in the graph.* Examine the pattern of the data values in the TI-83/84 Plus display (shown in the margin), and compare that pattern to the generic models shown earlier in this section. The pattern of those points is clearly not a straight line, so we rule out a linear model. Good candidates for the model appear to be the quadratic, exponential, and power functions.

2. *Find and compare values of R^2.* The TI-83/84 display for the quadratic model is shown in the margin. For the quadratic model, $R^2 = 0.9995$ (rounded), which is quite high. Table 10-8 includes this result with results from two other potential models. In comparing the values of the coefficient R^2, it appears that the quadratic model is best because it has the highest value of 0.9995. If we select the quadratic function as the best model, we conclude that the equation $y = 2.75x^2 - 5.80x + 9.66$ best describes the relationship between the year x (coded with $x = 1$ representing 1800, $x = 2$ representing 1820, and so on) and the population y (in millions).

    Based on its R^2 value of 0.9995, the quadratic model appears to be best, but the other values of R^2 are also quite high. Our general knowledge of population growth might suggest that the exponential model is most appropriate. (With a constant birth rate and no limiting factors, population will grow exponentially.)

TABLE 10-8 Models for the Population Data

Model	R^2	Equation
Quadratic	**0.9995**	$y = 2.75x^2 - 5.80x + 9.66$
Exponential	0.9573	$y = 5.76(1.45^x)$
Power	0.9779	$y = 3.26x^{1.79}$

To predict the U.S. population for the year 2040, first note that the year 2040 is coded as $x = 13$ (see Table 10-7). Substituting $x = 13$ into the quadratic model of $y = 2.75x^2 - 5.80x + 9.66$ results in $y = 399$, which indicates that the U.S. population is estimated to be 399 million in the year 2040.

continued

Clinical Trial Cut Short

What do you do when you're testing a new treatment and, before your study ends, you find that it is clearly effective? You should cut the study short and inform all participants of the treatment's effectiveness. This happened when hydroxyurea was tested as a treatment for sickle cell anemia. The study was scheduled to last about 40 months, but the effectiveness of the treatment became obvious and the study was stopped after 36 months. (See "Trial Halted as Sickle Cell Treatment Proves Itself," by Charles Marwick, *Journal of the American Medical Association*, Vol. 273, No. 8.)

TI-83/84 Plus

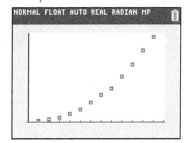

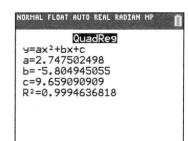

3. *Think.* The forecast result of 399 million in 2040 seems reasonable. (As of this writing, the latest figures from the U.S. Bureau of the Census use much more sophisticated methods to project that the U.S. population in 2040 will be 373 million.) However, there is considerable danger in making estimates for times that are beyond the scope of the available data. For example, the quadratic model suggests that in 1492, the U.S. population was 663 million, which is a result statisticians refer to as *ridiculous*. The quadratic model appears to be good for the available data (1800–2020), but other models might be better if it is necessary to make future population estimates.

YOUR TURN. Do Exercise 5 "Landing on the Moon."

EXAMPLE 2   Interpreting R^2

In Example 1, we obtained the value of $R^2 = 0.9995$ for the quadratic model. Interpret that value as it relates to the predictor variable of year and the response variable of population size.

SOLUTION

In the context of the year/population data from Table 10-7, the value of $R^2 = 0.9995$ can be interpreted as follows: 99.95% of the variation in the population size can be explained by the quadratic regression equation (given in Example 1) that relates year and population size.

YOUR TURN. Do Exercise 3 "Interpreting R^2."

EXAMPLE 3   COVID-19 Virus Pandemic

As this was being written in 2020, the COVID-19 virus was sweeping the world. In the United States and many other countries, residents were instructed to stay at home. Restaurants, movie theaters, and many other nonessential businesses were ordered closed. The 2020 Olympics were postponed for a year, and many other professional sports were cancelled or postponed.

Listed below are numbers of deaths in the United States resulting from the virus. The deaths occurred on consecutive days beginning with March 16, 2020, which was very early in the growth of the virus. Predicting future deaths becomes critical because those predictions could determine the distribution of important resources, such as hospital ventilators used in attempts to prevent deaths. Modeling the data became important as we all sought a return to normal life. Consequently, there were extensive and intensive efforts to develop and revise models. Use the listed data to find a mathematical model and use it to predict the number of deaths on the following day. How accurate is the prediction when compared to the actual number of 367 deaths that did occur?

19   22   48   59   53   126   73   203   225   264

SOLUTION

Use the days coded as 1, 2, 3, ... The quadratic and exponential models are very close with R^2 values of 0.918817 and 0.918732, respectively. Given that populations tend to grow exponentially, we choose the exponential model of $y = 15.1(1.34^x)$ as best, even though its R^2 value is very slightly lower than that of the quadratic model. The prediction for the next day is 378 deaths (388 if using unrounded coefficients), which is close to the actual number of 367 deaths. The quadratic model yields a prediction of 329 deaths.

YOUR TURN. Do Exercise 7 "CD Yields."

TECH CENTER

Nonlinear Regression

Access tech supplements, videos, and data sets at **www.TriolaStats.com**

Statdisk	Minitab	StatCrunch

Statdisk can find the quadratic model using the Multiple Regression *function. The following procedure features data from Table 10-7.*

1. Enter the population data from Table 10-7 in column 1 of the Sample Editor.
2. Enter the corresponding coded year values (1, 2, 3 . . . , 12) in column 2.
3. Enter the squares of the coded year values (1, 4, 9, . . . , 144) in column 3.
4. Click **Analysis** in the top menu.
5. Select **Multiple Regression** from the dropdown menu.
6. Select columns 1, 2, 3 and select column 1 as the dependent variable.
7. Click **Evaluate.** Statdisk provides the coefficients for the regression equation and value for R^2.

1. Click **Stat** in the top menu.
2. Select **Regression** from the dropdown menu and select **Fitted Line Plot** from the submenu.
3. Select the column to be used for the *Response y* variable and the column to be used for the *Predictor x* variable.
4. Choose the desired type of regression model: *Linear, Quadratic* or *Cubic*.
5. Click **OK.**

StatCrunch can find the model for a quadratic function (polynomial of order 2).

1. Click **Stat** in the top menu.
2. Select **Regression** from the dropdown menu, then select **Polynomial** from the submenu.
3. Select the column to be used for the *x* variable and *y* variable.
4. For a quadratic function select **2** under *Poly. order*.
5. Click **Compute!**

TI-83/84 Plus Calculator	Excel	R

1. Turn on the *Stat Diagnostics* feature by pressing the **MODE** button, scrolling down to **Stat Diagnostics**, highlighting **ON**, and pressing **ENTER**.
2. Press **STAT**, then select **CALC** in the top menu.
3. Select the desired model from the list of available options, then press **ENTER**.
4. Enter the desired data list names for *x* and *y* variables (for TI-83 calculators, enter the list names separated by **,**).
5. Select **Calculate** and press **ENTER**.

TIP: For TI-83 Plus calculators, turn Stat Diagnostics ON by pressing **2ND** **0** *for the Catalog menu. Scroll down to* **DiagnosticON** *and press* **ENTER** *twice.*

The XLSTAT add-in cannot be used to create nonlinear regression models, so Excel itself must be used.

1. Select the range of cells containing paired data.
2. Click the **Insert** tab in the Ribbon and select **Scatter** in the *Charts* section.
3. Right-click on any data point on the scatterplot and select **Add Trendline . . .**
4. Selected desired model and check **Display Equation on chart** and **Display R-squared value on chart.**

The basic syntax for creating a nonlinear least square test in R is provided below.

R command: **nls(formula, data, start)**

Where

- **formula** is a nonlinear model formula including variables and parameters.
- **data** is an optional data frame used to evaluate the variables in the formula.
- **start** is a named list or named numeric vector of starting estimates.

A complete list of R statistical commands is available at TriolaStats.com

10-5   Basic Skills and Concepts

Statistical Literacy and Critical Thinking

1. Identifying a Model and R^2 Samples of different square circuit boards are obtained. The sides of the squares are measured in cm (centimeters) and the areas are measured in cm^2. Let x represent the side of a square, and let y represent its area. What formula best describes the relationship between x and y? Which of the five models describes this relationship? What should be the value of R^2?

2. Super Bowl and R^2 Let x represent years coded as 1, 2, 3, . . . for years starting in 1980, and let y represent the numbers of points scored in each annual Super Bowl beginning in 1980. Using the data from 1980 to the last Super Bowl at the time of this writing, we obtain the following values of R^2 for the different models: linear: 0.008; quadratic: 0.023; logarithmic: 0.0004; exponential: 0.027; power: 0.007. Based on these results, which model is best? Is the best model a good model? What do the results suggest about predicting the number of points scored in a future Super Bowl game?

3. Interpreting R^2 In Exercise 2, the exponential model results in $R^2 = 0.027$. Identify the percentage of the variation in Super Bowl points that can be explained by the exponential model relating the variable of year and the variable of points scored. (*Hint:* See Example 2.) What does the result suggest about the usefulness of the exponential model?

4. Interpreting a Graph The accompanying graph plots the numbers of points scored in each Super Bowl from the first Super Bowl in 1967 (coded as year 1) to the last Super Bowl at the time of this writing. The graph of the quadratic equation that best fits the data is also shown in red. What feature of the graph justifies the value of $R^2 = 0.205$ for the quadratic model?

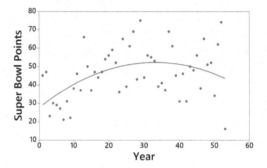

Finding the Best Model.   *In Exercises 5–16, construct a scatterplot and identify the mathematical model that best fits the given data. Assume that the model is to be used only for the scope of the given data, and consider only linear, quadratic, logarithmic, exponential, and power models.*

5. Landing on the Moon When the Apollo spacecraft landed on the Moon, the rocket engine would typically cut off at about 1.3 meters above the surface so that hot gases and dust and other surface materials would not cause damage. The landing module was in freefall starting at about 1 meter above the surface. The table below lists the time t (seconds) after being dropped and the distance d (meters) travelled by an object dropped near the surface of the Moon.

t	0.1	0.2	0.3	0.4	0.5	0.6	0.7	0.8
d	0.008	0.032	0.072	0.128	0.200	0.288	0.392	0.512

6. Dirt Cheap The Cherry Hill Construction company in Branford, CT sells screened topsoil by the "yard," which is actually a cubic yard. Let the variable x be the length (yd) of each side of a cube of screened topsoil. The table below lists the values of x along with the corresponding cost (dollars).

x	1	2	3	4	5	6	7	8
Cost	22	176	594	1408	2750	4752	7646	11,264

7. CD Yields The table lists the value y (in dollars) of $1000 deposited in a certificate of deposit at Bank of New York (based on rates currently in effect).

Year	1	2	3	4	5	6	10
Value	1010.00	1020.10	1030.30	1040.60	1051.01	1061.52	1104.62

8. Sound Intensity The table lists intensities of sounds as multiples of a basic reference sound. A scale similar to the decibel scale is used to measure the sound intensity.

Sound Intensity	316	500	750	2000	5000
Scale Value	25.0	27.0	28.75	33.0	37.0

9. Population Growth Here are the values of the world population (billions) beginning with the year 2000:

6.15	6.22	6.30	6.38	6.46	6.54	6.62	6.71	6.79	6.87
6.96	7.04	7.13	7.21	7.30	7.38	7.47	7.55	7.63	7.71

10. Deaths from Motor Vehicle Crashes Listed below are the numbers of deaths in the United States resulting from motor vehicle crashes. Use the best model to find the projected number of such deaths for the year 2025.

Year	1975	1980	1985	1990	1995	2000	2005	2010	2015
Deaths	44,525	51,091	43,825	44,599	41,817	41,945	43,443	32,708	35,485

11. Richter Scale The table lists different amounts (metric tons) of the explosive TNT and the corresponding value measured on the Richter scale resulting from explosions of the TNT.

TNT	2	10	15	50	100	500
Richter Scale	3.4	3.9	4.0	4.4	4.6	5.0

12. Detecting Fraud Leading digits of check amounts are often analyzed for the purpose of detecting fraud. The accompanying table lists frequencies of leading digits from checks written by the author (an honest guy).

Leading Digit	1	2	3	4	5	6	7	8	9
Frequency	83	58	27	21	21	21	6	4	9

13. Stock Market Listed below in order by row are the annual high values of the Dow Jones Industrial Average for each year beginning with 2000. Find the best model and then predict the value for the last year listed. Is the predicted value close to the actual value of 26,828.4?

11723.0	11337.9	10635.3	10453.9	10854.5	10940.5	12510.6	14164.5
13058.2	10548.5	11585.4	12810.5	13610.2	16576.7	18053.7	18312.4
19974.6	24837.5	26828.4					

14. Sunspot Numbers Listed below in order by row are annual sunspot numbers beginning with 1980. Is the best model a good model? Carefully examine the scatterplot and identify the pattern of the points. Which of the models fits that pattern?

154.6	140.5	115.9	66.6	45.9	17.9	13.4	29.2	100.2	157.6
142.6	145.7	94.3	54.6	29.9	17.5	8.6	21.5	64.3	93.3
119.6	123.3	123.3	65.9	40.4	29.8	15.2	7.5	2.9	3.1
16.5	55.7	57.6	64.7	79.3	44.6	24.5	13.8	4.0	

15. Earthquakes Listed below are earthquake depths (km) and magnitudes (Richter scale) of different earthquakes. Find the best model and then predict the magnitude for the last earthquake with a depth of 3.78 km. Is the predicted value close to the actual magnitude of 7.1?

Depth	6.00	7.00	5.4	17.60	15.90	11.70	17.30	22.40	15.90	3.78
Magnitude	3.62	3.06	3.3	2.58	2.91	3.38	2.79	2.61	3.13	7.10

16. Global Warming Listed below are mean annual temperatures (°C) of the earth for each decade, beginning with the decade of the 1880s. Find the best model and then predict the value for 2090–2099. Comment on the result.

13.819	13.692	13.741	13.788	13.906	14.016	14.052
13.983	13.938	14.014	14.264	14.396	14.636	

10-5 Beyond the Basics

17. Moore's Law In 1965, Intel cofounder Gordon Moore initiated what has since become known as *Moore's law:* The number of transistors per square inch on integrated circuits will double approximately every 18 months. In the table below, the first row lists different years and the second row lists the number of transistors (in thousands) for different years.

1971	1974	1978	1982	1985	1989	1993	1997	2000	2002	2003	2007	2011	2018
2.3	5	29	120	275	1180	3100	7500	42,000	220,000	410,000	789,000	2,600,000	19,200,000

a. Ignoring the listed data and assuming that Moore's law is correct and transistors per square inch double every 18 months, which mathematical model best describes this law: linear, quadratic, logarithmic, exponential, power? What specific function describes Moore's law?

b. Which mathematical model best fits the listed sample data?

c. Compare the results from parts (a) and (b). Does Moore's law appear to be working reasonably well?

18. Sum of Squares Criterion In addition to the value of R^2, another measurement used to assess the quality of a model is the *sum of squares of the residuals*. Recall from Section 10-2 that a residual is $y - \hat{y}$ (the difference between an observed y value and the value predicted from the model). Better models have smaller sums of squares. Refer to the U.S. population data in Table 10-7 on page 565.

a. Find $\Sigma (y - \hat{y})^2$, the sum of squares of the residuals resulting from the linear model.

b. Find the sum of squares of residuals resulting from the quadratic model.

c. Verify that according to the sum of squares criterion, the quadratic model is better than the linear model.

Chapter Quick Quiz

Exercises 1–10 are based on the following sample data consisting of costs of dinner (dollars) and the amounts of tips (dollars) left by diners. The data were collected by students of the author.

Cost of Dinner (dollars)	46.60	33.46	50.68	87.92	98.84	63.60	107.34	49.88
Tip (dollars)	7.50	5.50	5.00	8.08	17.00	12.00	16.00	7.00

1. Scatterplot Construct a scatterplot and comment on the pattern of points.

2. Conclusion The linear correlation coefficient r is found to be 0.846, the P-value is 0.008, and the critical values for a 0.05 significance level are ± 0.707. What should you conclude?

3. Fixed Percentage If a restaurant were to change its tipping policy so that a constant tip of 20% of the bill is added to the cost of the dinner, what would be the value of the linear correlation coefficient for the paired amounts of dinners/tips?

4. Fixed Percentage If a restaurant were to change its tipping policy so that a constant tip of 20% of the bill is added to the cost of the dinner, what would be the linear regression equation relating the cost of the dinner (x) and the amount of the tip (y)?

5. Switched Variables Which of the following values change if the two variables of dinner cost and amount of tip are switched: the value of $r = 0.846$, the P-value of 0.008, the critical values of ± 0.707?

6. Change in Scale Exercise 1 stated that for the given paired data, $r = 0.846$. How does that value change if all of the amounts of dinners are left unchanged but all of the tips are expressed in cents instead of dollars?

7. Values of r If you had computed the value of the linear correlation coefficient to be 1.200, what should you conclude?

8. Predictions The sample data result in a linear correlation coefficient of $r = 0.846$ and the regression equation $\hat{y} = -0.00777 + 0.145x$. What is the best predicted amount of tip, given that the cost of dinner was $84.62? How was the predicted value found?

9. Predictions Repeat the preceding exercise assuming that the linear correlation coefficient is $r = 0.132$.

10. Explained Variation Given that the linear correlation coefficient r is found to be 0.846, what is the proportion of the variation in tips that is explained by the linear relationship between amounts of dinner and amounts of tips? What is the proportion of the variation that cannot be explained by that linear relationship?

Review Exercises

1. Casino Size and Revenue Listed below are sizes (in thousands of square feet) and revenue (in millions of dollars) from casinos in Atlantic City (based on data from the *New York Times*). Is there sufficient evidence to conclude that there is a linear correlation between size and revenue of casinos? Can a casino increase its revenue by enlarging its physical size?

Size	160	227	140	144	161	147	141
Revenue	189	157	140	127	123	106	101

2. Casino Size and Revenue Use the same paired data from the preceding exercise.

a. Find the linear regression equation.

b. What is the best predicted amount of revenue for a casino with a size of 200 thousand square feet? Is it likely that the best predicted amount of revenue will be accurate?

3. Time and Motion In a physics experiment at Doane College, a soccer ball was thrown upward from the bed of a moving truck. The table below lists the time (sec) that has lapsed from the throw and the corresponding height (m) of the soccer ball.

a. Find the value of the linear correlation coefficient r.

b. Based on the result from part (a), what do you conclude about a linear correlation between time and height?

c. What horrible mistake would be easy to make if the analysis is conducted without a scatterplot?

Time (sec)	0.0	0.2	0.4	0.6	0.8	1.0	1.2	1.4	1.6	1.8
Height (m)	0.0	1.7	3.1	3.9	4.5	4.7	4.6	4.1	3.3	2.1

4. Multiple Regression with Cigarette Contents The table below lists measured amounts (mg) of tar, carbon monoxide (CO), and nicotine in king size cigarettes of different brands (from Data Set 16 "Cigarette Contents" in Appendix B).

a. Find the multiple regression equation with the response (y) variable of amount of nicotine and predictor (x) variables of amounts of tar and carbon monoxide.

b. Identify the value of the multiple coefficient of determination R^2, the adjusted R^2, and the P-value representing the overall significance of the multiple regression equation.

c. Use a 0.05 significance level and determine whether the multiple regression equation can be used to predict the amount of nicotine given the amounts of tar and carbon monoxide.

d. The Raleigh brand king size cigarette is not included in the table, and it has 23 mg of tar and 15 mg of carbon monoxide. What is the best predicted amount of nicotine? How does the predicted amount compare to the actual amount of 1.3 mg of nicotine?

Tar	25	27	20	24	20	20	21	24
CO	18	16	16	16	16	16	14	17
Nicotine	1.5	1.7	1.1	1.6	1.1	1.0	1.2	1.4

Cumulative Review Exercises

In Exercises 1–8, based on the nature of the given data, do the following:

a. Pose a key question that is relevant to the given data.

b. Identify a procedure or tool from this chapter or the preceding chapters to address the key question from part (a).

c. Analyze the data and state a conclusion.

1. IQ Scores In the table below, the values of x are IQ scores from randomly selected airline passengers and the values of y are IQ scores from randomly selected police officers.

x	105	103	118	137	95	89	89	79	103	103
y	111	108	112	107	108	110	110	109	118	110

2. IQ Scores Use the same table of values from Cumulative Review Exercise 1, but assume that the data are from ten randomly selected college students and for each student, the IQ score is measured before taking a training course and the IQ score is measured again after completion of the course. Each x value is the pre-course IQ score and each y value is the corresponding post-course IQ score.

3. Jockey Weight and IQ Score Use the same table of values from Cumulative Review Exercise 1, but assume that ten professional horse jockeys are randomly selected and their weights (lb) are measured along with the number of times they finished a race in the top three positions (i.e., "in the money"). Each x value is the weight of a horse jockey and each y value is their number of top three race finishes.

4. Digital Buyers A *digital buyer* is someone who purchases goods and services predominantly online. The table below lists the worldwide numbers (billions) of digital buyers for each of several recent years (based on data from eMarketer). What consequence do the data suggest for the business community?

Year	2014	2015	2016	2017	2018	2019
Digital Buyers (billions)	1.32	1.46	1.61	1.77	1.91	2.07

5. Wireless Earbuds In a survey of $n = 2016$ adults, the respondents were asked if they had wireless earbuds and 30% of them said "yes" (based on data from the Consumer Technology Association).

6. Height of Stephen Curry Heights of adult males are normally distributed with a mean of 174.12 cm and a standard deviation of 7.10 cm (based on Data Set 1 "Body Data" in Appendix B). Professional basketball player Stephen Curry has a height of 191 cm.

7. Cans of Motor Oil Automobile motor oil is commonly sold in plastic containers labelled as containing 16 ounces. A new motor oil filling device is being tested and listed below are the amounts (ounces) that the device poured in a sample of 16 containers.

  15.7   19.2   16.0   17.8   15.4   18.4   17.7   16.5   17.3   12.6   16.1   19.0   14.2   15.1

8. Drug Screening The company Drug Test Success provides a "1-Panel-THC" test for marijuana usage. Among 300 tested subjects, results from 27 subjects were wrong (either a false positive or a false negative).

Technology Project

Queues Data Set 30 "Queues" in Appendix B includes waiting times (seconds) from drivers in two lines (or queues) at a Delaware Department of Motor Vehicle emissions testing facility. Two-line wait times are actual times cars spent waiting in a line. Single-line wait times are modeled by assuming that there was a single line feeding the two service bays. Interarrival times are times (sec) since the previous car entered a line. Service times (sec) are times starting with a car entering a service bay and ending when it leaves the bay.

a. Using the actual two-line wait times and the modeled single-line wait times, generate a scatterplot and test for a correlation.

b. Using the independent variable of the two-line wait times and the dependent variable of the single-line wait times, find the equation of the regression line. How well does the regression line fit the data?

c. Using the independent variables of the interarrival times and the two-line wait times, and using the dependent variable of the single line wait times, find the best multiple regression equation. How well does the multiple regression equation fit the sample data?

d. Is the multiple regression equation from Part (c) better than the regression equation found in Part (b)? Why or why not?

Big (or Very Large) Data Project

Refer to Data Set 45 "Births in New York" in Appendix B, which contains records from 465,506 births.

a. Test for a correlation between birth weight and length of stay.

b. Find the equation of the regression line using length of stay as the independent x variable and using birth weight as the dependent y variable.

c. Can the regression equation from part (b) be used to predict birth weight based on length of stay? Why or why not?

FROM DATA TO DECISION

Critical Thinking: Do we report body measurements that are different from the actual measurements?

Use Data Set 4 "Measured and Reported' in Appendix B to address the following.

1. Correlation with Weights

a. For males, is there a significant linear correlation between measured weights and reported weights?

b. For females, is there a significant linear correlation between measured weights and reported weights?

2. Correlation with Heights

a. For males, is there a significant linear correlation between measured heights and reported heights?

b. For females, is there a significant linear correlation between measured heights and reported heights?

3. Conclusions

a. Does it appear that data are distorted when reported values are used in place of actual measurements?

b. Does there appear to be a difference between males and females in how they report weights?

c. Does there appear to be a difference between males and females in how they report heights?

Cooperative Group Activities

1. In-class activity For each student in the class, measure shoe print length and height. Test for a linear correlation and identify the equation of the regression line. Measure the shoe print length of the professor and use it to estimate his or her height. How close is the estimated height to the actual height?

2. Out-of-class activity Each student should estimate the number of footsteps that he or she would walk between the door of the classroom and the door used to exit the building. After recording all of the estimates, each student should then count the number of footsteps while walking from the classroom door to the door most students use to exit the building. After all of the estimates and actual counts have been compiled, explore correlation and regression using the tools presented in this chapter.

3. In-class activity Divide into groups of 8 to 12 people. For each group member, measure the person's height and also measure his or her navel height, which is the height from the floor to the navel. Is there a correlation between height and navel height? If so, find the regression equation with height expressed in terms of navel height. According to one theory, the average person's ratio of height to navel height is the golden ratio: $\left(1 + \sqrt{5} \right)/2 \approx 1.6$. Does this theory appear to be reasonably accurate?

4. In-class activity Divide into groups of 8 to 12 people. For each group member, use a string and ruler to measure head circumference and forearm length. Is there a relationship between these two variables? If so, what is it?

5. In-class activity Leonardo DaVinci did extensive research on human bodies and he formed many different conclusions including this one: "Length of arm span is equal to height." Arm span is the distance between the ends of the fingers when the arms are extended like the wings on an airplane. Divide into groups of two and use the ANSUR II data to investigate that claim. Is there a correlation between height and arm span? If so, find the regression equation with height expressed in terms of arm span. Can arm span be used as a reasonably good predictor of height?

6. In-class activity Divide into groups of 8 to 12 people. For each group member, measure height and arm span. For the arm span, the subject should stand with arms extended, like the wings on an airplane. Using the paired sample data, is there a correlation between height and arm span? If so, find the regression equation with height expressed in terms of arm span. Can arm span be used as a reasonably good predictor of height?

7. In-class activity Leonardo DaVinci did extensive research on human bodies and he formed many different conclusions including this one: "Length of foot is one seventh of height." Divide into groups of two and use the ANSUR II data to investigate that claim.

8. In-class activity Use a ruler as a device for measuring reaction time. One person should suspend the ruler by holding it at the top while the subject holds his or her thumb and forefinger at the bottom edge, ready to catch the ruler when it is released. Record the distance that the ruler falls before it is caught. Convert that distance to the time (in seconds) that it took the subject to react and catch the ruler. (If the distance is measured in inches, use $t = \sqrt{d/192}$. If the distance is measured in centimeters, use $t = \sqrt{d/487.68}$.) Test each subject once with the right hand and once with the left hand, and record the paired data. Test for a correlation. Find the equation of the regression line. Does the equation of the regression line suggest that the dominant hand has a faster reaction time?

9. In-class activity Divide into groups of 8 to 12 people. Record the pulse rate of each group member while he or she is seated. Then record the pulse rate of each group member while he or she is standing. Is there a relationship between sitting and standing pulse rate? If so, what is it?

10. Out-of-class activity Each student should use a sheet of paper and a paperclip to construct a "whirlybird" such as the one shown here. Instructions can be found on the Internet using the search term "*make a whirlybird from paper.*" Each whirlybird should be dropped from a height of six feet and a stopwatch should be used to record the time it takes to reach the floor. For each whirlybird, record the time it takes to fall and the length of its wings. Test for a correlation between the times and the lengths of wings.

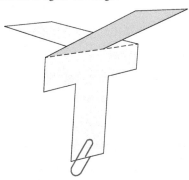

11. In-class activity Divide into groups of three or four people. Appendix B includes many data sets not yet included in examples or exercises in this chapter. Search Appendix B for a pair of variables of interest, then investigate correlation and regression. State your conclusions and try to identify practical applications.

12. Out-of-class activity Divide into groups of three or four people. Investigate the relationship between two variables by collecting your own paired sample data and using the methods of this chapter to determine whether there is a significant linear correlation. Also identify the regression equation and describe a procedure for predicting values of one of the variables when given values of the other variable. Suggested topics:

• Is there a relationship between taste and cost of different brands of chocolate chip cookies (or colas)? Taste can be measured on some number scale, such as 1 to 10.

• Is there a relationship between salaries of professional baseball (or basketball or football) players and their season achievements?

• Is there a relationship between student grade-point averages and the amount of television watched? If so, what is it?

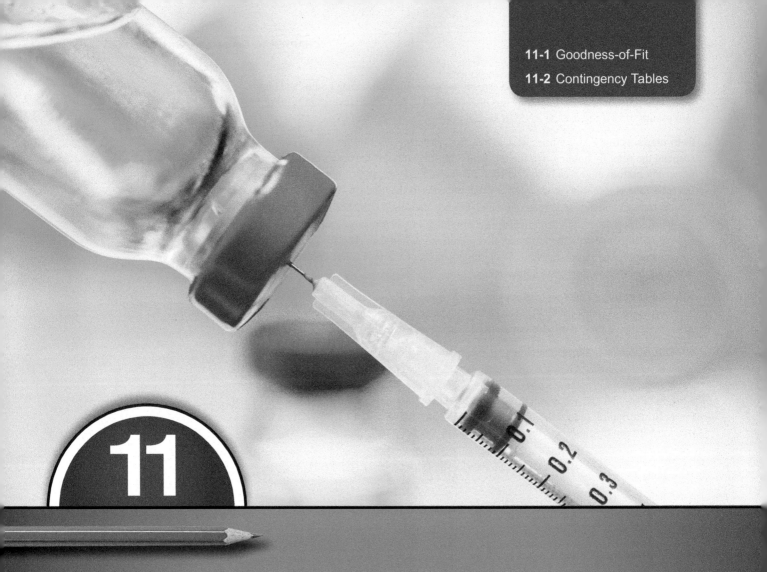

11

GOODNESS-OF-FIT AND CONTINGENCY TABLES

CHAPTER PROBLEM ──┤ **Is There a Link Between the Measles Vaccine and Autism?**

The World Health Organization reports that prior to mass vaccinations in the 1980s, measles killed around 2,600,000 people each year. As this is being written, about 100,000 people die from measles each year, and there is currently an outbreak of measles in the United States. Based on a belief that there is a link between the MMR (measles, mumps, rubella) vaccine and autism, some parents continue to prevent their children from being vaccinated.

The link between the vaccine and autism was fueled in part by research conducted by gastroenterologist Andrew Wakefield. In 1998, Wakefield and colleagues published results showing a vaccine/autism link in *Lancet*. Their small sample size of $n = 12$, the design of their studies, and the nature of their conclusions led to *retraction* of their published results, and those authors were accused of ethical violations, falsification of data, and fraud.

Table 11-1 includes more recent data (based on "Autism Occurrence by MMR Vaccine Status Among U.S. Children with Older Siblings With and Without Autism," by Jain et al., *Journal of the American Medical Association*, Vol. 313, No. 15). The 1878 subjects included in Table 11-1 were all children of age 4 with an older sibling having autism, and those who were vaccinated received one dose of the vaccine MMR (for measles, mumps, and rubella). In their conclusion, the authors of the study stated "these findings indicate no harmful association between MMR vaccine receipt and ASD (autism spectrum disorder) even among children already at higher risk for ASD." Do the data in Table 11-1 support this conclusion? That is, among four-year-old children, does having autism appear to be independent of whether the children are unvaccinated or vaccinated?

TABLE 11-1 Results From a Study of a Link Between the MMR Vaccine and Autism

	Unvaccinated	Vaccinated
Autism	25	64
No Autism	362	1427

CHAPTER OBJECTIVES

Chapters 7 and 8 introduced important methods of inferential statistics, including confidence intervals for estimating population parameters (Chapter 7) and methods for testing hypotheses or claims (Chapter 8). In Chapter 9 we considered inferences involving two populations, and in Chapter 10 we considered inferences involving correlation and regression with paired data. In this chapter we use statistical methods for analyzing categorical (or qualitative, or attribute) data that can be separated into different cells. The methods of this chapter use the same χ^2 (chi-square) distribution that was introduced in Section 7-3 and again in Section 8-4. See Section 7-3 or Section 8-4 for a quick review of properties of the χ^2 distribution. Here are the chapter objectives:

11-1 Goodness-of-Fit

- Use frequency counts of categorical data partitioned into different categories and determine whether the data fit some claimed distribution.

11-2 Contingency Tables

- Use categorical data summarized as frequencies in a two-way table with at least two rows and at least two columns to conduct a formal test of independence between the row variable and column variable.

- Be able to conduct a formal test of a claim that different populations have the same proportions of some characteristics.

11-1   Goodness-of-Fit

Key Concept By "goodness-of-fit" we mean that sample data consisting of observed frequency counts arranged in a single row or column (called a *one-way frequency table*) agree with some particular distribution (such as normal or uniform) being considered. We will use a hypothesis test for the claim that the observed frequency counts agree with the claimed distribution.

DEFINITION

A **goodness-of-fit test** is used to test the hypothesis that an observed frequency distribution fits (or conforms to) some claimed distribution.

KEY ELEMENTS

Testing for Goodness-of-Fit

Objective

Conduct a goodness-of-fit test, which is a hypothesis test to determine whether a single row (or column) of frequency counts agrees with some specific distribution (such as uniform or normal).

Notation

O represents the *observed frequency* of an outcome, found from the sample data.

E represents the *expected frequency* of an outcome, found by assuming that the distribution is as claimed.

k represents the *number of different categories* or cells.

n represents the total *number of trials* (or the total of observed sample values).

p represents the *probability* that a sample value falls within a particular category.

Requirements

1. The data have been randomly selected.

2. The sample data consist of frequency counts for each of the different categories.

3. For each category, the *expected* frequency is at least 5. (The expected frequency for a category is the frequency that would occur if the data actually have the distribution that is being claimed. There is no requirement that the *observed* frequency for each category must be at least 5.)

Null and Alternative Hypotheses

H_0: The frequency counts agree with the claimed distribution.
H_1: The frequency counts do not agree with the claimed distribution.

Test Statistic for Goodness-of-Fit Tests

$$\chi^2 = \sum \frac{(O - E)^2}{E}$$

***P*-values:** *P*-values are typically provided by technology, or a range of *P*-values can be found from Table A-4.

Critical values:

1. Critical values are found in Table A-4 by using $k - 1$ degrees of freedom, where k is the number of categories.

2. Goodness-of-fit hypothesis tests are always *right-tailed*.

Finding Expected Frequencies

Conducting a goodness-of-fit test requires that we identify the *observed* frequencies denoted by O, then find the frequencies *expected* (denoted by E) with the claimed distribution. There are two different approaches for finding expected frequencies E:

- **Equal Expected Frequencies:** If the expected frequencies are all equal, the expected frequency for each category (or cell) is $E = n/k$.

- **Unequal Expected Frequencies:** If the expected frequencies are not all equal, find the expected frequency for each individual category (or cell) by evaluating $E = np$ (where n is the total sample size and p is the probability for the individual category).

As good as these two preceding formulas for E might be, it is better to use an informal approach by simply asking,

> **"How can the observed frequencies be split up among the different categories so that there is perfect agreement with the claimed distribution?"**

Note: The *observed* frequencies must all be whole numbers because they represent actual counts, but the *expected* frequencies need not be whole numbers.

Examples:

a. **Equally Likely** A single die is rolled 45 times with the following results. Assuming that the die is fair and all outcomes are equally likely, find the expected frequency E for each empty cell.

Outcome	1	2	3	4	5	6
Observed Frequency O	13	6	12	9	3	2
Expected Frequency E						

With $n = 45$ outcomes and $k = 6$ categories, the expected frequency for each cell is the same: $E = n/k = 45/6 = 7.5$. If the die is fair and the outcomes are all equally likely, we expect that each outcome should occur about 7.5 times.

b. **Not Equally Likely** Using the same results from part (a), suppose that we claim that instead of being fair, the die is loaded so that the outcome of 1 occurs 50% of the time and the other five outcomes occur 10% of the time. The probabilities are listed in the second row below. Using $n = 45$ and the probabilities listed below, we find that for the first cell, $E = np = (45)(0.5) = 22.5$. Each of the other five cells will have the expected value of $E = np = (45)(0.1) = 4.5$.

Outcome	1	2	3	4	5	6
Probability	0.5	0.1	0.1	0.1	0.1	0.1
Observed Frequency O	13	6	12	9	3	2
Expected Frequency E	22.5	4.5	4.5	4.5	4.5	4.5

Measuring Disagreement with the Claimed Distribution

We know that sample frequencies typically differ somewhat from the values we theoretically expect, so we consider the key question:

> **Are the differences between the actual *observed* frequencies O and the theoretically *expected* frequencies E significant?**

To measure the discrepancy between the O and E values, we use the test statistic given in the preceding Key Elements box. (Later we will explain how this test statistic was developed, but it has differences of $O - E$ as a key component.)

$$\chi^2 = \sum \frac{(O - E)^2}{E}$$

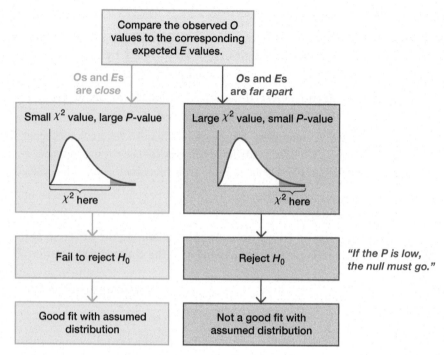

FIGURE 11-1   Relationships Among the χ^2 Test Statistic, P-Value, and Goodness-of-Fit

The χ^2 test statistic is based on differences between the observed and expected values. If the observed and expected values are *close,* the χ^2 test statistic will be small and the P-value will be large. If the observed and expected frequencies are *far apart,* the χ^2 test statistic will be large and the P-value will be small. Figure 11-1 summarizes this relationship. The hypothesis tests of this section are always right-tailed, because the critical value and critical region are located at the extreme right of the distribution. If you are confused, just remember this mnemonic:

"If the P is low, the null must go."

(If the P-value is small, reject the null hypothesis that the distribution is as claimed.)

EXAMPLE 1   Measured or Reported?

It is well known that when people *report* data, the results can be very different from those that are *measured,* especially when sensitive data such as weights or heights are involved. When weights of people are measured, the last digits of those weights tend to occur with about the same frequency. Data Set 4 "Measured and Reported" includes weights of subjects that were both reported and measured, and the data are from the National Center for Health Statistics. The last digits of weights (lb) of males are summarized in Table 11-2. Test the claim that the sample is from a population of weights in which the last digits do *not* occur with the same frequency. Based on the results, does it appear that the weights were reported or measured?

TABLE 11-2 Last Digits of Weights of Males

Last Digit	0	1	2	3	4	5	6	7	8	9
Frequency	1175	44	169	111	112	731	96	110	171	65

SOLUTION

REQUIREMENT CHECK (1) The data come from randomly selected subjects. (2) The data do consist of frequency counts, as shown in Table 11-2. (3) If the 2784 last digits are in 10 categories that are equally likely, each expected frequency is $2784/10 = 278.4$, so each expected frequency does satisfy the requirement of being a value that is at least 5. All of the requirements are satisfied. ☑

The claim that the digits do not occur with the same frequency is equivalent to the claim that the relative frequencies or probabilities of the 10 cells $(p_0, p_1, \ldots, p_9)$ are not all equal. (This is equivalent to testing the claim that the distribution of digits is not a uniform distribution.)

Step 1: The original claim is that the digits do not occur with the same frequency. That is, at least one of the probabilities, $p_0, p_1, \ldots, p_9$, is different from the others.

Step 2: If the original claim is false, then all of the probabilities are the same. That is, $p_0 = p_1 = p_2 = p_3 = p_4 = p_5 = p_6 = p_7 = p_8 = p_9$.

Step 3: The null hypothesis must contain the condition of equality, so we have

$$H_0: p_0 = p_1 = p_2 = p_3 = p_4 = p_5 = p_6 = p_7 = p_8 = p_9$$

H_1: At least one of the probabilities is different from the others.

Step 4: No significance level was specified, so we select the common choice of $\alpha = 0.05$.

Step 5: Because we are testing a claim about the distribution of the last digits being a uniform distribution (with all of the digits having the same probability), we use the goodness-of-fit test described in this section. The χ^2 distribution is used with the test statistic given in the preceding Key Elements box.

Step 6: The observed frequencies O are listed in Table 11-2. Each corresponding expected frequency E is equal to $2784/10 = 278.4$ (because the 2784 last digits would be uniformly distributed among the 10 categories). The Excel add-in XLSTAT is used to obtain the results shown in the accompanying screen display, and Table 11-3 shows the manual computation of the χ^2 test statistic. The test statistic is $\chi^2 = 4490.174$, the P-value is less than 0.0001, the critical value is $\chi^2 = 16.919$ (found in Table A-4 with $\alpha = 0.05$ in the right tail and degrees of freedom equal to $k - 1 = 10 - 1 = 9$). The test statistic and critical value are shown in Figure 11-2.

XLSTAT

Chi-square (Observed value)	4490.174
Chi-square (Critical value)	16.919
DF	9
p-value	< 0.0001
alpha	0.05

TABLE 11-3 Calculating the χ^2 Test Statistic for the Last Digits of Weights

Last Digit	Observed Frequency O	Expected Frequency E	$O - E$	$(O - E)^2$	$\dfrac{(O - E)^2}{E}$
0	1175	278.4	896.6	803,891.56	2887.5415
1	44	278.4	−234.4	54,943.36	197.3540
2	169	278.4	−109.4	11,968.36	42.9898
3	111	278.4	−167.4	28,022.76	100.6565
4	112	278.4	−166.4	27,688.96	99.4575
5	731	278.4	452.6	204,846.76	735.8001
6	96	278.4	−182.4	33,269.76	119.5034
7	110	278.4	−168.4	28,358.56	101.8626
8	171	278.4	−107.4	11,534.76	41.4323
9	65	278.4	−213.4	45,539.56	163.5760

$$\chi^2 = \sum \frac{(O - E)^2}{E} = 4490.174$$

continued

Which Car Seats Are Safest?

Many people believe that the back seat of a car is the safest place to sit, but is it? University of Buffalo researchers analyzed more than 60,000 fatal car crashes and found that the middle back seat is the safest place to sit in a car. They found that sitting in that seat makes a passenger 86% more likely to survive than those who sit in the front seats, and they are 25% more likely to survive than those sitting in either of the back seats nearest the windows. An analysis of seat belt use showed that when not wearing a seat belt in the back seat, passengers are three times more likely to die in a crash than those wearing seat belts in that same seat. Passengers concerned with safety should sit in the middle back seat and wear a seat belt.

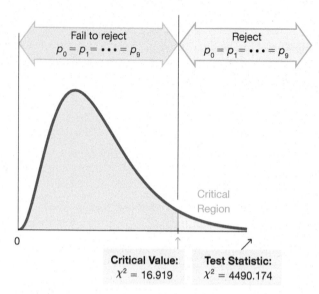

FIGURE 11-2 Test of $p_0 = p_1 = p_2 = p_3 = p_4 = p_5 = p_6 = p_7 = p_8 = p_9$

Step 7: If we use the *P*-value method of testing hypotheses, we see that the *P*-value is small (less than 0.0001), so we reject the null hypothesis. If we use the critical value method of testing hypotheses, Figure 11-2 shows that the test statistic falls in the critical region, so there is sufficient evidence to reject the null hypothesis.

Step 8: There is sufficient evidence to support the claim that the last digits do not occur with the same relative frequency.

> **INTERPRETATION**

This goodness-of-fit test suggests that the last digits do not provide a good fit with the claimed uniform distribution of equally likely frequencies. Instead of actually weighing the subjects, it appears that the subjects reported their weights. Visual examination of the frequencies in Table 11-2 reveals that the two highest frequencies correspond to the last digits of 0 and 5, and that also strongly suggests that the weights were reported instead of being measured. Because the weights are reported, the reliability of the data is questionable.

YOUR TURN. Do Exercise 5 "Heights: Measured or Reported?"

Example 1 involves a situation in which the expected frequencies *E* for the different categories are all equal. The methods of this section can also be used when the expected frequencies are different, as in Example 2.

Benford's Law

According to *Benford's law*, many data sets have the property that the leading (leftmost) digits of numbers have a distribution described by the top two rows of Table 11-4 in the following example. Data sets with values having leading digits that conform to Benford's law include numbers of Twitter followers, stock market prices, population sizes, amounts on tax returns, lengths of rivers, and check amounts. The real-world applications of Benford's law are widespread. In the *New York Times* article "Following Benford's Law, or Looking Out for No. 1," Malcolm Browne writes that "the income tax agencies of several nations and several states, including California, are using detection software to identify fraud based on Benford's Law. Many accounting firms and other large businesses use Benford's law to identify corporate fraud.

Cybersecurity Benford's law is also being used to detect cyberattacks on computer systems by analyzing Internet traffic in real time based on the time between the arrival of consecutive data packets, or "interarrival time." The basic idea is to detect anomalies in times of Internet traffic flow by analyzing leading digits of those times and determining whether the distribution of those leading digits is a significant departure from the distribution that follows Benford's law. Normal Internet traffic follows Benford's law, while a significant departure from Benford's law may indicate a cyberattack. (See "Benford's Law Behavior of Internet Traffic," by Arshadi and Jahangir, *Journal of Network and Computer Applications*, Vol. 40, No. 2014.) Major advantages of this approach are that it is relatively simple, it doesn't require difficult computations, it can be done in real time, and hackers would not be able to configure their malware to avoid detection.

EXAMPLE 2 **Benford's Law: Detecting Computer Intrusions**

The bottom row of Table 11-4 lists a sample of 271 leading digits of interarrival times of Internet traffic flow. Do these 271 leading digits appear to provide a good fit with the distribution indicated by Benford's law (as in the top two rows of Table 11-4)? What does the result suggest about a potential cyberattack?

TABLE 11-4 Leading Digits of Internet Traffic Interarrival Times

Leading Digit	1	2	3	4	5	6	7	8	9
Benford's Law: Distribution of Leading Digits	30.1%	17.6%	12.5%	9.7%	7.9%	6.7%	5.8%	5.1%	4.6%
Sample 2 of Leading Digits	69	40	42	26	25	16	16	17	20

SOLUTION

REQUIREMENT CHECK (1) The sample data are randomly selected from a larger population. (2) The sample data do consist of frequency counts. (3) Each expected frequency is at least 5. Because there are 271 leading digits and the lowest expected percentage is 4.6%, the lowest expected frequency is $271 \cdot 0.046 = 12.466$. All of the requirements are satisfied. ☑

Step 1: The original claim is that the leading digits fit the distribution given as Benford's law. Using subscripts corresponding to the leading digits, we can express this claim as $p_1 = 0.301$ and $p_2 = 0.176$ and $p_3 = 0.125$ and . . . and $p_9 = 0.046$.

Step 2: If the original claim is false, then at least one of the proportions does not have the value as claimed.

Step 3: The null hypothesis must contain the condition of equality, so we have

$$H_0: p_1 = 0.301 \text{ and } p_2 = 0.176 \text{ and } p_3 = 0.125 \text{ and } \ldots \text{ and } p_9 = 0.046.$$

H_1: At least one of the proportions is not equal to the given claimed value.

Step 4: The significance level is not specified, so we use the common choice of $\alpha = 0.05$.

Step 5: Because we are testing a claim that the distribution of leading digits fits the distribution given by Benford's law, we use the goodness-of-fit test described in this section. The χ^2 distribution is used with the test statistic given in the preceding Key Elements box.

continued

TI-84 Plus CE

NORMAL FLOAT AUTO REAL RADIAN MP

χ²GOF-Test
χ²=11.27917666
P=.1863768489
df=8
CNTRB={1.937331172 1.241...

Mendel's Data Falsified?

Because some of Mendel's data from his famous genetics experiments seemed too perfect to be true, statistician R. A. Fisher concluded that the data were probably falsified. He used a chi-square distribution to show that when a test statistic is extremely far to the left and results in a P-value very close to 1, the sample data fit the claimed distribution almost perfectly, and this is evidence that the sample data have not been randomly selected. It has been suggested that Mendel's gardener knew what results Mendel's theory predicted, and subsequently adjusted results to fit that theory.

Ira Pilgrim wrote in *The Journal of Heredity* that this use of the chi-square distribution is not appropriate. He notes that the question is not about goodness-of-fit with a particular distribution, but whether the data are from a sample that is truly random. Pilgrim used the binomial probability formula to find the probabilities of the results obtained in Mendel's experiments. Based on his results, Pilgrim concludes that "there is no reason whatever to question Mendel's honesty." It appears that Mendel's results are not too good to be true, and they could have been obtained from a truly random process.

Step 6: Table 11-5 shows the calculations of the components of the χ^2 test statistic for the leading digits of 1 and 2. If we include all nine leading digits, we get the test statistic of $\chi^2 = 11.2792$, as shown in the accompanying TI-84 Plus CE calculator display. The critical value is $\chi^2 = 15.507$ (found in Table A-4, with $\alpha = 0.05$ in the right tail and degrees of freedom equal to $k - 1 = 8$). The TI-84 Plus CE calculator display shows the value of the test statistic as well as the P-value of 0.186. (The entire bottom row of the display can be viewed by scrolling to the right. CNTRB is an abbreviated form of "contribution," and the values are the individual contributions to the total value of the χ^2 test statistic.)

TABLE 11-5 Calculating the χ^2 Test Statistic for Leading Digits in Table 11-4

Leading Digit	Observed Frequency O	Expected Frequency $E = np$	$O - E$	$(O - E)^2$	$\dfrac{(O - E)^2}{E}$
1	69	$271 \cdot 0.301 = 81.5710$	-12.5710	158.0300	1.9373
2	40	$271 \cdot 0.176 = 47.6960$	-7.6960	59.2284	1.2418

Step 7: The P-value of 0.186 is greater than the significance level of 0.05, so there is not sufficient evidence to reject the null hypothesis. (Also, the test statistic of $\chi^2 = 11.2792$ does not fall in the critical region bounded by the critical value of 15.507, so there is not sufficient evidence to reject the null hypothesis.)

Step 8: There is not sufficient evidence to warrant rejection of the claim that the 271 leading digits fit the distribution given by Benford's law.

INTERPRETATION

The sample of leading digits does not provide enough evidence to conclude that the Benford's law distribution is not being followed. There is not sufficient evidence to support a conclusion that the leading digits are from interarrival times that are not from normal traffic, so there is not sufficient evidence to conclude that a cyberattack has occurred.

YOUR TURN. Do Exercise 21 "Detecting Fraud."

In Figure 11-3 we use a green line to graph the expected proportions given by Benford's law (as in Table 11-4) along with a red line for the observed proportions from Table 11-4. Figure 11-3 allows us to visualize the "goodness-of-fit" between the distribution given by Benford's law and the frequencies that were observed. In Figure 11-3, the green and red lines agree reasonably well, so it appears that the observed data fit the expected values reasonably well.

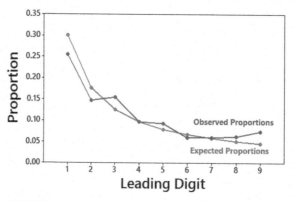

FIGURE 11-3   Interarrival Times: Observed Proportions and Proportions Expected with Benford's Law

Rationale for the Test Statistic Examples 1 and 2 show that the X^2 test statistic is a measure of the discrepancy between observed and expected frequencies. Simply summing the differences $O - E$ between observed and expected values tells us nothing because that sum is always 0. Squaring the $O - E$ values gives us a better statistic. (The reasons for squaring the $O - E$ values are essentially the same as the reasons for squaring the $x - \bar{x}$ values in the formula for standard deviation.) The value of $\Sigma(O - E)^2$ measures only the magnitude of the differences, but we need to find the magnitude of the differences relative to what was expected. We need a type of average instead of a cumulative total. This relative magnitude is found through division by the expected frequencies, as in the test statistic $\Sigma(O - E)^2/E$.

The theoretical distribution of $\Sigma(O - E)^2/E$ is a discrete distribution because the number of possible values is finite. The distribution can be approximated by a chi-square distribution, which is continuous. This approximation is generally considered acceptable, provided that all expected values E are at least 5. (There are ways of circumventing the problem of an expected frequency that is less than 5, such as combining some categories so that all expected frequencies are at least 5. Also, there are different procedures that can be used when not all expected frequencies are at least 5.)

The number of degrees of freedom reflects the fact that we can freely assign frequencies to $k - 1$ categories before the frequency for every category is determined. (Although we say that we can "freely" assign frequencies to $k - 1$ categories, we cannot have negative frequencies, nor can we have frequencies so large that their sum exceeds the total of the observed frequencies for all categories combined.)

TECH CENTER

Goodness-of-Fit Test

Access tech supplements, videos, and data sets at **www.TriolaStats.com**

Statdisk	Minitab	StatCrunch
1. Click **Analysis** in the top menu. 2. Select **Goodness-of-Fit** from the dropdown menu. 3. Select **Equal Expected Frequencies** or **Unequal Expected Frequencies**. 4. Enter the desired significance level and select the column containing the observed frequencies. For *Unequal Expected Frequencies* also indicate if data are in the format of counts or proportions and select the column containing expected data. 5. Click **Evaluate**.	1. Click **Stat** in the top menu. 2. Select **Tables** from the dropdown menu and select **Chi-Square Goodness-of-Fit Test** from the submenu. 3. Click **Observed Counts** and select the column containing the observed frequencies. 4. Under *Test* select **Equal proportions** if expected frequencies are all equal. For unequal expected frequencies or proportions, select **Proportions specified by historical counts** and select the column containing the expected frequencies or proportions. 5. Click **OK**.	1. Click **Stat** in the top menu. 2. Select **Goodness-of-fit** from the dropdown menu, then select **Chi-Square Test** from the submenu. 3. Select the column with the observed frequencies. 4. Select the column containing the expected frequencies if expected frequencies are not all equal. Otherwise, click **All cells in equal proportion**. 5. Click **Compute!**

continued

TECH CENTER *continued*

Goodness-of-Fit Test
Access tech supplements, videos, and data sets at **www.TriolaStats.com**

TI-83/84 Plus Calculator

TI-83/84 calculators require expected frequencies. Expected proportions cannot be used.

1. Enter the observed values in a list (*L1*) and expected frequencies in a separate list (*L2*).
2. Press **STAT**, then select **TESTS** in the top menu.
3. Select χ^2 **GOF-Test** in the menu and press **ENTER**.
4. Enter the list names for the observed and expected frequencies. For *df* enter the degrees of freedom, which is 1 less than the number of categories.
5. Select **Calculate** and press **ENTER**.

TIP: TI-83 calculators require the program **X2GOF**, which is available at TriolaStats.com.

Excel

XLSTAT Add-In

1. Click on the **XLSTAT** tab in the Ribbon and then click **Parametric tests**.
2. Select **Multinomial goodness of fit test** from the dropdown menu.
3. Under *Data format*, select **Frequencies** or **Proportions** for the expected data format.
4. In the *Frequencies* box enter the range of cells containing the observed frequencies. In the *Expected frequencies/ proportions* box enter the range of cells containing the expected data.
5. Check the **Chi-square test** box.
6. Enter a significance level and click **OK**. The test statistic is labeled *Chi-Square (Observed Value)*.

Excel

1. Click **Insert Function** f_x, select the category **Statistical**, and select the function **CHISQ.TEST**.
2. For *Actual_range* enter the cell range for observed frequencies. For *Expected_range* enter the cell range for the expected frequencies.
3. Click **OK** for the *P*-value.

R

R commands:

Equal expected frequencies:
chisq.test(x)

Unequal expected frequencies:
chisq.test($x, p = y$)

where *x* are the observed values and *y* are the expected proportions.

A complete list of R statistical commands is available at TriolaStats.com

11-1 Basic Skills and Concepts

Statistical Literacy and Critical Thinking

1. Cybersecurity The table below lists the frequency of leading digits of Internet traffic interarrival times for a computer, along with the percentages of each leading digit expected with Benford's law.

a. Identify the general notation used for observed and expected values.

b. Identify the observed and expected values for the leading digit of 2.

c. Use the results from part (b) to find the contribution to the χ^2 test statistic from the category representing the leading digit of 2.

Leading Digit	1	2	3	4	5	6	7	8	9
Benford's Law	30.1%	17.6%	12.5%	9.7%	7.9%	6.7%	5.8%	5.1%	4.6%
Leading Digits of Interarrival Traffic Times	76	62	29	33	19	27	28	21	22

2. Cybersecurity When using the data from Exercise 1 to test for goodness-of-fit with the distribution described by Benford's law, identify the null and alternative hypotheses.

3. Cybersecurity The accompanying Statdisk results shown in the margin are obtained from the data given in Exercise 1. What should be concluded when testing the claim that the leading digits have a distribution that fits well with Benford's law?

Test Statistic, X^2:	20.9222
Critical X^2:	15.5073
P-Value:	0.0074

4. Cybersecurity What do the results from the preceding exercises suggest about the possibility that the computer has been hacked? (Normal Internet traffic has a distribution that fits well with Benford's law.) Is there any corrective action that should be taken?

In Exercises 5–20, conduct the hypothesis test and provide the test statistic and the P-value and/or critical value, and state the conclusion.

5. *Heights* Measured or Reported? A random sample of the last digits of heights (in.) of males from Data Set 4 "Measured and Reported" is summarized in the table below. Use these last digits to determine whether they occur with about the same frequency. Use a 0.05 significance level. Do the corresponding heights appear to be measured or reported?

Last Digit	0	1	2	3	4	5	6	7	8	9
Frequency	12	9	8	7	9	9	12	10	11	14

6. *Heights* Measured or Reported? Repeat the preceding exercise using the frequencies in the following table, which summarizes all of the 2784 male heights listed in Data Set 4 "Measured and Reported." Does the larger data set have much of an effect on the results from Exercise 5?

Last Digit	0	1	2	3	4	5	6	7	8	9
Frequency	321	315	329	200	202	203	285	303	297	329

7. Testing a Slot Machine The author purchased a slot machine (Bally Model 809) and tested it by playing it 1197 times. There are 10 different categories of outcomes, including no win, win jackpot, win with three bells, and so on. When testing the claim that the observed outcomes agree with the expected frequencies, the author obtained a test statistic of $X^2 = 8.185$. Use a 0.05 significance level to test the claim that the actual outcomes agree with the expected frequencies. Does the slot machine appear to be functioning as expected?

8. Flat Tire and Missed Class A classic story involves four carpooling students who missed a test and gave as an excuse a flat tire. On the makeup test, the instructor asked the students to identify the particular tire that went flat. If they really didn't have a flat tire, would they be able to identify the same tire? The author asked 41 other students to identify the tire they would select. The results are listed in the following table (except for one student who selected the spare). Use a 0.05 significance level to test the author's claim that the results fit a uniform distribution. What does the result suggest about the likelihood of four students identifying the same tire when they really didn't have a flat?

Tire	Left Front	Right Front	Left Rear	Right Rear
Number Selected	11	15	8	6

9. Bias in Clinical Trials? Researchers investigated the issue of race and equality of access to clinical trials. The following table shows the population distribution and the numbers of participants in clinical trials involving lung cancer (based on data from "Participation in Cancer Clinical Trials," by Murthy, Krumholz, and Gross, *Journal of the American Medical Association*, Vol. 291, No. 22). Use a 0.01 significance level to test the claim that the distribution of clinical trial participants fits well with the population distribution. Is there a race/ethnic group that appears to be very underrepresented?

Race/ethnicity	White non-Hispanic	Hispanic	Black	Asian/Pacific Islander	American Indian/ Alaskan Native
Distribution of Population	75.6%	9.1%	10.8%	3.8%	0.7%
Number in Lung Cancer Clinical Trials	3855	60	316	54	12

10. Loaded Die The author drilled a hole in a die and filled it with a lead weight, then proceeded to roll it 200 times. Here are the observed frequencies for the outcomes of 1, 2, 3, 4, 5, and 6, respectively: 27, 31, 42, 40, 28, and 32. Use a 0.05 significance level to test the claim that the outcomes are not equally likely. Does it appear that the loaded die behaves differently than a fair die?

11. Mendelian Genetics Experiments are conducted with hybrids of two types of peas. If the offspring follow Mendel's theory of inheritance, the seeds that are produced are yellow-smooth, green-smooth, yellow-wrinkled, and green-wrinkled, and they should occur in the ratio of 9:3:3:1, respectively. An experiment is designed to test Mendel's theory, with the result that the offspring seeds consist of 307 that are yellow-smooth, 77 that are green-smooth, 98 that are yellow-wrinkled, and 18 that are green-wrinkled. Use a 0.05 significance level to test the claim that the results contradict Mendel's theory.

12. Do World War II Bomb Hits Fit a Poisson Distribution? In analyzing hits by V-1 buzz bombs in World War II, South London was subdivided into regions, each with an area of 0.25 km². Shown below is a table of actual frequencies of hits and the frequencies expected with the Poisson distribution. (The Poisson distribution is described in Section 5-3.) Use the values listed and a 0.05 significance level to test the claim that the actual frequencies fit a Poisson distribution. Does the result prove that the data conform to the Poisson distribution?

Number of Bomb Hits	0	1	2	3	4 or more
Actual Number of Regions	229	211	93	35	8
Expected Number of Regions (from Poisson Distribution)	227.5	211.4	97.9	30.5	8.7

13. Kentucky Derby The table below lists the frequency of wins for different post positions through the 144th running of the Kentucky Derby horse race. A post position of 1 is closest to the inside rail, so the horse in that position has the shortest distance to run. (Because the number of horses varies from year to year, only the first 10 post positions are included.) Use a 0.05 significance level to test the claim that the likelihood of winning is the same for the different post positions. Based on the result, should bettors consider the post position of a horse racing in the Kentucky Derby?

Post Position	1	2	3	4	5	6	7	8	9	10
Wins	19	14	11	15	16	7	9	12	5	11

14. Super Bowl Betting Pools Super Bowl parties often have a betting pool based on the last digits of scores at the end of each quarter. The table below lists the last digits of scores for all quarters of the Super Bowls up to the time of this writing. Using a 0.05 significance level, test the claim that the last digits occur with the same frequency. What do the results suggest about a betting strategy?

Last Digit	0	1	2	3	4	5	6	7	8	9
Frequency	113	25	12	68	46	10	34	80	16	20

15. World Series Games The table below lists the numbers of games played in 110 Major League Baseball (MLB) World Series. This table also includes the expected proportions for the numbers of games in a World Series, assuming that in each series, both teams have about the same chance of winning. Use a 0.05 significance level to test the claim that the actual numbers of games fit the distribution indicated by the expected proportions.

Games Played	4	5	6	7
World Series Contests	21	26	24	39
Expected Proportion	2/16	4/16	5/16	5/16

16. Baseball Player Births In his book *Outliers,* author Malcolm Gladwell argues that more baseball players have birth dates in the months immediately following July 31, because that was the age cutoff date for non-school baseball leagues. Here is a sample of frequency counts of months of birth dates of American-born Major League Baseball players starting with January: 387, 329, 366, 344, 336, 313, 313, 503, 421, 434, 398, 371. Using a 0.05 significance level, is there sufficient evidence to warrant rejection of the claim that American-born Major League Baseball players are born in different months with the same frequency? Do the sample values appear to support Gladwell's claim?

Exercises 17–20 are based on data sets included in Appendix B. The complete data sets can be found at www.TriolaStats.com.

17. Admissions for Birth Data Set 6 "Births" includes the days of the weeks that prospective mothers were admitted to a hospital to give birth. A physician claims that because many births are induced or involve cesarean section, they are scheduled for days other than Saturday or Sunday, so births do not occur on the seven different days of the week with equal frequency. Use a 0.01 significance level to test that claim.

18. Discharges After Birth Data Set 6 "Births" includes the days of the weeks that newborn babies were discharged from the hospital. A hospital administrator claims that such discharges occur on the seven different days of the week with equal frequency. Use a 0.01 significance level to test that claim.

19. M&M Candies Mars, Inc. claims that its M&M plain candies are distributed with the following color percentages: 16% green, 20% orange, 14% yellow, 24% blue, 13% red, and 13% brown. Refer to Data Set 38 "Candies" in Appendix B and use the sample data to test the claim that the color distribution is as claimed by Mars, Inc. Use a 0.05 significance level.

20. Last Digits of Weights Data Set 1 "Body Data" in Appendix B includes weights (kg) of 300 subjects. Use a 0.05 significance level to test the claim that the sample is from a population of weights in which the last digits do *not* occur with the same frequency. Do the results suggest that the weights were reported?

Benford's Law. *According to Benford's law, a variety of different data sets include numbers with leading (first) digits that follow the distribution shown in the table below. In Exercises 21–24, test for goodness-of-fit with the distribution described by Benford's law.*

Leading Digit	1	2	3	4	5	6	7	8	9
Benford's Law: Distribution of Leading Digits	30.1%	17.6%	12.5%	9.7%	7.9%	6.7%	5.8%	5.1%	4.6%

21. Detecting Fraud When working for the Brooklyn district attorney, investigator Robert Burton analyzed the leading digits of the amounts from 784 checks issued by seven suspect companies. The frequencies were found to be 0, 15, 0, 76, 479, 183, 8, 23, and 0, and those digits correspond to the leading digits of 1, 2, 3, 4, 5, 6, 7, 8, and 9, respectively. If the observed frequencies are substantially different from the frequencies expected with Benford's law, the check amounts appear to result from fraud. Use a 0.01 significance level to test for goodness-of-fit with Benford's law. Does it appear that the checks are the result of fraud?

22. Author's Check Amounts Exercise 21 lists the observed frequencies of leading digits from amounts on checks from seven suspect companies. Here are the observed frequencies of the leading digits from the amounts on 300 of the most recent checks written by the author at the time this exercise was created: 102, 45, 30, 34, 20, 27, 12, 18, 12. (Those observed frequencies correspond to the leading digits of 1, 2, 3, 4, 5, 6, 7, 8, and 9, respectively.) Using a 0.01 significance level, test the claim that these leading digits are from a population of leading digits that conform to Benford's law.

23. Tax Cheating? Frequencies of leading digits from IRS tax files are 152, 89, 63, 48, 39, 40, 28, 25, and 27 (corresponding to the leading digits of 1, 2, 3, 4, 5, 6, 7, 8, and 9, respectively, based on data from Mark Nigrini, who provides software for Benford data analysis). Using a 0.05 significance level, test for goodness-of-fit with Benford's law. Does it appear that the tax entries are legitimate?

24. Author's Computer Files The author recorded the leading digits of the sizes of the electronic document files for the current edition of this book. The leading digits have frequencies of 112, 28, 62, 47, 32, 40, 24, 11, and 11 (corresponding to the leading digits of 1, 2, 3, 4, 5, 6, 7, 8, and 9, respectively). Using a 0.05 significance level, test for goodness-of-fit with Benford's law.

11-1 Beyond the Basics

 25. Testing Goodness-of-Fit with a Normal Distribution Refer to Data Set 1 "Body Data" in Appendix B for the heights of females.

Height (cm)	Less than 155.45	155.45 – 162.05	162.05 – 168.65	Greater than 168.65
Frequency				

a. Enter the observed frequencies in the table above.

b. Assuming a normal distribution with mean and standard deviation given by the sample mean and standard deviation, use the methods of Chapter 6 to find the probability of a randomly selected height belonging to each class.

c. Using the probabilities found in part (b), find the expected frequency for each category.

d. Use a 0.01 significance level to test the claim that the heights were randomly selected from a normally distributed population. Does the goodness-of-fit test suggest that the data are from a normally distributed population?

 26. Weights Measured or Reported? Use the last digits of reported weights (lb) of females from Data Set 4 "Measured and Reported" and test to determine whether they occur with about the same frequency. Use a 0.05 significance level. How do the results confirm that the weights were reported and not measured? Also, what is it about the *measured* weights (lb) of females that strongly suggests that they were in fact measured and not reported?

11-2 Contingency Tables

Key Concept We now consider methods for analyzing *contingency tables* (or two-way frequency tables), which include frequency counts for categorical data arranged in a table with at least two rows and at least two columns. In Part 1 of this section, we present a method for conducting a hypothesis test of the null hypothesis that the row and column variables are independent of each other. This test of independence is widely used in real-world applications. In Part 2, we will consider three variations of the basic method presented in Part 1: (1) test of homogeneity, (2) Fisher's exact test, and (3) McNemar's test for matched pairs.

PART 1 Basic Concepts of Testing for Independence

In this section we use standard statistical methods to analyze frequency counts in a contingency table (or two-way frequency table).

> **DEFINITION**
>
> A **contingency table** (or **two-way frequency table**) is a table consisting of frequency counts of categorical data corresponding to two different variables. (One variable is used to categorize rows, and a second variable is used to categorize columns.)

The word *contingent* has a few different meanings, one of which refers to a *dependence* on some other factor. We use the term *contingency table* because we test for *independence* between the row and column variables. We first define a *test of independence* and we provide key elements of the test in the Key Elements box that follows.

DEFINITION

In a **test of independence,** we test the null hypothesis that in a contingency table, the row and column variables are independent. (That is, there is no dependency between the row variable and the column variable.)

KEY ELEMENTS

Contingency Table

Objective

Conduct a hypothesis test of independence between the row variable and column variable in a contingency table.

Notation

O represents the *observed frequency* in a cell of a contingency table.
E represents the *expected frequency* in a cell, found by assuming that the row and column variables are independent.
r represents the number of rows in a contingency table (not including labels or row totals).
c represents the number of columns in a contingency table (not including labels or column totals).

Requirements

1. The sample data are randomly selected.

2. The sample data are represented as frequency counts in a two-way table.

3. For every cell in the contingency table, the expected frequency E is at least 5. (There is no requirement that every *observed* frequency must be at least 5.)

Null and Alternative Hypotheses

The null and alternative hypotheses are as follows:

H_0: The row and column variables are independent.

H_1: The row and column variables are dependent.

Test Statistic for a Test of Independence

$$\chi^2 = \sum \frac{(O - E)^2}{E}$$

where O is the observed frequency in a cell and E is the expected frequency in a cell that is found by evaluating

$$E = \frac{(\text{row total})\,(\text{column total})}{(\text{grand total})}$$

P-values

P-values are typically provided by technology, or a range of P-values can be found from Table A-4.

Critical values:

1. The critical values are found in Table A-4 using

$$\textbf{Degrees of freedom } = (r - 1)(c - 1)$$

where r is the number of rows of data and c is the number of columns of data (not including labels).

2. Tests of independence with a contingency table are always *right-tailed.*

Caution

- If the P-value is greater than the significance level α, do not accept independence. Instead, conclude that there is not sufficient evidence to reject independence.

- If the P-value is less than or equal to the significance level α, do not conclude that one of the variables is the direct *cause* of the other variable.

The distribution of the test statistic χ^2 can be approximated by the chi-square distribution, provided that all cells have expected frequencies that are at least 5. The number of degrees of freedom $(r - 1)(c - 1)$ reflects the fact that because we know the total of all frequencies in a contingency table, we can freely assign frequencies to only $r - 1$ rows and $c - 1$ columns before the frequency for every cell is determined. However, we cannot have negative frequencies or frequencies so large that any row (or column) sum exceeds the total of the observed frequencies for that row (or column).

Observed and Expected Frequencies The test statistic allows us to measure the amount of disagreement between the frequencies actually observed and those that we would theoretically expect when the two variables are independent. Large values of the χ^2 test statistic are in the rightmost region of the chi-square distribution, and they reflect significant differences between observed and expected frequencies. As in Section 11-1, if observed and expected frequencies are close, the χ^2 test statistic will be small and the P-value will be large. If observed and expected frequencies are far apart, the χ^2 test statistic will be large and the P-value will be small. These relationships are summarized and illustrated in Figure 11-4.

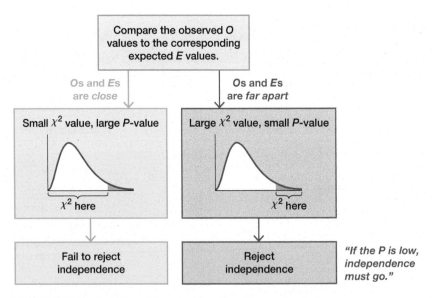

FIGURE 11-4 Relationships Among Key Components in a Test of Independence

Finding Expected Values E

An individual expected frequency E for a cell can be found by simply multiplying the total of the row frequencies by the total of the column frequencies, then dividing by the grand total of all frequencies, as shown in Example 1.

$$E = \frac{(\text{row total})\,(\text{column total})}{(\text{grand total})}$$

EXAMPLE 1   **Finding Expected Frequency**

Table 11-1 from the Chapter Problem is shown below. Also shown are the row totals and column totals. Find the expected frequency E for the cell with an observed frequency of 25.

TABLE 11-1 Results From a Study of a Link Between the MMR Vaccine and Autism

	Unvaccinated	Vaccinated	Total
Autism	25 (E = ?)	64	**89**
No Autism	362	1427	**1789**
Total	**387**	**1491**	**1878**

SOLUTION

The cell with the frequency of 25 lies in the first row (with a total frequency of 89) and in the first column (with total frequency of 387). The "grand total" is the sum of all frequencies in the table, which is 1878. For that first cell with an observed frequency of 25, the expected frequency is

$$E = \frac{(\text{row total})(\text{column total})}{(\text{grand total})} = \frac{(89)(387)}{1878} = 18.340$$

Using this formula, the expected frequency for the remaining three cells can be found. These expected frequencies are shown in Table 11-6.

TABLE 11-6 Expected Frequencies from Table 11-1

	Unvaccinated	Vaccinated
Autism	25(E = 18.340)	64(E = 70.660)
No Autism	362(E = 368.660)	1427(E = 1420.340)

INTERPRETATION

We know that the first cell has an *observed* frequency of $O = 25$ and an *expected* frequency of $E = 18.340$. We can interpret the expected value by stating that if we assume that autism is independent of vaccine, then we expect to find that 18.340 of the subjects would be unvaccinated and they would have autism. There is a discrepancy between $O = 25$ and $E = 18.340$, and such discrepancies are key components of the test statistic that is a collective measure of the overall disagreement between the observed frequencies and the frequencies expected with independence between the row and column variables.

YOUR TURN. Exercise 1: "Dogs Detecting Malaria."

 EXAMPLE 2   **Is There a Link Between the MMR Vaccine and Autism?**

Use the same sample data from Example 1 with a 0.05 significance level to test the claim that autism is independent of the MMR (measles, mumps, rubella) vaccine.

SOLUTION

REQUIREMENT CHECK (1) On the basis of the study description, we will treat the subjects as being randomly selected and randomly assigned to the different treatment groups. (2) The results are expressed as frequency counts in Table 11-6 in Example 1. (3) Table 11-6 shows that the expected frequencies are all at least 5. (The lowest expected frequency is 18.340.) The requirements are satisfied. ☑

continued

The null hypothesis and alternative hypothesis are as follows:

H_0: Autism is independent of the MMR vaccine.

H_1: Autism and the MMR vaccine are dependent.

The significance level is $\alpha = 0.05$.

Because the data in Table 11-6 are in the form of a contingency table, we use the χ^2 distribution with this test statistic:

$$\chi^2 = \sum \frac{(O - E)^2}{E} = \frac{(25 - 18.340)^2}{18.340} + \cdots + \frac{(1427 - 1420.340)^2}{1420.340}$$

$$= 3.198$$

TI-83/84

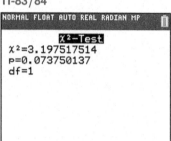

P-Value from Technology If using technology, results typically include the χ^2 test statistic and the P-value. For example, see the accompanying TI-83/84 Plus display showing the test statistic is $\chi^2 = 3.198$ and the P-value is 0.074.

P-Value from Table A-4 If using Table A-4 instead of technology, first find the number of degrees of freedom: $(r - 1)(c - 1) = (2 - 1)(2 - 1) = 1$ degree of freedom. Because the test statistic of $\chi^2 = 3.198$ is less than 3.841 in Table A-4 for the row corresponding to 1 degree of freedom, we know that P-value > 0.05.

Because the P-value is greater than the significance level of 0.05, we fail to reject the null hypothesis of independence between autism and the vaccine.

Critical Value If using the critical value method of hypothesis testing, the critical value of $\chi^2 = 3.841$ is found from Table A-4, with $\alpha = 0.05$ in the right tail and the number of degrees of freedom given by $(r - 1)(c - 1) = (2 - 1)(2 - 1) = 1$. The test statistic of $\chi^2 = 3.198$ does not fall in the critical region bounded by the critical value $\chi^2 = 3.841$, so we fail to reject the null hypothesis of independence between autism and the vaccine.

INTERPRETATION

Based on the data in Table 11-1, it appears that autism is not linked to the MMR vaccine. The data support the conclusion of the study that "these findings indicate no harmful association between MMR vaccine receipt and ASD (autism spectrum disorder) even among children already at higher risk for ASD." Within days of this writing, Peter Marks, director of the Center for Biologics Evaluation and Research for the FDA said that "vaccinating against measles, mumps and rubella not only protects us and our children, it protects people who can't be vaccinated, including children with compromised immune systems due to illness and its treatment, such as cancer."

YOUR TURN. Do Exercise 5 "Lie Detector."

2 × 2 Contingency Table vs Two Proportions The data in Table 11-1 can be expressed as two proportions:

- Unvaccinated Group: P(autism) $= 25/387$
- Vaccinated Group: P(autism) $= 64/1491$

Because we now have two proportions, why can't we use the methods of Section 9-1 "Two Proportions" instead of the methods of this section? Well, we can! See Exercise 21 for verifying that results from the two different methods are equivalent.

Rationale for Expected Frequencies E To better understand expected frequencies, pretend that we know only the row and column totals in Table 11-6. Let's assume that the row and column variables are independent and that 1 of the 1878 study subjects is randomly selected. First, note that 89 of the 1878 subjects had autism, and 387 of the 1878 subjects were unvaccinated, so we have the following:

$$P(\text{autism}) = 89/1878 \text{ and } P(\text{unvaccinated}) = 387/1878.$$

If the row and column variables are independent, as we are assuming in the null hypothesis, we can use the multiplication rule for independent events (see Section 4-2) as follows:

$$P(\text{autism } and \text{ unvaccinated}) = \frac{89}{1878} \cdot \frac{387}{1878} = 0.00976584$$

With a probability of 0.00976584 for the first cell, we expect that among 1878 subjects, there are $1878 \cdot 0.00976584 = 18.340$ subjects in the first cell. If we generalize these calculations, we get the following:

$$\text{Expected frequency } E = (\text{grand total}) \cdot \frac{(\text{row total})}{(\text{grand total})} \cdot \frac{(\text{column total})}{(\text{grand total})}$$

This expression can be simplified to

$$E = \frac{(\text{row total})\,(\text{column total})}{(\text{grand total})}$$

PART2 Test of Homogeneity, Fisher's Exact Test, and McNemar's Test for Matched Pairs

Test of Homogeneity

In Part 1 of this section, we focused on the test of *independence* between the row and column variables in a contingency table. In Part 1, the sample data are from one population, and individual sample results are categorized with the row and column variables. In a *chi-square test of homogeneity,* we have samples randomly selected from different populations, and we want to determine whether those populations have the same proportions of some characteristic being considered. (The word *homogeneous* means "having the same quality," and in this context, we are testing to determine whether the proportions are the same.) Section 9-1 presented a procedure for testing a claim about *two* populations with categorical data having two possible outcomes, but a chi-square test of homogeneity allows us to use two or more populations with outcomes from several categories.

> **DEFINITION**
>
> A **chi-square test of homogeneity** is a test of the claim that *different populations* have the same proportions of some characteristics.

Sampling from Different Populations In a typical test of independence, as described in Part 1 of this section, sample subjects are randomly selected from one population (such as people treated for stress fractures in a foot bone) and values of two different variables are observed (such as success/failure for people receiving different treatments). In a typical chi-square test of homogeneity, subjects are randomly selected from the different populations separately.

Procedure In conducting a test of homogeneity, we can use the same notation, requirements, test statistic, critical value, and procedures given in the Key Elements box from Part 1 on page 591 of this section, with this exception: Instead of testing the null hypothesis of independence between the row and column variables, we test the null hypothesis that *the different populations have the same proportion of some characteristic.*

EXAMPLE 3   The Lost Wallet Experiment

Table 11-7 lists results from a *Reader's Digest* experiment in which 12 wallets were intentionally lost in each of 16 different cities, including New York City, London, Amsterdam, and so on. Use a 0.05 significance level with the data from Table 11-7 to test the null hypothesis that the cities have the same proportion of returned wallets. The *Reader's Digest* headline "Most Honest Cities: The *Reader's Digest* Lost Wallet Test" implies that whether a wallet is returned is dependent on the city in which it was lost. Test the claim that the proportion of returned wallets is not the same in the 16 different cities.

TABLE 11-7 Lost Wallet Experiment

City	A	B	C	D	E	F	G	H	I	J	K	L	M	N	O	P
Wallet Returned	8	5	7	11	5	8	6	7	3	1	4	2	4	6	4	9
Wallet Not Returned	4	7	5	1	7	4	6	5	9	11	8	10	8	6	8	3

SOLUTION

REQUIREMENT CHECK (1) Based on the description of the study, we will treat the subjects as being randomly selected and randomly assigned to the different cities. (2) The results are expressed as frequency counts in Table 11-7. (3) The expected frequencies are all at least 5. (All expected values are either 5.625 or 6.375.) The requirements are satisfied. ☑

The null hypothesis and alternative hypothesis are as follows:

H_0: Whether a lost wallet is returned is independent of the city in which it was lost.

H_1: A lost wallet being returned depends on the city in which it was lost.

The accompanying StatCrunch display shows the test statistic of $X^2 = 35.388$ (rounded) and the *P*-value of 0.002 (rounded). Because the *P*-value of 0.002 is less than the significance level of 0.05, we reject the null hypothesis of independence between the two variables. ("If the *P* is low, the null must go.")

INTERPRETATION

We reject the null hypothesis of independence, so it appears that the proportion of returned wallets depends on the city in which they were lost. There is sufficient evidence to conclude that the proportion of returned wallets is not the same in the 16 different cities.

StatCrunch

Chi-Square test:			
Statistic	**DF**	**Value**	**P-value**
Chi-square	15	35.388235	0.0022

Fisher's Exact Test

The procedures for testing hypotheses with contingency tables have the requirement that every cell must have an expected frequency of at least 5. This requirement is necessary for the X^2 distribution to be a suitable approximation to the exact distribution of the X^2 test statistic. *Fisher's exact test* is often used for a 2×2 contingency table with one or more expected frequencies that are below 5. Fisher's exact test provides an *exact* P-value and does not require an approximation technique. Because the calculations are quite complex, it's a good idea to use technology when using Fisher's exact test. Statdisk, Minitab, XLSTAT, and StatCrunch all have the ability to perform Fisher's exact test.

EXAMPLE 4   **Does Yawning Cause Others to Yawn?**

The *MythBusters* show on the Discovery Channel tested the theory that when someone yawns, others are more likely to yawn. The results are summarized in Table 11-8. The methods of Part 1 in this Section should not be used because one of the cells has an expected frequency of 4.480, which violates the requirement that every cell must have an expected frequency E of at least 5. Using Fisher's exact test results in a P-value of 0.513, so there is not sufficient evidence to support the myth that people exposed to yawning actually yawn more than those not exposed to yawning. (For testing the claim of no difference, the P-value is 1.000, indicating that there is not a significant difference between the two groups.)

TABLE 11-8 Yawning Theory Experiment

		Subject Exposed to Yawning?	
		Yes	No
Did Subject Yawn?	Yes	10	4
	No	24	12

McNemar's Test for Matched Pairs

The methods in Part 1 of this section are based on independent data. For 2 × 2 tables consisting of frequency counts that result from matched pairs, the frequency counts within each matched pair are not independent and, for such cases, we can use McNemar's test of the null hypothesis that the frequencies from the discordant (different) categories occur in the same proportion.

Table 11-9 shows a general format for summarizing results from data consisting of frequency counts from matched pairs. Table 11-9 refers to two different treatments (such as two different eyedrop solutions) applied to two different parts of each subject (such as left eye and right eye). We should be careful when reading a table such as Table 11-9. If $a = 100$, then 100 subjects were cured with both treatments. If $b = 50$ in Table 11-9, then each of 50 subjects had no cure with treatment X but they were each cured with treatment Y. The total number of subjects is $a + b + c + d$, and each of those subjects yields results from each of two parts of a matched pair. Remember, the entries in Table 11-9 are frequency counts of subjects, not the total number of individual components in the matched pairs. If 500 people have each eye treated with two different ointments, the value of $a + b + c + d$ is 500 (the number of subjects), not 1000 (the number of treated eyes).

TABLE 11-9 2 × 2 Table with Frequency Counts from Matched Pairs

		Treatment X	
		Cured	Not Cured
Treatment Y	Cured	a	b
	Not Cured	c	d

continued

McNemar's test requires that for a table such as Table 11-9, the frequencies are such that $b + c \geq 10$. The test is a right-tailed chi-square test with the following test statistic:

$$\chi^2 = \frac{(|b - c| - 1)^2}{b + c}$$

P-values are typically provided by software, and critical values can be found in Table A-4 using 1 degree of freedom. *Caution:* When applying McNemar's test, be careful to use only the two frequency counts from *discordant* (different) pairs, such as the frequency *b* in Table 11-9 (with different pairs of cured/not cured) and frequency *c* in Table 11-9 (with different pairs of not cured/cured).

EXAMPLE 5 **Are Hip Protectors Effective?**

A randomized controlled trial was designed to test the effectiveness of hip protectors in preventing hip fractures in the elderly. Nursing home residents each wore protection on one hip, but not the other. Results are summarized in Table 11-10 (based on data from "Efficacy of Hip Protector to Prevent Hip Fracture in Nursing Home Residents," by Kiel et al., *Journal of the American Medical Association,* Vol. 298, No. 4). McNemar's test can be used to test the null hypothesis that the following two proportions are the same:

- The proportion of subjects with no hip fracture on the protected hip and a hip fracture on the unprotected hip.

- The proportion of subjects with a hip fracture on the protected hip and no hip fracture on the unprotected hip.

TABLE 11-10 Randomized Controlled Trial of Hip Protectors

		No Hip Protector Worn	
		No Hip Fracture	Hip Fracture
Hip Protector Worn	No Hip Fracture	309	10
	Hip Fracture	15	2

Using the discordant (different) pairs with the general format from Table 11-9 we have $b = 10$ and $c = 15$, so the test statistic is calculated as follows:

$$\chi^2 = \frac{(|b - c| - 1)^2}{b + c} = \frac{(|10 - 15| - 1)^2}{10 + 15} = 0.640$$

With a 0.05 significance level and degrees of freedom given by df $= 1$, we refer to Table A-4 to find the critical value of $\chi^2 = 3.841$ for this right-tailed test. The test statistic of $\chi^2 = 0.640$ does not exceed the critical value of $\chi^2 = 3.841$, so we fail to reject the null hypothesis. (Also, the *P*-value is 0.424, which is greater than 0.05, indicating that we fail to reject the null hypothesis.) The proportion of hip fractures with the protectors worn is not significantly different from the proportion of hip fractures without the protectors worn. The hip protectors do not appear to be effective in preventing hip fractures.

TECH CENTER

Contingency Tables
Access tech supplements, videos, and data sets at **www.TriolaStats.com**

Statdisk
1. Click **Analysis** in the top menu.
2. Select **Contingency Tables** from the dropdown menu.
3. Enter the desired significance level and select the columns to be included in the analysis.
4. Click **Evaluate.**

Minitab
1. Click **Stat** in the top menu.
2. Select **Tables** from the dropdown menu and select **Chi-Square Test for Association.**
3. Select **Summarized data in a two-way table** from the dropdown box.
4. Select the columns containing the observed frequencies.
5. Click **OK.**
TIP: Observed frequencies must be entered in columns just as they appear in the contingency table.

StatCrunch
1. Click **Stat** in the top menu.
2. Select **Tables** from the dropdown menu, then select **Contingency— With Summary** from the submenu.
3. Select the columns of data to be included in the analysis.
4. For *Row labels* select the column containing the row names.
5. Click **Compute!** The test statistic and *P*-value are displayed at the bottom of the results.
TIP: You must enter row names in the first column.

TI-83/84 Plus Calculator

1. Enter the contingency data as a matrix:

   Manually enter data: Press **2ND** then **x⁻¹** to get to the *MATRIX* menu, select **EDIT** from the top menu, select a matrix letter, and press **ENTER**. Enter the number of rows and columns needed, press **ENTER**, and proceed to enter the sample values.

   Using existing lists: Lists can be combined and stored in a matrix. Press **2ND** then **x⁻¹** to get to the *MATRIX* menu, select **MATH** from the top menu, and select the item **List → matr.** Enter the list names (the first list must contain values for the dependent *y* variable), followed by the matrix name, all separated by commas. *Important:* The matrix name must be entered by pressing **2ND** then **x⁻¹**, selecting the matrix letter, and pressing **ENTER**. The following is a summary of the commands used to create a matrix from three lists (L1, L2, L3): **List → matr(L1, L2, L3,[D]).**

2. Press **STAT**, then select **TESTS** in the top menu.
3. Select X^2**-Test** in the menu and press **ENTER**.
4. For *Observed* enter the matrix created in Step 1 by pressing **2ND** then **x⁻¹** and selecting the matrix letter. *Expected* shows the matrix that will be used to automatically store the expected frequencies that are calculated.
5. Select **Calculate** and press **ENTER**.

TIP: The list name *L1* (and *L2* . . . *L6*) can be quickly entered by pressing **2ND** **1**.

Excel

XLSTAT Add-In

1. Click on the **XLSTAT** tab in the Ribbon and then click **Correlation/ Association tests**.
2. Select **Tests on contingency tables** from the dropdown menu.
3. Under *Data format* select **Contingency table**.
4. In the *Contingency table* box enter the range of cells containing the frequency counts of the contingency table. If the range includes data labels, check the **Labels included** box.
5. Click the **Options** tab.
6. Check the **Chi-square test** box and enter a significance level if that option is available. If not, a 0.05 significance level will be used.
7. Click **OK** to display the results.

R

R command:

Equal expected frequencies: **chisq.test(Con_Table, correct=FALSE)**

where *Con_Table* is the contingency table name in R.

TIP: correct=FALSE results in no Yates's continuity correction being applied. *correct=TRUE* applies Yates's continuity correction.

A complete list of R statistical commands is available at TriolaStats.com

11-2 Basic Skills and Concepts

Statistical Literacy and Critical Thinking

1. Dogs Detecting Malaria The following table lists results from an experiment designed to test the ability of dogs to use their extraordinary sense of smell to detect malaria in samples of children's socks (based on data presented at an annual meeting of the American Society of Tropical Medicine, by principal investigator Steve Lindsay). Assuming that the dog being correct is independent of whether malaria is present, find the expected value for the observed frequency of 123.

	Malaria Was Present	Malaria Was Not Present
Dog Was Correct	123	131
Dog Was Wrong	52	14

2. Identifying Hypotheses Refer to the data given in Exercise 1 and assume that the requirements are all satisfied and we want to conduct a hypothesis test of independence using the methods of this section. Identify the null and alternative hypotheses.

3. Hypothesis Test The accompanying TI-83/84 Plus calculator display shows the results from the experiment described in Exercise 1. Assume that the hypothesis test requirements are all satisfied.

a. Identify the test statistic and the P-value (expressed in standard form and rounded to three decimal places), and then state the conclusion about the null hypothesis.

b. Does rejection of the null hypothesis of independence imply that dogs are good at identifying malaria?

4. Right-Tailed, Left-Tailed, Two-Tailed Is the hypothesis test described in Exercise 1 right-tailed, left-tailed, or two-tailed? Explain your choice.

In Exercises 5–18, test the given claim.

5. Lie Detector The table below includes results from polygraph (lie detector) experiments conducted by researchers Charles R. Honts (Boise State University) and Gordon H. Barland (Department of Defense Polygraph Institute). In each case, it was known if the subject lied or did not lie, so the table indicates when the polygraph test was correct. Use a 0.05 significance level to test the claim that whether a subject lies is independent of the polygraph test indication. Do the results suggest that polygraphs are effective in distinguishing between truths and lies?

	Did the Subject Actually Lie?	
	No (Did Not Lie)	Yes (Lied)
Polygraph test indicated that the subject lied.	15	42
Polygraph test indicated that the subject did not lie.	32	9

6. Ghosts The following table summarizes results from a Pew Research Center survey in which subjects were asked whether they had seen or been in the presence of a ghost. Use a 0.01 significance level to test the claim that gender is independent of response. Does the conclusion change if the significance level is changed to 0.05?

	Yes	No
Male	138	724
Female	228	913

7. Texting and Drinking In a study of high school students at least 16 years of age, researchers obtained survey results summarized in the accompanying table (based on data from "Texting While Driving and Other Risky Motor Vehicle Behaviors Among U.S. High School Students," by O'Malley, Shults, and Eaton, *Pediatrics,* Vol. 131, No. 6). Use a 0.05 significance level to test the claim of independence between texting while driving and driving when drinking alcohol. Are those two risky behaviors independent of each other?

	Drove When Drinking Alcohol?	
	Yes	No
Texted While Driving	731	3054
No Texting While Driving	156	4564

8. Accuracy of Fingerprint Identifications An experiment was conducted to compare the accuracy of fingerprint experts to the accuracy of novices (based on data from "Identifying Fingerprint Expertise," by Tangen, Thompson, and McCarthy, *Psychological Science,* Vol. 22, No. 8). The data in the table are based on trials in which the evaluators were given matching fingerprints. Use a 0.05 significance level to determine whether correct identification is independent of whether the evaluator is an expert or a novice.

	Correct	Wrong
Novice	331	113
Expert	409	35

9. Four Quarters the Same as $1? In a study of the "denomination effect," 43 college students were each given one dollar in the form of four quarters, while 46 other college students were each given one dollar in the form of a dollar bill. All of the students were then given two choices: (1) keep the money; (2) spend the money on gum. The results are given in the accompanying table (based on "The Denomination Effect," by Priya Raghubir and Joydeep Srivastava, *Journal of Consumer Research,* Vol. 36.) Use a 0.05 significance level to test the claim that whether students purchased gum or kept the money is independent of whether they were given four quarters or a $1 bill. Is there a "denomination effect"?

	Purchased Gum	Kept the Money
Students Given Four Quarters	27	16
Students Given a $1 Bill	12	34

10. Effect of the Football Overtime Coin Toss The accompanying table lists results of overtime football games before and after the overtime rule was changed in the National Football League in 2011. The data are current as of this writing. Use a 0.05 significance level to test the claim of independence between winning an overtime game and whether playing under the old rule or the new rule. What do the results suggest about the effectiveness of the rule change?

	Before Rule Change	After Rule Change
Overtime Coin Toss Winner Won the Game	252	59
Overtime Coin Toss Winner Lost the Game	208	52

11. Hawk-Eye and Tennis Challenges In 2006, use of the Hawk-Eye computer system was initiated at U.S. Open tennis matches. Players could challenge chair umpire and line judge calls, and the Hawk-Eye system was used to decide whether the call was correct or wrong. The table below shows results of player challenges in men's and women's singles games in which the Hawk-Eye system was used. The data are current at the time of this writing. Use a 0.05 significance level to test the claim that the gender of the tennis player is independent of whether the call is overturned. Do players of either gender appear to be better at challenging calls?

	Was the Challenge to the Call Successful?	
	Yes	No
Men	1757	4279
Women	887	2440

12. Nurse a Serial Killer? Alert nurses at the Veteran's Affairs Medical Center in Northampton, Massachusetts, noticed an unusually high number of deaths at times when another nurse, Kristen Gilbert, was working. Those same nurses later noticed missing supplies of the drug epinephrine, which is a synthetic adrenaline that stimulates the heart. Kristen Gilbert was arrested and charged with four counts of murder and two counts of attempted murder. When seeking a grand jury indictment, prosecutors provided a key piece of evidence consisting of the table below. Use a 0.01 significance level to test the defense claim that deaths on shifts are independent of whether Gilbert was working. What does the result suggest about the guilt or innocence of Gilbert?

	Shifts With a Death	Shifts Without a Death
Gilbert Was Working	40	217
Gilbert Was Not Working	34	1350

13. Gender and Eye Color The following table describes the distribution of eye colors reported by male and female statistics students (based on data from "Does Eye Color Depend on Gender? It Might Depend on Who or How You Ask," by Froelich and Stephenson, *Journal of Statistics Education*, Vol. 21, No. 2). Is there sufficient evidence to warrant rejection of the belief that gender and eye color are independent traits? Use a 0.01 significance level.

	Blue	Brown	Green	Hazel
Male	359	290	110	160
Female	370	352	198	187

14. Is Seat Belt Use Independent of Cigarette Smoking? A study of seat belt users and nonusers yielded the randomly selected sample data summarized in the given table (based on data from "What Kinds of People Do Not Use Seat Belts?" by Helsing and Comstock, *American Journal of Public Health*, Vol. 67, No. 11). Test the claim that the amount of smoking is independent of seat belt use. A plausible theory is that people who smoke more are less concerned about their health and safety and are therefore less inclined to wear seat belts. Is this theory supported by the sample data?

	Number of Cigarettes Smoked per Day			
	0	1–14	15–34	35 and over
Wear Seat Belts	175	20	42	6
Don't Wear Seat Belts	149	17	41	9

15. Clinical Trial of Echinacea In a clinical trial of the effectiveness of echinacea for preventing colds, the results in the table below were obtained (based on data from "An Evaluation of *Echinacea Angustifolia* in Experimental Rhinovirus Infections," by Turner et al., *New England Journal of Medicine*, Vol. 353, No. 4). Use a 0.05 significance level to test the claim that getting a cold is independent of the treatment group. What do the results suggest about the effectiveness of echinacea as a prevention against colds?

	Treatment Group		
	Placebo	Echinacea: 20% Extract	Echinacea: 60% Extract
Got a Cold	88	48	42
Did Not Get a Cold	15	4	10

16. Injuries and Motorcycle Helmet Color A case-control (or retrospective) study was conducted to investigate a relationship between the colors of helmets worn by motorcycle drivers and whether they are injured or killed in a crash. Results are given in the table below (based on data from "Motorcycle Rider Conspicuity and Crash Related Injury: Case-Control

Study," by Wells et al., *BMJ USA*, Vol. 4). Test the claim that injuries are independent of helmet color. Should motorcycle drivers choose helmets with a particular color? If so, which color appears best?

	Color of Helmet				
	Black	White	Yellow/Orange	Red	Blue
Controls (not injured)	491	377	31	170	55
Cases (injured or killed)	213	112	8	70	26

17. Survey Refusals A study of people who refused to answer survey questions provided the randomly selected sample data shown in the table below (based on data from "I Hear You Knocking But You Can't Come In," by Fitzgerald and Fuller, *Sociological Methods and Research,* Vol. 11, No. 1). At the 0.01 significance level, test the claim that the cooperation of the subject (response or refusal) is independent of the age category. Does any particular age group appear to be particularly uncooperative?

	Age					
	18–21	22–29	30–39	40–49	50–59	60 and over
Responded	73	255	245	136	138	202
Refused	11	20	33	16	27	49

18. Genetics and Handedness In a study of left-handedness as a possible inherited trait, the data in the table below were obtained (based on data from "Why Are Some People Left-Handed? An Evolutionary Perspective," by Laurens and Faurie, *Philosophical Transactions,* Vol. 364). Use a 0.01 significance level to test the claim that handedness of offspring is independent of parental handedness. What do the results suggest about the inheritability of handedness?

Handedness of Parents (Father/Mother)	Handedness of Offspring	
	Left	Right
Right/Right	5360	50,928
Right/Left	767	2736
Left/Right	741	3667
Left/Left	94	289

19. Car License Plates California, Connecticut, and New York are states with laws requiring that cars have license plates on the front and rear. The author randomly selected cars in those states and the results are given in the accompanying table. Use a 0.05 significance level to test the claim of independence between the state and whether a car has front and rear license plates. Does it appear that the license plate laws are followed at the same rates in the three states?

	California	Connecticut	New York
Car with Rear Plate Only	35	45	9
Car with Front and Rear Plates	528	289	541

20. Is the Home Field Advantage Independent of the Sport? Winning team data were collected for teams in different sports, with the results given in the table below (based on data from "Predicting Professional Sports Game Outcomes from Intermediate Game Scores," by Copper, DeNeve, and Mosteller, *Chance,* Vol. 5, No. 3–4). Use a 0.10 significance level to test the claim that home/visitor wins are independent of the sport. Given that among the four sports included here, baseball is the only sport in which the home team can modify field dimensions to favor its own players, does it appear that baseball teams are effective in using this advantage?

	Basketball	Baseball	Hockey	Football
Home Team Wins	127	53	50	57
Visiting Team Wins	71	47	43	42

11-2   Beyond the Basics

21. Equivalent Tests A X^2 test involving a 2×2 table is equivalent to the test for the difference between two proportions, as described in Section 9-1. Using Table 11-1 on page 577 from the Chapter Problem, verify that the X^2 test statistic and the z test statistic (found from the test of equality of two proportions) are related as follows: $z^2 = X^2$. Also show that the critical values have that same relationship.

22. Using Yates's Correction for Continuity The chi-square distribution is continuous, whereas the test statistic used in this section is discrete. Some statisticians use *Yates's correction for continuity* in cells with an expected frequency of less than 10 or in all cells of a contingency table with two rows and two columns. With Yates's correction, we replace

$$\sum \frac{(O - E)^2}{E} \quad \text{with} \quad \sum \frac{(|O - E| - 0.5)^2}{E}$$

Given the contingency table in Exercise 9 "Four Quarters the Same as \$1?" find the value of the X^2 test statistic using Yates's correction in all cells. What effect does Yates's correction have?

Chapter Quick Quiz

Exercises 1–5 refer to the sample data in the following table, which summarizes the frequencies of 500 digits randomly generated by Statdisk. Assume that we want to use a 0.05 significance level to test the claim that Statdisk generates the digits in a way that they are equally likely.

Last Digit	0	1	2	3	4	5	6	7	8	9
Frequency	45	45	54	61	45	43	48	53	50	56

1. What are the null and alternative hypotheses corresponding to the stated claim?

2. When testing the claim in Exercise 1, what are the observed and expected frequencies for the first digit of 0?

3. Is the hypothesis test left-tailed, right-tailed, or two-tailed?

4. If using a 0.05 significance level to test the stated claim, find the number of degrees of freedom.

5. Given that the *P*-value for the hypothesis test is 0.720, what do you conclude? Does it appear that Statdisk generates the digits so that they are equally likely?

*Questions 6–10 refer to the sample data in the following table, which describes the fate of the passengers and crew aboard the **Titanic** when it sank on April 15, 1912. Assume that the data are a sample from a large population and we want to use a 0.05 significance level to test the claim that surviving is independent of whether the person is a man, woman, boy, or girl.*

	Men	Women	Boys	Girls
Survived	332	318	29	27
Died	1360	104	35	18

6. Identify the null and alternative hypotheses corresponding to the stated claim.

7. What distribution is used to test the stated claim (normal, *t*, *F*, chi-square, uniform)?

8. Is the hypothesis test left-tailed, right-tailed, or two-tailed?

9. Find the number of degrees of freedom.

10. Given that the *P*-value for the hypothesis test is 0.000 when rounded to three decimal places, what do you conclude? What do the results indicate about the rule that women and children should be the first to be saved?

Review Exercises

1. Weather-Related Deaths For the most recent year as of this writing, the numbers of weather-related U.S. deaths for each month were 61, 14, 22, 26, 29, 42, 93, 49, 47, 35, 96, 16, listed in order beginning with January (based on data from the National Weather Service). Use a 0.01 significance level to test the claim that weather-related deaths occur in the different months with the same frequency. Provide an explanation for the result.

2. Benford and Cheating in Badminton According to Benford's law, for many data sets the leading digits of individual sample values follow the distribution shown in the first two rows of the following table. In normal and fair badminton play, leading digits in the numbers of rallies tend to follow the distribution of Benford's law. In a study of leading digits for the numbers of badminton rallies in international tournaments, the frequencies in the bottom row of the table were obtained (based on data from "Preliminary Study to Detect Match-Fixing: Benford's Law in Badminton Rally Data," by Park et al., *Journal of Physical Education and Sports Management*, Vol. 3, No. 1). Does it appear that the observed frequencies fit the distribution from Benford's law? What does the result suggest about cheating in those matches?

Leading Digit	1	2	3	4	5	6	7	8	9
Benford's Law: Distribution of Leading Digits	0.301	0.176	0.125	0.097	0.079	0.067	0.058	0.051	0.046
Leading Digits of Numbers of Rallies	3679	1515	974	898	866	757	740	743	649

3. Splint or Surgery? A randomized controlled trial was designed to compare the effectiveness of splinting versus surgery in the treatment of carpal tunnel syndrome. Results are given in the table below (based on data from "Splinting vs. Surgery in the Treatment of Carpal Tunnel Syndrome," by Gerritsen et al., *Journal of the American Medical Association*, Vol. 288, No. 10). The results are based on evaluations made one year after the treatment. Using a 0.01 significance level, test the claim that success is independent of the type of treatment. What do the results suggest about treating carpal tunnel syndrome?

	Successful Treatment	Unsuccessful Treatment
Splint Treatment	60	23
Surgery Treatment	67	6

4. Does the Treatment Affect Success? The following table lists frequencies of successes and failures for different treatments used for a stress fracture in a foot bone (based on data from "Surgery Unfounded for Tarsal Navicular Stress Fracture," by Bruce Jancin, *Internal Medicine News*, Vol. 42, No. 14). Use a 0.05 significance level to test the claim that success of the treatment is independent of the type of treatment. What does the result indicate about the increasing trend to use surgery?

	Success	Failure
Surgery	54	12
Weight-Bearing Cast	41	51
Non–Weight-Bearing Cast for 6 Weeks	70	3
Non–Weight-Bearing Cast for Less Than 6 Weeks	17	5

Cumulative Review Exercises

In Exercises 1–4, based on the nature of the given data, do the following:

a. Pose a key question that is relevant to the given data.

b. Identify a procedure or tool from this chapter or the preceding chapters to address the key question from part (a).

c. Analyze the data and state a conclusion.

1. Manual Dexterity In the following table, each column lists scores on a test of manual dexterity for brother/sister fraternal twins. The females are listed in the top row, and their corresponding brothers are listed in the bottom row.

14	22	11	12	18
20	15	16	17	15

2. Last Digits Use the same data from Exercise 1, but assume that the ten values are frequencies of last digits of weights of salmon captured in the Columbia River between Oregon and Washington. The frequencies are listed in order by row and they correspond to the last digits of 0, 1, 2, 3, 4, 5, 6, 7, 8, and 9.

3. Marathon Runners Use the same data from Exercise 1, but assume that the values in the top row are distances (miles) run by five randomly selected male runners and the values in the bottom row are distances (miles) run by five randomly selected female runners.

4. Last Digits Use the same data from Exercise 1, but assume that the columns correspond to the variable of day of the week (Monday, Tuesday, Wednesday, Thursday, Friday) and the rows correspond to the work shift (morning, afternoon) at an automobile brake manufacturer. The entries in the table are numbers of defective brake linings found during quality assurance inspections.

5. One Big Bill or Many Smaller Bills In a study of the "denomination effect," 150 women in China were given either a single 100 yuan bill or a total of 100 yuan in smaller bills. The value of 100 yuan is about $15. The women were given the choice of spending the money on specific items or keeping the money. The results are summarized in the table below (based on "The Denomination Effect," by Priya Raghubir and Joydeep Srivastava, *Journal of Consumer Research,* Vol. 36). Use a 0.05 significance level to test the claim that the form of the 100 yuan is independent of whether the money was spent. What does the result suggest about a denomination effect?

	Spent the Money	Kept the Money
Women Given a Single 100-Yuan Bill	60	15
Women Given 100 Yuan in Smaller Bills	68	7

6. Probability Refer to the results from the 150 subjects in Cumulative Review Exercise 5.

a. Find the probability that if 1 of the 150 subjects is randomly selected, the result is a woman who spent the money.

b. Find the probability that if 1 of the 150 subjects is randomly selected, the result is a woman who spent the money or was given a single 100-yuan bill.

c. If two different women are randomly selected, find the probability that they both spent the money.

Technology Project

Data Set 3 "ANSUR II 2012" includes measurements from $n = 6068$ U.S. Army personnel. Use software to find the frequencies in the following table. After finding those frequencies, test to determine whether handedness (right, left, or both) is independent of gender.

	Right-Handed	Left-Handed	Ambidextrous (Both Right and Left)
Female			
Male			

Big (or Very Large) Data Project

Refer to Data Set 45 "Births in New York" in Appendix B. Fill in the following table with the counts corresponding to gender and the given lengths of stay, then test the claim that the length of stay is independent of gender of the baby.

	Two Days	Three Days	Four Days
Males			
Females			

FROM DATA TO DECISION

Critical Thinking: Was Allstate wrong?

The Allstate insurance company once issued a press release listing zodiac signs along with the corresponding numbers of automobile crashes, as shown in the first and last columns in the table below.

In the original press release, Allstate included comments such as one stating that Virgos are worried and shy, and they were involved in 211,650 accidents, making them the worst offenders. Allstate quickly issued an apology and retraction. In a press release, Allstate included this: "Astrological signs have absolutely no role in how we base coverage and set rates. Rating by astrology would not be actuarially sound."

Zodiac Sign	Dates	Length (days)	Crashes
Capricorn	Jan. 18–Feb. 15	29	128,005
Aquarius	Feb. 16–March 11	24	106,878
Pisces	March 12–April 16	36	172,030
Aries	April 17–May 13	27	112,402
Taurus	May 14–June 19	37	177,503
Gemini	June 20–July 20	31	136,904
Cancer	July 21–Aug. 9	20	101,539
Leo	Aug. 10–Sept. 15	37	179,657
Virgo	Sept. 16–Oct. 30	45	211,650
Libra	Oct. 31–Nov. 22	23	110,592
Scorpio	Nov. 23–Nov. 28	6	26,833
Ophiuchus	Nov. 29–Dec. 17	19	83,234
Sagittarius	Dec. 18–Jan. 17	31	154,477

Analyzing the Results

The original Allstate press release did not include the lengths (days) of the different zodiac signs. The preceding table lists those lengths in the third column. A reasonable explanation for the different numbers of crashes is that they should be proportional to the lengths of the zodiac signs. For example, people are born under the Capricorn sign on 29 days out of the 365 days in the year, so they are expected to have 29/365 of the total number of crashes. Use the methods of this chapter to determine whether this appears to explain the results in the table. Write a brief report of your findings.

Cooperative Group Activities

1. Out-of-class activity Divide into groups of four or five students. Example 2 in Section 11-1 noted that according to Benford's law, a variety of different data sets include numbers with leading (first) digits that follow the distribution shown in the table below. Collect original data and use the methods of Section 11-1 to support or refute the claim that the data conform reasonably well to Benford's law. Here are some suggestions: (1) leading digits of smartphone passcodes; (2) leading digits of the prices of stocks; (3) leading digits of the numbers of Facebook friends; (5) leading digits of the lengths of rivers in the world; (6) leading digits of the amounts of checks written by each individual.

Leading Digit	1	2	3	4	5	6	7	8	9
Benford's Law	30.1%	17.6%	12.5%	9.7%	7.9%	6.7%	5.8%	5.1%	4.6%

2. Out-of-class activity Divide into groups of four or five students and collect past results from a state lottery. Such results are often available on websites for individual state lotteries. Use the methods of Section 11-1 to test the claim that the numbers are selected in such a way that all possible outcomes are equally likely.

3. Out-of-class activity Divide into groups of four or five students. Each group member should survey at least 15 male students and 15 female students at the same college by asking three questions: (1) Which political party does the subject favor most? (2) If the subject were to make up an absence excuse of a flat tire, which tire would he or she say went flat if the instructor asked? (See Exercise 8 in Section 11-1.) (3) What is the eye color of the subject? (See Exercise 13 in Section 11-2.) Ask the subject to write the three responses on an index card, and also record the gender of the subject and whether the subject wrote with the right or left hand. Use the methods of this chapter to analyze the data collected. Include these claims:

- The four possible choices for a flat tire are selected with equal frequency.

- The tire identified as being flat is independent of the gender of the subject.

- Political party choice is independent of the gender of the subject.

- Political party choice is independent of whether the subject is right- or left-handed.

- The tire identified as being flat is independent of whether the subject is right- or left-handed.

- Gender is independent of whether the subject is right- or left-handed.

- Eye color is independent of gender.

- Political party choice is independent of the tire identified as being flat.

4. Out-of-class activity Divide into groups of four or five students. Each group member should select about 15 other students and first ask them to "randomly" select four digits each. After the four digits have been recorded, ask each subject to write the last four digits of his or her Social Security number (for security, write these digits in any order). Take the "random" sample results of individual digits and mix them into one big sample, then mix the individual Social Security digits into a second big sample. Using the "random" sample set, test the claim that students select digits randomly. Then use the Social Security digits to test the claim that they come from a population of random digits. Compare the results. Does it appear that students can randomly select digits? Are they likely to select any digits more often than others? Are they likely to select any digits less often than others? Do the last digits of Social Security numbers appear to be randomly selected?

5. In-class activity Divide into groups of three or four students. Each group should be given a die along with the instruction that it should be tested for "fairness." Is the die fair or is it biased? Describe the analysis and results.

6. Out-of-class activity Divide into groups of two or three students. The analysis of last digits of data can sometimes reveal whether values are the results of actual measurements or whether they are reported estimates. Find the lengths of rivers in the world, then analyze the last digits to determine whether those lengths appear to be actual measurements or whether they appear to be reported estimates. Instead of lengths of rivers, you could use other variables, such as the following:

- Heights of mountains

- Heights of tallest buildings

- Lengths of bridges

- Heights of roller coasters

7. Out-of-class activity Divide into groups of two or three students. Each group should conduct a survey by asking subjects to draw the letter X. Observe how the X is drawn and identify it as one of those shown below or some other approach. Using the four different configurations shown below and a fifth category of "other," test the claim that the five different categories are all equally likely.

(a)　　　　(b)　　　　(c)　　　　(d)

ANALYSIS OF VARIANCE

CHAPTER PROBLEM — **Are Larger Cars Safer in Crashes?**

It is a common belief that larger cars are safer in crashes. Table 12-1 lists measurements of head injuries in car crash tests. These data are taken from Data Set 35 "Car Data" in Appendix B. Head injuries are the leading cause of death and disability in motor vehicle crashes. In car crash tests, head injuries are measured using HIC ("head injury criterion"), which is a measure of the likelihood of head injury arising from an impact. A higher HIC measure represents a higher probability of head injury in a crash. The data in Table 12-1 list HIC measures for a sample of different car models in four vehicle size categories: small, midsize, large, and SUV.

Before jumping into the application of a particular statistical method, we should first explore the data. Sample statistics are included in the table on the next page. See also the boxplots of the four vehicle size categories of HIC measurements.

TABLE 12-1 Measurements of Head Injuries (HIC) in Car Crash Tests

Small	Midsize	Large	SUV
253	117	249	121
143	121	90	112
124	204	178	261
301	195	114	145
422	186	183	198
324	178	87	193
258	157	180	193
271	203	103	111
467	132	154	276
298	212	129	156
315	229	266	213
304	235	338	143

Informal and subjective comparisons show that the "small" cars have a mean that is somewhat higher than the means of the "midsize," "large," and "SUV" vehicles. The boxplots overlap, so differences do not appear to be dramatic. But we need more formal methods that allow us to recognize any significant differences. We could use the methods of Section 9-2 "Two Means: Independent Samples" to compare means from samples collected from *two* different populations, but here we need to compare means from samples collected from *four* different populations. When we have samples from three or more populations, we can test for equality of the population means by using the method of *analysis of variance,* to be introduced in Section 12-1. In Section 12-1, we will use analysis of variance to test the claim that the four samples are from populations with the same mean.

	Small	Midsize	Large	SUV
n	12	12	12	12
$\bar{x}$	290.0	180.8	172.6	176.8
s	96.7	40.6	77.9	55.1
Distribution	Normal	Normal	Normal	Normal
Outliers	Low outliers of 124 and 143 and high outlier of 467	0	0	0

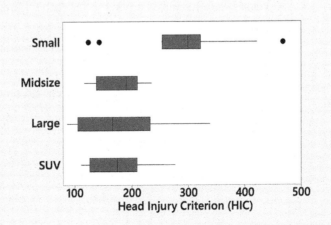

CHAPTER OBJECTIVES

Section 9-2 includes methods for testing equality of means from *two* independent populations, but this chapter presents a method for testing equality of *three or more* population means. Here are the chapter objectives:

12-1 One-Way ANOVA

- Apply the method of one-way analysis of variance to conduct a hypothesis test of equality of three or more population means. The focus of this section is the interpretation of results from technology.

12-2 Two-Way ANOVA

- Analyze sample data from populations separated into categories using two characteristics (or factors), such as gender and eye color.

- Apply the method of two-way analysis of variance to the following: (1) test for an *interaction* between two factors, (2) test for an effect from the *row* factor, and (3) test for an effect from the *column* factor. The focus of this section is the interpretation of results from technology.

12-1 One-Way ANOVA

Key Concept In this section we introduce the method of *one-way analysis of variance,* which is used for tests of hypotheses that three or more populations have means that are all equal, as in H_0: $\mu_1 = \mu_2 = \mu_3$. Because the calculations are very complicated, we emphasize the interpretation of results obtained by using technology.

F Distribution

The analysis of variance (ANOVA) methods of this chapter require the F distribution, which was first introduced in Section 9-4. In Section 9-4 we noted that the F distribution has the following properties (see Figure 12-1):

1. There is a different F distribution for each different pair of degrees of freedom for numerator and denominator.

2. The F distribution is not symmetric. It is skewed right.

3. Values of the F distribution cannot be negative.

4. The exact shape of the F distribution depends on the two different degrees of freedom.

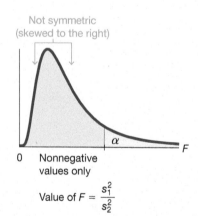

Not symmetric
(skewed to the right)

0   Nonnegative
    values only

Value of $F = \dfrac{s_1^2}{s_2^2}$

FIGURE 12-1 *F* **Distribution**

PART 1   Basics of One-Way Analysis of Variance

When testing for equality of three or more population means, use the method of one-way analysis of variance.

DEFINITION

One-way analysis of variance (ANOVA) is a method of testing the equality of three or more population means by analyzing sample variances. One-way analysis of variance is used with data categorized with *one* **factor** (or **treatment**), so there is one characteristic used to separate the sample data into the different categories.

The term *treatment* is used because early applications of analysis of variance involved agricultural experiments in which different plots of farmland were treated with different fertilizers, seed types, insecticides, and so on. Table 12-1 uses the one "treatment" (or factor) of size category of the automobile. That factor of size has four different categories: small, midsize, large, and SUV.

KEY ELEMENTS

One-Way Analysis of Variance for Testing Equality of Three or More Population Means

Objective

Use samples from three or more different populations to test a claim that the populations all have the same mean.

Requirements

1. The populations have distributions that are approximately normal. This is a loose requirement, because the method works well unless a population has a distribution that is very far from normal.

   ⬛**DETOUR**⮕ If a population does have a distribution that is far from normal, use the Kruskal-Wallis test described in Section 13-5.

2. The populations have the same variance σ^2 (or standard deviation σ). This is a loose requirement, because the method works well unless the population variances differ by large amounts. Statistician George E. P. Box showed that as long as the sample sizes are equal (or nearly equal), the largest variance can be up to nine times the smallest variance and the results of ANOVA will continue to be essentially reliable.

3. The samples are simple random samples of quantitative data.

4. The samples are independent of each other. (The samples are not matched or paired in any way.)

5. The different samples are from populations that are categorized in only one way.

Procedure for Testing $H_0: \mu_1 = \mu_2 = \mu_3 = \cdots = \mu_k$

1. Use technology to obtain results that include the test statistic and P-value.

2. Identify the P-value from the display. (The ANOVA test is right-tailed because only large values of the test statistic cause us to reject equality of the population means.)

3. Form a conclusion based on these criteria that use the significance level α:

   - **Reject:** If the P-value $\leq \alpha$, reject the null hypothesis of equal means and conclude that at least one of the population means is different from the others.

   - **Fail to Reject:** If the P-value $> \alpha$, fail to reject the null hypothesis of equal means.

Because the calculations required for one-way analysis of variance are messy, we recommend using technology with this study strategy:

1. Understand that a small *P*-value (such as 0.05 or less) leads to rejection of the null hypothesis of equal means. ("If the *P* is low, the null must go.") With a large *P*-value (such as greater than 0.05), fail to reject the null hypothesis of equal means.

2. Develop an understanding of the underlying rationale by studying the examples in this section.

CP — **EXAMPLE 1** **Size of Vehicle and Head Injury Measurements**

Use the head injury criterion (HIC) measurements listed in Table 12-1 and use a significance level of $\alpha = 0.5$ to test the claim that the four samples come from populations with means that are all equal.

SOLUTION

REQUIREMENT CHECK (1) Based on the four samples listed in Table 12-1, the four populations appear to have distributions that are approximately normal, as indicated by normal quantile plots that are not shown here. (2) The four samples in Table 12-1 have standard deviations that differ by considerable amounts, but those differences are not substantial, so we can consider the four population variances to be about the same. (3) On the basis of the study design, we can treat the samples as simple random samples. (4) The samples are independent of each other; the HIC measurements are not matched in any way. (5) The four samples are from populations categorized according to the single factor of vehicle size (small, midsize, large, SUV). The requirements are satisfied. ✓

The null hypothesis and the alternative hypothesis are as follows:

$$H_0: \mu_1 = \mu_2 = \mu_3 = \mu_4$$

H_1: At least one of the means is different from the others

The significance level is $\alpha = 0.05$.

Step 1: Use technology to obtain ANOVA results, such as one of those shown in the accompanying displays.

Statdisk

Source:	DF:	SS:	MS:
Treatment:	3	115887.08333	38629.02778
Error:	44	221158.83333	5026.33712
Total:	47	337045.91667	

Test Stat, F:	7.68532
Critical F:	2.81647
P-Value:	0.00031

Minitab

Analysis of Variance

Source	DF	Adj SS	Adj MS	F-Value	P-Value
Factor	3	115887	38629	7.69	0.000
Error	44	221159	5026		
Total	47	337046			

Excel

ANOVA						
Source of Variation	SS	df	MS	F	P-value	F crit
Between Groups	115887.1	3	38629.03	7.685324	0.000309	2.816466
Within Groups	221158.8	44	5026.337			
Total	337045.9	47				

StatCrunch

ANOVA table

Source	DF	SS	MS	F-Stat	P-value
Columns	3	115887.08	38629.028	7.6853237	0.0003
Error	44	221158.83	5026.3371		
Total	47	337045.92			

TI-83/84 Plus

```
NORMAL FLOAT AUTO REAL RADIAN MP

      One-way ANOVA
F=7.685323695
p=3.093850583ᴇ-4
Factor
  df=3
  SS=115887.0833
  MS=38629.02778
Error
↓ df=44
```

SPSS

ANOVA

HIC

	Sum of Squares	df	Mean Square	F	Sig.
Between Groups	115887.083	3	38629.028	7.685	.000
Within Groups	221158.833	44	5026.337		
Total	337045.917	47			

JMP

Analysis of Variance

Source	DF	Sum of Squares	Mean Square	F Ratio	Prob > F
Column 1	3	115887.08	38629.0	7.6853	0.0003*
Error	44	221158.83	5026.3		
C. Total	47	337045.92			

Step 2: In addition to the test statistic of $F = 7.6853$, the displays all show that the P-value is 0.000 when rounded.

Step 3: Because the P-value of 0.000 is less than the significance level of $\alpha = 0.05$, we reject the null hypothesis of equal means. (If the P is low, the null must go.)

INTERPRETATION

There is sufficient evidence to warrant rejection of the claim that the four samples come from populations with means that are all equal. Using the samples of measurements listed in Table 12-1, we conclude that those values come from populations having means that are not all the same. On the basis of this ANOVA test, we cannot conclude that any particular mean is different from the others, but we can informally note that the sample mean for the small cars is higher than the means for the midsize, large, and SUV vehicles. It appears that in crash tests, small cars are associated with higher head injury measurements.

YOUR TURN. Do Exercise 5 "Car Size and Left Femur in Crash Tests."

CAUTION When we conclude that there is sufficient evidence to reject the claim of equal population means, we cannot conclude from ANOVA that any particular mean is different from the others. (There are several other methods that can be used to identify the specific means that are different, and some of them are discussed in Part 2 of this section.)

How is the *P*-Value Related to the Test Statistic? *Larger* values of the test statistic result in *smaller P*-values, so the ANOVA test is right-tailed. Figure 12-2 on the next page shows the relationship between the F test statistic and the P-value. Assuming that the populations have the same variance σ^2 (as required for the test), the F test statistic is the ratio of these two estimates of σ^2: (1) variation *between* samples (based on variation among sample means); and (2) variation *within* samples (based on the sample variances).

Why 0.05?

In 1925, R. A. Fisher published a book that introduced the method of analysis of variance, and he needed a table of critical values based on numerator degrees of freedom and denominator degrees of freedom, as in Table A-5 in Appendix A. Because the table uses two different degrees of freedom, it becomes very long if many different critical values are used, so Fisher included a table using 0.05 only. In a later edition he also included the significance level of 0.01.

Stephen Stigler, a notable historian of statistics, wrote in *Chance* magazine that the choice of a significance level of 0.05 is a convenient round number that is somewhat arbitrary. Although it is arbitrary, the choice of 0.05 accomplishes the following important goals. (1) The value of a 0.05 significance level results in sample sizes that are reasonable and not too large. (2) The choice of 0.05 is large enough to give us a reasonable chance of identifying important effects (by correctly rejecting a null hypothesis of no effect when there really is an effect). (3) The choice of 0.05 is not so small that it forces us to miss important effects (by making the mistake of failing to reject a null hypothesis of no effect when there really is an effect).

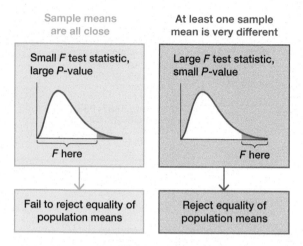

FIGURE 12-2   Relationship Between the *F* Test Statistic and the *P*-Value

Test Statistic for One-Way ANOVA: $F = \dfrac{\text{variance between samples}}{\text{variance within samples}}$

The numerator of the F test statistic measures variation between sample means. The estimate of variance in the denominator depends only on the sample variances and is not affected by differences among the sample means. Consequently, sample means that are close in value to each other result in a small F test statistic and a large P-value, so we conclude that there are no significant differences among the sample means. Sample means that are very far apart in value result in a large F test statistic and a small P-value, so we reject the claim of equal means.

Why Not Just Test Two Samples at a Time? If we want to test for equality among three or more population means, why do we need a new procedure when we can test for equality of two means using the methods presented in Section 9-2? For example, if we want to use the sample data from Table 12-1 to test the claim that the four populations have the same mean, why not simply pair them off and test two at a time by testing each of the following:

$$H_0: \mu_1 = \mu_2 \qquad H_0: \mu_1 = \mu_3 \qquad H_0: \mu_1 = \mu_4$$
$$H_0: \mu_2 = \mu_3 \qquad H_0: \mu_2 = \mu_4 \qquad H_0: \mu_3 = \mu_4$$

For the data in Table 12-1, the approach of testing equality of two means at a time requires six different hypothesis tests. If we use a 0.05 significance level for each of those six hypothesis tests, the actual overall confidence level could be as low as 0.95^6 (or 0.735). In general, as we increase the number of individual tests of significance, we increase the risk of finding a difference by chance alone (instead of a real difference in the means). The risk of a type I error—finding a difference in one of the pairs when no such difference actually exists—is far too high. The method of analysis of variance helps us avoid that particular pitfall (rejecting a true null hypothesis) by using *one test* for equality of several means, instead of several tests that each compare two means at a time.

> **CAUTION** When testing for equality of three or more populations, use analysis of variance. (Using multiple hypothesis tests with two samples at a time could adversely affect the significance level.)

PART 2 Calculations and Identifying Means That Are Different

Calculating the Test Statistic F with Equal Sample Sizes n

Table 12-2 can be very helpful in understanding the methods of ANOVA. In Table 12-2, compare Data Set A to Data Set B to see that Data Set A is the same as Data Set B with this notable exception: The Sample 1 values each differ by 10. If the data sets all have the same sample size (as in $n = 4$ for Table 12-2), the following calculations aren't too difficult, as shown here.

TABLE 12-2 Effect of a Mean on the F Test Statistic

			Add 10 to data in Sample 1 →		
Data Set A			**Data Set B**		
Sample 1	Sample 2	Sample 3	Sample 1	Sample 2	Sample 3
7	6	4	17	6	4
3	5	7	13	5	7
6	5	6	16	5	6
6	8	7	16	8	7
$n_1 = 4$	$n_2 = 4$	$n_3 = 4$	$n_1 = 4$	$n_2 = 4$	$n_3 = 4$
$\bar{x}_1 = 5.5$	$\bar{x}_2 = 6.0$	$\bar{x}_3 = 6.0$	$\bar{x}_1 = 15.5$	$\bar{x}_2 = 6.0$	$\bar{x}_3 = 6.0$
$s_1^2 = 3.0$	$s_2^2 = 2.0$	$s_3^2 = 2.0$	$s_1^2 = 3.0$	$s_2^2 = 2.0$	$s_3^2 = 2.0$

	Data Set A	**Data Set B**
Step 1: Variance *between* samples	$ns_{\bar{x}}^2 = 4(0.0833) = 0.3332$	$ns_{\bar{x}}^2 = 4(30.0833) = 120.3332$
Step 2: Variance *within* samples	$s_p^2 = \dfrac{3.0 + 2.0 + 2.0}{3} = 2.3333$	$s_p^2 = \dfrac{3.0 + 2.0 + 2.0}{3} = 2.3333$
Step 3: F test statistic	$F = \dfrac{ns_{\bar{x}}^2}{s_p^2} = \dfrac{0.3332}{2.3333} = 0.1428$	$F = \dfrac{ns_{\bar{x}}^2}{s_p^2} = \dfrac{120.3332}{2.3333} = 51.5721$
P-value	P-value $= 0.8688$	P-value $= 0.0000118$

Step 1: Find the Variance Between Samples

Calculate the variance *between* samples by evaluating $ns_{\bar{x}}^2$ where $s_{\bar{x}}^2$ is the variance of the sample means and n is the size of each of the samples. That is, consider the sample means to be an ordinary set of values and calculate the variance. (From the central limit theorem, $\sigma_{\bar{x}} = \sigma/\sqrt{n}$ can be solved for σ to get $\sigma = \sqrt{n} \cdot \sigma_{\bar{x}}$, so that we can estimate σ^2 with $ns_{\bar{x}}^2$.) For example, the sample means for Data Set A in Table 12-2 are 5.5, 6.0, and 6.0, and these three values have a variance of $s_{\bar{x}}^2 = 0.0833$, so that

$$\text{variance between samples} = ns_{\bar{x}}^2 = 4(0.0833) = 0.3332$$

Step 2: Find the Variance Within Samples

Estimate the variance *within* samples by calculating s_p^2, which is the pooled variance obtained by finding the mean of the sample variances. The sample variances in Table 12-2 are 3.0, 2.0, and 2.0, so that

$$\text{variance within samples} = s_p^2 = \frac{3.0 + 2.0 + 2.0}{3} = 2.3333$$

continued

Step 3:   Calculate the Test Statistic

Evaluate the F test statistic as follows:

$$F = \frac{\text{variance between samples}}{\text{variance within samples}} = \frac{ns_{\bar{x}}^2}{s_p^2} = \frac{0.3332}{2.3333} = 0.1428$$

Finding the Critical Value

The critical value of F is found by assuming a right-tailed test because large values of F correspond to significant differences among means. With k samples each having n values, the numbers of degrees of freedom are as follows.

Degrees of Freedom (using k = number of samples and n = sample size)

Numerator degrees of freedom = $k - 1$

Denominator degrees of freedom = $k(n - 1)$

For Data Set A in Table 12-2, $k = 3$ and $n = 4$, so the degrees of freedom are 2 for the numerator and $3(4 - 1) = 9$ for the denominator. With $\alpha = 0.05$, 2 degrees of freedom for the numerator, and 9 degrees of freedom for the denominator, the critical F value from Table A-5 is 4.2565. If we were to use the critical value method of hypothesis testing with Data Set A in Table 12-2, we would see that this right-tailed test has a test statistic of $F = 0.1428$ and a critical value of $F = 4.2565$, so the test statistic is not in the critical region. We therefore fail to reject the null hypothesis of equal means.

Understanding the Effect of a Mean on the F Test Statistic To really understand how the method of analysis of variance works, consider Data Set A and Data Set B in Table 12-2 and note the following.

- The three samples in Data Set A are identical to the three samples in Data Set B, except for this: Each value in Sample 1 of Data Set B is 10 more than the corresponding value in Data Set A.

- Adding 10 to each data value in the first sample of Data Set A has a significant effect on the test statistic, with F changing from 0.1428 to 51.5721.

- Adding 10 to each data value in the first sample of Data Set A has a dramatic effect on the P-value, which changes from 0.8688 (not significant) to 0.0000118 (significant).

- The three sample *means* in Data Set A (5.5, 6.0, 6.0) are very close, but the sample means in Data Set B (15.5, 6.0, 6.0) are not close.

- The three sample variances in Data Set A are identical to those in Data Set B.

- The *variance between samples* in Data Set A is 0.3332, but for Data Set B it is 120.3332 (indicating that the sample means in B are farther apart).

- The *variance within samples* is 2.3333 in both Data Set A and Data Set B, because the variance *within* a sample isn't affected when we add a constant to every sample value. *The change in the F test statistic and the P-value is attributable only to the change in $\bar{x}_1$.* This illustrates the key point underlying the method of one-way analysis of variance:

  > The *F* test statistic is very sensitive to sample *means,* even though it is obtained through two different estimates of the common population *variance.*

Calculations with Unequal Sample Sizes

While the calculations for cases with equal sample sizes are somewhat reasonable, they become much more complicated when the sample sizes are not all the same, but the same basic reasoning applies. Instead of providing the relevant messy formulas required for cases with unequal sample sizes, we wisely and conveniently assume that technology should be used to obtain the *P*-value for the analysis of variance. We become unencumbered by complex computations and we can focus on checking requirements and interpreting results.

We calculate an *F* test statistic that is the ratio of two different estimates of the common population variance σ^2. With unequal sample sizes, we must use *weighted* measures that take the sample sizes into account. The test statistic is essentially the same as the one given earlier, and its interpretation is also the same as described earlier.

Designing Experiments

With one-way (or single-factor) analysis of variance, we use one factor as the basis for partitioning the data into different categories. If we conclude that the differences among the means are significant, we can't be absolutely sure that the differences can be explained by the factor being used. It is possible that the variation of some other unknown factor is responsible. One way to reduce the effect of the extraneous factors is to design the experiment so that it has a **completely randomized design,** in which each sample value is given the same chance of belonging to the different factor groups. For example, you might assign subjects to two different treatment groups and a third placebo group through a process of random selection equivalent to picking slips of paper from a bowl. Another way to reduce the effect of extraneous factors is to use a **rigorously controlled design,** in which sample values are carefully chosen so that all other factors have no variability. In general, good results require that the experiment be carefully designed and executed.

Identifying Which Means Are Significantly Different

After conducting an analysis of variance test, we might conclude that there is sufficient evidence to reject a claim of equal population means, but we cannot conclude from ANOVA that any *particular* means are significantly different from the others. There are several formal and informal procedures that can be used to identify the specific means that are significantly different. Here are two *informal* methods for comparing means:

- Construct boxplots of the different samples and examine any overlap to see if one or more of the boxplots is very different from the others.

- Construct confidence interval estimates of the means for each of the different samples, then compare those confidence intervals to see if one or more of them does not overlap with the others.

There are several formal procedures for identifying which means are significantly different. Some of the tests, called **range tests,** allow us to identify subsets of means that are not significantly different from each other. Other tests, called **multiple comparison tests,** use pairs of means, but they make adjustments to overcome the problem of having a significance level that increases as the number of individual tests increases. There is no consensus on which test is best, but some of the more common tests are the Duncan test, Student-Newman-Keuls test (or SNK test), Tukey test (or Tukey honestly significant difference test), Scheffé test, Dunnett test, least significant difference test, and the Bonferroni test. Let's consider the Bonferroni test to see one example of a multiple comparison test. Here is the procedure.

Bonferroni Multiple Comparison Test

Step 1: Do a separate t test for each pair of samples, but make the adjustments described in the following steps.

Step 2: For an estimate of the variance σ^2 that is common to all of the involved populations, use the value of MS(error), which uses all of the available sample data. The value of MS(error) is typically obtained with the results when conducting the analysis of variance test. Using the value of MS(error), calculate the value of the test statistic t, as shown below. The particular test statistic calculated below is based on the choice of Sample 1 and Sample 2; change the subscripts and use another pair of samples until all of the different possible pairs of samples have been tested.

$$ t = \frac{\bar{x}_1 - \bar{x}_2}{\sqrt{\text{MS(error)} \cdot \left(\dfrac{1}{n_1} + \dfrac{1}{n_2} \right)}} $$

Step 3: After calculating the value of the test statistic t for a particular pair of samples, find either the critical t value or the P-value, but make the following adjustment so that the overall significance level does not increase.

> **P-Value** Use the test statistic t with df $= N - k$, where N is the total number of sample values and k is the number of samples, and find the P-value using technology or Table A-3, but *adjust the P-value by multiplying it by the number of different possible pairings of two samples.* (For example, with three samples, there are three different possible pairings, so adjust the P-value by multiplying it by 3.)

> **Critical Value** When finding the critical value, adjust the significance level α by dividing it by the number of different possible pairings of two samples. (For example, with three samples, there are three different possible pairings, so adjust the significance level by dividing it by 3.)

Note that in Step 3 of the preceding Bonferroni procedure, either an individual test is conducted with a much lower significance level or the P-value is greatly increased. Rejection of equality of means therefore requires differences that are much farther apart. This adjustment in Step 3 compensates for the fact that we are doing several tests instead of only one test.

(CP) **EXAMPLE 2**   Bonferroni Test

Example 1 in this section used analysis of variance with the sample data in Table 12-1. We concluded that there is sufficient evidence to warrant rejection of the claim of equal means. Use the Bonferroni test with a 0.05 significance level to identify which mean is significantly different from the others.

SOLUTION

The Bonferroni test requires a separate t test for each of six different possible pair of samples. Here are the null hypotheses to be tested:

$$ H_0: \mu_1 = \mu_2 \qquad H_0: \mu_1 = \mu_3 \qquad H_0: \mu_1 = \mu_4 $$
$$ H_0: \mu_2 = \mu_3 \qquad H_0: \mu_2 = \mu_4 \qquad H_0: \mu_3 = \mu_4 $$

We begin with $H_0: \mu_1 = \mu_2$. Using the sample data given in Table 12-1, we have $n_1 = 12$ and $\bar{x}_1 = 290.0$. Also, $n_2 = 12$ and $\bar{x}_2 = 180.75$. From the technology results shown in Example 1 we also know that MS(error) $= 5026.337121$.

We now evaluate the test statistic using the unrounded sample means:

$$t = \frac{\bar{x}_1 - \bar{x}_2}{\sqrt{MS(\text{error}) \cdot \left(\frac{1}{n_1} + \frac{1}{n_2}\right)}}$$

$$= \frac{290.0 - 180.75}{\sqrt{5026.337121 \cdot \left(\frac{1}{12} + \frac{1}{12}\right)}} = 3.775$$

The number of degrees of freedom is df $= N - k = 48 - 4 = 44$. ($N = 48$ because there are 48 different sample values in all four samples combined, and $k = 4$ because there are four different samples.) With a test statistic of $t = 3.775$ and with df $= 44$, the two-tailed P-value is 0.000476, but we adjust this P-value by multiplying it by 6 (the number of different possible pairs of samples) to get a final adjusted P-value of 0.002856 or 0.003 when rounded. Because this P-value is small (less than 0.05), we reject the null hypothesis. It appears that Samples 1 and 2 do have significantly different means.

Instead of continuing with separate hypothesis tests for the other five pairings, see the SPSS display showing all of the Bonferroni test results. In these results, the vehicle size categories are represented as follows: 1 = small, 2 = midsize, 3 = large, 4 = SUV. The first row of results corresponds to the results found here; see the P-value of 0.003 that was previously calculated and see the same significance ("Sig") value of 0.003 shown in the display. Consequently, there is a significance difference between small cars and medium cars. In addition, the SPSS display shows that the pairing of small/large yields a P-value of 0.001, so there is a significant difference between small cars and large cars. Also, the pairing of small/SUV yields a P-value of 0.002, so there is a significant difference between small cars and SUVs.

SPSS Bonferroni Results

Dependent Variable: HIC
Bonferroni

(I) Size	(J) Size	Mean Difference (I-J)	Std. Error	Sig.
1	2	109.250*	28.943	.003
	3	117.417*	28.943	.001
	4	113.167*	28.943	.002
2	1	-109.250*	28.943	.003
	3	8.167	28.943	1.000
	4	3.917	28.943	1.000
3	1	-117.417*	28.943	.001
	2	-8.167	28.943	1.000
	4	-4.250	28.943	1.000
4	1	-113.167*	28.943	.002
	2	-3.917	28.943	1.000
	3	4.250	28.943	1.000

* The mean difference is significant at the 0.05 level.

INTERPRETATION

Although the analysis of variance test tells us that at least one of the means is significantly different from the others, the Bonferroni test results do show that the first sample (small cars) has HIC values with a mean that is significantly different from the three other means. Examining all of the P-values ("Sig") in the last column of the SPSS display, we see that the only significant differences in means occur when one of the means is from the small cars. None of the other three samples yields a mean that is significantly different. In this case, the Bonferroni test results did identify which mean appears to be significantly different from the others.

YOUR TURN. Do Exercise 18 "Bonferroni Test."

TECH CENTER

One-Way Analysis of Variance
Access tech supplements, videos, and data sets at **www.TriolaStats.com**

Statdisk	Minitab	StatCrunch
1. Click **Analysis** in the top menu. 2. Select **One-Way Analysis of Variance** from the dropdown menu. 3. Enter the desired significance level and select at least 3 columns to be included in the analysis. 4. Click **Evaluate.**	1. Click **Stat** in the top menu. 2. Select **ANOVA** from the dropdown menu and select **One-Way** from the submenu. 3. Select **Response data are in a separate column for each factor level.** 4. In the *Responses* box select the columns to be included in the analysis. 5. Click the **Options** button and check the **Assume equal variances** box. 6. Click **OK** twice.	1. Click **Stat** in the top menu. 2. Select **ANOVA** from the dropdown menu, then select **One Way** from the submenu. 3. Select the columns to be included in the analysis. 4. Click **Compute!**

TI-83/84 Plus Calculator

1. Press **STAT**, then select **TESTS** in the top menu.
2. Select **ANOVA** in the menu and press **ENTER**.
3. Enter list names that include the data to be included in the analysis. Separate list names with **,** so the command appears in the format **ANOVA(L1, L2, L3).**
4. Press **ENTER** and use the arrow buttons to scroll through the results.

TIP: The list name *L1 (and L2 . . . L6)* can be quickly entered by pressing **2ND** **1**.

Excel

XLSTAT Add-In

Data can be in the format of columns or a table. The procedure below is for the default "column" format which requires all data to be stacked in a single column with the corresponding category name for each data value in a separate column.

1. Click on the **XLSTAT** tab in the Ribbon and then click **Modeling data.**
2. Select **ANOVA** from the dropdown menu.
3. Enter the range of cells containing the *Y/Dependent variable* data values.
4. Select **Qualitative** box and enter the range of cells containing the qualitative values (category names) for the *X/Explanatory variable*.
5. If the first data row includes a label, check the **Variable labels** box.
6. Click **OK.** The Analysis of Variance table includes the *F* test statistic and *P*-value.

Excel Data Analysis Add-In

1. Click on the **Data** tab in the Ribbon and then select **Data Analysis** in the top menu.
2. Select **Anova: Single Factor** under *Analysis Tools* and click **OK.**
3. Enter the desired data range for **Input Range.**
4. For *Grouped By* select **Columns** if data for each category are contained in separate columns; select **Rows** if data are organized by rows.
5. Check the **Labels in First Row** box if the first cell contains a category label.
6. Click **OK** for the results, including the *F* test statistic and *P*-value.

R

Requires all data to be stacked in a single vector with the corresponding category name for each data value in a separate vector.

R command: **aov($y \sim x$)**

Additional ANOVA details: **summary(aov($y \sim x$))**

Where *y* contains the data values and *x* contains the corresponding category names.

A complete list of R statistical commands is available at TriolaStats.com

12-1 Basic Skills and Concepts

Statistical Literacy and Critical Thinking

*In Exercises 1–4, use the following listed measured amounts of chest compression (mm)
from car crash tests (from Data Set 35 "Car Data" in Appendix B). Also shown are the SPSS
results from analysis of variance. Assume that we plan to use a 0.05 significance level to test
the claim that the different car sizes have the same mean amount of chest compression.*

Small	29	31	35	33	26	32	21	26	25	34	26	34
Midsize	32	28	26	23	25	26	19	29	26	20	22	22
Large	27	32	39	27	31	26	34	30	34	26	24	31
SUV	24	31	31	25	30	39	22	33	34	35	29	26

SPSS

ANOVA					
CHEST					
	Sum of Squares	df	Mean Square	F	Sig.
Between Groups	223.750	3	74.583	3.815	.016
Within Groups	860.167	44	19.549		
Total	1083.917	47			

1. ANOVA

a. What characteristic of the data above indicates that we should use *one-way* analysis of variance?

b. If the objective is to test the claim that the four car sizes have the same *mean* chest compression, why is the method referred to as analysis of *variance?*

2. Why Not Test Two at a Time? Refer to the sample data given in Exercise 1. If we want to test for equality of the four means, why don't we use the methods of Section 9-2 "Two Means: Independent Samples" for the following six separate hypothesis tests?

$$H_0: \mu_1 = \mu_2 \qquad H_0: \mu_1 = \mu_3 \qquad H_0: \mu_1 = \mu_4$$
$$H_0: \mu_2 = \mu_3 \qquad H_0: \mu_2 = \mu_4 \qquad H_0: \mu_3 = \mu_4$$

3. Test Statistic What is the value of the test statistic? What distribution is used with the test statistic?

4. *P*-Value If we use a 0.05 significance level in analysis of variance with the sample data given in Exercise 1, what is the *P*-value? What should we conclude? If the four populations have means that do not appear to be the same, does the analysis of variance test enable us to identify which populations have means that are significantly different?

In Exercises 5–16, use analysis of variance for the indicated test.

5. Car Size and Left Femur in Crash Tests Example 1 used measured amounts of chest compression from car crash tests for four different vehicle size categories. If we use the same four categories of vehicle size with measured amounts of left leg femur force (kN), we get the following Minitab display. (The data are listed in Data Set 35 "Car Data" in Appendix B.) Using a 0.05 significance level, test the claim that the four vehicle size categories have the same mean force on the femur of the left leg. Does size of the car appear to have an effect on the force on the left femur in crash tests?

Analysis of Variance					
Source	DF	Adj SS	Adj MS	F-Value	P-Value
Size	3	0.6742	0.2247	0.57	0.638
Error	44	17.3583	0.3945		
Total	47	18.0325			

6. Does Candy Increase Restaurant Tips? A study was conducted to determine whether amounts of tips left for servers are affected by giving guests free candy along with the bill. Four different groups were used: (1) No candy, (2) one piece of candy, (3) two pieces of candy, (4) the offer of an additional piece of candy after the customer selected one piece of candy. The results of analysis of variance are shown in the accompanying TI-83/84 Plus display (based on data from "Sweetening the Till: The Use of Candy to Increase Restaurant Tipping," by Strohmetz et al., *Journal of Applied Social Psychology*, Vol. 32, No. 2). Use a 0.05 significance level to test the claim that tip amounts are affected by giving guests candy.

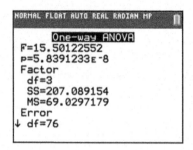

```
NORMAL FLOAT AUTO REAL RADIAN MP

        One-way ANOVA
 F=15.50122552
 p=5.8391233E-8
 Factor
  df=3
  SS=207.089154
  MS=69.0297179
 Error
↓ df=76
```

7. Chocolate Chip Cookies Data Set 39 "Chocolate Chip Cookies" in Appendix B includes the counts of chocolate chips from the three different types of Chips Ahoy cookies. The accompanying StatCrunch display results from analysis of variance used with those three types of cookies. Use a 0.05 significance level to test the claim that the three different types of Chips Ahoy cookies have the same mean number of chocolate chips.

ANOVA table

Source	DF	SS	MS	F-Stat	P-value
Columns	2	542.77232	271.38616	28.1666	<0.0001
Error	109	1050.2188	9.6350344		
Total	111	1592.9911			

8. Secondhand Smoke Data Set 15 "Passive and Active Smoke" in Appendix B includes measured serum cotinine levels (mg/mL) from the three groups of subjects: 902 smokers, 433 nonsmokers exposed to tobacco smoke, and 358 nonsmokers not exposed to tobacco smoke. When nicotine is absorbed by the body, cotinine is produced. The results from analysis of variance are shown in the accompanying XLSTAT display. Use a 0.05 significance level to test the claim that the three samples are from populations with the same mean. What do the results suggest about the effects of secondhand smoke?

Source	DF	Sum of squares	Mean squares	F	Pr > F
Model	2	26357005.145	13178502.572	969.744	< 0.0001
Error	1690	22966554.662	13589.677		
Corrected	1692	49323559.806			

9. Clancy, Rowling, and Tolstoy Ease of Reading Pages were randomly selected from three books: *The Bear and the Dragon* by Tom Clancy, *Harry Potter and the Sorcerer's Stone* by J.K. Rowling, and *War and Peace* by Leo Tolstoy. Listed below are Flesch Reading Ease Scores for those pages. Use a 0.05 significance level to test the claim that pages from books by those three authors have the same mean Flesch Reading Ease score. Given that higher scores correspond to text that is easier to read, which author appears to be different, and how is that author different?

Clancy	58.2	73.4	73.1	64.4	72.7	89.2	43.9	76.3	76.4	78.9	69.4	72.9
Rowling	85.3	84.3	79.5	82.5	80.2	84.6	79.2	70.9	78.6	86.2	74.0	83.7
Tolstoy	69.4	64.2	71.4	71.6	68.5	51.9	72.2	74.4	52.8	58.4	65.4	73.6

10. Clancy, Rowling, and Tolstoy Characters per Word Numbers of characters per word were found from the same three books used in the preceding exercise. Use a 0.05 significance level to test the claim that the three books have the same mean number of characters per word. Does it appear that any of the authors use words with more characters?

Clancy	4.8	4.5	4.6	4.5	4.0	4.0	4.6	4.5	4.4	4.4	4.3	4.3
Rowling	4.1	4.2	4.2	4.4	4.3	4.2	4.5	4.5	4.3	4.0	4.4	4.3
Tolstoy	4.3	4.5	4.5	4.5	4.5	4.8	4.3	4.2	4.7	4.3	4.4	4.5

11. Triathlon Times Jeff Parent is a statistics instructor who participates in triathlons. Listed below are times (in minutes and seconds) he recorded while riding a bicycle for five stages through each mile of a 3-mile loop. Use a 0.05 significance level to test the claim that it takes the same time to ride each of the miles. Does one of the miles appear to have a hill?

Mile 1	3:15	3:24	3:23	3:22	3:21
Mile 2	3:19	3:22	3:21	3:17	3:19
Mile 3	3:34	3:31	3:29	3:31	3:29

12. Arsenic in Rice Listed below are amounts of arsenic in samples of brown rice from three different states. The amounts are in micrograms of arsenic and all samples have the same serving size. The data are from the Food and Drug Administration. Use a 0.05 significance level to test the claim that the three samples are from populations with the same mean. Do the amounts of arsenic appear to be different in the different states? Given that the amounts of arsenic in the samples from Texas have the highest mean, can we conclude that brown rice from Texas poses the greatest health problem?

Arkansas	4.8	4.9	5.0	5.4	5.4	5.4	5.6	5.6	5.6	5.9	6.0	6.1
California	1.5	3.7	4.0	4.5	4.9	5.1	5.3	5.4	5.4	5.5	5.6	5.6
Texas	5.6	5.8	6.6	6.9	6.9	6.9	7.1	7.3	7.5	7.6	7.7	7.7

In Exercises 13–16, use the data set in Appendix B.

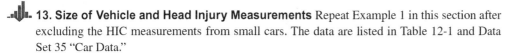 **13. Size of Vehicle and Head Injury Measurements** Repeat Example 1 in this section after excluding the HIC measurements from small cars. The data are listed in Table 12-1 and Data Set 35 "Car Data."

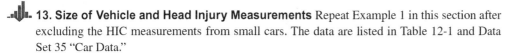 **14. M&M Candies** Refer to Data Set 38 "Candies" in Appendix B and use the weights of the M&M candies for each of the six colors. Use a 0.05 significance level to test the claim that the six different colors of M&M candies have the same mean weight. Is the result as expected?

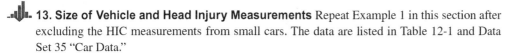 **15. Disney World Wait Times** Refer to Data Set 33 "Disney World Wait Times" in Appendix B and use the 10 AM wait times for Space Mountain, Rock 'n' Roller Coaster, Tower of Terror, and Flight of Passage. Use a 0.05 significance level to test the claim that the four rides have the same mean wait time at 10 AM.

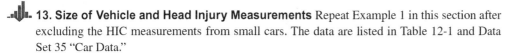 **16. Disney World Wait Times** Repeat the preceding exercise using the wait times at 5 PM instead of at 10 AM.

12-1 Beyond the Basics

17. Tukey Test A display of the Bonferroni test results from Table 12-1 (which is part of the Chapter Problem) is provided on page 621. Shown on the top of the next page is the SPSS-generated display of results from the Tukey test using the same data. Compare the Tukey test results to those from the Bonferroni test.

continued

SPSS

Dependent Variable: HIC Tukey				
(I) Size	(J) Size	Mean Difference (I-J)	Std. Error	Sig.
1	2	109.250*	28.943	.003
	3	117.417*	28.943	.001
	4	113.167*	28.943	.002
2	1	-109.250*	28.943	.003
	3	8.167	28.943	.992
	4	3.917	28.943	.999
3	1	-117.417*	28.943	.001
	2	-8.167	28.943	.992
	4	-4.250	28.943	.999
4	1	-113.167*	28.943	.002
	2	-3.917	28.943	.999
	3	4.250	28.943	.999

* The mean difference is significant at the 0.05 level.

18. Bonferroni Test Shown below are weights (kg) of poplar trees obtained from trees planted in a rich and moist region. The trees were given different treatments identified in the table below. The data are from a study conducted by researchers at Pennsylvania State University and were provided by Minitab, Inc. Also shown are partial results from using the Bonferroni test with the sample data.

No Treatment	Fertilizer	Irrigation	Fertilizer and Irrigation
1.21	0.94	0.07	0.85
0.57	0.87	0.66	1.78
0.56	0.46	0.10	1.47
0.13	0.58	0.82	2.25
1.30	1.03	0.94	1.64

a. Use a 0.05 significance level to test the claim that the different treatments result in the same mean weight.

b. What do the displayed Bonferroni SPSS results tell us?

c. Use the Bonferroni test procedure with a 0.05 significance level to test for a significant difference between the mean amount of the irrigation treatment group and the group treated with both fertilizer and irrigation. Identify the test statistic and either the P-value or critical values. What do the results indicate?

Bonferroni Results from SPSS

(I) TREATMENT	(J) TREATMENT	Mean Difference (I-J)	Std. Error	Sig.	95% Confidence Interval	
					Lower Bound	Upper Bound
1.00	2.00	-.02200	.26955	1.000	-.8329	.7889
	3.00	.23600	.26955	1.000	-.5749	1.0469
	4.00	-.84400*	.26955	.039	-1.6549	-.0331

12-2 Two-Way ANOVA

Key Concept Section 12-1 considered data partitioned using *one* factor, but this section describes the method of *two-way analysis of variance,* which is used with data partitioned into categories according to *two* factors. The method of this section requires that we first test for an *interaction* between the two factors; then we test for an effect from the row factor, and we test for an effect from the column factor.

Table 12-3 includes data of the measured force on femurs (or thighbones) in car crash tests. The data are measured in kilonewtons (kN). Table 12-3 has data categorized according to the two factors:

1. **Femur Side:** One factor is whether the femur is in the *left* leg or the *right* leg.

2. **Vehicle Size Category:** The second factor is the vehicle size category (small, midsize, large, SUV).

TABLE 12-3 Crash Test Force on Femur with Two Factors: Femur Side and Vehicle Size Category

	Small	Midsize	Large	SUV
Left Femur	1.6 1.4 0.5 0.2 0.4	0.4 0.7 1.1 0.7 0.5	0.6 1.8 0.3 1.3 1.1	0.4 0.4 0.6 0.2 0.2
Right Femur	2.8 1.0 0.3 0.3 0.2	0.6 0.8 1.3 0.5 1.1	1.5 1.7 0.2 0.6 0.9	0.7 0.7 3.0 0.2 0.2

The subcategories in Table 12-3 are called *cells*, so Table 12-3 has eight cells containing five values each.

In analyzing the sample data in Table 12-3, we have already discussed one-way analysis of variance for a single factor (Section 12-1), so it might seem reasonable to simply proceed with one-way ANOVA for the factor of femur side and another one-way ANOVA for the factor of vehicle size category. However, that approach wastes information and totally ignores a very important feature: the possible effect of an *interaction* between the two factors.

> **DEFINITION**
>
> There is an **interaction** between two factors if the effect of one of the factors changes for different categories of the other factor.

As an example of an *interaction* between two factors, consider food pairings. Peanut butter and jelly interact well, but ketchup and ice cream interact in a way that results in a bad taste, so we rarely see someone eating ice cream topped with ketchup. In general, consider an interaction to be an effect due to the combination of the two factors.

Explore Data with Means and an Interaction Graph

Let's explore the data in Table 12-3 by calculating the mean for each cell and by constructing a graph. The individual cell means are shown in Table 12-4. Those means vary from a low of 0.68 to a high of 1.02, so they vary considerably. Figure 12-3 is an *interaction graph,* which shows graphs of those means. We can interpret an interaction graph as follows:

- **Interaction Effect:** An interaction effect is suggested when line segments are far from being parallel.

- **No Interaction Effect:** If the line segments are approximately *parallel*, as in Figure 12-3, it appears that the different categories of a variable have the same effect for the different categories of the other variable, so there does not appear to be an interaction effect.

TABLE 12-4 Means of Cells from Table 12-3

	Small	Midsize	Large	SUV
Left Femur	0.82	0.68	1.02	0.36
Right Femur	0.92	0.86	0.98	0.96

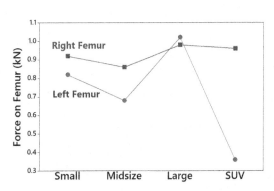

FIGURE 12-3   Interaction Graph of Femur Side and Vehicle Size Category from Table 12-4

Instead of relying only on subjective judgments made by examining the means in Table 12-4 and the interaction graph in Figure 12-3, we will proceed with the more objective procedure of two-way analysis of variance. Here are the requirements and basic procedure for two-way analysis of variance (ANOVA). The procedure is also summarized in Figure 12-4, which follows the Key Elements box.

KEY ELEMENTS

Two-Way Analysis of Variance

Objective

With sample data categorized with two factors (a row variable and a column variable), use two-way analysis of variance to conduct the following three tests:

1. Test for an effect from an *interaction* between the row factor and the column factor.

2. Test for an effect from the *row* factor.

3. Test for an effect from the *column* factor.

Requirements

1. Normality For each cell, the sample values come from a population with a distribution that is approximately normal. (This procedure is robust against reasonable departures from normal distributions.)

2. Variation The populations have the same variance σ^2 (or standard deviation σ). (This procedure is robust against reasonable departures from the requirement of equal variances.)

3. Sampling The samples are simple random samples of quantitative data.

4. Independence The samples are independent of each other. (This procedure does not apply to samples lacking independence.)

5. Two-Way The sample values are categorized two ways. (This is the basis for the name of the method: *two-way* analysis of variance.)

6. Balanced Design All of the cells have the same number of sample values. (This is called a *balanced* design. This section does not include methods for a design that is not balanced.)

Procedure for Two-Way ANOVA (See Figure 12-4)

Step 1: *Interaction Effect:* In two-way analysis of variance, begin by testing the null hypothesis that there is no interaction between the two factors. Use technology to find the P-value corresponding to the following test statistic:

$$F = \frac{MS(\text{interaction})}{MS(\text{error})}$$

Conclusion:

- **Reject:** If the P-value corresponding to the above test statistic is small (such as less than or equal to 0.05), reject the null hypothesis of no interaction. Conclude that there is an interaction effect.

- **Fail to Reject:** If the P-value is large (such as greater than 0.05), fail to reject the null hypothesis of no interaction between the two factors. Conclude that there is no interaction effect.

Step 2: *Row/Column Effects:* If we conclude that there is an interaction effect, then we should stop now; we should not proceed with the two additional tests. (If there is an interaction between factors, we shouldn't consider the effects of either factor without considering those of the other.)

If we conclude that there is no interaction effect, then we should proceed with the following two hypothesis tests.

Row Factor

For the row factor, test the null hypothesis H_0: There are no effects from the row factor (that is, the row values are from populations with the same mean). Find the P-value corresponding to the test statistic $F = MS(\text{row})/MS(\text{error})$.

Conclusion:

- **Reject:** If the *P*-value corresponding to the test statistic is small (such as less than or equal to 0.05), reject the null hypothesis of no effect from the row factor. Conclude that there is an effect from the row factor.

- **Fail to Reject:** If the *P*-value is large (such as greater than 0.05), fail to reject the null hypothesis of no effect from the row factor. Conclude that there is no effect from the row factor.

Column Factor

For the column factor, test the null hypothesis H_0: There are no effects from the column factor (that is, the column values are from populations with the same mean). Find the *P*-value corresponding to the test statistic $F = \text{MS(column)}/\text{MS(error)}$.

Conclusion:

- **Reject:** If the *P*-value corresponding to the test statistic is small (such as less than or equal to 0.05), reject the null hypothesis of no effect from the column factor. Conclude that there is an effect from the column factor.

- **Fail to Reject:** If the *P*-value is large (such as greater than 0.05), fail to reject the null hypothesis of no effect from the column factor. Conclude that there is no effect from the column factor.

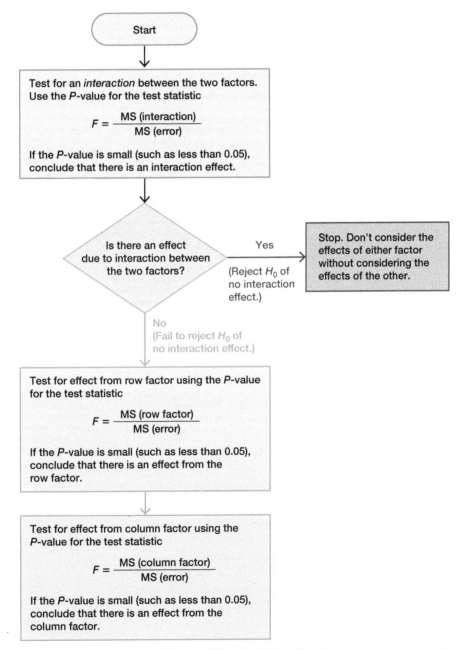

FIGURE 12-4   Procedure for Two-Way Analysis of Variance

CP EXAMPLE 1 **Femur Impact in Car Crash Tests**

Given the Table 12-3 measurements of crash forces on the left and right femurs in car crash tests, use two-way analysis of variance to test for an interaction effect, an effect from the row factor of femur side (left, right), and an effect from the column factor of vehicle size category (small, midsize, large, SUV). Use a 0.05 significance level.

SOLUTION

REQUIREMENT CHECK (1) Except for the right/small and right/SUV cells, the sample values appear to be from populations with distributions that are approximately normal, as indicated by normal quantile plots. The right/small and right/SUV cells appear to be normal using a 0.01 significance level, so they don't deviate from normal distributions by substantial amounts. (2) The variances of the cells (0.40, 0.07, 0.35, 0.03, 1.21, 0.11, 0.39, 1.36) differ considerably, but the test is robust against departures from equal variances. (3) The samples are simple random samples of vehicles. (4) The samples are independent of each other; the vehicles are not matched in any way. (5) The sample values are categorized in two ways (femur side and vehicle size category). (6) All of the cells have the same number (five) of sample values. The requirements are satisfied. ✓

The calculations are quite involved, so we use technology. The StatCrunch two-way analysis of variance display for the data in Table 12-3 is shown here.

StatCrunch

Source	DF	SS	MS	F-Stat	P-value
Femur Side	1	0.441	0.441	0.90022965	0.3498
Car Size	3	0.629	0.20966667	0.42800034	0.7343
Interaction	3	0.569	0.18966667	0.3871736	0.763
Error	32	15.676	0.489875		
Total	39	17.315			

Step 1: Interaction Effect: We begin by testing the null hypothesis that there is no interaction between the two factors. Using StatCrunch for the data in Table 12-3, we get the results shown in the preceding StatCrunch display, and we can see that the test statistic for the interaction is $F = 0.3872$. This test statistic can be calculated as follows:

$$F = \frac{\text{MS(interaction)}}{\text{MS(error)}} = \frac{0.18966667}{0.489875} = 0.3872$$

Interpretation: The corresponding *P*-value is shown in the StatCrunch display as 0.763, so we fail to reject the null hypothesis of no interaction between the two factors. It does not appear that femur crash force measurements are affected by an interaction between the femur side (left, right) and vehicle size category. There does not appear to be an interaction effect.

Step 2: Row/Column Effects: Because there does not appear to be an interaction effect, we proceed to test for effects from the row and column factors. The two hypothesis tests use these null hypotheses:

H_0: There are no effects from the row factor (that is, the row values are from populations with equal means).

H_0: There are no effects from the column factor (that is, the column values are from populations with equal means).

Row Factor: For the row factor (femur side), we refer to the preceding StatCrunch display of results to see that the test statistic for the row factor is $F = 0.9002$ (rounded). This test statistic can be calculated as follows:

$$F = \frac{MS(\text{leg side})}{MS(\text{error})} = \frac{0.441}{0.489875} = 0.9002$$

Conclusion: The corresponding P-value is shown in the StatCrunch display as 0.3498. Because that P-value is greater than the significance level of 0.05, we fail to reject the null hypothesis of no effects from femur side. That is, the car crash force measurements do not appear to be affected by whether the femur is in the left leg or right leg.

Column Factor: For the column factor (vehicle size category), we refer to the preceding StatCrunch display of results to see that the test statistic for the column factor is $F = 0.4280$ (rounded). This test statistic can be calculated as follows:

$$F = \frac{MS(\text{size})}{MS(\text{error})} = \frac{0.2096667}{0.489875} = 0.4280$$

Conclusion: The corresponding P-value is shown in the StatCrunch display as 0.7343. Because that P-value is not less than the significance level of 0.05, we fail to reject the null hypothesis of no effects from vehicle size category. The femur crash force measurements do not appear to be affected by the size of the vehicle.

INTERPRETATION

On the basis of the sample data in Table 12-3, we conclude that the crash force measurements on the femur are not affected by an interaction between the femur side (left, right) and the vehicle size category, they are not affected by the femur side (left, right), and they are not affected by the vehicle size category.

 YOUR TURN. Do Exercise 5 "Car Crash Test Measurements."

CAUTION Two-way analysis of variance is not one-way analysis of variance done twice. When conducting a two-way analysis of variance, be sure to test for an *interaction* between the two factors.

TECH CENTER

Two-Way Analysis of Variance
Access tech supplements, videos, and data sets at **www.TriolaStats.com**

Statdisk	Minitab	StatCrunch
1. Click **Analysis** in the top menu. 2. Select **Two-Way Analysis of Variance** from the dropdown menu. 3. Enter the number of categories for row variables and column variables. 4. Enter the number of values in each cell and click **Generate Table.** 5. In the table, enter or paste the data in the *Value* column. 6. Click **Evaluate.**	1. Enter all of the sample values in column C1. 2. Enter the corresponding row numbers (or names) in column C2. 3. Enter the corresponding column numbers (or names) in column C3. 4. Click **Stat** in the top menu. 5. Select **ANOVA** from the dropdown menu and select **General Linear Model—Fit General Linear Model.** 6. For *Responses* select **C1** and select **C2** and **C3** as *Factors*. 7. Click the **Model** button. 8. Under *Factors and covariates* select **C2** and **C3** and click the **Add** button. 9. Click **OK** twice. See *Analysis of Variance* in the results. *TIP:* Use descriptive labels rather than C1, C2, and C3 to avoid confusion.	1. Enter all sample values in one column named "Responses." 2. Enter corresponding *row* numbers (or names) in a second column named "Row Factor." 3. Enter the corresponding *column* numbers (or names) in a third column named "Column Factor." 4. Click **Stat** in the top menu. 5. Select **ANOVA** from the dropdown menu, then select **Two Way** from the submenu. 6. Select the columns to be used for responses, row factor and column factor. 7. Click **Compute!**

TI-83/84 Plus Calculator

Requires program *A1ANOVA* (available at www.TriolaStats.com).

1. The program A1ANOVA requires that we first create a Matrix [D] containing the sample data:
   Manually enter data: Press **2ND** then **x⁻¹** to get to the *MATRIX* menu, select **EDIT** from the top menu, select **[D]**, and press **ENTER**.
   Enter the number of rows and columns needed, press **ENTER**, and proceed to enter the sample values.

   Using existing lists: Lists can be combined and stored in a matrix. Press **2ND** then **x⁻¹** to get to the *MATRIX* menu, select **MATH** from the top menu, and select the item **List → matr**. Enter the list names, followed by the matrix name **[D]**, all separated by commas. *Important:* The matrix name must be entered by pressing **2ND** then **x⁻¹**, selecting **[D]**, and pressing **ENTER**. The following is a summary of the commands used to create a matrix from three lists (L1, L2, L3):
   List → matr(L1, L2, L3,[D]).
2. Press **PRGM**, then select **A1ANOVA** and press **ENTER** twice.
3. Select **RAN BLOCK DESIGN** and press **ENTER** twice. Select **Continue** and press **ENTER**.
4. The program will work with data in Matrix **[D]** and display the results. The results do not fit on a single screen, so press **ENTER** to see the remaining results.

TIP: In the results, F(A) is the *F* test statistic for the row factor, F(B) is the *F* test statistic for the column factor, and F(AB) is the *F* test statistic for the interaction effect.

TECH CENTER *continued*

Two-Way Analysis of Variance

Access tech supplements, videos, and data sets at **www.TriolaStats.com**

Excel

XLSTAT Add-In

Data can be in the format of columns or a table. The procedure below is for the default "column" format which requires all data to be stacked in a single column with the corresponding category names for each data value in two separate and adjacent columns. The row names should be in one of those columns and the column names should be in the other column.

1. Click on the **XLSTAT** tab in the Ribbon and then click **Modeling data.**
2. Select **ANOVA** from the dropdown menu.
3. Enter the range of cells containing sample values in the *Y/Dependent variables* box.
4. Select **Qualitative** box and enter the range of cells containing the row and column names in the *X/Explanatory variables* box, such as B1:C30.
5. If a variable label is included in the data range, check the **Variable labels** box.
6. Click the **Options** tab and confirm the **Interactions/Level** box is checked and set to **2.**
7. Click the **Outputs** tab and check the box labeled **Type I/II/III SS.**
8. Click **OK**. Click **All** in the *Factors and interactions* window and click **OK** for the results. Look for key results under the heading of "Type I Sum of Squares analysis." *P*-values are labeled *Pr > F.*

Excel Data Analysis Add-In

More than one entry per cell

For two-way tables with more than one entry per cell, entries from the same cell must be listed down a column, not across a row. Enter the labels corresponding to the data set in column A and row 1, as shown in this example:

	A	B	C	D
1		Low	Medium	High
2	Male	85	78	93
3	Male	90	107	97
⋮	⋮	⋮	⋮	⋮

1. Click on the **Data** tab in the Ribbon and then select **Data Analysis** in the top menu.
2. Select **Anova: Two-Factor With Replication** under *Analysis Tools* and click **OK.**
3. Enter the desired data range for **Input Range.**
4. In *Rows per sample* enter the number of values in each cell.
5. Click **OK.**

R

Requires all data to be stacked in a single vector with the corresponding row category names in a separate vector and the corresponding column category names in a separate vector

R command: **aov($y \sim x1 + x2 + x1{*}x2$)**

Additional Two-Way ANOVA details: **summary(aov($y \sim x1 + x2 + x1{*}x2$))**

where *y* contains the data values and *x1*, *x2* contain the corresponding row and column category names.

*TIP: **x1*x2** tests for an interaction effect.*

A complete list of R statistical commands is available at TriolaStats.com

12-2   Basic Skills and Concepts

Statistical Literacy and Critical Thinking

1. Two-Way ANOVA The measurements of crash test forces on the femur in Table 12-3 from Example 1 are reproduced below with fabricated measurement data (in **red**) used for the left femur in a small car. What characteristic of the data suggests that the appropriate method of analysis is *two-way* analysis of variance? That is, what is "two-way" about the data entered in this table?

	Small	Midsize	Large	SUV
Left Femur	**8.0 7.0 2.5 1.0 2.0**	0.4 0.7 1.1 0.7 0.5	0.6 1.8 0.3 1.3 1.1	0.4 0.4 0.6 0.2 0.2
Right Femur	2.8 1.0 0.3 0.3 0.2	0.6 0.8 1.3 0.5 1.1	1.5 1.7 0.2 0.6 0.9	0.7 0.7 3.0 0.2 0.2

2. Two-Way ANOVA If we have a goal of using the data given in Exercise 1 to (1) determine whether the femur side (left, right) has an effect on the crash force measurements and (2) to determine whether the vehicle size has an effect on the crash force measurements, should we use one-way analysis of variance for the two individual tests? Why or why not?

3. Interaction

a. What is an interaction between two factors?

b. In general, when using two-way analysis of variance, if we find that there is an interaction effect, how does that affect the procedure?

c. Shown below is an interaction graph constructed from the data in Exercise 1. What does the graph suggest?

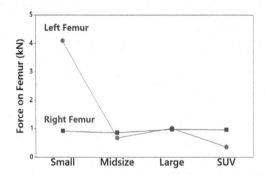

4. Balanced Design Does the table given in Exercise 1 constitute a *balanced design?* Why or why not?

5. Car Crash Test Measurements If we use the data given in Exercise 1 with two-way analysis of variance and a 0.05 significance level, we get the accompanying display. What do you conclude?

Statdisk

Source:	DF:	SS:	MS:	Test Stat, F:	Critical F:	P-Value:
Interaction:	3	22.54500	7.51500	4.43134	2.90111	0.01028
Row Variable:	1	3.72100	3.72100	2.19415	4.14911	0.14832
Column Variable:	3	22.27700	7.42567	4.37866	2.90111	0.01084

6. Weights from ANSUR I and ANSUR II The following table lists weights (kg) of randomly selected U.S. Army personnel obtained from the ANSUR I study conducted in 1988 and the ANSUR II study conducted in 2012. If we use the data with two-way analysis of variance and a 0.05 significance level, we get the accompanying display. What do you conclude?

	ANSUR I - 1998						ANSUR II - 2012					
Female	72.6	56.0	66.7	53.6	54.5	77.9	57.3	58.2	55.3	69.8	64.0	59.0
Male	70.7	77.1	77.3	74.4	75.4	83.0	82.4	65.0	96.1	97.9	54.0	60.8

XLSTAT

Source	DF	Sum of squares	Mean squares	F	Pr > F
Gender	1	1192.860	1192.860	9.459	**0.006**
ANSUR	1	15.682	15.682	0.124	0.728
Gender*ANSUR	1	10.667	10.667	0.085	0.774

7. Distance Between Pupils The following table lists distances (mm) between pupils of randomly selected U.S. Army personnel collected as part of the ANSUR II study. Results from two-way analysis of variance are also shown. Use the displayed results and use a 0.05 significance level. What do you conclude? Are the results as you would expect?

	Right-Handed					Left-Handed				
Female	65	64	60	59	56	71	63	62	70	63
Male	66	63	67	69	70	68	68	64	67	65

Statdisk

Source:	DF:	SS:	MS:	Test Stat, F:	Critical F:	P-Value:
Interaction:	1	39.2	39.2	3.62963	4.49401	0.07489
Row Variable:	1	57.8	57.8	5.35185	4.49401	0.03433
Column Variable:	1	24.2	24.2	2.24074	4.49401	0.15388

8. Pancake Experiment Listed below are ratings of pancakes made by experts (based on data from Minitab). Different pancakes were made with and without a supplement and with different amounts of whey. The results from two-way analysis of variance are shown. Use the displayed results and a 0.05 significance level. What do you conclude?

	Whey											
	0%			10%			20%			30%		
No Supplement	4.4	4.5	4.3	4.6	4.5	4.8	4.5	4.8	4.8	4.6	4.7	5.1
Supplement	3.3	3.2	3.1	3.8	3.7	3.6	5.0	5.3	4.8	5.4	5.6	5.3

Minitab

Two-way ANOVA: Quality versus Supplement, Whey

Source	DF	SS	MS	F	P
Supplement	1	0.5104	0.51042	17.01	0.001
Whey	3	6.6912	2.23042	74.35	0.000
Interaction	3	3.7246	1.24153	41.38	0.000
Error	16	0.4800	0.03000		
Total	23	11.4062			

9. Sitting Heights The sitting height of a person is the vertical distance between the sitting surface and the top of the head. The following table lists sitting heights (mm) of randomly selected U.S. Army personnel collected as part of the ANSUR II study. Using the data with a 0.05 significance level, what do you conclude? Are the results as you would expect?

	Right-Handed					Left-Handed				
Female	857	878	875	786	897	871	858	885	846	812
Male	944	908	902	913	946	1001	917	1030	915	977

10. Smoking, Gender, and Body Temperature The table below lists body temperatures obtained from randomly selected subjects (based on Data Set 5 "Body Temperatures" in Appendix B). Using a 0.05 significance level, test for an interaction between gender and smoking, test for an effect from gender, and test for an effect from smoking. What do you conclude?

	Smokes	Does not smoke
Male	98.8 97.6 98.0 98.5	98.4 97.8 98.0 97.0
Female	98.0 98.5 98.3 98.7	97.7 98.0 98.2 99.1

12-2 Beyond the Basics

11. Transformations of Data Example 1 illustrated the use of two-way ANOVA to analyze the sample data in Table 12-3 on page 627. How are the results affected in each of the following cases?

a. The same constant is added to each sample value.

b. Each sample value is multiplied by the same nonzero constant.

c. The format of the table is transposed so that the row and column factors are interchanged.

d. The first sample value in the first cell is changed so that it becomes an outlier.

Chapter Quick Quiz

1. Cola Weights Data Set 37 "Cola Weights and Volumes" in Appendix B lists the weights (lb) of the contents of cans of cola from four different samples: (1) regular Coke, (2) Diet Coke, (3) regular Pepsi, and (4) Diet Pepsi. The results from analysis of variance are shown in the Minitab display below. What is the null hypothesis for this analysis of variance test? Based on the displayed results, what should you conclude about H_0? What do you conclude about equality of the mean weights from the four samples?

Minitab

Source	DF	Adj SS	Adj MS	F-Value	P-Value
Factor	3	0.047979	0.015993	503.06	0.000
Error	140	0.004451	0.000032		
Total	143	0.052430			

2. Cola Weights For the four samples described in Exercise 1, the sample of regular Coke has a mean weight of 0.81682 lb, the sample of Diet Coke has a mean weight of 0.78479 lb, the sample of regular Pepsi has a mean weight of 0.82410 lb, and the sample of Diet Pepsi has a mean weight of 0.78386 lb. If we use analysis of variance and reach a conclusion to reject equality of the four sample means, can we then conclude that any of the specific samples have means that are significantly different from the others?

3. Cola Weights For the analysis of variance test described in Exercise 1, is that test left-tailed, right-tailed, or two-tailed?

4. Cola Weights Identify the value of the test statistic in the display included with Exercise 1. In general, do larger test statistics result in larger P-values, smaller P-values, or P-values that are unrelated to the value of the test statistic?

5. Cola Weights The displayed results from Exercise 1 are from one-way analysis of variance. What is it about this test that characterizes it as one-way analysis of variance instead of two-way analysis of variance?

6. One-Way ANOVA In general, what is one-way analysis of variance used for?

7. One vs. Two What is the fundamental difference between one-way analysis of variance and two-way analysis of variance?

8. Pulse Rates Shown below are pulse rates from Data Set 1 "Body Data" in Appendix B, and the StatCrunch display from two-way analysis of variance of these data. In analyzing these data, what important feature is addressed with two-way analysis of variance that is not addressed with two separate tests of (1) difference between mean pulse rates based on gender, or (2) differences among the mean pulse rates in the different age brackets?

	Female										Male									
18–29	104	82	80	78	80	84	82	66	70	78	72	64	72	64	64	70	72	64	54	52
30–49	66	74	96	86	98	88	82	72	80	80	80	90	58	74	96	72	58	66	80	92
50–80	94	72	82	86	72	90	64	72	72	100	54	102	52	52	62	82	82	60	52	74

ANOVA table

Source	DF	SS	MS	F-Stat	P-value
Age	2	526.93333	263.46667	1.8156202	0.1725
Gender	1	1972.2667	1972.2667	13.591424	0.0005
Interaction	2	272.53333	136.26667	0.93905054	0.3973
Error	54	7836	145.11111		
Total	59	10607.733			

9. Interaction

a. Based on the display included with the preceding exercise, what do you conclude about an interaction between gender and age bracket?

b. If there does appear to be an interaction between gender and age bracket, how should we continue with the procedure for two-way analysis of variance?

10. Gender and Age Bracket Based on the display included with Exercise 8, what are the final conclusions?

Review Exercises

1. Cholesterol If we record all of the LDL cholesterol measures from Data Set 1: "Body Data" that fall into the four age brackets of 20–29, 30–39, 40–49, and 50–59, we obtain the Statdisk analysis of variance results shown below. What do you conclude?

Source:	DF:	SS:	MS:	Test Stat, F:	Critical F:	P-Value:
Treatment:	3	7953.154561	2651.05152	2.143564	2.653431	0.096256
Error:	185	228798.654963	1236.749486			
Total:	188	236751.809524				

2. Cholesterol Listed below are LDL cholesterol measurements (mg/dL) from subjects in four different age brackets. Use a 0.05 significance level to test the claim that subjects in those different age brackets have the same mean cholesterol level.

Age										
20-29	144	104	116	52	124	102	117	84	56	66
30-39	150	137	118	104	94	69	103			
40-49	60	68	94	57	75	136	119	122		
50-59	152	91	147	130	140					

3. Birth Weights Data Set 6 "Births" includes birth weights (g), hospitals, and the day of the week that mothers were admitted to the hospital. Using rows to represent the four hospitals (Albany Medical Center, Bellevue Hospital Center, Olean General Hospital, Strong Memorial Hospital), and using columns to represent the seven different days of the week, a two-way table has 28 individual cells. Using five birth weights for each of those 28 cells and using StatCrunch for two-way analysis of variance, we get the results displayed below. What do you conclude?

Source	DF	SS	MS	F-Stat	P-value
Hospital	3	660214.29	220071.43	0.35487215	0.7857
Day	6	3120428.6	520071.43	0.83863165	0.5426
Interaction	18	9461285.7	525626.98	0.84759016	0.6413
Error	112	69456000	620142.86		
Total	139	82697929			

4. Birth Weights The table below lists some of the same data used in the preceding exercise, but the seven days of the week are combined into weekday (Monday, Tuesday, Wednesday, Thursday, Friday) and weekend days (Saturday, Sunday). Also, the birth weights are converted to kilograms. What do you conclude?

	Weekday					Weekend				
Albany	3.5	3.4	3.3	2.8	3.3	3.1	3.6	3.5	0.3	1.7
Bellevue	3.4	3.0	3.2	0.6	3.2	3.5	2.5	3.1	1.0	3.2
Olean	2.6	2.6	3.2	2.9	3.2	3.3	3.0	3.1	3.5	3.7
Strong	2.9	3.4	2.7	3.5	3.3	3.6	2.8	2.3	3.3	2.7

Cumulative Review Exercises

In Exercises 1–5, refer to the following list of numbers of years that deceased U.S. presidents, popes, and British monarchs lived after their inauguration, election, or coronation, respectively. (As of this writing, the last president is George H. W. Bush, the last pope is John Paul II, and the last British monarch is George VI.) Assume that the data are samples from larger populations.

Longevity (years)

Presidents	10	29	26	28	15	23	17	25	0	20	4	1	24	16	12
	4	10	17	16	0	7	24	12	4	18	21	11	2	9	36
	12	28	3	16	9	25	23	32	30						
Popes	2	9	21	3	6	10	18	11	6	25	23	6	2	15	32
	25	11	8	17	19	5	15	0	26						
Monarchs	17	6	13	12	13	33	59	10	7	63	9	25	36	15	

1. Exploring the Data Include appropriate units in all answers.

a. Find the mean for presidents, find the mean for popes, and find the mean for the monarchs.

b. Find the standard deviation for presidents, find the standard deviation for popes, and find the standard deviation for monarchs.

c. Find the variances for presidents, popes, and monarchs.

d. Are there any obvious outliers?

e. What is the level of measurement of the data (nominal, ordinal, interval, ratio)?

2. Comparing Two Means Treating the data as samples from larger populations, test the claim that there is a significant difference between the mean of presidents and the mean of popes.

3. Normal Quantile Plot The accompanying normal quantile plot was obtained from the longevity times of presidents. What does this graph tell us?

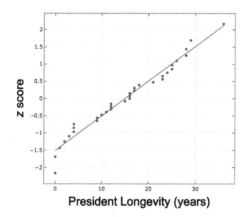

4. Confidence Interval Use the longevity times of presidents and construct a 95% confidence interval estimate of the population mean. Write a brief statement that interprets the confidence interval.

5. ANOVA The XLSTAT display below results from using the one-way analysis of variance test with the three samples.

a. What is the null hypothesis?

b. Assuming a 0.05 significance level, what conclusion is indicated by the displayed results?

Source	DF	Sum of squares	Mean squares	F	Pr > F
Model	2	824.964	412.482	3.038	0.054
Error	74	10047.841	135.782		
Corrected Total	76	10872.805			

6. Quarters Assume that weights of quarters minted after 1964 are normally distributed with a mean of 5.670 g and a standard deviation of 0.062 g (based on U.S. Mint specifications).

a. Find the probability that a randomly selected quarter weighs between 5.600 g and 5.700 g.

b. If 25 quarters are randomly selected, find the probability that their mean weight is greater than 5.675 g.

c. Find the probability that when eight quarters are randomly selected, they all weigh less than 5.670 g.

d. If a vending machine is designed to accept quarters with weights above the 10th percentile P_{10}, find the weight separating acceptable quarters from those that are not acceptable.

7. Concussions The following table summarizes results from a study of concussions in children (based on data from "Association Between Early Participation in Physical Activity Following Acute Concussion and Persistent Postconcussive Symptoms in Children and Adolescents," by Grool et al., *Journal of the American Medical Association*, Vol. 216, No. 23). Use a 0.05 significance level and determine whether physical activity within 7 days after an acute concussion appears to have an effect on symptoms 28 days after a concussion.

		Symptoms 28 days after concussion?	
		Yes	No
Physical activity within 7 days after acute concussion?	Yes	413	1264
	No	320	416

8. Win 4 Lottery Shown below is a histogram of digits selected in California's Win 4 lottery. Each drawing involves the random selection (with replacement) of four digits between 0 and 9 inclusive.

a. What is fundamentally wrong with the graph?

b. Does the display depict a normal distribution? Why or why not? What should be the shape of the histogram?

c. Identify the frequencies, then test the claim that the digits are selected from a population in which the digits are all equally likely. Is there a problem with the lottery?

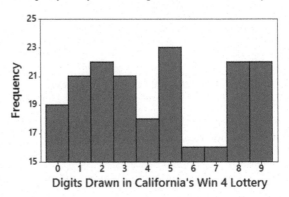

Digits Drawn in California's Win 4 Lottery

Technology Project

Does Weight Change with Age? Refer to Data Set 1 "Body Data" in Appendix B and use the weights of males partitioned into the three different age brackets of 18–25, 26–40, and 41–80. Test the claim that men in those three age brackets have the same mean weight.

Sorting One challenge in this project is identifying the weights of men in the three age brackets. First, use the *sort* feature of your technology to sort all of the columns using *Gender* as the basis for sorting. You can then delete all of the rows representing females. Next, sort all of the columns using *Age* as the basis for sorting. It will then be much easier to identify the weights in the different age brackets.

Big (or Very Large) Data Project

Refer to Data Set 46 "Dow Jones Industrial Average (DJIA)" in Appendix B. That data set includes 31,784 records of opening, high, low, and closing values of the Dow Jones Industrial Average. Test the claim that the values from those four variables have the same mean.

FROM DATA TO DECISION

Critical Thinking: Does Exposure to Lead Affect IQ Scores of Children?

An important environment/health study involved children who lived within 7 km (about 4 miles) of a large ore smelter in El Paso, Texas. A smelter is used to melt the ore in order to separate the metals in it. Because the smelter emitted

lead pollution, there was concern that these children would somehow suffer negative health effects. Data from the study are included in Data Set 11 "IQ and Lead" in Appendix B. The focus of this Project is to investigate the possible effect of lead exposure on IQ scores as measured by the Wechsler intelligence scale.

Data Set 11 "IQ and Lead" includes the following IQ scores:

- Verbal IQ: Measured verbal IQ scores

- Performance IQ: Measured with a performance test that includes components such as picture analysis, picture arrangement, and matching patterns

- Full IQ: The full IQ score is a combination of the verbal IQ score and the performance IQ score.

Based on measured blood lead levels, the children were partitioned into a low lead level group, a medium lead level group, or a high lead level group.

First explore the data using sample statistics. Then use analysis of variance to investigate the effect of lead on verbal IQ scores, performance IQ scores, and full IQ scores. What do you conclude?

Cooperative Group Activities

1. Out-of-class activity Flesch Reading Ease scores and Flesch-Kincaid Grade Level scores measure readability of text. Some programs, such as Microsoft Word, include features that allow you to automatically obtain readability scores. Divide into groups of three or four students. Using at least three different writing samples, such as the *New York Times, USA Today,* and the *Onion,* obtain readability scores for ten samples of text from each source. Use the methods of this chapter to determine whether there are any differences.

2. In-class activity Divide the class into three groups. One group should record the pulse rate of each member while he or she remains seated. The second group should record the pulse rate of each member while he or she is standing. The third group should record the pulse rate of each member immediately after he or she stands and sits 10 times. Analyze the results. What do the results indicate?

3. In-class activity Ask each student in the class to estimate the length of the classroom. Specify that the length is the distance between the whiteboard and the opposite wall. On the same sheet of paper, each student should also write his or her gender (male/female) and major. Then divide into groups of three or four, and use the data from the entire class to address these questions:

• Is there a significant difference between the mean estimate for males and the mean estimate for females?

• Is there sufficient evidence to reject equality of the mean estimates for different majors? Describe how the majors were categorized.

• Does an interaction between gender and major have an effect on the estimated length?

• Does gender appear to have an effect on estimated length?

• Does major appear to have an effect on estimated length?

4. Out-of-class activity Biographyonline.net includes information on the lives of notable artists, politicians, scientists, actors, and others. Design and conduct an observational study that begins with choosing samples from select groups, followed by a comparison of life spans of people from the different groups. Do any particular groups appear to have life spans that are different from those of the other groups? Can you explain such differences?

5. Out-of-class activity Divide into groups of three or four students. Each group should survey other students at the same college by asking them to identify their major and gender. You might include other factors, such as employment (none, part-time, full-time) and age (under 21, 21–30, over 30). For each surveyed subject, determine the number of Twitter followers or Facebook friends.

• Does gender appear to have an effect on the number of followers/friends?

• Does major have an effect on the number of followers/friends?

• Does an interaction between gender and major have an effect on the number of followers/friends?

13

NONPARAMETRIC TESTS

CHAPTER PROBLEM — **Do Better Smartphones Cost More?**

Table 13-1 lists ranks and costs (dollars) of smartphones (based on data from *Consumer Reports*). Lower rank numbers correspond to better smartphones, based on quality scores determined by *Consumer Reports*. Among the smartphones included in Table 13-1, the best smartphone has a rank of 1, and its cost is $1000. Is there a correlation between ranks and cost? If so, does it appear that better smartphones cost more? Do you get what you pay for?

It would be wise to begin the analysis with a basic exploration of the data. Because we want to address the issue of correlation, we create the scatterplot shown below. There appears to be a straight-line pattern, so there does appear to be a linear correlation. We could move beyond this subjective judgment and proceed to compute a linear correlation coefficient r, but let's consider the nature of the data. Specifically, the ranks simply identify an order, and they do not really measure or count anything. Instead of using the linear correlation method from Section 10-1, we can use the rank correlation method described in Section 13-6.

We can then provide objective results that are better than a subjective judgment.

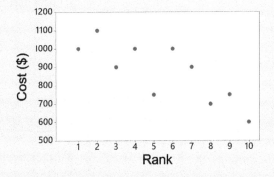

TABLE 13-1 Ranks and Costs of Smartphones

Rank	1	2	3	4	5	6	7	8	9	10
Cost (dollars)	1000	1100	900	1000	750	1000	900	700	750	600

CHAPTER OBJECTIVES

Here are the chapter objectives:

13-1 Basics of Nonparametric Tests

- Develop the ability to describe the difference between parametric tests and nonparametric tests.
- Identify advantages and disadvantages of nonparametric tests.
- Know how nonparametric tests are generally less *efficient* than the corresponding parametric tests.
- Develop the ability to convert data into *ranks*.

13-2 Sign Test

- Develop the ability to conduct a sign test for claims involving matched pairs of sample data, or claims involving nominal data, or claims made about the median of a population.

13-3 Wilcoxon Signed-Ranks Test for Matched Pairs

- Develop the ability to apply the Wilcoxon signed-ranks test for sample data consisting of matched pairs.

13-4 Wilcoxon Rank-Sum Test for Two Independent Samples

- Develop the ability to apply the Wilcoxon rank-sum test for sample data from two independent populations.

13-5 Kruskal-Wallis Test for Three or More Samples

- Develop the ability to apply the Kruskal-Wallis test for sample data from three or more independent populations.

13-6 Rank Correlation

- Develop the ability to compute the value of the rank correlation coefficient r_s, and use it to determine whether there is a correlation between two variables.

13-7 Runs Test for Randomness
- Develop the ability to use the runs test for randomness to determine whether sample data occur in a random sequence.

13-1   Basics of Nonparametric Tests

This chapter introduces methods of *nonparametric* tests, which do not have the stricter requirements of corresponding parametric tests, which are based on samples from populations with specific parameters such as μ or σ.

> **DEFINITIONS**
>
> **Parametric tests** have requirements about the distribution of the populations involved; **nonparametric (or distribution-free) tests** do not require that samples come from populations with normal distributions or any other particular distributions.

Misleading Terminology The term *distribution-free test* correctly indicates that a test does not require a particular distribution. The term *nonparametric tests* is misleading in the sense that it suggests that the tests are not based on a parameter, but there are some nonparametric tests that are based on a parameter such as the median. Due to the widespread use of the term *nonparametric test,* we use that terminology, but we define it to be a test that does not require a particular distribution.

Advantages and Disadvantages

Advantages of Nonparametric Tests

1. Because nonparametric tests have less rigid requirements than parametric tests, they can be applied to a wider variety of situations.

2. Nonparametric tests can be applied to more data types than parametric tests. For example, nonparametric tests can be used with data consisting of ranks, and they can be used with categorical data, such as genders of survey respondents.

Disadvantages of Nonparametric Tests

1. Nonparametric tests tend to waste information because exact numerical data are often reduced to a qualitative form. For example, with the nonparametric sign test (Section 13-2), weight losses by dieters are recorded simply as negative signs, and the actual magnitudes of the weight losses are ignored.

2. Nonparametric tests are not as *efficient* as parametric tests, so a nonparametric test generally needs stronger evidence (such as a larger sample or greater differences) in order to reject a null hypothesis.

Efficiency of Nonparametric Tests When the requirements of population distributions are satisfied, nonparametric tests are generally less efficient than their corresponding parametric tests. For example, Section 13-6 presents the concept of *rank correlation,* which has an efficiency rating of 0.91 when compared to linear correlation in Section 10-1. This means that with all other things being equal, the nonparametric rank correlation method in Section 13-6 requires 100 sample observations to achieve the same results as 91 sample observations analyzed through the parametric linear correlation in Section 10-1, assuming the stricter requirements for using the parametric test are met. Table 13-2 lists nonparametric tests along with the corresponding parametric test and **efficiency** rating. Table 13-2 shows that several nonparametric tests have efficiency ratings above 0.90, so the lower efficiency might not be an important factor in choosing between parametric and nonparametric tests. However, because parametric tests do have higher efficiency ratings than their nonparametric counterparts, it's generally better to use the parametric tests when their required assumptions are satisfied.

TABLE 13-2 Efficiency: Comparison of Parametric and Nonparametric Tests

Application	Parametric Test	Nonparametric Test	Efficiency Rating of Nonparametric Test with Normal Populations
Matched pairs of sample data	*t* test	Sign test or	0.63
		Wilcoxon signed-ranks test	0.95
Two independent samples	*t* test	Wilcoxon rank-sum test	0.95
Three or more independent samples	Analysis of variance (*F* test)	Kruskal-Wallis test	0.95
Correlation	Linear correlation	Rank correlation test	0.91
Randomness	No parametric test	Runs test	No basis for comparison

Ranks

Sections 13-2 through 13-5 use methods based on ranks, defined as follows.

DEFINITION

Data are *sorted* when they are arranged according to some criterion, such as smallest to largest or best to worst. A **rank** is a number assigned to an individual sample item according to its order in the sorted list. The first item is assigned a rank of 1, the second item is assigned a rank of 2, and so on.

Handling Ties Among Ranks If a tie in ranks occurs, one very common procedure is to find the mean of the ranks involved in the tie and then assign this mean rank to each of the tied items, as in the following example.

EXAMPLE 1   **Handling Ties Among Ranks**

The golf scores (for one hole) of 4, 5, 5, 5, 10, 11, 12, and 12 are given ranks of 1, 3, 3, 3, 5, 6, 7.5, and 7.5, respectively. The table below illustrates the procedure for handling ties.

Sorted Data	Preliminary Ranking	Rank
4	1	1
5 5 5	2 3 } Mean is 3. 4	3 3 3
10	5	5
11	6	6
12 12	7 } Mean is 7.5. 8	7.5 7.5

13-2   Sign Test

Key Concept This section introduces the *sign test,* which involves converting data values to positive and negative signs, then testing to determine whether either sign occurs significantly more often than the other sign.

> **DEFINITION**
>
> The **sign test** is a nonparametric (distribution-free) test that uses positive and negative signs to test different claims, including these:
>
> **1.** Claims involving matched pairs of sample data
>
> **2.** Claims involving nominal data with two categories
>
> **3.** Claims about the median of a single population

Basic Concept of the Sign Test The basic idea underlying the sign test is to analyze the frequencies of positive and negative signs to determine whether they are significantly different. For example, consider the results of clinical trials of the XSORT method of gender selection. Among 726 couples who used the XSORT method in trying to have a baby girl, 668 couples did have baby girls. Is 668 girls in 726 births *significant?* Common sense should suggest that 668 girls in 726 births is significant, but what about 365 girls in 726 births? Or 400 girls in 726 births? The sign test allows us to determine when such results are significant. Figure 13-1 summarizes the sign test procedure.

For consistency and simplicity, we will use a test statistic based on the number of times that the *less frequent* sign occurs.

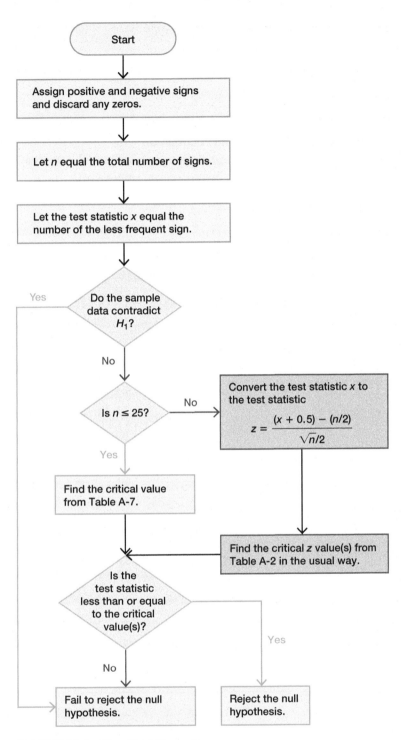

FIGURE 13-1   Sign Test Procedure

Sign Test

Objective

Use positive and negative signs to test a claim falling into one of the following three categories:

1. **Matched Pairs**
   - Subtract the second value in each pair from the first, record the sign of the difference, and ignore any 0s.

2. **Nominal Data with Two Categories**
   - Represent each member of one category by a positive sign and represent each member of the other category by a negative sign.

3. **Median of a Single Population**
   - Subtract the median from each sample value, record the sign of the difference, and ignore any 0s.

Notation

x = the number of times the *less frequent* sign occurs
n = the total number of positive and negative signs combined

Requirements

The sample data are a simple random sample.

Note: There is *no* requirement that the sample data come from a population with a particular distribution, such as a normal distribution.

Test Statistic

If $n \le 25$: Test statistic is x = the number of times the less frequent sign occurs.
If $n > 25$: Test statistic is

$$z = \frac{(x + 0.5) - \left(\dfrac{n}{2}\right)}{\dfrac{\sqrt{n}}{2}}$$

P-Values

P-values are often provided by technology, or *P*-values can often be found using the z test statistic.

Critical Values

1. If $n \le 25$, critical x values are found in Table A-7.   2. If $n > 25$, critical z values are found in Table A-2.

Hint: Because x or z is based on the *less* frequent sign, all one-sided tests are treated as if they were left-tailed tests.

CAUTION When using the sign test in a one-tailed test, be very careful to avoid making the wrong conclusion when one sign occurs significantly more often or less often than the other sign, but the sample data *contradict* the alternative hypothesis. A sample of 7% boys can never be used to support the claim that boys occur *more than* 50% of the time, as in Example 1.

EXAMPLE 1 **Data Contradicting the Alternative Hypothesis**

Among 945 couples who used the XSORT method of gender selection, 66 had boys, so the sample proportion of boys is 66/945, or 0.0698 (based on data from the Genetics & IVF Institute). Consider the claim that the XSORT method of gender selection *increases* the likelihood of baby *boys* so that the probability of a boy is $p > 0.5$. This claim of $p > 0.5$ becomes the alternative hypothesis.

Using common sense, we see that with a sample proportion of boys of 0.0698, we can never support a claim that $p > 0.5$. (We would need a sample proportion of boys *greater* than 0.5 by a significant amount.) Here, the sample proportion of 66/945, or 0.0698, *contradicts* the alternative hypothesis because it is not greater than 0.5.

INTERPRETATION

An alternative hypothesis can never be supported with data that contradict it. The sign test will show that 66 boys in 945 births is significant, but it is significant in the wrong direction. We can never support a claim that $p > 0.5$ with a sample proportion of 66/945, or 0.0698, which is *less than* 0.5.

 YOUR TURN. Exercise 3 "Contradicting H_1."

Claims About Matched Pairs

When using the sign test with data that are matched pairs, we convert the raw data to positive and negative signs as follows:

1. Subtract each value of the second variable from the corresponding value of the first variable.

2. Record only the *sign* of the difference found in Step 1. Exclude *ties* by deleting any matched pairs in which both values are equal.

The main concept underlying this use of the sign test is as follows:

If the two sets of data have equal medians, the number of positive signs should be approximately equal to the number of negative signs.

EXAMPLE 2 **Is There a Difference Between Measured and Reported Weights?**

Listed below are measured and reported weights (lb) of random male subjects (from Data Set 4 "Measured and Reported" in Appendix B). Use a 0.05 significance level to test the claim that for males, the differences "measured weight–reported weight" have a median equal to 0.

TABLE 13-3 Measured and Reported Male Weights

Measured	220.0	268.7	213.4	201.3	107.1	172.0	187.4	132.5	122.1	151.9
Reported	220	267	210	204	107	176	187	135	122	150
Sign of Difference	0	+	+	−	+	−	+	−	+	+

SOLUTION

REQUIREMENT CHECK The only requirement of the sign test is that the sample data are a simple random sample, and that requirement is satisfied. ☑

If there is no difference between measured weights and reported weights, the numbers of positive and negative signs should be approximately equal. In Table 13-3 we have 6 positive signs, 3 negative signs, and 1 difference of 0. We discard the difference of 0 and proceed using only the 6 positive signs and 3 negative signs. The sign test tells us whether or not the numbers of positive and negative signs are approximately equal.

continued

The null hypothesis is the claim of no difference between measured weights and reported weights of males, and the alternative hypothesis is the claim that there is a difference.

H_0: There is no difference. (The median of the differences is equal to 0.)

H_1: There is a difference. (The median of the differences is not equal to 0.)

Following the sign test procedure summarized in Figure 13-1, we let $n = 9$ (the total number of positive and negative signs) and we let $x = 3$ (the number of the less frequent sign, or the smaller of 3 and 6).

The sample data do not contradict H_1, because there is a difference between the 6 positive signs and the 3 negative signs. The sample data show a difference, and we need to continue with the test to determine whether that difference is significant.

Figure 13-1 shows that with $n = 9$, we should proceed to find the critical value from Table A-7. We refer to Table A-7, where the critical value of 1 is found for $n = 9$ and $\alpha = 0.05$ in two tails.

Since $n \leq 25$, the test statistic is $x = 3$ (and we do not convert x to a z score). With a test statistic of $x = 3$ and a critical x value of 1, we fail to reject the null hypothesis of no difference. (See Note 2 included with Table A-7: "Reject the null hypothesis if the number of the less frequent sign (x) is less than or equal to the value in the table." Because $x = 3$ is *not* less than or equal to the critical value of 1, we fail to reject the null hypothesis.) There is not sufficient evidence to warrant rejection of the claim that for males, the median of the differences "measured weight – reported weight" is equal to 0.

INTERPRETATION

We conclude that there is not sufficient evidence to reject the claim that for males, there is no difference between measured weights and reported weights.

> **YOUR TURN.** Do Exercise 5 "Measured and Reported Weights."

Claims Involving Nominal Data with Two Categories

In Chapter 1 we defined nominal data to be data that consist of names, labels, or categories only. The nature of nominal data limits the calculations that are possible, but we can identify the *proportion* of the sample data that belong to a particular category, and we can test claims about the corresponding population proportion p. The following example uses nominal data consisting of genders (girls/boys). The sign test is used by representing girls with positive ($+$) signs and boys with negative ($-$) signs. (Those signs are chosen arbitrarily—honest.)

EXAMPLE 3   **Gender Selection**

The Genetics & IVF Institute conducted a clinical trial of its methods for gender selection for babies. Before the clinical trials were concluded, 879 of 945 babies born to parents using the XSORT method of gender selection were girls. Use the sign test and a 0.05 significance level to test the claim that this method of gender selection is effective in increasing the likelihood of a baby girl.

SOLUTION

REQUIREMENT CHECK   The only requirement is that the sample is a simple random sample. Based on the design of this experiment, we can assume that the sample data are a simple random sample.

Let p denote the population proportion of baby girls. The claim that girls are more likely with the XSORT method can be expressed as $p > 0.5$, so the null and alternative hypotheses are as follows:

H_0: $p = 0.5$ (the proportion of girls is equal to 0.5)

H_1: $p > 0.5$ (girls are more likely)

Denoting girls by positive signs $(+)$ and boys by negative signs $(-)$, we have 879 positive signs and 66 negative signs. Using the sign test procedure summarized in Figure 13-1, we let the test statistic x be the smaller of 879 and 66, so $x = 66$ boys. *Instead of trying to determine whether 879 girls is high enough to be significantly high, we proceed with the equivalent goal of trying to determine whether 66 boys is low enough to be significantly low, so we treat the test as a* left-tailed *test.*

The sample data do not contradict the alternative hypothesis because the sample proportion of girls is $879/945$, or 0.930, which is greater than 0.5, as in the above alternative hypothesis. Continuing with the procedure in Figure 13-1, we note that the value of $n = 945$ is greater than 25, so the test statistic $x = 66$ is converted (using a correction for continuity) to the test statistic z as follows:

$$z = \frac{(x + 0.5) - \left(\dfrac{n}{2}\right)}{\dfrac{\sqrt{n}}{2}}$$

$$= \frac{(66 + 0.5) - \left(\dfrac{945}{2}\right)}{\dfrac{\sqrt{945}}{2}} = -26.41$$

P-Value We could use the test statistic of $z = -26.41$ to find the left-tailed P-value of 0.0000 (Table: 0.0001). That low P-value causes us to reject the null hypothesis.

Critical Value With $\alpha = 0.05$ in a left-tailed test, the critical value is $z = -1.645$. Figure 13-2 shows that the test statistic $z = -26.41$ is in the critical region bounded by $z = -1.645$, so we reject the null hypothesis that the proportion of girls is equal to 0.5.

There is sufficient sample evidence to support the claim that girls are more likely with the XSORT method.

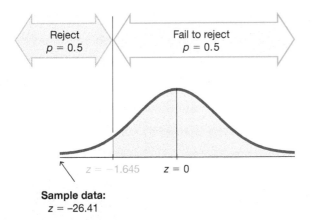

FIGURE 13-2   Testing Effectiveness of the XSORT Gender Selection Method

INTERPRETATION

The XSORT method of gender selection does appear to be associated with an increase in the likelihood of a girl, so this method appears to be effective (but this hypothesis test does not prove that the XSORT method is the *cause* of the increase).

YOUR TURN. Do Exercise 9 "Buttered Toast Drop Test."

Claims About the Median of a Single Population

The next example illustrates the procedure for using the sign test in testing a claim about the median of a single population. See how the negative and positive signs are based on the claimed value of the median.

EXAMPLE 4   **Body Temperatures**

Data Set 5 "Body Temperatures" in Appendix B includes measured body temperatures of adults. Use the 106 temperatures listed for 12 AM on Day 2 with the sign test to test the claim that the median is less than 98.6°F. Use a 0.05 significance level. Of the 106 subjects, 68 had temperatures below 98.6°F, 23 had temperatures above 98.6°F, and 15 had temperatures equal to 98.6°F.

SOLUTION

REQUIREMENT CHECK   The only requirement is that the sample is a simple random sample. Based on the design of this experiment, we assume that the sample data are a simple random sample. ☑

The claim that the median is less than 98.6°F is the alternative hypothesis, while the null hypothesis is the claim that the median is equal to 98.6°F.

H_0: Median is equal to 98.6°F. (median $= 98.6$°F)

H_1: Median is less than 98.6°F. (median < 98.6°F)

Following the procedure outlined in Figure 13-1, we use a negative sign to represent each temperature below 98.6°F, and we use a positive sign for each temperature above 98.6°F. We discard the 15 data values of 98.6, since they result in differences of zero. We have 68 negative signs and 23 positive signs, so $n = 91$ and $x = 23$ (the number of the less frequent sign). The sample data do not contradict the alternative hypothesis, because most of the 91 temperatures are below 98.6 °F. The value of n exceeds 25, so we convert the test statistic x to the test statistic z:

$$z = \frac{(x + 0.5) - \left(\dfrac{n}{2}\right)}{\dfrac{\sqrt{n}}{2}}$$

$$= \frac{(23 + 0.5) - \left(\dfrac{91}{2}\right)}{\dfrac{\sqrt{91}}{2}} = -4.61$$

P-Value In this left-tailed test, the test statistic of $z = -4.61$ yields a P-value of 0.0000 (Table: 0.0001). Because that P-value is so small, we reject the null hypothesis.

Critical Value In this left-tailed test with $\alpha = 0.05$, use Table A-2 to get the critical z value of -1.645. From Figure 13-3 on the next page we see that the test statistic of $z = -4.61$ is within the critical region, so reject the null hypothesis.

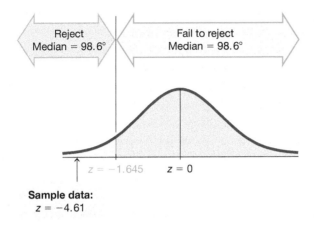

Sample data:
$z = -4.61$

**FIGURE 13-3   Testing the Claim That the Median
Is Less Than 98.6°F**

INTERPRETATION

There is sufficient sample evidence to support the claim that the median body temperature of healthy adults is less than 98.6°F. It is not equal to 98.6°F, as is commonly believed.

YOUR TURN. Do Exercise 13 "Body Temperatures."

In Example 4, the sign test of the claim that the median is below 98.6°F results in a test statistic of $z = -4.61$ and a P-value of 0.00000202. However, a parametric test of the claim that $\mu < 98.6$°F results in a test statistic of $t = -6.611$ with a P-value of 0.000000000813. Because the P-value from the sign test is not as low as the P-value from the parametric test, we see that the sign test isn't as sensitive as the parametric test. Both tests lead to rejection of the null hypothesis, but the sign test doesn't consider the sample data to be as extreme, partly because the sign test uses only information about the *direction* of the data, ignoring the *magnitudes* of the data values. The next section introduces the Wilcoxon signed-ranks test, which largely overcomes that disadvantage.

Rationale for the Test Statistic Used When $n > 25$ When finding critical values for the sign test, we use Table A-7 only for n up to 25. When $n > 25$, the test statistic z is based on a normal approximation to the binomial probability distribution with $p = q = 1/2$. Section 6-6 (available at *www.TriolaStats.com*) shows that the normal approximation to the binomial distribution is acceptable when both $np \geq 5$ and $nq \geq 5$. In Section 5-2 we saw that $\mu = np$ and $\sigma = \sqrt{npq}$ for binomial probability distributions. Because this sign test assumes that $p = q = 1/2$, we meet the $np \geq 5$ and $nq \geq 5$ prerequisites whenever $n \geq 10$. Also, with the assumption that $p = q = 1/2$, we get $\mu = np = n/2$ and $\sigma = \sqrt{npq} = \sqrt{n/4} = \sqrt{n}/2$, so the standard z score

$$z = \frac{x - \mu}{\sigma}$$

becomes

$$z = \frac{x - \left(\dfrac{n}{2}\right)}{\dfrac{\sqrt{n}}{2}}$$

continued

We replace x by $x + 0.5$ as a correction for continuity (as discussed in Section 6-6). That is, the values of x are discrete, but since we are using a continuous probability distribution, a discrete value such as 10 is actually represented by the interval from 9.5 to 10.5. Because x represents the less frequent sign, we act conservatively by concerning ourselves only with $x + 0.5$; we get the test statistic z shown below and in the Key Elements box.

$$z = \frac{(x + 0.5) - \left(\dfrac{n}{2}\right)}{\dfrac{\sqrt{n}}{2}}$$

TECH CENTER

Sign Test

Access tech supplements, videos, and data sets at **www.TriolaStats.com**

Statdisk	Minitab	StatCrunch
1. Click **Analysis** in the top menu. 2. Select **Sign Test** from the dropdown menu. 3. *Known number of signs* Select **Given Number of Signs,** choose the format for the claim, enter the significance level and numbers of positive and negative signs. *Pairs of values* Select **Given Pairs of Values,** choose the format for the claim, enter the significance level, and select the two data columns to include. 4. Click **Evaluate.**	*Minitab requires a single column of values.* ***Matched pairs:*** *Enter a column consisting of the differences.* ***Nominal data in two categories:*** *Enter a 1 for each value of one category and −1 for each value of the other category. Enter 0 for the claimed value of the median.* ***Individual values to be tested with claimed median:*** *Enter sample values in a single column.* 1. Click **Stat** in the top menu. 2. Select **Nonparametrics** from the dropdown menu and select **1-Sample Sign** from the submenu. 3. Under *Variables* select the column containing the data to be analyzed. 4. Select **Test Median** and enter the claimed median value. 5. Choose the format of the alternative hypothesis. 6. Click **OK.**	*StatCrunch is able to test the claim that a single list of values is from a population with a median equal to some specified value.* 1. Click **Stat** in the top menu. 2. Select **Nonparametrics** from the dropdown menu and **Sign Test** from the submenu. 3. Select the column containing the data to be analyzed. 4. Select **Hypothesis test for median** and for H_0 enter the claimed median value. For H_A select the desired format. 5. Click **Compute!**

TI-83/84 Plus Calculator

The TI-83/84 Plus calculator does not have a function dedicated to the sign test, but the calculator's binomcdf *function can be used to find the P-value for a sign test.*

1. Press **2ND** then **VARS** keys to access the *DISTR* (distributions) menu.
2. Select **binomcdf** and click **ENTER**.
3. Enter the values for trials *n, p,* and *x* to complete the command **binomcdf(n,p,x)**. For *trials* enter the total number of positive and negative signs. For *p* enter **0.5**. For *x* enter the number of the less frequent sign.
4. Press **ENTER**. The result is the probability of getting *x* or fewer trials. *Double this value for two-tailed tests.*

TIP: The final result is the P-value, so reject the null hypothesis if the P-value is less than or equal to the significance level. Otherwise, fail to reject the null hypothesis.

TECH CENTER *continued*

Sign Test

Access tech supplements, videos, and data sets at **www.TriolaStats.com**

Excel

XLSTAT Add-In

1. Click on the **XLSTAT** tab in the Ribbon and then click **Nonparametric tests.**
2. Select **Comparison of two samples** from the dropdown menu.
3. Enter the data range for each sample in the *Sample 1 & 2 boxes.* Check the **Column labels** box if the data range includes labels.
4. Select **Paired samples** under *Data format.*
5. Check the **Sign test** option only.
6. Click the **Options** tab.
7. Under *Alternative hypothesis* select **Sample 1 – Sample 2 ≠ D.** Confirm *Hypothesized difference (D)* is **0.**
8. Enter a significance level and check the **Exact p-value** box.
9. Click **OK.**

Excel

Excel does not have a function dedicated to the sign test, but can be used to find the P-value for a sign test.

1. Click on the **Insert Function** f_x button, select the category **Statistical,** and select the function **BINOM.DIST** and click **OK.**
2. For *Number_s* enter the number of times the *less frequent* sign occurs. For *Trials* enter the total number of positive and negative signs. For *probability_s* enter **0.5.** For *Cumulative* enter **1** for "True."
3. Click **OK.** The single-tail *P*-value will be displayed. *Double this value for two-tailed tests.*

TIP: The final result is the *P*-value, so reject the null hypothesis if the *P*-value is less than or equal to the significance level. Otherwise, fail to reject the null hypothesis.

R

R does not have a function dedicated to the sign test, but the *binom.test* command can be used to find the *P*-value for a sign test.

R command: **binom.test(*x*, *n*, *p* = 0.5, alternative = c("less" or "two.sided")**

where *x* is the number of the less frequent sign and *n* is the number of positive and negative signs.

TIP: The final result is the *P*-value, so reject the null hypothesis if the *P*-value is less than or equal to the significance level. Otherwise, fail to reject the null hypothesis.

A complete list of R statistical commands is available at TriolaStats.com

13-2 Basic Skills and Concepts

Statistical Literacy and Critical Thinking

1. Is Friday the 13th Unlucky? Listed below are numbers of hospital admissions in one region due to traffic accidents on different Fridays falling on the 6th day of a month and the following 13th day of the month (based on data from "Is Friday the 13th Bad for Your Health," by Scanlon et al., *British Medical Journal*, Vol. 307). Assume that we plan to use the sign test to test the claim of no difference between traffic accidents that occur on Friday the 6th and those that occur on the following Friday the 13th.

a. What requirements must be satisfied for this test?

b. Is there any requirement that the samples must be from populations having a normal distribution or any other specific distribution?

c. In what sense is this sign test a "distribution-free test"?

Friday 6th	9	6	11	11	3	5	8
Friday 13th	13	12	14	10	4	12	8

2. Identifying Signs For the sign test described in Exercise 1, identify the number of positive signs, the number of negative signs, the number of ties, the sample size *n* that is used for the sign test, and the value of the test statistic.

3. Contradicting H_1 An important step in conducting the sign test is to determine whether the sample data contradict the alternative hypothesis H_1. For the sign test described in Exercise 1, identify the null hypothesis and the alternative hypothesis, and explain how the sample data contradict or do not contradict the alternative hypothesis.

4. Efficiency of the Sign Test Refer to Table 13-2 on page 645 and identify the efficiency of the sign test. What does that value tell us about the sign test?

Matched Pairs. *In Exercises 5–8, use the sign test for the data consisting of matched pairs.*

5. Measured and Reported Weights Listed below are measured and reported weights (lb) of random female subjects (from Data Set 4 "Measured and Reported" in Appendix B). Use a 0.05 significance level to test the claim that for females, there is no difference between measured weights and reported weights.

Measured	147.3	268.7	213.4	201.3	107.1	172.0	187.4	132.5	122.1	151.9
Reported	142	267	210	204	107	176	187	135	122	150

6. Do Men and Women Talk the Same Amount? Listed below are word counts of males and females in couple relationships (from Data Set 14 "Word Counts" in Appendix B). Use a 0.05 significance level to test the claim that there is no significant difference between the numbers of words spoken by males and females in couple relationships.

Men	13,560	18,876	13,825	9274	20,547	17,190
Women	21,261	12,964	33,789	8709	10,508	11,909

7. Do Men and Women Talk the Same Amount? Repeat Exercise 6 using all of the paired word counts of males and females in couple relationships listed in the first two columns from Data Set 14 "Word Counts" in Appendix B.

8. Oscars Refer to Data Set 21 "Oscar Winner Age" in Appendix B and use all of the ages of actresses and actors when they won Academy Awards for their performances. Each pair of ages is from the same year. Use a 0.05 significance level to test the claim that there is no significant difference between ages of Oscar-winning actresses and Oscar-winning actors.

Nominal Data. *In Exercises 9–12, use the sign test for the claim involving nominal data.*

9. Buttered Toast Drop Test The Discovery channel television show *MythBusters* conducted an experiment to study what happens when buttered toast is dropped on the floor. When 48 buttered slices of toast were dropped, 29 of them landed with the buttered side up and 19 landed with the buttered side down. Use a 0.05 significance level to test the claim that toast will land with the buttered side down 50% of the time.

10. Medical Malpractice In a study of 1228 randomly selected medical malpractice lawsuits, it was found that 856 of them were dropped or dismissed (based on data from the Physicians Insurers Association of America). Use a 0.01 significance level to test the claim that there is a difference between the rate of medical malpractice lawsuits that go to trial and the rate of such lawsuits that are dropped or dismissed.

11. Overtime Rule in Football Before the overtime rule in the National Football League was changed in 2011, among 460 overtime games, 252 were won by the team that won the coin toss at the beginning of overtime. Using a 0.05 significance level, test the claim that the coin toss is fair in the sense that neither team has an advantage by winning it. Does the coin toss appear to be fair?

12. Overtime Rule in Football Repeat the preceding exercise using these results from 111 overtime games (excluding ties) played *after* the overtime rule in the National Football League was changed in 2011: Among 111 overtime games, 59 were won by the team that won the coin toss at the beginning of overtime, and 52 were lost by the team that won the coin toss at the beginning of overtime. These results are current as of this writing.

Appendix B Data Sets. *In Exercises 13–16, refer to the indicated data set in Appendix B and use the sign test for the claim about the median of a population.*

13. Body Temperatures Data Set 5 "Body Temperatures" in Appendix B includes measured body temperatures of adults. Use the body temperatures listed for 12 AM on Day 1 with the sign test to test the claim that the median is equal to 98.6°F. Use a 0.01 significance level.

14. Peanut Butter Cups Data Set 38 "Candies" includes weights (grams) of randomly selected Reese's Peanut Butter Cup Miniatures. They are from a package of 38 cups, and the package label states that the total weight is 12 oz, or 340.2 g. If the 38 cups have a total weight of 340.2 g, then the cups should have a median weight of 340.2 g/38 = 8.953 g. Use the listed sample data to test the claim that the sample is from a population with a median weight equal to 8.953 g. Use a significance level of $\alpha = 0.05$.

15. Cotinine in Smokers Data Set 15 "Passive and Active Smoke" includes cotinine measurements from 902 smokers. Cotinine is a biomarker of nicotine in the body. Use a 0.01 significance level to test the claim that smokers have cotinine levels with a median of 2.84 ng/mL, which is the median for nonsmokers not exposed to tobacco smoke.

16. Tower of Terror Data Set 33 "Disney World Wait Times" includes wait times (minutes) for the Tower of Terror ride at 5:00 PM. Use those times to test the claim that the median of all such wait times is equal to 30 minutes. Use a 0.01 significance level.

13-2 Beyond the Basics

17. Procedures for Handling Ties In the sign test procedure described in this section, we exclude ties (represented by 0 instead of a sign of + or −). A second approach is to treat half of the 0s as positive signs and half as negative signs. (If the number of 0s is odd, exclude one so that they can be divided equally.) With a third approach, in two-tailed tests make half of the 0s positive and half negative; in one-tailed tests make all 0s either positive or negative, whichever supports the null hypothesis. Repeat Example 4 "Body Temperatures" using the second and third approaches to handling ties, and use a significance level of 0.05. Do the different approaches lead to very different test statistics, *P*-values, and conclusions?

18. Finding Critical Values Table A-7 lists critical values for limited choices of α. Use Table A-1 to add a new column in Table A-7 (from $n = 1$ to $n = 8$) that represents a significance level of 0.03 in one tail or 0.06 in two tails. For any particular n, use $p = 0.5$, because the sign test requires the assumption that $P(\text{positive sign}) = P(\text{negative sign}) = 0.5$. The probability of x or fewer like signs is the sum of the probabilities for values up to and including x.

13-3 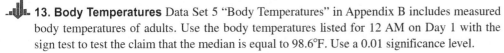 Wilcoxon Signed-Ranks Test for Matched Pairs

Key Concept This section introduces the *Wilcoxon signed-ranks test,* which begins with the conversion of the sample data into ranks. This test can be used for the two different applications described in the following definition.

DEFINITION

The **Wilcoxon signed-ranks test** is a nonparametric test that uses ranks for these applications:

1. Testing a claim that a population of matched pairs has the property that the matched pairs have differences with a median equal to zero

2. Testing a claim that a single population of individual values has a median equal to some claimed value

When testing a claimed value of a median for a population of individual values, we create matched pairs by pairing each sample value with the claimed median, so the same procedure is used for both of the applications above.

Claims Involving Matched Pairs

The sign test (Section 13-2) can be used with matched pairs, but the sign test uses only the *signs* of the differences. By using ranks instead of signs, the Wilcoxon signed-ranks test takes the magnitudes of the differences into account, so it includes and uses more information than the sign test and therefore tends to yield conclusions that better reflect the true nature of the data.

KEY ELEMENTS

Wilcoxon Signed-Ranks Test

Objective: Use the Wilcoxon signed-ranks test for the following tests:

- **Matched Pairs:**   Test the claim that a population of matched pairs has the property that the matched pairs have differences with a median equal to zero.

- **One Population of Individual Values:**   Test the claim that a population has a median equal to some claimed value. (By pairing each sample value with the claimed median, we again work with matched pairs.)

Notation

T = the smaller of the following two sums:

1. The sum of the positive ranks of the nonzero differences d

2. The absolute value of the sum of the negative ranks of the nonzero differences d

(Details for evaluating T are given in the procedure following this Key Elements box.)

Requirements

1. The data are a simple random sample.

2. The population of differences has a distribution that is approximately *symmetric,* meaning that the left half of its histogram is roughly a mirror image of its right half. (For a sample of matched pairs, obtain differences by subtracting the second value from the first value in each

pair; for a sample of individual values, obtain differences by subtracting the value of the claimed median from each sample value.)

Note: There is *no* requirement that the data have a normal distribution.

Test Statistic

If $n \leq 30$, the test statistic is T.

If $n > 30$, the test statistic is $z = \dfrac{T - \dfrac{n(n+1)}{4}}{\sqrt{\dfrac{n(n+1)(2n+1)}{24}}}$

P-Values

P-values are often provided by technology, or P-values can be found using the z test statistic and Table A-2.

Critical Values

1. If $n \leq 30$, the critical T value is found in Table A-8.

2. If $n > 30$, the critical z values are found in Table A-2.

Wilcoxon Signed-Ranks Procedure The following example includes the eight steps of the Wilcoxon signed-ranks procedure. This procedure requires that you sort data, then assign ranks. When working with larger data sets, sorting and ranking become tedious, but technology can be used to automate that process. Stemplots can also be very helpful in sorting data.

EXAMPLE 1 **Measured and Reported Weights**

The first two rows of Table 13-4 include measured and reported weights from a simple random sample of eight different male subjects (from Data Set 4 "Measured and Reported" in Appendix B). The data are matched, so each measured weight is paired with the corresponding reported weight. Assume that we want to use the Wilcoxon signed-ranks test with a 0.05 significance level to test the claim that there is a significant difference between measured weights and reported weights of males. That is, assume that we want to test the null hypothesis that the matched pairs are from a population of matched pairs with differences having a median equal to zero.

TABLE 13-4 Measured and Reported Weights (kg)

Measured Weights	152.6	149.3	174.8	119.5	194.9	180.3	215.4	239.6
Reported Weights	150	148	170	119	185	180	224	239
d (difference)	2.6	1.3	4.8	0.5	9.9	0.3	−8.6	0.6
Rank of $\lvert d \rvert$	5	4	6	2	8	1	7	3
Signed rank	5	4	6	2	8	1	−7	3

SOLUTION

REQUIREMENT CHECK (1) The data are a simple random sample, as required. (2) The second requirement is that the population of differences has a distribution that is approximately *symmetric,* meaning that the left half of its histogram is roughly a mirror image of its right half. A histogram of the differences in the third row of Table 13-4 shows that the difference between the left and right sides is not too extreme, so we will consider this requirement to be satisfied. ✓

Wilcoxon Signed-Ranks Procedure

Step 1: For each pair of data, find the difference d by subtracting the second value from the first value. Discard any pairs that have a difference of 0.

> *EXAMPLE:* The third row of Table 13-4 lists the differences found by subtracting the reported weights from the measured weights. Ignore any differences equal to 0.

Step 2: *Ignore the signs of the differences,* then sort the differences from lowest to highest and replace the differences by the corresponding rank value (as described in Section 13-1). When differences have the same numerical value, assign to them the mean of the ranks involved in the tie.

> *EXAMPLE:* The fourth row of Table 13-4 shows the ranks of the values of $\lvert d \rvert$. The smallest value of $\lvert d \rvert$ is 0.3, so it is assigned the rank of 1. The next smallest value of $\lvert d \rvert$ is 0.5, so it is assigned the rank of 2. If there had been any ties, they would have been assigned the mean of the ranks involved in the tie.

continued

Step 3: Attach to each rank the sign of the difference from which it came. That is, insert the signs that were ignored in Step 2.

EXAMPLE: The bottom row of Table 13-4 lists the same ranks found in the fourth row, but the signs of the differences shown in the third row are inserted.

Step 4: Find the sum of the ranks that are positive. Also find the absolute value of the sum of the negative ranks.

EXAMPLE: The bottom row of Table 13-4 lists the signed ranks. The sum of the positive ranks is $5 + 4 + 6 + 2 + 8 + 1 + 3 = 29$. The sum of the negative ranks is -7, and the absolute value of this sum is 7. The two rank sums are 29 and 7.

Step 5: Let T be the *smaller* of the two sums found in Step 4. Either sum could be used, but for a simplified procedure we arbitrarily select the smaller of the two sums.

EXAMPLE: The data in Table 13-4 result in the rank sums of 29 and 7, so the smaller of those two sums is 7.

Step 6: Let n be the number of pairs of data for which the difference d is not 0.

EXAMPLE: The data in Table 13-4 have 8 differences that are not 0, so $n = 8$.

Step 7: Determine the test statistic and critical values based on the sample size, as shown in the preceding Key Elements box.

EXAMPLE: For the data in Table 13-4 the test statistic is $T = 7$. The sample size is $n = 8$, so the critical value is found in Table A-8. Using a 0.05 significance level with a two-tailed test, the critical value from Table A-8 is 4.

Step 8: Reject the null hypothesis if the sample data lead to a test statistic that is in the critical region—that is, the test statistic is less than or equal to the critical value(s). Otherwise, fail to reject the null hypothesis.

EXAMPLE: For the sample of matched pairs in the first two rows of Table 13-4, the test statistic is $T = 7$ and the critical value is 4, so the test statistic is *not* less than or equal to the critical value. Consequently, we fail to reject the null hypothesis that the matched pairs are from a population of matched pairs with differences having a median equal to zero.

Conclusion Table A-8 includes a note stating that we should reject the null hypothesis if the test statistic T is less than or equal to the critical value. Because the test statistic of $T = 7$ is *not* less than or equal to the critical value of 4, we fail to reject the null hypothesis.

> **INTERPRETATION**

We conclude that there is not sufficient evidence to support the claim that for males, there is a significant difference between measured weights and reported weights. Based on the very small sample, it appears that males do not tend to report weights that are much different from their actual weights. It is possible that a much larger sample would lead to a different conclusion.

YOUR TURN. Do Exercise 5 "Measured and Reported Weights."

Claims About the Median of a Single Population

The Wilcoxon signed-ranks test can also be used to test a claim that a single population has some claimed value of the median. The preceding procedures can be used with one simple adjustment:

> **When testing a claim about the median of a single population, create matched pairs by pairing each sample value with the claimed value of the median. The procedure included in Example 1 can then be used.**

EXAMPLE 2 **Body Temperatures**

Data Set 5 "Body Temperatures" in Appendix B includes measured body temperatures of adults. Use the 106 temperatures listed for 12 AM on Day 2 with the Wilcoxon signed-ranks test to test the claim that the median is less than 98.6°F. Use a 0.05 significance level.

SOLUTION

REQUIREMENT CHECK   (1) The design of the experiment that led to the data in Data Set 5 justifies treating the sample as a simple random sample. (2) The requirement of an approximately symmetric distribution of differences is satisfied, because a histogram of those differences is approximately symmetric. ☑

By pairing each individual sample value with the median of 98.6°F, we are working with matched pairs. Shown in the margin is the Statdisk display showing the test statistic of $T = 661$, which converts to the test statistic $z = -5.67$. (The display is from a two-tailed test; for this left-tailed test, the critical value is -1.645.) The test statistic of $z = -5.67$ yields a P-value of 0.000, so we reject the null hypothesis that the population of differences between body temperatures and the claimed median of 98.6°F is zero. There is sufficient evidence to support the claim that the median body temperature is less than 98.6°F. This is the same conclusion that results from the sign test in Example 4 in Section 13-2.

> YOUR TURN. Do Exercise 9 "Body Temperatures."

Statdisk

> Num Unequal pairs: 91
>
> Using Approximation
> Test Statistic, T: 661.0000
> Mean, μ: 2093
> Standard Deviation: 252.6589
> Test Statistic, z: -5.6677
> Critical z: ±1.959962

Rationale: In Example 1, the unsigned ranks of 1 through 8 have a total of 36, so if there are no significant differences, each of the two signed-rank totals should be around $36 \div 2 = 18$. That is, the negative ranks and positive ranks should split up as 18–18 or something close, such as 17–19. Table A-8, the table of critical values, shows that at the 0.05 significance level with 8 pairs of data, the critical value is 4, so a split of 4–32 represents a significant departure from the null hypothesis, and any split that is farther apart will also represent a significant departure from the null hypothesis. Conversely, splits like 5–31 do not represent significant departures from an 18–18 split, and they would not justify rejecting the null hypothesis. The Wilcoxon signed-ranks test is based on the lower rank total, so instead of analyzing both numbers constituting the split, we consider only the lower number.

The sum of all the ranks $1 + 2 + 3 + \cdots + n$ is equal to $n(n + 1)/2$. If this rank sum is to be divided equally between two categories (positive and negative), each of the two totals should be near $n(n + 1)/4$, which is half of $n(n + 1)/2$. Recognition of this principle helps us understand the test statistic used when $n > 30$.

TECH CENTER

Wilcoxon Signed-Ranks Test
Access tech supplements, videos, and data sets at **www.TriolaStats.com**

Statdisk	Minitab	StatCrunch
1. Click **Analysis** in the top menu. 2. Select **Wilcoxon Tests** from the dropdown menu and **Wilcoxon (Matched Pairs)** from the submenu. 3. Enter a significance level and select the two data columns to include. 4. Click **Evaluate**.	1. Create a column consisting of the differences between the matched pairs. To do this, enter paired data in columns *C1* and *C2*, and enter the command **Let C3 = C1 − C2** in the *Command Line* pane. Click *Run*. 2. Click **Stat** in the top menu. 3. Select **Nonparametrics** from the dropdown menu and select **1-Sample Wilcoxon** from the submenu. 4. Under *Variables* select the column containing the differences between matched pairs (**C3**). 5. Select **Test Median** and enter the median value **0**. 6. Choose the format of the alternative hypothesis. 7. Click **OK**.	1. Click **Stat** in the top menu. 2. Select **Nonparametrics** from the dropdown menu and **Wilcoxon Signed Ranks** from the submenu. 3. Choose **Paired** and select the columns containing the paired data to be analyzed. 4. Select **Hypothesis test for median** and for H_0 enter **0** for the claimed median value. For H_A select the desired format. 5. Click **Compute!**

TI-83/84 Plus Calculator	Excel	R
Requires programs *SRTEST* and *ZZRANK* (available at TriolaStats.com) 1. Create a list of differences between values in the matched pairs. To do this, enter paired data in lists *L1* and *L2* and store the differences in *L3* by entering L1 ⊖ L2 **STO▸** L3. 2. Press **PRGM**, select **SRTEST**, and press **ENTER** twice. 3. For **DATA =** enter the name of the list containing the differences (*L3*) and press **ENTER**. 4. The sample size (*N*), sum of positive ranks (*T+*), and sum of negative ranks (*T−*) will be displayed. Press **ENTER** to see the mean and standard deviation. Press **ENTER** again to see the *z* score. 5. If $n \le 30$, get the critical *T* value from Table A-8. If $n > 30$, get the critical *z* values from Table A-2. *TIP:* The list name *L1* (and *L2 . . . L6*) can be quickly entered by pressing **2ND** ①.	**XLSTAT Add-In (Required)** 1. Click on the **XLSTAT** tab in the Ribbon and then click **Nonparametric tests**. 2. Select **Comparison of two samples** from the dropdown menu. 3. Enter the data range for each sample in the *Sample 1 & 2 boxes*. Check the **Column labels** box if the data range includes labels. 4. Select **Paired samples** under *Data format*. 5. Check the **Wilcoxon signed-rank test** option only. 6. Click the **Options** tab. 7. Under *Alternative hypothesis* select the desired format. Confirm *Hypothesized difference (D)* is **0**. 8. Enter a significance level and check the **Exact p-value** box. 9. Click **OK**.	R command: **wilcox.test(x, y, paired = TRUE)** where *x, y* include paired data. *A complete list of R statistical commands is available at TriolaStats.com*

13-3 Basic Skills and Concepts

Statistical Literacy and Critical Thinking

1. Is Friday the 13th Unlucky? Listed below are numbers of hospital admissions in one region due to traffic accidents on different Fridays falling on the 6th day of a month and the following 13th day of the month (based on data from "Is Friday the 13th Bad for Your Health," by Scanlon et al., *British Medical Journal*, Vol. 307). Assume that we want to use the Wilcoxon signed-ranks test to test the claim of no difference between traffic accidents that occur on Friday the 6th and those that occur on the following Friday the 13th. Identify the null hypothesis and alternative hypothesis.

a. What requirements must be satisfied for this test?

b. Is there any requirement that the samples must be from populations having a normal distribution or any other specific distribution?

c. In what sense is the Wilcoxon signed-ranks test a "distribution-free test"?

Friday 6th	9	6	11	11	3	5
Friday 13th	13	12	14	10	4	12

2. Hospital Admissions For the matched pairs listed in Exercise 1, identify the following components used in the Wilcoxon signed-ranks test:

a. Differences d

b. The ranks corresponding to the nonzero values of $|d|$

c. The signed ranks

d. The sum of the positive ranks and the sum of the absolute values of the negative ranks

e. The value of the test statistic T

f. The critical value of T (assuming a 0.05 significance level in a test of no difference between hospital admissions of Friday 6th and the following Friday 13th).

3. Sign Test vs. Wilcoxon Signed-Ranks Test Using the data in Exercise 1, we can test for no difference between hospital admissions on Friday 6th and Friday 13th by using the sign test or the Wilcoxon signed-ranks test. In what sense does the Wilcoxon signed-ranks test incorporate and use more information than the sign test?

4. Efficiency of the Wilcoxon Signed-Ranks Test Refer to Table 13-2 on page 645 and identify the efficiency of the Wilcoxon signed-ranks test. What does that value tell us about the test?

Using the Wilcoxon Signed-Ranks Test. *In Exercises 5–8, refer to the sample data for the given exercises in Section 13-2 on page 656. Use the Wilcoxon signed-ranks test to test the claim that the matched pairs have differences that come from a population with a median equal to zero. Use a 0.05 significance level.*

5. Exercise 5 "Measured and Reported Weights"

6. Exercise 6 "Do Men and Women Talk the Same Amount?"

7. Exercise 7 "Do Men and Women Talk the Same Amount?"

8. Exercise 8 "Oscars"

In Exercises 9–12, refer to the sample data from the given exercises in Section 13-2 on page 657. Use the Wilcoxon signed-ranks test for the claim about the median of a population.

 9. Exercise 13 "Body Temperatures"

 10. Exercise 14 "Peanut Butter Cups"

 11. Exercise 15 "Cotinine in Smokers"

12. Exercise 16 "Tower of Terror"

13-3 Beyond the Basics

13. Rank Sums Exercise 12 uses Data Set 33 "Disney World Wait Times" in Appendix B, and the sample size for the 5:00 PM Tower of Terror wait times is $n = 50$.

a. If we have sample paired data with 50 nonzero differences, what are the smallest and largest possible values of T?

b. If we have sample paired data with 50 nonzero differences, what is the expected value of T if the population consists of matched pairs with differences having a median of 0?

c. If we have sample paired data with 50 nonzero differences and the sum of the positive ranks is 165, find the absolute value of the sum of the negative ranks.

d. If we have sample paired data with n nonzero differences and one of the two rank sums is k, find an expression for the other rank sum.

Wilcoxon Rank-Sum Test for Two Independent Samples

Key Concept This section describes the *Wilcoxon rank-sum test,* which uses ranks of values from two *independent* samples to test the null hypothesis that the samples are from populations having equal medians. The Wilcoxon rank-sum test is equivalent to the **Mann-Whitney U test** (see Exercise 13), which is included in some textbooks and technologies (such as Minitab, StatCrunch, and XLSTAT). Here is the basic idea underlying the Wilcoxon rank-sum test: If two samples are drawn from identical populations and the individual values are all *ranked* as one combined collection of values, then the high and low ranks should fall evenly between the two samples. If the low ranks are found predominantly in one sample and the high ranks are found predominantly in the other sample, we have an indication that the two populations have different medians.

Unlike the parametric t tests for two independent samples in Section 9-2, the Wilcoxon rank-sum test does *not* require normally distributed populations and it can be used with data at the ordinal level of measurement, such as data consisting of ranks. In Table 13-2 we noted that the Wilcoxon rank-sum test has a 0.95 efficiency rating when compared to the parametric test. Because this test has such a high efficiency rating and involves easier calculations, it is often preferred over the parametric t test, even when the requirement of normality is satisfied.

CAUTION Don't confuse the Wilcoxon rank-sum test for two *independent* samples with the Wilcoxon signed-ranks test for matched pairs. Use "Internal Revenue Service" as the mnemonic for IRS to remind yourself of "**I**ndependent: **R**ank **S**um."

DEFINITION

The **Wilcoxon rank-sum test** is a nonparametric test that uses ranks of sample data from two independent populations to test this null hypothesis:

H_0: Two independent samples come from populations with equal medians.

(The alternative hypothesis H_1 can be any one of the following three possibilities: The two populations have *different* medians, or the first population has a median *greater than* the median of the second population, or the first population has a median *less than* the median of the second population.)

Wilcoxon Rank-Sum Test

Objective

Use the Wilcoxon rank-sum test with samples from two independent populations for the following null and alternative hypotheses:

H_0: The two samples come from populations with equal medians.

H_1: The median of the first population is different from (or greater than, or less than) the median from the second population.

Notation

n_1 = size of Sample 1
n_2 = size of Sample 2
R_1 = sum of ranks for Sample 1
R_2 = sum of ranks for Sample 2
R = same as R_1 (sum of ranks for Sample 1)

μ_R = mean of the sample R values that is expected when the two populations have equal medians
σ_R = standard deviation of the sample R values that is expected with two populations having equal medians

Requirements

1. There are two independent simple random samples.

2. Each of the two samples has more than 10 values. (For samples with 10 or fewer values, special tables are available in special reference books, such as

CRC Standard Probability and Statistics Tables and Formulae, published by CRC Press.)

Note: There is *no* requirement that the two populations have a normal distribution or any other particular distribution.

Test Statistic

$$z = \frac{R - \mu_R}{\sigma_R}$$

where $\mu_R = \dfrac{n_1(n_1 + n_2 + 1)}{2}$ and $\sigma_R = \sqrt{\dfrac{n_1 n_2(n_1 + n_2 + 1)}{12}}$

n_1 = size of the sample from which the rank sum R is found
n_2 = size of the other sample
R = sum of ranks of the sample with size n_1

P-Values

P-values can be found from technology or by using the z test statistic and Table A-2.

Critical Values

Critical values can be found in Table A-2 (because the test statistic is based on the normal distribution).

Procedure for Finding the Value of the Test Statistic

To see how the following steps are applied, refer to the sample data listed in Table 13-5 on the next page. The data are heights (mm) of males randomly selected from Data Set 2 "ANSUR I 1988" and Data Set 3 "ANSUR II 2012." Both data sets are in Appendix B.

Step 1: Temporarily combine the two samples into one big sample, then replace each sample value with its rank. (The lowest value gets a rank of 1, the next lowest value gets a rank of 2, and so on. If values are tied, assign to them the

continued

TABLE 13-5 Heights (mm) of Males from ANSUR I and ANSUR II

ANSUR I 1988	ANSUR II 2012
1698 (5)	1810 (21)
1727 (8)	1850 (25)
1734 (11)	1777 (16)
1684 (3)	1811 (22)
1667 (1)	1780 (17.5)
1680 (2)	1733 (10)
1785 (19)	1814 (23)
1885 (27)	1861 (26)
1841 (24)	1709 (7)
1702 (6)	1740 (13)
1738 (12)	1694 (4)
1732 (9)	1766 (15)
	1748 (14)
	1794 (20)
	1780 (17.5)
$n_1 = 12$	$n_2 = 15$
$R_1 = 127$	$R_2 = 251$

mean of the ranks involved in the tie. See Section 13-1 for a description of ranks and the procedure for handling ties.)

EXAMPLE: In Table 13-5, the ranks of the 27 male heights are shown in parentheses. The rank of 1 is assigned to the lowest sample value of 1667, the rank of 2 is assigned to the next lowest value of 1680, and the rank of 3 is assigned to the next lowest value of 1684. The 17th and 18th values are tied at 1780, so we assign the rank of 17.5 to both of those tied values.

Step 2: Find the sum of the ranks for either one of the two samples.

EXAMPLE: In Table 13-5, the sum of the ranks from the first sample is 127. (That is, $R_1 = 5 + 8 + 11 + \cdots + 9 = 127$.) The sum of the ranks from the second sample is 251.

Step 3: Calculate the value of the z test statistic as shown in the preceding Key Elements box, where either sample can be used as "Sample 1." (If both sample sizes are greater than 10, then the sampling distribution of R is approximately normal with mean μ_R and standard deviation σ_R, and the test statistic is as shown in the preceding Key Elements box.)

EXAMPLE: Calculations of μ_R and σ_R and z are shown in Example 1, which follows.

EXAMPLE 1   **Heights of Males from ANSUR I 1988 and ANSUR II 2012**

Table 13-5 lists samples of heights of males from the ANSUR I 1988 and ANSUR II 2012 data sets. Use a 0.05 significance level to test the claim that the two samples are from populations with the same median.

SOLUTION

REQUIREMENT CHECK (1) The sample data are two independent simple random samples. (2) The sample sizes are 12 and 15, so both sample sizes are greater than 10. The requirements are satisfied. ☑

The null and alternative hypotheses are as follows:

H_0: The two samples are from populations with the same median.

H_1: The two samples are from populations with different medians.

Rank the combined list of all 27 male heights, beginning with a rank of 1 (assigned to the lowest value of 1667). The ranks corresponding to the individual sample values are shown in parentheses in Table 13-5. R denotes the sum of the ranks for the sample we choose as Sample 1. If we choose the ANSUR I 1988 sample, we get

$$R = 5 + 8 + 11 + \cdots + 9 = 127$$

Because there are 12 heights in the first sample, we have $n_1 = 12$. Also, $n_2 = 15$ because there are 15 heights in the second sample. The values of μ_R and σ_R and the test statistic z can now be found as follows.

$$\mu_R = \frac{n_1(n_1 + n_2 + 1)}{2} = \frac{12(12 + 15 + 1)}{2} = 168$$

$$\sigma_R = \sqrt{\frac{n_1 n_2(n_1 + n_2 + 1)}{12}} = \sqrt{\frac{(12)(15)(12 + 15 + 1)}{12}} = 20.4939$$

$$z = \frac{R - \mu_R}{\sigma_R} = \frac{127 - 168}{20.4939} = -2.00$$

The test is two-tailed because a large positive value of z would indicate that disproportionately more higher ranks are found in Sample 1, and a large negative value of z would indicate that disproportionately more lower ranks are found in Sample 1. In either case, we would have strong evidence against the claim that the two samples come from populations with equal medians.

The significance of the test statistic z can be treated as in previous chapters. We are testing (with $\alpha = 0.05$) the hypothesis that the two populations have equal medians, so we have a two-tailed test.

P-Value: Using the unrounded z score, the P-value is 0.045, so we reject the null hypothesis that the two samples are from populations with the same median.

Critical Values: If we use the critical values of $z = \pm 1.96$, we see that the test statistic of $z = -2.00$ does fall within the critical region, so we reject the null hypothesis that the two samples are from populations with the same median.

> **INTERPRETATION**
>
> There is sufficient evidence to warrant rejection of the claim that the sample of male heights from ANSUR I 1988 and the sample of male heights from ANSUR II 2012 are from populations with the same median. It appears that the medians are different. Based on the listed sample data, it appears that the heights from 1988 are different than the heights from 2012. Because the heights from 2012 have a larger median, it appears that males became taller as time passed from 1988 to 2012, although a one-sided hypothesis test would be better for testing that conclusion. A one-sided test would lead to the conclusion that the 2012 heights are significantly larger than the 1988 heights.

YOUR TURN. Do Exercise 5 "Heights of Females from ANSUR I and ANSUR II."

In Example 1, if we interchange the two sets of sample values and consider the ANSUR II 2012 heights to be the first sample, then $R = 251$, $\mu_R = 210$, $\sigma_R = 20.4939$, and $z = 2.00$, so the conclusion is exactly the same.

EXAMPLE 2 **Large Samples of Heights of Males from ANSUR I (in 1988) and ANSUR II (in 2012)**

Example 1 uses samples of sizes 12 and 15. Data Set 2 "ANSUR I 1988" includes 1774 heights of males and Data Set 3 "ANSUR II 2012" includes 4082 heights of males. Repeating the manual calculations of Example 1 using these much larger samples would not be much fun. But alas, technology comes to the rescue. If we use Statdisk to repeat Example 1 with the much larger data sets, we get the accompanying display. We can see that the test statistic is $z = -0.11$ rounded. The unrounded test statistic of $z = -0.10546$ can be used to find that the P-value in this two-tailed test is 0.9160. Although Example 1 led to a conclusion of a difference between the two population medians, the larger data sets lead to a conclusion of no significant difference between the two population medians.

Statdisk

Total Number of Values:	5856
Rank Sum 1:	5188889.00000
Rank Sum 2:	11960407.00000
Mean, μ:	5195159.00000
Standard Deviation:	59451.15507
Test Statistic, z:	-0.10546
Critical z:	±1.95996

YOUR TURN. Do Exercise 9 "Queues."

TECH CENTER

Wilcoxon Rank-Sum Test
Access tech supplements, videos, and data sets at **www.TriolaStats.com**

Statdisk	Minitab	StatCrunch
1. Click **Analysis** in the top menu. 2. Select **Wilcoxon Tests** from the dropdown menu and **Wilcoxon (Independent Samples)** from the submenu. 3. Enter a significance level and select the two data columns to include. 4. Click **Evaluate.**	1. Enter the two sets of sample data into columns *C1* and *C2*. 2. Click **Stat** in the top menu. 3. Select **Nonparametrics** from the dropdown menu and select **Mann-Whitney** from the submenu. 4. For *First Sample* select **C1** and for *Second Sample* select **C2**. 5. Enter the confidence level (95.0 corresponds to a significance level of $\alpha = 0.05$). 6. For *Alternative*, choose the format of the alternative hypothesis (*not equal* corresponds to a two-tailed hypothesis test). 7. Click **OK.**	1. Click **Stat** in the top menu. 2. Select **Nonparametrics** from the dropdown menu and **Mann-Whitney** from the submenu. 3. Select the columns to be used for the two samples. 4. Select **Hypothesis test for m1-m2** and for H_0 enter the value of the claimed difference. For H_A select the desired format. 5. Click **Compute!**

TI-83/84 Plus Calculator	Excel	R
Requires programs *RSTEST* and *ZZRANK* (available at TriolaStats.com) 1. Enter the two sets of sample data in list *L1* and *L2*. 2. Press **PRGM**, select **RSTEST,** and press **ENTER** twice. 3. For **GROUP A** = enter **L1** and press **ENTER**. For **GROUP B** = enter **L2** and press **ENTER**. 4. The rank sum *R*, mean, standard deviation and test statistic *z* will be calculated based on the sample with the fewer number of values. Press **ENTER** again to get the test statistic *z*. Find the critical value by referring to Table A-2 or using the *normalcdf* function as described in the Tech Center in Section 6-1. *TIP:* The list name *L1* (and *L2 . . . L6)* can be quickly entered by pressing **2ND** **①**.	**XLSTAT Add-In (Required)** 1. Click on the **XLSTAT** tab in the Ribbon and then click **Nonparametric tests.** 2. Select **Comparison of two samples** from the dropdown menu. 3. Enter the data range for each sample in the *Sample 1 & 2 boxes*. Check the **Column labels** box if the data range includes labels. 4. Select **One column per sample** under *Data format*. 5. Check the **Mann-Whitney test** option only. 6. Click the **Options** tab. 7. Under *Alternative hypothesis* select **Sample 1 – Sample 2 ≠ D.** Confirm *Hypothesized difference (D)* is **0**. 8. Enter a significance level and check the **Exact p-value** box. 9. Click **OK.** *TIP: Because XLSTAT uses a different procedure than the one described in this section, results may be somewhat different, especially for small samples.*	R command: **wilcox.test(*x, y*, paired = FALSE)** where *x, y* include independent data. *A complete list of R statistical commands is available at TriolaStats.com*

13-4   Basic Skills and Concepts

Statistical Literacy and Critical Thinking

1. Heights of Females from ANSUR I and ANSUR II Example 1 in this section used samples of heights of males from Data Set 1 "ANSUR I 1988" and Data Set 2 "ANSUR II 2012." Listed below are samples of heights (mm) of females from those same data sets. Are the requirements for using the Wilcoxon rank-sum test satisfied? Why or why not?

ANSUR I 1988	1620	1693	1558	1783	1609	1649	1628	1597
	1640	1660	1597	1569				
ANSUR II 2012	1672	1621	1623	1633	1526	1570	1616	1690
	1637	1718	1588	1520	1618	1631	1642	

2. Rank Sum After ranking the combined list of female heights given in Exercise 1, find the sum of the ranks for the ANSUR I sample.

3. What Are We Testing? Refer to the sample data in Exercise 1. Assuming that we use the Wilcoxon rank-sum test with those data, identify the null hypothesis and all possible alternative hypotheses.

4. Efficiency Refer to Table 13-2 on page 645 and identify the efficiency of the Wilcoxon rank-sum test. What does that value tell us about the test?

Wilcoxon Rank-Sum Test. *In Exercises 5–8, use the Wilcoxon rank-sum test.*

5. Heights of Females from ANSUR I and ANSUR II Use the sample data given in Exercise 1 and test the claim that the sample of female heights from ANSUR I and the sample of female heights from ANSUR II are from populations with the same median. Use a 0.05 significance level.

6. Radiation in Baby Teeth Listed below are amounts of strontium-90 (in millibecquerels, or mBq, per gram of calcium) in a simple random sample of baby teeth obtained from Pennsylvania residents and New York residents born after 1979 (based on data from "An Unexpected Rise in Strontium-90 in U.S. Deciduous Teeth in the 1990s," by Mangano et al., *Science of the Total Environment*). Use a 0.05 significance level to test the claim that the median amount of strontium-90 from Pennsylvania residents is the same as the median from New York residents.

Pennsylvania	155	142	149	130	151	163	151	142	156	133	138	161
New York	133	140	142	131	134	129	128	140	140	140	137	143

7. Clinical Trials of Lipitor The sample data below are changes in LDL cholesterol levels in clinical trials of Lipitor (atorvastatin). It was claimed that Lipitor had an effect on LDL cholesterol. (The data are based on results given in a Parke-Davis memo from David G. Orloff, M.D., the medical team leader for clinical trials of Lipitor. Pfizer declined to provide the author with the original data values.) Negative values represent decreases in LDL cholesterol. Use a 0.05 significance level to test the claim that for those treated with 20 mg of Lipitor and those treated with 80 mg of Lipitor, changes in LDL cholesterol have the same median. What do the results suggest?

Group Treated with 20 mg of Lipitor:													
−28	−32	−29	−39	−31	−35	−25	−36	−35	−26	−29	−34	−30	

Group Treated with 80 mg of Lipitor:													
−42	−41	−38	−42	−41	−41	−40	−44	−32	−37	−41	−37	−34	−31

8. Queues Listed below are observed waiting times (seconds) of cars at a Delaware vehicle inspection station. The data from two waiting lines are real observations and the data from the single waiting line are modeled from those real observations. These data are from Data Set 30 "Queues" in Appendix B. The data were collected by the author. Use a 0.01 significance level to test the claim that cars in two lines have a median waiting time equal to that of cars in a single common line.

Two Lines	64	216	86	340	200	630	333	329	915	553
	597	865	1090	663	518	566	268	350	95	100
	163	101								
One Line	64	157	142	279	253	476	478	474	402	722
	761	692	837	903	734	606	268	310	129	133
	122	129	233	461	482	518	509	580		

Appendix B Data Sets. *In Exercises 9–12, refer to the indicated data set in Appendix B and use the Wilcoxon rank-sum test.*

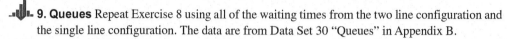

9. Queues Repeat Exercise 8 using all of the waiting times from the two line configuration and the single line configuration. The data are from Data Set 30 "Queues" in Appendix B.

10. Do Men and Women Talk the Same Amount? Refer to Data Set 14 "Word Counts" in Appendix B and use the measured word counts from men in the third column ("M2") and the measured word counts from women in the fourth column ("F2"). Use a 0.01 significance level to test the claim that contrary to a popular belief, the median of the numbers of words spoken by men in a day is the same as the median of the numbers of words spoken by women in a day.

11. IQ and Lead Exposure Data Set 11 "IQ and Lead" in Appendix B lists *full* IQ scores for a random sample of subjects with "medium" lead levels in their blood and another random sample of subjects with "high" lead levels in their blood. Use a 0.05 significance level to test the claim that subjects with medium lead levels have a higher median of the full IQ scores than subjects with high lead levels. Does lead level appear to affect full IQ scores?

12. IQ and Lead Exposure Data Set 11 "IQ and Lead" in Appendix B lists *performance* IQ scores for a random sample of subjects with low lead levels in their blood and another random sample of subjects with high lead levels in their blood. Use a 0.05 significance level to test the claim that subjects with low lead levels have a higher median of the performance IQ score than those with high lead levels. Does lead exposure appear to have an adverse effect?

13-4 Beyond the Basics

13. Using the Mann-Whitney *U* Test The Mann-Whitney *U* test is equivalent to the Wilcoxon rank-sum test for independent samples in the sense that they both apply to the same situations and always lead to the same conclusions. In the Mann-Whitney *U* test we calculate

$$z = \frac{U - \dfrac{n_1 n_2}{2}}{\sqrt{\dfrac{n_1 n_2 (n_1 + n_2 + 1)}{12}}}$$

where

$$U = n_1 n_2 + \frac{n_1 (n_1 + 1)}{2} - R$$

and R is the sum of the ranks for Sample 1. Use the male height values in Table 13-5 on page 666 to find the z test statistic for the Mann-Whitney U test. Compare this value to the z test statistic found using the Wilcoxon rank-sum test.

14. Finding Critical Values Assume that we have two treatments (A and B) that produce quantitative results, and we have only two observations for treatment A and two observations for treatment B. We cannot use the Wilcoxon signed-ranks test given in this section because both sample sizes do not exceed 10.

Rank				Rank Sum for Treatment A
1	2	3	4	
A	A	B	B	3

a. Complete the accompanying table by listing the five rows corresponding to the other five possible outcomes, and enter the corresponding rank sums for treatment A.

b. List the possible values of R and their corresponding probabilities. (Assume that the rows of the table from part (a) are equally likely.)

c. Is it possible, at the 0.10 significance level, to reject the null hypothesis that there is no difference between treatments A and B? Explain.

13-5 Kruskal-Wallis Test for Three or More Samples

Key Concept This section describes the *Kruskal-Wallis test,* which uses *ranks* of data from three or more independent simple random samples to test the null hypothesis that the samples come from populations with the same median.

Section 12-1 described one-way analysis of variance (ANOVA) as a method for testing the null hypothesis that three or more populations have the same *mean*, but that ANOVA procedure requires that all of the involved populations have normal distributions. The Kruskal-Wallis test for equal *medians* does not require normal distributions, so it is a distribution-free or nonparametric test.

> **DEFINITION**
>
> The **Kruskal-Wallis test** (also called the **H test**) is a nonparametric test that uses ranks of combined simple random samples from three or more independent populations to test the null hypothesis that the populations have the same median. (The alternative hypothesis is the claim that the populations have medians that are not all equal.)

In applying the Kruskal-Wallis test, we compute the test statistic H, which has a distribution that can be approximated by the chi-square distribution provided that each sample has at least five observations. (For a quick review of the key features of the chi-square distribution, see Section 7-3.)

The H test statistic measures the variance of the rank sums $R_1, R_2, \ldots, R_k$ from the different samples. If the ranks are distributed evenly among the sample groups, then H should be a relatively small number. If the samples are very different, then the ranks will be excessively low in some groups and high in others, with the net effect that H will be large. Consequently, only large values of H lead to rejection of the null hypothesis that the samples come from identical populations. *The Kruskal-Wallis test is therefore a right-tailed test.*

KEY ELEMENTS

Kruskal-Wallis Test

Objective

Use the Kruskal-Wallis test with simple random samples from three or more independent populations for the following null and alternative hypotheses:

H_0: The samples come from populations with the same median.

H_1: The samples come from populations with medians that are not all equal.

Notation

N = total number of observations in all samples combined
k = number of different samples
R_1 = sum of ranks for Sample 1
n_1 = number of observations in Sample 1

For Sample 2, the sum of ranks is R_2 and the number of observations is n_2, and similar notation is used for the other samples.

Requirements

1. We have at least three independent simple random samples.

2. Each sample has at least five observations. (If samples have fewer than five observations, refer to special tables of critical values, such as *CRC Standard Probability*

and Statistics Tables and Formulae, published by CRC Press.)

Note: There is *no* requirement that the populations have a normal distribution or any other particular distribution.

continued

Test Statistic

$$H = \frac{12}{N(N+1)}\left(\frac{R_1^2}{n_1} + \frac{R_2^2}{n_2} + \cdots + \frac{R_k^2}{n_k}\right) - 3(N+1)$$

P-Values

P-values are often provided by technology. By using the test statistic H and the number of degrees of freedom $(k-1)$, Table A-4 can be used to find a range of values for the P-value.

Critical Values

1. The test is *right-tailed* and critical values can be found from technology or from the chi-square distribution in Table A-4.

2. df $= k - 1$ (where df is the number of degrees of freedom and k is the number of different samples)

Procedure for Finding the Value of the H Test Statistic To see how the following steps are applied, refer to the sample data in Table 13-6. Table 13-6 includes only some of the head injury data from Data Set 35 "Car Data." This shortened data set is more suitable for illustrating the method of the Kruskal-Wallis test.

Step 1: Temporarily combine all samples into one big sample and assign a rank to each sample value. (Sort the values from lowest to highest, and in cases of ties, assign to each observation the mean of the ranks involved.)

EXAMPLE: In Table 13-6, the numbers in parentheses are the ranks of the combined data set. The rank of 1 is assigned to the lowest value of 90, the rank of 2 is assigned to the next lowest value of 114, and so on. In the case of ties, each of the tied values is assigned the mean of the ranks involved in the tie. (The seventh and eighth values are tied at 178, so they are each assigned a rank of 7.5.)

Step 2: For each sample, find the sum of the ranks and find the sample size.

EXAMPLE: In Table 13-6, the sum of the ranks from the first sample is 110, the sum of the ranks for the second sample is 47.5, and the sum of the ranks for the third sample is 32.5.

Step 3: Calculate H using the results of Step 2 and the notation and test statistic given in the preceding Key Elements box.

EXAMPLE: The test statistic is computed in Example 1.

TABLE 13-6 Head Injury Criterion (HIC) Measurements in Car Crash Tests (Ranks in parentheses)

Small	Midsize	Large
253 **(14)**	117 **(3)**	249 **(13)**
143 **(6)**	121 **(4)**	90 **(1)**
124 **(5)**	204 **(12)**	178 **(7.5)**
301 **(17)**	195 **(11)**	114 **(2)**
422 **(19)**	186 **(10)**	183 **(9)**
324 **(18)**	178 **(7.5)**	
258 **(15)**		
271 **(16)**		
$n_1 = 8$	$n_2 = 6$	$n_3 = 5$
$R_1 = 110$	$R_2 = 47.5$	$R_3 = 32.5$

EXAMPLE 1 Head Injuries in Small, Midsize, and Large Cars

Table 13-6 lists head injury criterion (HIC) measurements of small, midsize, and large car crash tests. Use a 0.05 significance level to test the claim that the three samples of HIC measurements are from populations with medians that are all equal.

REQUIREMENT CHECK (1) Each of the three samples is a simple random independent sample. (2) Each sample size is at least 5. The requirements are satisfied. ☑
The null and alternative hypotheses are as follows:

H_0: The populations of small cars, midsize cars, and large cars all have the same median HIC measurement in crash tests.

H_1: The three populations of small, midsize, and large cars have median HIC measurements that are not all the same.

Test Statistic First combine all of the sample data and rank them, then find the sum of the ranks for each category. In Table 13-6, ranks are shown in parentheses next to the original sample values. Next, find the sample size (n) and sum of ranks (R) for each sample. Those values are shown at the bottom of Table 13-6. Because the total number of observations is 19, we have $N = 19$. We can now evaluate the test statistic as follows:

$$H = \frac{12}{N(N+1)}\left(\frac{R_1^2}{n_1} + \frac{R_2^2}{n_2} + \cdots + \frac{R_k^2}{n_k}\right) - 3(N+1)$$

$$= \frac{12}{19(19+1)}\left(\frac{110^2}{8} + \frac{47.5^2}{6} + \frac{32.5^2}{5}\right) - 3(19+1)$$

$$= 6.309$$

Because each sample has at least five observations, the distribution of H is approximately a chi-square distribution with $k - 1$ degrees of freedom. The number of samples is $k = 3$, so we have $3 - 1 = 2$ degrees of freedom.

P-Value With $H = 6.309$ and df $= 2$, Table A-4 shows that the P-value is less than 0.05. Using technology, we get P-value $= 0.043$. Because the P-value is less than the significance level of 0.05, we reject the null hypothesis of equal population medians.

Critical Value Refer to Table A-4 to find the critical value of 5.991, which corresponds to 2 degrees of freedom and a 0.05 significance level (with an area of 0.05 in the right tail). In this right-tailed test with test statistic $H = 6.309$ and critical value of 5.991, the test statistic does exceed the critical value, so it does fall within the critical region. We reject the null hypothesis of equal population medians.

INTERPRETATION

There is sufficient evidence to reject the claim that the three samples of HIC measurements come from populations with medians that are all equal. At least one of the population medians appears to be different from the others.

YOUR TURN. Do Exercise 5 "HIC Measurements."

Rationale: The Kruskal-Wallis H test statistic is the rank version of the F test statistic used in analysis of variance discussed in Chapter 12. When we deal with ranks R instead of original values x, many components are predetermined. For example, the sum of all ranks can be expressed as $N(N + 1)/2$, where N is the total number of values in all samples combined. The expression

$$H = \frac{12}{N(N + 1)} \Sigma n_i (\overline{R}_i - \overline{\overline{R}})^2$$

where

$$\overline{R}_i = \frac{R_i}{n_i} \quad and \quad \overline{\overline{R}} = \frac{\Sigma R_i}{\Sigma n_i}$$

combines weighted variances of ranks to produce the H test statistic given here, and this expression for H is algebraically equivalent to the expression for H given earlier as the test statistic.

TECH CENTER

Kruskal-Wallis Test

Access tech supplements, videos, and data sets at **www.TriolaStats.com**

Statdisk	Minitab	StatCrunch
1. Click **Analysis** in the top menu. 2. Select **Kruskal-Wallis Test** from the dropdown menu. 3. Enter a significance level and select the columns to be included in the analysis. 4. Click **Evaluate**.	1. List all of the sample data in column *C1* and identify the sample (using names or numbers) for the corresponding value in a second column *C2*. • For the data of Table 13-6 in this section, enter the 19 sample values in *C1* and in *C2* enter eight *1*s followed by six *2*s followed by five *3*s. 2. Click **Stat** in the top menu. 3. Select **Nonparametrics** from the dropdown menu and select **Kruskal-Wallis** from the submenu. 4. For *Response* select column **C1** and for *Factor* select column **C2**. 5. Click **OK**.	1. Click **Stat** in the top menu. 2. Select **Nonparametrics** in the dropdown menu and **Kruskal-Wallis** in the submenu. 3. Select the columns to be used in the analysis. 4. Check **Adjust for ties** under *Options*. 5. Click **Compute!** *TIP: Checking Adjust for ties provides more accurate results that may be different from those in this section of the textbook.*

TI-83/84 Plus Calculator

Requires programs *KWTEST* and *ZZRANK* (available at TriolaStats.com)

1. Data must be entered as columns in *Matrix A*:
   Manually enter data: Press **2ND** then **x⁻¹** to get to the *MATRIX* menu, select **EDIT** from the top menu, select **[A]**, and press **ENTER**.
   Enter the number of rows and columns needed, press **ENTER**, and proceed to enter the sample values.

   Using existing lists: Lists can be combined and stored in *Matrix A*. Press **2ND** then **x⁻¹** to get to the *MATRIX* menu, select **MATH** from the top menu, and select the item **List → matr**. Enter the list names followed by the matrix name **[A]**, all separated by commas. *Important:* The matrix name must be entered by pressing **2ND** then **x⁻¹**, selecting **[A]**, and pressing **ENTER**. The following is a summary of the commands used to create a matrix from three lists (*L1, L2, L3*): **List → matr(L1, L2, L3, [A])**.

2. Press **PRGM**, select **KWTEST**, and press **ENTER** twice. The value of the H test statistic and the number of degrees of freedom will be provided. Refer to Table A-4 to find the critical value.

TIP: If the samples have different sizes, some of the matrix entries will be zeros. If any of the original data values are zero, add some convenient constant to all of the sample values so that no zeros are present among the original data values.

TECH CENTER *continued*

 Kruskal-Wallis Test

Access tech supplements, videos, and data sets at **www.TriolaStats.com**

Excel
XLSTAT Add-In (Required)
1. Click the **XLSTAT** tab in the Ribbon and click **Nonparametric tests.**
2. Select **Comparison of k samples** from the dropdown menu.
3. In the *Samples* box enter the data range for the sample values. If the range includes labels, check the **Column labels** box.
4. Select **One column per sample** under *Data format.*
5. Check the **Kruskal-Wallis test** option only.
6. Click the **Options** tab, enter a significance level and check the **Asymptotic p-value** box.
7. Click the **Missing Data** tab and select *Ignore missing data* if the data samples do not have an equal number of observations.
8. Click **OK.**

R
R command: **kruskal.test(list(*x*, *y*, *z*))**
A complete list of R statistical commands is available at TriolaStats.com

13-5 Basic Skills and Concepts

Statistical Literacy and Critical Thinking

1. HIC Measurements Listed below are head injury criterion (HIC) measurements from crash tests of small, midsize, large, and SUV vehicles. In using the Kruskal-Wallis test, we must rank all of the data combined, and then we must find the sum of the ranks for each sample. Find the sum of the ranks for each of the four samples.

Small	29	31	35	33	26	32	21
Midsize	32	28	26	23	25		
Large	27	32	39	27	31	26	
SUV	24	31	31	25	30	39	22

2. Requirements Assume that we want to use the data from Exercise 1 with the Kruskal-Wallis test. Are the requirements satisfied? Explain.

3. Notation For the data given in Exercise 1, identify the values of n_1, n_2, n_3, and N.

4. Efficiency Refer to Table 13-2 on page 645 and identify the efficiency of the Kruskal-Wallis test. What does that value tell us about the test?

Using the Kruskal-Wallis Test. *In Exercises 5–8, use the Kruskal-Wallis test.*

5. HIC Measurements Use the sample data from Exercise 1 with a 0.05 significance level to test the claim that small, midsize, large, and SUV vehicles have the same median HIC measurement in car crash tests.

6. Arsenic in Rice Listed below are amounts of arsenic in samples of brown rice from three different states. The amounts are in micrograms of arsenic and all samples have the same serving size. The data are from the Food and Drug Administration. Use a 0.01 significance level to test the claim that the three samples are from populations with the same median.

Arkansas	4.8	4.9	5.0	5.4	5.4	5.4	5.6	5.6	5.6	5.9	6.0	6.1
California	1.5	3.7	4.0	4.5	4.9	5.1	5.3	5.4	5.4	5.5	5.6	5.6
Texas	5.6	5.8	6.6	6.9	6.9	6.9	7.1	7.3	7.5	7.6	7.7	7.7

7. Clancy, Rowling, and Tolstoy Ease of Reading Pages were randomly selected from three books: *The Bear and the Dragon* by Tom Clancy, *Harry Potter and the Sorcerer's Stone* by J. K. Rowling, and *War and Peace* by Leo Tolstoy. Listed below are Flesch Reading Ease Scores for those pages. Higher scores correspond to pages that are easier to read. Use a 0.01 significance level to test the claim that pages from books by those three authors have the same median Flesch Reading Ease score.

Clancy	58.2	73.4	73.1	64.4	72.7	89.2	43.9	76.3	76.4	78.9	69.4	72.9
Rowling	85.3	84.3	79.5	82.5	80.2	84.6	79.2	70.9	78.6	86.2	74.0	83.7
Tolstoy	69.4	64.2	71.4	71.6	68.5	51.9	72.2	74.4	52.8	58.4	65.4	73.6

8. Clancy, Rowling, and Tolstoy Characters Per Word Numbers of characters per word were found from the same three books used in the preceding exercise. These data are shown below. Use a 0.05 significance level to test the claim that the three books have the same median number of characters per word. Does it appear that any of the authors use longer words?

Clancy	4.8	4.5	4.6	4.5	4.0	4.0	4.6	4.5	4.4	4.4	4.3	4.3
Rowling	4.1	4.2	4.2	4.4	4.3	4.2	4.5	4.5	4.3	4.0	4.4	4.3
Tolstoy	4.3	4.5	4.5	4.5	4.5	4.8	4.3	4.2	4.7	4.3	4.4	4.5

Appendix B Data Sets.   *In Exercises 9–12, use the Kruskal-Wallis test with the data set in Appendix B.*

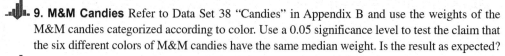 **9. M&M Candies** Refer to Data Set 38 "Candies" in Appendix B and use the weights of the M&M candies categorized according to color. Use a 0.05 significance level to test the claim that the six different colors of M&M candies have the same median weight. Is the result as expected?

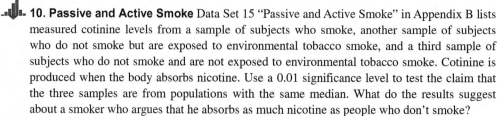 **10. Passive and Active Smoke** Data Set 15 "Passive and Active Smoke" in Appendix B lists measured cotinine levels from a sample of subjects who smoke, another sample of subjects who do not smoke but are exposed to environmental tobacco smoke, and a third sample of subjects who do not smoke and are not exposed to environmental tobacco smoke. Cotinine is produced when the body absorbs nicotine. Use a 0.01 significance level to test the claim that the three samples are from populations with the same median. What do the results suggest about a smoker who argues that he absorbs as much nicotine as people who don't smoke?

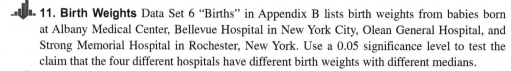 **11. Birth Weights** Data Set 6 "Births" in Appendix B lists birth weights from babies born at Albany Medical Center, Bellevue Hospital in New York City, Olean General Hospital, and Strong Memorial Hospital in Rochester, New York. Use a 0.05 significance level to test the claim that the four different hospitals have different birth weights with different medians.

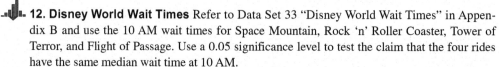 **12. Disney World Wait Times** Refer to Data Set 33 "Disney World Wait Times" in Appendix B and use the 10 AM wait times for Space Mountain, Rock 'n' Roller Coaster, Tower of Terror, and Flight of Passage. Use a 0.05 significance level to test the claim that the four rides have the same median wait time at 10 AM.

13-5   Beyond the Basics

13. Correcting the *H* Test Statistic for Ties In using the Kruskal-Wallis test, there is a correction factor that should be applied whenever there are many ties: Divide *H* by

$$1 - \frac{\Sigma T}{N^3 - N}$$

First combine all of the sample data into one list, and then, in that combined list, identify the different groups of sample values that are tied. For each individual group of tied observations, identify the *number* of sample values that are tied and designate that number as *t*; then calculate $T = t^3 - t$. Next, add the *T* values to get ΣT. The value of *N* is the total number of observations in all samples combined.

Listed below are performance (non-verbal) IQ scores from samples of subjects with low blood lead level, medium blood lead level, and high blood lead level (from Data Set 11 "IQ and Lead" in Appendix B). For the test of equal medians, find the value of the test statistic H using the methods of this section, and then find the corrected value of H using the above correction factor. Does the corrected value of H differ substantially from the uncorrected value?

Low	85	90	107	85	100	97	101	64
Medium	78	97	107	80	90	83		
High	93	100	97	79	97			

13-6 Rank Correlation

Key Concept This section describes the nonparametric method of the *rank correlation test,* which uses *ranks* of paired data to test for an association between two variables. In Section 10-1, paired sample data were used to compute values for the linear correlation coefficient r, but in this section we use *ranks* as the basis for computing the rank correlation coefficient r_s. As in Chapter 10, we should begin an analysis of paired data by exploring with a scatterplot so that we can identify any patterns in the data as well as outliers.

> **DEFINITION**
>
> The **rank correlation test** (or **Spearman's rank correlation test**) is a nonparametric test that uses ranks of sample data consisting of matched pairs. It is used to test for an association between two variables.

We use the notation r_s for the rank correlation coefficient so that we don't confuse it with the linear correlation coefficient r. The subscript s does *not* refer to a standard deviation; it is used in honor of Charles Spearman (1863–1945), who originated the rank correlation approach. In fact, r_s is often called **Spearman's rank correlation coefficient.** Key components of the rank correlation test are given in the following Key Elements box, and the procedure is summarized in Figure 13-4 on page 679.

KEY ELEMENTS

Rank Correlation

Objective

Compute the rank correlation coefficient r_s and use it to test for an association between two variables. The null and alternative hypotheses are as follows:

H_0: $\rho_s = 0$ (There is no correlation.)

H_1: $\rho_s \neq 0$ (There is a correlation.)

Notation

r_s = rank correlation coefficient for sample paired data (r_s is a sample statistic)

ρ_s = rank correlation coefficient for all the population data (ρ_s is a population parameter)

n = number of pairs of sample data

d = difference between ranks for the two values within an individual pair

continued

Requirements

1. The paired data are a simple random sample.
2. The data are ranks or can be converted to ranks.

Note: Unlike the parametric methods of Section 10-1, there is *no* requirement that the sample pairs of data have a bivariate normal distribution (as described in Section 10-1). There is *no* requirement of a normal distribution for any population.

Test Statistic

Within each sample, first convert the data to *ranks,* then find the exact value of the rank correlation coefficient r_s by using Formula 10-1:

FORMULA 10-1

$$r_s = \frac{n(\Sigma xy) - (\Sigma x)(\Sigma y)}{\sqrt{n(\Sigma x^2) - (\Sigma x)^2}\sqrt{n(\Sigma y^2) - (\Sigma y)^2}}$$

Simpler Test Statistic if There Are No Ties: After converting the data in each sample to ranks, if there are no ties among ranks for the first variable and there are no ties among ranks for the second variable, the exact value of the test statistic can be calculated using Formula 10-1 or with the following relatively simple formula, but it is probably easier to use Formula 10-1 with technology:

$$r_s = 1 - \frac{6\Sigma d^2}{n(n^2 - 1)}$$

P-Values

P-values are sometimes provided by technology, but use them only if they result from Spearman's rank correlation. (*Caution: Do not use P-values from linear correlation for methods of rank correlation.* When working with data having ties among ranks, the rank correlation coefficient r_s can be calculated using Formula 10-1. Technology can be used instead of manual calculations with Formula 10-1, but the displayed *P*-values from *linear* correlation do not apply to the methods of *rank* correlation.)

Critical Values

1. If $n \leq 30$, critical values are found in Table A-9.

2. If $n > 30$, critical values of r_s are found using Formula 13-1.

FORMULA 13-1

$$r_s = \frac{\pm z}{\sqrt{n - 1}} \quad (\text{critical values for } n > 30)$$

where the value of z corresponds to the significance level. (For example, if $\alpha = 0.05$, $z = 1.96$.)

Advantages of Rank Correlation: Rank correlation has these advantages over the parametric methods discussed in Chapter 10:

1. Rank correlation can be used with paired data that are ranks or can be converted to ranks. Unlike the parametric methods of Chapter 10, the method of rank correlation does *not* require a normal distribution for any population.

2. Rank correlation can be used to detect some (not all) relationships that are not linear.

Disadvantage of Rank Correlation: Efficiency A minor disadvantage of rank correlation is its efficiency rating of 0.91, as described in Section 13-1. This efficiency rating shows that with all other circumstances being equal, the nonparametric approach of rank correlation requires 100 pairs of sample data to achieve the same results as only 91 pairs of sample observations analyzed through the parametric approach, assuming that the stricter requirements of the parametric approach are met.

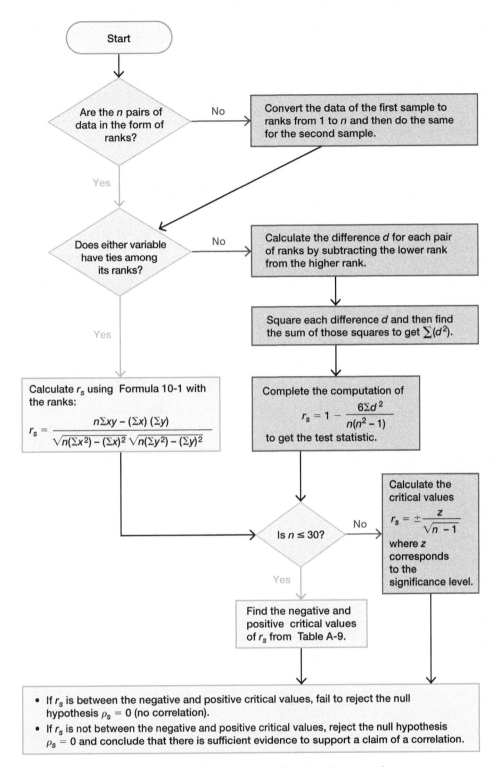

FIGURE 13-4   Rank Correlation Procedure for Testing H_0: $\rho_s = 0$

CP ┤ **EXAMPLE 1** Do Better Smartphones Cost More?

Table 13-1 from the Chapter Problem lists ranks and costs (dollars) of smartphones (based on data from *Consumer Reports*). Lower ranks correspond to better smartphones. Find the value of the rank correlation coefficient and use it to determine whether there is sufficient evidence to support the claim of a correlation between quality and price. Use a 0.05 significance level. Based on the result, does it appear that you get a better quality smartphone by spending more?

TABLE 13-1 Ranks and Costs of Smartphones

Quality Rank	1	2	3	4	5	6	7	8	9	10
Cost (dollars)	1000	1100	900	1000	750	1000	900	700	750	600

SOLUTION

REQUIREMENT CHECK The sample data are a simple random sample from the smartphones that were tested. The data are ranks or can be converted to ranks. ☑

The quality ranks are consecutive integers and are not from a population that is normally distributed, so we use the rank correlation coefficient instead of the linear correlation coefficient to test for a relationship between quality and price. The null and alternative hypotheses are as follows:

$$H_0: \rho_s = 0 \text{ (There is } no \text{ correlation between quality and price.)}$$

$$H_1: \rho_s \neq 0 \text{ (There is a correlation between quality and price.)}$$

Following the procedure of Figure 13-4, we begin by converting the costs in Table 13-1 into their corresponding ranks shown in Table 13-7. The lowest cost of $600 in Table 13-1 is assigned a rank of 1, the next lowest cost of $700 is assigned a rank of 2, and so on. When ties occur, each of the tied values is assigned the mean of the ranks involved in the tie. For example, there are two costs of $750 and they are tied for the ranks of 3 and 4, so they are both assigned a rank of 3.5. The ranks corresponding to the costs from Table 13-1 are shown in the second row of Table 13-7.

TABLE 13-7 Ranks of All Data from Table 13-1

Quality Rank	1	2	3	4	5	6	7	8	9	10
Cost Rank	8	10	5.5	8	3.5	8	5.5	2	3.5	1

Because there are ties among ranks, we must use Formula 10-1 to find that the rank correlation coefficient r_s is equal to -0.796.

FORMULA 10-1

$$r_s = \frac{n\Sigma xy - (\Sigma x)(\Sigma y)}{\sqrt{n(\Sigma x^2) - (\Sigma x)^2}\sqrt{n(\Sigma y^2) - (\Sigma y)^2}}$$

$$= \frac{10(238) - (55)(55)}{\sqrt{10(385) - (55)^2}\sqrt{10(382) - (55)^2}} = -0.796$$

Now we refer to Table A-9 to find the critical values of ± 0.648 (based on $\alpha = 0.05$ and $n = 10$). Because the test statistic $r_s = -0.796$ is outside of the range between the critical values of -0.648 and 0.648, we reject the null hypothesis. There is sufficient evidence to support a claim of a correlation between quality and cost. It appears that you do get better quality by paying more, but this conclusion incorrectly implies causation.

↱ **YOUR TURN.** Do Exercise 7 "Colombian Coffee."

EXAMPLE 2   Large Sample Case

Example 1 used a sample size of $n = 10$, but if we use 33 smartphones, we get the following costs (dollars) that correspond to ranks of 1 through 33, respectively. Use a 0.05 significance level to test the claim that there is a correlation between the quality rank and the costs of these smartphones.

1000	1100	900	1000	750	1000	900	700	750	600	550
700	600	470	900	850	800	400	400	800	490	470
230	850	500	255	800	400	330	800	550	850	120

SOLUTION

REQUIREMENT CHECK   The data are a simple random sample and can be converted to ranks. ☑

Test Statistic The value of the rank correlation coefficient is $r_s = -0.572$, which can be found by using technology.

Critical Values Because there are 33 pairs of data, we have $n = 33$. Because n exceeds 30, we find the critical values from Formula 13-1 instead of Table A-9. With $\alpha = 0.05$ in two tails, we let $z = 1.96$ to get the critical values of -0.346 and 0.346, as shown below.

$$r_s = \frac{\pm z}{\sqrt{n-1}} = \frac{\pm 1.96}{\sqrt{33-1}} = \pm 0.346$$

The test statistic of $r_s = -0.572$ falls outside of the range between the critical values of -0.346 and 0.346, so we reject the null hypothesis of $r_s = 0$. There is sufficient evidence to support the claim that there is a correlation between costs of smartphones and their quality.

 **YOUR TURN.** Do Exercise 13 "Taxis."

Detecting Nonlinear Patterns *Rank correlation* methods sometimes allow us to detect relationships that we cannot detect with the *linear correlation* methods of Chapter 10. See scatterplot on the following page, which shows an S-shaped pattern of points suggesting that there is a correlation between x and y. The methods of Chapter 10 result in the linear correlation coefficient of $r = 0.627$ and critical values of ± 0.632, suggesting that there is not sufficient evidence to support the claim of a linear correlation between x and y. If we use rank correlation and the methods of this section, we get $r = 0.997$ and critical values of ± 0.648, suggesting that there is sufficient evidence to support the claim of a correlation between x and y. Linear correlation missed it, but rank correlation recognized it.

With rank correlation, we can sometimes detect relationships that are not linear.

Direct Link Between Smoking and Cancer

When we find a statistical correlation between two variables, we must be extremely careful to avoid the mistake of concluding that there is a cause-effect link. The tobacco industry has consistently emphasized that correlation does not imply causality as they denied that tobacco products cause cancer. However, Dr. David Sidransky of Johns Hopkins University and other researchers found a direct physical link that involves mutations of a specific gene among smokers. Molecular analysis of genetic changes allows researchers to determine whether cigarette smoking is the cause of a cancer. (See "Association Between Cigarette Smoking and Mutation of the p53 Gene in Squamous-Cell Carcinoma of the Head and Neck," by Brennan, Boyle, et al., *New England Journal of Medicine*, Vol 332, No. 11.) Although statistical methods cannot prove that smoking *causes* cancer, statistical methods can be used to identify an association, and physical proof of causation can then be sought by researchers.

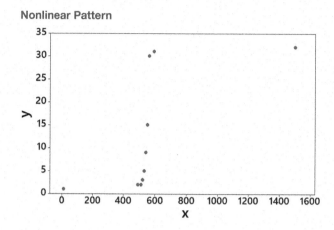

Nonlinear Pattern

TECH CENTER

Rank Correlation

Access tech supplements, videos, and data sets at **www.TriolaStats.com**

Statdisk	Minitab	StatCrunch
1. Click **Analysis** from the top menu.	1. Enter the paired data in columns *C1* and *C2*.	1. Click **Stat** in the top menu.
2. Select **Rank Correlation** from the dropdown menu.	2. Click **Stat** in the top menu.	2. Select **Nonparametrics** from the dropdown menu and **Spearman's Correlation** from the submenu.
3. Enter a significance level and select the two data columns to be included.	3. Select **Basic Statistics** from the dropdown menu and select **Correlation** from the submenu.	3. Select the columns to be used in the analysis.
4. Click **Evaluate.**	4. Select the columns *C1* and *C2* to be included under *Variables*.	4. Under *Display* check **Two-sided P-value.**
	5. Click the **Options** button, select **Spearman correlation** for *Method* and enter the desired confidence level.	5. Click **Compute!**
	6. Click **OK** twice.	

TI-83/84 Plus Calculator

The TI-83/84 Plus calculator is not designed to calculate rank correlation, but we can replace each value with its corresponding rank and calculate the value of the linear correlation coefficient r.

1. Replace each sample value with its corresponding rank and enter the paired ranks in lists *L1* and *L2*.
2. Press **STAT**, then select **TESTS** in the top menu.
3. Select **LinRegTTest** in the menu and press **ENTER**.
4. Enter the list names for the *x* and *y* variables. Enter **1** for *Freq* and for β & ρ select $\neq$ **0** to test the null hypothesis of no correlation.
5. Select **Calculate** and press **ENTER**. Because the calculation of *r* is done using ranks, the value shown as *r* is actually the rank correlation coefficient r_s. Ignore the *P*-value because it is using the methods of Chapter 10, not the methods of this section.

TECH CENTER *continued*

 Rank Correlation
Access tech supplements, videos, and data sets at **www.TriolaStats.com**

Excel

XLSTAT Add-In
1. Click on the **XLSTAT** tab in the Ribbon and then click **Correlation/Association tests.**
2. Select **Correlation tests** from the dropdown menu.
3. For **Observations/Quantitative variables** enter the cell range for the data values. If the data range includes a data label, check the **Variable labels** box.
4. For *Type of correlation* select **Spearman.**
5. Enter the desired significance level.
6. Click **OK.** The rank correlation coefficient is displayed in the *Correlation Matrix.* If the value displayed is in **bold font,** we can reject the claim of no correlation.

Excel
Excel does not have a function that calculates the rank correlation coefficient from the original sample values, but the following procedure can be used.
1. Replace each of the original sample values with its corresponding rank.
2. Click **Insert Function f_x,** select the category **Statistical,** select the function **CORREL,** and click **OK.**
3. For *Array1* enter the data range for the first variable. For *Array2* enter the data range for the second variable.
4. Click **OK** for the rank correlation coefficient r_s.

R

R command:
cor.test(x, y, method = "spearman")

A complete list of R statistical commands is available at TriolaStats.com

13-6 Basic Skills and Concepts

Statistical Literacy and Critical Thinking

1. Lottery Tickets Sold and Jackpot Amounts The following table includes the same paired data used for the Chapter Problem at the beginning of Chapter 10. The table lists paired data consisting of Powerball lottery jackpot amounts (millions of dollars) and numbers of lottery tickets sold (millions). Convert the data to ranks that would be used for finding the rank correlation coefficient.

Jackpot	334	127	300	227	202	180	164	145	255
Tickets	54	16	41	27	23	18	18	16	26

2. Rank Correlation Use the ranks from Exercise 1 to find the value of the rank correlation coefficient. Also, use a 0.05 significance level and find the critical value of the rank correlation coefficient. What do you conclude about correlation?

3. Notation What do r, r_s, ρ, and ρ_s denote? Why is the subscript s used? Does the subscript s represent the same standard deviation s introduced in Section 3-2?

4. Efficiency Refer to Table 13-2 on page 645 and identify the efficiency of the rank correlation test. What does that value tell us about the test?

In Exercises 5 and 6, use the scatterplot to find the value of the rank correlation coefficient r_s and the critical values corresponding to a 0.05 significance level used to test the null hypothesis of $\rho_s = 0$. Determine whether there is a correlation.

5. Altitude and Temperature Shown below is a scatterplot of altitudes (thousands of feet) and outside air temperatures (degrees Fahrenheit) recorded by the author during a Delta flight from New Orleans to Atlanta.

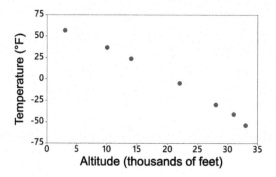

6. First Moon Landing Shown below is a scatterplot of vertical distance traveled (meters) and time of travel (seconds) during the final descent of the Apollo 11 Lunar Module when it first landed on the Moon.

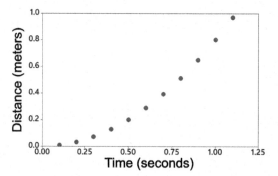

Testing for Rank Correlation. *In Exercises 7–12, use the rank correlation coefficient to test for a correlation between the two variables. Use a significance level of $\alpha = 0.05$.*

7. Colombian Coffee The following table lists quality rankings and costs (dollars) for a pound of different brands of Colombian coffee (based on data from *Consumer Reports*). Lower values of the quality rankings correspond to better coffee. Do the more expensive brands appear to have better quality?

Rank	1	2	3	4	5	6	7	8	9	10
Cost	23	16	10	25	14	9	13	5	9	11

8. Computers The following table lists quality rankings and costs (dollars) for different brands of laptop computers with 12 in. or 13 in. screens (based on data from *Consumer Reports*). Lower values of the quality rankings correspond to better computers. Do the more expensive brands appear to have better quality?

Rank	1	2	3	4	5	6	7	8	9	10
Cost	1800	950	1265	1260	1200	1500	1200	880	1600	800

9. Measuring Seals from Photos Listed below are the overhead widths (cm) of seals measured from photographs and the weights of the seals (kg). The data are based on "Mass Estimation of Weddell Seals Using Techniques of Photogrammetry," by R. Garrott of Montana State University.

The purpose of the study was to determine if weights of seals could be determined from overhead photographs. Is there sufficient evidence to conclude that there is a correlation between overhead widths and the weights of the seals?

Overhead width (cm)	7.2	7.4	9.8	9.4	8.8	8.4
Weight (kg)	116	154	245	202	200	191

10. Cheese and Engineering Listed below are annual data for various years. The data are weights (pounds) of per capita consumption of mozzarella cheese and the numbers of civil engineering PhD degrees awarded (based on data from the U.S. Department of Agriculture and the National Science Foundation). Is there sufficient evidence to conclude that there is a correlation between the two variables? What important comment should be made about the conclusion?

Cheese Consumption	9.3	9.7	9.7	9.7	9.9	10.2	10.5	11.0	10.6	10.6
Civil Engineering PhDs	480	501	540	552	547	622	655	701	712	708

11. POTUS Media periodically discuss the issue of heights of winning presidential candidates and heights of their main opponents. Listed below are those heights (cm) from several recent presidential elections (from Data Set 22 "Presidents" in Appendix B). Is there sufficient evidence to conclude that there is a correlation between heights of winning presidential candidates and heights of their main opponents? Should there be such a correlation?

President	192	182	177	185	188	188	183	188	191
Opponent	180	180	183	177	173	188	185	175	169

12. Crickets and Temperature The association between the temperature and the number of times a cricket chirps in 1 min was studied. Listed below are the numbers of chirps in 1 min and the corresponding temperatures in degrees Fahrenheit (based on data from *The Song of Insects* by George W. Pierce, Harvard University Press). Is there sufficient evidence to conclude that there is a relationship between the number of chirps in 1 min and the temperature?

Chirps in 1 min	882	1188	1104	864	1200	1032	960	900
Temperature (°F)	69.7	93.3	84.3	76.3	88.6	82.6	71.6	79.6

Appendix B Data Sets. *In Exercises 13–16, use the data in Appendix B to test for rank correlation with a 0.05 significance level.*

13. Taxis Refer to Data Set 32 "Taxis" in Appendix B and use the distances (miles) and tip amounts (dollars) of all of the rides. Is there sufficient evidence to support the claim that there is a correlation between the distance of the ride and the tip amount? Does it appear that riders base their tips on the distance of the ride?

14. Taxis Refer to Data Set 32 "Taxis" in Appendix B and use the distances (miles) and the times (minutes) of all of the rides. Is there sufficient evidence to support the claim that there is a correlation between the distance of the ride and the time of the ride?

15. Ages of Best Actresses and Best Actors Use the ages of Best Actresses and Best Actors at the times they won Oscars (from Data Set 21 "Oscar Winner Age" in Appendix B). Do these data suggest that there is a correlation between ages of Best Actresses and Best Actors?

16. IQ and Brain Volume Refer to Data Set 12 "IQ and Brain Size" in Appendix B and test for a correlation between brain volume (cm^3) and IQ score.

13-6 Beyond the Basics

 17. Finding Critical Values An alternative to using Table A-9 to find critical values for rank correlation is to compute them using this approximation:

$$r_s = \pm\sqrt{\frac{t^2}{t^2 + n - 2}}$$

Here, t is the critical t value from Table A-3 corresponding to the desired significance level and $n - 2$ degrees of freedom. Use this approximation to find critical values of r_s for Exercise 15 "Ages of Best Actresses and Best Actors." How do the resulting critical values compare to the critical values that would be found by using Formula 13-1 on page 678?

13-7 Runs Test for Randomness

Key Concept This section describes the *runs test for randomness,* which is used to determine whether a sequence of sample data has a random order. This test requires a criterion for categorizing each data value into one of two separate categories, and it analyzes *runs* of those two categories to determine whether the runs appear to result from a random process, or whether the runs suggest that the order of the data is not random.

DEFINITIONS

After characterizing each data value as one of two separate categories, a **run** is a sequence of data having the same characteristic; the sequence is preceded and followed by data with a different characteristic or by no data at all.

The **runs test** uses the number of runs in a sequence of sample data to test for randomness in the order of the data.

Fundamental Principle of the Runs Test

Here is the key idea underlying the runs test:

Reject randomness if the number of runs is very *low* or very *high.*

- Example: The sequence of genders FFFFFMMMMM is not random because it has only 2 runs, so the number of runs is very *low*.

- Example: The sequence of genders FMFMFMFMFM is not random because there are 10 runs, which is very *high*.

The exact criteria for determining whether a number of runs is very high or low are found in the Key Elements box. The procedure for the runs test for randomness is also summarized in Figure 13-5.

CAUTION The runs test for randomness is based on the *order* in which the data occur; it is *not* based on the *frequency* of the data. For example, a sequence of 3 men and 20 women might appear to be random, but the issue of whether 3 men and 20 women constitute a *biased* sample (with disproportionately more women) is *not* addressed by the runs test.

Runs Test for Randomness

Objective

Apply the runs test for randomness to a *sequence* of sample data to test for randomness in the *order* of the data. Use the following null and alternative hypotheses:

H_0: The data are in a random order. H_1: The data are in an order that is not random.

Notation

n_1 = number of elements in the sequence that have one particular characteristic. (The characteristic chosen for n_1 is arbitrary.)

n_2 = number of elements in the sequence that have the other characteristic

G = number of runs

Requirements

1. The sample data are arranged according to some ordering scheme, such as the order in which the sample values were obtained.

2. Each data value can be categorized into one of *two* separate categories (such as male/female).

Test Statistic and Critical Values

For Small Samples and $\alpha = 0.05$: If $n_1 \leq 20$ and $n_2 \leq 20$ and the significance level is $\alpha = 0.05$, the test statistic, critical values, and decision criteria are as follows:

- **Test statistic:** number of runs G

- **Critical values of G:** Use Table A-10.

- **Decision criteria:** Reject randomness if the number of runs G is such that

    - $G \leq$ smaller critical value found in Table A-10.

    - or $G \geq$ larger critical value found in Table A-10.

For Large Samples or $\alpha \neq 0.05$: If $n_1 > 20$ or $n_2 > 20$ or $\alpha \neq 0.05$, the test statistic, critical values, and decision criteria are as follows:

- **Test statistic:** $z = \dfrac{G - \mu_G}{\sigma_G}$

    where $\mu_G = \dfrac{2n_1 n_2}{n_1 + n_2} + 1$

    and $\sigma_G = \sqrt{\dfrac{(2n_1 n_2)\,(2n_1 n_2 - n_1 - n_2)}{(n_1 + n_2)^2 (n_1 + n_2 - 1)}}$

- **Critical values of z:** Use Table A-2.

- **Decision criteria:** Reject randomness if the test statistic z is such that

    - $z \leq$ negative critical z score (such as -1.96).

    - or $z \geq$ positive critical z score (such as 1.96).

Sports Hot Streaks

It is a common belief that athletes often have "hot streaks"— that is, brief periods of extraordinary success. Stanford University psychologist Amos Tversky and other researchers used statistics to analyze the thousands of shots taken by the Philadelphia 76ers for one full season and half of another. They found that the number of "hot streaks" was no different than you would expect from random trials with the outcome of each trial independent of any preceding results. That is, the probability of making a basket doesn't depend on the preceding make or miss.

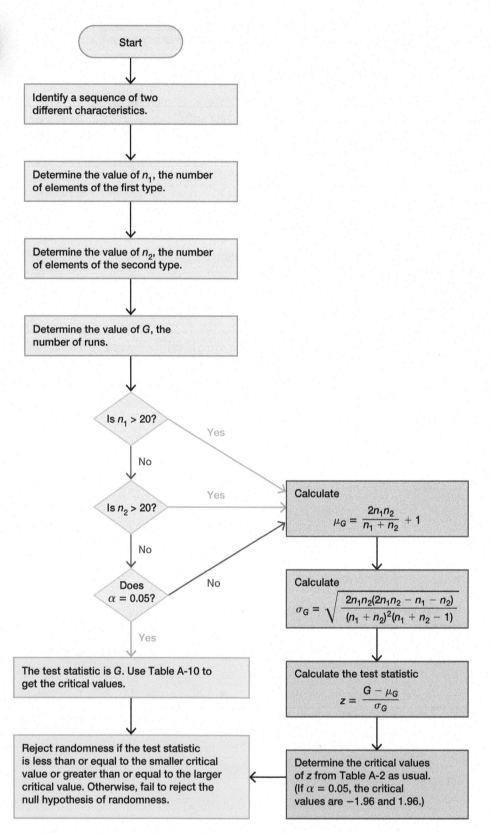

FIGURE 13-5   Procedure for Runs Test for Randomness

Testing for Randomness Above and Below the Mean or Median

Some sequential data are naturally categorized according to two characteristics, such as a sequence of male and female genders from consecutive births. (See Example 1.) Additionally, we can also test for randomness in the way numerical data fluctuate above or below a mean or median. To test for randomness above and below the median, for example, use the sample data to find the value of the median, then replace each individual value with the letter A if it is *above* the median and replace it with B if it is *below* the median. Delete any values that are equal to the median. (It is helpful to write the A's and B's directly above or below the numbers they represent because this makes checking easier and also reduces the chance of having the wrong number of letters.) After finding the sequence of A and B letters, we can proceed to apply the runs test as described earlier. (See Example 2.)

Economists use the runs test for randomness above and below the median to identify trends or cycles. An upward economic trend would contain a predominance of B's at the beginning and A's at the end, so the number of runs would be very small. A downward trend would have A's dominating at the beginning and B's at the end, with a small number of runs. A cyclical pattern would yield a sequence that systematically changes, so the number of runs would tend to be large.

EXAMPLE 1   Small Sample: Political Parties of Presidents

Listed below are the political parties of the past 15 presidents of the United States (as of this writing). The letter R represents a Republican president and the letter D represents a Democratic president. Use a 0.05 significance level to test for randomness in the sequence.

$$\text{R} \quad \text{D} \quad \text{D} \quad \text{R} \quad \text{D} \quad \text{D} \quad \text{R} \quad \text{R} \quad \text{D} \quad \text{R} \quad \text{R} \quad \text{D} \quad \text{R} \quad \text{D} \quad \text{R}$$

SOLUTION

REQUIREMENT CHECK   (1) The data are arranged in order. (2) Each data value is categorized into one of two separate categories (Republican/Democrat). The requirements are satisfied. ✅

We will follow the procedure summarized in Figure 13-5. The sequence of two characteristics (Republican/Democrat) has been identified. We must now find the values of n_1, n_2, and the number of runs G. The sequence is shown below with spacing adjusted to better identify the different runs.

R	DD	R	DD	RR	D	RR	D	R	D	R
1st run	2nd run	3rd run	4th run	5th run	6th run	7th run	8th run	9th run	10th run	11th run

The above display shows that there are 8 Republican presidents and 7 Democratic presidents, and the number of runs is 11. We represent those results with the following notation.

$$n_1 = \text{number of Republican presidents} = 8$$
$$n_2 = \text{number of Democratic presidents} = 7$$
$$G = \text{number of runs} = 11$$

Because $n_1 \leq 20$ and $n_2 \leq 20$ and the significance level is $\alpha = 0.05$, the test statistic is $G = 11$ (the number of runs), and we refer to Table A-10 to find the critical values of 4 and 13. Because $G = 11$ is neither less than or equal to the lower critical value of 4, nor is it greater than or equal to the upper critical value of 13, *we do not reject randomness*. There is not sufficient evidence to reject randomness in the sequence of political parties of recent presidents. Based on the given data, it appears that Republicans and Democrats become presidents in random order.

▶ **YOUR TURN.** Do Exercise 5 "Law Enforcement Fatalities."

EXAMPLE 2 Large Sample: Testing Temperatures for Randomness Above and Below the Mean

Use the following mean global temperatures (°C) for 50 recent and consecutive years to test for randomness above and below the mean. Use a 0.05 significance level. The data are listed in order by row.

13.98	14.10	14.05	14.03	13.65	13.75	13.93	13.98	13.91	14.00
14.04	13.90	13.95	14.18	13.94	13.98	13.79	14.16	14.07	14.13
14.27	14.40	14.10	14.34	14.16	14.13	14.19	14.35	14.42	14.28
14.49	14.44	14.16	14.18	14.31	14.47	14.36	14.40	14.71	14.44
14.41	14.56	14.70	14.64	14.60	14.77	14.64	14.66	14.68	14.70

SOLUTION

REQUIREMENT CHECK (1) The data are arranged in order. (2) Each data value can be categorized into one of two separate categories: below the mean or above the mean. The requirements are satisfied. ☑️

The null and alternative hypotheses are as follows:

$$H_0: \text{The sequence is random.}$$

$$H_1: \text{The sequence is not random.}$$

The mean of those 50 temperatures is 14.250°C. If we replace each temperature with B if it is below the mean and A if it is above the mean, we get the following sequence. For example, the first temperature of 13.98°C is *below* the mean of 14.250°C, so 13.98 is replaced with B.

B	B	B	B	B	B	B	B	B	B
B	B	B	B	B	B	B	B	B	B
A	A	B	A	B	B	B	A	A	A
A	A	B	B	A	A	A	A	A	A
A	A	A	A	A	A	A	A	A	A

Examination of the sequence of B's and A's shows that the letter B occurs 26 times, the letter A occurs 24 times, and the number of runs is 8, so we have the following:

$$n_1 = \text{number of B's} = 26$$

$$n_2 = \text{number of A's} = 24$$

$$G = \text{number of runs} = 8$$

Since, $n_1 > 20$, we need to calculate the test statistic z, so we must first evaluate μ_G and σ_G as follows:

$$\mu_G = \frac{2n_1n_2}{n_1 + n_2} + 1 = \frac{2(26)(24)}{26 + 24} + 1 = 25.96$$

$$\sigma_G = \sqrt{\frac{(2n_1n_2)(2n_1n_2 - n_1 - n_2)}{(n_1 + n_2)^2(n_1 + n_2 - 1)}}$$

$$= \sqrt{\frac{(2)(26)(24)[2(26)(24) - 26 - 24]}{(26 + 24)^2(26 + 24 - 1)}} = 3.49355558$$

We now find the test statistic:

$$z = \frac{G - \mu_G}{\sigma_G} = \frac{8 - 25.96}{3.49355558} = -5.14$$

We can use the test statistic $z = -5.14$ to find that the P-value is 0.000, which is less than the significance level of $\alpha = 0.05$, so we reject the null hypothesis of randomness.

Also, because the significance level is $\alpha = 0.05$ and we have a two-tailed test, the critical values are $z = -1.96$ and $z = 1.96$. The test statistic of $z = -5.14$ does fall within the critical region, so we again reject the null hypothesis of randomness.

INTERPRETATION

We have sufficient evidence to reject randomness of the sequence of 50 mean global temperatures. If we simply examine the list of B's and A's, we see that the B's are mostly in the beginning of the sequence and the A's are mostly at the end, suggesting that over this period of 50 years, the mean global temperature is *increasing*.

 YOUR TURN. Do Exercise 9 "Testing for Randomness of Super Bowl Victories."

TECH CENTER

 ## Runs Test for Randomness
Access tech supplements, videos, and data sets at **www.TriolaStats.com**

Statdisk	Minitab	StatCrunch
1. Determine the number of elements in the first category, the number of elements in the second category, and count the number of runs. 2. Click **Analysis** in the top menu. 3. Select **Runs Test for Randomness** from the dropdown menu. 4. Enter a significance level and the values for number of runs, number of elements in the first category *(Element 1)*, and number of elements in the second category *(Element 2)*. 5. Click **Evaluate.**	*Minitab will do a runs test with a sequence of numerical data only. The Minitab Student Laboratory Manual and Workbook provides additional information on how to circumvent this constraint.* 1. Enter numerical data in column *C1*. 2. Click **Stat** in the top menu. 3. Select **Nonparametrics** from the dropdown menu and select **Runs Test** from the submenu. 4. Select column **C1** under *Variables*. 5. Select to test above and below the mean or enter a desired value to be used. 6. Click **OK.**	Not available.

TI-83/84 Plus Calculator	Excel	R
Not available.	Not available.	**R command not available at time of publication.** *R is rapidly evolving, and an updated list of statistical commands is available at TriolaStats.com.*

13-7 Basic Skills and Concepts

Statistical Literacy and Critical Thinking

*In Exercises 1–4, use the following sequence of political party affiliations of recent presidents of the United States, where **R** represents **Republican** and **D** represents **Democrat**.*

R R R D R D R R R D R R R D D R D D R R D R R D R D R

1. Testing for Bias Can the runs test be used to show the proportion of Republicans is significantly greater than the proportion of Democrats?

2. Notation Identify the values of n_1, n_2, and G that would be used in the runs test for randomness.

3. Runs Test If we use a 0.05 significance level to test for randomness, what are the critical values from Table A-10? Based on those values and the number of runs from Exercise 2, what should be concluded about randomness?

4. Good Sample? Given the sequence of data, if we fail to reject randomness, does it follow that the sampling method is suitable for statistical methods? Explain.

Using the Runs Test for Randomness. *In Exercises 5–8, use the runs test with a significance level of $\alpha = 0.05$. (All data are listed in order by row.)*

5. Law Enforcement Fatalities Listed below are numbers of law enforcement fatalities for recent and consecutive years. First find the median, and then test for randomness above and below the median. Is there a trend?

196	195	162	149	163	158	179	184	140	174	172	146	162	242	159
151	167	166	160	203	159	139	171	185	141	120	148	160	159	129

6. Odd and Even Digits in Pi A *New York Times* article about the calculation of decimal places of π noted that "mathematicians are pretty sure that the digits of π are indistinguishable from any random sequence." Given below are the first 25 decimal places of π. Test for randomness in the way that odd (O) and even (E) digits occur in the sequence. Based on the result, does the statement from the *New York Times* appear to be accurate?

1 4 1 5 9 2 6 5 3 5 8 9 7 9 3 2 3 8 4 6 2 6 4 3 3

7. Draft Lottery In 1970, a lottery was used to determine who would be drafted into the U.S. Army. The 366 dates in the year were placed in individual capsules, they were mixed, and then capsules were selected to identify birth dates of men to be drafted first. The first 30 results are listed below. Test for randomness before and after the middle of the year, which is July 1.

Sept. 14	Apr. 24	Dec. 30	Feb. 14	Oct. 18	Sept. 6	Oct. 26	Sept. 7	Nov. 22
Dec. 6	Aug 31	Dec. 7	July 8	Apr. 11	July 12	Dec. 29	Jan. 15	Sept. 26
Nov. 1	June 4	Aug. 10	June 26	July 24	Oct. 5	Feb. 19	Dec. 14	July 21
June 5	Mar. 2	Mar. 31						

8. CD Sales Listed below are amounts of CD sales in billions of dollars (based on data from the Recording Industry Association of America). The amounts are listed in order by year beginning with the year 1984. First find the mean, identify each value as being above the mean (A) or below the mean (B), then test for randomness above and below the mean. Is there a trend?

0.1	0.4	0.9	1.6	2.1	2.6	3.5	4.3	5.3	6.5
8.5	9.4	9.9	9.9	11.4	12.8	13.2	12.9	12.0	11.2
11.4	10.5	9.4	7.5	5.5	4.3	3.4	3.1	2.3	2.1
1.8	1.4	1.1	1.1	0.9					

Runs Test with Large Samples. *In Exercises 9–12, use the runs test with a significance level of $\alpha = 0.05$. (All data are listed in order by row.)*

9. Testing for Randomness of Super Bowl Victories Listed below are the conference designations of teams that won the Super Bowl, where N denotes a team from the NFC and A denotes a team from the AFC. Do the results suggest that either conference is superior?

N	N	A	A	A	N	A	A	A	A	N	A	A	A	N	N	A	N	N	N	N	N	N	N	N	N	N
N	N	N	N	A	A	N	A	A	N	A	A	A	A	N	A	N	N	N	A	N	A	A	A	N	A	

10. Baseball World Series Victories Test the claim that the sequence of World Series wins by American League and National League teams is random. Given are recent results, with A = American League and N = National League.

A	N	A	N	N	N	A	A	A	A	N	A	A	A	A	N	A	N	N	A	A	N	N	A
A	A	A	N	A	N	N	N	A	A	A	A	A	N	A	N	A	N	A	N	A	A	A	A
A	A	N	N	A	N	A	N	N	N	A	A	N	N	N	A	N	A	N	A	N	A	A	A	N
N	A	A	N	N	N	N	A	A	A	N	A	N	A	N	A	A	A	N	A	N	A	A	A
N	A	N	A	A	N	A	N	A	N	N	N	A	N	A	N	A	A						

11. Stock Market: Testing for Randomness Above and Below the Median Listed below are the annual high values of the Dow Jones Industrial Average for a recent sequence of years. Find the median, then test for randomness below and above the median. What does the result suggest about the stock market as an investment consideration?

969	995	943	985	969	842	951	1036	1052	892	882	1015
1000	908	898	1000	1024	1071	1287	1287	1553	1956	2722	2184
2791	3000	3169	3413	3794	3978	5216	6561	8259	9374	11568	11401
11350	10635	10454	10855	10941	12464	14198	13279	10580	11625	12929	13589
16577	18054	18312	19975	24838	26828						

12. Kentucky Derby Listed below are the post positions of Kentucky Derby winners arranged in order by year. Find the mean, then test for randomness above and below the mean. Is there any other analysis that would be better for bettors?

7	5	13	11	8	10	5	1	1	5	1	4	3	5	4	12	2	13	1	2
14	9	1	10	7	8	1	6	2	9	9	14	4	1	7	8	12	7	13	8
2	12	9	10	2	3	2	4	2	3	10	7	18	10	15	10	1	3	11	10
8	5	10	6	8	16	15	5	3	16	15	16	5	5	13	10	8	7	20	8
4	16	19	15	5	15	13													

13-7   Beyond the Basics

13. Finding Critical Values

a. Using all of the elements A, A, A, B, B, B, B, B, B, B, list the 84 different possible sequences.

b. Find the number of runs for each of the 84 sequences.

c. Use the results from parts (a) and (b) to find your own critical values for *G*.

d. Compare your results to those given in Table A-10.

Chapter Quick Quiz

1. Nicotine in Cigarettes Some of the nonparametric methods in this chapter use ranks of data. Find the ranks corresponding to the following amounts (milligrams) of nicotine in king-sized cigarettes (from Data Set 16 "Cigarette Contents" in Appendix B).

1.1   1.7   1.7   1.1   1.4   1.0   1.2   1.8   1.6   1.1

2. Efficiency What does it mean when we say that the rank correlation test has an efficiency rating of 0.91 when compared to the parametric test for linear correlation?

3. Nonparametric Tests

a. Which of the following terms is sometimes used instead of "nonparametric test": *normality test; abnormality test; distribution-free test; last testament; test of patience?*

b. Why is the answer to part (a) better than "nonparametric test"?

4. Dropped Object The table below describes the behavior of an object dropped near the surface of the Earth. The time is in seconds, and the distance traveled is in meters. Find the rank correlation coefficient, then form a conclusion based on its value.

Time	0.1	0.2	0.3	0.4	0.5	0.6	0.7	0.8	0.9
Distance	0.049	0.196	0.441	0.784	1.225	1.764	2.401	3.136	3.969

5. Dropped Object For paired sample data such as those given in Exercise 4, identify at least one advantage of using the appropriate nonparametric test over the parametric test.

6. Sign Test Identify three different configurations of data that can be analyzed using the sign test.

7. Runs Test Assume that we use the runs test of randomness above and below the mean for the annual gross revenue of Amazon.com, Inc. each year for the past 25 years. If the number of runs is $G = 2$, what do we know about Amazon.com?

8. Sign Test and Wilcoxon Signed-Ranks Test Paired data consist of pulse rates before and after a training program. What is a major advantage of the Wilcoxon signed-ranks test over the sign test when analyzing data consisting of matched pairs of the before/after differences?

9. Wilcoxon Tests What is the difference between the Wilcoxon signed-ranks test and the Wilcoxon rank-sum test?

10. Kruskal-Wallis Test What parametric test can also be conducted instead of the Kruskal-Wallis test? What is an advantage of using the Kruskal-Wallis test instead of the parametric test?

Review Exercises

Using Nonparametric Tests. *In Exercises 1–10, use a 0.05 significance level with the indicated test. If no particular test is specified, use the appropriate nonparametric test from this chapter.*

1. The Freshman 15 The "Freshman 15" refers to the belief that college students gain 15 lb (or 6.8 kg) during their freshman year. Listed below are weights (kg) of randomly selected male college freshmen (from Data Set 13 "Freshman 15" in Appendix B). The weights were measured in September and later in April. Use the sign test to test the claim that for the population of freshman male college students there is not a significant difference between the weights in September and the weights in the following April. What do you conclude about the Freshman 15 belief?

September	67	68	87	81	60	70	68	68	80
April	67	68	88	82	61	71	69	69	82

2. Wilcoxon Signed-Ranks Test Repeat the preceding exercise using the Wilcoxon signed-ranks test.

3. Rank Correlation Use the paired sample data from Exercise 1 and analyze the data using the rank correlation coefficient. What does the result tell us about the belief that college students gain 15 lb (or 6.8 kg) during their freshman year?

4. Length of Hospital Stay Listed below are lengths of stay (days) for mothers who gave birth at Albany Medical Center, Bellevue Hospital Center, and Olean General Hospital (based on Data Set 6 "Births" from Appendix B). Use a 0.05 significance level to test the claim that the lengths of stay at the three hospitals have the same median.

Albany	2	2	36	5	2	4	3	2	2	2	19	3	2
Bellevue	2	3	53	2	3	2	6	44	3	3	2	3	2
Olean	3	2	2	3	2	4	3	4	2	2	2	3	3

5. World Series The last 114 baseball World Series ended with 66 wins by American League teams and 48 wins by National League teams. Use the sign test to test the claim that in each World Series, the American League team has a 0.5 probability of winning.

6. Taxis In a study of the length of time for a taxi ride in New York City, the following sample of times (minutes) was obtained (from Data Set 32 "Taxis" in Appendix B). Use the sign test to test the claim that the sample is from a population with a median equal to 15 minutes.

$$38 \quad 4 \quad 7 \quad 16 \quad 13 \quad 20 \quad 4 \quad 7 \quad 10 \quad 12$$

7. Taxis Repeat the preceding Review Exercise 6 using the Wilcoxon signed-ranks test.

8. California Lottery Listed below are consecutive first-digits drawn in the California Daily 4 lottery. Test for randomness of even and odd integers. Does the lottery appear to be working as it should?

8 7 7 8 0 5 7 4 7 0 0 3 1 2 9 4 7 7 0 4 9 5 1 7 8 8 5 5 8 2

9. Old Faithful Listed below are time intervals (min) between eruptions of the Old Faithful geyser. The "recent" times are within the past few years, and the "past" times are from 1995. Test the claim that the two samples are from populations with the same median. Does the conclusion change with a 0.01 significance level?

Recent	78	91	89	79	57	100	62	87	70	88	82	83	56	81	74	102	61
Past (1995)	89	88	97	98	64	85	85	96	87	95	90	95					

10. Student and *U.S. News & World Report* Rankings of Colleges Each year, *U.S. News & World Report* publishes rankings of colleges based on statistics such as admission rates, graduation rates, class size, faculty–student ratio, faculty salaries, and peer ratings of administrators. Economists Christopher Avery, Mark Glickman, Caroline Minter Hoxby, and Andrew Metrick took an alternative approach of analyzing the college choices of 3240 high-achieving school seniors. They examined the colleges that offered admission along with the colleges that the students chose to attend. The table below lists rankings for a small sample of colleges. Find the value of the rank correlation coefficient and use it to determine whether there is a correlation between the student rankings and the rankings of the magazine.

Student ranks	1	2	3	4	5	6	7	8
U.S. News & World Report ranks	1	2	5	4	7	6	3	8

Cumulative Review Exercises

Hershey's Kisses   *In Exercises 1–10, use the following weights (g) of Hershey's Kisses from Data Set 38 "Candies" in Appendix B.*

4.488	4.781	4.697	4.54	4.458	4.524	4.395	4.513	4.512	4.666

1. Statistics Find the mean, median, range, standard deviation, and variance. Include appropriate units in the answers.

2. Normality Do the weights appear to be from a population having a normal distribution? Explain.

3. *t* Test The bag of Hershey's Kisses includes 75 of the candies. According to the label, the total weight is 340 g, so the candies should have a mean weight of $340/75 = 4.5333$ g. Use the sample of weights listed above to test the claim that they are from a population with a mean of 4.5333 g. Use a 0.05 significance level with a *t* test. What does the conclusion suggest about the claim of 340 g printed on the label?

4. Sign Test Repeat Exercise 3 using the sign test to test the claim that the sample of weights is from a population with a median of 4.5333 g.

5. Wilcoxon Signed-Ranks Test Repeat Exercise 3 using the Wilcoxon signed-ranks test to test the claim that the sample of weights is from a population with a median of 4.5333 g.

6. Confidence Interval Use the sample of Hershey's Kisses weights on the previous page to construct a 95% confidence interval estimate of the population mean μ. What does the confidence interval suggest about the claim that Hershey's Kisses have a mean weight of 4.5333 g?

7. Bootstrap Resampling Use the bootstrap resampling method with the sample of Hershey's Kisses weights to construct a 95% confidence interval estimate of the population mean μ. What does the confidence interval suggest about the claim that Hershey's Kisses have a mean weight of 4.5333 g?

8. Randomness Refer to the following ages at inauguration of the elected presidents of the United States (from Data Set 22 "Presidents" in Appendix B). Test for randomness above and below the mean. Do the results suggest an upward trend or a downward trend?

57	61	57	57	58	57	61	54	68	49	64	48	65	52	46	54	49	47
55	54	42	51	56	55	51	54	51	60	62	43	55	56	52	69	64	46
54	47	70															

9. Sample Size Advances in technology are dramatically affecting different aspects of our lives. For example, the number of daily print newspapers is decreasing because of easy access to Internet and television news. To help address such issues, we want to estimate the percentage of adults in the United States who use a computer at least once each day. Find the sample size needed to estimate that percentage. Assume that we want 95% confidence that the sample percentage is within two percentage points of the true population percentage.

10. Cell Phones and Crashes: Analyzing Newspaper Report In an article from the Associated Press, it was reported that researchers "randomly selected 100 New York motorists who had been in an accident and 100 who had not been in an accident. Of those in accidents, 13.7 percent owned a cellular phone, while just 10.6 percent of the accident-free drivers had a phone in the car." What is wrong with these results?

Technology Project

Past attempts to identify or contact extraterrestrial intelligent life have involved efforts to send radio messages carrying information about us earthlings. Dr. Frank Drake of Cornell University developed such a radio message that could be transmitted as a series of pulses and gaps. The pulses and gaps can be considered to be 1s and 0s. Listed on the next page is a message consisting of 77 entries of 0s and 1s. If we factor 77 into the prime numbers of 7 and 11 and then make an 11 × 7 grid and put a dot at those positions corresponding to a pulse of 1, we can get a simple picture of something. Assume that the sequence of 77 entries of 1s and 0s is sent as a radio message that is intercepted by extraterrestrial life with enough intelligence to have studied this book. If the radio message is tested using the methods of this chapter, will the sequence appear to be "random noise" or will it be identified as a pattern that is not random? Also, construct the image represented by the digits and identify it.

0	0	1	1	1	0	0	0	0	1	1	1	0	0	0	0	0	1	0	0	0
1	1	1	1	1	1	1	0	0	1	1	1	0	0	0	0	1	1	1	0	0
0	0	1	1	1	0	0	0	1	0	0	0	1	0	1	0	0	0	0	1	0
1	0	0	0	0	1	0	1	0	0	0	0	1	0							

Big (or Very Large) Data Project

Data Set 25 "Tornadoes" in Appendix B includes lengths (miles) and widths (yards) of 63,160 tornadoes. Use rank correlation to test for an association between those two variables.

FROM DATA TO DECISION

Critical Thinking: Was the draft lottery random?

On December 1, 1969, during the Vietnam War, a lottery was used to determine who would be drafted into the U.S. Army, but the lottery generated considerable controversy. The different dates in a year were placed in 366 individual capsules. First, the 31 January capsules were placed in a box; then the 29 February capsules were added and the two months were mixed. Next, the 31 March capsules were added and the three months were mixed. This process continued until all months were included. The first capsule selected was September 14, so men born on that date were drafted first. The accompanying list shows the 366 priority dates in the order of selection. These data are available in Appendix B Data Set 43 "Draft Lottery."

Analyzing the Results

a. Use the runs test to test the sequence for randomness above and below the median of 183.5.

b. Use the Kruskal-Wallis test to test the claim that the 12 months had priority numbers drawn from the same population.

c. Calculate the 12 monthly means. Then plot those 12 means on a graph. (The horizontal scale lists the 12 months, and the vertical scale ranges from 100 to 260.) Note any pattern suggesting that the original priority numbers were not randomly selected.

d. Based on the results from parts (a), (b), and (c), decide whether this particular draft lottery was fair. Write a statement explaining why you believe that it was or was not fair. If you decided that this lottery was unfair, describe a process for selecting lottery numbers that would have been fair.

Day	Jan.	Feb.	Mar.	Apr.	May	Jun.	Jul.	Aug.	Sep.	Oct.	Nov.	Dec.
1	305	86	108	32	330	249	93	111	225	359	19	129
2	159	144	29	271	298	228	350	45	161	125	34	328
3	251	297	267	83	40	301	115	261	49	244	348	157
4	215	210	275	81	276	20	279	145	232	202	266	165
5	101	214	293	269	364	28	188	54	82	24	310	56
6	224	347	139	253	155	110	327	114	6	87	76	10
7	306	91	122	147	35	85	50	168	8	234	51	12
8	199	181	213	312	321	366	13	48	184	283	97	105
9	194	338	317	219	197	335	277	106	263	342	80	43
10	325	216	323	218	65	206	284	21	71	220	282	41
11	329	150	136	14	37	134	248	324	158	237	46	39
12	221	68	300	346	133	272	15	142	242	72	66	314
13	318	152	259	124	295	69	42	307	175	138	126	163
14	238	4	354	231	178	356	331	198	1	294	127	26

continued

Day	Jan.	Feb.	Mar.	Apr.	May	Jun.	Jul.	Aug.	Sep.	Oct.	Nov.	Dec.
15	17	89	169	273	130	180	322	102	113	171	131	320
16	121	212	166	148	55	274	120	44	207	254	107	96
17	235	189	33	260	112	73	98	154	255	288	143	304
18	140	292	332	90	278	341	190	141	246	5	146	128
19	58	25	200	336	75	104	227	311	177	241	203	240
20	280	302	239	345	183	360	187	344	63	192	185	135
21	186	363	334	62	250	60	27	291	204	243	156	70
22	337	290	265	316	326	247	153	339	160	117	9	53
23	118	57	256	252	319	109	172	116	119	201	182	162
24	59	236	258	2	31	358	23	36	195	196	230	95
25	52	179	343	351	361	137	67	286	149	176	132	84
26	92	365	170	340	357	22	303	245	18	7	309	173
27	355	205	268	74	296	64	289	352	233	264	47	78
28	77	299	223	262	308	222	88	167	257	94	281	123
29	349	285	362	191	226	353	270	61	151	229	99	16
30	164		217	208	103	209	287	333	315	38	174	3
31	211		30		313		193	11		79		100

Cooperative Group Activities

1. Out-of-class activity Half of the students should make up results for 200 coin flips and the other half should collect results from 200 actual tosses of a coin. Then use the runs test to determine whether the results appear to be random.

2. In-class activity Use the existing seating arrangement in your class and apply the runs test to determine whether the students are arranged randomly according to gender. After recording the seating arrangement, analysis can be done in subgroups of three or four students.

3. In-class activity Divide into groups of 8 to 12 people. For each group member, *measure* his or her height and *measure* his or her arm span. For the arm span, the subject should stand with arms extended, like the wings on an airplane. Divide the following tasks among subgroups of three or four people.

a. Use rank correlation with the paired sample data to determine whether there is a correlation between height and arm span.

b. Use the sign test to test for a difference between the two variables.

c. Use the Wilcoxon signed-ranks test to test for a difference between the two variables.

4. In-class activity Do Activity 3 using pulse rate instead of arm span. Measure pulse rates by counting the number of heartbeats in 1 min.

5. Out-of-class activity Divide into groups of three or four students. Investigate the relationship between two variables by collecting your own paired sample data and using the methods of Section 13-6 to determine whether there is a correlation. Suggested topics:

• Is there a correlation between taste and cost of different brands of chocolate chip cookies (or colas)? (Taste can be measured on some number scale, such as 1 to 10.)

• Is there a correlation between salaries of professional baseball (or basketball or football) players and their season achievements (such as batting average or points scored)?

• Is there a correlation between car fuel consumption rates and car weights?

• Is there a correlation between the lengths of men's (or women's) feet and their heights?

• Is there a correlation between student grade-point averages and the amount of television watched?

• Is there a correlation between heights of fathers (or mothers) and heights of their first sons (or daughters)?

6. Out-of-class activity See this chapter's "From Data to Decision" project, which involves analysis of the 1970 lottery used for drafting men into the U.S. Army. Because the 1970 results raised concerns about the randomness of selecting draft priority numbers, design a new procedure for generating the 366 priority numbers. Use your procedure to generate the 366 numbers and test your results using the techniques suggested in parts (a), (b), and (c) of the "From Data to Decision" project. How do your results compare to those obtained in 1970? Does your random selection process appear to be better than the one used in 1970? Write a report that clearly describes the process you designed. Also include your analyses and conclusions.

7. Out-of-class activity Divide into groups of three or four. Survey other students by asking them to identify their major and gender. For each surveyed subject, determine the number of Twitter followers or Facebook friends. Use the sample data to address these questions:

• Do the numbers of Twitter followers or Facebook friends appear to be the same for both genders?

• Do the numbers of Twitter followers or Facebook friends appear to be the same for the different majors?

8. In-class activity Divide into groups of 8 to 12 people. For each group member, measure the person's height and also measure his or her navel height, which is the height from the floor to the navel. Use the rank correlation coefficient to determine whether there is a correlation between height and navel height.

9. In-class activity Divide into groups of three or four people. Appendix B includes many data sets not yet addressed by the methods of this chapter. Search Appendix B for variables of interest, then investigate using appropriate methods of nonparametric statistics. State your conclusions and try to identify practical applications.

14

STATISTICAL PROCESS CONTROL

CHAPTER PROBLEM — **Global Warming: Is It Real?**

The principles of statistical process control are widely used to monitor the quality of services and manufactured goods. Scientists also use statistical process control in the monitoring of global temperatures to better understand and predict atmospheric and climatic changes. In this Chapter Problem, we consider the process of monitoring the surface temperature of Earth. Table 14-1 lists the global mean surface temperature (in °C) of Earth for each year from 1880, with projections used

for the last two years. This data set is based on measurements provided by NASA Goddard's Global Surface Temperature Analysis (GISTEMP).

Note: Annual global temperature is calculated by comparing each daily measurement to what is "normal" for that specific location and time. For the GISS analysis, "normal" is defined as the mean temperature for the 30-year period 1951–1980. The differences are called "anomalies," and it is these anomalies that scientists monitor and evaluate. The data in Table 14-1 are not actual global temperature data, but are based on data from NASA's Goddard Institute for Space Studies (GISS).

Most scientists agree that global warming is occurring and that this increase in temperature is caused by an increase in greenhouse gases (e.g., CO_2). Others deny global warming and claim that human activity is *not* driving an increase in global temperature. We will see how methods of statistics can be used to monitor and evaluate trends in the Earth's temperature. Specifically, we will determine whether the Earth's temperature results from a process that is out of control, or whether the Earth's temperature is behaving as it should.

TABLE 14-1 Annual Temperatures (°C) of Earth

	0	1	2	3	4	5	6	7	8	9	$\bar{x}$	Range
1880s	13.88	13.88	14.00	13.96	13.59	13.77	13.75	13.55	13.77	14.04	13.819	0.490
1890s	13.78	13.44	13.60	13.61	13.68	13.68	13.73	13.85	13.79	13.76	13.692	0.410
1900s	13.95	13.95	13.70	13.64	13.58	13.75	13.85	13.60	13.70	13.69	13.741	0.370
1910s	13.79	13.74	13.67	13.72	13.98	14.06	13.80	13.54	13.67	13.91	13.788	0.520
1920s	13.85	13.95	13.91	13.84	13.89	13.85	14.04	13.95	14.00	13.78	13.906	0.260
1930s	13.97	14.03	14.04	13.89	14.05	13.92	14.01	14.12	14.15	13.98	14.016	0.260
1940s	14.14	14.11	14.10	14.06	14.11	13.99	14.01	14.12	13.97	13.91	14.052	0.230
1950s	13.83	13.98	14.03	14.12	13.91	13.91	13.82	14.08	14.10	14.05	13.983	0.300
1960s	13.98	14.10	14.05	14.03	13.65	13.75	13.93	13.98	13.91	14.00	13.938	0.450
1970s	14.04	13.90	13.95	14.18	13.94	13.98	13.79	14.16	14.07	14.13	14.014	0.390
1980s	14.27	14.40	14.10	14.34	14.16	14.13	14.19	14.35	14.42	14.28	14.264	0.320
1990s	14.49	14.44	14.16	14.18	14.31	14.47	14.36	14.40	14.71	14.44	14.396	0.550
2000s	14.41	14.56	14.70	14.64	14.60	14.77	14.64	14.66	14.68	14.70	14.636	0.360
2010s	14.52	14.40	14.60	14.81	14.59	14.96	14.83	15.61	15.49	14.97	14.878	1.210

CHAPTER OBJECTIVES

This chapter presents methods for constructing and interpreting *control charts* that are commonly used to monitor changing characteristics of data over time. A control chart is a graph with a centerline, an upper control limit, and a lower control limit. A control chart can be used to determine whether a process is statistically stable (or within statistical control) with only natural variation and no patterns, cycles, or unusual points.

Here are the chapter objectives:

14-1 Control Charts for Variation and Mean

- Develop the ability to construct a run chart.

- Develop the ability to construct a control chart for R (range).

- Develop the ability to construct a control chart for $\bar{x}$.

- Identify out-of-control criteria and apply them to determine whether process data are within statistical control.

14-2 Control Charts for Attributes

- Develop the ability to construct a control chart for p, the proportion corresponding to some attribute, such as being a defect.

- Identify out-of-control criteria and apply them to determine whether attribute data are within statistical control with only natural variation and no patterns, cycles, or unusual points.

14-1 Control Charts for Variation and Mean

Key Concept This section presents run charts, R charts, and $\bar{x}$ charts as tools that enable us to monitor characteristics of data over time. We can use such charts to determine whether a process is statistically stable (or within statistical control).

Process Data

The following definition formally describes the type of data that will be considered in this chapter.

> **DEFINITION**
>
> **Process data** are data arranged according to some time sequence. They are measurements of a characteristic of goods or services that result from some combination of equipment, people, materials, methods, and conditions.

 EXAMPLE 1 Global Temperatures of Earth as Process Data

Table 14-1 includes process data consisting of the measured global temperatures (°C) of Earth. Because the values in Table 14-1 are arranged according to the time at which they were measured, they are process data.

Continuous process monitoring is critical for identifying problems before they get out of hand. Countless companies have gone bankrupt because they allowed manufacturing processes to deteriorate without constant monitoring. This section introduces three tools commonly used to monitor process data: run charts, R charts, and $\bar{x}$ charts. We begin with run charts.

Run Chart

A run chart is one of several different tools commonly used to monitor a process to ensure that desired characteristics don't change. A run chart is basically the same as a time-series graph, which was introduced in Section 2-3.

> **DEFINITION**
>
> A **run chart** is a sequential plot of *individual* data values over time. One axis (usually the vertical axis) is used for the data values, and the other axis (usually the horizontal axis) is used for the time sequence. Run charts are used to monitor process data for any patterns of changes over time.

CP — EXAMPLE 2 Run Chart of Earth Temperatures

Treating the 140 global Earth temperatures from Table 14-1 as a string of consecutive measurements, construct a run chart using the vertical axis for the temperatures and the horizontal axis to identify the chronological order of the temperatures.

SOLUTION

Figure 14-1 is the Minitab-generated run chart for the data in Table 14-1. In Figure 14-1, the horizontal scale identifies the sample number, so the number 1 corresponds to the first temperature measurement in 1880, the number 2 corresponds to the second temperature measurement in 1881, and so on. The vertical scale represents the mean global temperatures (°C).

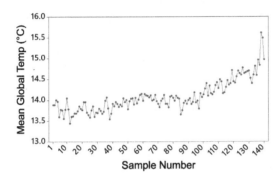

FIGURE 14-1 Run Chart of Earth Temperatures

INTERPRETATION

Examine Figure 14-1 and try to identify any *patterns*. From Figure 14-1 we see that as time progresses from left to right, the points appear to be rising. If this pattern continues, rising temperatures will cause melting of large ice formations, widespread flooding, and many other climatic changes. Figure 14-1 is evidence of global warming, which threatens us in many different ways.

 YOUR TURN. Do Exercise 6 "Pepsi Cans: Run Chart."

DEFINITION

A process is **statistically stable** (or **within statistical control**) if it has only natural variation, with no patterns, cycles, or unusual points.

Interpreting Run Charts

A run chart with no obvious pattern suggests that the data are from a process that is *statistically stable,* and the data can be treated as if they came from a population with a constant mean, standard deviation, distribution, and other characteristics. Figure 14-1 shows a pattern of increasing values, and that is one of several criteria for determining that a process is *not statistically stable* (or out of statistical control). Violating one or more of the following criteria indicates that a process is not statistically stable or out of statistical control.

Improving Quality in Cars by Reducing Variation

Ford and Mazda were producing similar transmissions that were supposed to be made with the same specifications, but it soon became apparent that the Ford transmissions required many more warranty repairs than the Japanese-made Mazda transmissions. Ford researchers investigated this and found that their transmissions were meeting the required specifications, but the *variation* in the Ford transmissions was much greater than those from Mazda. Mazda was using a better and more expensive grinder, but the increased cost was offset through fewer warranty repairs. Armed with these important results, Ford made changes and proceeded not only to meet the required specifications but also to improve quality by reducing variation. (See *Taguchi Techniques for Quality Engineering* by Phillip J. Ross.)

Out of Control Criteria

- **Increasing Variation:** As the run chart proceeds from left to right, the vertical variation of the points is increasing, so the corresponding data values are experiencing an increase in variation. This is a common problem in quality control. The net effect is that products vary more and more until almost all of them are considered defective.

- **Upward Trend:** The points are rising from left to right, (as in Figure 14-1), so the corresponding values are increasing over time.

- **Downward Trend:** The points are falling from left to right, so the corresponding values are decreasing over time.

- **Upward Shift:** The points near the beginning are noticeably lower than those near the end, so the corresponding values have shifted upward.

- **Downward Shift:** The points near the beginning are noticeably higher than those near the end, so the corresponding values have shifted downward.

- **Exceptional Value:** There is a single point that is exceptionally high or low.

- **Cyclical Pattern:** There is a repeating cycle.

Causes of Variation

Many different methods of quality control attempt to *reduce variation* in the product or service. Variation in a process can result from two types of causes as defined below.

> **DEFINITIONS**
>
> **Random variation** is due to chance; it is the type of variation inherent in any process that is not capable of producing every good or service exactly the same way every time.
>
> **Assignable variation** results from causes that can be identified (such as defective machinery or untrained employees).

Later in the chapter we will consider ways to distinguish between assignable variation and random variation.

The run chart is one tool for monitoring the stability of a process. We will now consider *control charts,* which are also useful for monitoring the stability of a process.

Control Charts

Because control charts were first introduced by Walter Shewhart in 1924, they are sometimes called Shewhart charts. We begin with a basic definition.

> **DEFINITION**
>
> A **control chart** (or **Shewhart chart** or **process-behavior chart**) of a process characteristic (such as mean or variation) consists of values plotted sequentially over time, and it includes a **centerline** as well as a **lower control limit** (LCL) and an **upper control limit** (UCL). The centerline represents a central value of the characteristic measurements, whereas the control limits are boundaries used to separate and identify any points considered to be *significantly high or significantly low.*

We will assume that the population standard deviation σ is not known as we now consider two of several different types of *control charts:*

1. R charts (or range charts) used to monitor variation

2. $\bar{x}$ charts used to monitor means

When using control charts to monitor a process, it is common to consider R charts and $\bar{x}$ charts together, because a statistically unstable process may be the result of increasing *variation,* changing *means,* or both.

Interpreting Control Charts

When interpreting control charts, the following caution is important:

CAUTION Upper and lower control limits of a control chart are based on the *actual* behavior of the process, not the *desired* behavior. Upper and lower control limits do not correspond to any process *specifications* that may have been decreed by the manufacturer.

When investigating the quality of some process, typically two key questions need to be addressed:

1. Based on the current behavior of the process, can we conclude that the process is within statistical control?

2. Do the process goods or services meet design specifications?

In this chapter we address the first question, but not the second; we are focusing on the behavior of the process with the objective of determining whether the process is within statistical control. Also, we should clearly understand the following specific criteria for determining whether a process is in statistical control (or is statistically stable).

Out-of-Control-Criteria

DEFINITION

A process is **not statistically stable** or is **out of statistical control** if one or more of the following out-of-control criteria are satisfied.

1. There is a pattern, trend, or cycle that is obviously not random.

2. There is at least one point above the upper control limit or at least one point below the lower control limit.

3. *Run of 8 Rule:* There are at least eight consecutive points all above or all below the centerline. (With a statistically stable process, there is a 0.5 probability that a point will be above or below the centerline, so it is very unlikely that eight consecutive points will all be above the centerline or all below it.)

In this book we will use only the three out-of-control criteria listed above, but some companies use additional criteria such as these:

- There are at least six consecutive points all increasing or all decreasing.

- There are at least 14 consecutive points all alternating between up and down (such as up, down, up, down, and so on).

continued

Don't Tamper!

Nashua Corp. had trouble with its paper-coating machine and considered spending a million dollars to replace it. The machine was working well with a stable process, but samples were taken every so often and, based on the results, unnecessary adjustments were made. These overadjustments, called *tampering,* caused shifts away from the distribution that had been good. The effect was an increase in defects. When statistician and quality expert W. Edwards Deming studied the process, he recommended that no adjustments be made unless warranted by a signal that the process had shifted or had become unstable. The company was better off with no adjustments than with the tampering that took place.

- Two out of three consecutive points are beyond control limits that are 2 standard deviations away from the centerline.

- Four out of five consecutive points are beyond control limits that are 1 standard deviation away from the centerline.

Control Chart for Monitoring Variation: The *R* Chart

> **DEFINITION**
>
> An *R* **chart** (or **range chart**) is a plot of sample ranges instead of individual sample values. In addition to plotting the values of the ranges, we include a centerline located at $\overline{R}$, which denotes the mean of all sample ranges, as well as another line for the lower control limit and a third line for the upper control limit. It is used to monitor the *variation* in a process.

For monitoring variation in a process, it might make more sense to use standard deviations, but range charts are quite effective for cases in which the size of the samples (or subgroups) is 10 or fewer. If the samples all have a size greater than 10, the use of an *s* chart is recommended instead of an *R* chart. (See Exercise 13.) The following is a summary of notation and the components of the *R* chart.

KEY ELEMENTS

Monitoring Process Variation: Control Chart for *R*

Objective

Construct a control chart for *R* (or an "*R* chart") that can be used to determine whether the *variation* of process data is within statistical control.

Requirements

1. The data are process data consisting of a sequence of samples all of the same size *n*.

2. The distribution of the process data is essentially normal.

3. The individual sample data values are independent.

Notation

n = size of each sample or *subgroup*

$\overline{R}$ = mean of the sample ranges (the sum of the sample ranges divided by the number of samples)

Graph

Points plotted: sample ranges (each point represents the range for each subgroup)

Centerline: $\overline{R}$ (the mean of the sample ranges)

Upper control limit (UCL): $D_4\overline{R}$ (where D_4 is a constant found in Table 14-2)

Lower control limit (LCL): $D_3\overline{R}$ (where D_3 is a constant found in Table 14-2)

TABLE 14-2 Control Chart Constants

n: Number of Observations in Subgroup	R Chart		x̄ Chart		s Chart	
	D_3	D_4	A_2	A_3	B_3	B_4
2	0.000	3.267	1.880	2.659	0.000	3.267
3	0.000	2.574	1.023	1.954	0.000	2.568
4	0.000	2.282	0.729	1.628	0.000	2.266
5	0.000	2.114	0.577	1.427	0.000	2.089
6	0.000	2.004	0.483	1.287	0.030	1.970
7	0.076	1.924	0.419	1.182	0.118	1.882
8	0.136	1.864	0.373	1.099	0.185	1.815
9	0.184	1.816	0.337	1.032	0.239	1.761
10	**0.223**	**1.777**	**0.308**	**0.975**	**0.284**	**1.716**

Source: Adapted from *ASTM Manual on the Presentation of Data and Control Chart Analysis,*
© 1976 ASTM, pp. 134–136. Reprinted with permission of American Society for Testing and Materials.

The values of D_4 and D_3 are constants computed by quality-control experts, and they are intended to simplify calculations. The upper and lower control limits of $D_4\overline{R}$ and $D_3\overline{R}$ are values that are roughly equivalent to 99.7% confidence interval limits. It is therefore highly unlikely that values from a statistically stable process would fall beyond those limits. If a value does fall beyond the control limits, it's very likely that the process is not statistically stable.

CP EXAMPLE 3 **R Chart of Earth Global Temperatures**

Construct a control chart for R using the temperatures listed in Table 14-1. Use the samples of size $n = 10$ for each of the decades.

SOLUTION

Refer to Table 14-1 in the Chapter Problem on page 701 to see the column of sample ranges R. The value of $\overline{R}$ is the mean of those 14 sample ranges, so its value is found as follows:

$$\overline{R} = \frac{0.490 + 0.410 + \cdots + 1.210}{14} = 0.4371$$

The centerline for our R chart is therefore located at $\overline{R} = 0.4371°C$. To find the upper and lower control limits, we must first find the values of D_3 and D_4. Referring to Table 14-2 for $n = 10$, we get $D_4 = 1.777$ and $D_3 = 0.223$, so the control limits are as follows:

Upper control limit (UCL): $D_4\overline{R} = (1.777)(0.4371) = 0.7767$

Lower control limit (LCL): $D_3\overline{R} = (0.223)(0.4371) = 0.0975$

Using a centerline value of $\overline{R} = 0.4371$ and control limits of 0.7767 and 0.0975, we now proceed to plot the 14 sample ranges as 14 individual points. The result is shown in the following display.

continued

Costly Assignable Variation

The Mars Climate Orbiter was launched by NASA and sent to Mars, but it was destroyed when it flew too close to Mars. The loss was estimated at $125 million. The cause of the crash was found to be confusion over the units used for calculations. Acceleration data were provided in the English units of pounds of force, but the Jet Propulsion Laboratory assumed that those units were in metric "newtons" instead of pounds. The thrusters of the spacecraft subsequently provided wrong amounts of force in adjusting the position of the spacecraft. The errors caused by the discrepancy were fairly small at first, but the cumulative error over months of the spacecraft's journey proved to be fatal to its success.

In 1962, the rocket carrying the *Mariner 1* satellite was destroyed by ground controllers when it went off course due to a missing minus sign in a computer program.

Bribery Detected with Control Charts

Control charts were used to help convict a person who bribed Florida jai alai players to lose. (See "Using Control Charts to Corroborate Bribery in Jai Alai," by Charnes and Gitlow, *The American Statistician*, Vol. 49, No. 4.) An auditor for one jai alai facility noticed that abnormally large sums of money were wagered for certain types of bets, and some contestants didn't win as much as expected when those bets were made. *R* charts and $\bar{x}$ charts were used in court as evidence of highly unusual patterns of betting. Examination of the control charts clearly shows points well beyond the upper control limit, indicating that the process of betting was out of statistical control. The statistician was able to identify a date at which assignable variation appeared to stop, and prosecutors knew that it was the date of the suspect's arrest.

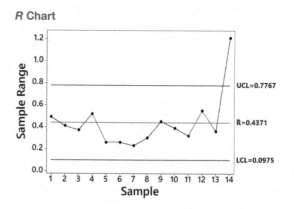

R Chart

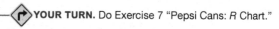

INTERPRETATION

Examination of the *R* chart shows that there is a point that lies beyond the upper control limit, so we conclude that the variation of the process is out of statistical control.

YOUR TURN. Do Exercise 7 "Pepsi Cans: *R* Chart."

Control Chart for Monitoring Means: The $\bar{x}$ Chart

DEFINITION

An **$\bar{x}$ chart** is a plot of sample means. It includes a centerline located at $\bar{\bar{x}}$, which denotes the mean of all sample means (equal to the mean of all sample values combined), as well as another line for the lower control limit and a third line for the upper control limit. It is used to monitor the *center* in a process.

Using the approach common in business and industry, the control limits are based on ranges instead of standard deviations. (See Exercise 14 for an $\bar{x}$ chart based on standard deviations.)

Monitoring Process Mean: Control Chart for $\bar{x}$

Objective

Construct a control chart for $\bar{x}$ (or an $\bar{x}$ chart) that can be used to determine whether the *center* of process data is within statistical control.

Requirements

1. The data are process data consisting of a sequence of samples all of the same size *n*.

2. The distribution of the process data is essentially normal.

3. The individual sample data values are independent.

Notation

n = size of each sample, or *subgroup*

$\bar{\bar{x}}$ = mean of all sample means (equal to the mean of all sample values combined)

Graph

Points plotted: sample means

Centerline: $\bar{\bar{x}}$ = mean of all sample means

Upper control limit (UCL): $\bar{\bar{x}} + A_2\bar{R}$ (where A_2 is a constant found in Table 14-2)

Lower control limit (LCL): $\bar{\bar{x}} - A_2\bar{R}$ (where A_2 is a constant found in Table 14-2)

CP | **EXAMPLE 4** $\bar{x}$ **Chart of Global Earth Temperatures**

Using the temperatures in Table 14-1 on page 701 with samples of size $n = 10$ for each of the 14 decades, construct a control chart for $\bar{x}$. Based on the result, determine whether the process mean is within statistical control.

SOLUTION

Before plotting the 14 points corresponding to the 14 values of $\bar{x}$, we must first find the values for the centerline and control limits. We get

$$\bar{\bar{x}} = \frac{13.819 + 13.692 + \cdots + 14.878}{14} = 14.0802$$

$$\bar{R} = \frac{0.490 + 0.410 + \cdots + 1.210}{14} = 0.4371$$

Referring to Table 14-2 on page 707, we find that for $n = 10$, $A_2 = 0.308$. Knowing the values of $\bar{\bar{x}}$, A_2, and $\bar{R}$, we can now evaluate the control limits.

Upper control limit (UCL): $\bar{\bar{x}} + A_2\bar{R} = 14.0802 + (0.308)(0.4371) = 14.2148$

Lower control limit (LCL): $\bar{\bar{x}} - A_2\bar{R} = 14.0802 - (0.308)(0.4371) = 13.9456$

The resulting control chart for $\bar{x}$ will be as shown in the accompanying display.

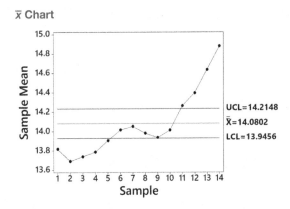

$\bar{x}$ Chart

INTERPRETATION

Examination of the $\bar{x}$ chart shows that the process mean is out of statistical control because there are points lying beyond the upper and lower control limits and there are at least eight consecutive points lying below the centerline.

YOUR TURN. Do Exercise 8 "Pepsi Cans: $\bar{x}$ Chart."

By analyzing the global Earth temperatures in Table 14-1 with a run chart, an R chart, and an $\bar{x}$ chart, we can see that the process is out of statistical control. It appears that the temperatures of Earth are increasing, so it appears that global warming is a real phenomenon.

TECH CENTER

Control Charts
Access tech supplements, videos, and data sets at www.TriolaStats.com

Statdisk	Minitab	StatCrunch

Statdisk

Visit TriolaStats.com for detailed instructions.

Minitab

Run Chart
1. Enter all of the sample data in column *C1*.
2. Click **Stat** in the top menu.
3. Select **Quality Tools** from the dropdown menu and select **Run Chart** from the submenu.
4. In the *Single column* box enter **C1**. In *Subgroup* size enter **1**.
5. Click **OK.**

R Chart and $\bar{x}$ Chart
1. Enter sample values sequentially in column *C1* or enter the sample values in columns or rows as in Table 14-1.
2. Click **Stat** in the top menu.
3. Select **Control Charts** from the dropdown menu and select **Variables Charts for Subgroups**
4. Select **Xbar-R** from the submenu.
5. Select the format of data entered in Step 1 and then select the appropriate columns in the entry box.
6. Enter the *subgroup size* if all observations are in one column.
7. Click the **Xbar-R Options** button and then click the **Estimate** tab and select **Rbar.**
8. Click **OK** twice.

StatCrunch

1. Click **Stat** in the top menu.
2. Select **Control Charts** from the dropdown menu and **X-bar, R** from the submenu.
3. Select the columns to be used.
4. Click **Compute!**
5. Click the arrow buttons to switch between the charts and numerical results.

TI-83/84 Plus Calculator	Excel	R

TI-83/84 Plus Calculator

Creating Run Charts, R Charts, and Charts using a TI-83/84 Plus calculator is possible but not recommended due to the complex procedures required and limited information displayed. Visit TriolaStats.com for detailed instructions.

Excel

XLSTAT Add-In *(not available with all XLSTAT licenses)*
1. Click on the **XLSTAT** tab in the Ribbon and then click **SPC.**
2. Select **Subgroup charts** from the dropdown menu.
3. For *Chart Family* click **Subgroup charts** and select **X-bar–R chart** under *Chart type*.
4. Click the **General** tab.
5. Under *Data format* select **Column** if the data are listed in separate columns or **One column** if the data are stacked in a single column.
6. If **One column** is selected, enter the sample size common to all data entries under *Common subgroup size*.
7. In the *Data* box enter the cell range of the data. If the data range includes a label, check the **Column labels** box.
8. Click the **Estimation** tab and select **R bar.**
9. Click **OK** twice.

R

R command not available at time of publication. Control charts are available in some R packages.

R is rapidly evolving, and an updated list of statistical commands is available at TriolaStats.com.

14-1   Basic Skills and Concepts

Statistical Literacy and Critical Thinking

1. Run Charts and Control Charts

a. What is a run chart and what is its purpose?

b. What is an R chart and what is its purpose?

c. What is an $\bar{x}$ chart and what is its purpose?

2. Control Limits In a control chart, what are upper and lower control limits, and what is their purpose?

3. Statistically Stable Process What does it mean to have a statistically stable process?

4. Lake Mead Water Elevations Many people in Nevada, Arizona, and California get water and electricity from Lake Mead and Hoover Dam. Shown below are an $\bar{x}$ chart (top) and an R chart (bottom) obtained by using the monthly water elevations (ft) of Lake Mead at Hoover Dam (based on data from the U.S. Department of the Interior). The control charts are based on the 12 monthly water elevations for each of 83 consecutive and recent years. What do these control charts tell us about Lake Mead?

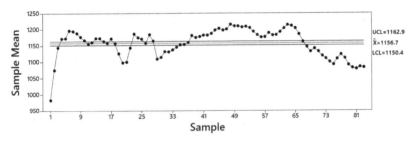

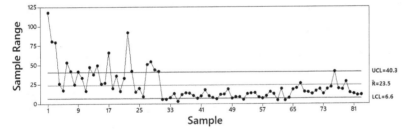

Pepsi Cans. In Exercises 5–8, refer to the axial loads (pounds) of aluminum Pepsi cans that are 0.0109 in. thick, as listed in Data Set 41 "Aluminum Cans" in Appendix B. An axial load of a can is the maximum weight supported by the side, and it is important to have an axial load high enough so that the can isn't crushed when the top lid is pressed onto the top. There are seven measurements from each of 25 days of production. If the 175 axial loads are in one column, the first 7 are from the first day, the next 7 are from the second day, and so on, so that the "subgroup size" is 7.

5. Pepsi Cans: Notation After finding the sample mean and sample range for each of the 25 days, find the values of $\bar{\bar{x}}$ and $\bar{R}$. Also find the values of LCL and UCL for an R chart, then find the values of LCL and UCL for an $\bar{x}$ chart.

6. Pepsi Cans: Run Chart Treat the 175 axial loads as a string of consecutive measurements and construct a run chart. What does the result suggest?

7. Pepsi Cans: R Chart Treat the seven measurements from each day as a sample and construct an R chart. What does the result suggest?

8. Pepsi Cans: $\bar{x}$ Chart Treat the seven measurements from each day as a sample and construct an $\bar{x}$ chart. What does the result suggest?

Quarters. *In Exercises 9–12, refer to the accompanying table of weights (grams) of quarters minted by the U.S. government. This table is available in Data Set 44 "Weights of Minted Quarters" in Appendix B.*

Day	Hour 1	Hour 2	Hour 3	Hour 4	Hour 5	$\bar{x}$	s	Range
1	5.543	5.698	5.605	5.653	5.668	5.6334	0.0607	0.155
2	5.585	5.692	5.771	5.718	5.720	5.6972	0.0689	0.186
3	5.752	5.636	5.660	5.680	5.565	5.6586	0.0679	0.187
4	5.697	5.613	5.575	5.615	5.646	5.6292	0.0455	0.122
5	5.630	5.770	5.713	5.649	5.650	5.6824	0.0581	0.140
6	5.807	5.647	5.756	5.677	5.761	5.7296	0.0657	0.160
7	5.686	5.691	5.715	5.748	5.688	5.7056	0.0264	0.062
8	5.681	5.699	5.767	5.736	5.752	5.7270	0.0361	0.086
9	5.552	5.659	5.770	5.594	5.607	5.6364	0.0839	0.218
10	5.818	5.655	5.660	5.662	5.700	5.6990	0.0689	0.163
11	5.693	5.692	5.625	5.750	5.757	5.7034	0.0535	0.132
12	5.637	5.628	5.646	5.667	5.603	5.6362	0.0235	0.064
13	5.634	5.778	5.638	5.689	5.702	5.6882	0.0586	0.144
14	5.664	5.655	5.727	5.637	5.667	5.6700	0.0339	0.090
15	5.664	5.695	5.677	5.689	5.757	5.6964	0.0359	0.093
16	5.707	5.890	5.598	5.724	5.635	5.7108	0.1127	0.292
17	5.697	5.593	5.780	5.745	5.470	5.6570	0.1260	0.310
18	6.002	5.898	5.669	5.957	5.583	5.8218	0.1850	0.419
19	6.017	5.613	5.596	5.534	5.795	5.7110	0.1968	0.483
20	5.671	6.223	5.621	5.783	5.787	5.8170	0.2380	0.602

9. Quarters: Notation Find the values of $\bar{\bar{x}}$ and $\bar{R}$. Also find the values of LCL and UCL for an R chart, then find the values of LCL and UCL for an $\bar{x}$ chart.

10. Quarters: R Chart Treat the five measurements from each day as a sample and construct an R chart. What does the result suggest?

11. Quarters: $\bar{x}$ Chart Treat the 5 measurements from each day as a sample and construct an $\bar{x}$ chart. What does the result suggest?

12. Quarters: Run Chart Treat the 100 consecutive measurements from the 20 days as individual values and construct a run chart. What does the result suggest?

14-1 Beyond the Basics

13. s Chart In this section we described control charts for R and $\bar{x}$ based on *ranges*. Control charts for monitoring variation and center (mean) can also be based on *standard deviations*. An s chart for monitoring variation is constructed by plotting sample standard deviations with a centerline at $\bar{s}$ (the mean of the sample standard deviations) and control limits at $B_4\bar{s}$ and $B_3\bar{s}$, where B_4 and B_3 are found in Table 14-2 on page 707 in this section. Construct an s chart for the data of Table 14-1 on page 701. Compare the result to the R chart given in Example 3 "R Chart of Earth Global Temperatures."

14. $\bar{x}$ Chart Based on Standard Deviations An $\bar{x}$ chart based on *standard deviations* (instead of ranges) is constructed by plotting sample means with a centerline at $\bar{\bar{x}}$ and control limits at $\bar{\bar{x}} + A_3\bar{s}$ and $\bar{\bar{x}} - A_3\bar{s}$, where A_3 is found in Table 14-2 on page 707 and $\bar{s}$ is the mean of the sample standard deviations. Use the data in Table 14-1 on page 701 to construct an $\bar{x}$ chart based on standard deviations. Compare the result to the $\bar{x}$ chart based on sample ranges in Example 4 "$\bar{x}$ Chart of Global Earth Temperatures."

Control Charts for Attributes

Key Concept This section presents a method for constructing a control chart to monitor the proportion p for some *attribute,* such as whether a service or manufactured item is defective or nonconforming. (A good or a service is nonconforming if it doesn't meet specifications or requirements. Nonconforming goods are sometimes discarded, repaired, or called "seconds" and sold at reduced prices.) The control chart is interpreted using the same three out-of-control criteria from Section 14-1 to determine whether the process is statistically stable:

Out-of-Control-Criteria

> **DEFINITION**
>
> A process is **not statistically stable** or is **out of statistical control** if one or more of the following out-of-control criteria are satisfied.
>
> **1.** There is a pattern, trend, or cycle that is obviously not random.
>
> **2.** There is at least one point above the upper control limit or at least one point below the lower control limit.
>
> **3.** *Run of 8 Rule:* There are at least eight consecutive points all above or all below the centerline. (With a statistically stable process, there is a 0.5 probability that a point will be above or below the centerline, so it is very unlikely that eight consecutive points will all be above the centerline or all below it.)

As in Section 14-1, we select samples of size n at regular time intervals and plot points in a sequential graph with a centerline and control limits. (There are ways to deal with samples of different sizes, but we don't consider them here.)

> **DEFINITION**
>
> A **control chart for p** (or **p chart**) is a graph of proportions of some attribute (such as whether products are defective) plotted sequentially over time, and it includes a centerline, a lower control limit (LCL), and an upper control limit (UCL).

The notation and control chart values are as summarized in the following Key Elements box. In this box, the attribute of "defective" can be replaced by any other relevant attribute (so that each sample item belongs to one of two distinct categories).

KEY ELEMENTS

Monitoring a Process Attribute: Control Chart for p

Objective

Construct a control chart for p (or a "p chart") that can be used to determine whether the proportion of some attribute (such as whether products are defective) from process data is within statistical control.

Requirements

1. The data are process data consisting of a sequence of samples all of the same size n.

2. Each sample item belongs to one of two categories (such as defective or not defective).

3. The individual sample data values are independent.

continued

Notation

$$\bar{p} = \text{estimate of the proportion of defective items in the process}$$

$$= \frac{\text{total number of defects found among all items sampled}}{\text{total number of items sampled}}$$

$$\bar{q} = \text{estimate of the proportion of process items that are not defective}$$

$$= 1 - \bar{p}$$

$$n = \text{size of each individual sample or subgroup}$$

Graph

Points plotted: proportions from the individual samples of size n

Centerline: $\bar{p}$

Upper control limit: $\bar{p} + 3\sqrt{\dfrac{\bar{p}\,\bar{q}}{n}}$ (Use 1 if this result is greater than 1.)

Lower control limit: $\bar{p} - 3\sqrt{\dfrac{\bar{p}\,\bar{q}}{n}}$ (Use 0 if this result is less than 0.)

> **CAUTION** Note this distinction in the calculations: When evaluating $\bar{p}$, divide the total number of defects by the *total* number of items sampled. The computations for UCL and LCL, however, require division by n, the size of each individual sample.

We use $\bar{p}$ for the centerline because it is the best estimate of the proportion of defects from the process. The expressions for the control limits correspond to 99.7% confidence interval limits for the confidence intervals described in Section 7-1. (Section 7-1 did not include any 99.7% confidence intervals, but the z score used for a 99.7% confidence interval is $z = 2.97$, which is rounded to 3 in the expressions used for the LCL and UCL in this section.)

EXAMPLE 1   Defective Aircraft Altimeters

The accuracy of aircraft altimeters is important because pilots rely on this instrument to maintain safe altitudes at all times. Pilots and passengers have been killed in crashes caused by wrong altimeter readings that led pilots to believe that they were safely above the ground when they were actually flying dangerously low.

Because aircraft altimeters are so critically important to aviation safety, their accuracy is carefully controlled by government regulations. Federal Aviation Administration (FAA) Regulation 91.411 requires periodic testing of aircraft altimeters, and those altimeters must comply with specifications included in Appendix E to Part 43 of the FAA regulations. One of those FAA specifications is that an altimeter must give a reading with an error of no more than 30 ft when tested for an altitude of 2000 ft.

The Orange Avionics Company manufactures altimeters in batches of 100, and each altimeter is tested and determined to be acceptable or defective. Listed below are the numbers of defective altimeters in successive batches of 100. Construct a control chart for the proportion p of defective altimeters and determine whether the process is within statistical control. If not, identify which of the three out-of-control criteria apply.

Defects: 2   0   1   3   1   2   2   4   3   5   12   7

SOLUTION

The centerline for the control chart is located by the value of $\bar{p}$:

$$\bar{p} = \frac{\text{total number of defects from all samples combined}}{\text{total number of altimeters sampled}},$$

$$= \frac{2 + 0 + 1 + \cdots + 7}{12 \cdot 100} = \frac{42}{1200} = 0.035$$

Because $\bar{p} = 0.035$, it follows that $\bar{q} = 1 - \bar{p} = 0.965$. Using $\bar{p} = 0.035$, $\bar{q} = 0.965$, and $n = 100$, we find the control limits as follows:

Upper control limit:

$$\bar{p} + 3\sqrt{\frac{\bar{p}\,\bar{q}}{n}} = 0.035 + 3\sqrt{\frac{(0.035)(0.965)}{100}} = 0.090$$

Lower control limit:

$$\bar{p} - 3\sqrt{\frac{\bar{p}\,\bar{q}}{n}} = 0.035 - 3\sqrt{\frac{(0.035)(0.965)}{100}} = -0.020$$

Because the lower control limit is less than 0, we use 0 instead.

Having found the values for the centerline and control limits, we can proceed to plot the control chart for proportions of defective altimeters. The Minitab control chart for p is shown in the accompanying display.

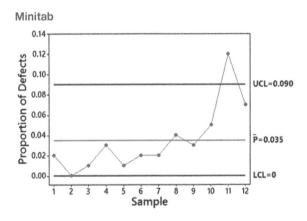

INTERPRETATION

We can interpret the control chart for p by considering the three out-of-control criteria listed earlier in this section. Using those criteria, we conclude that this process is out of statistical control for these reasons: There appears to be an upward trend, and there is point lying beyond the upper control limit. The company should take immediate corrective action.

YOUR TURN. Do Exercise 5 "Euro Coins."

CAUTION Upper and lower control limits of a control chart for a proportion p are based on the *actual* behavior of the process, not the *desired* behavior. Upper and lower control limits are totally unrelated to any process *specifications* that may have been decreed by the manufacturer.

TECH CENTER

Control Chart for *p*
Access tech supplements, videos, and data sets at **www.TriolaStats.com**

Statdisk	Minitab	StatCrunch
Visit TriolaStats.com for detailed instructions.	1. Enter the numbers of defects (or items with any particular attribute) in column *C1*. 2. Click **Stat** in the top menu. 3. Select **Control Charts** from the dropdown menu and select **Attribute Charts** and **P** from the submenu. 4. In the *Variables* box enter column **C1**. 5. In *Subgroup sizes* enter the size of the individual samples. 6. Click **OK**.	1. Click **Stat** in the top menu. 2. Select **Control Charts** from the dropdown menu and **p** from the submenu. 3. Select the column to be used, select **Constant,** and enter the size of the individual samples. 4. Click **Compute!** 5. Click the arrow buttons to switch between the chart and numerical results.

TI-83/84 Plus Calculator	Excel	R
Not available.	**XLSTAT Add-In (not available with all XLSTAT licenses)** 1. Click on the **XLSTAT** tab in the Ribbon and then click **SPC**. 2. Select **Attribute charts** from the dropdown menu. 3. For *Chart Family* click **Attribute charts** and select **P chart** under *Chart type*. 4. Click the **General** tab. 5. In the *Data* box enter the cell range of the data. If the data range includes a label, check the **Column labels** box. 6. In the *Common subgroup size* box enter the sample size that is common to all data entries. 7. Click **OK**. The results include a *p* chart.	R command not available at time of publication. Control charts are available in some R packages. *R is rapidly evolving, and an updated list of statistical commands is available at TriolaStats.com.*

14-2 Basic Skills and Concepts

Statistical Literacy and Critical Thinking

1. Minting Quarters Specifications for a quarter require that it be 8.33% nickel and 91.67% copper; it must weigh 5.670 g and have a diameter of 24.26 mm and a thickness of 1.75 mm; and it must have 119 reeds on the edge. A quarter is considered to be defective if it deviates substantially from those specifications. A production process is monitored, defects are recorded and the accompanying control chart is obtained. Does this process appear to be within statistical control? If not, identify any out-of-control criteria that are satisfied. Is the manufacturing process deteriorating?

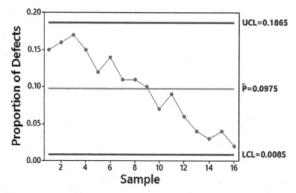

2. Notation The control chart for Exercise 1 shows a value of $\bar{p} = 0.0975$. What does that value denote, and how is it obtained? What do UCL and LCL indicate?

3. Control Limits In constructing a control chart for the proportions of defective dimes, it is found that the lower control limit is -0.00325. How should that value be adjusted?

4. Euro Coins After constructing a control chart for the proportions of defective one-euro coins, it is concluded that the process is within statistical control. Does it follow that almost all of the coins meet the desired specifications? Explain.

Control Charts for p. *In Exercises 5–12, use the given process data to construct a control chart for p. In each case, use the three out-of-control criteria listed near the beginning of this section and determine whether the process is within statistical control. If it is not, identify which of the three out-of-control criteria apply.*

5. Euro Coins Consider a process of minting coins with a value of one euro. Listed below are the numbers of defective coins in successive batches of 10,000 coins randomly selected on consecutive days of production.

$$32 \quad 21 \quad 25 \quad 19 \quad 35 \quad 34 \quad 27 \quad 30 \quad 26 \quad 33$$

6. Euro Coins Repeat Exercise 5, assuming that the size of each batch is 100 instead of 10,000. Compare the control chart to the one found for Exercise 5. Comment on the general quality of the manufacturing process described in Exercise 5 compared to the manufacturing process described in this exercise.

7. Aspirin Tablets Bottles of aspirin tablets typically have labels indicating that each tablet contains 325 mg of aspirin, but the actual amounts can vary between 315 mg and 335 mg. A tablet is defective if it has less than 315 mg of aspirin or more than 335 mg of aspirin. Listed below are numbers of defects found in batches of 1000 tablets.

$$16 \quad 18 \quad 13 \quad 9 \quad 10 \quad 8 \quad 6 \quad 5 \quad 5 \quad 3$$

8. Defibrillators At least one corporation was sued for manufacturing defective heart defibrillators. Listed below are the numbers of defective defibrillators in successive batches of 1000. Construct a control chart for the proportion p of defective defibrillators and determine whether the process is within statistical control. If not, identify which of the three out-of-control criteria apply.

$$8 \quad 5 \quad 6 \quad 4 \quad 9 \quad 3 \quad 12 \quad 7 \quad 8 \quad 5 \quad 22 \quad 4 \quad 9 \quad 10 \quad 11 \quad 8 \quad 7 \quad 6 \quad 8 \quad 5$$

9. Voting Rate In each of recent and consecutive years of national elections held every two years, 1000 people of voting age in the United States were randomly selected and the number who voted was determined, with the results listed below. Comment on the voting behavior of the population.

$$549 \quad 725 \quad 560 \quad 780 \quad 576 \quad 660 \quad 516 \quad 638 \quad 453 \quad 688 \quad 475 \quad 644 \quad 486 \quad 644 \quad 425 \quad 654$$

10. Car Batteries Defective car batteries are a nuisance because they can strand and inconvenience drivers, and drivers could be put in danger. A car battery is considered to be defective if it fails before its warranty expires. Defects are identified when the batteries are returned under the warranty program. The Powerco Battery corporation manufactures car batteries in batches of 250, and the numbers of defects are listed below for each of 12 consecutive batches. Does the manufacturing process require correction?

$$3 \quad 4 \quad 2 \quad 5 \quad 3 \quad 6 \quad 8 \quad 9 \quad 12 \quad 14 \quad 17 \quad 20$$

11. Motor Oil Motor oil is commonly provided in cans labeled as containing 1 quart of the oil. It is common for a car to require 6 quarts of motor oil. If cans are underfilled or overfilled, engine damage can occur. Consider a can to be defective if it contains less than 0.95 qt or more than 1.05 qt. Listed below are numbers of defects in batches of 100 cans randomly selected on 15 different days of production. What action should be taken?

$$9 \quad 6 \quad 12 \quad 14 \quad 8 \quad 7 \quad 11 \quad 11 \quad 7 \quad 8 \quad 9 \quad 12 \quad 10 \quad 5 \quad 8$$

12. Li-ion Batteries Rechargeable lithium ion batteries are used for mobile computing devices and portable power systems. Consider batteries manufactured to provide a capacity of 2200 mAh (milliampere hour) with a minimum of 2150 mAh. Batteries not meeting those specifications are defects. Listed below are numbers of defects in batches of 300 randomly selected batteries in each of 12 consecutive days of production. What action should be taken?

4   3   5   8   12   7   11   9   9   7   6   19

14-2   Beyond the Basics

13. *np* Chart A variation of the control chart for p is the ***np* chart,** in which the *actual numbers* of defects are plotted instead of the *proportions* of defects. The np chart has a centerline value of $n\bar{p}$, and the control limits have values of $n\bar{p} + 3\sqrt{n\bar{p}\,\bar{q}}$ and $n\bar{p} - 3\sqrt{n\bar{p}\,\bar{q}}$. The p chart and the np chart differ only in the scale of values used for the vertical axis. Construct the np chart for Example 1 "Defective Aircraft Altimeters" in this section. Compare the np chart to the control chart for p given in this section.

Chapter Quick Quiz

1. What are *process* data?

2. What is the difference between *random variation* and *assignable variation*?

3. Identify three specific criteria for determining when a process is out of statistical control.

4. What is the difference between an R chart and an $\bar{x}$ chart?

In Exercises 5–8, use the following two control charts that result from testing batches of newly manufactured aircraft altimeters, with 100 in each batch. The original sample values are errors (in feet) obtained when the altimeters are tested in a pressure chamber that simulates an altitude of 6000 ft. The Federal Aviation Administration requires an error of no more than 40 ft at that altitude.

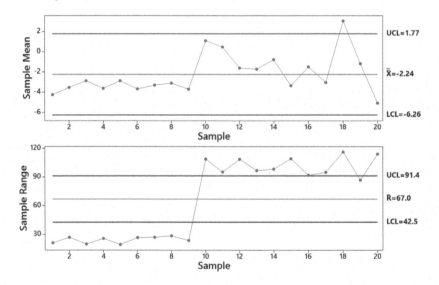

5. Is the process variation within statistical control? Why or why not?

6. What is the value of $\bar{R}$? In general, how is a value of $\bar{R}$ obtained?

7. Is the process mean within statistical control? Why or why not?

8. What is the value of $\bar{\bar{x}}$? In general, how is a value of $\bar{\bar{x}}$ found?

9. If the R chart and $\bar{x}$ chart both showed that the process of manufacturing aircraft altimeters is within statistical control, can we conclude that the altimeters satisfy the Federal Aviation Administration requirement of having errors of no more than 40 ft when tested at an altitude of 6000 ft?

10. Examine the following p chart for defective calculator batteries and briefly describe the action that should be taken.

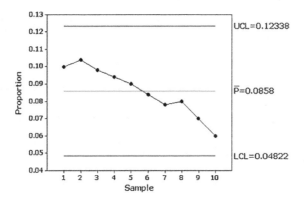

Review Exercises

Energy Consumption. *Exercises 1–4 refer to the amounts of energy consumed in the author's home. (Most of the data are real, but some are fabricated.) Each value represents energy consumed (kWh) in a two-month period. Let each subgroup consist of the six amounts within the same year. Data are available for download at www.TriolaStats.com.*

	Jan.–Feb.	Mar.–April	May–June	July–Aug.	Sept.–Oct.	Nov.–Dec.
Year 1	3637	2888	2359	3704	3432	2446
Year 2	4463	2482	2762	2288	2423	2483
Year 3	3375	2661	2073	2579	2858	2296
Year 4	2812	2433	2266	3128	3286	2749
Year 5	3427	578	3792	3348	2937	2774
Year 6	4016	3458	3395	4249	4003	3118
Year 7	5261	2946	3063	5081	2919	3360
Year 8	3853	3174	3370	4480	3710	3327

1. Energy Consumption: Notation After finding the values of the mean and range for each year, find the values of $\bar{\bar{x}}$ and $\bar{R}$. Then find the values of LCL and UCL for an R chart and find the values of LCL and UCL for an $\bar{x}$ chart.

2. Energy Consumption: R Chart Let each subgroup consist of the 6 values within a year. Construct an R chart and determine whether the process variation is within statistical control. If it is not, identify which of the three out-of-control criteria lead to rejection of statistically stable variation.

3. Energy Consumption: $\bar{x}$ Chart Let each subgroup consist of the 6 values within a year. Construct an $\bar{x}$ chart and determine whether the process mean is within statistical control. If it is not, identify which of the three out-of-control criteria lead to rejection of a statistically stable mean.

4. Energy Consumption: Run Chart Construct a run chart for the 48 values. Does there appear to be a pattern suggesting that the process is not within statistical control?

5. Service Times A manager of a McDonald's franchise has developed a service criterion whereby a dinner order is considered to be defective if it takes longer than 180 seconds. Listed below are numbers of such defects among groups of 50 different customers on each of several consecutive days (based on Data Set 36 "Fast Food" in Appendix B). Construct an appropriate control chart and determine whether the process is within statistical control. What should the manager conclude from the result?

19 21 21 17 15 12 24 26 28 21 22 23 21 20 25

Cumulative Review Exercises

1. Federal Criminal Defendants The following graph depicts results from a study of defendants in federal crime cases (based on data from the Administrative Office of the U.S. Courts).

a. If a defendant is randomly selected what is the probability that this person had their case dismissed before going to trial?

b. If a defendant goes to trial, what is the probability of an acquittal from the trial?

c. If a defendant is randomly selected, what is the probability of getting someone who went to trial and was subsequently convicted?

d. If three defendants are randomly selected, what is the probability that they all pleaded guilty?

e. If a defense attorney is assigned a random defendant, what seems like a reasonable strategy for the client?

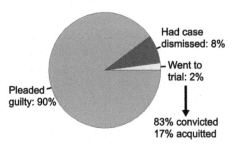

2. Are Nuclear Plants Safe? In a Gallup poll of 1038 adults, 47% said that nuclear plants are safe, 49% said that they are not safe, and 4% had no opinion. Construct a 95% confidence interval estimate of the proportion of all adults who say that nuclear plants are safe. Based on the result, can we conclude that fewer than half of all adults say that nuclear plants are safe?

3. Are Nuclear Plants Safe? Use the data from the preceding exercise to test the claim that fewer than half of all adults say that nuclear plants are safe. Use a 0.05 significance level. Does the conclusion contradict the conclusion from the preceding exercise?

4. Are Nuclear Plants Safe? Using the survey results from Exercise 2 and ignoring those respondents with no opinion, is the following graph somehow misleading? If so, how?

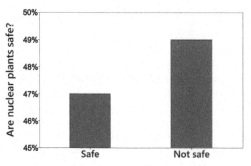

5. Carbon Dioxide and Temperature The table below lists the annual amount of carbon dioxide (parts per million) and the mean annual temperature (°C) of Earth for several different years. Is there a correlation? Can we conclude that human activity that increases carbon dioxide emissions is the cause of the rise in temperatures?

CO_2	390	392	394	397	399	401	404	407	273	415
Temp.	14.52	14.4	14.6	14.81	14.59	14.96	14.83	15.61	15.49	14.97

6. Carbon Dioxide and Temperature Use the sample data from the preceding exercise to find the equation of the regression line. What is the best predicted temperature for a year with a CO_2 level of 420? Is that predicted value likely to be accurate?

7. Heights On the basis of Data Set 1 "Body Data" in Appendix B, assume that heights of men are normally distributed, with a mean of 68.6 in. and a standard deviation of 2.8 in.

a. The U.S. Coast Guard requires that men must have a height between 60 in. and 80 in. Find the percentage of men who satisfy that height requirement.

b. Find the probability that 4 randomly selected men have heights with a mean greater than 70 in.

8. Defective Child Restraint Systems The Tracolyte Manufacturing Company produces plastic frames used for child booster seats in cars. During each week of production, 120 frames are selected and tested for conformance to all regulations by the Department of Transportation. Frames are considered defective if they do not meet all requirements. Listed below are the numbers of defective frames among the 120 that are tested each week. Use a control chart for p to verify that the process is within statistical control. If it is not in control, explain why it is not.

$$3 \quad 2 \quad 4 \quad 6 \quad 5 \quad 9 \quad 7 \quad 10 \quad 12 \quad 15$$

9. Child Restraint Systems Use the numbers of defective child restraint systems given in Exercise 8. Find the mean, median, and standard deviation. What important characteristic of the sample data is missed if we explore the data using those statistics?

10. Eyewitness Accuracy of Police Does stress affect the recall ability of police eyewitnesses? This issue was studied in an experiment that tested police eyewitness memory a week after a non-stressful interrogation of a cooperative suspect and a stressful interrogation of an uncooperative and belligerent suspect. The numbers of details recalled a week after the incident were recorded, and the summary statistics are given below (based on data from "Eyewitness Memory of Police Trainees for Realistic Role Plays," by Yuille et al., *Journal of Applied Psychology*, Vol. 79, No. 6). Use a 0.01 significance level to test the claim in the article that "stress decreases the amount recalled."

$$\text{Nonstress:} \quad n = 40, \bar{x} = 53.3, s = 11.6$$
$$\text{Stress:} \quad n = 40, \bar{x} = 45.3, s = 13.2$$

Technology Project

Carbon Dioxide Listed below are annual mean amounts of carbon dioxide (parts per million) measured at the Mauna Loa Observatory in Hawaii. The amounts are listed in order starting with 1960. Construct and print a run chart. Then use subgroups consisting of the decades and construct and print an R chart and an $\bar{x}$ chart. What do you conclude?

1960s:	317	318	318	319	320	320	321	322	323	325
1970s:	326	326	327	330	330	331	332	334	335	337
1980s:	339	340	341	343	345	346	347	349	352	353
1990s:	354	356	356	357	359	361	363	364	367	368
2000s:	370	371	373	376	378	380	382	384	386	387
2010s:	390	392	394	397	399	401	404	407	273	415

Big (or Very Large) Data Project

Refer to Data Set 46 "Dow Jones Industrial Average" in Appendix B. This data set includes opening values, high values, low values, and closing values for each day from May 27, 1896 to December 28, 2018, and there are records for 31,784 days. Use the closing values to construct a run chart, and comment on the result. *Hint:* For a technology that does not include a function for generating a run chart, create a new column of consecutive integers from 1 to 31,784, then construct a scatterplot using the consecutive integers for *x* (horizontal scale) and use the closing values for *y* (vertical scale).

FROM DATA TO DECISION

Critical Thinking: Are the axial loads within statistical control? Is the process of manufacturing cans proceeding as it should?

Exercises 5–8 in Section 14-1 used process data from the manufacture of 0.0109-in.-thick aluminum cans. Refer to Data Set 41 "Aluminum Cans" in Appendix B and conduct an analysis of the process data for the cans that are 0.0111 in. thick. The values in the data set are the measured axial loads of cans, and the top lids are pressed into place with pressures that vary between 158 lb and 165 lb. The 175 axial loads are in one column, the first 7 are from the first day, the next 7 are from the second day, and so on, so that the "subgroup size" is 7.

Analyzing the Results

Based on the given process data, should the company take any corrective action? Write a report summarizing your conclusions. Address not only the issue of statistical stability but also the ability of the cans to withstand the pressures applied when the top lids are pressed into place. Also compare the behavior of the 0.0111-in. cans to the behavior of the 0.0109-in. cans, and recommend which thickness should be used.

Cooperative Group Activities

1. Out-of-class activity Collect your own process data and analyze them using the methods of this chapter. It would be ideal to collect data from a real manufacturing process, but that might be difficult. Instead, consider using a simulation or referring to published data. Obtain a copy of computer results and write a brief report summarizing your conclusions. Here are some suggestions:

• Shoot five basketball foul shots (or shoot five crumpled sheets of paper into a wastebasket) and record the number of shots made; then repeat this procedure 20 times. Use a *p* chart to test for statistical stability in the proportion of shots made.

• Measure your pulse rate by counting the number of times your heart beats in 1 min. Measure your pulse rate four times each hour for several hours, then construct appropriate control charts. What factors contribute to random variation? Assignable variation?

• Search the Internet and record the closing of the Dow Jones Industrial Average (DJIA) for each business day of the past 12 weeks. Use run and control charts to explore the statistical stability of the DJIA. Identify at least one practical consequence of having this process statistically stable, and identify at least one practical consequence of having this process out of statistical control.

• Find the marriage rate per 10,000 population for several years. Assume that in each year 10,000 people were randomly selected and surveyed to determine whether they were married. Use a p chart to test for statistical stability of the marriage rate. (Other possible rates: death, accident fatality, crime.)

• Search the Internet and find the numbers of runs scored by your favorite baseball team in recent games, then use run and control charts to explore statistical control.

2. In-class activity If the instructor can distribute the numbers of absences for each class meeting, groups of three or four students can analyze them for statistical stability and make recommendations based on the conclusions.

3. Out-of-class activity Conduct research to find a description of Deming's funnel experiment, then use a funnel and marbles to collect data for the different rules for adjusting the funnel location. Construct appropriate control charts for the different rules of funnel adjustment. What does the funnel experiment illustrate? What do you conclude?

4. Out-of-class activity This chapter included annual global mean temperatures and annual carbon dioxide amounts. Identify another factor that should be considered in an investigation of global warming. Find annual data and use the methods of this chapter to conduct an analysis.

15

HOLISTIC STATISTICS

CHAPTER PROBLEM — **Is the Body Temperature of 98.6°F a Myth?**

In this final chapter, we revisit the process of statistical and critical thinking that was introduced in Chapter 1. See Figure 1-3 for a summary of this process and note that the focus is on critical thinking, not mathematical calculations. Instead of jumping into an analysis of data with one particular statistical method, it is wise to begin by considering what the data represent and identifying the goal of the study. Question the source of the data and the sampling

method. Explore the data with relevant graphs, identify any outliers and important statistics. Use two or more technologies to obtain results. Form a conclusion and determine whether the results have statistical significance and/or practical significance.

In this chapter, we will apply statistical and critical thinking to investigate the following question: Is the body temperature of 98.6°F a myth?

```
┌─────────────────────────────────────────────────────────────────────┐
│                             Prepare                                   │
│  1. Context                                                           │
│       • What do the data represent?                                   │
│       • What is the goal of study?                                    │
│  2. Source of the Data                                                │
│       • Are the data from a source with a special interest so that    │
│         there is pressure to obtain results that are favorable to     │
│         the source?                                                   │
│  3. Sampling Method                                                   │
│       • Were the data collected in a way that is unbiased, or were    │
│         the data collected in a way that is biased (such as a         │
│         procedure in which respondents volunteer to participate)?     │
└─────────────────────────────────────────────────────────────────────┘
                                  ↓
┌─────────────────────────────────────────────────────────────────────┐
│                             Analyze                                   │
│  1. Graph the Data                                                    │
│  2. Explore the Data                                                  │
│       • Are there any outliers (numbers very far away from almost     │
│         all of the other data)?                                       │
│       • What important statistics summarize the data (such as the     │
│         mean and standard deviation described in Chapter 3)?          │
│       • How are the data distributed?                                 │
│       • Are there missing data?                                       │
│       • Did many selected subjects refuse to respond?                 │
│  3. Apply Statistical Methods                                         │
│       • Use technology to obtain results.                             │
└─────────────────────────────────────────────────────────────────────┘
                                  ↓
┌─────────────────────────────────────────────────────────────────────┐
│                            Conclude                                   │
│  1. Significance                                                      │
│       • Do the results have statistical significance?                 │
│       • Do the results have practical significance?                   │
└─────────────────────────────────────────────────────────────────────┘
```

FIGURE 1-3   **Statistical and Critical Thinking**

CHAPTER OBJECTIVES

Here are the chapter objectives:

Approach an application of statistics by using appropriate statistical methods. Be thorough by using a variety of methods.

- Begin by considering the context of the data, the source of the data, and the sampling method. Explore the data and include relevant graphs.

- Use a variety of different relevant statistical methods, and use at least two different technologies to generate graphs and conduct data analyses.

- Write a conclusion that highlights the most important features of the data. Address the issues of statistical significance and practical significance.

- Start from the beginning and replicate the study by collecting *new* sample data, then repeat the entire process of analyzing the data. Confirm that the results of the original study continue to appear to be valid.

Is the Body Temperature of 98.6°F a Myth?

Let's consider the common belief that us humans have a body temperature of 98.6°F. Data Set 5 "Body Temperatures" includes body temperatures collected as part of a study reported in the article "A Critical Appraisal of 98.6 Degrees F, the Upper Limit of the Normal Body Temperature, and Other Legacies of Carl Reinhold August Wunderlich," by Mackowiak, Wasserman, and Levine, *Journal of the American Medical Association*, Volume 268, Number 12. Data Set 5 "Body Temperatures" includes four columns of body temperatures, but for the purposes of this analysis, we will use only the values included in the last column, which are body temperatures collected at 12 AM on the second day (Day 2) of the study.

Prepare

Context The data represent body temperatures (°F) measured from subjects who participated in the study. The subjects were healthy volunteers recruited for inpatient vaccine trials that were conducted at the Center for Vaccine Development, University of Maryland School of Medicine. Temperatures were measured during a two-day period preceding treatment with a vaccine.

Source The source of the measured body temperatures is from the authors (Mackowiak, Wasserman, Levine) of the journal article cited above. The study was supported by the U.S. Department of Veterans Affairs and the U.S. Army. The source of the data does not appear to be at all questionable.

Sampling Method The subjects were recruited for a study of a vaccine. A substantial issue would have been hospitalized patients who were not healthy and may have abnormal body temperatures, but the recruited subjects were healthy. Also, the temperatures were measured by the researchers instead of being reported by the subjects. The sampling method appears to be sound.

Analyze

Graph the Data Shown below are a histogram and boxplot (Figure 15-1), and normal quantile plot (Figure 15-2) of the sample of body temperatures. The histogram and normal quantile plot suggest that the data are from a normally distributed population.

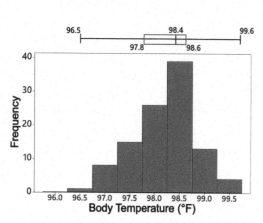

FIGURE 15-1 **Histogram and Boxplot of Body Temperatures (°F)**

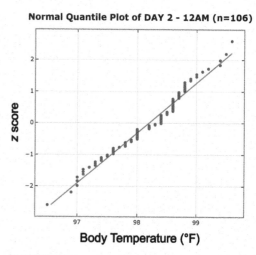

FIGURE 15-2 **Normal Quantile Plot of Body Temperatures (°F)**

Explore the Data Here are important statistics from the sample of measured body temperatures. Note that the sample mean is 98.2°F, not 98.6°F.

Sample Size	106	Five-Number Summary	
Mean	98.2	Minimum:	96.5
Median	98.4	1st Quartile:	97.8
Midrange	98.05	2nd Quartile:	98.4
Variance	0.388	3rd Quartile:	98.6
St. Dev.	0.6228965	Maximum:	99.6
Range	3.1		

Any Outliers? Examination of the normal quantile plot and the minimum and maximum body temperatures reveals that there is one potential outlier: the minimum body temperature of 96.5°F. But when viewed as part of the lowest ten body temperatures (96.5, 96.9, 97.0, 97.0, 97.0, 97.1, 97.1, 97.1, 97.2, 97.3), the minimum of 96.5°F does not appear to be very far from the other lowest values, so that minimum value is not likely to have much of an impact on results.

Apply Statistical Methods

Hypothesis test using the parametric t test with a 0.05 significance level: Example 5 in Section 8-3 involved a hypothesis test of the common belief that the population mean is equal to 98.6°F. Results: With H_0: $\mu = 98.6$°F and H_1: $\mu \neq 98.6$°F, the test statistic is $t = -6.611$, the P-value is 0.0000 (Table: P-value <0.005), the critical values are $t = \pm 1.983$, so we reject H_0 and conclude that there is sufficient evidence to warrant rejection of the common belief that the mean body temperature is equal to 98.6°F. (See the following Statdisk and Minitab displays for this hypothesis test.)

Statdisk Results

```
Alternative Hypothesis:
  μ not equal to μ(hyp)

t Test
Test Statistic, t: -6.61146
Critical t:       ±1.98281
P-Value:          0.00000

95% Confidence interval:
98.08004 <  μ < 98.31996
```

Minitab Results

```
Test

Null hypothesis        H₀: μ = 98.6
Alternative hypothesis H₁: μ ≠ 98.6

 T-Value   P-Value
  -6.61     0.000
```

95% confidence interval using the t distribution: Based on the preceding hypothesis test, we rejected the common belief that the mean body temperature is equal to 98.6°F, but that begs this question: *If the mean body temperature is not 98.6°F, then what is it?* A confidence interval gives us valuable information about that mean. The 95% confidence interval estimate of μ is 98.08°F $< \mu <$ 98.32°F. We have 95% confidence that the mean body temperature is between 98.08°F and 98.32°F. Because the confidence interval does not include 98.6°F, we have strong evidence suggesting that the mean body temperature is *not* equal to 98.6°F.

Randomization: Using the resampling method of randomization, shift the sample values so that the sample mean changes from 98.2°F to the claimed value of 98.6°F, and then use bootstrapping to generate 1000 samples. Using the sorted 1000 sample means, find the number of those sample means that are at least as extreme as 98.2°F. A typical randomization procedure will yield 1000 sample means such that the number of sample means that are at least as extreme as 98.2°F is 0 or close to 0. See the following displays from Statdisk and Minitab. (The Minitab P-value of less than

continued

0.002 shows that among 1000 randomizations, fewer than 2 yielded sample means at least as extreme as 98.2°F.) This shows that if the population mean is really 98.6°F, it is highly unlikely that we would ever get a sample with a mean of 98.2°F, but we really *did* get a sample with a mean of 98.2°F. The reasonable explanation for that result is that it could not have come from a population with a mean of 98.6°F, so we have strong evidence against 98.6°F being the population mean.

Statdisk Randomization

Mean of Original Data:	98.20000
Number of means 98.20000 or below: 0	
Number of means 99.00000 or above: 0	
Proportion of means 98.20000 or below:	0.00000
Proportion of means 99.00000 or above:	0.00000

Minitab Randomization

Randomization Test

Null hypothesis H_0: μ = 98.6
Alternative hypothesis H_1: $\mu \neq$ 98.6

Number of Resamples	Mean	StDev	P-Value
1000	98.5976	0.0621	< 0.0020

Bootstrap Resampling: Using the bootstrap resampling method results in the 95% confidence interval of 98.07°F $< \mu <$ 98.31°F, which is very close to the 95% confidence interval obtained by using the t distribution. (Due to the randomness used in the bootstrap method, the confidence interval could vary somewhat.)

Nonparametric test using the Wilcoxon signed-ranks test with a 0.05 significance level: Test statistic is $z = -5.67$ and the critical values are $z = \pm 1.96$, so conclude that there is sufficient evidence to warrant rejection of the claim that the median body temperature is equal to 98.6°F. Note that this nonparametric test is not greatly affected by the presence of outliers.

Nonparametric test using the sign test for matched pairs with a 0.05 significance level: Test statistic is $z = -4.61$ and the critical values are $z = \pm 1.96$, so conclude that there is sufficient evidence to warrant rejection of the claim that body temperatures have a median of 98.6°F.

Simulation: For the simulation, use a technology to generate samples of size 106 (as in the sample), a normal distribution (as in the sample), an assumed mean of 98.6°F, and a standard deviation of 0.6228965°F (as in the sample). Listed below in ascending order are the means from 50 samples generated with the assumption that the population mean is 98.6°F. *See that the actual sample mean of 98.2°F is not even close to any of the simulated means.* We now reason as follows:

1. If the population mean is really 98.6°F, the sample mean of 98.2°F is very unlikely.

2. Because the sample mean of 98.2°F actually did occur, either the sample is very unusual, or the assumed mean of 98.6°F is wrong.

3. Given that none of the simulated samples has a mean close to the sample mean of 98.2°F, it appears that the better explanation is that the assumed population mean of 98.6°F is wrong.

98.5	98.5	98.5	98.5	98.5	98.5	98.5	98.6	98.6	98.6
98.6	98.6	98.6	98.6	98.6	98.6	98.6	98.6	98.6	98.6
98.6	98.6	98.6	98.6	98.6	98.6	98.6	98.6	98.6	98.6
98.6	98.6	98.6	98.6	98.6	98.6	98.6	98.6	98.6	98.6
98.6	98.6	98.6	98.6	98.7	98.7	98.7	98.7	98.7	98.8

Conclusion

Statistical and Practical Significance The preceding results use a variety of different approaches, and they are all in agreement that the population does not have a mean body temperature equal to 98.6°F. Because there is sufficient evidence to warrant rejection of the common belief that the mean body temperature is 98.6°F, the results do have *statistical* significance. Based on the sample mean of 98.20°F and the preceding confidence intervals, the discrepancy between 98.6°F and the actual mean appears to be somewhere between 0.28°F and 0.55°F, and that difference is fairly substantial, so the difference does appear to have *practical* significance.

There's More to the Story

Replication The preceding example led to the conclusion that the mean body temperature is not 98.6°F. Also, the preceding results suggest that the actual population mean is likely to be somewhere between 98.08°F and 98.32°F. These results are based on the 1992 study conducted by Mackowiak, Wasserman, and Levine. A more recent study conducted by Jonathan Hausmann et al. used smartphone crowdsourcing to collect a sample of 5038 body temperatures from 329 subjects. The subjects used a variety of different thermometers and an app to manually report their temperatures. The results from this 2018 study suggest that the population mean body temperature is 97.7°F. (See "Using Smartphone Crowdsourcing to Redefine Normal and Febrile Temperatures in Adults: Results from the Feverprints Study," by Jonathan S. Hausmann et al., in *Journal of General Internal Medicine*.) Therefore, we don't have agreement on the true value of the mean body temperature, but there is agreement that it is not 98.6°F. There is also agreement that there isn't a single value that should be used for the "normal" body temperature. Body temperatures vary throughout the day, and they vary for different people.

Where Did 98.6°F Come From?

The value of 98.6°F came from the nineteenth century German physician Carl Wunderlich. He collected data from 25,000 patients by holding a foot-long thermometer in patients' armpits for 20 minutes. His value of 98.6°F was used until the 1992 study by Mackowiak et al. Current thermometers are more accurate, and they are typically placed in the patient's mouth instead of the armpit, so results are more reliable. Even though we now have better data showing that the value of 98.6°F is wrong, many people continue to believe that 98.6°F is the correct value.

Key Takeaways

The preceding analyses illustrate the different approaches that can be used. Here are some important takeaways for conducting an important statistical analysis:

- **Preliminary Analysis** Start by questioning what the data represent, and identifying the goal of the study. Question the source of the data and the sampling method. Explore the data with relevant graphs, identify any outliers and important statistics.

- **Go Beyond the *P*-Value!** It is wise to not rely solely on a conclusion suggested by a *P*-value. The *P*-value leads us to a binary conclusion equivalent to either rejecting the null hypothesis or failing to reject the null hypothesis, but a confidence interval can give us information about the size of an effect, and graphs can give us deep insight that might not be otherwise obtained. Instead of relying on a single statistical method, use a variety of different methods. Use parametric methods if they satisfy distribution requirements, and also use nonparametric methods that don't require particular distributions. Use randomization and bootstrapping methods.

- **Multiple Technologies** It is wise to not rely solely on a single technology. Some technologies are a bit quirky and can provide results that can be easily misunderstood or misinterpreted.

- **Replicate** Repeat the entire study after collecting a new set of sample data. Compare results from the original study and the new study.

Holistic Exercises

1. Differences from Matched Pairs Use the second-day 8 AM temperatures paired with the second-day 12 AM temperatures from Data Set 5 "Body Temperatures." Test the null hypothesis that the matched pairs have differences with a mean equal to 0°F. Use relevant parametric and nonparametric methods.

2. Differences from Matched Pairs Use the first-day 12 AM temperatures paired with the second-day 12 AM temperatures from Data Set 5 "Body Temperatures." Test the null hypothesis that the matched pairs have differences with a mean equal to 0°F. Use relevant parametric and nonparametric methods.

3. Correlation Use the second-day 8 AM temperatures paired with the second-day 12 AM temperatures from Data Set 5 "Body Temperatures." Test for a correlation using the linear correlation coefficient r and the rank correlation coefficient r_s.

4. Correlation Use the first-day 12 AM temperatures paired with the second-day 12 AM temperatures from Data Set 5 "Body Temperatures." Test for a correlation using the linear correlation coefficient r and the rank correlation coefficient r_s.

5. Fevers Use the sample statistics from the study conducted by Mackowiak et al. ($\bar{x} = 98.20°F$ and $s = 0.62°F$). Find the 99th percentile to be used as the cutoff for determining that a patient has a fever. Compare the result to the 99th percentile that would be obtained by using the mean of 98.6°F instead of 98.2°F. Compare the results.

The body temperatures included in this chapter used only the values of the 12 AM temperatures from the second day (Day 2) as listed in Data Set 5 "Body Temperatures." For Exercises 6-8, use the indicated samples of temperatures from Data Set 5 "Body Temperatures" and repeat the test of the claim that the mean body temperature is equal to 98.6°F using at least several different methods. Also, compare the results to those found previously in this chapter.

6. Replication Use the 8 AM temperatures from the second day to test the claim that the mean body temperature is 98.6°F.

7. Replication Use the 12 AM temperatures from the first day (Day 1).

8. Replication Use the 8 AM temperatures from the first day (Day 1).

9. Simulation This chapter included a simulation method for testing the claim that the mean body temperature is equal to 98.6°F. Use a technology to generate samples of size 106 (as in the sample), a normal distribution (as in the sample), an assumed mean of 98.6°F, and a standard deviation of 0.6228965°F (as in the sample). Find the means of the simulated samples, then arrange them in ascending order, and determine how many of the simulated means are at least as extreme as the sample mean of 98.2°F that was obtained in the 1992 study. Write a conclusion and provide an explanation justifying the conclusion.

TABLE A-1 Binomial Probabilities

n	x	.01	.05	.10	.20	.30	.40	.50	.60	.70	.80	.90	.95	.99	x
2	0	.980	.903	.810	.640	.490	.360	.250	.160	.090	.040	.010	.003	0+	0
	1	.020	.095	.180	.320	.420	.480	.500	.480	.420	.320	.180	.095	.020	1
	2	0+	.003	.010	.040	.090	.160	.250	.360	.490	.640	.810	.903	.980	2
3	0	.970	.857	.729	.512	.343	.216	.125	.064	.027	.008	.001	0+	0+	0
	1	.029	.135	.243	.384	.441	.432	.375	.288	.189	.096	.027	.007	0+	1
	2	0+	.007	.027	.096	.189	.288	.375	.432	.441	.384	.243	.135	.029	2
	3	0+	0+	.001	.008	.027	.064	.125	.216	.343	.512	.729	.857	.970	3
4	0	.961	.815	.656	.410	.240	.130	.063	.026	.008	.002	0+	0+	0+	0
	1	.039	.171	.292	.410	.412	.346	.250	.154	.076	.026	.004	0+	0+	1
	2	.001	.014	.049	.154	.265	.346	.375	.346	.265	.154	.049	.014	.001	2
	3	0+	0+	.004	.026	.076	.154	.250	.346	.412	.410	.292	.171	.039	3
	4	0+	0+	0+	.002	.008	.026	.063	.130	.240	.410	.656	.815	.961	4
5	0	.951	.774	.590	.328	.168	.078	.031	.010	.002	0+	0+	0+	0+	0
	1	.048	.204	.328	.410	.360	.259	.156	.077	.028	.006	0+	0+	0+	1
	2	.001	.021	.073	.205	.309	.346	.313	.230	.132	.051	.008	.001	0+	2
	3	0+	.001	.008	.051	.132	.230	.313	.346	.309	.205	.073	.021	.001	3
	4	0+	0+	0+	.006	.028	.077	.156	.259	.360	.410	.328	.204	.048	4
	5	0+	0+	0+	0+	.002	.010	.031	.078	.168	.328	.590	.774	.951	5
6	0	.941	.735	.531	.262	.118	.047	.016	.004	.001	0+	0+	0+	0+	0
	1	.057	.232	.354	.393	.303	.187	.094	.037	.010	.002	0+	0+	0+	1
	2	.001	.031	.098	.246	.324	.311	.234	.138	.060	.015	.001	0+	0+	2
	3	0+	.002	.015	.082	.185	.276	.312	.276	.185	.082	.015	.002	0+	3
	4	0+	0+	.001	.015	.060	.138	.234	.311	.324	.246	.098	.031	.001	4
	5	0+	0+	0+	.002	.010	.037	.094	.187	.303	.393	.354	.232	.057	5
	6	0+	0+	0+	0+	.001	.004	.016	.047	.118	.262	.531	.735	.941	6
7	0	.932	.698	.478	.210	.082	.028	.008	.002	0+	0+	0+	0+	0+	0
	1	.066	.257	.372	.367	.247	.131	.055	.017	.004	0+	0+	0+	0+	1
	2	.002	.041	.124	.275	.318	.261	.164	.077	.025	.004	0+	0+	0+	2
	3	0+	.004	.023	.115	.227	.290	.273	.194	.097	.029	.003	0+	0+	3
	4	0+	0+	.003	.029	.097	.194	.273	.290	.227	.115	.023	.004	0+	4
	5	0+	0+	0+	.004	.025	.077	.164	.261	.318	.275	.124	.041	.002	5
	6	0+	0+	0+	0+	.004	.017	.055	.131	.247	.367	.372	.257	.066	6
	7	0+	0+	0+	0+	0+	.002	.008	.028	.082	.210	.478	.698	.932	7
8	0	.923	.663	.430	.168	.058	.017	.004	.001	0+	0+	0+	0+	0+	0
	1	.075	.279	.383	.336	.198	.090	.031	.008	.001	0+	0+	0+	0+	1
	2	.003	.051	.149	.294	.296	.209	.109	.041	.010	.001	0+	0+	0+	2
	3	0+	.005	.033	.147	.254	.279	.219	.124	.047	.009	0+	0+	0+	3
	4	0+	0+	.005	.046	.136	.232	.273	.232	.136	.046	.005	0+	0+	4
	5	0+	0+	0+	.009	.047	.124	.219	.279	.254	.147	.033	.005	0+	5
	6	0+	0+	0+	.001	.010	.041	.109	.209	.296	.294	.149	.051	.003	6
	7	0+	0+	0+	0+	.001	.008	.031	.090	.198	.336	.383	.279	.075	7
	8	0+	0+	0+	0+	0+	.001	.004	.017	.058	.168	.430	.663	.923	8

NOTE: 0+ represents a positive probability value less than 0.0005.
From Frederick C. Mosteller, Robert E. K. Rourke, and George B. Thomas, Jr., *Probability with Statistical Applications,* 2nd ed., © 1970. Reprinted and electronically reproduced by permission of Pearson Education, Inc., Upper Saddle River, New Jersey.

NEGATIVE z Scores

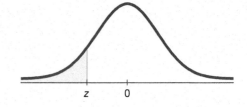

TABLE A-2 Standard Normal (z) Distribution: Cumulative Area from the LEFT

z	.00	.01	.02	.03	.04	.05	.06	.07	.08	.09
−3.50 and lower	.0001									
−3.4	.0003	.0003	.0003	.0003	.0003	.0003	.0003	.0003	.0003	.0002
−3.3	.0005	.0005	.0005	.0004	.0004	.0004	.0004	.0004	.0004	.0003
−3.2	.0007	.0007	.0006	.0006	.0006	.0006	.0006	.0005	.0005	.0005
−3.1	.0010	.0009	.0009	.0009	.0008	.0008	.0008	.0008	.0007	.0007
−3.0	.0013	.0013	.0013	.0012	.0012	.0011	.0011	.0011	.0010	.0010
−2.9	.0019	.0018	.0018	.0017	.0016	.0016	.0015	.0015	.0014	.0014
−2.8	.0026	.0025	.0024	.0023	.0023	.0022	.0021	.0021	.0020	.0019
−2.7	.0035	.0034	.0033	.0032	.0031	.0030	.0029	.0028	.0027	.0026
−2.6	.0047	.0045	.0044	.0043	.0041	.0040	.0039	.0038	.0037	.0036
−2.5	.0062	.0060	.0059	.0057	.0055	.0054	.0052	.0051 *	.0049	.0048
−2.4	.0082	.0080	.0078	.0075	.0073	.0071	.0069	.0068	.0066	.0064
−2.3	.0107	.0104	.0102	.0099	.0096	.0094	.0091	.0089	.0087	.0084
−2.2	.0139	.0136	.0132	.0129	.0125	.0122	.0119	.0116	.0113	.0110
−2.1	.0179	.0174	.0170	.0166	.0162	.0158	.0154	.0150	.0146	.0143
−2.0	.0228	.0222	.0217	.0212	.0207	.0202	.0197	.0192	.0188	.0183
−1.9	.0287	.0281	.0274	.0268	.0262	.0256	.0250	.0244	.0239	.0233
−1.8	.0359	.0351	.0344	.0336	.0329	.0322	.0314	.0307	.0301	.0294
−1.7	.0446	.0436	.0427	.0418	.0409	.0401	.0392	.0384	.0375	.0367
−1.6	.0548	.0537	.0526	.0516	.0505 *	.0495	.0485	.0475	.0465	.0455
−1.5	.0668	.0655	.0643	.0630	.0618	.0606	.0594	.0582	.0571	.0559
−1.4	.0808	.0793	.0778	.0764	.0749	.0735	.0721	.0708	.0694	.0681
−1.3	.0968	.0951	.0934	.0918	.0901	.0885	.0869	.0853	.0838	.0823
−1.2	.1151	.1131	.1112	.1093	.1075	.1056	.1038	.1020	.1003	.0985
−1.1	.1357	.1335	.1314	.1292	.1271	.1251	.1230	.1210	.1190	.1170
−1.0	.1587	.1562	.1539	.1515	.1492	.1469	.1446	.1423	.1401	.1379
−0.9	.1841	.1814	.1788	.1762	.1736	.1711	.1685	.1660	.1635	.1611
−0.8	.2119	.2090	.2061	.2033	.2005	.1977	.1949	.1922	.1894	.1867
−0.7	.2420	.2389	.2358	.2327	.2296	.2266	.2236	.2206	.2177	.2148
−0.6	.2743	.2709	.2676	.2643	.2611	.2578	.2546	.2514	.2483	.2451
−0.5	.3085	.3050	.3015	.2981	.2946	.2912	.2877	.2843	.2810	.2776
−0.4	.3446	.3409	.3372	.3336	.3300	.3264	.3228	.3192	.3156	.3121
−0.3	.3821	.3783	.3745	.3707	.3669	.3632	.3594	.3557	.3520	.3483
−0.2	.4207	.4168	.4129	.4090	.4052	.4013	.3974	.3936	.3897	.3859
−0.1	.4602	.4562	.4522	.4483	.4443	.4404	.4364	.4325	.4286	.4247
−0.0	.5000	.4960	.4920	.4880	.4840	.4801	.4761	.4721	.4681	.4641

NOTE: For values of z below −3.49, use 0.0001 for the area.

(continued)

*Use these common values that result from interpolation:

z Score	Area
−1.645	0.0500
−2.575	0.0050

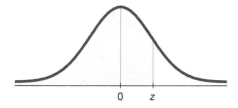

POSITIVE z Scores

TABLE A-2 *(continued)* Cumulative Area from the LEFT

z	.00	.01	.02	.03	.04	.05	.06	.07	.08	.09
0.0	.5000	.5040	.5080	.5120	.5160	.5199	.5239	.5279	.5319	.5359
0.1	.5398	.5438	.5478	.5517	.5557	.5596	.5636	.5675	.5714	.5753
0.2	.5793	.5832	.5871	.5910	.5948	.5987	.6026	.6064	.6103	.6141
0.3	.6179	.6217	.6255	.6293	.6331	.6368	.6406	.6443	.6480	.6517
0.4	.6554	.6591	.6628	.6664	.6700	.6736	.6772	.6808	.6844	.6879
0.5	.6915	.6950	.6985	.7019	.7054	.7088	.7123	.7157	.7190	.7224
0.6	.7257	.7291	.7324	.7357	.7389	.7422	.7454	.7486	.7517	.7549
0.7	.7580	.7611	.7642	.7673	.7704	.7734	.7764	.7794	.7823	.7852
0.8	.7881	.7910	.7939	.7967	.7995	.8023	.8051	.8078	.8106	.8133
0.9	.8159	.8186	.8212	.8238	.8264	.8289	.8315	.8340	.8365	.8389
1.0	.8413	.8438	.8461	.8485	.8508	.8531	.8554	.8577	.8599	.8621
1.1	.8643	.8665	.8686	.8708	.8729	.8749	.8770	.8790	.8810	.8830
1.2	.8849	.8869	.8888	.8907	.8925	.8944	.8962	.8980	.8997	.9015
1.3	.9032	.9049	.9066	.9082	.9099	.9115	.9131	.9147	.9162	.9177
1.4	.9192	.9207	.9222	.9236	.9251	.9265	.9279	.9292	.9306	.9319
1.5	.9332	.9345	.9357	.9370	.9382	.9394	.9406	.9418	.9429	.9441
1.6	.9452	.9463	.9474	.9484	.9495 *	.9505	.9515	.9525	.9535	.9545
1.7	.9554	.9564	.9573	.9582	.9591	.9599	.9608	.9616	.9625	.9633
1.8	.9641	.9649	.9656	.9664	.9671	.9678	.9686	.9693	.9699	.9706
1.9	.9713	.9719	.9726	.9732	.9738	.9744	.9750	.9756	.9761	.9767
2.0	.9772	.9778	.9783	.9788	.9793	.9798	.9803	.9808	.9812	.9817
2.1	.9821	.9826	.9830	.9834	.9838	.9842	.9846	.9850	.9854	.9857
2.2	.9861	.9864	.9868	.9871	.9875	.9878	.9881	.9884	.9887	.9890
2.3	.9893	.9896	.9898	.9901	.9904	.9906	.9909	.9911	.9913	.9916
2.4	.9918	.9920	.9922	.9925	.9927	.9929	.9931	.9932	.9934	.9936
2.5	.9938	.9940	.9941	.9943	.9945	.9946	.9948	.9949 *	.9951	.9952
2.6	.9953	.9955	.9956	.9957	.9959	.9960	.9961	.9962	.9963	.9964
2.7	.9965	.9966	.9967	.9968	.9969	.9970	.9971	.9972	.9973	.9974
2.8	.9974	.9975	.9976	.9977	.9977	.9978	.9979	.9979	.9980	.9981
2.9	.9981	.9982	.9982	.9983	.9984	.9984	.9985	.9985	.9986	.9986
3.0	.9987	.9987	.9987	.9988	.9988	.9989	.9989	.9989	.9990	.9990
3.1	.9990	.9991	.9991	.9991	.9992	.9992	.9992	.9992	.9993	.9993
3.2	.9993	.9993	.9994	.9994	.9994	.9994	.9994	.9995	.9995	.9995
3.3	.9995	.9995	.9995	.9996	.9996	.9996	.9996	.9996	.9996	.9997
3.4	.9997	.9997	.9997	.9997	.9997	.9997	.9997	.9997	.9997	.9998
3.50 and up	.9999									

NOTE: For values of *z* above 3.49, use 0.9999 for the area.

*Use these common values that result from interpolation:

z Score	Area
1.645	0.9500
2.575	0.9950

Common Critical Values

Confidence Level	Critical Value
0.90	1.645
0.95	1.96
0.99	2.575

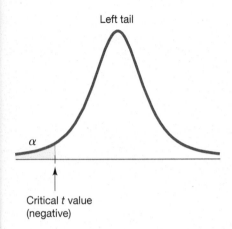

Left tail

α

Critical t value
(negative)

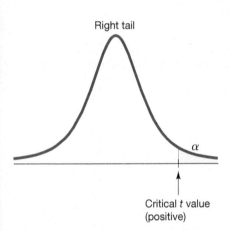

Right tail

α

Critical t value
(positive)

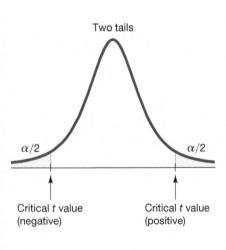

Two tails

α/2   α/2

Critical t value   Critical t value
(negative)   (positive)

TABLE A-3 t Distribution: Critical t Values

Degrees of Freedom	Area in One Tail				
	0.005	0.01	0.025	0.05	0.10
	Area in Two Tails				
	0.01	0.02	0.05	0.10	0.20
1	63.657	31.821	12.706	6.314	3.078
2	9.925	6.965	4.303	2.920	1.886
3	5.841	4.541	3.182	2.353	1.638
4	4.604	3.747	2.776	2.132	1.533
5	4.032	3.365	2.571	2.015	1.476
6	3.707	3.143	2.447	1.943	1.440
7	3.499	2.998	2.365	1.895	1.415
8	3.355	2.896	2.306	1.860	1.397
9	3.250	2.821	2.262	1.833	1.383
10	3.169	2.764	2.228	1.812	1.372
11	3.106	2.718	2.201	1.796	1.363
12	3.055	2.681	2.179	1.782	1.356
13	3.012	2.650	2.160	1.771	1.350
14	2.977	2.624	2.145	1.761	1.345
15	2.947	2.602	2.131	1.753	1.341
16	2.921	2.583	2.120	1.746	1.337
17	2.898	2.567	2.110	1.740	1.333
18	2.878	2.552	2.101	1.734	1.330
19	2.861	2.539	2.093	1.729	1.328
20	2.845	2.528	2.086	1.725	1.325
21	2.831	2.518	2.080	1.721	1.323
22	2.819	2.508	2.074	1.717	1.321
23	2.807	2.500	2.069	1.714	1.319
24	2.797	2.492	2.064	1.711	1.318
25	2.787	2.485	2.060	1.708	1.316
26	2.779	2.479	2.056	1.706	1.315
27	2.771	2.473	2.052	1.703	1.314
28	2.763	2.467	2.048	1.701	1.313
29	2.756	2.462	2.045	1.699	1.311
30	2.750	2.457	2.042	1.697	1.310
31	2.744	2.453	2.040	1.696	1.309
32	2.738	2.449	2.037	1.694	1.309
33	2.733	2.445	2.035	1.692	1.308
34	2.728	2.441	2.032	1.691	1.307
35	2.724	2.438	2.030	1.690	1.306
36	2.719	2.434	2.028	1.688	1.306
37	2.715	2.431	2.026	1.687	1.305
38	2.712	2.429	2.024	1.686	1.304
39	2.708	2.426	2.023	1.685	1.304
40	2.704	2.423	2.021	1.684	1.303
45	2.690	2.412	2.014	1.679	1.301
50	2.678	2.403	2.009	1.676	1.299
60	2.660	2.390	2.000	1.671	1.296
70	2.648	2.381	1.994	1.667	1.294
80	2.639	2.374	1.990	1.664	1.292
90	2.632	2.368	1.987	1.662	1.291
100	2.626	2.364	1.984	1.660	1.290
200	2.601	2.345	1.972	1.653	1.286
300	2.592	2.339	1.968	1.650	1.284
400	2.588	2.336	1.966	1.649	1.284
500	2.586	2.334	1.965	1.648	1.283
1000	2.581	2.330	1.962	1.646	1.282
2000	2.578	2.328	1.961	1.646	1.282
Large	2.576	2.326	1.960	1.645	1.282

TABLE A-4 Chi-Square (X^2) Distribution

Degrees of Freedom	Area to the *Right* of the Critical Value									
	0.995	0.99	0.975	0.95	0.90	0.10	0.05	0.025	0.01	0.005
1	—	—	0.001	0.004	0.016	2.706	3.841	5.024	6.635	7.879
2	0.010	0.020	0.051	0.103	0.211	4.605	5.991	7.378	9.210	10.597
3	0.072	0.115	0.216	0.352	0.584	6.251	7.815	9.348	11.345	12.838
4	0.207	0.297	0.484	0.711	1.064	7.779	9.488	11.143	13.277	14.860
5	0.412	0.554	0.831	1.145	1.610	9.236	11.071	12.833	15.086	16.750
6	0.676	0.872	1.237	1.635	2.204	10.645	12.592	14.449	16.812	18.548
7	0.989	1.239	1.690	2.167	2.833	12.017	14.067	16.013	18.475	20.278
8	1.344	1.646	2.180	2.733	3.490	13.362	15.507	17.535	20.090	21.955
9	1.735	2.088	2.700	3.325	4.168	14.684	16.919	19.023	21.666	23.589
10	2.156	2.558	3.247	3.940	4.865	15.987	18.307	20.483	23.209	25.188
11	2.603	3.053	3.816	4.575	5.578	17.275	19.675	21.920	24.725	26.757
12	3.074	3.571	4.404	5.226	6.304	18.549	21.026	23.337	26.217	28.299
13	3.565	4.107	5.009	5.892	7.042	19.812	22.362	24.736	27.688	29.819
14	4.075	4.660	5.629	6.571	7.790	21.064	23.685	26.119	29.141	31.319
15	4.601	5.229	6.262	7.261	8.547	22.307	24.996	27.488	30.578	32.801
16	5.142	5.812	6.908	7.962	9.312	23.542	26.296	28.845	32.000	34.267
17	5.697	6.408	7.564	8.672	10.085	24.769	27.587	30.191	33.409	35.718
18	6.265	7.015	8.231	9.390	10.865	25.989	28.869	31.526	34.805	37.156
19	6.844	7.633	8.907	10.117	11.651	27.204	30.144	32.852	36.191	38.582
20	7.434	8.260	9.591	10.851	12.443	28.412	31.410	34.170	37.566	39.997
21	8.034	8.897	10.283	11.591	13.240	29.615	32.671	35.479	38.932	41.401
22	8.643	9.542	10.982	12.338	14.042	30.813	33.924	36.781	40.289	42.796
23	9.260	10.196	11.689	13.091	14.848	32.007	35.172	38.076	41.638	44.181
24	9.886	10.856	12.401	13.848	15.659	33.196	36.415	39.364	42.980	45.559
25	10.520	11.524	13.120	14.611	16.473	34.382	37.652	40.646	44.314	46.928
26	11.160	12.198	13.844	15.379	17.292	35.563	38.885	41.923	45.642	48.290
27	11.808	12.879	14.573	16.151	18.114	36.741	40.113	43.194	46.963	49.645
28	12.461	13.565	15.308	16.928	18.939	37.916	41.337	44.461	48.278	50.993
29	13.121	14.257	16.047	17.708	19.768	39.087	42.557	45.722	49.588	52.336
30	13.787	14.954	16.791	18.493	20.599	40.256	43.773	46.979	50.892	53.672
40	20.707	22.164	24.433	26.509	29.051	51.805	55.758	59.342	63.691	66.766
50	27.991	29.707	32.357	34.764	37.689	63.167	67.505	71.420	76.154	79.490
60	35.534	37.485	40.482	43.188	46.459	74.397	79.082	83.298	88.379	91.952
70	43.275	45.442	48.758	51.739	55.329	85.527	90.531	95.023	100.425	104.215
80	51.172	53.540	57.153	60.391	64.278	96.578	101.879	106.629	112.329	116.321
90	59.196	61.754	65.647	69.126	73.291	107.565	113.145	118.136	124.116	128.299
100	67.328	70.065	74.222	77.929	82.358	118.498	124.342	129.561	135.807	140.169

Source: Donald B. Owen, *Handbook of Statistical Tables.*

Degrees of Freedom

$n - 1$	**Confidence interval or hypothesis test** for a standard deviation σ or variance σ^2
$k - 1$	**Goodness-of-fit test** with k different categories
$(r - 1)(c - 1)$	**Contingency table test** with r rows and c columns
$k - 1$	**Kruskal-Wallis test** with k different samples

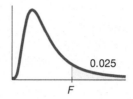

TABLE A-5 F Distribution ($\alpha = 0.025$ in the right tail)

Denominator degrees of freedom (df₂)	Numerator degrees of freedom (df₁)								
	1	2	3	4	5	6	7	8	9
1	647.79	799.50	864.16	899.58	921.85	937.11	948.22	956.66	963.28
2	38.506	39.000	39.165	39.248	39.298	39.331	39.335	39.373	39.387
3	17.443	16.044	15.439	15.101	14.885	14.735	14.624	14.540	14.473
4	12.218	10.649	9.9792	9.6045	9.3645	9.1973	9.0741	8.9796	8.9047
5	10.007	8.4336	7.7636	7.3879	7.1464	6.9777	6.8531	6.7572	6.6811
6	8.8131	7.2599	6.5988	6.2272	5.9876	5.8198	5.6955	5.5996	5.5234
7	8.0727	6.5415	5.8898	5.5226	5.2852	5.1186	4.9949	4.8993	4.8232
8	7.5709	6.0595	5.4160	5.0526	4.8173	4.6517	4.5286	4.4333	4.3572
9	7.2093	5.7147	5.0781	4.7181	4.4844	4.3197	4.1970	4.1020	4.0260
10	6.9367	5.4564	4.8256	4.4683	4.2361	4.0721	3.9498	3.8549	3.7790
11	6.7241	5.2559	4.6300	4.2751	4.0440	3.8807	3.7586	3.6638	3.5879
12	6.5538	5.0959	4.4742	4.1212	3.8911	3.7283	3.6065	3.5118	3.4358
13	6.4143	4.9653	4.3472	3.9959	3.7667	3.6043	3.4827	3.3880	3.3120
14	6.2979	4.8567	4.2417	3.8919	3.6634	3.5014	3.3799	3.2853	3.2093
15	6.1995	4.7650	4.1528	3.8043	3.5764	3.4147	3.2934	3.1987	3.1227
16	6.1151	4.6867	4.0768	3.7294	3.5021	3.3406	3.2194	3.1248	3.0488
17	6.0420	4.6189	4.0112	3.6648	3.4379	3.2767	3.1556	3.0610	2.9849
18	5.9781	4.5597	3.9539	3.6083	3.3820	3.2209	3.0999	3.0053	2.9291
19	5.9216	4.5075	3.9034	3.5587	3.3327	3.1718	3.0509	2.9563	2.8801
20	5.8715	4.4613	3.8587	3.5147	3.2891	3.1283	3.0074	2.9128	2.8365
21	5.8266	4.4199	3.8188	3.4754	3.2501	3.0895	2.9686	2.8740	2.7977
22	5.7863	4.3828	3.7829	3.4401	3.2151	3.0546	2.9338	2.8392	2.7628
23	5.7498	4.3492	3.7505	3.4083	3.1835	3.0232	2.9023	2.8077	2.7313
24	5.7166	4.3187	3.7211	3.3794	3.1548	2.9946	2.8738	2.7791	2.7027
25	5.6864	4.2909	3.6943	3.3530	3.1287	2.9685	2.8478	2.7531	2.6766
26	5.6586	4.2655	3.6697	3.3289	3.1048	2.9447	2.8240	2.7293	2.6528
27	5.6331	4.2421	3.6472	3.3067	3.0828	2.9228	2.8021	2.7074	2.6309
28	5.6096	4.2205	3.6264	3.2863	3.0626	2.9027	2.7820	2.6872	2.6106
29	5.5878	4.2006	3.6072	3.2674	3.0438	2.8840	2.7633	2.6686	2.5919
30	5.5675	4.1821	3.5894	3.2499	3.0265	2.8667	2.7460	2.6513	2.5746
40	5.4239	4.0510	3.4633	3.1261	2.9037	2.7444	2.6238	2.5289	2.4519
60	5.2856	3.9253	3.3425	3.0077	2.7863	2.6274	2.5068	2.4117	2.3344
120	5.1523	3.8046	3.2269	2.8943	2.6740	2.5154	2.3948	2.2994	2.2217
∞	5.0239	3.6889	3.1161	2.7858	2.5665	2.4082	2.2875	2.1918	2.1136

(continued)

TABLE A-5 *(continued)* F Distribution ($\alpha = 0.025$ in the right tail)

		Numerator degrees of freedom (df$_1$)									
		10	12	15	20	24	30	40	60	120	∞
	1	968.63	976.71	984.87	993.10	997.25	1001.4	1005.6	1009.8	1014.0	1018.3
	2	39.398	39.415	39.431	39.448	39.456	39.465	39.473	39.481	39.490	39.498
	3	14.419	14.337	14.253	14.167	14.124	14.081	14.037	13.992	13.947	13.902
	4	8.8439	8.7512	8.6565	8.5599	8.5109	8.4613	8.4111	8.3604	8.3092	8.2573
	5	6.6192	6.5245	6.4277	6.3286	6.2780	6.2269	6.1750	6.1225	6.0693	6.0153
	6	5.4613	5.3662	5.2687	5.1684	5.1172	5.0652	5.0125	4.9589	4.9044	4.8491
	7	4.7611	4.6658	4.5678	4.4667	4.4150	4.3624	4.3089	4.2544	4.1989	4.1423
	8	4.2951	4.1997	4.1012	3.9995	3.9472	3.8940	3.8398	3.7844	3.7279	3.6702
	9	3.9639	3.8682	3.7694	3.6669	3.6142	3.5604	3.5055	3.4493	3.3918	3.3329
	10	3.7168	3.6209	3.5217	3.4185	3.3654	3.3110	3.2554	3.1984	3.1399	3.0798
	11	3.5257	3.4296	3.3299	3.2261	3.1725	3.1176	3.0613	3.0035	2.9441	2.8828
	12	3.3736	3.2773	3.1772	3.0728	3.0187	2.9633	2.9063	2.8478	2.7874	2.7249
	13	3.2497	3.1532	3.0527	2.9477	2.8932	2.8372	2.7797	2.7204	2.6590	2.5955
	14	3.1469	3.0502	2.9493	2.8437	2.7888	2.7324	2.6742	2.6142	2.5519	2.4872
Denominator degrees of freedom (df$_2$)	15	3.0602	2.9633	2.8621	2.7559	2.7006	2.6437	2.5850	2.5242	2.4611	2.3953
	16	2.9862	2.8890	2.7875	2.6808	2.6252	2.5678	2.5085	2.4471	2.3831	2.3163
	17	2.9222	2.8249	2.7230	2.6158	2.5598	2.5020	2.4422	2.3801	2.3153	2.2474
	18	2.8664	2.7689	2.6667	2.5590	2.5027	2.4445	2.3842	2.3214	2.2558	2.1869
	19	2.8172	2.7196	2.6171	2.5089	2.4523	2.3937	2.3329	2.2696	2.2032	2.1333
	20	2.7737	2.6758	2.5731	2.4645	2.4076	2.3486	2.2873	2.2234	2.1562	2.0853
	21	2.7348	2.6368	2.5338	2.4247	2.3675	2.3082	2.2465	2.1819	2.1141	2.0422
	22	2.6998	2.6017	2.4984	2.3890	2.3315	2.2718	2.2097	2.1446	2.0760	2.0032
	23	2.6682	2.5699	2.4665	2.3567	2.2989	2.2389	2.1763	2.1107	2.0415	1.9677
	24	2.6396	2.5411	2.4374	2.3273	2.2693	2.2090	2.1460	2.0799	2.0099	1.9353
	25	2.6135	2.5149	2.4110	2.3005	2.2422	2.1816	2.1183	2.0516	1.9811	1.9055
	26	2.5896	2.4908	2.3867	2.2759	2.2174	2.1565	2.0928	2.0257	1.9545	1.8781
	27	2.5676	2.4688	2.3644	2.2533	2.1946	2.1334	2.0693	2.0018	1.9299	1.8527
	28	2.5473	2.4484	2.3438	2.2324	2.1735	2.1121	2.0477	1.9797	1.9072	1.8291
	29	2.5286	2.4295	2.3248	2.2131	2.1540	2.0923	2.0276	1.9591	1.8861	1.8072
	30	2.5112	2.4120	2.3072	2.1952	2.1359	2.0739	2.0089	1.9400	1.8664	1.7867
	40	2.3882	2.2882	2.1819	2.0677	2.0069	1.9429	1.8752	1.8028	1.7242	1.6371
	60	2.2702	2.1692	2.0613	1.9445	1.8817	1.8152	1.7440	1.6668	1.5810	1.4821
	120	2.1570	2.0548	1.9450	1.8249	1.7597	1.6899	1.6141	1.5299	1.4327	1.3104
	∞	2.0483	1.9447	1.8326	1.7085	1.6402	1.5660	1.4835	1.3883	1.2684	1.0000

Based on data from Maxine Merrington and Catherine M. Thompson, "Tables of Percentage Points of the Inverted Beta (*F*) Distribution," *Biometrika 33* (1943): 80–84.

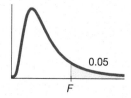

TABLE A-5 *(continued)* F Distribution ($\alpha = 0.05$ in the right tail)

				Numerator degrees of freedom (df$_1$)					
	1	**2**	**3**	**4**	**5**	**6**	**7**	**8**	**9**
1	161.45	199.50	215.71	224.58	230.16	233.99	236.77	238.88	240.54
2	18.513	19.000	19.164	19.247	19.296	19.330	19.353	19.371	19.385
3	10.128	9.5521	9.2766	9.1172	9.0135	8.9406	8.8867	8.8452	8.8123
4	7.7086	6.9443	6.5914	6.3882	6.2561	6.1631	6.0942	6.0410	6.9988
5	6.6079	5.7861	5.4095	5.1922	5.0503	4.9503	4.8759	4.8183	4.7725
6	5.9874	5.1433	4.7571	4.5337	4.3874	4.2839	4.2067	4.1468	4.0990
7	5.5914	4.7374	4.3468	4.1203	3.9715	3.8660	3.7870	3.7257	3.6767
8	5.3177	4.4590	4.0662	3.8379	3.6875	3.5806	3.5005	3.4381	3.3881
9	5.1174	4.2565	3.8625	3.6331	3.4817	3.3738	3.2927	3.2296	3.1789
10	4.9646	4.1028	3.7083	3.4780	3.3258	3.2172	3.1355	3.0717	3.0204
11	4.8443	3.9823	3.5874	3.3567	3.2039	3.0946	3.0123	2.9480	2.8962
12	4.7472	3.8853	3.4903	3.2592	3.1059	2.9961	2.9134	2.8486	2.7964
13	4.6672	3.8056	3.4105	3.1791	3.0254	2.9153	2.8321	2.7669	2.7144
14	4.6001	3.7389	3.3439	3.1122	2.9582	2.8477	2.7642	2.6987	2.6458
15	4.5431	3.6823	3.2874	3.0556	2.9013	2.7905	2.7066	2.6408	2.5876
16	4.4940	3.6337	3.2389	3.0069	2.8524	2.7413	2.6572	2.5911	2.5377
17	4.4513	3.5915	3.1968	2.9647	2.8100	2.6987	2.6143	2.5480	2.4943
18	4.4139	3.5546	3.1599	2.9277	2.7729	2.6613	2.5767	2.5102	2.4563
19	4.3807	3.5219	3.1274	2.8951	2.7401	2.6283	2.5435	2.4768	2.4227
20	4.3512	3.4928	3.0984	2.8661	2.7109	2.5990	2.5140	2.4471	2.3928
21	4.3248	3.4668	3.0725	2.8401	2.6848	2.5727	2.4876	2.4205	2.3660
22	4.3009	3.4434	3.0491	2.8167	2.6613	2.5491	2.4638	2.3965	2.3419
23	4.2793	3.4221	3.0280	2.7955	2.6400	2.5277	2.4422	2.3748	2.3201
24	4.2597	3.4028	3.0088	2.7763	2.6207	2.5082	2.4226	2.3551	2.3002
25	4.2417	3.3852	2.9912	2.7587	2.6030	2.4904	2.4047	2.3371	2.2821
26	4.2252	3.3690	2.9752	2.7426	2.5868	2.4741	2.3883	2.3205	2.2655
27	4.2100	3.3541	2.9604	2.7278	2.5719	2.4591	2.3732	2.3053	2.2501
28	4.1960	3.3404	2.9467	2.7141	2.5581	2.4453	2.3593	2.2913	2.2360
29	4.1830	3.3277	2.9340	2.7014	2.5454	2.4324	2.3463	2.2783	2.2229
30	4.1709	3.3158	2.9223	2.6896	2.5336	2.4205	2.3343	2.2662	2.2107
40	4.0847	3.2317	2.8387	2.6060	2.4495	2.3359	2.2490	2.1802	2.1240
60	4.0012	3.1504	2.7581	2.5252	2.3683	2.2541	2.1665	2.0970	2.0401
120	3.9201	3.0718	2.6802	2.4472	2.2899	2.1750	2.0868	2.0164	1.9588
∞	3.8415	2.9957	2.6049	2.3719	2.2141	2.0986	2.0096	1.9384	1.8799

Denominator degrees of freedom (df$_2$)

(continued)

TABLE A-5 *(continued)* F Distribution ($\alpha = 0.05$ in the right tail)

	Numerator degrees of freedom (df_1)									
	10	12	15	20	24	30	40	60	120	∞
1	241.88	243.91	245.95	248.01	249.05	250.10	251.14	252.20	253.25	254.31
2	19.396	19.413	19.429	19.446	19.454	19.462	19.471	19.479	19.487	19.496
3	8.7855	8.7446	8.7029	8.6602	8.6385	8.6166	8.5944	8.5720	8.5494	8.5264
4	5.9644	5.9117	5.8578	5.8025	5.7744	5.7459	5.7170	5.6877	5.6581	5.6281
5	4.7351	4.6777	4.6188	4.5581	4.5272	4.4957	4.4638	4.4314	4.3985	4.3650
6	4.0600	3.9999	3.9381	3.8742	3.8415	3.8082	3.7743	3.7398	3.7047	3.6689
7	3.6365	3.5747	3.5107	3.4445	3.4105	3.3758	3.3404	3.3043	3.2674	3.2298
8	3.3472	3.2839	3.2184	3.1503	3.1152	3.0794	3.0428	3.0053	2.9669	2.9276
9	3.1373	3.0729	3.0061	2.9365	2.9005	2.8637	2.8259	2.7872	2.7475	2.7067
10	2.9782	2.9130	2.8450	2.7740	2.7372	2.6996	2.6609	2.6211	2.5801	2.5379
11	2.8536	2.7876	2.7186	2.6464	2.6090	2.5705	2.5309	2.4901	2.4480	2.4045
12	2.7534	2.6866	2.6169	2.5436	2.5055	2.4663	2.4259	2.3842	2.3410	2.2962
13	2.6710	2.6037	2.5331	2.4589	2.4202	2.3803	2.3392	2.2966	2.2524	2.2064
14	2.6022	2.5342	2.4630	2.3879	2.3487	2.3082	2.2664	2.2229	2.1778	2.1307
15	2.5437	2.4753	2.4034	2.3275	2.2878	2.2468	2.2043	2.1601	2.1141	2.0658
16	2.4935	2.4247	2.3522	2.2756	2.2354	2.1938	2.1507	2.1058	2.0589	2.0096
17	2.4499	2.3807	2.3077	2.2304	2.1898	2.1477	2.1040	2.0584	2.0107	1.9604
18	2.4117	2.3421	2.2686	2.1906	2.1497	2.1071	2.0629	2.0166	1.9681	1.9168
19	2.3779	2.3080	2.2341	2.1555	2.1141	2.0712	2.0264	1.9795	1.9302	1.8780
20	2.3479	2.2776	2.2033	2.1242	2.0825	2.0391	1.9938	1.9464	1.8963	1.8432
21	2.3210	2.2504	2.1757	2.0960	2.0540	2.0102	1.9645	1.9165	1.8657	1.8117
22	2.2967	2.2258	2.1508	2.0707	2.0283	1.9842	1.9380	1.8894	1.8380	1.7831
23	2.2747	2.2036	2.1282	2.0476	2.0050	1.9605	1.9139	1.8648	1.8128	1.7570
24	2.2547	2.1834	2.1077	2.0267	1.9838	1.9390	1.8920	1.8424	1.7896	1.7330
25	2.2365	2.1649	2.0889	2.0075	1.9643	1.9192	1.8718	1.8217	1.7684	1.7110
26	2.2197	2.1479	2.0716	1.9898	1.9464	1.9010	1.8533	1.8027	1.7488	1.6906
27	2.2043	2.1323	2.0558	1.9736	1.9299	1.8842	1.8361	1.7851	1.7306	1.6717
28	2.1900	2.1179	2.0411	1.9586	1.9147	1.8687	1.8203	1.7689	1.7138	1.6541
29	2.1768	2.1045	2.0275	1.9446	1.9005	1.8543	1.8055	1.7537	1.6981	1.6376
30	2.1646	2.0921	2.0148	1.9317	1.8874	1.8409	1.7918	1.7396	1.6835	1.6223
40	2.0772	2.0035	1.9245	1.8389	1.7929	1.7444	1.6928	1.6373	1.5766	1.5089
60	1.9926	1.9174	1.8364	1.7480	1.7001	1.6491	1.5943	1.5343	1.4673	1.3893
120	1.9105	1.8337	1.7505	1.6587	1.6084	1.5543	1.4952	1.4290	1.3519	1.2539
∞	1.8307	1.7522	1.6664	1.5705	1.5173	1.4591	1.3940	1.3180	1.2214	1.0000

Based on data from Maxine Merrington and Catherine M. Thompson, "Tables of Percentage Points of the Inverted Beta (F) Distribution," *Biometrika* 33 (1943): 80–84.

TABLE A-6 Critical Values of the Pearson Correlation Coefficient r

n	$\alpha = .05$	$\alpha = .01$
4	.950	.990
5	.878	.959
6	.811	.917
7	.754	.875
8	.707	.834
9	.666	.798
10	.632	.765
11	.602	.735
12	.576	.708
13	.553	.684
14	.532	.661
15	.514	.641
16	.497	.623
17	.482	.606
18	.468	.590
19	.456	.575
20	.444	.561
25	.396	.505
30	.361	.463
35	.335	.430
40	.312	.402
45	.294	.378
50	.279	.361
60	.254	.330
70	.236	.305
80	.220	.286
90	.207	.269
100	.196	.256

NOTE: To test H_0: $\rho = 0$ (no correlation) against H_1: $\rho \neq 0$ (correlation), reject H_0 if the absolute value of r is greater than or equal to the critical value in the table.

TABLE A-7 Critical Values for the Sign Test

	α			
	.005 (one tail)	.01 (one tail)	.025 (one tail)	.05 (one tail)
n	.01 (two tails)	.02 (two tails)	.05 (two tails)	.10 (two tails)
1	*	*	*	*
2	*	*	*	*
3	*	*	*	*
4	*	*	*	*
5	*	*	*	0
6	*	*	0	0
7	*	0	0	0
8	0	0	0	1
9	0	0	1	1
10	0	0	1	1
11	0	1	1	2
12	1	1	2	2
13	1	1	2	3
14	1	2	2	3
15	2	2	3	3
16	2	2	3	4
17	2	3	4	4
18	3	3	4	5
19	3	4	4	5
20	3	4	5	5
21	4	4	5	6
22	4	5	5	6
23	4	5	6	7
24	5	5	6	7
25	5	6	7	7

NOTES:
1. *indicates that it is not possible to get a value in the critical region, so fail to reject the null hypothesis.
2. Reject the null hypothesis if the number of the less frequent sign (x) is less than or equal to the value in the table.
3. For values of n greater than 25, a normal approximation is used with

$$z = \frac{(x + 0.5) - \left(\dfrac{n}{2}\right)}{\dfrac{\sqrt{n}}{2}}$$

TABLE A-8 Critical Values of T for the Wilcoxon Signed-Ranks Test

	α			
	.005 (one tail)	.01 (one tail)	.025 (one tail)	.05 (one tail)
n	.01 (two tails)	.02 (two tails)	.05 (two tails)	.10 (two tails)
5	*	*	*	1
6	*	*	1	2
7	*	0	2	4
8	0	2	4	6
9	2	3	6	8
10	3	5	8	11
11	5	7	11	14
12	7	10	14	17
13	10	13	17	21
14	13	16	21	26
15	16	20	25	30
16	19	24	30	36
17	23	28	35	41
18	28	33	40	47
19	32	38	46	54
20	37	43	52	60
21	43	49	59	68
22	49	56	66	75
23	55	62	73	83
24	61	69	81	92
25	68	77	90	101
26	76	85	98	110
27	84	93	107	120
28	92	102	117	130
29	100	111	127	141
30	109	120	137	152

NOTES:

1. *indicates that it is not possible to get a value in the critical region, so fail to reject the null hypothesis.

2. Conclusions:

   Reject the null hypothesis if the test statistic T is less than or equal to the critical value found in this table.

   Fail to reject the null hypothesis if the test statistic T is greater than the critical value found in the table.

Based on data from *Some Rapid Approximate Statistical Procedures*, Copyright © 1949, 1964 Lederle Laboratories Division of American Cyanamid Company.

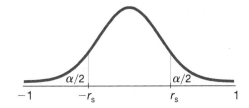

TABLE A-9 Critical Values of Spearman's Rank
Correlation Coefficient r_s

n	$\alpha = 0.10$	$\alpha = 0.05$	$\alpha = 0.02$	$\alpha = 0.01$
5	.900	—	—	—
6	.829	.886	.943	—
7	.714	.786	.893	.929
8	.643	.738	.833	.881
9	.600	.700	.783	.833
10	.564	.648	.745	.794
11	.536	.618	.709	.755
12	.503	.587	.678	.727
13	.484	.560	.648	.703
14	.464	.538	.626	.679
15	.446	.521	.604	.654
16	.429	.503	.582	.635
17	.414	.485	.566	.615
18	.401	.472	.550	.600
19	.391	.460	.535	.584
20	.380	.447	.520	.570
21	.370	.435	.508	.556
22	.361	.425	.496	.544
23	.353	.415	.486	.532
24	.344	.406	.476	.521
25	.337	.398	.466	.511
26	.331	.390	.457	.501
27	.324	.382	.448	.491
28	.317	.375	.440	.483
29	.312	.368	.433	.475
30	.306	.362	.425	.467

NOTES:
1. For $n > 30$ use $r_s = \pm z/\sqrt{n-1}$, where z corresponds to the level of
significance. For example, if $\alpha = 0.05$, then $z = 1.96$.
2. If the absolute value of the test statistic r_s is greater than or equal to the positive
critical value, then reject H_0: $\rho_s = 0$ and conclude that there is sufficient evidence to
support the claim of a correlation.

Based on data from *Biostatistical Analysis*, 4th edition © 1999, by Jerrold Zar, Prentice
Hall, Inc., Upper Saddle River, New Jersey, and "Distribution of Sums of Squares of Rank
Differences to Small Numbers with Individuals," *The Annals of Mathematical Statistics*,
Vol. 9, No. 2.

TABLE A-10 Runs Test for Randomness: Critical Values for Number of Runs G

Value of n_1		n_2=2	3	4	5	6	7	8	9	10	11	12	13	14	15	16	17	18	19	20
2		1	1	1	1	1	1	1	1	1	1	2	2	2	2	2	2	2	2	2
		6	6	6	6	6	6	6	6	6	6	6	6	6	6	6	6	6	6	6
3		1	1	1	1	2	2	2	2	2	2	2	2	2	3	3	3	3	3	3
		6	8	8	8	8	8	8	8	8	8	8	8	8	8	8	8	8	8	8
4		1	1	1	2	2	2	3	3	3	3	3	3	3	3	4	4	4	4	4
		6	8	9	9	9	10	10	10	10	10	10	10	10	10	10	10	10	10	10
5		1	1	2	2	3	3	3	3	3	4	4	4	4	4	4	4	5	5	5
		6	8	9	10	10	11	11	12	12	12	12	12	12	12	12	12	12	12	12
6		1	2	2	3	3	3	3	4	4	4	4	5	5	5	5	5	5	6	6
		6	8	9	10	11	12	12	13	13	13	13	14	14	14	14	14	14	14	14
7		1	2	2	3	3	3	4	4	5	5	5	5	5	6	6	6	6	6	6
		6	8	10	11	12	13	13	14	14	14	14	15	15	15	16	16	16	16	16
8		1	2	3	3	3	4	4	5	5	5	6	6	6	6	6	7	7	7	7
		6	8	10	11	12	13	14	14	15	15	16	16	16	16	17	17	17	17	17
9		1	2	3	3	4	4	5	5	5	6	6	6	7	7	7	7	8	8	8
		6	8	10	12	13	14	14	15	16	16	16	17	17	18	18	18	18	18	18
10		1	2	3	3	4	5	5	5	6	6	7	7	7	7	8	8	8	8	9
		6	8	10	12	13	14	15	16	16	17	17	18	18	18	19	19	19	20	20
11		1	2	3	4	4	5	5	6	6	7	7	7	8	8	8	9	9	9	9
		6	8	10	12	13	14	15	16	17	17	18	19	19	19	20	20	20	21	21
12		2	2	3	4	4	5	6	6	7	7	7	8	8	8	9	9	9	10	10
		6	8	10	12	13	14	16	16	17	18	19	19	20	20	21	21	21	22	22
13		2	2	3	4	5	5	6	6	7	7	8	8	9	9	9	10	10	10	10
		6	8	10	12	14	15	16	17	18	19	19	20	20	21	21	22	22	23	23
14		2	2	3	4	5	5	6	7	7	8	8	9	9	9	10	10	10	11	11
		6	8	10	12	14	15	16	17	18	19	20	20	21	22	22	23	23	23	24
15		2	3	3	4	5	6	6	7	7	8	8	9	9	10	10	11	11	11	12
		6	8	10	12	14	15	16	18	18	19	20	21	22	22	23	23	24	24	25
16		2	3	4	4	5	6	6	7	8	8	9	9	10	10	11	11	11	12	12
		6	8	10	12	14	16	17	18	19	20	21	21	22	23	23	24	25	25	25
17		2	3	4	4	5	6	7	7	8	9	9	10	10	11	11	11	12	12	13
		6	8	10	12	14	16	17	18	19	20	21	22	23	23	24	25	25	26	26
18		2	3	4	5	5	6	7	8	8	9	9	10	10	11	11	12	12	13	13
		6	8	10	12	14	16	17	18	19	20	21	22	23	24	25	25	26	26	27
19		2	3	4	5	6	6	7	8	8	9	10	10	11	11	12	12	13	13	13
		6	8	10	12	14	16	17	18	20	21	22	23	23	24	25	26	26	27	27
20		2	3	4	5	6	6	7	8	9	9	10	10	11	12	12	13	13	13	14
		6	8	10	12	14	16	17	18	20	21	22	23	24	25	25	26	27	27	28

NOTES:

1. The entries in this table are the critical G values, assuming a two-tailed test with a significance level of $\alpha = 0.05$.
2. Reject the null hypothesis of randomness if either of these conditions is satisfied:
   - The number of runs G is less than or equal to the smaller entry in the table.
   - The number of runs G is greater than or equal to the larger entry in the table.

From "Tables for Testing Randomness of Groupings in a Sequence of Alternatives," *The Annals of Mathematical Statistics*, Vol. 14, No. 1. Reprinted with permission of the Institute of Mathematical Statistics.

Formulas by Mario F. Triola
Copyright 2022 Pearson Education, Inc.

Ch. 3: Descriptive Statistics

$\bar{x} = \dfrac{\Sigma x}{n}$ Mean

$\bar{x} = \dfrac{\Sigma(f \cdot x)}{\Sigma f}$ Mean (frequency table)

$s = \sqrt{\dfrac{\Sigma(x - \bar{x})^2}{n - 1}}$ Standard deviation

$s = \sqrt{\dfrac{n(\Sigma x^2) - (\Sigma x)^2}{n(n - 1)}}$ Standard deviation (shortcut)

$s = \sqrt{\dfrac{n[\Sigma(f \cdot x^2)] - [\Sigma(f \cdot x)]^2}{n(n - 1)}}$ Standard deviation (frequency table)

$\text{variance} = s^2$

Ch. 4: Probability

$P(A \text{ or } B) = P(A) + P(B)$ if A, B are mutually exclusive

$P(A \text{ or } B) = P(A) + P(B) - P(A \text{ and } B)$
  if A, B are not mutually exclusive

$P(A \text{ and } B) = P(A) \cdot P(B)$ if A, B are independent

$P(A \text{ and } B) = P(A) \cdot P(B|A)$ if A, B are dependent

$P(\bar{A}) = 1 - P(A)$ Rule of complements

${}_nP_r = \dfrac{n!}{(n - r)!}$ Permutations (no elements alike)

$\dfrac{n!}{n_1! \, n_2! \, \ldots \, n_k!}$ Permutations (n_1 alike, ...)

${}_nC_r = \dfrac{n!}{(n - r)! \, r!}$ Combinations

Ch. 5: Probability Distributions

$\mu = \Sigma[x \cdot P(x)]$ Mean (prob. dist.)

$\sigma = \sqrt{\Sigma[x^2 \cdot P(x)] - \mu^2}$ Standard deviation (prob. dist.)

$P(x) = \dfrac{n!}{(n - x)! \, x!} \cdot p^x \cdot q^{n-x}$ Binomial probability

$\mu = n \cdot p$ Mean (binomial)

$\sigma^2 = n \cdot p \cdot q$ Variance (binomial)

$\sigma = \sqrt{n \cdot p \cdot q}$ Standard deviation (binomial)

$P(x) = \dfrac{\mu^x \cdot e^{-\mu}}{x!}$ Poisson distribution where $e = 2.71828$

Ch. 6: Normal Distribution

$z = \dfrac{x - \mu}{\sigma}$ or $\dfrac{x - \bar{x}}{s}$ Standard score

$\mu_{\bar{x}} = \mu$ Central limit theorem

$\sigma_{\bar{x}} = \dfrac{\sigma}{\sqrt{n}}$ Central limit theorem (Standard error)

Ch. 7: Confidence Intervals (one population)

$\hat{p} - E < p < \hat{p} + E$ Proportion

  where $E = z_{\alpha/2}\sqrt{\dfrac{\hat{p}\hat{q}}{n}}$

$\bar{x} - E < \mu < \bar{x} + E$ Mean

  where $E = t_{\alpha/2}\dfrac{s}{\sqrt{n}}$ (σ unknown)

  or $E = z_{\alpha/2}\dfrac{\sigma}{\sqrt{n}}$ (σ known)

$\dfrac{(n - 1)s^2}{\chi_R^2} < \sigma^2 < \dfrac{(n - 1)s^2}{\chi_L^2}$ Variance

Ch. 7: Sample Size Determination

$n = \dfrac{[z_{\alpha/2}]^2 0.25}{E^2}$ Proportion

$n = \dfrac{[z_{\alpha/2}]^2 \hat{p}\hat{q}}{E^2}$ Proportion ($\hat{p}$ and $\hat{q}$ are known)

$n = \left[\dfrac{z_{\alpha/2}\sigma}{E}\right]^2$ Mean

Ch. 8: Test Statistics (one population)

$z = \dfrac{\hat{p} - p}{\sqrt{\dfrac{pq}{n}}}$ Proportion—one population

$t = \dfrac{\bar{x} - \mu}{\dfrac{s}{\sqrt{n}}}$ Mean—one population (σ unknown)

$z = \dfrac{\bar{x} - \mu}{\dfrac{\sigma}{\sqrt{n}}}$ Mean—one population (σ known)

$\chi^2 = \dfrac{(n - 1)s^2}{\sigma^2}$ Standard deviation or variance—one population

Formulas by Mario F. Triola
Copyright 2022 Pearson Education, Inc.

Ch. 9: Confidence Intervals (two populations)

$$(\hat{p}_1 - \hat{p}_2) - E < (p_1 - p_2) < (\hat{p}_1 - \hat{p}_2) + E$$

$$\text{where } E = z_{\alpha/2}\sqrt{\frac{\hat{p}_1 \hat{q}_1}{n_1} + \frac{\hat{p}_2 \hat{q}_2}{n_2}}$$

$$(\bar{x}_1 - \bar{x}_2) - E < (\mu_1 - \mu_2) < (\bar{x}_1 - \bar{x}_2) + E \quad \text{(Indep.)}$$

$$\text{where } E = t_{\alpha/2}\sqrt{\frac{s_1^2}{n_1} + \frac{s_2^2}{n_2}} \quad \begin{array}{l} (\text{df} = \text{smaller of} \\ n_1 - 1, n_2 - 1) \end{array}$$

(σ_1 and σ_2 unknown and not assumed equal)

$$E = t_{\alpha/2}\sqrt{\frac{s_p^2}{n_1} + \frac{s_p^2}{n_2}} \quad (\text{df} = n_1 + n_2 - 2)$$

$$s_p^2 = \frac{(n_1 - 1)s_1^2 + (n_2 - 1)s_2^2}{(n_1 - 1) + (n_2 - 1)}$$

(σ_1 and σ_2 unknown but assumed equal)

$$E = z_{\alpha/2}\sqrt{\frac{\sigma_1^2}{n_1} + \frac{\sigma_2^2}{n_2}}$$

(σ_1, σ_2 known)

$$\bar{d} - E < \mu_d < \bar{d} + E \quad \text{(Matched pairs)}$$

$$\text{where } E = t_{\alpha/2}\frac{s_d}{\sqrt{n}} \quad (\text{df} = n - 1)$$

Ch. 9: Test Statistics (two populations)

$$z = \frac{(\hat{p}_1 - \hat{p}_2) - (p_1 - p_2)}{\sqrt{\frac{\bar{p}\,\bar{q}}{n_1} + \frac{\bar{p}\,\bar{q}}{n_2}}} \quad \text{Two proportions} \qquad \bar{p} = \frac{x_1 + x_2}{n_1 + n_2}$$

$$t = \frac{(\bar{x}_1 - \bar{x}_2) - (\mu_1 - \mu_2)}{\sqrt{\frac{s_1^2}{n_1} + \frac{s_2^2}{n_2}}} \quad \begin{array}{l} \text{df} = \text{smaller of} \\ n_1 - 1, n_2 - 1 \end{array}$$

Two means—independent; σ_1 and σ_2 unknown, and not assumed equal.

$$t = \frac{(\bar{x}_1 - \bar{x}_2) - (\mu_1 - \mu_2)}{\sqrt{\frac{s_p^2}{n_1} + \frac{s_p^2}{n_2}}} \quad (\text{df} = n_1 + n_2 - 2)$$

$$s_p^2 = \frac{(n_1 - 1)s_1^2 + (n_2 - 1)s_2^2}{n_1 + n_2 - 2}$$

Two means—independent; σ_1 and σ_2 unknown, but assumed equal.

$$z = \frac{(\bar{x}_1 - \bar{x}_2) - (\mu_1 - \mu_2)}{\sqrt{\frac{\sigma_1^2}{n_1} + \frac{\sigma_2^2}{n_2}}} \quad \begin{array}{l} \text{Two means—independent;} \\ \sigma_1, \sigma_2 \text{ known.} \end{array}$$

$$t = \frac{\bar{d} - \mu_d}{\frac{s_d}{\sqrt{n}}} \quad \text{Two means—matched pairs (df} = n - 1)$$

$$F = \frac{s_1^2}{s_2^2} \quad \begin{array}{l} \text{Standard deviation or variance—} \\ \text{two populations (where } s_1^2 \geq s_2^2) \end{array}$$

Ch. 10: Linear Correlation/Regression

$$\text{Correlation } r = \frac{n\Sigma xy - (\Sigma x)(\Sigma y)}{\sqrt{n(\Sigma x^2) - (\Sigma x)^2}\sqrt{n(\Sigma y^2) - (\Sigma y)^2}}$$

$$\text{or } r = \frac{\Sigma(z_x z_y)}{n - 1} \quad \begin{array}{l} \text{where } z_x = z \text{ score for } x \\ z_y = z \text{ score for } y \end{array}$$

$$\text{Slope: } b_1 = \frac{n\Sigma xy - (\Sigma x)(\Sigma y)}{n(\Sigma x^2) - (\Sigma x)^2} \text{ or } b_1 = r\frac{s_y}{s_x}$$

y-Intercept:

$$b_0 = \bar{y} - b_1\bar{x} \text{ or } b_0 = \frac{(\Sigma y)(\Sigma x^2) - (\Sigma x)(\Sigma xy)}{n(\Sigma x^2) - (\Sigma x)^2}$$

$$\hat{y} = b_0 + b_1 x \quad \text{Estimated eq. of regression line}$$

$$r^2 = \frac{\text{explained variation}}{\text{total variation}}$$

$$s_e = \sqrt{\frac{\Sigma(y - \hat{y})^2}{n - 2}} \text{ or } \sqrt{\frac{\Sigma y^2 - b_0\Sigma y - b_1\Sigma xy}{n - 2}}$$

$$\hat{y} - E < y < \hat{y} + E \quad \text{Prediction interval}$$

$$\text{where } E = t_{\alpha/2}s_e\sqrt{1 + \frac{1}{n} + \frac{n(x_0 - \bar{x})^2}{n(\Sigma x^2) - (\Sigma x)^2}}$$

Ch. 11: Goodness-of-Fit and Contingency Tables

$$\chi^2 = \Sigma\frac{(O - E)^2}{E} \quad \text{Goodness-of-fit (df} = k - 1)$$

$$\chi^2 = \Sigma\frac{(O - E)^2}{E} \quad \text{Contingency table [df} = (r - 1)(c - 1)]$$

$$\text{where } E = \frac{(\text{row total})(\text{column total})}{(\text{grand total})}$$

$$\chi^2 = \frac{(|b - c| - 1)^2}{b + c} \quad \text{McNemar's test for matched pairs (df} = 1)$$

Ch. 12: One-Way Analysis of Variance

Procedure for testing H_0: $\mu_1 = \mu_2 = \mu_3 = \ldots$

1. Use software or calculator to obtain results.
2. Identify the P-value.
3. Form conclusion:

   If P-value $\leq \alpha$, reject the null hypothesis
   of equal means.
   If P-value $> \alpha$, fail to reject the null hypothesis
   of equal means.

Ch. 12: Two-Way Analysis of Variance

Procedure:

1. Use software or a calculator to obtain results.
2. Test H_0: There is no interaction between the row factor and
   column factor.
3. Stop if H_0 from Step 2 is rejected.

   If H_0 from Step 2 is not rejected (so there does not appear to be an
   interaction effect), proceed with these two tests:
   Test for effects from the row factor.
   Test for effects from the column factor.

Formulas by Mario F. Triola
Copyright 2022 Pearson Education, Inc.

Ch. 13: Nonparametric Tests

$$z = \frac{(x + 0.5) - (n/2)}{\frac{\sqrt{n}}{2}}$$ Sign test for $n > 25$

$$z = \frac{T - n(n + 1)/4}{\sqrt{\frac{n(n + 1)(2n + 1)}{24}}}$$ Wilcoxon signed ranks (matched pairs and $n > 30$)

$$z = \frac{R - \mu_R}{\sigma_R} = \frac{R - \frac{n_1(n_1 + n_2 + 1)}{2}}{\sqrt{\frac{n_1 n_2 (n_1 + n_2 + 1)}{12}}}$$ Wilcoxon rank-sum (two independent samples)

$$H = \frac{12}{N(N + 1)}\left(\frac{R_1^2}{n_1} + \frac{R_2^2}{n_2} + \cdots + \frac{R_k^2}{n_k}\right) - 3(N + 1)$$

Kruskal-Wallis (chi-square df $= k - 1$)

$$r_s = 1 - \frac{6\Sigma d^2}{n(n^2 - 1)}$$ Rank correlation

$$\left(\text{critical values for } n > 30: \frac{\pm z}{\sqrt{n - 1}}\right)$$

$$z = \frac{G - \mu_G}{\sigma_G} = \frac{G - \left(\frac{2n_1 n_2}{n_1 + n_2} + 1\right)}{\sqrt{\frac{(2n_1 n_2)(2n_1 n_2 - n_1 - n_2)}{(n_1 + n_2)^2(n_1 + n_2 - 1)}}}$$ Runs test for $n > 20$

Ch. 14: Control Charts

R chart: Plot sample ranges

  UCL: $D_4\bar{R}$

  Centerline: $\bar{R}$

  LCL: $D_3\bar{R}$

$\bar{x}$ chart: Plot sample means

  UCL: $\bar{\bar{x}} + A_2\bar{R}$

  Centerline: $\bar{\bar{x}}$

  LCL: $\bar{\bar{x}} - A_2\bar{R}$

p chart: Plot sample proportions

  UCL: $\bar{p} + 3\sqrt{\frac{\bar{p}\,\bar{q}}{n}}$

  Centerline: $\bar{p}$

  LCL: $\bar{p} - 3\sqrt{\frac{\bar{p}\,\bar{q}}{n}}$

Control Chart Constants

Subgroup Size n	D_3	D_4	A_2
2	0.000	3.267	1.880
3	0.000	2.574	1.023
4	0.000	2.282	0.729
5	0.000	2.114	0.577
6	0.000	2.004	0.483
7	0.076	1.924	0.419

Inferences about μ: choosing between t and normal distributions	
t distribution: or	σ not known and normally distributed population σ not known and $n > 30$
Normal distribution: or	σ known and normally distributed population σ known and $n > 30$
Nonparametric method or bootstrapping: Population not normally distributed and $n \leq 30$	

Procedure for Hypothesis Tests

Hypothesis Tests: Wording of Final Conclusion

Finding *P*-Values

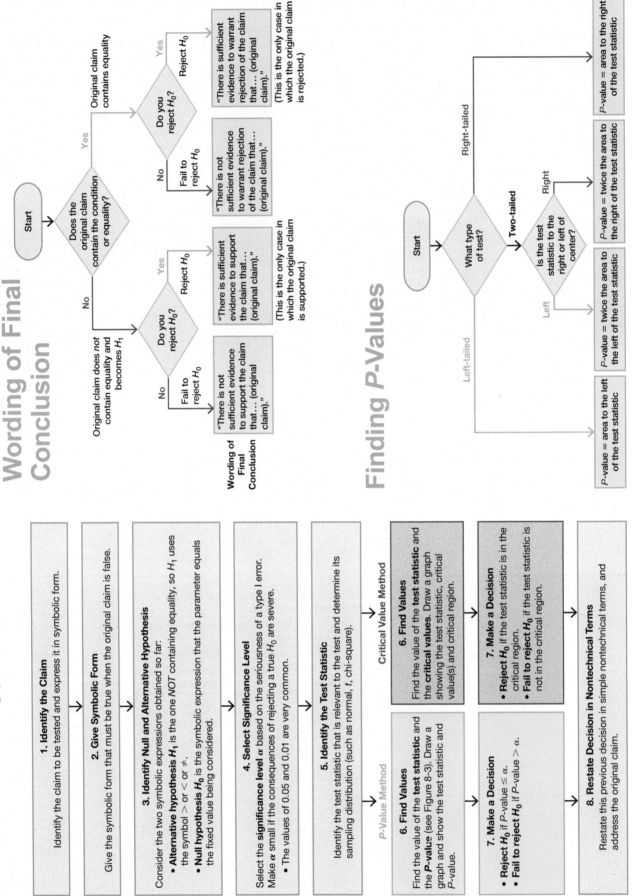

Complete data sets are available at www.TriolaStats.com

This appendix lists only the first five rows of each data set. The complete data sets are available for download at www.TriolaStats.com for a variety of technologies, including Excel, TI-83/84 Plus calculators, and Minitab. These data sets are included with Statdisk, which is available for free to users of this textbook and can be accessed at www.statdisk.com.

Data Set 1:   Body Data

Data Set 2:   ANSUR I 1988

Data Set 3:   ANSUR II 2012

Data Set 4:   Measured and Reported

Data Set 5:   Body Temperatures

Data Set 6:   Births

Data Set 7:   Audiometry

Data Set 8:   Vision

Data Set 9:   Foot and Height

Data Set 10:   Family Heights

Data Set 11:   IQ and Lead

Data Set 12:   IQ and Brain Size

Data Set 13:   Freshman 15

Data Set 14:   Word Counts

Data Set 15:   Passive and Active Smoke

Data Set 16:   Cigarette Contents

Data Set 17:   Arsenic in Rice

Data Set 18:   Bear Measurements

Data Set 19:   Manatee Boat Deaths

Data Set 20:   Alcohol and Tobacco in Movies

Data Set 21:   Oscar Winner Age

Data Set 22:   Presidents

Data Set 23:   Nobel Laureates and Chocolate

Data Set 24:   Earthquakes

Data Set 25:   Tornadoes

Data Set 26:   Old Faithful

Data Set 27:   Internet Traffic

Data Set 28:   Course Evaluations

Data Set 29:   Speed Dating

Data Set 30:   Queues

Data Set 31:   Commute Times

Data Set 32:   Taxis

Data Set 33:   Disney World Wait Times

Data Set 34:   Airport Data Speeds

Data Set 35:   Car Data

Data Set 36:   Fast Food

Data Set 37:   Cola Weights and Volumes

Data Set 38:   Candies

Data Set 39:   Chocolate Chip Cookies

Data Set 40:   Coin Weights

Data Set 41:   Aluminum Cans

Data Set 42:   Garbage Weight

Data Set 43:   Draft Lottery

Data Set 44:   Weights of Minted Quarters

Large Data Sets

Data Set 45:   Births in New York

Data Set 46:   Dow Jones Industrial Average (DJIA)

Data Set 1: Body Data

Body and exam measurements are from 300 subjects (first five rows shown here). **AGE** is in years, for **GENDER** 1 = male and 0 = female, **PULSE** is pulse rate (beats per minute), **SYSTOLIC** is systolic blood pressure (mm Hg), **DIASTOLIC** is diastolic blood pressure (mm Hg), **HDL** is HDL cholesterol (mg/dL), **LDL** is LDL cholesterol (mg/dL), **WHITE** is white blood cell count

(1000 cells/μL), **RED** is red blood cell count (million cells/μL), **PLATE** is platelet count (1000 cells/μL), **WEIGHT** is weight (kg), **HEIGHT** is height (cm), **WAIST** is waist circumference (cm), **ARM CIRC** is arm circumference (cm), and **BMI** is body mass index (kg/m^2). Data are from the National Center for Health Statistics.

TI-83/84 list names (BODY): AGE, GENDR, PULSE, SYS, DIAS, HDL, LDL, WHITE, REDBC, PLATE, WT, HT, WAIST, ARMC, BMI

AGE	GENDER (1 = M)	PULSE	SYSTOLIC	DIASTOLIC	HDL	LDL	WHITE	RED	PLATE	WEIGHT	HEIGHT	WAIST	ARM CIRC	BMI
43	0	80	100	70	73	68	8.7	4.80	319	98.6	172.0	120.4	40.7	33.3
57	1	84	112	70	35	116	4.9	4.73	187	96.9	186.0	107.8	37.0	28.0
38	0	94	134	94	36	223	6.9	4.47	297	108.2	154.4	120.3	44.3	45.4
80	1	74	126	64	37	83	7.5	4.32	170	73.1	160.5	97.2	30.3	28.4
34	1	50	114	68	50	104	6.1	4.95	140	83.1	179.0	95.1	34.0	25.9

Data Set 2: ANSUR I 1988

ANSUR is an abbreviation of "anthropometric survey." The ANSUR I study was conducted in 1988. (See also the following ANSUR II data set.) This data set consists of body measurements from 3982 U.S. Army personnel (first five rows shown here, not all data columns shown). **AGE** is in years, **WEIGHT** is in kilograms (kg), for **GENDER** 1 = male and 0 = female, for **WRITING HAND** 1 = right and 2 = left and 3 = both, and the other body measurements are in

millimeters (mm). Additional detail on body measurements in this data set can be found at TriolaStats.com/ansur. Data are from the U.S. Army.

TI-83/84 list names (ANSUR1)*: A1AGE, A1HT, A1WGT, A1FTL, A1HC, A1CC, A1NC, A1WC, A1SW, A1SH, A1SKH, A1SEH, A1NHT, A1PPD, A1ARM, A1WH, A1GND

*NOTE: TI lists are limited to 500 rows due to calculator memory constraints.

AGE	HEIGHT	WEIGHT	FOOT LENGTH	HEAD CIRC	CHEST CIRC	SHOULDER WIDTH	SITTING HT	ARM SPAN	WRITING HAND	GENDER (1 = M)
34	1735	88.3	260	572	1052	490	888	1813	1	1
37	1830	86.5	290	590	1029	485	905	1916	1	1
38	1726	71.3	254	572	995	500	907	1827	1	1
33	1783	81.6	271	593	966	484	948	1846	1	1
42	1669	75.6	240	546	1032	479	856	1712	1	1

Data Set 3: ANSUR II 2012

ANSUR is an abbreviation of "anthropometric survey." The ANSUR II study was conducted in 2012. (See also the preceding ANSUR I data set.) This data set consists of body measurements from 6068 U.S. Army personnel (first five rows shown here, not all data columns shown). **AGE** is in years, **WEIGHT** is in kilograms (kg), for **GENDER** 1 = male and 0 = female, for **WRITING HAND** 1 = right and 2 = left and 3 = both, and the other body measurements are in

millimeters (mm). Additional detail on body measurements can be found at TriolaStats.com/ansur. Data are from the U.S. Army.

TI-83/84 list names (ANSUR2)*: A2AGE, A2HT, A2WGT, A2FTL, A2HC, A2CC, A2NC, A2WC, A2SW, A2SH, A2SKH, A2SEH, A2NHT, A2PPD, A2ARM, A2WH, A2GND

*NOTE: TI lists are limited to 500 rows due to calculator memory constraints.

AGE	HEIGHT	WEIGHT	FOOT LENGTH	HEAD CIRC	CHEST CIRC	SHOULDER WIDTH	SITTING HT	ARM SPAN	WRITING HAND	GENDER (1 = M)
41	1776	81.5	273	583	1074	493	928	1782	1	1
35	1702	72.6	263	568	1021	479	884	1745	2	1
42	1735	92.9	270	573	1120	544	917	1867	2	1
31	1655	79.4	267	576	1114	518	903	1708	1	1
21	1914	94.6	305	566	1048	524	919	2035	1	1

(Complete data sets available at www.TriolaStats.com)

Data Set 4: Measured and Reported

Measured weights and heights matched with the weights and heights that were reported when 5755 subjects (first five rows shown here) aged 16 and over were asked for those values. Values are given in both Imperial and metric systems. Weights are given in pounds and kilograms. Heights are given in inches and centimeters. Data are from the National Center for Health Statistics.

TI-83/84 list names (MESREPT)*: MRGND, MWTLB, RWLB, MHTIN, RHTIN, MWTKG, RWKG, MHTCM, RHTCM

*NOTE: TI lists are limited to 500 rows due to calculator memory constraints.

GENDER (1 = M)	MEASURED WEIGHT (LB)	REPORTED WEIGHT (LB)	MEASURED HEIGHT (IN)	REPORTED HEIGHT (IN)	MEASURED WEIGHT (KG)	REPORTED WEIGHT (KG)	MEASURED HEIGHT (CM)	REPORTED HEIGHT (CM)
1	209.0	212	72.6	74	94.8	96.2	184.5	188.0
1	199.3	193	67.5	68	90.4	87.5	171.4	172.7
1	183.9	182	67.0	69	83.4	82.6	170.1	175.3
0	242.1	220	63.3	64	109.8	99.8	160.9	162.6
0	121.7	125	64.9	64	55.2	56.7	164.9	162.6

Data Set 5: Body Temperatures

Body temperatures (°F) are from 107 subjects taken on two consecutive days at 8 AM and 12 AM (first five rows shown here). **SEX** is gender of subject, and **SMOKE** indicates if subject smokes (Y) or does not smoke (N). Data provided by Dr. Steven Wasserman, Dr. Philip Mackowiak, and Dr. Myron Levine of the University of Maryland.

TI-83/84 Plus list names (BODYTEMP): D1T8, D1T12, D2T8, D2T12 (no list for SEX and SMOKE). **Missing data values are represented by 9999.**

SEX	SMOKE	DAY 1—8 AM	DAY 1—12 AM	DAY 2—8 AM	DAY 2—12 AM
M	Y	98.0	98.0	98.0	98.6
M	Y	97.0	97.6	97.4	—
M	Y	98.6	98.8	97.8	98.6
M	N	97.4	98.0	97.0	98.0
M	N	98.2	98.8	97.0	98.0

Data Set 6: Births

Data are from 400 births (first five rows shown here). For **GENDER** 1 = male and 0 = female. **LENGTH OF STAY** is in days, **BIRTH WEIGHT** is in grams, and **TOTAL CHARGES** are in dollars.

TI-83/84 list names (BIRTHS): FLOS, MLOS, FBWT, MBWT, FCHRG, MCHRG [Separate lists provided for female (F) and male (M) babies. No list for FACILITY, INSURANCE, ADMITTED, and DISCHARGED]

FACILITY	INSURANCE	GENDER (1 = M)	LENGTH OF STAY	ADMITTED	DISCHARGED	BIRTH WEIGHT	TOTAL CHARGES
Albany Medical Center Hospital	Insurance Company	0	2	FRI	SUN	3500	13986
Albany Medical Center Hospital	Blue Cross	1	2	FRI	SUN	3900	3633
Albany Medical Center Hospital	Blue Cross	0	36	WED	THU	800	359091
Albany Medical Center Hospital	Insurance Company	1	5	MON	SAT	2800	8537
Albany Medical Center Hospital	Insurance Company	1	2	FRI	SUN	3700	3633

(Complete data sets available at www.TriolaStats.com)

Data Set 7: Audiometry

Data are from 350 subjects (first five rows shown here). **AGE** is in years, for **GENDER** 0 = female and 1 = male, and **RIGHT/LEFT THRESHOLD** are hearing measurements in each ear using pure tone sounds sent through earphones. Intensity of sound is varied until hearing threshold at frequency of 1000 Hz (db) is identified. Data are from the National Center for Health Statistics.

TI-83/84 list names   AUDAG, AUDGN, AUDRT, AUDLT **(AUDIO):**

AGE	GENDER	RIGHT THRESHOLD	LEFT THRESHLOD
42	1	5	5
46	0	5	15
51	0	5	10
70	0	15	20
78	1	5	10

Data Set 8: Vision

Data are from 300 subjects (first five rows shown here). **AGE** is in years, for **GENDER** 0 = female and 1 = male, and **RIGHT/LEFT EYE** is measure of visual acuity with "usual correction," which could be eyeglasses, contacts, or no correction. Data are from the National Center for Health Statistics.

TI-83/84 list names   VISAG, VISGN, VISRT, VISLT **(VISION):**

AGE	GENDER	RIGHT EYE	LEFT EYE
39	1	20	20
48	1	20	20
84	0	25	20
55	0	25	20
41	1	50	50

Data Set 9: Foot and Height

Foot and height measurements are from 40 subjects (first five rows shown here). **SEX** is gender of subject, **AGE** is age in years, **FOOT LENGTH** is length of foot (cm), **SHOE PRINT** is length of shoe (cm), **SHOE SIZE** is reported shoe size, and **HEIGHT** is height (cm) of the subject.

Data from Rohren, Brenda, "Estimation of Stature from Foot and Shoe Length: Applications in Forensic Science." Copyright © 2006. Reprinted by permission of the author. Brenda Rohren (MA, MFS, LIMHP, LADC, MAC) was a graduate student at Nebraska Wesleyan University when she conducted the research and wrote the report.

TI-83/84 list names   FTSEX (1 = male), FTAGE, FTLN, SHOPT, **(FOOTHT):**   SHOSZ, FHT

SEX	AGE	FOOT LENGTH	SHOE PRINT	SHOE SIZE	HEIGHT
M	67	27.8	31.3	11.0	180.3
M	47	25.7	29.7	9.0	175.3
M	41	26.7	31.3	11.0	184.8
M	42	25.9	31.8	10.0	177.8
M	48	26.4	31.4	10.0	182.3

(Complete data sets available at www.TriolaStats.com)

Data Set 10: Family Heights

Height data are from 134 families (first five rows shown here). Heights are in inches. Only families with at least one child of each gender are included, and only heights of the first son and first daughter are included. The data are from a journal of Francis Galton (1822–1911), who developed the concepts of standard deviation, regression line, and correlation between two variables.

TI-83 / 84 list names   DAD, MOM, SON1, DGHT1
(FAMHT):

FATHER	MOTHER	FIRST SON	FIRST DAUGHTER
70.0	64.0	68.0	65.0
71.0	65.5	72.0	66.0
69.0	63.5	70.5	65.0
69.5	66.0	71.0	66.5
70.0	58.0	72.0	66.0

Data Set 11: IQ and Lead

Data are from 121 subjects (first five rows shown here). Data are measured from children in two consecutive years, and the children were living close to a lead smelter. **LEAD** is blood lead level group [1 = *low lead level* (blood lead levels < 40 micrograms/100 mL in both years), 2 = *medium lead level* (blood lead levels ≥ 40 micrograms/100 mL in exactly one of two years), 3 = *high lead level* (blood lead level ≥ 40 micrograms/100 mL in both years)]. **AGE** is age in years, **SEX** is sex of subject (1 = male; 2 = female).

YEAR1 is blood lead level in first year, and **YEAR2** is blood lead level in second year. **IQ VERB** is measured verbal IQ score. **IQ PERF** is measured performance IQ score. **IQ FULL** is measured full IQ score.

Data are from "Neuropsychological Dysfunction in Children with Chronic Low-Level Lead Absorption," by P. J. Landrigan, R. H. Whitworth, R. W. Baloh, N. W. Staehling, W. F Barthel, and B. F. Rosenblum, *Lancet*, Vol. 1, No. 7909.

TI-83 / 84 list names   LEAD, IQAGE, IQSEX, YEAR1, YEAR2,
(IQLEAD):   IQV, IQP, IQF

LEAD	AGE	SEX	YEAR1	YEAR2	IQ VERB	IQ PERF	IQ FULL
1	11	1	25	18	61	85	70
1	9	1	31	28	82	90	85
1	11	1	30	29	70	107	86
1	6	1	29	30	72	85	76
1	11	1	2	34	72	100	84

Data Set 12: IQ and Brain Size

Data are from 20 monozygotic (identical) twins (first five rows shown here). **PAIR** identifies the set of twins, **SEX** is the gender of the subject (1 = male, 2 = female), **ORDER** is the birth order, **IQ** is measured full IQ score, **VOL** is total brain volume (cm^3), **AREA** is total brain surface area (cm^2), **CCSA** is corpus callosum (fissure connecting left and right cerebral hemispheres) surface area (cm^2), **CIRC** is head circumference (cm), and **WT** is body weight (kg).

Data provided by M. J. Tramo, W. C. Loftus, T. A. Stukel, J. B. Weaver, M. S. Gazziniga. See "Brain Size, Head Size, and IQ in Monozygotic Twins," *Neurology*, Vol. 50.

TI-83 / 84 list names   PAIR, SEX, ORDER, IQ, VOL, AREA,
(IQBRAIN):   CCSA, CIRC, BWT

PAIR	SEX (1 = M)	ORDER	IQ	VOL	AREA	CCSA	CIRC	WT
1	2	1	96	1005	1913.88	6.08	54.7	57.607
1	2	2	89	963	1684.89	5.73	54.2	58.968
2	2	1	87	1035	1902.36	6.22	53.0	64.184
2	2	2	87	1027	1860.24	5.80	52.9	58.514
3	2	1	101	1281	2264.25	7.99	57.8	63.958

(Complete data sets available at www.TriolaStats.com)

Data Set 13: Freshman 15

Weights of 67 college students are provided (first five rows shown here). **SEX** is gender of subject, **WT** is weights in kilograms, and **BMI** is measured body mass index. Measurements were made in September of freshman year and then later in April of freshman year.

Results are published in Hoffman, D. J., Policastro, P., Quick, V., and Lee, S. K.: "Changes in Body Weight and Fat Mass of Men and Women in the First Year of College: A Study of the 'Freshman 15.'" *Journal of American College Health*, July 1, 2006, Vol. 55, No. 1, p. 41. Copyright © 2006. Reprinted by permission.

TI-83/84 list names (FRESH15): WTSP, WTAPR, BMISP, BMIAP (no list for SEX)

SEX	WT SEPT	WT APRIL	BMI SEPT	BMI APRIL
M	72	59	22.02	18.14
M	97	86	19.70	17.44
M	74	69	24.09	22.43
M	93	88	26.97	25.57
F	68	64	21.51	20.10

Data Set 14: Word Counts

Data are from counts of the numbers of words spoken in a day by 396 male (M) and female (F) subjects in six different sample groups (first five rows shown here). Column **M1** denotes the word counts for males in Sample 1, **F1** is the count for females in Sample 1, and so on.

Sample 1: Recruited couples ranging in age from 18 to 29
Sample 2: Students recruited in introductory psychology classes, aged 17 to 23
Sample 3: Students recruited in introductory psychology classes in Mexico, aged 17 to 25
Sample 4: Students recruited in introductory psychology classes, aged 17 to 22
Sample 5: Students recruited in introductory psychology classes, aged 18 to 26
Sample 6: Students recruited in introductory psychology classes, aged 17 to 23

Results were published in "Are Women Really More Talkative Than Men?" by Mehl, Vazire, Ramirez-Esparza, Slatcher, Pennebaker, *Science*, Vol. 317, No. 5834.

TI-83/84 list names (WORDS): M1, F1, M2, F2, M3, F3, M4, F4, M5, F5, M6, F6.

M1	F1	M2	F2	M3	F3	M4	F4	M5	F5	M6	F6
27531	20737	23871	16109	21143	6705	47016	11849	39207	15962	28408	15357
15684	24625	5180	10592	17791	21613	27308	25317	20868	16610	10084	13618
5638	5198	9951	24608	36571	11935	42709	40055	18857	22497	15931	9783
27997	18712	12460	13739	6724	15790	20565	18797	17271	5004	21688	26451
25433	12002	17155	22376	15430	17865	21034	20104		10171	37786	12151

Data Set 15: Passive and Active Smoke

Data are from 1693 subjects (first five rows shown here) in three groups: **SMOKER** includes subjects who reported smoking at least one cigarette every day, **ETS** (Exposed to Tobacco Smoke) includes nonsmokers who reported living in a household with at least one smoker, **NOETS** (Nonsmoker and No Exposure to Tobacco Smoke) includes nonsmokers who reported living in a household with no smokers and had no exposure to second-hand smoke over the last seven days. All values are measured levels of serum cotinine (in ng/mL), a metabolite of nicotine. (When nicotine is absorbed by the body, cotinine is produced.) Data are from the U.S. Department of Health and Human Services, National Center for Health Statistics, Third National Health and Nutrition Examination Survey.

TI-83/84 Plus list names (SMOKE)*: SMKR, ETS, NOETS

NOTE: TI lists are limited to 500 rows due to calculator memory constraints.

SMOKER	ETS	NOETS
362	1.700	0.046
210	0.029	0.124
400	0.042	0.030
520	28.700	0.011
360	0.520	0.011

(Complete data sets available at www.TriolaStats.com)

Data Set 16: Cigarette Contents

Data are from 75 cigarettes (first five rows shown here) from three categories: **KING** includes king-sized cigarettes that are nonfiltered, nonmenthol, and nonlight; **MENTH** includes menthol cigarettes that are 100 mm long, filtered, and nonlight; and **100** includes 100-mm-long cigarettes that are filtered, nonmenthol, and nonlight.

TAR is the amount of tar per cigarette (milligrams), **NICOTINE** is the amount of nicotine per cigarette (milligrams), and **CO** is the amount of carbon monoxide per cigarette (milligrams). Data are from the Federal Trade Commission.

TI-83/84 list names (CIGARET):   KGTAR, KGNIC, KGCO, MNTAR, MNNIC, MNCO, FLTAR, FLNIC, FLCO

KING TAR	KING NICOTINE	KING CO	MENTH TAR	MENTH NICOTINE	MENTH CO	100 TAR	100 NICOTINE	100 CO
20	1.1	16	16	1.1	15	5	0.4	4
27	1.7	16	13	0.8	17	16	1.0	19
27	1.7	16	16	1.0	19	17	1.2	17
20	1.1	16	9	0.9	9	13	0.8	18
20	1.1	16	14	0.8	17	13	0.8	18

Data Set 17: Arsenic in Rice

Measures of inorganic arsenic from samples of brown rice in California, Arkansas, and Texas (first five rows shown here). All values are based on samples of the same serving size, and amounts of arsenic are in micrograms (μg) per serving. Data are from the U.S. Food and Drug Administration.

TI-83/84 list names (ARSENIC):   ARSCA, ARSAK, ARSTX

CALIFORNIA	ARKANSAS	TEXAS
1.5	4.8	5.6
3.7	4.9	5.8
4.0	5.0	6.6
4.5	5.4	6.9
4.9	5.4	6.9

Data Set 18: Bear Measurements

Data are from 54 anesthetized wild bears (first five rows shown here). **AGE** is in months, **MONTH** is the month of measurement 1 = January, **SEX** is coded with 0 = female and 1 = male, **HEADLEN** is head length (inches), **HEADWDTH** is width of head (inches), **NECK** is distance around neck (in inches), **LENGTH** is length of body (inches), **CHEST** is distance around chest (inches), and **WEIGHT** is measured in pounds. Data are from Gary Alt and Minitab, Inc.

TI-83/84 list names (BEARS):   BAGE, BSEX, BHDLN, BHDWD, BNECK, BLEN, BCHST, BWGHT (no list for MONTH)

AGE	MONTH	SEX (1 = M)	HEADLEN	HEADWDTH	NECK	LENGTH	CHEST	WEIGHT
19	7	1	11.0	5.5	16.0	53.0	26.0	80
55	7	1	16.5	9.0	28.0	67.5	45.0	344
81	9	1	15.5	8.0	31.0	72.0	54.0	416
115	7	1	17.0	10.0	31.5	72.0	49.0	348
104	8	0	15.5	6.5	22.0	62.0	35.0	166

(Complete data sets available at www.TriolaStats.com)

Data Set 19: Manatee Boat Deaths

Annual Florida data for 28 years are provided (first five rows shown here). **DEATHS** is the annual number of Manatee deaths caused by boats, **BOATS** is the number of registered pleasure boats (tens of thousands), **FLORIDA POP** is the Florida population (millions).

TI-83/84 list names   DEATH, BOATS, FLPOP (no list for YEAR)
(MANATEE):

YEAR	DEATHS	BOATS	FLORIDA POP
1991	53	68	13.3
1992	38	68	13.5
1993	35	67	13.7
1994	49	70	14.0
1995	42	71	14.3

Data Set 20: Alcohol and Tobacco in Movies

Data are from 50 animated children's movies (first five rows shown here). **LENGTH** is movie length in minutes, **TOBACCO** is tobacco use time in seconds, and **ALCOHOL** is alcohol use time in seconds.

The data are based on Goldstein, Adam O., Sobel, Rachel A., Newman, Glen R., "Tobacco and Alcohol Use in G-Rated Children's Animated Films." *Journal of the American Medical Association,* March 24/31, 1999, Vol. 281, No. 12, p. 1132. Copyright © 1999. All rights reserved.

TI-83/84 list names   CHLEN, CHTOB, CHALC (no list for
(CHMOVIE):   MOVIE and STUDIO)

MOVIE	STUDIO	LENGTH (MIN)	TOBACCO (SEC)	ALCOHOL (SEC)
Snow White	Disney	83	0	0
Pinocchio	Disney	88	223	80
Fantasia	Disney	120	0	0
Dumbo	Disney	64	176	88
Bambi	Disney	69	0	0

Data Set 21: Oscar Winner Age

Data are from 91 years (first five rows shown here). Data values are ages (years) of actresses and actors at the times that they won Oscars in the categories of Best Actress and Best Actor. The ages are listed in chronological order by row, so that each row has paired ages from the same year. (*Note:* In 1968 there was a tie in the Best Actress category, and the mean of the two ages is used; in 1932 there was a tie in the Best Actor category, and the mean of the two ages is used).

These data are suggested by the article "Ages of Oscar-Winning Best Actors and Actresses," by Richard Brown and Gretchen Davis, *Mathematics Teacher* magazine. In that article, the year of birth of the award winner was subtracted from the year of the awards ceremony, but the ages listed here are calculated from the birth date of the winner and the date of the awards ceremony.

TI-83/84 list names   OSCRF, OSCRM
(OSCARS):

ACTRESSES	ACTORS
22	44
37	41
28	62
63	52
32	41

(Complete data sets available at www.TriolaStats.com)

Data Set 22: Presidents

Data are from 39 presidents of the United States (first five rows shown here). Presidents who took office as the result of an assassination or resignation are not included. **AGE** is age in years at time of inauguration. **DAYS** is the number of days served as president. **YEARS** is the number of years lived after the first inauguration. **HEIGHT** is height (cm) of the president. **HEIGHT OPP** is the height (cm) of the major opponent for the presidency.

TI-83/84 list names (POTUS): PRAGE, DAYS, YEARS, PRHT, HTOPP (no list for PRESIDENT). **Missing data values are represented by 9999.**

PRESIDENT	AGE	DAYS	YEARS	HEIGHT	HEIGHT OPP
Washington	57	2864	10	188	
J. Adams	61	1460	29	170	189
Jefferson	57	2921	26	189	170
Madison	57	2921	28	163	
Monroe	58	2921	15	183	

Data Set 23: Nobel Laureates and Chocolate

Data are from 23 countries (first five rows shown here). **CHOCOLATE** includes chocolate consumption (kg per capita), **NOBEL** includes the numbers of Nobel Laureates (per 10 million people), **POPULATION** includes population (in millions), and **INTERNET** includes the number of Internet users per 100 people.

The data are from "The Real Secret to Genius? Reading Between the Lines," by McClintock, Stangle, and Cetinkaya-Rundel, *Chance*, Vol. 27, No. 1; and "Chocolate Consumption, Cognitive Function, and Nobel Laureates," by Franz Messerli, *New England Journal of Medicine*, Vol. 367, No. 16.

TI-83/84 list names (NOBEL): CHOC, NOBEL, POPUL, INTNT (no list for COUNTRY)

COUNTRY	CHOCOLATE	NOBEL	POPULATION	INTERNET
Australia	4.5	5.5	22	79.5
Austria	10.2	24.3	8	79.8
Belgium	4.4	8.6	11	78.0
Brazil	2.9	0.1	197	45.0
Canada	3.9	6.1	34	83.0

Data Set 24: Earthquakes

Data are from 600 matched pairs (first five rows shown here) of magnitude/depth measurements randomly selected from 10,594 earthquakes recorded in one year from a location in southern California. Only earthquakes with a magnitude of at least 1.00 are used.

MAGNITUDE is magnitude measured on the Richter scale and **DEPTH** is depth in km. The magnitude and depth both describe the source of the earthquake. The data are from the Southern California Earthquake Data Center.

TI-83/84 list names (QUAKE): MAG, DEPTH

MAGNITUDE	DEPTH
2.45	0.7
3.62	6.0
3.06	7.0
3.30	5.4
1.09	0.5

(Complete data sets available at www.TriolaStats.com)

Data Set 25: Tornadoes

Data are from 63,160 tornadoes (first five rows shown here) arranged chronologically. **MONTH** is the month of the tornado (1 = January), **F SCALE** is the Fujita scale rating of tornado intensity, **FATALITIES** is number of deaths caused by the tornado, **LENGTH (MI)** is the distance the tornado traveled in miles, and **WIDTH (YD)** is the tornado width in yards. Data are from the National Weather Service.

TI-83/84 list names (TORNADO)*: FSCAL, FATAL, TLEN, TWDTH (no list for YEAR and MONTH). **Missing F-scale values are represented by 9999.**

NOTE: TI lists are limited to 500 rows due to calculator memory constraints.

YEAR	MONTH	F SCALE	FATALITIES	LENGTH (MI)	WIDTH (YD)
1950	1	3	0	9.5	150
1950	1	3	0	3.6	130
1950	1	1	0	0.1	10
1950	1	3	1	0.6	17
1950	1	2	0	2.3	300

Data Set 26: Old Faithful

Data are from 250 eruptions (first five rows shown here) of the Old Faithful geyser in Yellowstone National Park. **INT BEFORE** is the time interval (min) before the eruption, **DURATION** is the time (sec) of the eruption, **INT AFTER** is the time interval (min) after the eruption, **HEIGHT** (ft) is the height of the eruption, and **PRED ERROR** is the error (min) of the predicted time of eruption. Based on data from the Geyser Observation and Study Association.

TI-83/84 list names (OLDFAITH): INTBF, DUR, INTAF, OFHT, PRED

INT BEFORE (MIN)	DURATION (SEC)	INT AFTER (MIN)	HEIGHT (FT)	PRED ERROR (MIN)
82	251	83	130	4
99	243	76	125	−13
88	250	86	120	−2
92	240	82	120	−6
86	243	87	130	0

Data Set 27: Internet Traffic

Data from 9000 arrivals of Internet traffic at Digital Equipment Corporation (first five rows shown here). **ARRIVAL TIME** is in thousandths of a minute. **INTERARRIVAL TIME** is the time between consecutive traffic arrivals, in thousandths of a minute. **DATA** are the numbers of bytes, where a byte is a letter or digit or symbol.

TI-83/84 list names (INTERNET)*: ARRVL, INTER, BYTES

NOTE: TI lists are limited to 500 rows due to calculator memory constraints.

ARRIVAL TIME	INTERARRIVAL TIME	DATA (BYTES)
419	2	0
421	2	5
427	6	512
427	0	512
428	1	512

(Complete data sets available at www.TriolaStats.com)

Data Set 28: Course Evaluations

Data are from 93 college student course evaluations (first five rows shown here). **COURSE EVAL** includes the mean course rating, **PROF EVAL** includes the mean professor rating, **PROF AGE** includes the professor age in years, **SIZE** includes the number of course evaluations per course, **PROF BEAUTY** includes the mean beauty rating based on the professor's photo.

Based on data from Andrew Gelman and Jennifer Hill, 2007, "Replication Data for Data Analysis Using Regression Multilevel/Hierarchical Models," http://hdl.handle.net/1902.1/10285.

TI-83/84 list names (EVALS): CEVAL, PEVAL, PAGE, SIZE, PBTY (no list for PROF, PROF GENDER, PROF PHOTO, and CLASS LEVEL)

PROF	COURSE EVAL	PROF EVAL	PROF GENDER	PROF AGE	SIZE	PROF BEAUTY	PROF PHOTO	CLASS LEVEL
1	4.3	4.7	female	36	24	5.000	color	upper
2	4.5	4.6	male	59	17	3.000	color	upper
3	3.7	4.1	male	51	55	3.333	color	upper
4	4.3	4.5	female	40	40	3.167	color	upper
5	4.4	4.8	female	31	42	7.333	color	upper

Data Set 29: Speed Dating

Data are from 199 dates (first five rows shown here). **DEC BY FEM** is decision (1 = yes) of female to date again, **AGE FEM** is age of female, **LIKE BY FEM** is "like" rating by female of male (scale of 1−10), **ATTRACT BY FEM** is "attractive" rating by female of male (scale of 1−10), **ATTRIB BY FEM** is sum of ratings of five attributes (sincerity, intelligence, fun, ambitious, shared interests) by female of male. Data for males use corresponding descriptors. Higher scale ratings correspond to more positive impressions.

Based on replication data from *Data Analysis Using Regression and Multilevel/Hierarchical Models,* by Andrew Gelman and Jennifer Hill, Cambridge University Press.

TI-83/84 list names (DATE): DBYF, DBYM, AGEF, AGEM, LBYF, LBYM, ABYF, ABYM, ATBYF, ATBYM

DEC BY FEM	DEC BY MALE	AGE FEM	AGE MALE	LIKE BY FEM	LIKE BY MALE	ATTRACT BY FEM	ATTRACT BY MALE	ATTRIB BY FEM	ATTRIB BY MALE
0	1	27	28	7	7	5	8	38	36
0	0	24	26	7	7	7	6	36	38
1	0	26	28	6	3	7	8	29	35
1	0	34	27	8	6	8	6	38	28
1	0	22	25	5	5	7	5	33	34

Data Set 30: Queues

Data from 85 drivers (first five rows shown here) waiting in two queues (or lines) at a Delaware Department of Motor Vehicle emissions testing facility. All times are in seconds. The data for a single line are modeled from the actual times and are based on the assumption that all drivers enter a single waiting line and then move to one of the service stations as vacancies become available. Data observed and collected by the author.

CAR is the sequence number for each vehicle based on arrival time. **INTERARRIVAL TIME** is the time (sec) since the previous car entered a line. **SERVICE TIME** is the time (sec) starting with a car entering a service bay and ending when it leaves the bay. **TWO LINE WAIT - ACTUAL** is the actual time (sec) a car spent waiting in a line. **TWO-LINE BAY - ACTUAL** indicates whether a car entered the left or right service bay. **SINGLE LINE WAIT – MODELED** is modeled by assuming that there was a single line feeding the two service bays. **SINGLE LINE BAY - MODELED** is the modeled service bay (left or right) that the car entered from a single line feeding two service bays.

TI-83/84 list names (QUEUES): QCAR, QARRV, QINTA, QSERV, Q2WAT, Q2BAY, Q1WAT, Q1BAY

CAR	ARRIVAL TIME	INTERARRIVAL TIME	SERVICE TIME	TWO LINE WAIT - ACTUAL	TWO LINE BAY - ACTUAL (1 = L)	SINGLE LINE WAIT - MODELED	SINGLE LINE BAY - MODELED (1 = L)
1	0	94	102	64	1	64	1
2	9	9	223	216	2	157	1
3	83	74	177	86	1	142	2
4	110	27	342	340	2	279	1
5	149	39	239	200	1	253	2

(Complete data sets available at www.TriolaStats.com)

Data Set 31: Commute Times

Reported daily commute times (minutes) to work from 7494 workers (first five rows shown here) of age 16 and older in different cities. Data are from the U.S. Census Bureau's 2017 American Community Survey.

TI-83/84 list names (COMMUTE)*:   BOSTN, NYNY, LACA, CHCGO, DALLS, BOISE, POK, BURLT

NOTE: TI lists are limited to 500 rows due to calculator memory constraints.

BOSTON MA	NEW YORK NY	LOS ANGELES CA	CHICAGO IL	DALLAS TX	BOISE ID	POUGHKEEPSIE NY	BURLINGTON VT
10	10	18	60	20	45	10	45
30	20	25	15	16	30	15	60
45	60	45	35	25	151	38	10
20	25	75	30	10	10	30	30
5	20	60	15	30	25	25	15

Data Set 32: Taxis

NYC Taxi and Limousine Commission data from 703 taxicab rides (first five rows shown here) in New York City yellow cabs during a Friday morning of the same day in a recent year. The fare structure is somewhat complicated and includes such items as a $2.50 fee upon entry, a 50¢ New York State tax surcharge, a 30¢ fee for "improvement," a 50¢ fee for each one-fifth of a mile while the taxi is going at least 6 mi/h, and a 50¢ fee for each minute the taxi is going less than 6 mi/h. There is a flat fare of $52.80 for a trip to or from JFK International Airport.

TI-83/84 list names (TAXI):   TXDIS, TXTIM, TXFAR, TXTOL, TXTIP, TXPAY

DISTANCE (MI)	TIME (MIN)	FARE ($)	TOLLS ($)	TIP ($)	TOTAL PAID ($)
0.68	6	6.3	0	1.89	8.19
2.47	18	14.3	0	4.29	18.59
8.51	31	31.75	0	2.98	34.73
12.71	27	36.8	5.76	0	42.56
1.65	11	9.8	0	1.96	11.76

Data Set 33: Disney World Wait Times

Wait times (minutes) from six rides located in three different Walt Disney World theme parks: Magic Kingdom, Hollywood Studios, and Animal Kingdom (first five rows shown here). Wait times were reported by Disney and wait times at 10 AM and 5 PM were recorded on 50 different days. **Magic Kingdom** rides include **Space Mountain** and **It's a Small World**; **Hollywood Studios** rides include **Rock 'n' Roller Coaster** and **Tower of Terror**; **Animal Kingdom** rides include **Avatar Flight of Passage** and **Na'vi River Journey**.

TI-83/84 list names (DISNY):   SPM10, SPM5, SMW10, SMW5, RRC10, RRC5, TOT10, TOT5, FOP10, FOP5, NAV10, NAV5

SPACE MT 10AM	SPACE MT 5PM	SMALL WORLD 10AM	SMALL WORLD 5PM	ROCK N ROLLER 10AM	ROCK N ROLLER 5PM	TOWER TERROR 10AM	TOWER TERROR 5PM	FLIGHT PASSAGE 10AM	FLIGHT PASSAGE 5PM	NAVI RIVER 10AM	NAVI RIVER 5PM
50	70	10	30	55	65	35	45	180	95	70	70
25	110	5	35	50	70	35	50	195	125	50	70
75	45	5	25	75	75	20	30	110	90	60	45
35	45	10	25	50	85	50	35	150	85	60	75
50	110	10	45	60	45	95	55	180	115	60	75

(Complete data sets available at www.TriolaStats.com)

Data Set 34: Airport Data Speeds

Data are from 50 airports (first five rows shown here) consisting of data speeds (Mbps) from four different cell phone carriers. Based on data from CNN.

TI-83/84 list names (DATASPED): VRZN, SPRNT, ATT, TMOBL (no list for AIRPORT CODE)

AIRPORT CODE	VERIZON	SPRINT	ATT	T-MOBILE
RSW	38.5	13.0	9.7	8.6
ORD	55.6	30.4	8.2	7.0
SNA	22.4	15.2	7.1	18.5
MEM	14.1	2.4	14.4	16.7
MKE	23.1	2.7	13.4	5.6

Data Set 35: Car Data

Measurements and crash test results from 48 cars (first five shown here). There are 12 cars in each category of small, midsize, large, and SUV. Crash test results are from cars crashed into a fixed barrier at 35 mi/h with a crash test dummy in the driver's seat. For car measurements, **WEIGHT** is car weight (lb), **LENGTH** is car length (inches), **BRAKING** is braking distance (feet) from 60 mi/h, **CYLINDERS** is the number of cylinders, **DISPLACEMENT** is the engine displacement (liters), **CITY** is the fuel consumption (mi/gal) for city driving conditions, **HWY** is highway fuel consumption (mi/gal) for highway driving conditions, and **GHG** is a measure of greenhouse gas emissions (in tons/year, expressed as CO_2 equivalents). For crash test results, **HIC** is a measurement of a standard "head injury criterion," **CHEST** is chest maximum compression (mm), **LEFT FEMUR** is left leg femur force (in kilonewtons, kN), **RIGHT FEMUR** is right leg femur force (kN), **MAXIMUM NIJ** is a measure of "neck injury criteria." Data are from the National Highway Traffic Safety Administration, the Insurance Institute for Highway Safety, the Environmental Protection Agency, and *Consumer Reports*.

TI-83/84 list names (CARDATA): CWGT, CLNGT, CBRAK, CCYL, CDISPL, CCITY, CHWY, CGHG, CHIC, CCHST, CLFEM, CRFEM, CNIJ (no list for MODEL and SIZE)

MODEL	SIZE	WEIGHT	LENGTH	BRAKING	CYLINDERS	DISPLACEMENT	CITY	HWY	GHG	HIC	CHEST	LEFT FEMUR	RIGHT FEMUR	MAXIMUM NIJ
Toyota Corolla	Small	2844	183	138	4	1.8	29	36	4.6	253	29	1.6	2.8	0.27
Subaru Impreza	Small	3109	176	124	4	2.0	28	38	4.7	143	31	1.4	1.0	0.28
Mazda 3	Small	2870	180	133	4	2.0	30	41	4.4	124	35	0.5	0.3	0.24
Volkswagen Golf	Small	3095	168	130	4	2.0	25	33	5.3	301	33	0.2	0.3	0.33
Honda Civic	Small	2915	182	129	4	1.5	31	42	4.2	422	26	0.4	0.2	0.20

Data Set 36: Fast Food

Data are from 400 observations (first five rows shown here) of drive-thru service times (sec) at different fast-food restaurants. Times begin when a vehicle stops at the order window and end when the vehicle leaves the pickup window. Lunch times were measured between 11:00 AM and 2:00 PM, and dinner times were measured between 4:00 PM and 7:00 PM. Data collected by the author.

TI-83/84 list names (FASTFOOD): MCDL, MCDD, BKL, BKD, WL, WD, DDL, DDD

MCDONALDS LUNCH	MCDONALDS DINNER	BURGER KING LUNCH	BURGER KING DINNER	WENDYS LUNCH	WENDYS DINNER	DUNKIN DONUTS LUNCH	DUNKIN DONUTS DINNER
107	84	116	101	466	56	86	181
139	121	131	126	387	82	201	50
197	119	147	153	368	120	179	177
209	146	120	116	219	116	131	107
281	266	126	175	177	121	126	68

(Complete data sets available at www.TriolaStats.com)

Data Set 37: Cola Weights and Volumes

Data are from 144 cans of cola (first five rows shown here). **WT** is weight in pounds and **VOL** is volume in ounces.

TI-83/84 list names (COLA):   CRGWT, CRGVL, CDTWT, CDTVL, PRGWT, PRGVL, PDTWT, PDTVL

COKE REG WT	COKE REG VOL	COKE DIET WT	COKE DIET VOL	PEPSI REG WT	PEPSI REG VOL	PEPSI DIET WT	PEPSI DIET VOL
0.8192	12.3	0.7773	12.1	0.8258	12.4	0.7925	12.3
0.8150	12.1	0.7758	12.1	0.8156	12.2	0.7868	12.2
0.8163	12.2	0.7896	12.3	0.8211	12.2	0.7846	12.2
0.8211	12.3	0.7868	12.3	0.8170	12.2	0.7938	12.3
0.8181	12.2	0.7844	12.2	0.8216	12.2	0.7861	12.2

Data Set 38: Candies

Weights (grams) from M&M plain candies listed by color, Hershey's Kisses, and Reese's Peanut Butter Cup Miniatures (first five rows shown here). Data collected and later eaten by the author.

TI-83/84 list names (CANDY):   MMRED, MMORG, MMYEL, MMBWN, MMBLU, MMGRN, HKISS, PBCUP

RED	ORANGE	YELLOW	BROWN	BLUE	GREEN	HERSHEYS KISSES	REESES PB CUPS
0.889	0.976	0.853	0.874	0.843	0.892	4.488	9.029
0.937	0.878	0.822	0.842	0.845	0.861	4.781	8.689
0.877	0.886	0.875	0.907	0.829	0.968	4.697	8.909
0.839	0.867	0.855	0.904	0.880	0.968	4.540	8.969
0.810	0.858	0.934	0.877	0.871	0.905	4.458	9.012

Data Set 39: Chocolate Chip Cookies

Data are from 170 chocolate chip cookies (first five rows shown here). Brands are Chips Ahoy regular, Chips Ahoy Chewy, Chips Ahoy Reduced Fat, Keebler, and Hannaford. Values are counts of numbers of chocolate chips in each cookie. Data collected by the author.

TI-83/84 list names (CHIPS):   CAREG, CACHW, CARF, KEEB, HANNA.

CHIPS AHOY REG	CHIPS AHOY CHEWY	CHIPS AHOY RED FAT	KEEBLER	HANNAFORD
22	21	13	29	13
22	20	24	31	15
26	16	18	25	16
24	17	16	32	21
23	16	21	27	15

Data Set 40: Coin Weights

Data are from 222 coins (first five rows shown here) consisting of coin weights (grams). The "pre-1983 pennies" were made after the Indian and wheat pennies, and they are 97% copper and 3% zinc. The "post-1983 pennies" are 3% copper and 97% zinc. The "pre-1964 silver quarters" are 90% silver and 10% copper. The "post-1964 quarters" are made with a copper-nickel alloy.

TI-83/84 list names (COINS):   CPIND, CPWHT, CPPRE, CPPST, CPCAN, CQPRE, CQPST, CDOL

INDIAN PENNIES	WHEAT PENNIES	PRE-1983 PENNIES	POST-1983 PENNIES	CANADIAN PENNIES	PRE-1964 QUARTERS	POST-1964 QUARTERS	DOLLAR COINS
3.0630	3.1366	3.1582	2.5113	3.2214	6.2771	5.7027	8.1008
3.0487	3.0755	3.0406	2.4907	3.2326	6.2371	5.7495	8.1072
2.9149	3.1692	3.0762	2.5024	2.4662	6.1501	5.7050	8.0271
3.1358	3.0476	3.0398	2.5298	2.8357	6.0002	5.5941	8.0813
2.9753	3.1029	3.1043	2.4950	3.3189	6.1275	5.7247	8.0241

(Complete data sets available at www.TriolaStats.com)

Data Set 41: Aluminum Cans

Data are from 350 cans (first five rows shown here) consisting of measured maximum axial loads (pounds). Axial loads are applied when the tops are pressed into place. **CANS 109** includes cans that are 0.0109 inch thick, and **CANS 111** includes cans that are 0.0111 inch thick.

TI-83/84 list names CN109, CN111
(CANS):

CANS 109	CANS 111
270	287
273	216
258	260
204	291
254	210

Data Set 42: Garbage Weight

Data are from 62 households (first five rows shown here) consisting of weights (pounds) of discarded garbage in different categories. **HH SIZE** is household size. Data provided by Masakuza Tani, the Garbage Project, University of Arizona.

TI-83/84 list names HHSIZ, METAL, PAPER, PLAS, GLASS,
(GARBAGE): FOOD, YARD, TEXT, OTHER, TOTAL

HH SIZE	METAL	PAPER	PLASTIC	GLASS	FOOD	YARD	TEXTILE	OTHER	TOTAL
2	1.09	2.41	0.27	0.86	1.04	0.38	0.05	4.66	10.76
3	1.04	7.57	1.41	3.46	3.68	0.00	0.46	2.34	19.96
3	2.57	9.55	2.19	4.52	4.43	0.24	0.50	3.60	27.60
6	3.02	8.82	2.83	4.92	2.98	0.63	2.26	12.65	38.11
4	1.50	8.72	2.19	6.31	6.30	0.15	0.55	2.18	27.90

Data Set 43: Draft Lottery

Data are from the 1969 Vietnam War U.S. Army draft lottery (first five rows shown here). The data represent the order in which dates were drawn from a box (1 is the first date drawn of September 14; 366 is the last date drawn of June 8). Men were drafted into the U.S. Army based on the order in which their birthday was drawn. See "From Data to Decision" in Chapter 13 for more information.

TI-83/84 list names DRDAY, DRJAN, DRFEB, DRMAR, DRAPR,
(DRAFT): DRMAY, DRJUN, DRJUL, DRAUG, DRSEP,
DROCT, DRNOV, DRDEC

DAY	JAN	FEB	MAR	APR	MAY	JUNE	JULY	AUG	SEPT	OCT	NOV	DEC
1	305	86	108	32	330	249	93	111	225	359	19	129
2	159	144	29	271	298	228	350	45	161	125	34	328
3	251	297	267	83	40	301	115	261	49	244	348	157
4	215	210	275	81	276	20	279	145	232	202	266	165
5	101	214	293	269	364	28	188	54	82	24	310	56

(Complete data sets available at www.TriolaStats.com)

Data Set 44: Weights of Minted Quarters

Data are the weights (grams) of quarters selected during each of the first 5 hours of U.S. Mint production on each of 25 consecutive days (first five rows shown here).

TI-83/84 list names (QUARTER):   MQDAY, MQHR1, MQHR2, MQHR3, MQHR4, MQHR5, MQXBR, MQS, MQRNG.

DAY	HOUR 1	HOUR 2	HOUR 3	HOUR 4	HOUR 5	$\bar{x}$	s	RANGE
1	5.543	5.698	5.605	5.653	5.668	5.6334	0.060690	0.155
2	5.585	5.692	5.771	5.718	5.720	5.6972	0.068947	0.186
3	5.752	5.636	5.660	5.680	5.565	5.6586	0.067925	0.187
4	5.697	5.613	5.575	5.615	5.646	5.6292	0.045499	0.122
5	5.630	5.770	5.713	5.649	5.650	5.6824	0.058140	0.140

Data Set 45: Births in New York

Data are from 465,506 births (first five rows shown here) in New York State hospitals. **GENDER** is the gender of the baby, **LENGTH OF STAY** is the number of days the mother remained in the hospital, **BIRTH WEIGHT** is the weight of the baby at birth in grams.

TI-83/84 list names (BIRTHS)*:   BBLOS, BBWGT (no list for GENDER)

*NOTE: TI lists are limited to 500 rows due to calculator memory constraints.

GENDER	LENGTH OF STAY	BIRTH WEIGHT
M	3	2500
F	1	3400
F	2	3000
M	4	2800
M	2	2900

Data Set 46: Dow Jones Industrial Average (DJIA)

Data are from the Dow Jones Industrial Average (DJIA) on 31,784 days (first five rows shown here) dating back to May 1896. For each date, **OPEN** is the opening DJIA value, **HIGH** is the maximum DJIA value reached, **LOW** is the minimum DJIA value reached, and **CLOSE** is the DJIA value when the stock market closed.

TI-83/84 list names (DJIA)*:   DJOPN, DJHI, DJLOW, DJCLS (No list for DATE)

*NOTE: TI lists are limited to 500 rows due to calculator memory constraints.

DATE	OPEN	HIGH	LOW	CLOSE
1896-05-27	29.39	29.39	29.39	29.39
1896-05-28	29.11	29.11	29.11	29.11
1896-05-29	29.43	29.43	29.43	29.43
1896-06-01	29.40	29.40	29.40	29.40
1896-06-02	29.00	29.00	29.00	29.00

(Complete data sets available at www.TriolaStats.com)

APPENDIX C

Websites

Triola Stats: www.TriolaStats.com

Access continually updated digital resources for the Triola Statistics Series, including downloadable data sets, textbook supplements, online instructional videos, and more.

Statdisk: www.Statdisk.com

Access the free Statdisk statistical software that is designed specifically for this book and contains all Appendix B data sets.

StatCrunch: www.statcrunch.com

Books

*An asterisk denotes a book recommended for reading. Other books are recommended as reference texts.

Bennett, D. 1998. *Randomness.* Cambridge, Mass.: Harvard University Press.

*Best, J. 2012. *Damned Lies and Statistics.* Berkeley, Calif.: University of California Press.

*Best, J. 2004. *More Damned Lies and Statistics.* Berkeley, Calif.: University of California Press.

*Campbell, S. 2004. *Flaws and Fallacies in Statistical Thinking.* Mineola, N.Y.: Dover Publications.

*Crossen, C. 1996. *Tainted Truth: The Manipulation of Fact in America.* New York: Simon & Schuster.

*Freedman, D., R. Pisani, R. Purves, and A. Adhikari. 2007. *Statistics.* 4th ed. New York: W. W. Norton & Company.

*Gonick, L., and W. Smith. 1993. *The Cartoon Guide to Statistics.* New York: Harper Collins.

*Heyde, C., and E. Seneta, eds. 2001. *Statisticians of the Centuries.* New York: Springer-Verlag.

*Hollander, M., and F. Proschan. 1984. *The Statistical Exorcist: Dispelling Statistics Anxiety.* New York: Marcel Dekker.

*Holmes, C. 1990. *The Honest Truth About Lying with Statistics.* Springfield, Ill.: Charles C Thomas.

*Hooke, R. 1983. *How to Tell the Liars from the Statisticians.* New York: Marcel Dekker.

*Huff, D. 1993. *How to Lie with Statistics.* New York: W. W. Norton & Company.

*Jaffe, A., and H. Spirer. 1998. *Misused Statistics.* New York: Marcel Dekker.

Kaplan, M. 2007. *Chances Are.* New York: Penguin Group.

Kotz, S., and D. Stroup. 1983. *Educated Guessing—How to Cope in an Uncertain World.* New York: Marcel Dekker.

Lapp, James. 2022. *Student Solutions Manual to Accompany Elementary Statistics.* 14th ed. Boston: Pearson.

Mlodinow, L. 2009. *The Drunkard's Walk.* New York: Vintage Books.

*Moore, D., and W. Notz. 2017. *Statistics: Concepts and Controversies.* 9th ed. San Francisco: Freeman.

*Paulos, J. 2001. *Innumeracy: Mathematical Illiteracy and Its Consequences.* New York: Hill and Wang.

*Reichmann, W. 1981. *Use and Abuse of Statistics.* New York: Penguin.

*Rossman, A., and B. Chance. 2011. *Workshop Statistics: Discovery with Data.* 4th ed. Emeryville, Calif.: Key Curriculum Press.

*Salsburg, D. 2001. *The Lady Tasting Tea: How Statistics Revolutionized the Twentieth Century.* New York: W. H. Freeman.

Sheskin, D. 2011. *Handbook of Parametric and Nonparametric Statistical Procedures.* 5th ed. Boca Raton, Fla.: CRC Press.

*Silver, N. 2015. *The Signal and the Noise.* New York: Penguin Books.

Simon, J. 1997. *Resampling: The New Statistics.* 2nd ed. Arlington, Va.: Resampling Stats.

Spiegelhalter, D. 2019. *The Art of Statistics: How to Learn from Data.* New York: Hachette Book Group.

*Stigler, S. 1986. *The History of Statistics.* Cambridge, Mass.: Harvard University Press.

Stigler, S. 2016. *The Seven Pillars of Statistical Wisdom.* Cambridge, Mass.: Harvard University Press.

Taleb, N. 2010. *The Black Swan.* 2nd ed. New York: Random House.

Triola, M. 2022. *Statdisk Student Laboratory Manual and Workbook.* 14th ed. Boston: Pearson.

Triola, M., and L. Franklin. 1994. *Business Statistics.* Boston: Addison-Wesley.

Triola, M., M. Triola, and J. Roy. 2018. *Biostatistics for the Biological and Health Sciences.* 2nd ed. Boston: Pearson.

*Tufte, E. 2001. *The Visual Display of Quantitative Information.* 2nd ed. Cheshire, Conn.: Graphics Press.

Tukey, J. 1977. *Exploratory Data Analysis.* Boston: Pearson.

Vickers, A. 2009. *What Is a P-Value Anyway?* Boston: Pearson.

Whelan, C. 2013. *Naked Statistics.* New York: W. W. Norton & Company.

Zwillinger, D., and S. Kokoska. 2000. *CRC Standard Probability and Statistics Tables and Formulae.* Boca Raton, Fla.: CRC Press.

APPENDIX D

Chapter 1 Answers

Section 1-1

1. The respondents are a voluntary response sample or a self-selected sample. Because those with strong interests in the topic are more likely to respond, it is very possible that their responses do not reflect the opinions or behavior of the general population.

3. Statistical significance is indicated when methods of statistics are used to reach a conclusion that a treatment is effective, but common sense might suggest that the treatment does not make enough of a difference to justify its use or to be practical. Yes, it is possible for a study to have statistical significance, but not practical significance.

5. Yes, there does appear to be a potential to create a bias.

7. No, there does not appear to be a potential to create a bias.

9. The sample is a voluntary response sample and has strong potential to be flawed.

11. The sampling method appears to be sound.

13. The Ornish weight loss program has statistical significance, because the results are so unlikely (3 chances in 1000) to occur by chance. It does not have practical significance because the amount of lost weight (3.3 lb) is so small.

15. The difference between Mendel's 25% rate and the result of 26% is not statistically significant. According to Mendel's theory, 145 of the 580 peas would have yellow pods, but the results consisted of 152 peas with yellow pods. The difference of 7 peas with yellow pods among the 580 offspring does not appear to be statistically significant. The difference does not appear to have practical significance.

17. With 40 out of 41 ballots having the Democrat first, it appears that the result is statistically significant. Because of the great advantage enjoyed by Democrats, the results also have practical significance.

19. There appears to be statistical significance given the large discrepancy between 79.1% and 39%. Because the results are so far from yielding a jury of peers, it appears that the results have practical significance.

21. Yes. Each column of 8 AM and 12 AM temperatures is recorded from the same subject, so each pair is matched.

23. The data can be used to address the issue of whether there is a correlation between body temperatures at 8 AM and at 12 AM. Also, the data can be used to determine whether there are differences between body temperatures at 8 AM and at 12 AM.

25. No. The lemon imports are weights in metric tons and the crash fatality rates are fatalities per 100,000 population, so their differences are meaningless.

27. No. The author of an article for the *Journal of Chemical Information and Modeling* has no reason to collect or present the data in a way that is biased.

29. It is questionable that the sponsor is the Idaho Potato Commission and the favorite vegetable is potatoes.

31. The correlation, or association, between two variables does not mean that one of the variables is the cause of the other. Correlation does not imply causation. Clearly, sour cream consumption is not directly related in any way to motorcycle fatalities.

33. The correlation, or association, between two variables does not mean that one of the variables is the cause of the other. Correlation does not imply causation.

35. The sample is a voluntary response sample, so there is a good chance that the results do not accurately reflect the larger population.

37. a. 700 adults   b. 55%

39. a. 559.2 respondents
    b. No. Because the result is a count of respondents among the 1165 engaged or married women who were surveyed, the result must be a whole number.
    c. 559 respondents   d. 8%

41. Because a reduction of 100% would eliminate all of the size, it is not possible to reduce the size by 100% or more.

43. Because a reduction of 100% would eliminate all plaque, it is not possible to reduce it by more than 100%.

45. If one subgroup receives a 4% raise and another subgroup receives a 4% raise, the combined group will receive a 4% raise, not an 8% raise. The percentages should not be added in this case.

47. All percentages of success should be multiples of 5. The given percentages cannot be correct.

Section 1-2

1. The population consists of all adults in the United States, and the sample is the 1001 adults who were surveyed. Because the value of 69% refers to the sample, it is a statistic.

3. Only part (b) describes discrete data.

5. Statistic   7. Parameter   9. Statistic
11. Parameter   13. Continuous   15. Discrete
17. Continuous   19. Discrete   21. Nominal
23. Ordinal   25. Interval   27. Ratio

29. The numbers are not counts or measures of anything. They are at the nominal level of measurement, and it makes no sense to compute the average (mean) of them.

31. The temperatures are at the interval level of measurement. Because there is no natural starting point with 0°F representing "no heat," ratios such as "twice" make no sense, so it is wrong to say that it is twice as warm in Paris as it is in Anchorage.

33. a. Continuous, because the number of possible values is infinite and not countable
    b. Discrete, because the number of possible values is finite
    c. Discrete, because the number of possible values is finite
    d. Discrete, because the number of possible values is infinite and countable

Section 1-3

1. The study is an experiment because subjects were given treatments.

3. The group sample sizes are large enough so that the researchers could see the effects of the two treatments, but it would have been better to have larger samples.

5. The sample appears to be a convenience sample. By e-mailing the survey to a readily available group of Internet users, it was easy to obtain results. Although there is a real potential for getting a sample group that is not representative of the population, indications of which ear is used for cell phone calls and which hand is dominant do not appear to be factors that would be distorted much by a sample bias.

7. With 717 responses, the response rate is 14%, which does appear to be quite low. In general, a very low response rate creates a serious potential for getting a biased sample that consists of those with a special interest in the topic.

9. Systematic   11. Random   13. Cluster

15. Stratified   17. Random   19. Convenience

21. Observational study. The sample is a convenience sample consisting of subjects who decided themselves to respond. Such voluntary response samples have a high chance of not being representative of the larger population, so the sample may well be biased. The question was posted in an electronic edition of a newspaper, so the sample is biased from the beginning.

23. Experiment. This experiment would create an *extremely* dangerous and illegal situation that has a real potential to result in injury or death. It's difficult enough to drive in New York City while being completely sober.

25. Experiment. The biased sample created by using a small sample of college students cannot be fixed by using a larger sample. The larger sample will still be a biased sample that is not representative of the population of all adults.

27. Observational study. Respondents who have been convicted of felonies are not likely to respond honestly to the second question. The survey will suffer from a "social desirability bias" because subjects will tend to respond in ways that will be viewed favorably by those conducting the survey.

29. Prospective study   31. Cross-sectional study

33. Matched pairs design   35. Completely randomized design

37. a. Not a simple random sample, but it is a random sample.
    b. Simple random sample and also a random sample.
    c. Not a simple random sample and not a random sample.

Chapter 1: Quick Quiz

1. No. The numbers do not measure or count anything.
2. Nominal   3. Continuous   4. Quantitative data
5. Ratio   6. Statistic   7. No
8. Observational study
9. The subjects did not know whether they were getting aspirin or the placebo.
10. Simple random sample

Chapter 1: Review Exercises

1. The respondents are a voluntary response sample or a self-selected sample. Because those with strong interests in the topic are more likely to respond, it is very possible that their responses do not reflect the opinions or behavior of the general population.
2. a. The sample is a voluntary response sample, so the results are questionable.
   b. Statistic   c. Observational study

3. Randomized: Subjects were assigned to the different groups through a process of random selection, whereby they had the same chance of belonging to each group. Double-blind: The subjects did not know which of the two groups they were in, and the people who evaluated results did not know either.

4. No. Correlation does not imply causality.

5. a. Systematic   b. Stratified
   c. Simple random sample   d. Convenience
   e. Cluster

6. Yes. The two questions give the false impression that they are addressing very different issues. Most people would be in favor of defending marriage, so the first question is likely to receive a substantial number of "yes" responses. The second question better describes the issue and subjects are much more likely to have varied responses.

7. a. Discrete   b. Ratio
   c. The mailed responses would be a voluntary response sample, so those with strong opinions or greater interest in the topics are more likely to respond. It is very possible that the results do not reflect the true opinions of the population of all state residents.
   d. Stratified   e. Cluster

8. a. If they have no fat at all, they have 100% less than any other amount with fat, so the 125% figure cannot be correct.
   b. 686   c. 28%

9. a. Interval data; systematic sample
   b. Nominal data; stratified sample
   c. Ordinal data; convenience sample

10. Because there is less than a 1% chance of getting the results by chance, the method does appear to have statistical significance. The result of 239 boys in 291 births is a rate of 82% so it is above the 50% rate expected by chance, and it does appear to be high enough to have practical significance. The procedure appears to have both statistical significance and practical significance.

Chapter 1: Cumulative Review Exercises

1. 133.0. The IQ score of 188 appears to be substantially higher than the other IQ scores.
2. 0.000122   3. 4.50 is a significantly high value.
4. −6.64   5. 1068
6. 20.25   7. 0.364
8. 0.20   9. 0.000729
10. 68,719,476,736 (or about 68,719,477,000)
11. 377,149,515,625 (or about 377,149,520,000)
12. 0.000000004096

Chapter 2 Answers

Section 2-1

1. The table summarizes 1000 commute times. It is not possible to identify the exact values of all of the original data amounts.

3.

Daily Commute Time in Boston (minutes)	Relative Frequency
0–29	46.8%
30–59	42.2%
60–89	9.2%
90–119	1.0%
120–149	0.8%

5. Class width: 10. Class midpoints: 24.5, 34.5, 44.5, 54.5, 64.5, 74.5, 84.5. Class boundaries: 19.5, 29.5, 39.5, 49.5, 59.5, 69.5, 79.5, 89.5. Number: 91.

7. Class width: 100. Class midpoints: 49.5, 149.5, 249.5, 349.5, 449.5, 549.5, 649.5. Class boundaries: −0.5, 99.5, 199.5, 299.5, 399.5, 499.5, 599.5, 699.5. Number: 153.

9. No. The maximum frequency is in the second class instead of being near the middle, so the frequencies below the maximum do not mirror those above the maximum.

11. Yes. Except for the single value that lies between 600 and 699, the frequencies start low, reach a maximum of 90, and then decrease. The values below the maximum are very roughly a mirror image of those above it. (That single value between 600 and 699 is an outlier that makes the determination of a normal distribution somewhat questionable, but using a *loose interpretation* of the criteria for normality, it is reasonable to conclude that the distribution is normal.)

13. The data amounts do not appear to have a normal distribution. The distribution does not appear to be symmetric because the frequencies preceding the maximum frequency of 16 are far outweighed by the frequencies following the maximum.

Daily Commute Time in Chicago (Minutes)	Frequency
0–14	5
15–29	16
30–44	14
45–59	9
60–74	5
75–89	1

15.

Duration (sec)	Frequency
125–149	1
150–174	0
175–199	0
200–224	3
225–249	34
250–274	12

17.

Burger King Lunch Service Times (sec)	Frequency
70–109	11
110–149	23
150–189	7
190–229	6
230–269	3

19. The distribution does appear to be a normal distribution.

Weight (kg)	Frequency
40–49	2
50–59	22
60–69	23
70–79	13
80–89	3
90–99	4

21. Because there are disproportionately more 0s and 5s, it appears that the heights were reported instead of measured. It is likely that the results are not very accurate.

Last Digit	Frequency
0	9
1	2
2	1
3	3
4	1
5	15
6	2
7	0
8	3
9	1

23. The actresses appear to be generally younger than the actors.

Age (yr)	Actresses	Actors
20–29	34.1%	1.1%
30–39	37.4%	31.9%
40–49	16.5%	41.8%
50–59	3.3%	17.6%
60–69	6.6%	6.6%
70–79	1.1%	1.1%
80–89	1.1%	0.0%

25.

Age (yr) of Best Actress When Oscar Was Won	Cumulative Frequency
Less than 30	31
Less than 40	65
Less than 50	80
Less than 60	83
Less than 70	89
Less than 80	90
Less than 90	91

27. No. The United States has 37.1% of the cost of piracy for only the five countries listed, not the total cost of piracy for all countries. Because only the top five costs of piracy are listed, we know only that any other country must have a cost less than $1.9 billion.

Country	Relative Frequency
United States	37.1%
China	35.5%
India	11.0%
France	8.6%
United Kingdom	7.8%

29. It is very similar to Table 2-2. Both frequency distributions begin with a low frequency in the first class, followed by the maximum frequency in the second class, and the frequencies are generally lower as you progress from top to bottom in the table. (TI data: Frequencies are 79, 148, 157, 43, 49, 6, 9, 0, 0, 9.)

Daily Commute Time in Los Angeles (minutes)	Frequency
0–14	157
15–29	324
30–44	282
45–59	103
60–74	98
75–89	7
90–104	18
105–119	0
120–134	0
135–149	11

31. Yes, the frequency distribution appears to be a normal distribution.

Systolic Blood Pressure (mm Hg)	Frequency
80–99	11
100–119	116
120–139	131
140–159	34
160–179	7
180–199	1

33. Yes, the frequency distribution appears to be a normal distribution.

Magnitude	Frequency
1.00–1.49	19
1.50–1.99	97
2.00–2.49	187
2.50–2.99	147
3.00–3.49	100
3.50–3.99	38
4.00–4.49	8
4.50–4.99	4

35. An outlier can dramatically increase the number of classes.

Weight (lb)	With Outlier	Without Outlier
200–219	6	6
220–239	5	5
240–259	12	12
260–279	36	36
280–299	87	87
300–319	28	28
320–339	0	
340–359	0	
360–379	0	
380–399	0	
400–419	0	
420–439	0	
440–459	0	
460–479	0	
480–499	0	
500–519	1	

Section 2-2

1. The histogram should be bell-shaped.
3. With a data set that is so small, the true nature of the distribution cannot be seen with a histogram.
5. 40
7. The shape of the graph would not change. The vertical scale would be different, but the relative heights of the bars would be the same.
9. Because the data are skewed to the right, the histogram does not appear to depict data from a population with a normal distribution.

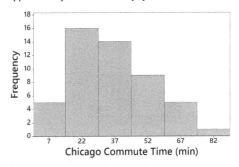

11. Because it is far from being bell-shaped, the histogram does not appear to depict data from a population with a normal distribution.

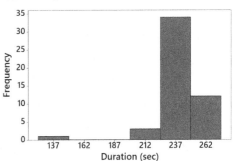

13. Using a loose interpretation of "normal," the histogram appears to be approximately normal. The histogram does show skewness to the right.

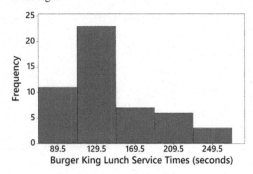
Burger King Lunch Service Times (seconds)

15. Because the histogram is roughly bell-shaped, it does appear to depict a normal distribution.

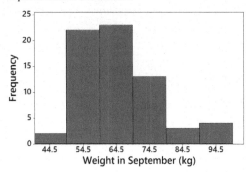
Weight in September (kg)

17. The digits 0 and 5 appear to occur more often than the other digits, so it appears that the heights were reported and not actually measured. This suggests that the data might not be very useful.

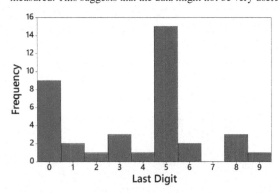
Last Digit

19. Only part (c) appears to represent data from a normal distribution. Part (a) has a systematic pattern that is not that of a straight line, part (b) has points that are not close to a straight-line pattern, and part (d) is really bad because it shows a systematic pattern and points that are not close to a straight-line pattern.

Section 2-3

1. The data set is too small for a dotplot to reveal important characteristics of the data. Because the data are listed in order for each of the last several years, a time-series graph would be most effective for these data.

3. No. Graphs should be constructed in a way that is fair and objective. The readers should be allowed to make their own judgments, instead of being manipulated by misleading graphs.

5. The pulse rate of 36 beats per minute appears to be an outlier.

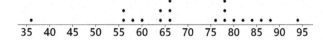

7. The data are arranged in order from lowest to highest, as 36, 56, 56, and so on.

```
3 | 6
4 |
5 | 668
6 | 044666
7 | 6888
8 | 02468
9 | 4
```

9. There is a gradual upward trend that appears to be leveling off in recent years. An upward trend would be helpful to women so that their earnings become equal to those of men.

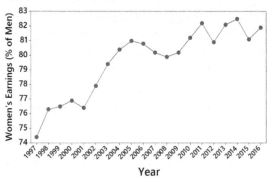
Year

11. Given that box office receipts are closely tracked and widely reported, these data are very accurate.

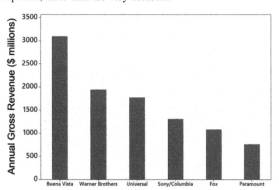

13.

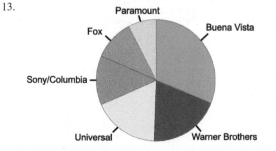

15. The distribution does not have much skewness.

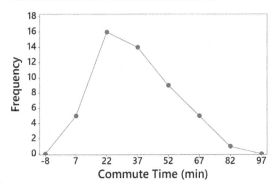

17. Because the vertical scale starts with a frequency of 200 instead of 0, the difference between the "no" and "yes" responses is greatly exaggerated. The graph makes it appear that about *five* times as many respondents said "no," when the ratio is actually a little less than 2.5 to 1.

19. The two costs are one-dimensional in nature, but the baby bottles are three-dimensional objects. The $4500 cost isn't even twice the $2600 cost, but the baby bottles make it appear that the larger cost is about five times the smaller cost.

21.
```
96. | 59
97. | 0001112333444
97. | 5566666788888999
98. | 00000000000002222233444444444444
98. | 5555666666666666666677777888888899
99. | 001244
99. | 56
```

Section 2-4

1. The term *linear* refers to a straight *line,* and *r* measures how well a scatterplot of the sample paired data fits a straight-line pattern.

3. A scatterplot is a graph of paired (x, y) quantitative data. It helps us by providing a visual image of the data plotted as points, and such an image is helpful in enabling us to see patterns in the data and to recognize that there may be a correlation between the two variables.

5. There does not appear to be a correlation. The given data suggest that five-day predicted high temperatures are not very accurate.

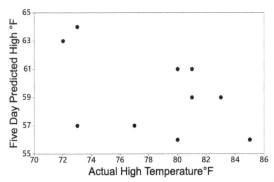

7. There does appear to be a linear correlation between the amounts of tar and the amounts of nicotine in cigarettes.

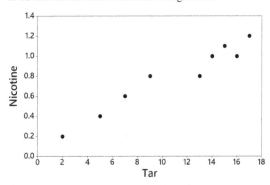

9. With $n = 10$ pairs of data, the critical values are ± 0.632. Because $r = -0.475$ is between -0.632 and 0.632, there is not sufficient evidence to conclude that there is a linear correlation.

11. With $n = 9$ pairs of data, the critical values are ± 0.666. Because $r = 0.971$ is in the right tail region beyond 0.666, there is sufficient evidence to conclude that there is a linear correlation.

13. Because the *P*-value is 0.166, which is not small (such as 0.05 or less), there is a high chance (16.6%) of getting the sample results when there is no correlation, so there is not sufficient evidence to conclude that there is linear correlation.

15. Because the *P*-value of 0.000 is small (such as 0.05 or less), there is a small chance of getting the sample results when there is no correlation, so there is sufficient evidence to conclude that there is a linear correlation.

Chapter 2: Quick Quiz

1. Class width: 20. It is not possible to identify the original data values.

2. Class limits: 0 and 19. Class boundaries: -0.5 and 19.5.

3. 69

4.

Annual Tornadoes in Oklahoma	Relative Frequency
0–19	4.3%
20–39	26.1%
40–59	30.4%
60–79	21.7%
80–99	8.7%
100–119	7.2%
120–139	0.0%
140–159	1.4%

5. 30, 30, 30, 31, 34, 34, 36, 36, 39

6. Pareto chart

7. Scatterplot

8. No, the term "normal distribution" has a different meaning than the term "normal" that is used in ordinary speech. A normal distribution has a bell shape, but the randomly selected lottery digits will have a uniform or flat shape.

9. Variation

10. Parts a, d, e describe normally distributed data.

Chapter 2: Review Exercises

1. Both distributions are skewed to the right.

Email Interarrival Time (minutes)	Frequency
0–9	27
10–19	15
20–29	7
30–39	7
40–49	1
50–59	2
60–69	1

2. Because the histogram has a shape that is far from being bell-shaped, it suggests that the data are from a population *not* having a normal distribution.

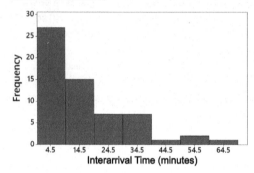

3. By using fewer classes, the histogram does a better job of illustrating the distribution.

4. There are no outliers.

```
0 | 111111122333555666677788999
1 | 012335567888899
2 | 0014589
3 | 3457789
4 | 1
5 | 38
6 | 1
```

5. No. There is no pattern suggesting that there is a relationship.

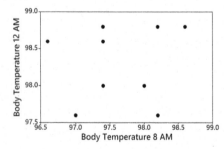

6. a. Time-series graph   b. Scatterplot   c. Pareto chart

7. A pie chart wastes ink on components that are not data; pie charts lack an appropriate scale; pie charts don't show relative sizes of different components as well as some other graphs, such as a Pareto chart.

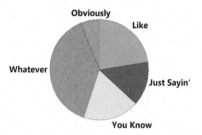

8. The Pareto chart does a better job. It draws attention to the most annoying words or phrases and shows the relative sizes of the different categories.

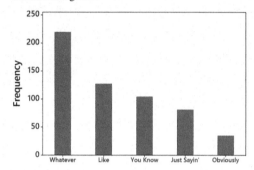

Chapter 2: Cumulative Review Exercises

1.

Magnitude	Frequency
1.00–1.49	1
1.50–1.99	1
2.00–2.49	5
2.50–2.99	7
3.00–3.49	5
3.50–3.99	1

2. a. 1.00 and 1.49   b. 0.995 and 1.495   c. 1.245

3. The distribution is closer to being a normal distribution than the others. Only the single lowest value of 1.09 prevents perfect symmetry, but that one value should not be a basis for stating that the distribution is skewed left.

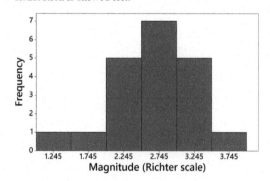

4. a. Continuous   b. Quantitative   c. Ratio   d. Sample

5. The scatterplot does not show any pattern. There does not appear to be correlation between magnitude and depth.

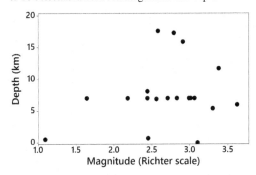

Chapter 3 Answers

Section 3-1

1. The term *average* is not used in statistics. The term *mean* should be used for the result obtained by adding all of the sample values and dividing the total by the number of sample values.

3. They use different approaches for providing a value (or values) of the center or middle of the sorted list of data.

5. $\bar{x} = 47.8$; median $= 60.0$; mode $=$ none; midrange $= 49.0$. The resulting statistics are meaningless because the jersey numbers are nominal data that are just replacements for names, and they do not measure or count anything.

7. $\bar{x} = \$2281$ million; median $= \$1450$ million; mode $= \$1000$ million; midrange $= \$3225$ million. Apart from the fact that all other celebrities have amounts of net worth lower than those given, nothing meaningful can be known about the population of net worth of all celebrities. The numbers all end in 0, and they appear to be rounded estimates (which is the reason for rounding to the nearest whole number).

9. $\bar{x} = 76.4$ attacks; median $= 77.5$ attacks; mode $=$ no mode; midrange $= 76.0$ attacks. The data are time-series data, but the measures of center do not reveal anything about a trend consisting of a pattern of change over time.

11. $\bar{x} = \$198.2$; median $= \$200.0$; mode $= \$250$; midrange $= \$175.0$. The lowest price is a relevant statistic for someone planning to buy one of the smart thermostats.

13. $\bar{x} = 32.6$ mg; median $= 39.5$ mg; mode $= 0$ mg; midrange $= 27.5$ mg. Americans consume some brands much more often than others, but the 20 brands are all weighted equally in the calculations, so the statistics are not necessarily representative of the population of all cans of the same 20 brands consumed by Americans.

15. $\bar{x} = 1.2$; median $= 1.0$; mode $= 1$; midrange $= 1.5$. The statistics are meaningless because the data are at the nominal level of measurement with the numbers being replacements for "right" and "left." Because the measurements were made in 1988, they are not necessarily representative of the current population of all Army women.

17. $\bar{x} = \$365.3$; median $= \$200.0$; mode $= \$500$; midrange $= \$1269.5$. The amounts of $1500 and $2500 appear to be outliers.

19. $\bar{x} = 2.8$ cigarettes; median $= 0.0$ cigarettes; mode $= 0$ cigarettes; midrange $= 25.0$ cigarettes. Because the selected subjects *report* the number of cigarettes smoked, it is very possible that

the data are not at all accurate. And what about that person who smokes 50 cigarettes (or 2.5 packs) a day? What are they thinking?

21. Systolic: $\bar{x} = 127.6$ mm Hg; median $= 124.0$ mm Hg. Diastolic: $\bar{x} = 73.6$ mm Hg; median $= 75.0$ mm Hg. Given that systolic and diastolic blood pressures measure different characteristics, a comparison of the measures of center doesn't make sense. Because the data are matched, it would make more sense to investigate whether there is an association or *correlation* between systolic blood pressure measurements and diastolic blood pressure measurements.

23. Males: $\bar{x} = 69.5$ beats per minute; median $= 66.0$ beats per minute. Females: $\bar{x} = 82.1$ beats per minute; median $= 84.0$ beats per minute. The pulse rates of males appear to be lower than those of females.

25. ANSUR I 1988: $\bar{x} = 78.49$ kg and median $= 77.70$ kg. ANSUR II 2012: $\bar{x} = 85.52$ kg and median $= 84.60$ kg. It does appear that males have become heavier. (TI data: ANSUR I 1988: $\bar{x} = 78.82$ kg and median $= 77.70$ kg. ANSUR II 2012: $\bar{x} = 84.53$ kg and median $= 84.00$ kg.)

27. $\bar{x} = 98.20°$F; median $= 98.40°$F. These results suggest that the mean is less than 98.6°F.

29. $\bar{x} = 34.6$ minutes, which is reasonably close to the mean of 31.4 minutes obtained by using the original list of values.

31. $\bar{x} = 55.1$ years. The mean from the frequency distribution is quite close to the mean of 55.2 years obtained by using the original list of values.

33. 3.14; yes

35. a. 70 years   b. $n - 1$

37. 504 lb is an outlier. Median: 285.5 lb; mean: 294.4 lb; 10% trimmed mean: 285.4 lb; 20% trimmed mean: 285.8 lb. The median, 10% trimmed mean, and 20% trimmed mean are all quite close, but the untrimmed mean of 294.4 lb differs from them because it is strongly affected by the inclusion of the outlier.

39. 0.247%

41. The median found using the given expression is 30.5 minutes. The median of the 1000 times from Data Set 31 is 30.0 minutes. The difference is 0.5 minute.

Section 3-2

1. 9.58 cm is in the general ballpark of the standard deviation of 7.10 cm calculated using the 153 heights. The range rule of thumb does not necessarily give an estimate of s that is very accurate.

3. 50.41 cm^2

5. Range $= 76.0$; $s^2 = 755.4$; $s = 27.5$. Because the jersey numbers are really just replacements for names, they are at the nominal level of measurement, so the results are meaningless.

7. Range $= \$4550$ million; $s^2 = 2,825,670$ (million dollars)^2; $s = \$1681$ million dollars. Because the data are from celebrities with the highest net worth, the measures of variation are not at all typical for all celebrities. Because all of the amounts end with 0, it appears that they are rounded to the nearest ten million dollars, so it would make sense to round the results to the nearest million dollars, as is done here.

9. Range $= 44.0$ attacks; $s^2 = 132.7$ attacks^2; $s = 11.5$ attacks. The measures of variation are blind to any trend for these time-series data.

11. Range = $150.0; s^2 = 2513.9 dollars²; s = $50.1. These statistics are measuring variation among the sample of prices. The minimum price would be a particularly helpful statistic, but none of these statistics is helpful for selecting a smart thermostat for purchase.

13. Range = 55.0 mg; s^2 = 413.4 mg²; s = 20.3 mg. Americans consume some brands much more often than others, but the 20 brands are all weighted equally in the calculations, so the statistics are not necessarily representative of the population of all cans of the same 20 brands consumed by Americans.

15. Range = 1.0; s^2 = 0.2; s = 0.4. Because the numbers are replacements for "right" and "left," they are at the nominal level of measurement, and the results are meaningless.

17. Range = $2461.0; s^2 = 290,400.4 (dollars)²; s = $538.9. The amounts of $1500 and $2500 appear to be outliers, and it is likely that they have a large effect on the measures of variation.

19. Range = 50.0 cigarettes; s^2 = 89.7 cigarettes²; s = 9.5 cigarettes. Because the selected subjects *report* the number of cigarettes smoked, it is very possible that the data are not at all accurate, so the results might not reflect the actual smoking behavior of California adults.

21. Systolic: 14.6%. Diastolic: 16.9%. The variation is roughly about the same.

23. Males: 16.2%. Females: 11.2%. Pulse rates of males appear to vary more than pulse rates of females.

25. Range = 3.10°F; s^2 = 0.39(°F)²; s = 0.62°F

27. Right Threshold: Range = 70.0; s^2 = 160.7; s = 12.7.
Left Threshold: Range = 75.0; s^2 = 164.9; s = 12.8. Amounts of variation for the left and right thresholds do not appear to be very different.

29. 0.78°F, which is not substantially different from s = 0.62°F found using all of the data.

31. Right Threshold: 17.5, which is reasonably close to s = 12.7 found using all of the data.
Left Threshold: 18.8, which is in the ballpark of 12.8 found using all of the data.

33. Significantly low values are less than or equal to 41.4 years, and significantly high values are greater than or equal to 69.0 years. An age of 35 years would be significantly low.

35. Significantly low values are less than or equal to 24.74 cm, and significantly high values are greater than or equal to 29.90 cm. A foot length of 30 cm is significantly high.

37. s = 20.4 minutes is very close to the exact value of 18.5 minutes.

39. s = 7.1 years is very close to the exact value of 6.9 years.

41. a. 95%   b. 68%

43. At least 89% of women have platelet counts within 3 standard deviations of the mean. The minimum is 58.9 and the maximum is 451.3.

45. a. 24.7 cigarettes²   b. 24.7 cigarettes²   c. 12.3 cigarettes²
d. Part (b), because repeated samples result in variances that target the same value (24.7 cigarettes²) as the population variance. Use division by $n - 1$.
e. No. The mean of the sample variances (24.7 cigarettes²) equals the population variance (24.7 cigarettes²), but the mean of the sample standard deviations (3.5 cigarettes) does not equal the population standard deviation (5.0 cigarettes).

Section 3-3

1. Brady's height is 2.66 standard deviations above the mean.

3. It appears that weights of U.S. Army males increased from 1988 to 2012.

5. a. 27.8 mm Hg   b. 2.48 standard deviations   c. z = 2.48
d. The diastolic blood pressure of 98 mm Hg is significantly high.

7. a. 52.4 minutes   b. 2.00 standard deviations   c. z = 2.00
d. The commute time of 95.0 minutes is significantly high because $z \geq 2.0$.

9. Significantly low values are less than or equal to 10.7; significantly high values are greater than or equal to 31.5; values that are not significant are between 10.7 and 31.5.

11. Significantly low values are less than or equal to 19.0 in.; significantly high values are greater than or equal to 23.8 in.; values that are not significant are between 19.0 in. and 23.8 in.

13. With z scores of 13.79 and −16.83, the z score of −16.83 is farther from the mean, so Chandra Bahadur Dangi has a height that is more extreme.

15. Male: z score = −2.69; female: z score = −2.18. The male has the more extreme weight.

17. 6th percentile   19. 40th percentile

21. 0.95 W/kg (Tech: Minitab: 0.942 W/kg; Excel: 0.958 W/kg)

23. 1.28 W/kg (Tech: Minitab: 1.285 W/kg)

25. 1.155 W/kg

27. 0.91 W/kg

29. 5-number summary: 2, 6.0, 7.0, 8.0, 10.

31. 5-number summary: 128 mBq, 140.0 mBq, 150.0 mBq, 158.5 mBq, 172 mBq (Tech: Minitab yields Q_1 =139.0 mBq and Q_3 = 159.75 mBq. Excel yields Q_1 = 141.0 mBq and Q_3 = 157.25 mBq.)

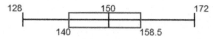

33. The top boxplot represents males. Males appear to have slightly lower pulse rates than females. (Tech: For males, Minitab yields Q_3 = 77.)

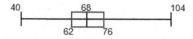

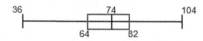

35. The top boxplot represents the weights from ANSUR I 1988 and the bottom boxplot represents weights from ANSUR II 2012. It appears that the weights of male Army personnel increased somewhat from 1988 to 2012. (Tech: For ANSUR II 2012, Minitab yields Q_1 = 75.575 and Q_3 = 94.425. TI data: The values of the five-number summary for ANSUR I are

49.8, 70.7, 77.7, 86.0, 116.9, and for ANSUR II those values are 47.8, 75.2, 84.0, 93.2, 137.1.)

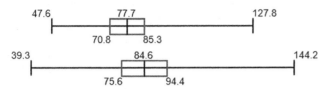

37. Top boxplot represents males. Males appear to have slightly lower pulse rates than females. Outliers for males: 40 beats per minute, 102 beats per minute, 104 beats per minute. Outliers for females: 36 beats per minute.

Chapter 3: Quick Quiz

1. 93.6 km/h
2. 78.5 km/h
3. 65 km/h
4. 1857.6 $(km/h)^2$
5. The speed of 194 km/h appears to be an outlier because it is substantially greater than the other speeds.
6. −1.81; no
7. About 75% or 69 speeds are less than Q_3.
8. Minimum, first quartile Q_1, second quartile Q_2 (or median), third quartile Q_3, maximum
9. 46.0 km/h (from range/4)
10. $\bar{x}, \mu, s, \sigma, s^2, \sigma^2$

Chapter 3: Review Exercises

1. a. −1.00 in.   b. 0.30 in.   c. None   d. −4.75 in.
   e. 12.90 in.   f. 3.52 in.   g. 12.39 in.^{2}
   h. −1.75 in. (Tech: Minitab: −1.83 in.; Excel: −1.675 in.)
   i. 1.05 in. (Tech: Minitab: 1.07 in.; Excel: 1.025 in.)
2. The difference of −11.2 in. appears to be an outlier. If that outlier is excluded, the mean changes from −1.00 in. to −0.07 in., the median changes from 0.30 in. to 0.50 in., and the standard deviation changes from 3.52 in. to 1.51 in. The outlier has a strong effect on the mean and standard deviation, but very little effect on the median.
3. $z = -2.90$. The difference of −11.2 in. is significantly low (because its z score is less than or equal to −2).
4. 5-number summary: −11.2 in., −1.75 in., 0.30 in., 1.05 in., 1.70 in. (Tech: Minitab yields $Q_1 = -1.83$ in. and $Q_3 = 1.07$ in. Excel yields $Q_1 = -1.675$ in. and $Q_3 = 1.025$ in.)

5. 23.0. The numbers don't measure or count anything. They are used as replacements for the names of the categories, so the numbers are at the nominal level of measurement. In this case the mean is a meaningless statistic.

6. Significantly low values are less than or equal to 485.9; significantly high values are greater than or equal to 523.5.
7. The minimum is 119 mm, the first quartile Q_1 is 128 mm, the second quartile Q_2 (or median) is 131 mm, the third quartile Q_3 is 135 mm, and the maximum is 141 mm.
8. With a minimum of 0.799 g and a maximum of 0.944 g, s is estimated to be range/4 = 0.0363 g, which is very close to the standard deviation of 0.0366 g.
9. $P_{25} = 0.871$ g. The value of P_{25} is the same as the value of Q_1. (Tech: Minitab yields 0.8705 and Excel yields 0.8715.)
10. The female has the larger relative birth weight because her z score of 0.23 is larger than the z score of 0.19 for the male.

Chapter 3: Cumulative Review Exercises

1. a. Quantitative   b. Ratio level of measurement   c. Continuous
   d. Sample   e. Statistic

2.

Weight (mg)	Frequency
3500–3549	6
3550–3599	3
3600–3649	7
3650–3699	3
3700–3749	1

3.

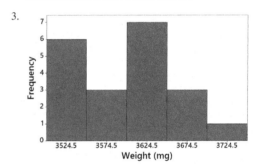

4. 75th percentile
5. a. 3605.2 mg   b. 3619.0 mg   c. 62.4 mg
   d. 3895.3 mg^2 e. 212.0 mg
6. The vertical scale does not begin at 0, so the differences among the different outcomes are exaggerated.
7. No. A normal distribution would appear in a histogram as being bell-shaped, but the histogram is not bell-shaped.
8. Based on the scatterplot, there does appear to be a correlation between heights of fathers and heights of their first sons. Because the points are not very close to a straight-line pattern, the correlation does not appear to be very strong.

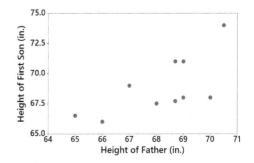

Chapter 4 Answers

Section 4-1

1. $P(A) = 1/10,000$, or 0.0001. $P(\overline{A}) = 9999/10,000$, or 0.9999.
3. a. 1/6 or 0.167   b. 1/2 or 0.5   c. 0
5. 0, 3/5, 1, 0.135   7. 1/10 or 0.1
9. Neither significantly low nor significantly high
11. Significantly high
13. 1/2 or 0.5   15. 0.33
17. 1/10 or 0.1   19. 0
21. 239/291 or 0.821. Yes, the technique appears to be effective.
23. 428/580 or 0.738; yes
25. 0.730. The result suggests that it is likely for someone to use a social networking site.
27. a. brown/brown, brown/blue, blue/brown, blue/blue
    b. 1/4   c. 3/4
29. 3/8 or 0.375   31. 4/16 or 1/4 or 0.25.
33. Because the probability of a result such as 40 is small (less than or equal to 0.05), and because 40 is much higher than what is expected with randomness, the result of 40 is significantly high.
35. Because the probability of a result as low as 14 is 0.029792, that probability is small (less than or equal to 0.05). The result of 14 Democrats being placed on the first line is significantly low.
37. If pregnant women have no ability to predict the genders of their babies, then among 104 predictions, we expect about half of them (or 52) to be correct. The 57 correct predictions is greater than 52. The high probability of 0.189 is greater than 0.05, so 57 correct predictions is not significantly high (and it is not significantly low). It does not appear that pregnant women can correctly predict the genders of their babies.
39. Because the probability of getting 604 or more respondents who have made new friends online is 0.00000306 (less than or equal to 0.05), it appears that 604 is significantly high. This suggests that the true rate is not 50%.
41. a. 999:1   b. 499:1
    c. Yes. If payoffs were made according to the actual odds, the payoff for a winning ticket would be a profit of $999 instead of only $499.
43. a. $5.80   b. 5.80:2 or 29:10 (or roughly 3:1)
    c. 4.168:1 (or roughly 4:1)
    d. $10.34 or about $10 (instead of the actual payoff of $7.80)

Section 4-2

1. $P(D)$ represents the probability of selecting a smartphone with a manufacturing defect, and $P(\overline{D})$ represents the probability that the selected smartphone does not have a manufacturing defect.
3. Because the selections are made without replacement, the events are dependent. Because the sample size of 1068 is less than 5% of the population size of 30,488,983, the selections can be treated as being independent (based on the 5% guideline for cumbersome calculations).
5. 0.318; 0.5   7. 0.87
9. 887/8505 or 0.104   11. 3941/8505 or 0.463
13. a. 0.0109. Yes, the events are independent.
    b. 0.0109. The events are dependent, not independent.

c. In this case, the results are the same when rounded to three significant digits, but with more significant digits, the results of 0.0108767364 and 0.0108657516 are different.
15. a. 0.0309. Yes, the events are independent.
    b. 0.0308. The events are dependent, not independent.
17. 731/8505 or 0.0859   19. 0.000118
21. a. 300   b. 154   c. 0.513
23. 0.990
25. a. 0.0366   b. 0.00133956 or 0.00134 rounded
    c. 0.000049027896 or 0.0000490 rounded
    d. By using one drive without a backup, the probability of total failure is 0.0366, and with three independent drives, the probability drops to 0.0000490 (rounded). By changing from one drive to three, the probability of total failure drops from 0.0366 to 0.0000490, and that is a very substantial improvement in reliability. Back up your data!
27. 0.838. The probability of 0.838 is high, so it is likely that the entire batch will be accepted, even though it includes many firmware defects.
29. a. 0.299
    b. Using the 5% guideline for cumbersome calculations: 0.00239 [using the rounded result from part (a)] or 0.00238
31. a. 0.999775   b. 0.970225
    c. The series arrangement provides better protection.
33. a. $P(A \text{ or } B) = P(A) + P(B) - 2P(A \text{ and } B)$
    b. 3210/8505 or 0.377

Section 4-3

1. The event of not getting at least 1 defect among the 4 calculators, which means that all 4 calculators are good.
3. The probability that the polygraph indicated a lie given that the subject did tell a lie.
5. 15/16 or 0.938
7. a. 0.488   b. 0.134   c. 0.116   d. 0.866
9. a. 0.999   b. 0.00100
11. 0.965. The probability is high enough so that she can be reasonably sure of getting a defect for her work.
13. a. 27/43 or 0.628   b. 16/43 or 0.372
    c. It appears that when students are given four quarters, they are more likely to spend the money than keep it.
15. a. 27/43 or 0.628   b. 12/46 or 0.261
    c. It appears that students are more likely to spend the money when given four quarters than when given a $1 bill.
17. 15/47 or 0.319. This is the probability of the polygraph making it appear that the subject lied when the subject did not lie, so the subject would be unfairly characterized as a liar.
19. 42/57 or 0.737. To be truly effective, the probability should be much higher. There is not sufficient evidence to conclude that the polygraph is effective.
21. a. 0.999851
    b. 0.999998. The usual round-off rule for probabilities would result in a probability of 1.00, which would incorrectly indicate that we are certain to have at least one working hard drive.
23. 0.490. The probability is not low, so further testing of the individual samples will be necessary in 49% of the combined samples.
25. 0.569

Section 4-4

1. The symbol ! is the factorial symbol, which represents the product of decreasing whole numbers, as in $5! = 5 \cdot 4 \cdot 3 \cdot 2 \cdot 1 = 120$. Five NBA players can stand in line 120 different ways.

3. Because repetition is allowed, numbers are selected *with replacement*, so the combinations rule and the two permutation rules do not apply. The multiplication counting rule can be used to show that the number of possible outcomes is $10 \cdot 10 \cdot 10 = 1000$.

5. 1/10,000   7. 1/190

9. 50,400; 1/50,400   11. 1/5,527,200

13. 1/100,000,000. No, there are far too many different possibilities.

15. 360; 1/360 (RHYTHM)

17. 1/292,201,338   19. 1/100,000

21. Area codes: 792. Phone numbers: 6,272,640,000. Yes. (With a total population of about 400,000,000, there would be roughly 16 phone numbers for every adult and child.)

23. a. 360,360   b. 3003   c. 1/3003

25. a. 1,048,576   b. 184,756   c. 0.176
    d. With a probability of 0.176, the result is common, but it should not happen consistently.

27. 653,837,184,000

29. a. 1/302,575,350
    b. There is a *much* better chance of being struck by lightning.
    c. Probability for the old Mega Millions game: 1/258,890,850. The current Mega Millions game has a substantially lower probability of winning when compared to the old Mega Millions game.

31. There are 62 different possible characters. The alphabet requires 26 characters and there are 10 digits, so the Morse code system is more than adequate.

33. 12

35. a. 1/177,100   b. $88,550
    c. No, because the jackpot is too small.

37. 2,095,681,645,538 (about 2 trillion)

39. 0.000000112 $\left[\text{from } \left({}_{20}C_{10} \right) / \left({}_{80}C_{10} \right) \right]$

Section 4-5

1. No. The generated numbers between 2 and 12 would be equally likely, but they are not equally likely with actual dice.

3. Yes, it does. Each of the 365 birthdays has the same chance of being selected, and the cards are replaced, so it is possible to select the same birthday more than once.

5. Randomly generate 50 integers, with each integer between 1 and 100. Consider the numbers 1 through 95 to be adults who recognize the brand name of McDonald's, while the numbers 96 through 100 represent adults who do not recognize McDonald's.

7. Randomly generate an integer between 1 and 1000 inclusive. Consider an outcome of 1 through 640 to be a pass that was caught and consider an outcome between 641 and 1000 to be a pass that was not caught.

9. Answers vary, but here is a typical result: Among 100 generated samples, the sample mean of $\bar{x} = 97.49°F$ or lower never occurred, so the conclusions are essentially the same as in Example 1: With the assumption that the mean body temperature is 98.6°F, we have found that the sample mean of 97.49°F is highly unlikely and is significantly low. Because we did get the sample mean of 97.49°F from Data Set 5, we have strong evidence suggesting that the assumed population mean of 98.6°F is likely to be wrong.

11. Sample statistics: $n = 15$, $\bar{x} = 62.7$ seconds, $s = 19.5$ seconds. Generate random samples from a normally distributed population with the assumed mean of 60 seconds, a standard deviation of 19.5 seconds, and a sample size of $n = 15$. Answers vary, but here is a typical result: Among 100 generated samples, the sample mean of $\bar{x} = 62.7$ seconds or higher occurred 33 times, so 62.7 seconds is not significantly high. The sample mean of 62.7 seconds could easily occur with a population mean of 60 seconds, so there isn't strong evidence against 60 seconds as the population mean.

13. With switching, $P(\text{win}) = 2/3$. With sticking, $P(\text{win}) = 1/3$.

15. The reasoning is not correct. The proportion of girls will not increase.

Chapter 4: Quick Quiz

1. 0.2 or 1/5   2. 4/5 or 0.8   3. 1/365

4. 1/100 or 0.01

5. Answer varies, but the probability should be somewhat low, such as 0.02.

6. 0.0680   7. 0.727   8. 0.00874

9. 0.00459   10. 0.0131

Chapter 4: Review Exercises

1. 0.684, which does not appear to be reasonably close to the proportion of females in the general population. It does not seem that the study subjects were randomly selected from the general population.

2. 0.125   3. 0.739   4. 0.714

5. 0.401   6. 0.0133   7. 0.0134

8. $\bar{L}$ is the event of randomly selecting one of the study subjects and getting someone who does not write with their left hand. $P(\bar{L}) = 0.884$.

9. $\bar{M}$ is the event of randomly selecting one of the study subjects and getting someone who is not a male. $P(\bar{M}) = 0.684$.

10. 0.00151. Yes, because the probability of getting three lefties is so small.

11. $(15/65)(14/64)(13/63)(12/62) = 32,760/16,248,960 = 0.00202$. Because that probability is so low, it is very unlikely that the seats were randomly assigned.

12. a. 0.25   b. 0.316
    c. A result of x successes among n trials is a *significantly high* number of successes if the probability of x or more successes is unlikely with a probability of 0.05 or less. That is, x is a significantly high number of successes if $P(x \text{ or more}) \leq 0.05$. (The value 0.05 is not absolutely rigid. Other values, such as 0.01, could be used to distinguish between results that are significant and those that are not significant.)
    d. No, the probability of getting all four people using vision correction is 0.316, which is not unlikely with a small probability such as 0.05 or less. Because the probability of four people using vision correction is so high, that event can easily occur and it is not a significant event.

13. a. 1/365   b. 31/365
    c. Answer varies, but it is probably quite small, such as 0.01 or less.
    d. Yes
14. 0.0422. No.
15. 1/1,832,600. No, the jackpot seems disproportionately small given the probability of winning it. But then, no lotteries are fair.

Chapter 4: Cumulative Review Exercises

1. a. 6.919 rnfl   b. 6.485 rnfl   c. 9.485 rnfl
   d. 12.090 rnfl   e. 3.400 rnfl   f. 11.558 rnfl^2
2. a. 3.44 rnfl, 4.480 rnfl, 6.485 rnfl, 7.845 rnfl, 15.53 rnfl
   b.

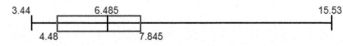

   c. The amount of 15.53 rnfl appears to be an outlier.
3. a. 46%   b. 0.460   c. Stratified sample
4. a. Convenience sample
   b. If the students at the college are mostly from a surrounding region that includes a large proportion of one ethnic group, the results might not reflect the general population of the United States.
   c. 0.75   d. 0.64
5. Based on the scatterplot, it is reasonable to conclude that there is no association between heights of presidents and the heights of the presidential candidates who were runners-up. It is also reasonable to conclude that there is a very weak association with increasing heights of winners corresponding to decreasing heights of runners-up. (More objective criteria will be introduced in Chapter 10.)

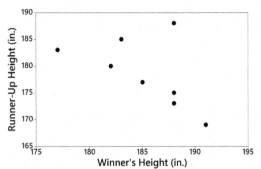

Chapter 5 Answers

Section 5-1

1. The random variable is x, which is the number of unlicensed software packages. The possible values of x are 0, 1, 2, 3, and 4. The values of the random variable x are numerical.
3. $\Sigma P(x) = 0.008 + 0.076 + 0.265 + 0.412 + 0.240 = 1.001$. The sum is not exactly 1 because of a round-off error. The sum is close enough to 1 to satisfy the requirement. Also, the variable x is a numerical random variable and its values are associated with probabilities, and each of the probabilities is between 0 and 1 inclusive, as required. The table does describe a probability distribution.

5. a. Discrete random variable   b. Continuous random variable
   c. Discrete random variable   d. Not a random variable
   e. Discrete random variable
7. Not a probability distribution because the causes are not values of a numerical random variable.
9. Probability distribution with $\mu = 1.6$, $\sigma = 0.9$.
11. Not a probability distribution because the responses are not values of a numerical random variable.
13. Probability distribution with $\mu = 2.4$, $\sigma = 1.0$.
15. $\mu = 0.4$, $\sigma = 0.6$
17. Significantly high numbers of matches are greater than or equal to $\mu + 2\sigma$, and $\mu + 2\sigma = 0.4 + 2(0.6) = 1.6$ matches. Because 4 matches is greater than or equal to 1.6 matches, it is a significantly high number of matches.
19. a. 0.004   b. 0.004   c. Part (b)
    d. Yes, because the probability of 0.004 is low (less than or equal to 0.05).
21. $\mu = 2.1$, $\sigma = 1.1$
23. Significantly low numbers of drivers who say that they text while driving is less than or equal to $\mu - 2\sigma = 2.1 - 2(1.1) = -0.1$. Because 1 driver is not less than or equal to -0.1, 1 is not a significantly low number of drivers who say that they text while driving.
25. a. 0.344   b. 0.648   c. Part (b)
    d. No, because the probability of 2 or fewer drivers who say that they text while driving is not low (less than or equal to 0.05).
27. Because the probability of 270 or more saying that we should use biometrics is 0.0995, which is not low (less than or equal to 0.05), 270 is not significantly high. Given that 270 is not significantly greater than 50%, there is not sufficient evidence to conclude that the majority of the population says that we should replace passwords with biometric security.
29. a. 1000   b. 1/1000   c. $499   d. −50¢
    e. The $1 bet on the pass line in craps is better because its expected value of −1.4¢ is much greater than the expected value of −50¢ for the Florida Pick 3 lottery.
31. a. −39¢
    b. The bet on the number 27 is better because its expected value of −26¢ is greater than the expected value of −39¢ for the other bet.

Section 5-2

1. The given calculation assumes that the first two speaking characters are females and the last three are not females, but there are other arrangements consisting of two females and three males. The probabilities corresponding to those other arrangements should also be included in the result.
3. Because the 50 selections are made without replacement, they are dependent, not independent. Based on the 5% guideline for cumbersome calculations, the 50 selections can be treated as being independent. (The 50 selections constitute 3.33% of the population of 1500 speaking characters, and 3.33% is not more than 5% of the population.)
5. Not binomial. Each of the ages has more than two possible outcomes.

7. Not binomial. Each response has more than two possible outcomes.

9. Not binomial. Because the senators are selected without replacement, the selections are not independent. (The 5% guideline for cumbersome calculations should not be used because the 40 selected senators constitute 40% of the population of 100 senators, and 40% exceeds 5%.)

11. Binomial. Although the events are not independent, they can be treated as being independent by applying the 5% guideline for cumbersome calculations. The sample size of 3600 is not more than 5% of the population of all households.

13. a. 0.128   b. WWC, WCW, CWW; 0.128 for each
    c. 0.384

15. 0.0413 (Table: 0.041)   17. 0.315 (Table: 0.316)

19. 0.0168 (Table: 0.017)   21. 0.238   23. 0.0121

25. 0.00000451. The result of 7 minorities is significantly low. The probability shows that it is very highly unlikely that a process of random selection would result in 7 or fewer minorities. (The Supreme Court rejected the claim that the process was random.)

27. a. 0.00128
    b. Yes, because the probability of 12 or more is 0.00149, which is low (such as less than 0.05).
    c. 0.999

29. a. $\mu = 18.0$ girls; $\sigma = 3.0$ girls
    b. Values of 12.0 girls or fewer are significantly low, values of 24.0 girls or greater are significantly high, and values between 12.0 girls and 24.0 girls are not significant.
    c. Yes, because the result of 26 girls is greater than or equal to 24.0 girls. A result of 26 girls would suggest that the XSORT method is effective.

31. a. $\mu = 7.5$ peas; $\sigma = 1.4$ peas
    b. Values of 4.7 or less are significantly low, values of 10.3 or greater are significantly high, and values between 4.7 and 10.3 are not significant.
    c. No, because the result of 9 peas with green pods is not greater than or equal to 10.3.

33. With a probability of 0.158 that the combined sample tests positive, it is not unlikely because the probability of 0.158 is not very low.

35. 0.985. The high probability shows that a high percentage of ammo cans will be accepted, so it does not appear that there is a production problem.

37. a. 32.4 and 57.3 (or 32.5 and 57.3 if using the rounded σ). The result of 36 brown M&Ms lies between those limits, so it is neither significantly low nor significantly high.
    b. 0.0241
    c. The probability of 36 or fewer brown M&Ms is 0.0878.
    d. The probability from part (c) is relevant. The result of 36 brown M&Ms is not significantly low.
    e. The results do not provide strong evidence against the claim that 13% of M&Ms are brown.

39. a. 238.3 and 287.2 (or 287.1 if using the rounded σ). Because 308 is greater than 287.2, the value of 308 is significantly high.
    b. 0.0000369
    c. The probability of 308 or more is 0.000136.
    d. The probability from part (c) is relevant. The result of 308 voters who voted for the winner is significantly high.

    e. The results suggest that the surveyed voters either lied or had defective memory of how they voted.

41. 0.0468

43. 0.000969 (Use $A = 6$, $B = 43$, $n = 6$, and $x = 4$.)

Section 5-3

1. $\mu = 0.470$ arrivals; $x = 2$ arrivals; $e \approx 2.71828$, which is a constant used in all applications of Formula 5-9.

3. The probability of exactly 2 Internet arrivals in one thousandth of a minute is $P(x) = 0.0690$ (or 0.0691 if using the unrounded value of μ).

5. a. $P(4) = 0.123$
   b. In 118 years, the expected number of years with 7 hurricanes is 14.5.
   c. The expected value of 14.5 years is very close to the actual value of 14 years, so in this case the Poisson distribution works quite well.

7. a. $P(3) = 0.113$
   b. In 118 years, the expected number of years with 3 hurricanes is 13.3.
   c. The expected value of 13.3 years is close to the actual value of 17 years, so in this case the Poisson distribution works well.

9. a. 16.3 births
   b. 0.0989 (or 0.0990 if using the unrounded mean)
   c. 0+ (or 0.0000000834 or 0.0000000851 if using the unrounded mean). Yes, 0 births in a day would be a significantly low number of births.

11. a. 62.2
    b. 0.0155 (0.0156 using the rounded mean)

13. a. 0.170
    b. The expected number is between 97.9 and 98.2, depending on rounding.
    c. The expected number of regions with 2 hits is close to 93, which is the actual number of regions with 2 hits.

15. a. $\mu = 30.41176471$ chocolate chips (or 30.4 rounded).
    b. $P(26) = 0.0557$ (or 0.0558 if using the rounded mean).
    c. Expected number: 1.9 cookies. The expected number of cookies is 1.9, and that is very close to the actual number of cookies with 26 chocolate chips, which is 2.

17. 0.0000172. No, it is highly unlikely that at least one jackpot win will occur in 50 years. You would need to play for more than 306,534 years to reach a 10% chance of winning at least one jackpot. Don't hold your breath.

Chapter 5: Quick Quiz

1. 0+ indicates that the probability is a very small positive number. It does not indicate that it is impossible for event A to occur.

2. No, the sum of the probabilities is 1.5, which is greater than 1.

3. Yes. The random variable x has numerical values, the sum of the probabilities is 1, and each probability is between 0 and 1.

4. $\mu = 3.0$

5. The mean is a parameter.

6. Yes. The sum of the probabilities is 0.999, but because of rounding errors, it can be considered to be 1.

7. 0.827 or 0.828   8. $\mu = 1.5$ sleepwalkers

9. 1.0 sleepwalker^2

10. Yes. If using the range rule of thumb, significantly high numbers of sleepwalkers are greater than or equal to $\mu + 2\sigma = 1.5 + 2(1.0) = 3.5$ sleepwalkers, and 4 sleepwalkers is greater than or equal to 3.5 sleepwalkers. If using probabilities, the probability of 4 or more sleepwalkers is 0.029, which is small (less than 0.05).

Chapter 5: Review Exercises

1. 0.0563   2. 0.349

3. $\mu = 0.4$ workers and $\sigma = 0.6$ workers.

4. No, 0 is not significantly low. If using the range rule of thumb with $\mu = 0.4$ workers and $\sigma = 0.6$ workers, values are significantly low if they are less than or equal to $\mu - 2\sigma = -0.8$, but 0 is not less than or equal to -0.8. If using probabilities, the probability of 0 workers testing positive is 0.651, which is not low (less than or equal to 0.05).

5. Yes, 4 is significantly high. If using the range rule of thumb with $\mu = 0.4$ workers and $\sigma = 0.6$ workers, values are significantly high if they are greater than or equal to $\mu + 2\sigma = 1.6$, and 4 is greater than or equal to 1.6. If using probabilities, the probability of 4 or more workers testing positive is 0.000533, which is low (less than or equal to 0.05).

6. No. The responses are not *numerical* as required.

7. No, because $\Sigma P(x) = 0.9686$, but the sum should be 1. (There is a little leeway allowed for rounding errors, but the sum of 0.9686 is too far from 1.)

8. Yes, probability distribution with $\mu = 4.6$ people, $\sigma = 1.0$ people. (The sum of the probabilities is 0.999, but that is due to rounding errors.)

9. a. 236.0 checks
   b. $\mu = 236.0$ checks and $\sigma = 12.8$ checks
   c. 210.4 checks (or 210.3 checks if using the unrounded σ)
   d. Yes, because 0 is less than or equal to 210.4 checks (or 210.3 checks).

10. a. $7/365$ or 0.0192   b. 0.981   c. 0.000182
    d. No, because the event is so rare. (But it is possible that more than one death occurs in a car crash or some other such event, so it might be wise to consider a contingency plan.)

Chapter 5: Cumulative Review Exercises

1. a. 9.6 moons   b. 5.0 moons   c. 0 moons
   d. 28.0 moons   e. 11.0 moons   f. 120.3 moons²
   g. -12.4 moons, 31.6 moons
   h. No, because none of the planets have a number of moons less than or equal to -12.4 moons (which is impossible, anyway) and none of the planets have a number of moons equal to or greater than 31.6 moons.
   i. Ratio   j. Discrete

2. a. $1/10,000$ or 0.0001   b. 0.0365
   c. 0.964   d. $-75¢$

3. a. 0.270   b. 0.373   c. 0.0726   d. 0.691   e. 0.627

4. a. 663   b. 557   c. 24.4%   d. Statistic

5. No vertical scale is shown, but a comparison of the numbers shows that 7,066,000 is roughly 1.2 times the number 6,000,000; however, the graph makes it appear that the goal of 7,066,000 people is roughly 3 times the number of people enrolled. The

graph is misleading in the sense that it creates the false impression that actual enrollments are far below the goal, which is not the case. Fox News apologized for their graph and provided a corrected graph.

6. Two wins is not significantly high because $P(2 \text{ or more wins}) = 0.380$, which is not low (0.05 or less). The probability of making a profit with two or more wins is 0.380, which is not very likely. Things aren't looking too good for this gambler.

7. a. 0.254   b. 0.255 (Table: 0.256)
   c. $\mu = 5.6$ adults, $\sigma = 1.3$ adults
   d. Yes. Using the range rule of thumb, 1 is less than $\mu - 2\sigma = 3.0$; using probabilities, the probability of 1 or fewer is 0.00129 (Table: 0.001), which is low, such as less than 0.05.

8. Not a probability distribution because the responses are not values of a numerical random variable.

Chapter 6 Answers

Section 6-1

1. The word "normal" has a special meaning in statistics. It refers to a specific bell-shaped distribution that can be described by Formula 6-1. The lottery digits do not have a normal distribution.

3. The mean is $\mu = 0$ and the standard deviation is $\sigma = 1$.

5. 0.4   7. 0.2   9. 0.6700   11. 0.6993 (Table: 0.6992)

13. 1.23   15. -1.45 17. 0.0228   19. 0.9082   21. 0.1587

23. 0.9599   25. 0.0441 (Table: 0.0440)

27. 0.1021   29. 0.8789 (Table: 0.8788)

31. 0.9770 (Table: 0.9771)   33. 0.9999 (Table: 0.9999 or 0.9998)

35. 0.9999 (Table: 0.9998)   37. 2.33   39. $-2.33, 2.33$

41. 0.67   43. 2.05   45. 68.27% (Table: 68.26%)

47. 99.73% (Table: 99.74%)

49. a. 2.28%   b. 2.28%   c. 95.45% (Table: 95.44%)

Section 6-2

1. a. $\mu = 0; \sigma = 1$
   b. The z scores are numbers without units of measurement.

3. No. A standard normal distribution has a mean of 0 and a standard deviation of 1, but the distribution described in the preceding exercise has a mean different from 0 and a standard deviation different from 1. The distribution is a normal distribution, but not a standard normal distribution.

5. 0.8849   7. 0.9053   9. 136   11. 69

13. 0.1978 (Table: 0.1977)   15. 0.3156   17. 0.5252

19. 0.4504 (Table: 0.4489)   21. 84.1 beats per minute

23. 43.3 beats per minute and 95.9 beats per minute. No, 90 beats per minute is not significantly high.

25. a. 72.11% (Table: 72.23%). Yes, about 28% of women are not qualified because of their heights.
    b. 58.2 in. to 69.2 in.

27. a. 0.92% (Table: 0.90%). Because so few men can meet the height requirement, it is likely that most Mickey Mouse characters are women.
    b. 64.0 in. to 68.6 in.

29. 539.9 mm and 600.1 mm   31. 16.4 in.

33. a. 0.0038; either a very rare event occurred or the husband is not the father.
    b. 240 days
35. 97.41% (Table: 97.38%). The design is feasible if the loss of 2.59% (Table: 2.62%) of adult drivers is acceptable.
37. a. 75; 12
    b. No, the conversion should also account for variation.
    c. B grade: 66.3 to 75.4 (Table: 66.2 to 75.4)
    d. Use a scheme like the one given in part (c), because variation is included in the curving process.

Section 6-3

1. a. In the long run, the sample proportions will have a mean of 0.00559.
   b. The sample proportions will tend to have a distribution that is approximately normal.
3. Sample mean; sample variance; sample proportion
5. No. The sample is not a simple random sample from the population of all college students in the United States. It is very possible that incomes of college students in Maine differ substantially from the incomes of college students in the other states.
7. a. 4.7
   b.

Sample Variance s^2	Probability
0.0	3/9
0.5	2/9
8.0	2/9
12.5	2/9

   c. 4.7
   d. Yes. The mean of the sampling distribution of the sample variances (4.7) is equal to the value of the population variance (4.7), so the sample variances target the value of the population variance.
9. a. 5
   b.

Sample Median	Probability
4.0	1/9
4.5	2/9
5.0	1/9
6.5	2/9
7.0	2/9
9.0	1/9

   c. 6.0
   d. No. The mean of the sampling distribution of the sample medians is 6.0, and it is not equal to the value of the population median (5.0), so the sample medians do not target the value of the population median.

11. a.

$\bar{x}$	Probability
2	1/16
2.5	2/16
3	1/16
3.5	2/16
4	2/16
5	1/16
5.5	2/16
6	2/16
7	2/16
9	1/16

    b. The mean of the population is 4.75 and the mean of the sample means is also 4.75.
    c. The sample means target the population mean. Sample means make good estimators of population means because they target the value of the population mean instead of systematically underestimating or overestimating it.

13. a.

Range	Probability
0	4/16
1	2/16
2	2/16
3	2/16
4	2/16
6	2/16
7	2/16

    b. The range of the population is 7.0, but the mean of the sample ranges is 2.875. Those values are not equal.
    c. The sample ranges do not target the population range of 7.0, so sample ranges do not make good estimators of population ranges.

15.

Proportion of Girls	Probability
0	0.25
0.5	0.50
1	0.25

Yes. The proportion of girls in 2 births is 0.5, and the mean of the sample proportions is 0.5. The result suggests that a sample proportion is an unbiased estimator of a population proportion.

17. a.

Proportion Correct	Probability
0	16/25
0.5	8/25
1	1/25

    b. 0.2
    c. Yes. The sampling distribution of the sample proportions has a mean of 0.2 and the population proportion is also 0.2 (because there is 1 correct answer among 5 choices). Yes, the mean of the sampling distribution of the sample proportions is always equal to the population proportion.

19. The formula yields $P(0) = 0.25$, $P(0.5) = 0.5$, and $P(1) = 0.25$, which does describe the sampling distribution of the sample proportions. The formula is just a different way of presenting the same information in the table that describes the sampling distribution.

Section 6-4

1. The sample must have more than 30 values, or there must be evidence that the population of systolic blood pressures has a normal distribution.

3. $\mu_{\bar{x}}$ represents the mean of all sample means, and $\sigma_{\bar{x}}$ represents the standard deviation of all sample means. For the samples of 36 IQ scores, $\mu_{\bar{x}} = 100$ and $\sigma_{\bar{x}} = 15/\sqrt{36} = 2.5$.

5. a. 0.4033 (Table: 0.4052)
   b. 0.1104 (Table: 0.1112)
   c. Because the original population has a normal distribution, the distribution of sample means is a normal distribution for any sample size.

7. a. 0.2401 (Table: 0.2391)
   b. 0.6335 (Table: 0.6316)
   c. Because the original population has a normal distribution, the distribution of sample means is normal for any sample size.

9. a. 0.8534 (Table: 0.8531)
   b. 0.99999998 (Table: 0.9999)
   c. It appears that the elevator would be overloaded with 27 adult males, which is probably unlikely but possible. Also, it is likely that a safety factor is built in so that the elevator can safely take a load greater than the 4000 lb capacity on the placard. But to be safe, instead of boarding the elevator full of adult men, it would be wiser to wait for another elevator.

11. a. 140 lb
    b. 0.9999999998 (Table: 0.9999)
    c. 0.9458 (Table: 0.9463)
    d. The new capacity of 20 passengers does not appear to be safe enough because the probability of overloading is too high.

13. a. 0.5575 (Table: 0.5564)
    b. 0.9996 (Table: 0.9995)
    c. Part (a) because the ejection seats will be occupied by individual women, not groups of women.

15. a. 0.8877 (Table: 0.8869)
    b. 1.0000 when rounded to four decimal places (Table: 0.9999)
    c. The probability from part (a) is more relevant because it shows that 89% of male passengers will not need to bend. The result from part (b) gives us information about the mean for a group of 100 men, but it doesn't give us useful information about the comfort and safety of individual male passengers.
    d. Because men are generally taller than women, a design that accommodates a suitable proportion of men will necessarily accommodate a greater proportion of women.

17. If we assume that the true mean weight gain is 15 lb, the probability of getting a sample of 67 college students having a mean weight gain of 2.6 lb or less is 0+ (Table: 0.0001). Because it is so unlikely to get a sample such as the one obtained, it appears that the assumption of a mean weight gain of 15 lb is an incorrect assumption. The "Freshman 15" claim of a mean weight gain of 15 lb appears to be an incorrect claim.

19. 0.0000540 (Table: 0.0001). If the mean really is 0 lb as assumed, the probability of getting a sample with a mean of 3.0 lb or higher is very small, so the mean of 3.0 lb is significantly high. There is strong evidence suggesting that the mean is actually higher than 0 lb, so the diet does appear to be effective. However, the mean weight loss of only 3.0 lb is not very much, so even though the diet appears to be effective, it doesn't appear to be worth using this diet. The amount of weight loss appears to have statistical significance but not practical significance.

Section 6-5

1. The requirement is satisfied because the sample size of 147 is greater than 30.

3. Either the points are not reasonably close to a straight-line pattern, or there is some systematic pattern that is not a straight-line pattern.

5. Normal. The points are reasonably close to a straight-line pattern, and there is no other pattern that is not a straight-line pattern.

7. Not normal. The points are not reasonably close to a straight-line pattern, and there appears to be a pattern that is not a straight-line pattern.

9. Normal   11. Not normal

13. Normal

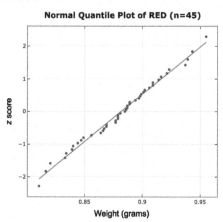

Normal Quantile Plot of RED (n=45)

15. Not normal

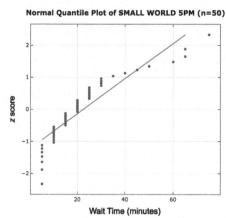

Normal Quantile Plot of SMALL WORLD 5PM (n=50)

17. Normal. The points have coordinates $(97.9, -1.28)$, $(98.0, -0.52)$, $(98.2, 0)$, $(98.4, 0.52)$, $(98.7, 1.28)$.

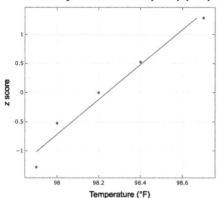

Normal Quantile Plot of Body Temp (n=5)

19. Not normal. The points have coordinates $(963, -1.53)$, $(1027, -0.89)$, $(1029, -0.49)$ $(1034, -0.16)$, $(1070, 0.16)$, $(1079, 0.49)$, $(1079, 0.89)$, $(1439, 1.53)$.

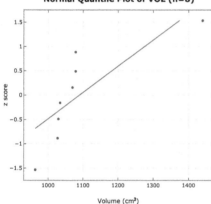

Normal Quantile Plot of VOL (n=8)

21. a. Yes   b. Yes   c. No

Chapter 6: Quick Quiz

1.

2. $z = 1.28$ 3. 0.0606   4. 0.8186 (Table: 0.8185)
5. a. $\mu = 0$ and $\sigma = 1$
   b. $\mu_{\bar{x}}$ represents the mean of all sample means, and $\sigma_{\bar{x}}$ represents the standard deviation of all sample means.
6. Normal distribution   7. 0.0863 (Table: 0.0869)
8. 0.9021 (Table: 0.9015)   9. 0.9137 (Table: 0.9131)
10. The normal quantile plot suggests that the scores are from a normally distributed population.

Chapter 6: Review Exercises

1. a. 0.9147   b. 0.9904   c. 0.6500 (Table: 0.6501)
   d. -0.67 e. 0.2451

2. a. An unbiased estimator is a statistic that targets the value of the population parameter in the sense that the sampling distribution of the statistic has a mean that is equal to the corresponding parameter.
   b. Mean; variance; proportion
   c. True
3. a. -2.33 b. 2.33   c. 1.96
4. a. Normal   b. 33.64 cm   c. 0.83 cm
5. a. 1   b. 3037.1 g   c. 3037.1 g
   d. $498{,}859.7\,\text{g}^2$
6. a. 131   b. 0.0000179 (Table: 0.0001)
   c. No. It is very possible that the 4 subjects have a mean of 131 while some of them have scores below 131.
7. a. 1.49% (Table: 1.50%)   b. 69.4 in.
8. a. 1.13%   b. 63.8 in.
9. 53.9 in. and 65.5 in. Yes, 67 in. is significantly high.
10. No. A histogram is far from bell-shaped. A normal quantile plot reveals a pattern of points that is far from a straight-line pattern.

Chapter 6: Cumulative Review Exercises

1. a. 44.2 minutes   b. 35.0 minutes   c. 21.4 minutes
   d. $458.3\,\text{minutes}^2$ e. $z = 2.37$
   f. Yes. The z score of 2.37 is greater than 2, so the longest wait time of 95 minutes is significantly high.
   g. Ratio level of measurement
   h. The exact unrounded wait times would have been continuous, but the listed wait times are all multiples of 5, so these rounded wait times are discrete data.
2. a. 30.0 minutes, 35.0 minutes, 50.0 minutes
   b.

   c. No. The distribution appears to be skewed instead of being normal.
   d. No. The points don't fit a straight-line pattern very well, and there appears to be some other pattern that is not a straight line.
3. a. 0.0228   b. 0.6003 (Table: 0.6009)
   c. 266.7 mm   d. 0.1163 (Table: 0.1170)
   e. The result from part (c) is more helpful because it provides a foot length that is potentially the maximum to be used for shoe sizes. The result from part (d) is based on the distribution of means from groups of 16 women, which is irrelevant for planning shoe sizes.
4. a. $\bar{B}$ is the event of selecting someone who does not have blue eyes.
   b. 0.65   c. 0.0429
   d. Using normal approximation: 0.1727 (Table: 0.1736); Tech using binomial: 0.1724.
   e. No
5. a. 196.54°F is far too high to be reasonable as the mean body temperature of a group of adult males.
   b. The value of 980°F is an outlier and an error because it is not a possible body temperature of an adult male.

c. If the value of 980°F is discarded as an error, the mean appears to be 98.61°F. It is also reasonable to believe that the value of 980°F was incorrectly entered without the decimal point, and if 980°F is changed to 98.0°F, the mean appears to be 98.54°F.

Chapter 7 Answers

Section 7-1

1. The confidence level, such as 95%, was not provided.
3. $\hat{p} = 0.51$ is the sample proportion; $\hat{q} = 0.49$ (found from evaluating $1 - \hat{p}$); $n = 1144$ is the sample size; $E = 0.035$ is the margin of error; p is the population proportion, which is unknown. The value of α is 0.05.
5. 1.645   7. 2.81
9. 0.154 ± 0.038 11. $0.0847 < p < 0.153$
13. a. 0.367   b. $E = 0.0610$
    c. $0.306 < p < 0.428$
    d. We have 95% confidence that the interval from 0.306 to 0.428 contains the true value of the population proportion of successful challenges.
15. a. $\hat{p} = 0.143$ b. $E = 0.00815$
    c. $0.135 < p < 0.152$
    d. We have 90% confidence that the interval from 0.135 to 0.152 actually does contain the true value of the population proportion of returned surveys.
17. $0.462 < p < 0.529$. Because 0.512 is contained within the confidence interval, there is not strong evidence against 0.512 as the value of the proportion of boys in all births.
19. a. $14.7\% < p < 33.5\%$
    b. Because the two confidence intervals overlap, it is very possible that both genders have the same success rates. Neither gender appears to be substantially more successful in their challenges.
21. a. 0.5   b. 0.439   c. $0.363 < p < 0.516$
    d. If the touch therapists really had an ability to select the correct hand by sensing an energy field, their success rate would be significantly greater than 0.5, but the sample success rate of 0.439 and the confidence interval suggest that they do not have the ability to select the correct hand by sensing an energy field.
23. a. 236
    b. $0.402 < p < 0.516$ (Using $x = 236$: $0.403 < p < 0.516$)
    c. $0.431 < p < 0.487$
    d. The 99% confidence interval is wider than the 80% confidence interval. A confidence interval must be wider in order to be more confident that it captures the true value of the population proportion.
25. 95% CI: $0.0419 < p < 0.0421$. 99% CI: $0.0418 < p < 0.0422$. For both confidence levels, the upper and lower confidence interval limits are very close to each other, suggesting that the estimates are very accurate. Also, there is not much difference between the 95% CI and the 99% CI. The extremely large sample size is giving us confidence interval estimates with a very narrow range, so we are getting very precise estimates.
27. Sustained care: $77.6\% < p < 88.1\%$ (using $x = 164$). Standard care: $56.1\% < p < 69.5\%$ (using $x = 125$). The two confidence intervals do not overlap. It appears that the success rate is higher with sustained care.

29. $\hat{p} = 19/35$, or 0.543. CI: $37.8\% < p < 70.8\%$. Greater height does not appear to be an advantage for presidential candidates. If greater height is an advantage, then taller candidates should win substantially more than 50% of the elections, but the confidence interval shows that the percentage of elections won by taller candidates is likely to be anywhere between 37.8% and 70.8%.
31. a. 1844 (Table: 1842)   b. 1266 (Table: 1265)
33. a. 4269   b. 609
    c. Yes, there is a substantial decrease in the sample size.
35. a. 1537   b. 1449
37. a. 752   b. 295
    c. No. A sample of the people you know is a convenience sample, not a simple random sample, so it is very possible that the results would not be representative of the population.
39. 1238 (Table: 1237)
41. a. The requirement of at least 5 successes and at least 5 failures is not satisfied, so the normal distribution cannot be used.
    b. 6.67%

Section 7-2

1. a. $85.74 \text{ min} < \mu < 91.76 \text{ min}$
   b. The best point estimate is $\bar{x} = 88.75$ minutes. The margin of error is $E = 3.01$ minutes.
3. We have 95% confidence that the limits of 85.74 minutes and 91.76 minutes contain the true value of the mean of the population of all times between eruptions.
5. a. $t_{\alpha/2} = 2.030$ b. $E = 235.3 \text{ g}$
   c. $2914.7 \text{ g} < \mu < 3385.3 \text{ g}$
   d. We have 95% confidence that the limits of 2914.7 g and 3385.3 g contain the true value of the mean birth weight of all girls.
7. a. $t_{\alpha/2} = 2.724$ b. $E = 0.00259 \text{ lb}$
   c. $0.82151 \text{ lb} < \mu < 0.82669 \text{ lb}$
   d. We have 99% confidence that the limits of 0.82151 lb and 0.82669 lb contain the true value of the mean weight of Pepsi in cans.
9. $98.08°F < \mu < 98.32°F$. Because the confidence interval does not contain 98.6°F, it appears that the mean body temperature is not 98.6°F, as is commonly believed.
11. $71.4 \text{ min} < \mu < 126.4 \text{ min}$. The confidence interval includes the mean of 102.8 min that was measured before the treatment, so the mean could be the same after the treatment. This result suggests that the zopiclone treatment does not have a significant effect.
13. $126.3 \text{ mm} < \mu < 141.2 \text{ mm}$
15. $9.2 \text{ minutes} < \mu < 35.8 \text{ minutes}$. Five of the listed values are 5, so the data do not appear to be from a normally distributed population. Also, the sample size is not greater than 30, so the requirement of a "normal distribution or $n > 30$" is not satisfied. It is very possible that the confidence interval is not a good estimate of the population mean.
17. $1.8 < \mu < 3.4$. The given numbers are just substitutes for the four DNA base names, so the numbers don't measure or count anything, and they are at the nominal level of measurement. The confidence interval has no practical use.
19. $0.284 \text{ ppm} < \mu < 1.153 \text{ ppm}$. Using the FDA guideline, the confidence interval suggests that there could be too much

mercury in fish because it is possible that the mean is greater than 1 ppm. Also, one of the sample values exceeds the FDA guideline of 1 ppm, so at least some of the fish have too much mercury.

21. The sample size is 97, and it does appear to be very practical.

23. 925 (Table: 927). The sample should not be obtained from one movie at one theater, because that sample could be easily biased. Instead, a simple random sample of the broader population should be obtained.

25. a. 425   b. 212
    c. The result from part (a) is substantially larger than the result from part (b). The result from part (b) is likely to be better because it uses s instead of the estimated σ obtained from the range rule of thumb.

27. The required sample size is 38,415 (Table: 38,416). The sample appears to be too large to be practical for a telephone survey.

29. Females: 72.0 bpm $< \mu <$ 76.1 bpm.
Males: 67.8 bpm $< \mu <$ 71.4 bpm. Adult females appear to have a mean pulse rate that is higher than the mean pulse rate of adult males. Good to know.

31. 41.0 minutes $< \mu <$ 44.3 minutes
(TI data: 40.0 minutes $< \mu <$ 44.9 minutes)

33. Using the class limits of 66-75 for the "over 65" group, the summary statistics are $n = 195$, $\bar{x} = 40.1$ years, $s = 11.3$ years. CI: 38.5 years $< \mu <$ 41.7 years.

Section 7-3

1. a. Unlike confidence interval estimates of p or μ, confidence interval estimates of σ or σ^2 are not created using a distribution that is symmetric, so there is no "$\pm E$" as in confidence interval estimates of p or μ.
    b. The format of 10.9 bpm $\pm$ 3.3 bpm implies that $s = 10.9$ bpm, which is not the case. Because the chi-square distribution is not symmetric, confidence interval estimates of σ or σ^2 cannot be expressed in the format of $s \pm E$.

3. 0.130 (million cells/μL)$^2 < \sigma^2 <$ 0.206 (million cells/μL)^2

5. df = 24. $X_L^2 = 12.401$ and $X_R^2 = 39.364$. CI: 0.19 mg $< \sigma <$ 0.33 mg.

7. df = 146. $X_L^2 = 105.741$ (Table: 67.328) and $X_R^2 = 193.761$ (Table: 140.169).
CI: 1.70 (1000 cells/μL) $< \sigma <$ 2.30 (1000 cells/μL).
[Table: 2.00 (1000 cells/μL) $< \sigma <$ 2.89 (1000 cells/μL).]

9. 0.55°F $< \sigma <$ 0.72°F (Table: 0.56°F $< \sigma <$ 0.74°F)

11. 29.6 min $< \sigma <$ 71.6 min. No, the confidence interval does not indicate whether the treatment is effective.

13. 1.9 in. $< \sigma <$ 3.4 in. Because the confidence interval includes the value of 2.9 in., it is very possible that the standard deviation of heights of women who are professional soccer players is the same as the standard deviation of heights of women in the general population. There is not sufficient evidence to support the claim that women who are professional soccer players have heights that vary less than women in the general population.

15. Female: 0.50 $< \sigma <$ 1.32. Male: 0.24 $< \sigma <$ 0.64. Because the two confidence intervals overlap, it is possible that females and males have the same amount of variation, so there does not appear to be a significant difference in variation.

17. The sample size is 85, which is very practical.

19. The sample size is 192, which is practical.

21. Two-line wait times: 208.8 sec $< \sigma <$ 283.0 sec
(Table: 213.3 sec $< \sigma <$ 291.3 sec.)
Single-line wait times: 174.3 sec $< \sigma <$ 236.3 sec
(Table: 178.0 sec $< \sigma <$ 243.2 sec.)
Because the confidence intervals overlap, it is possible that the different line configurations have the same variation, so these results do not support the expectation that the single line has less variation. Requirements: The strict normality requirement is questionable for both data sets, especially the two-line wait times.

23. $X_L^2 = 78.085$ and $X_R^2 = 134.756$.
The values from the given approximation are quite close to the actual critical values.

Section 7-4

1. (1) The sample must be collected in an appropriate way, such as a simple random sample. (2) The sample means found from the generated bootstrap samples should have a distribution that is approximately symmetric.

3. There is no universal exact number, but there should be at least 1000 bootstrap samples, and the use of 10,000 or more is common.

5. $0.000 < p < 0.500$

7. a. 0.1 kg $< \mu <$ 8.6 kg   b. 1.9 kg $< \sigma <$ 6.3 kg

9. Answers vary, but here are typical answers.
    a. -0.8 kg $< \mu <$ 7.8 kg
    b. 1.2 kg $< \sigma <$ 7.0 kg

11. a. Answers vary, but here is a typical answer:
     128.4 mm $< \mu <$ 139.3 mm.
    b. The confidence interval obtained from the bootstrap method is very close to this confidence interval from Exercise 13 in Section 7-2: 126.3 mm $< \mu <$ 141.2 mm.

13. a. Answers vary, but here is a typical answer:
     11.9 minutes $< \mu <$ 34.3 minutes.
    b. The confidence interval given in part (a) is likely to be better. Given that the sample data do not appear to be from a normally distributed population, the use of the t distribution is questionable, so the confidence interval found in Exercise 15 in Section 7-2 might not be a good estimate of μ.

15. a. Answers vary, but here is a typical answer:
     1.5 in. $< \sigma <$ 3.1 in.
    b. The confidence interval obtained from the bootstrap method is close to this confidence interval from Exercise 13 in Section 7-3: 1.9 in. $< \sigma <$ 3.4 in.

17. a. Answers vary, but here is a typical answer:
     1080.0 cm$^3 < \mu <$ 1169.0 cm^3
    b. Answers vary, but here is a typical answer:
     79.0 cm$^3 < \sigma <$ 152.8 cm^3

19. Answers vary, but here is a typical result: $0.135 < p < 0.152$. The result is essentially the same as the confidence interval of $0.135 < p < 0.152$ found in Exercise 15 from Section 7-1.

21. Answers vary, but here is a typical result: $0.0208 < p < 0.0317$. This is quite close to the confidence interval of $0.0205 < p < 0.0311$ found in Exercise 14 from Section 7-1.

23. a. Answers vary, but here is a typical result: $2.5 < \sigma < 3.3$.
    b. $2.4 < \sigma < 3.7$

c. The confidence interval from the bootstrap method is not very different from the confidence interval found using the methods of Section 7-3. Because a histogram or normal quantile plot shows that the sample appears to be from a population not having a normal distribution, the bootstrap confidence interval of $2.5 < \sigma < 3.3$ would be a better estimate of σ.

25. Answers vary, but here is a typical result using 10,000 bootstrap samples: $1.7 < \mu < 3.3$. This result is very close to the confidence interval of $1.6 < \mu < 3.3$ found using 1000 bootstrap samples. In this case, increasing the number of bootstrap samples from 1000 to 10,000 does not have much of an effect on the confidence interval.

27. The histogram of the 1000 bootstrap sample means is approximately symmetric as required.

Chapter 7: Quick Quiz

1. 19.1%
2. We have 95% confidence that the limits of 17.5% and 20.6% contain the true value of the percentage of motorcycle owners who are women.
3. $z = 2.576$ (Table: 2.575)
4. $36.9\% < p < 43.1\%$
5. 2401   6. 374 (Table: 373)
7. There is a loose requirement that the sample values are from a normally distributed population.
8. The degrees of freedom is the number of sample values that can vary after restrictions have been imposed on all of the values. For the sample data described in Exercise 7, df $= 5$.
9. $t = 2.571$
10. No, the use of the χ^2 distribution has a fairly strict requirement that the data must be from a normal distribution. The bootstrap method could be used to find a 95% confidence interval estimate of σ.

Chapter 7: Review Exercises

1. a. 97   b. 93
   c. No, in this case the sample size doesn't change much at all.
2. 163
3. a. 701   b. $67.1\% < p < 72.8\%$
   c. 70%; ± 2.8 percentage points [or ± 2.9 percentage points if using the confidence interval limits from part (b)]
   d. No. Because 61% is not included in the confidence interval, it does not appear that the responses are consistent with the actual voter turnout.
4. 30.7 minutes $< \mu < 52.3$ minutes. We have 95% confidence that the limits of 30.7 minutes and 52.3 minutes contain the true value of the population mean μ.
5. a. Student t distribution
   b. None of the three distributions is appropriate, but a confidence interval could be constructed by using bootstrap methods.
   c. χ^2 (chi-square distribution)
   d. Normal distribution
   e. None of the three distributions is appropriate, but a confidence interval could be constructed by using bootstrap methods.

6. -19.9 min $< \mu < 50.4$ min. The confidence interval includes 0 (on time), so the on-time performance looks reasonably good. The confidence interval is wide, so the population mean delay time is not estimated with much accuracy.
7. 27.8 min $< \sigma < 85.6$ min
8. Answer varies, but this result is typical: 10.1 min $< \sigma < 58.8$ min.
9. a. Yes, the requirements are satisfied. 8.8 seconds $< \mu <$ 59.3 seconds.
   b. Construction of a confidence interval estimate of σ has a fairly strict requirement that the sample should be from a population with a normal distribution, regardless of the sample size. That requirement is not satisfied. 19 of the 36 times are 0 seconds, so the sample does not appear to be from a population having a normal distribution.
10. a. The requirements are satisfied, and here is the confidence interval: 27.03 cm $< \mu < 33.07$ cm.
    b. The requirements are satisfied, and here is the confidence interval: 2.91 cm $< \sigma < 7.72$ cm.

Chapter 7: Cumulative Review Exercises

1. $\bar{x} = 1.28$ W/kg, median $= 1.30$ W/kg, $s = 0.18$ W/kg, $s^2 = 0.03$ (W/kg)^2, range $= 0.60$ W/kg. These results are statistics.
2. Significantly low values are two standard deviations below the mean or lower, so significantly low values are 0.92 W/kg or lower; significantly high values are two standard deviations above the mean or higher, so significantly high values are 1.64 W/kg or higher. Because the lowest value of 0.9 W/kg is less than 0.92 W/kg, it is significantly low.
3. Ratio level of measurement; continuous data.
4. The graphs suggest that the sample appears to be from a population having a distribution that is *approximately* normal.
5. 1.16 W/kg $< \mu < 1.40$ W/kg. We have 95% confidence that the limits of 1.16 W/kg and 1.40 W/kg contain the actual value of the population mean μ.
6. 130 cell phones
7. a. 0.0691 (Table: 0.0694)   b. 1.37 W/kg (Table: 1.36 W/kg)
8. a. $0.932 < p < 0.959$
   b. Based on the result from part (a), it is clear that the majority of the population does not feel that the song is too offensive.
   c. Because the respondents chose to respond, the survey involves a self-selected or voluntary response sample, so the results are very questionable. Given that the respondents are a self-selected sample, we don't really know anything about the population.
9. $63.9\% < p < 68.1\%$. CVS Pharmacy sells flu shots and could potentially benefit from the widespread belief that there will be high demand for flu shots, so there is a potential for bias (although the Harris Poll would likely conduct the survey without any bias).
10. a. 39.909 km/h $< \mu < 40.531$ km/h
    b. Given that the speeds are listed in order by year, another tool that would be more helpful is a time series graph of the speeds. The time series graph could reveal any pattern of change over time. The time series graph of the listed data (see next page) does not reveal any notable pattern of change over time.

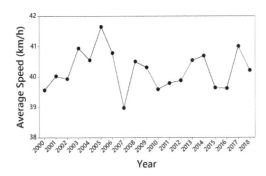

Chapter 8 Answers

Section 8-1

1. a. H_0: $\mu = 40$ minutes   b. H_1: $\mu \neq 40$ minutes
   c. Reject the null hypothesis or fail to reject the null hypothesis.
   d. No. In this case, the original claim becomes the null hypothesis. For the claim that the mean wait time is equal to 40 minutes, we can either reject that claim or fail to reject it, but we cannot state that there is sufficient evidence to *support* that claim.

3. The P-value of 0.001 is preferred because it corresponds to the sample evidence that most strongly supports the alternative hypothesis that the method is effective.

5. a. $p < 0.10$ b. H_0: $p = 0.10$; H_1: $p < 0.10$

7. a. $\mu < 123$ mm Hg
   b. H_0: $\mu = 123$ mm Hg; H_1: $\mu < 123$ mm Hg

9. $z = -17.77$ (or $z = -17.76$ if using $x = 935$)

11. $t = -0.044$

13. a. Left-tailed   b. P-value $= 0.2266$ c. Fail to reject H_0.

15. a. Two-Tailed   b. P-value $= 0.0719$ (Table: 0.0718)
    c. Fail to reject H_0.

17. a. $z = -1.645$ b. Fail to reject H_0.

19. a. $z = \pm 1.96$ b. Fail to reject H_0.

21. a. Fail to reject H_0.
    b. There is not sufficient evidence to support the claim that more than 58% of adults would erase all of their personal information online if they could.

23. a. Reject H_0.
    b. There is sufficient evidence to warrant rejection of the claim that the mean pulse rate (in beats per minute) of adult males is 72 bpm.

25. Type I error: In reality $p = 0.1$, but we reject the claim that $p = 0.1$. Type II error: In reality $p \neq 0.1$, but we fail to reject the claim that $p = 0.1$.

27. Type I error: In reality $p = 0.25$, but we support the claim that $p > 0.25$. Type II error: In reality $p > 0.25$, but we fail to support that claim.

29. The power of 0.96 shows that there is a 96% chance of rejecting the null hypothesis of $p = 0.08$ when the true proportion is actually 0.18. That is, if the proportion of Chantix users who experience abdominal pain is actually 0.18, then there is a 96% chance of supporting the claim that the proportion of Chantix users who experience abdominal pain is greater than 0.08.

31. 617 (or 618 or 619 depending on precision used)

Section 8-2

1. a. 877   b. $\hat{p} = 0.86$ c. $p = 3/4$ or 0.75

3. (1) It was stated that the sample is a simple random sample. (2) There is a fixed number of trials (1020), the trials are independent because any respondent is independent of the others, there are two categories of success, and the probability remains the same for all respondents. (3) With $n = 1020$ and $p = 3/4$, the conditions $np \geq 5$ and $nq \geq 5$ are both satisfied (because 765 and 255 are both greater than 5).

5. a. Left-tailed   b. $z = -4.46$ c. P-value: 0.000004
   d. H_0: $p = 0.10$. Reject the null hypothesis.
   e. There is sufficient evidence to support the claim that fewer than 10% of treated subjects experience headaches.

7. a. Left-tailed.   b. $z = -6.32$ c. P-value: 0.000
   d. H_0: $p = 0.50$. Reject the null hypothesis.
   e. There is sufficient evidence to support the claim that fewer than 50% of adults search for themselves online.

9. H_0: $p = 0.40$. H_1: $p > 0.40$. Test statistic: $z = 0.41$. P-value $= 0.3399$ (Table: 0.3409). Critical value: $z = 1.645$. Fail to reject H_0. There is not sufficient evidence to support the claim that the sample of cast and crew members is from a population in which the rate of cancer is greater than 40%. There is not sufficient evidence to support a conclusion that the movie was cursed because of a significantly high number of cancer cases.

11. 11% of 2005 is 221, so 221 of those surveyed knew what the symbol designates. H_0: $p = 0.5$. H_1: $p < 0.5$. Test statistic: $z = -34.91$. P-value $= 0.0000$ (Table: 0.0001). Critical value: $z = -2.33$. Reject H_0. There is sufficient evidence to support the claim that fewer than half of all Americans know what the symbol designates. Because it appears that so few Americans know what the symbol designates, the symbol should be replaced with one that is much more obvious.

13. H_0: $p = 0.20$. H_1: $p > 0.20$. Test statistic: $z = 1.10$. P-value $= 0.1367$ (Table: 0.1357). Critical value: $z = 1.645$. Fail to reject H_0. There is not sufficient evidence to support the claim that more than 20% of OxyContin users develop nausea. However, with $\hat{p} = 0.229$, we see that a large percentage of OxyContin users experience nausea, so that rate does appear to be very high.

15. H_0: $p = 0.50$. H_1: $p < 0.50$. Test statistic: $z = -4.06$. P-value $= 0.00002$ (Table: 0.0001). Critical value $z = -2.33$. Reject H_0. There is sufficient evidence to support the claim that fewer than half of Americans prefer to watch the news rather than read or listen to it.

17. H_0: $p = 0.512$. H_1: $p \neq 0.512$. Test statistic: $z = -0.98$. P-value $= 0.3286$ (Table: 0.3270). Critical values: $z = \pm 1.96$. Fail to reject H_0. There is not sufficient evidence to warrant rejection of the claim that 51.2% of newborn babies are boys. The results do not *support* the belief that 51.2% of newborn babies are boys; the results merely show that there is not strong evidence against the rate of 51.2%.

19. H_0: $p = 0.80$. H_1: $p < 0.80$. Test statistic: $z = -1.11$. P-value $= 0.1332$ (Table: 0.1335). Critical value: $z = -1.645$. Fail to reject H_0. There is not sufficient evidence to support the claim that the polygraph results are correct less than 80% of the time. However, based on the sample proportion of correct results in 75.5% of the 98 cases, polygraph results do not appear to have the high

degree of reliability that would justify the use of polygraph results in court, so polygraph test results should be prohibited as evidence in trials.

21. H_0: $p = 0.5$. H_1: $p \neq 0.5$. Test statistic: $z = -2.03$. P-value $= 0.0422$ (Table: 0.0424). Critical values: $z = \pm 1.645$. Reject H_0. There is sufficient evidence to warrant rejection of the claim that touch therapists use a method equivalent to random guesses. However, their success rate of $123/280$, or 43.9%, indicates that they performed *worse* than random guesses, so they do not appear to be effective.

23. H_0: $p = 0.35$. H_1: $p \neq 0.35$. Test statistic: $z = -2.17$. P-value $= 0.0303$ (Table: 0.0300). Critical values: $z = \pm 1.96$. Reject H_0. There is sufficient evidence to warrant rejection of the claim that the percentage who make angry gestures while driving is equal to 35%. If the significance level is changed to 0.01, the conclusion does change to this: "There is not sufficient evidence to warrant rejection of the claim that the percentage who make angry gestures while driving is equal to 35%."

25. H_0: $p = 0.5$. H_1: $p > 0.5$. Test statistic: $z = 0.14$. P-value $= 0.4454$ (Table: 0.4443). Critical value: $z = 1.645$. Fail to reject H_0. There is not sufficient evidence to support the claim that NFC teams win the majority of Super Bowl games.

27. H_0: $p = 0.5$. H_1: $p \neq 0.5$. Test statistic: $z = 2.05$. P-value $= 0.0402$ (Table: 0.0404). Critical values: $z = \pm 1.96$. Reject H_0. There is sufficient evidence to warrant rejection of the claim that the coin toss is fair in the sense that neither team has an advantage by winning it. The coin toss rule does not appear to be fair. This helps explain why the overtime rules were changed.

29. H_0: $p = 1/3$. H_1: $p > 1/3$. Test statistic: $z = 8.72$. P-value $= 0.0000$ (Table: 0.0001). Critical value: $z = 2.33$. Reject H_0. There is sufficient evidence to support the claim that more than $1/3$ of adults believe in ghosts.

31. H_0: $p = 0.791$. H_1: $p < 0.791$. Test statistic: $z = -29.09$ (using $\hat{p} = 0.39$) or $z = -29.11$ (using $x = 339$). P-value $= 0.0000$ (Table: 0.0001). Critical value: $z = -2.33$. Reject H_0. There is sufficient evidence to support the claim that the percentage of selected Americans of Mexican ancestry is less than 79.1%, so the jury selection process appears to be biased.

33. The P-values agree reasonably well with the large sample size of $n = 926$. The normal approximation to the binomial distribution works better as the sample size increases. Normal approximation entries: 0.0114, 0.0012, 0.1059. Exact entries: 0.0215, 0.0034, 0.1120. Exact with simple continuity correction: 0.0117, 0.0018, 0.1060.

35. a. 0.7219 (Table: 0.7224)   b. 0.2781 (Table: 0.2776)
    c. The power of 0.7219 shows that there is a reasonably good chance of making the correct decision of rejecting the false null hypothesis. It would be better if the power were even higher, such as greater than 0.8 or 0.9.

Section 8-3

1. Requirement: (1) the sample must be a simple random sample, and (2) either or both of these conditions must be satisfied: The population is normally distributed or $n > 30$. There is not enough information given to determine whether the sample is a simple random sample. Because the sample size is not greater than 30, we must check for normality, but the value of $36 million appears

to be an outlier, and a normal quantile plot or histogram suggests that the sample does not appear to be from a normally distributed population. The requirements are not satisfied.

3. A t test is a hypothesis test that uses the Student t distribution, such as the method of testing a claim about a population mean as presented in this section. The letter t is used in reference to the Student t distribution, which is used in a t test. The z test methods require a known value of σ, but it would be very rare to conduct a hypothesis test for a claim about an unknown value of μ while we somehow know the value of σ.

5. P-value $= 0.0033$ (Table: P-value < 0.01). There is sufficient evidence to warrant rejection of the claim that the mean weight of quarters is equal to 5.670 g.

7. P-value $= 0.0000$ (Table: P-value < 0.005). There is sufficient evidence to support the claim that the mean cotinine level of smokers is greater than 2.84 ng/mL.

9. H_0: $\mu = 8.953$ g. H_1: $\mu \neq 8.953$ g. Test statistic: $t = -3.423$. P-value $= 0.0015$. Critical values assuming a 0.05 significance level: $t = \pm 2.026$. Reject H_0. There is sufficient evidence to warrant rejection of the claim that the sample is from a population with a mean equal to 8.953 g.

11. H_0: $\mu = 30$ min. H_1: $\mu > 30$ min. Test statistic: $t = 0.940$. P-value $= 0.177$. Critical value assuming a 0.05 significance level: $t = 1.685$. Fail to reject H_0. There is not sufficient evidence to support the claim that the mean wait time is more than 30 min.

13. H_0: $\mu = 120$ mm Hg. H_1: $\mu > 120$ mm Hg. Test statistic: $t = 3.234$. P-value $= 0.0007$ (Table: P-value < 0.005). Critical value: $t = 2.339$. Reject H_0. There is sufficient evidence to support the claim that the sample is from a population with a mean greater than 120 mm Hg.

15. H_0: $\mu = 100$. H_1: $\mu \neq 100$. Test statistic: $t = -6.676$. P-value $= 0.0000$ (Table: P-value < 0.01). Critical values: $t = \pm 2.086$. Reject H_0. There is sufficient evidence to warrant rejection of the claim that the sample of children is from a population with mean IQ equal to 100. These results do not "prove" that exposure to lead has an adverse effect on IQ scores of children, but it strongly suggests that such an adverse effect is very possible.

17. H_0: $\mu = 0$ lb. H_1: $\mu > 0$ lb. Test statistic: $t = 3.872$. P-value $= 0.0002$ (Table: <0.005). Critical value: $t = 2.426$. Reject H_0. There is sufficient evidence to support the claim that the mean weight loss is greater than 0. Although the diet appears to have statistical significance, it does not appear to have practical significance, because the mean weight loss of only 3.0 lb does not seem to be worth the effort and cost.

19. H_0: $\mu = 12.00$ oz. H_1: $\mu \neq 12.00$ oz. Test statistic: $t = 10.364$. P-value $= 0.0000$ (Table: <0.01). Critical values: $t = \pm 2.030$. Reject H_0. There is sufficient evidence to warrant rejection of the claim that the mean volume is equal to 12.00 oz. Because the mean appears to be greater than 12.00 oz, consumers are not being cheated because they are getting slightly more than 12.00 oz.

21. The sample data meet the loose requirement of having a normal distribution. H_0: $\mu = 14$ μg/g. H_1: $\mu < 14$ μg/g. Test statistic: $t = -1.444$. P-value $= 0.0913$ (Table: >0.05). Critical value: $t = -1.833$. Fail to reject H_0. There is not sufficient evidence to support the claim that the mean lead concentration for all such medicines is less than 14 μg/g.

23. H_0: $\mu = 1.6$ W/kg. H_1: $\mu < 1.6$ W/kg. Test statistic: $t = -4.256$. P-value $= 0.0019$ (Table: P-value < 0.005). Critical value: $t = -2.998$. Reject H_0. There is sufficient evidence to support the claim that the sample is from a population of cell phones with a mean amount of radiation that is less than the FCC standard of 1.6 W/kg.

25. H_0: $\mu = 35$ minutes. H_1: $\mu < 35$ minutes. Test statistic: $t = -5.820$. P-value $= 0.000$ (Table: P-value < 0.005). Critical value: $t = -2.330$. Reject H_0. There is sufficient evidence to support the claim that the mean commute time is less than 35 minutes. The sample mean is 31.0 minutes, and the claimed mean is 35 minutes. That difference is statistically significant, but does not appear to have much practical significance. (TI data: Test statistic is $t = -2.62$ and P-value $= 0.005$.)

27. H_0: $\mu = 1818$ mm. H_1: $\mu < 1818$ mm. Test statistic: $t = -2.903$. P-value $= 0.0019$ (Table: P-value < 0.005). Critical value: $t = -2.327$ (Table: -2.326). Reject H_0. There is sufficient evidence to support the claim that the sample is from a population with a mean arm span less than 1818 mm. The sample mean is 1814.154 mm, and the claimed mean is 1818 mm. The difference of 3.846 mm (or 0.15 in.) is statistically significant, but does not appear to have practical significance. (TI data: Test statistic: $t = 0.126$, P-value $= 0.550$, critical value: $t = -2.334$. Fail to reject H_0. There is not sufficient evidence to support the claim that the sample is from a population with a mean arm span less than 1818 mm.)

29. The hypothesis test yields a P-value of 0.0009, so the difference between $\bar{x} = 100.05$ and the claimed mean of 100 is statistically significant, but that difference is so small that it does not have practical significance.

31. The critical t score found using the given approximation is 1.645, which is the same value of 1.645 found from technology. The approximation appears to work quite well, and it provides us with a method for finding critical t scores when the number of degrees of freedom cannot be found from Table A-3 and suitable technology is unavailable.

Section 8-4

1. The sample must be a simple random sample, and the sample must be from a normally distributed population. The normality requirement for a hypothesis test of a claim about a standard deviation is different in these ways: (1) It is much more strict, meaning that the distribution of the population must be much closer to a normal distribution; (2) the normality requirement applies for any sample size, not just for small samples with $n \leq 30$.

3. a. Reject H_0.

   b. There is sufficient evidence to support the claim that the standard deviation is less than 0.04000 g.

   c. It appears that with the new minting process, the variation among weights has decreased, so the weights are more consistent. The new minting process appears to be better than the original minting process.

5. H_0: $\sigma = 10$ bpm. H_1: $\sigma \neq 10$ bpm. Test statistic: $\chi^2 = 195.172$. P-value $= 0.0208$. Reject H_0. There is sufficient evidence to warrant rejection of the claim that pulse rates of men have a standard deviation equal to 10 beats per minute. Using the range rule of thumb with the normal range of 60 to 100 beats per minute is not very good for estimating σ in this case.

7. H_0: $\sigma = 2.08°$F. H_1: $\sigma < 2.08°$F. Test statistic: $\chi^2 = 9.329$. P-value $= 0.0000$ (Table: <0.005). Critical value: $\chi^2 = 74.252$ (Table: 70.065 approximately). Reject H_0. There is sufficient evidence to support the claim that body temperatures have a standard deviation less than 2.08°F. It is very highly unlikely that the conclusion in the hypothesis test in Example 5 from Section 8-3 would change because of a standard deviation from a different sample.

9. H_0: $\sigma = 0.0400$ g. H_1: $\sigma < 0.0400$ g. Test statistic: $\chi^2 = 13.486$. P-value $= 0.1872$. Critical value: $\chi^2 = 7.633$. Fail to reject H_0. There is not sufficient evidence to support a claim that M&Ms are manufactured so that they have weights with a standard deviation less than 0.0400 g. It does not appear that the goal is being satisfied.

11. H_0: $\sigma = 9.9$ min. H_1: $\sigma > 9.9$ min. Test statistic: $\chi^2 = 19.556$. P-value $= 0.0518$ (Table: $0.05 <$ P-value < 0.10). Critical value: $\chi^2 = 19.675$. Fail to reject H_0. There is not sufficient evidence to support a claim that Friday afternoon ride times have greater variation than the Friday morning ride times.

13. H_0: $\sigma = 32.2$ ft. H_1: $\sigma > 32.2$ ft. Test statistic: $\chi^2 = 29.176$. P-value: 0.0021. Critical value: $\chi^2 = 19.675$. Reject H_0. There is sufficient evidence to support the claim that the new production method has errors with a standard deviation greater than 32.2 ft. The variation appears to be greater than in the past, so the new method appears to be worse because there will be more altimeters that have larger errors. The company should take immediate action to reduce the variation.

15. H_0: $\sigma = 0.2000$ g. H_1: $\sigma \neq 0.2000$ g. Test statistic: $\chi^2 = 5.275$. P-value $= 0.7664$ (Table: P-value > 0.20). Critical values: 0.831, 12.833. Fail to reject H_0. There is not sufficient evidence to warrant rejection of the claim that the sample is from a population having weights with a standard deviation equal to 0.2000 g.

17. H_0: $\sigma = 20$ minutes. H_1: $\sigma \neq 20$ minutes. Test statistic: $\chi^2 = 1153.950$. P-value $= 0.0009$. Critical values: 887.620, 1117.889. Reject H_0. There is sufficient evidence to warrant rejection of the claim that the sample is from a population with a standard deviation equal to 20 minutes. A histogram or normal quantile plot shows that the distribution is far from being normal, so a requirement of the hypothesis test is violated and the results of this hypothesis test are not necessarily valid. (TI data: Test statistic: $\chi^2 = 679.168$, P-value $= 0.0000$. Critical values: 421.384, 584.125.)

19. Critical $\chi^2 = 81.540$ (or 81.494 if using $z = 2.326348$ found from technology), which is close to the value of 82.292 obtained from Statdisk and Minitab.

Section 8-5

1. a. A sample of the same size ($n = 5$) is randomly selected from the given sample.

   b. The sampling is done with replacement. If we were to sample without replacement, we would always obtain the same sample consisting of the same five waiting times, and those results would have no real value.

   c. A resampling method does not require that the sample data are from a population having a particular distribution (such as normal) or that the sample size meets some minimum requirement.

3. a. $\hat{p} = 426/860 = 0.495$ and $p = 0.512$.

   b. The sample proportions that are at least as extreme as $\hat{p} = 0.495$ are those that are 0.495 or lower and those that are 0.529 or higher.

   c. The result of 310 samples (among 1000) with a proportion at least as extreme as $426/860$ shows that the event of getting such a sample proportion is quite common and can easily occur. It appears that there is not sufficient evidence to warrant rejection of the claim that the proportion of male births is equal to 0.512.

5. Answers vary, but the following is typical. Resample 1000 times to find that 364 of the results have a proportion of $91/220 = 0.414$ or greater. There is a likelihood of 0.364 of getting a sample proportion that is at least as extreme as the one obtained, so there is not sufficient evidence to support the claim that the sample of cast and crew members is from a population in which the rate of cancer is greater than 40%.

7. Answers vary, but the following is typical. Create a column of 2005 ones and zeros, with 0.5 of them being 1 (as assumed in the null hypothesis). The sample proportion is 0.11, so in this left-tailed case, the values "at least as extreme" as 0.11 are those that are 0.11 or lower. Resample 1000 times to find that none of the results have a proportion of 0.11 or lower. There is a very small likelihood of getting a sample proportion that is at least as extreme as the one obtained, so there is sufficient evidence to support the claim that fewer than half of all Americans know what the symbol designates.

9. Answers vary, but the following is typical. With $\bar{x} = 11.05\ \mu g/g$ and $\mu = 14\ \mu g/g$ (as assumed in the null hypothesis), add $2.95\ \mu g/g$ to each sample value (as Statdisk does) so that the sample has the claimed mean of $14\ \mu g/g$. Resample the modified sample 1000 times to find that 53 of the results have a mean of $11.05\ \mu g/g$ or less. There appears to be a likelihood of 0.053 of getting a sample mean of $11.05\ \mu g/g$ or lower, so there is not sufficient evidence to support the claim that the mean lead concentration for all such medicines is less than $14\ \mu g/g$. (Note: Because the likelihood of 0.053 is so close to the significance level of 0.05, it is very possible to find that the likelihood is less than 0.05, so the conclusion would be that there is sufficient evidence to support the claim.)

11. Answers vary, but the following is typical. With $\bar{x} = 1.04875\ \text{W}/\text{kg}$ and $\mu = 1.6\ \text{W}/\text{kg}$ (as assumed in the null hypothesis), add $0.55125\ \text{W}/\text{kg}$ to each sample value (as Statdisk does) so that the sample has the claimed mean of $1.6\ \text{W}/\text{kg}$. Resample the modified sample 1000 times. The sample means at least as extreme as $1.04875\ \text{W}/\text{kg}$ are those that are $1.04875\ \text{W}/\text{kg}$ or lower. Among the 1000 generated samples, there are none that are at least as extreme as $1.04875\ \text{W}/\text{kg}$, so there appears to be a likelihood of 0.000 of getting a sample mean at least as extreme as $1.04875\ \text{W}/\text{kg}$. There is sufficient evidence to support the claim that the sample is from a population of cell phones with a mean amount of radiation that is less than the FCC standard of $1.6\ \text{W}/\text{kg}$.

13. For the data in Example 4, $s = 0.0480164$ g. For testing the claim that $\sigma < 0.062$ g, we assume in the null hypothesis that $\sigma = 0.062$ g. To modify the data set so that s becomes 0.062 g, multiply each of the data values by

$\sigma/s = 0.062/0.0480164 = 1.2912255$, then resample 1000 times. A typical result is that among the 1000 resulting values of s, 69 of them are 0.0480164 or lower. That is, 69 of the 1000 resamples are at least as extreme as the value of $s = 0.0480164$ g that was obtained. That result corresponds to an estimated P-value of 0.069, which is greater than the significance level of 0.05 used in Example 4. We therefore conclude that there is not sufficient evidence to support the claim that the listed weights are from a population with a standard deviation that is less than 0.062 g. These results from randomization agree quite well with those from Example 1 in Section 8-4, and this suggests that randomization is very effective in this case.

Chapter 8: Quick Quiz

1. H_0: $\mu = 2.000$ pounds. H_1: $\mu < 2.000$ pounds.
2. $t = -0.658$
3. a. t distribution
   b. No. The relevant requirement is that the population is normally distributed or $n > 30$. With $n = 62$, that requirement is satisfied and it is not necessary to test for normality.
4. a. Fail to reject H_0.
   b. There is not sufficient evidence to support the claim that the sample is from a population with a mean less than 2.000 pounds.
5. H_0: $p = 0.45$. H_1: $p > 0.45$.   6. $z = 2.76$
7. a. Reject H_0.
   b. There is sufficient evidence to support the claim that for the population of all TV households, more than 45% have at least one stand-alone streaming device.
8. a. t distribution   b. Normal distribution
   c. Chi-square distribution
9. a. True   b. False   c. False   d. False   e. False
10. The t test requires that the sample is from a normally distributed population, and the test is robust in the sense that the test works reasonably well if the departure from normality is not too extreme. The χ^2 (chi-square) test is not robust against a departure from normality, meaning that the test does not work well if the population has a distribution that is far from normal.

Chapter 8: Review Exercises

1. H_0: $p = 0.50$. H_1: $p > 0.50$. Test statistic: $z = 8.85$. P-value $= 0.0000$ (Table: 0.0001). Critical value: $z = 2.33$. Reject H_0. There is sufficient evidence to support the claim that the majority of employees are searching for new jobs.
2. H_0: $\mu = 27.2$ km/h. H_1: $\mu \neq 27.2$ km/h. Test statistic: $t = 92.116$. P-value $= 0.0000$ (Table: 0.0002). Critical values: $t = \pm 2.093$. Reject H_0. There is sufficient evidence to reject the claim that current winning speeds are not significantly different from the 27.2 km/h overall speed of winners from the first few races. Current winning speeds appear to be significantly higher.
3. H_0: $\mu = 5.4$ million cells per microliter. H_1: $\mu < 5.4$ million cells per microliter. Test statistic: $t = -5.873$. P-value $= 0.0000$ (Table: <0.005). Critical value: $t = -2.426$. Reject H_0. There is sufficient evidence to support the claim that the sample is from a population with a mean less than 5.4 million cells per microliter. The test deals with the distribution of sample means, not

individual values, so the result does not suggest that each of the 40 males has a red blood cell count below 5.4 million cells per microliter.

4. H_0: $p = 0.43$. H_1: $p \neq 0.43$. Test statistic: $z = 3.70$. P-value: 0.0002. Critical values: $z = \pm 1.96$. Reject H_0. There is sufficient evidence to warrant rejection of the claim that the percentage who believe that they voted for the winning candidate is equal to 43%. There appears to be a substantial discrepancy between how people said that they voted and how they actually did vote.

5. a. A type I error is the mistake of rejecting a null hypothesis when it is actually true. A type II error is the mistake of failing to reject a null hypothesis when in reality it is false.

   b. Type I error: In reality, the percentage who voted for the winning candidate is equal to 43%, but we conclude that the percentage is different from 43%. Type II error: In reality, the percentage who voted for the winning candidate is different from 43%, but we fail to support that claim that the percentage is different from 43%.

6. a. False   b. True   c. False   d. False   e. False

Chapter 8: Cumulative Review Exercises

1. a. 34.8 deaths   b. 33.0 deaths   c. 10.7 deaths
   d. 114.7 deaths^2 e. 35.0 deaths
   f. The pattern of the data over time is not revealed by the statistics. A time-series graph would be very helpful in understanding the pattern over time. The data appear to be trending downward.

2. a. Ratio   b. Discrete   c. Quantitative
   d. No. The data are from recent and consecutive years, so they are not randomly selected.

3. a. 27.9 deaths $< \mu < 41.6$ deaths.
   b. We have 99% confidence that the limits of 27.9 deaths and 41.6 deaths contain the value of the population mean.
   c. No. The data appear to be trending downward. Instead of having a stable population, the population characteristics appear to be changing over time.

4. H_0: $\mu = 72.6$ deaths. H_1: $\mu < 72.6$ deaths. Test statistic: $t = -15.804$. P-value = 0.0000 (Table: P-value < 0.005). Critical value: $t = -2.539$. Reject H_0: $\mu = 72.6$ deaths. There is sufficient evidence to support the claim that the mean number of annual lightning deaths is now less than the mean of 72.6 deaths from the 1980s. Possible factors: Shift in population from rural to urban areas; better lightning protection and grounding in electric and cable and phone lines; better medical treatment of people struck by lightning; fewer people use phones attached to cords; better weather predictions.

5. Because the vertical scale starts at 50 and not at 0, the difference between the number of males and the number of females is exaggerated, so the graph is deceptive by creating the false impression that males account for nearly all lightning strike deaths. A comparison of the numbers of deaths shows that the number of male deaths is roughly 4 times the number of female deaths, but the graph makes it appear that the number of male deaths is around 12 times the number of female deaths.

6. H_0: $p = 0.5$. H_1: $p > 0.5$. Test statistic: $z = 10.18$. P-value = 0.0000 (Table: 0.0001). Critical value: $z = 2.33$. Reject H_0. There is sufficient evidence to support the claim that the proportion of male deaths is greater than $1/2$. More males are involved in certain outdoor activities such as construction, fishing, and golf.

7. $0.745 < p < 0.836$. Because the entire confidence interval is greater than 0.5, it does not seem feasible that males and females have equal chances of being killed by lightning. The confidence interval indicates that the proportion of male lightning deaths is substantially greater than 0.5.

8. a. 0.512   b. 0.008   c. 0.992   d. 0.205
   e. $\mu = 40.0$ males; $\sigma = 2.8$ males
   f. Yes. Using the range rule of thumb, significantly high values are $\mu + 2\sigma$ or greater. With $\mu + 2\sigma = 45.6$, values above 45.6 are significantly high, so 46 would be a significantly high number of male victims in a group of 50. Using probabilities, $P(46$ or more male victims among 50$) = 0.0185$, which is very small, suggesting that 46 is significantly high.

Chapter 9 Answers

Section 9-1

1. The samples are simple random samples that are independent. For each of the two groups, the number of successes is at least 5 and the number of failures is at least 5. (Depending on what we call a success, the four numbers are 33, 115, 201,196, and 200,630 and all of those numbers are at least 5.) The requirements are satisfied.

3. a. H_0: $p_1 = p_2$. H_1: $p_1 < p_2$.
   b. There is sufficient evidence to support the claim that the rate of polio is less for children given the Salk vaccine than for children given a placebo. The Salk vaccine appears to be effective.

5. H_0: $p_1 = p_2$. H_1: $p_1 > p_2$. Test statistic: $z = 12.82$. P-value: 0.0000. Critical value: $z = 2.33$. Reject H_0. There is sufficient evidence to support the claim that vinyl gloves have a greater virus leak rate than latex gloves.

7. a. H_0: $p_1 = p_2$. H_1: $p_1 \neq p_2$. Test statistic: $z = -0.62$. P-value: 0.5359 (Table: 0.5352). Critical values: $z = \pm 1.96$. Fail to reject H_0. There is not sufficient evidence to warrant rejection of the claim that when dropped, buttered toast and toast marked with an X have the same proportion that land with the buttered/X side down.
   b. 95% CI: $-0.260 < p_1 - p_2 < 0.135$. Because the confidence interval limits do contain 0, there is a not a significant difference between the two sample proportions. There is not sufficient evidence to warrant rejection of the claim that when dropped, buttered toast and toast marked with an X have the same proportion that land with the buttered/X side down.

9. a. H_0: $p_1 = p_2$. H_1: $p_1 < p_2$. Test statistic: $z = -7.94$. P-value: 0.0000 (Table: 0.0001). Critical value: $z = -2.33$. Reject H_0. There is sufficient evidence to support the claim that the rate of right-handedness for those who prefer to use their left ear for cell phones is less than the rate of right-handedness for those who prefer to use their right ear for cell phones.

b. 98% CI: $-0.266 < p < -0.126$. Because the confidence interval limits do not contain 0, there is a significant difference between the two proportions. Because the interval consists of negative numbers only, it appears that the claim is supported. The difference between the populations does appear to have practical significance.

11. a. H_0: $p_1 = p_2$. H_1: $p_1 > p_2$. Test statistic: $z = 6.44$. P-value $= 0.0000$ (Table: 0.0001). Critical value: $z = 2.33$. Reject H_0. There is sufficient evidence to support the claim that the proportion of people over 55 who dream in black and white is greater than the proportion of those under 25.

b. 98% CI: $0.117 < p_1 - p_2 < 0.240$. Because the confidence interval limits do not include 0, it appears that the two proportions are not equal. Because the confidence interval limits include only positive values, it appears that the proportion of people over 55 who dream in black and white is greater than the proportion of those under 25.

c. The results suggest that the proportion of people over 55 who dream in black and white is greater than the proportion of those under 25, but the results cannot be used to verify the cause of that difference.

13. a. H_0: $p_1 = p_2$. H_1: $p_1 > p_2$. Test statistic: $z = 6.11$. P-value $= 0.0000$ (Table: 0.0001). Critical value: $z = 1.645$. Reject H_0. There is sufficient evidence to support the claim that the fatality rate is higher for those not wearing seat belts.

b. 90% CI: $0.00559 < p_1 - p_2 < 0.0123$. Because the confidence interval limits do not include 0, it appears that the two fatality rates are not equal. Because the confidence interval limits include only positive values, it appears that the fatality rate is higher for those not wearing seat belts.

c. The results suggest that the use of seat belts is associated with fatality rates lower than those associated with not using seat belts.

15. a. H_0: $p_1 = p_2$. H_1: $p_1 \neq p_2$. Test statistic: $z = -4.41$. P-value: 0.00001 (Table: 0.0002). Critical values: $z = \pm 1.96$. Reject H_0. There is sufficient evidence to reject the claim of no difference between the two rates of correct responses. It appears that the dogs do a better job of correctly identifying subjects without malaria.

b. 95% CI: $-0.284 < p_1 - p_2 < -0.118$. Because the confidence interval limits do not contain 0, there is a significant difference between the two sample proportions. Because the confidence interval consists of negative values only, it appears that the proportion of correct identifications made with subjects having malaria is less than the proportion of correct identifications made with subjects not having malaria.

c. With correct identification rates of 70.3% and 90.3%, the dogs are doing quite well for subjects with malaria and subjects without malaria, but they do a much better job of correctly identifying patients without malaria.

17. a. H_0: $p_1 = p_2$. H_1: $p_1 \neq p_2$. Test statistic: $z = 7.11$. P-value: 0.0000 (Table: 0.0002). Critical values: $z = \pm 1.96$. Reject H_0. There is sufficient evidence to warrant rejection of the claim that Connecticut and New York have the same proportion of cars with rear license plates only.

b. 95% CI: $0.0828 < p_1 - p_2 < 0.118$. Because the confidence interval limits do not contain 0, there is sufficient evidence to warrant rejection of the claim that Connecticut and New York have the same proportion of cars with rear license plates only. There appears to be a significant difference between the proportions of cars with rear license plates only.

19. a. H_0: $p_1 = p_2$. H_1: $p_1 \neq p_2$. Test statistic: $z = -2.63$. P-value: 0.0085 (Table: 0.0086). Critical values: $z = \pm 2.575$. Reject H_0. There is sufficient evidence to reject the claim that the proportions of blue eyes are the same for females and males.

b. 99% CI: $-0.112 < p_1 - p_2 < -0.00116$. Because the confidence interval limits do not contain 0, there appears to be a significant difference between the two sample proportions. Because the confidence interval consists of negative values only, it appears that the proportion of blue eyes among females is less than the proportion of blue eyes among males.

c. The professors used a convenience sample of their students. Convenience samples are typically problematic for making inferences about population parameters, but in this case there isn't anything about eye color that would seem to make someone more or less likely to be a student in a statistics class, so the data do not appear to have the typical bias of a convenience sample.

21. a. H_0: $p_1 = p_2$. H_1: $p_1 < p_2$. Test statistic: $z = -1.17$. P-value $= 0.1214$ (Table: 0.1210). Critical value: $z = -2.33$. Fail to reject H_0. There is not sufficient evidence to support the claim that the rate of left-handedness among males is less than that among females.

b. 98% CI: $-0.0848 < p_1 - p_2 < 0.0264$ (Table: $-0.0849 < p_1 - p_2 < 0.0265$). Because the confidence interval limits include 0, there does not appear to be a significant difference between the rate of left-handedness among males and the rate among females. There is not sufficient evidence to support the claim that the rate of left-handedness among males is less than that among females.

c. The rate of left-handedness among males does not appear to be less than the rate of left-handedness among females.

23. The samples should include 4802 men and 4802 women.

25. a. $0.0227 < p_1 - p_2 < 0.217$; because the confidence interval limits do not contain 0, it appears that $p_1 = p_2$ can be rejected.

b. $0.491 < p_1 < 0.629$; $0.371 < p_2 < 0.509$; because the confidence intervals do overlap, it appears that $p_1 = p_2$ cannot be rejected.

c. H_0: $p_1 = p_2$. H_1: $p_1 \neq p_2$. Test statistic: $z = 2.40$. P-value: 0.0164. Critical values: $z = \pm 1.96$. Reject H_0. There is sufficient evidence to reject $p_1 = p_2$.

d. Reject $p_1 = p_2$. Least effective method: Using the overlap between the individual confidence intervals.

27. ANSUR I 1988: $\hat{p}_1 = 1774/3982$. ANSUR II 2012: $\hat{p}_2 = 4082/6068$.
H_0: $p_1 = p_2$. H_1: $p_1 \neq p_2$. Test statistic: $z = -22.59$. P-value: 0.0000 (Table: 0.0002). Critical values: $z = \pm 2.575$. 99% CI: $-0.253 < p_1 - p_2 < -0.202$. Reject H_0. There is sufficient evidence to warrant rejection of the claim that the proportion of males in the sample in Data Set 1 "ANSUR I 1988" is the same as the proportion of males in the sample in Data Set 2 "ANSUR

II 2012." The proportion of males in ANSUR II 2012 appears to be significantly higher than in ANSUR I 1988. (TI data: With sample proportions of $227/500$ and $319/500$, test statistic is $z = -5.84$, P-value $= 0.0000$, and the confidence interval is $-0.264 < p_1 - p_2 < -0.104$.)

Section 9-2

1. Only parts (b) and (c) describe independent samples.

3. a. Yes   b. Yes   c. 98%

5. a. H_0: $\mu_1 = \mu_2$. H_1: $\mu_1 < \mu_2$. Test statistic: $t = -4.084$. P-value $= 0.0001$ (Table: P-value < 0.005). Critical value: $t = -1.695$ (Table: -1.729). Reject H_0. There is sufficient evidence to support the claim that giving candy does result in greater tips.
   b. 90% CI: $-3.78 < \mu_1 - \mu_2 < -1.56$ (Table: $-3.80 < \mu_1 - \mu_2 < -1.54$)

7. a. H_0: $\mu_1 = \mu_2$. H_1: $\mu_1 > \mu_2$. Test statistic: $t = 2.095$. P-value $= 0.0196$ (Table: P-value > 0.01). Critical value: $t = 2.372$ (Table: 2.403). Fail to reject H_0. There is not sufficient evidence to support the claim that rubbing with alcohol results in a lower bacteria count.
   b. 98% CI: $-4 < \mu_1 - \mu_2 < 72$ (Table: $-5 < \mu_1 - \mu_2 < 73$)
   c. Yes, the null hypothesis is rejected with a 0.05 significance level, so the conclusion changes to this: There is sufficient evidence to support the claim that rubbing with alcohol results in a lower bacteria count.

9. a. H_0: $\mu_1 = \mu_2$. H_1: $\mu_1 \neq \mu_2$. Test statistic: $t = 2.647$. P-value $= 0.0101$ (Table: < 0.02). Critical values: $t = \pm 1.995$ (Table: ± 2.032). Reject H_0. There is sufficient evidence to warrant rejection of the claim that the samples are from populations with the same mean. Color does appear to have an effect on word recall scores. Red appears to be associated with higher word memory recall scores.
   b. 95% CI: $0.88 < \mu_1 - \mu_2 < 6.28$ (Table: $0.83 < \mu_1 - \mu_2 < 6.33$). The confidence interval includes positive numbers only, so the mean score with a red background appears to be greater than the mean score with a blue background.
   c. The background color does appear to have an effect on word recall scores. Red appears to be associated with higher word memory recall scores.

11. a. H_0: $\mu_1 = \mu_2$. H_1: $\mu_1 > \mu_2$. Test statistic: $t = 0.132$. P-value $= 0.4480$ (Table: > 0.10). Critical value: $t = 1.691$ (Table: 1.729). Fail to reject H_0. There is not sufficient evidence to support the claim that the magnets are effective in reducing pain.
    b. 90% CI: $-0.59 < \mu_1 - \mu_2 < 0.69$ (Table: $-0.61 < \mu_1 - \mu_2 < 0.71$).
    c. Magnets do not appear to be effective in treating back pain. It is valid to argue that the magnets *might* appear to be effective if the sample sizes were larger.

13. a. H_0: $\mu_1 = \mu_2$. H_1: $\mu_1 \neq \mu_2$. Test statistic: $t = -0.393$. P-value $= 0.6959$ (Table: P-value > 0.20). Critical value: $t = \pm 2.012$ (Table: ± 2.060). Fail to reject H_0. There is not sufficient evidence to warrant rejection of the claim that the mean commuting time with the heavier bicycle is the same as the mean commuting time with the lighter bicycle.
    b. 95% CI: -3.7 min $< \mu_1 - \mu_2 < 2.5$ min

15. a. H_0: $\mu_1 = \mu_2$. H_1: $\mu_1 > \mu_2$. Test statistic: $t = 32.771$. P-value $= 0.0000$ (Table: < 0.005). Critical value: $t = 1.667$ (Table: 1.685). Reject H_0. There is sufficient evidence to support the claim that pre-1964 quarters have a mean weight that is greater than the mean weight of post-1964 quarters.
    b. 90% CI: 0.52522 lb $< \mu_1 - \mu_2 < 0.58152$ (Table: 0.52492 lb $< \mu_1 - \mu_2 < 0.58182$)
    c. Yes. Vending machines are not affected very much because pre-1964 quarters are mostly out of circulation.

17. a. H_0: $\mu_1 = \mu_2$. H_1: $\mu_1 < \mu_2$. Test statistic: $t = -1.085$. P-value $= 0.1442$ (Table: P-value > 0.10). Critical value: $t = -1.708$ (Table: -1.796). Fail to reject H_0. There is not sufficient evidence to support the claim that the mean weight of the 1988 male population is less than the mean weight of the 2012 male population.
    b. 90% CI: -11.77 kg $< \mu_1 - \mu_2 < 2.63$ kg (Table: -12.14 kg $< \mu_1 - \mu_2 < 3.00$ kg)

19. a. H_0: $\mu_1 = \mu_2$. H_1: $\mu_1 > \mu_2$. Test statistic: $t = 16.084$. P-value $= 0.0000$ (Table: < 0.005). Critical value: $t = 2.538$ (Table: 2.718). Reject H_0. There is sufficient evidence to support the claim that the contents of cans of regular Coke have weights with a mean that is greater than the mean for Diet Coke.
    b. 98% CI: 0.02794 lb $< \mu_1 - \mu_2 < 0.03841$ lb (Table: 0.02756 lb $< \mu_1 - \mu_2 < 0.03878$ lb)
    c. The contents in cans of regular Coke appear to weigh more, probably due to the sugar present in regular Coke but not diet Coke.

21. a. H_0: $\mu_1 = \mu_2$. H_1: $\mu_1 < \mu_2$. Test statistic: $t = -20.393$. P-value $= 0.0000$ (Table: P-value < 0.005). Critical value: $t = -1.645$. Reject H_0. There is sufficient evidence to support the claim that the mean weight of the 1988 male population is less than the mean weight of the 2012 male population. It does appear that the male population is getting heavier. (TI data: Test statistic is $t = -5.282$, P-value is 0.0000, critical value is $t = -1.648$.)
    b. 90% CI: -7.60 kg $< \mu_1 - \mu_2 < -6.47$ kg (TI data: -7.50 kg $< \mu_1 - \mu_2 < -3.93$ kg)

23. H_0: $\mu_1 = \mu_2$. H_1: $\mu_1 < \mu_2$. Test statistic: $t = -0.132$. P-value $= 0.4477$ (Table: >0.10). Critical value: $t = -1.669$ (Table: -1.688). Fail to reject H_0. There is not sufficient evidence to support the claim that men talk less than women.

25. With pooling, df increases dramatically to 97, but the test statistic decreases from 2.282 to 1.705 (because the estimated standard deviation increases from 2.620268 to 3.507614), the P-value increases to 0.0457, and the 90% confidence interval becomes wider. With pooling, these results do not show greater significance.

27. H_0: $\mu_1 = \mu_2$. H_1: $\mu_1 \neq \mu_2$. Test statistic: $t = 15.322$. P-value $= 0.0000$ (Table: P-value < 0.01). Critical values: $t = \pm 2.080$. Reject H_0. There is sufficient evidence to warrant rejection of the claim that the two populations have the same mean.

Section 9-3

1. $H_0: \mu_d = 0.\ H_1: \mu_d < 0.$
3. a. 90% b. 2.015
   c. Because the confidence interval limits do not include 0 admissions and the range of values consists of negative values only, there is sufficient evidence to support the claim that fewer hospital admissions due to traffic accidents occur on Friday the 6th than on the following Friday the 13th.
5. a. $H_0: \mu_d = 0.\ H_1: \mu_d > 0.$ Test statistic: $t = 0.407.$
   P-value $= 0.3469$ (Table: P-value > 0.10). Critical value: $t = 1.833$. Fail to reject H_0. There is not sufficient evidence to support the claim that for females, the measured weights tend to be higher than the reported weights.
   b. 90% CI: -1.30 lb $< \mu_d < 2.04$ lb. Because the confidence interval includes 0, fail to reject H_0. There is not sufficient evidence to support the claim that for females, the measured weights tend to be higher than the reported weights.
7. a. $H_0: \mu_d = 0.\ H_1: \mu_d < 0.$ Test statistic: $t = -4.438.$
   P-value $= 0.0011$ (Table: P-value < 0.005). Critical value: $t = -2.896$. Reject H_0. There is sufficient evidence to support the claim that for the population of freshman male college students, the weights in September are less than the weights in the following April.
   b. 98% CI: -1.5 kg $< \mu_d < -0.3$ kg. Because the confidence interval does not include 0 kg, reject H_0. There is sufficient evidence to support the claim that for the population of freshman male college students, the weights in September are less than the weights in the following April.
   c. The test does not address the specific weight gain of 15 lb, but it does suggest that males gain weight during their freshman year.
9. a. $H_0: \mu_d = 0.\ H_1: \mu_d \neq 0.$ Test statistic: $t = 0.890.$
   P-value $= 0.3924$ (Table: P-value > 0.20). Critical values: $t = \pm 2.201$. Fail to reject H_0. There is not sufficient evidence to warrant rejection of the claim that the population of differences has a mean equal to 0.
   b. 95% CI: $-3.1 < \mu_d < 7.2$. Because the confidence interval includes 0, fail to reject H_0. There is not sufficient evidence to warrant rejection of the claim that the population of differences has a mean equal to 0.
11. a. $H_0: \mu_d = 0$ year. $H_1: \mu_d < 0$ year. Test statistic: $t = -2.609.$
   P-value $= 0.0142$ (Table: < 0.025). Critical value: $t = -1.833$. Reject H_0. There is sufficient evidence to support the claim that for the population of ages of Best Actresses and Best Actors, the differences have a mean less than 0. There is sufficient evidence to conclude that Best Actresses are generally younger than Best Actors.
   b. 90% CI: -16.5 years $< \mu_d < -2.9$ years. The confidence interval consists of negative numbers only and does not include 0.
13. $H_0: \mu_d = 0$ in. $H_1: \mu_d \neq 0$ in. Test statistic: $t = -1.379.$
   P-value $= 0.2013$ (Table: >0.20). Critical values: $t = \pm 2.262$. Fail to reject H_0. There is not sufficient evidence to warrant rejection of the claim that there is no difference in heights between mothers and their first daughters.

15. $0.69 < \mu_d < 5.56$. Because the confidence interval limits do not contain 0 and they consist of positive values only, it appears that the "before" measurements are greater than the "after" measurements, so hypnotism does appear to be effective in reducing pain.
17. The larger data set changed the results and conclusion.
    a. $H_0: \mu_d = 0.\ H_1: \mu_d > 0.$ Test statistic: $t = 17.611.$
    P-value $= 0.0000$ (Table: P-value < 0.005). Critical value: $t = 1.645$. Reject H_0. There is sufficient evidence to support the claim that for females, the measured weights tend to be higher than the reported weights. (TI data: Test statistic is $t = 4.864$, the critical value is $t = 1.651$, and the P-value is 0.0000.)
    b. 90% CI: 2.94 lb $< \mu_d < 3.55$ lb. Because the confidence interval does not include 0 lb, reject H_0. There is sufficient evidence to support the claim that for females, the measured weights tend to be higher than the reported weights. (TI data: 1.02 lb $< \mu_d < 2.08$ lb.)
19. a. $H_0: \mu_d = 0$ year. $H_1: \mu_d < 0$ year. Test statistic: $t = -5.269.$
    P-value $= 0.0000$ (Table: < 0.005). Critical value: $t = -1.662$. Reject H_0. There is sufficient evidence to support the claim that actresses are generally younger than actors.
    b. 90% CI: -10.2 years $< \mu_d < -5.3$ years. The confidence interval consists of negative numbers only and does not include 0.
21. a. $H_0: \mu_d = 0.\ H_1: \mu_d \neq 0.$ Test statistic: $t = -77.006.$
    P-value $= 0.0000$ (Table: P-value < 0.005). Critical values: $t = \pm 1.961$. Reject H_0. There is sufficient evidence to warrant rejection of the claim that for males, their height is the same as their arm span. (TI data: Test statistic is $t = -22.16$, critical values are $t = \pm 1.967$, and the P-value is 0.0000.)
23. $H_0: \mu_d = 0$ in. $H_1: \mu_d \neq 0$ in. Test statistic: $t = -4.090.$
    P-value $= 0.0001$ (Table: <0.01). Critical values: $t = \pm 1.978$ (Table: ± 1.984 approximately). Reject H_0. There is sufficient evidence to warrant rejection of the claim of no difference in heights between mothers and their first daughters.
25. a. 95% CI: -1.31 in. $< \mu_d < 1.35$ in. Because the confidence interval includes the value of 0 in., fail to reject H_0. There is not sufficient evidence to warrant rejection of the claim of no difference in heights between fathers and their first sons. There does not appear to be a significant difference.
    b. Answers vary, but here is a typical 95% confidence interval: -0.98 in. $< \mu_d < 1.20$ in. Because the confidence interval includes the value of 0 in., fail to reject H_0. There is not sufficient evidence to warrant rejection of the claim of no difference in heights between fathers and their first sons. There does not appear to be a significant difference.
    c. The two confidence intervals do not differ by amounts that are very substantial. The conclusions from the two confidence intervals are the same. It appears that the confidence interval constructed using the t distribution and the confidence interval constructed using the bootstrap method are reasonably consistent with each other.

Section 9-4

1. a. No. b. No.
   c. The two samples have standard deviations (or variances) that are very close in value.
   d. Skewed right

3. No. Unlike some other tests that have a requirement that samples must be from normally distributed populations or the samples must have more than 30 values, the F test has a requirement that the samples must be from normally distributed populations, regardless of how large the samples are.

5. $H_0: \sigma_1 = \sigma_2$ and $H_1: \sigma_1 > \sigma_2$. Test statistic: $F = 1.9728$. P-value: 0.0184. Critical F value is 1.7045 (Table: Approximately 1.6928). Reject H_0. There is sufficient evidence to support the claim that the variation of weights before 1964 is greater than the variation of weights after 1964. Here is one advantage of the change in variation: Weights of quarters now have less variation than they did before 1964, so vending machines can be calibrated to accept a narrower range of weights, and counterfeit coins will be less likely to be accepted.

7. $H_0: \sigma_1 = \sigma_2$. $H_1: \sigma_1 \neq \sigma_2$. Test statistic: $F = 2.3706$. P-value: 0.0129. Upper critical F value: 1.9678 (Table: Upper critical F value is between 1.8752 and 2.0739). Reject H_0. There is sufficient evidence to warrant rejection of the claim that creative task scores have the same variation with a red background and a blue background.

9. $H_0: \sigma_1 = \sigma_2$ and $H_1: \sigma_1 \neq \sigma_2$. Test statistic: $F = 9.3364$. P-value: 0.0000. Critical F value is 2.4086 (Table: Critical F value is between 2.3675 and 2.4247). Reject H_0. There is sufficient evidence to reject the claim that the treatment and placebo groups have the same amount of variation among the errors.

11. $H_0: \sigma_1 = \sigma_2$ and $H_1: \sigma_1 > \sigma_2$. Test statistic: $F = 1.6531$. P-value: 0.0966. Critical F value is 1.8915 (Table: Between 1.8543 and 1.9005). Fail to reject H_0. There is not sufficient evidence to support the claim that commuting times with the lighter bicycle have more variation than commuting times with the heavier bicycle.

13. $H_0: \sigma_1 = \sigma_2$ and $H_1: \sigma_1 > \sigma_2$. Test statistic: $F = 3.8134$. P-value: 0.0340. Critical F value is 3.3129 (Table: Between 3.3472 and 3.2839). Reject H_0. There is sufficient evidence to support the claim that the variation among pulse rates of females is greater than the variation among males.

15. $H_0: \sigma_1 = \sigma_2$ and $H_1: \sigma_1 > \sigma_2$. Test statistic: $F = 2.5285$. P-value: 0.0213. Critical F value is 2.1124 (Table: Critical F value is between 2.0825 and 2.1242). Reject H_0. There is sufficient evidence to support the claim that IQ scores of subjects with medium lead levels vary more than IQ scores of subjects with high lead levels.

17. $c_1 = 3$, $c_2 = 0$, critical value is 7.4569. Fail to reject H_0. There is not sufficient evidence to support a claim that the two populations of scores have different amounts of variation.

19. $F_L = 0.4103$; $F_R = 2.7006$

Section 9-5

1. Bootstrapping is used for obtaining a confidence interval estimate, and it involves sampling with replacement of selected sample values. Randomization is used for testing hypotheses. When working with two independent samples, randomization involves sampling without replacement; when working with matched pairs, randomization involves sampling with replacement.

3. Only part (b) is a randomization. Only part (b) has the same original sample sizes with the sample data selected without replacement.

5. a. **Randomization:** The difference between the two sample proportions is 0.0625. Results vary but this is typical: Among 1000 resamplings, differences at least as extreme as 0.0625 occurred 695 times. It appears that by chance, it is easy to get a difference like the one obtained, so there is not sufficient evidence to warrant rejection of the claim that when dropped, buttered toast and toast marked with an X have the same proportion that land with the buttered/X side down.

   b. **Bootstrapping:** Results vary but this is typical: 95% CI: $-0.250 < p_1 - p_2 < 0.125$. Because the confidence interval limits do contain 0, there is a not a significant difference between the two sample proportions. There is not sufficient evidence to warrant rejection of the claim that when dropped, buttered toast and toast marked with an X have the same proportion that land with the buttered/X side

7. a. **Randomization:** The difference between the two sample proportions is 0.196. Results vary but this is typical: Among 1000 resamplings, differences at least as extreme as -0.196 never occurred. It appears that by chance, it is very difficult to get a difference like the one obtained, so there is sufficient evidence to support the claim that the rate of right-handedness for those who prefer to use their left ear for cell phones is less than the rate of right-handedness for those who prefer to use their right ear for cell phones.

   b. **Bootstrapping:** Results vary but this is typical: 98% CI: $-0.266 < p_1 - p_2 < -0.127$. Because the confidence interval limits do not contain 0, there is a significant difference between the two sample proportions. There is sufficient evidence to support the claim that the rate of right-handedness for those who prefer to use their left ear for cell phones is less than the rate of right-handedness for those who prefer to use their right ear for cell phones.

9. a. **Randomization:** Using the sample data, we get $\bar{x}_1 - \bar{x}_2 = -4.57$ kg. If we use randomization with the two sets of sample data to generate 1000 simulated differences, a typical result is that 150 of those differences will be -4.57 kg or below, so it appears that such differences can easily occur. There is not sufficient evidence to support the claim that the mean weight of the 1988 male population is less than the mean weight of the 2012 male population.

   b. **Bootstrapping:** Results vary but this is typical: 90% CI: -11.38 kg $< \mu_1 - \mu_2 < 2.21$ kg. Because the confidence interval does include 0, it appears that there is not a significant difference between the mean weight in 1988 and the mean weight in 2012. There is not sufficient evidence to support the claim that the mean weight of the 1988 male population is less than the mean weight of the 2012 male population.

11. a. **Randomization:** Using the sample data, we get $\bar{x}_1 - \bar{x}_2 = 0.03317$ lb. If we use randomization to generate 1000 simulated differences, a typical result is that none of those differences will be at least as extreme as 0.03317 lb, so it appears that such differences are very rare. There is sufficient evidence to support the claim that the contents of cans of regular Coke have weights with a mean that is greater than the mean for Diet Coke.

b. **Bootstrapping:** Results vary but this is typical: 98% CI: 0.02844 lb $< \mu_1 - \mu_2 <$ 0.03773 lb. Because the confidence interval does not include 0, it appears that there is a significant difference between the two sample means. There is sufficient evidence to support the claim that the contents of cans of regular Coke have weights with a mean that is greater than the mean for Diet Coke.

13. a. **Randomization:** Typical result: With 1000 resamples, 336 of the values of $\overline{d}$ are 0.37 lb or greater, so the value of $\overline{d} = 0.37$ lb can easily occur by chance. There is not sufficient evidence to support the claim that for females, the measured weights tend to be higher than the reported weights.

   b. **Bootstrapping:** Typical result: 90% CI: -1.02 lb $< \mu_d <$ 1.78 lb. Because the confidence interval does include 0, there is not sufficient evidence to support the claim that for females, the measured weights tend to be higher than the reported weights.

15. a. **Randomization:** Typical result: With 1000 resamples, 5 of the values of $\overline{d}$ are -0.889 kg or less, so the value of $\overline{d} = -0.889$ kg is very unlikely to occur by chance. There is sufficient evidence to support the claim that for the population of freshman male college students, the weights in September are less than the weights in the following April.

   b. **Bootstrapping:** Typical result: 98% CI: -1.3 kg $< \mu_d < -0.4$ kg. Because the confidence interval does not include 0 and consists of negative values only, there is sufficient evidence to support the claim that for the population of freshman male college students, the weights in September are less than the weights in the following April.

17. Typical result from 1000 resamples: 95% CI: 0.02909 lb $< \mu_1 - \mu_2 <$ 0.03478 lb. Typical result from 10,000 resamples: 0.02908 lb $< \mu_1 - \mu_2 <$ 0.03474 lb. The differences are very small, so the larger number of resamples does not have much of an effect on the results.

Chapter 9: Quick Quiz

1. H_0: $p_1 = p_2$. H_1: $p_1 \neq p_2$.
2. $\hat{p}_1 = 102/288 = 0.354$, $\hat{p}_2 = 75/277 = 0.271$, $\overline{p} = 0.313$
3. a. 0.0324
   b. Reject H_0 and conclude that there is sufficient evidence to warrant rejection of the claim that patients treated with dexamethasone and patients given a placebo have the same rate of complete resolution. It appears that the rates of complete resolution are different.
4. a. 95% CI: 0.00732 $< p_1 - p_2 <$ 0.159
   b. The confidence interval does not include 0, so it appears that the two proportions are not equal. There appears to be a significant difference between the success rate in the treatment group and the success rate in the placebo group.
5. a. The two samples are independent because they are not matched or paired in any way.
   b. $t = 22.092$ (or 22.095 if using original data)
6. $F = 2.9265$ (or 2.9233 if using original data)
7. a. Because each pair of data is matched by the same subject, the two sets of data are dependent.
   b. H_0: $\mu_d = 0°F$. H_1: $\mu_d \neq 0°F$.

8. Because the confidence interval includes the value of 0°F, it appears that there is not a significant difference between the temperatures at 8 AM and the temperatures at 12 AM.
9. True   10. False

Chapter 9: Review Exercises

1. H_0: $p_1 = p_2$. H_1: $p_1 < p_2$. Test statistic: $z = -3.49$. P-value: 0.0002. Critical value: $z = -1.645$. Reject H_0. There is sufficient evidence to support the claim that money in a large denomination is less likely to be spent relative to an equivalent amount in smaller denominations.
2. 90% CI: $-0.528 < p_1 - p_2 < -0.206$. The confidence interval limits do not contain 0, so it appears that there is a significant difference between the two proportions. Because the confidence interval consists of negative values only, it appears that p_1 is less than p_2, so it appears that money in a large denomination is less likely to be spent relative to an equivalent amount in smaller denominations.
3. H_0: $\mu_d = 0°F$. H_1: $\mu_d \neq 0°F$. Test statistic: $t = -0.262$. P-value $= 0.7995$ (Table: P-value > 0.10). Critical values: $t = \pm 2.262$. Fail to reject H_0. There is not sufficient evidence to warrant rejection of the claim that differences between actual temperatures and temperatures forecast five days earlier are from a population with a mean of 0°F. There does not appear to be a difference between actual temperatures and temperatures forecast five days earlier.
4. 95% CI: $-3.9°F < \mu_d < 3.1°F$. Because the confidence interval includes 0°F, fail to reject H_0. There is not sufficient evidence to warrant rejection of the claim that differences between actual temperatures and temperatures forecast five days earlier are from a population with a mean of 0°F. There does not appear to be a difference between actual temperatures and temperatures forecast five days earlier. It appears that weather forecasters are doing a good job.
5. a. H_0: $p_1 = p_2$. H_1: $p_1 > p_2$. Test statistic: $z = 2.64$. P-value: 0.0041. Critical value: $z = 2.33$. Reject H_0. There is sufficient evidence to support the claim that the rate of success for smoking cessation is greater with the sustained care program.
6. a. 98% CI: 0.0135 $< p_1 - p_2 <$ 0.200 (Table: 0.0134 $< p <$ 0.200). Because the confidence interval limits do not contain 0, there is a significant difference between the two proportions. Because the interval consists of positive numbers only, it appears that the success rate for the sustained care program is greater than the success rate for the standard care program.
   b. Based on the samples, the success rates of the programs are 25.8% (sustained care) and 15.1% (standard care). That difference does appear to be substantial, so the difference between the programs does appear to have practical significance.
   c. The more successful of the two programs has a success rate of only 25.8%, so there is a failure rate of about 74% for those who try to stop smoking with the sustained care program. The time required and cost of the sustained program relative to standard care must be considered when determining practical significance. If sustained care is much more time consuming and expensive, the practical significance will be lower.

7. $H_0: \mu_1 = \mu_2$ $H_1: \mu_1 < \mu_2$ Test statistic: $t = -2.330$.
   P-value $= 0.0102$ (Table: < 0.025). Critical value: $t = -1.649$
   (Table: -1.660). Reject H_0. There is sufficient evidence to support the claim that children wearing seat belts have a lower mean length of time in an ICU than the mean for children not wearing seat belts. Buckle up!

8. 90% CI: -0.96 day $< \mu_1 - \mu_2 < -0.16$ day. The confidence interval does not include 0 days, so there appears to be a significant difference. Because the confidence interval consists of negative values only, it appears that children wearing seat belts spend less time in intensive care units than children who don't wear seat belts. Children should wear seat belts (except for young children who should use properly installed car seats).

9. The waist circumferences from 1988 are measured from eight males, and the waist circumferences from 2012 are from eight *different* males, so the data are not paired or matched in any meaningful way. The stated claim makes no sense for these two *independent* samples. Here are the results that would be obtained by blindly following the instruction to test the claim that the differences between the pairs of data are from a population with a mean of 0 mm: $H_0: \mu_d = 0$. $H_1: \mu_d \neq 0$. Test statistic: $t = -0.834$. P-value $= 0.4320$ (Table: P-value > 0.20). Critical values: $t = \pm 2.365$. Fail to reject H_0. There is not sufficient evidence to warrant rejection of the claim that the differences between the pairs of data are from a population with a mean of 0 mm. However, these results are not valid and they make no sense with the two independent samples.

10. $H_0: \sigma_1 = \sigma_2$. $H_1: \sigma_1 \neq \sigma_2$. Test statistic: $F = 2.9888$. P-value: 0.0000. Upper critical F value: 1.3630. Reject H_0. There is sufficient evidence to warrant rejection of the claim that for children hospitalized after motor vehicle crashes, the numbers of days in intensive care units for those wearing seat belts and for those not wearing seat belts have the same variation.

Chapter 9: Cumulative Review Exercises

1. a. Key question: Does the bar graph correctly depict the data or is it somehow misleading? (Another reasonable question would be to ask whether significantly more males play video games than females, but no sample sizes are provided to help address that question.)
   b. Just examine the graph to determine whether it is misleading.
   c. Because the vertical scale begins with 40% instead of 0%, the bottom portion of the bar graph is cut off, so the differences are visually exaggerated. The graph makes it appear that about 3.5 times as many males play video games as females, but examination of the percentage values shows that the ratio is closer to 1.5.

2. a. Key question: Estimate the proportion of all females aged 18–29 who play video games. Another reasonable question is this: Are females aged 18–29 who play video games in the minority (with a proportion less than 0.5 or 50%)?
   b. The population proportion can be estimated with a confidence interval. Determination of whether the population proportion is less than 0.5 can be addressed with a hypothesis test of the claim that $p < 0.5$.

   c. The 95% confidence interval estimate of the population proportion is $0.459 < p < 0.521$. For determining whether the proportion of females aged 18–29 who play video games is less than 0.5, the test statistic is $z = -0.64$ and the P-value is 0.2619 (Table: 0.2611), and these values show that the sample proportion of 0.49 is not significantly below 0.5. There is not sufficient evidence to support a claim that the proportion is less than 0.5. (Also, there is not sufficient evidence to support a claim that the proportion is significantly different from 0.5.)

3. a. Key question: Do significantly more males play video games than females? Or is there a significant difference between the proportion of male video game players and the proportion of female video game players?
   b. Use a hypothesis test or confidence interval with two proportions (as in Section 9-1).
   c. Conclude that the proportion of male video game players is greater than (or different from) the proportion of female video game players. Using the methods of Section 9-1, the test statistic of $z = 10.53$ and the P-value of 0.0000 support that claim. Or the 95% confidence interval of $0.188 < p_1 - p_2 < 0.272$ consists of positive values only, which also supports that claim.

4. a. Key question: Based on the differences between the IQ scores of each matched pair in the sample, is there no difference between the IQ scores of pairs of twins in the population?
   b. Use the methods of Section 9-3 for matched pairs.
   c. There does not appear to be a difference between the IQ scores of first-born and second-born twins in the population. Use $H_0: \mu_d = 0$ and $H_1: \mu_d \neq 0$. Fail to reject H_0. Test statistic: $t = 0.150$. P-value $= 0.8843$ (Table: P-value > 0.20). Critical values: ± 2.262 (assuming a 0.05 significance level). 95% CI: $-5.6 < \mu_d < 6.4$.

5. a. The data are time series data. Key question: What is the trend of the data over time?
   b. A time series graph would reveal a trend over time.
   c. A time series graph clearly shows that there is a distinct trend of declining sales of CDs.

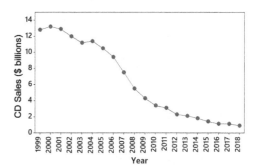

6. a. Key question: Is eyewitness memory of police better (or the same as) with a non-stressful interrogation than with a stressful interrogation?
   b. Use the methods for inferences from two independent means (Section 9-2).

c. It appears that eyewitness memory of police is better with a non-stressful interrogation than with a stressful interrogation. $H_0: \mu_1 = \mu_2$ and $H_1: \mu_1 > \mu_2$. Test statistic: $t = 2.843$. P-value $= 0.0029$ (Table: P-value < 0.005). Critical value: $t = 1.665$ (Table: 1.685). 90% CI: $3.27 < \mu_1 - \mu_2 < 12.53$ (Table: $3.22 < \mu_1 - \mu_2 < 12.58$). Reject H_0. There is sufficient evidence to support the claim that eyewitness memory of police is better with a non-stressful interrogation than with a stressful interrogation.

7. a. Key question: How do the different categories compare in terms of the numbers of deaths?

   b. Construct an effective graph such as a Pareto chart so that we can see which causes of death are most significant.

   c. A Pareto chart or bar chart or pie chart shows that pollution is the largest cause of deaths, followed by tobacco use. Deaths from the other causes are relatively much lower.

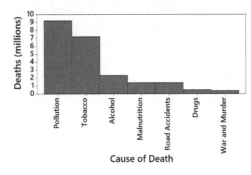

8. a. Key question: Is the mean height of supermodels greater than (or different from) 162 cm, so that supermodels are generally taller than (or have heights different from) adult women in the general population?

   b. Use a hypothesis test or confidence interval for an inference involving a single population mean (as in Section 8-3).

   c. The data support the claim that supermodels are taller than (or have heights different from) the mean of 162 cm for adult women in the general population. $H_0: \mu = 162$ cm. $H_1: \mu > 162$ cm. Test statistic: $t = 33.082$. P-value $= 0.0000$ (Table: < 0.005). Critical value: $t = 1.753$ (assuming a 0.05 significance level). 90% confidence interval: 176.4 cm $< \mu < 178.1$ cm. Reject H_0. (If testing H_1: $\mu \neq 162$ cm, the test statistic and P-value will be the same.) There is sufficient evidence to support the claim that supermodels have heights with a mean that is greater than the mean height of 162 cm for women in the general population. Supermodels appear to be taller than typical women.

9. a. Key question: Are the numbers selected in a way that appears to be random, with roughly the same frequency for each number?

   b. Construct a histogram or dotplot to visualize the frequencies.

   c. The graph shows that the numbers do appear to be drawn with roughly the same frequency. (Chapter 11 will introduce a procedure for testing "goodness-of-fit" with a uniform distribution, and that procedure is much more thorough and objective.)

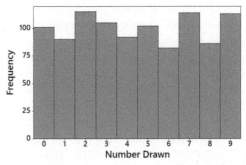

10. a. Key question: Is there a correlation between the numbers of pleasure boats and the numbers of manatee fatalities?

    b. A scatterplot (see Section 2-2) would be helpful in visualizing whether there is a correlation. (The following chapter will introduce much more thorough and objective criteria for analyzing correlations.)

    c. A scatterplot reveals that there does not appear to be a correlation between the numbers of pleasure boats and the numbers of manatee deaths.

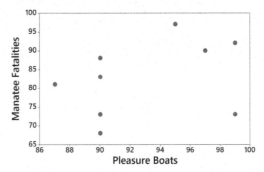

Chapter 10 Answers

Section 10-1

1. a. r is a statistic that represents the value of the linear correlation coefficient computed from the paired sample data, and ρ is a parameter that represents the value of the linear correlation coefficient that would be computed by using all of the paired data in the population of all statistics students.

   b. The value of r is estimated to be 0, because it is likely that there is no correlation between heights of statistics students and their scores on the first statistics test.

   c. The value of r does not change if the heights are converted from centimeters to inches.

3. No. A correlation between two variables indicates that they are somehow associated, but that association does not necessarily imply that one of the variables has a direct effect on the other variable. Correlation does not imply causality.

5. Yes. $r = 0.963$. P-value $= 0.000$. Critical values: ± 0.268 (Table: ± 0.279 approximately). There is sufficient evidence to support the claim that there is a linear correlation between the weights of bears and their chest sizes. It is easier to measure the chest size of a bear than the weight, which would require lifting the bear onto a scale. It does appear that chest size could be used to predict weight.

7. Yes. $r = 0.319$ and with $n = 56$, the critical values are ± 0.263 (Table: ± 0.254 approximately). There is sufficient evidence to support the claim that there is a linear correlation between the numbers of words spoken in a day by men and women in couple relationships.

9. a. Answer varies. Because there appears to be an upward pattern, it is reasonable to think that there is a linear correlation.
   b. $r = 0.906$. P-value $= 0.000$ (Table: <0.01). Critical values: $r = \pm 0.632$ (for a 0.05 significance level). There is sufficient evidence to support the claim of a linear correlation.
   c. $r = 0$. P-value $= 1.000$ (Table: >0.05). Critical values: $r = \pm 0.666$ (for a 0.05 significance level). There is not sufficient evidence to support the claim of a linear correlation.
   d. The effect from a single pair of values can be very substantial, and it can change the conclusion.

11. a.
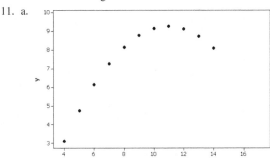

   b. $r = 0.816$. P-value $= 0.002$ (Table: <0.01). Critical values: $r = \pm 0.602$ assuming a 0.05 significance level. There is sufficient evidence to support the claim of a linear correlation between the two variables.
   c. The scatterplot reveals a distinct pattern that is not a straight-line pattern.

13. $r = 0.532$. P-value $= 0.114$ (Table: >0.05). Critical values: $r = \pm 0.632$. There is not sufficient evidence to support the claim that there is a linear correlation between lottery jackpots and numbers of tickets sold. The pair of data in the last column correspond to a point in the scatterplot that is an outlier. The outlier had a significant effect on the results and the conclusion changed from the one reached in Example 4. Also, the added pair of values represent a huge jackpot of 400 million dollars, but the relatively low number of ticket sales is not consistent with known lottery behavior. It appears that the added pair of values is in error.

15. $r = 0.298$. P-value $= 0.473$ (Table: >0.05). Critical values: $r = \pm 0.707$. There is not sufficient evidence to support the claim that there is a linear correlation between the time of the ride and the tip amount. It does not appear that riders base their tips on the time of the ride.

17. $r = 0.986$. P-value $= 0.000$ (Table: <0.01). Critical values: $r = \pm 0.707$. There is sufficient evidence to support the claim that there is a linear correlation between the distance of the ride and the fare.

19. $r = -0.139$. P-value $= 0.667$ (Table: >0.05). Critical values: $r = \pm 0.576$. There is not sufficient evidence to support the claim that there is a significant linear correlation between the ages of Best Actresses and Best Actors. Because Best Actresses and Best Actors typically appeared in different movies, we should not expect that there would be a correlation between their ages at the time that they won the awards.

21. $r = 0.990$. P-value $= 0.000$ (Table: <0.01). Critical values: $r = \pm 0.632$. There is sufficient evidence to support the claim that there is a linear correlation between New York City prices of a slice of pizza and a subway ride.

23. $r = 0.857$. P-value $= 0.007$ (Table: <0.01). Critical values: $r = \pm 0.707$. There is sufficient evidence to support the claim that there is a linear correlation between footprint lengths and heights of males. The given results suggest that police can use a footprint length to estimate the height of a male.

25. $r = 0.174$. P-value $= 0.681$ (Table: >0.05). Critical values: $r = \pm 0.707$. There is not sufficient evidence to support the claim that there is a linear correlation between the numbers of cars sold (thousands) and the numbers of points scored in the Super Bowl. Common sense suggests that it would be unreasonable to expect a correlation between car sales and points scored in the Super Bowl.

27. $r = -0.959$. P-value $= 0.010$. Critical values: $r = \pm 0.878$. There is sufficient evidence to support the claim that there is a linear correlation between weights of lemon imports from Mexico and U.S. car fatality rates. The results do not suggest any cause-effect relationship between the two variables.

29. $r = 0.571$. P-value $= 0.000$ (Table: <0.05). Critical values found from technology: $r = \pm 0.074$. There is sufficient evidence to support the claim that there is a linear correlation between the time of the ride and the tip amount. It does appear that riders base their tips on the time of the ride. While the smaller sample of eight pairs of data listed in Exercise 15 did not provide sufficient evidence to support a claim of a linear correlation, the larger data set of 703 pairs of data does provide sufficient evidence to support that claim.

31. $r = 0.934$. P-value $= 0.000$ (Table: <0.05). Critical values found from technology: $r = \pm 0.074$. There is sufficient evidence to support the claim that there is a linear correlation between the distance of the ride and the fare. The smaller sample of eight pairs of data leads to the same conclusion as the larger data set of 703 pairs of data, and the values of the linear correlation coefficient r are not dramatically different.

33. Answers vary, but the following is typical. Resampling 1000 times, there are 108 results that are at least as extreme as $r = 0.532$ found from the sample data. (The results "at least as extreme" are those with $r = 0.532$ or greater and those that with $r = -0.532$ or lower.) It appears that the likelihood of getting a result at least as extreme as the one obtained is 0.108, so there is not sufficient evidence to support the claim that there is a linear correlation between lottery jackpots and numbers of tickets sold.

35. Answers vary, but the following is typical. Resampling 1000 times, there are 473 results that are at least as extreme as $r = 0.298$ found from the sample data. (The results "at least as extreme" are those with $r = 0.298$ or greater and those that with $r = -0.298$ or lower.) It appears that the likelihood of getting a result at least as extreme as the one obtained is 0.473, so there is not sufficient evidence to support the claim that there is a linear correlation between the time of the ride and the tip amount.

37. With $n = 703$, there are 701 degrees of freedom. From Table A-3 use the closest t value of 1.965 in the given formula to get the critical values of ± 0.074. Using a more accurate value of $t = 1.963354$ from technology leads to the same critical values of ± 0.074.

Section 10-2

1. a. $\hat{y}$ represents the predicted value of highway fuel consumption.
   b. Slope: -0.00749; y-intercept: 58.9
   c. The predictor variable is weight which is represented by x.
   d. 36.4 mi/gal
3. a. A residual is a value of $y - \hat{y}$, which is the difference between an observed value of y and a predicted value of y.
   b. The regression line has the property that the sum of squares of the residuals is the lowest possible sum.
5. With no significant linear correlation, the best predicted value is $\bar{y} = 37.3$ mi/gal.
7. With a significant linear correlation, the best predicted value is 92.0 kg.
9. $\hat{y} = 3.00 + 0.500x$. The data have a pattern that is not a straight line.
11. a. $\hat{y} = 0.264 + 0.906x$
    b. $\hat{y} = 2 + 0x$ (or $\hat{y} = 2$)
    c. The results are very different, indicating that one point can dramatically affect the regression equation.
13. $\hat{y} = 7.97 + 0.0756x$. Best predicted value: $\bar{y} = 25.6$ million tickets. The best predicted value is very different from the actual value of 90 million tickets that were sold.
15. $\hat{y} = 1.06 + 0.0452x$. Best predicted value: $\bar{y} = \$1.68$. The best predicted value is very different from the actual tip of $4.55.
17. $\hat{y} = 5.19 + 2.70x$. Best predicted value: $13.55 (or $13.56). The best predicted value is close to the actual fare of $15.30.
19. $\hat{y} = 50.0 - 0.0886x$. Best predicted value: $\bar{y} = 46.4$ years. The best predicted value isn't close to the actual value of 60 years.
21. $\hat{y} = 0.0329 + 0.969x$. Best predicted value: $3.91.
23. $\hat{y} = 350 + 5.21x$. Best predicted value: 1772 mm. The best predicted height is close to the actual height.
25. $\hat{y} = 0.923 + 0.00665x$. Best predicted value: $\bar{y} = 57$ points. The best predicted value isn't close to the actual value of 37 points.
27. $\hat{y} = 16.5 - 0.00282x$. Best predicted value: 15.1 fatalities per 100,000 population. Common sense suggests that the prediction doesn't make much sense.
29. $\hat{y} = 0.174 + 0.116x$. Best predicted value: $2.49. (Unlike Exercise 15, this larger data set results in a significant linear correlation, so the predicted value is not $\bar{y}$.) The best predicted value isn't very close to the actual tip of $4.55.
31. $\hat{y} = 5.95 + 2.86x$. Best predicted value: $14.80 (or $14.82). The best predicted value is close to the actual fare of $15.30.
33. a. 6.784, 4.802, -0.300, -1.598, -1.248, -2.420, 0.364, 1.670, -7.470
    b. 137.862
    c. Using $\hat{y} = -10.0 + 0.200x$, the sum of squares of the residuals is 535.560, which is larger than 137.862, which is the sum of squares of the residuals for the regression line.

Section 10-3

1. The value of $s_e = 16.27555$ cm is the standard error of estimate, which is a measure of the differences between the observed weights and the weights predicted from the regression equation. It is a measure of the variation of the sample points about the regression line.
3. The coefficient of determination is $r^2 = 0.155$. We know that 15.5% of the variation in weight is explained by the linear correlation between height and weight, and 84.5% of the variation in weight is explained by other factors and/or random variation.
5. $r^2 = 0.089$. 8.9% of the variation in tips is explained by the linear correlation between times and tips, and 91.1% of the variation in tips is explained by other factors and/or random variation.
7. $r^2 = 0.972$. 97.2% of the variation in fares is explained by the linear correlation between distances and fares, and 2.8% of the variation in fares is explained by other factors and/or random variation.
9. $r = -0.788$. Critical values: $r = \pm 0.576$, assuming a 0.05 significance level. There is sufficient evidence to support a claim of a linear correlation between weights of large cars and the highway fuel consumption amounts.
11. 29.0 mi/gal
13. 27.9 mi/gal $< y <$ 37.7 mi/gal
15. 24.2 mi/gal $< y <$ 36.9 mi/gal
17. a. 10,626.59
    b. 68.83577
    c. 38.0°F $< y <$ 60.4°F
19. a. 352.7278
    b. 109.3722
    c. 71.09°F $< y <$ 88.71°F
21. 76.1 million tickets $< \bar{y} <$ 120 million tickets

Section 10-4

1. The response variable is Speed (the mean speed of the winner) and the predictor variables are Distance, the number of Stages, and the number of Finishers.
3. The unadjusted R^2 increases (or remains the same) as more variables are included, but the adjusted R^2 is adjusted for the number of variables and sample size. The unadjusted R^2 incorrectly suggests that the best multiple regression equation is obtained by including all of the available variables, but by taking into account the sample size and number of predictor variables, the adjusted R^2 is much more helpful in weeding out variables that should not be included.
5. Son $= 18.0 + 0.504$ Father$+0.277$ Mother
7. P-value less than 0.0001 is low, but the values of $R^2(0.3649)$ and adjusted $R^2(0.3552)$ are not high. Although the multiple regression equation fits the sample data best, it is not a good fit, so it should not be used for predicting the height of a son based on the height of his father and the height of his mother.
9. The weight of discarded paper, because it has the best combination of small P-value (0.000) and highest adjusted R^2 (0.411).
11. PLAS $= -0.170 + 0.290$ METAL $+ 0.122$ PAPER $+ 0.0777$ GLASS. That equation has a low P-value of 0.000 and its adjusted R^2 value of 0.540 is the largest and it is substantially higher than any of the other values of adjusted R^2.

13. The best regression equation is HWY $= 58.9 - 0.00749$ Weight. The three different possible regression equations all have a P-value of 0.000. Given that the single predictor variable of Weight yields an adjusted R^2 of 0.787 that is only slightly less than the adjusted R^2 of 0.791 obtained by using the two predictor variables of Weight and Displacement, it is better to use the single predictor variable instead of two predictor variables. (The single predictor variable of Displacement has an adjusted R^2 of 0.506.) Because the adjusted R^2 of 0.787 isn't very close to 1, it is likely that predicted values will not be very accurate.

15. The best regression equation is $\hat{y} = 109 - 0.00670x_1$, where x_1 represents volume. It is best because it has the highest adjusted R^2 value of -0.0513 and the lowest P-value of 0.791. The three regression equations all have adjusted values of R^2 that are very close to 0, so none of them are good for predicting IQ. It does not appear that people with larger brains have higher IQ scores.

17. For H_0: $\beta_1 = 0$, the test statistic is $t = 10.814$, the P-value is less than 0.0001, so reject H_0 and conclude that the regression coefficient of $b_1 = 0.769$ should be kept. For H_0: $\beta_2 = 0$, the test statistic is $t = 29.856$, the P-value is less than 0.0001, so reject H_0 and conclude that the regression coefficient of $b_2 = 1.01$ should be kept. It appears that the regression equation should include both independent variables of height and waist circumference.

19. $\hat{y} = 3.06 + 82.4x_1 + 2.91x_2$, where x_1 represents sex and x_2 represents age. Female: 61 lb; male: 144 lb. The sex of the bear does appear to have an effect on its weight. The regression equation indicates that the predicted weight of a male bear is about 82 lb more than the predicted weight of a female bear with other characteristics being the same.

Section 10-5

1. $y = x^2$. The quadratic model describes the relationship, and $R^2 = 1$.

3. 2.7% of the variation in Super Bowl points can be explained by the exponential model that relates the variable of year and the variable of points scored. Because such a small percentage of the variation is explained by the model, the model is not very useful.

5. The quadratic and power models both yield the same result: $d = 0.8t^2$.

7. Exponential: $y = 1000(1.01^x)$

9. Quadratic: $y = 0.000154x^2 + 0.0799x + 6.06$, where x is the year with 2000 coded as 1, and y is the world population in billions.

11. Logarithmic: $y = 3.22 + 0.293 \ln x$

13. Quadratic: $y = 84.0x^2 - 953x + 13,289$. (Result is based on the year 2000 coded as 1.) Using the rounded coefficients, the projected value for the last year is 25,506.0, which isn't too far from the actual value of 26,828.4. Because $R^2 = 0.925$ for the quadratic model, which is high, predicted values are likely to be reasonably accurate, but we should remember that stock market values can be dramatically affected by events that cannot be foreseen by our most creative minds.

15. Power: $y = 7.89(x^{-0.371})$, where x is the depth and y is the magnitude. The predicted magnitude is 4.82, which is far from the actual magnitude of 7.10. Because $R^2 = 0.613$ for the power model, which isn't very high, predicted values are not likely to be very accurate.

17. a. Exponential: $y = 2^{\frac{2}{3}(x-1)}$ [or $y = (0.629961)(1.587401)^x$ for an initial value of 1 that doubles every 1.5 years].

b. Exponential: $y = (1.49724152)(1.419450033)^x$, where 1971 is coded as 1.

c. Moore's law does appear to be working reasonably well. With $R^2 = 0.991$, the model appears to be very good.

Chapter 10: Quick Quiz

1. The points appear to approximate a straight-line pattern that rises from left to right.

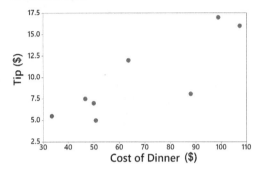

2. Conclude that there is sufficient evidence to support the claim of a linear correlation between amount of the dinner and the amount of the tip.

3. $r = 1$

4. $y = 0 + 0.20x$ (or simply $y = 0.20x$)

5. None of the given values change when the variables are switched.

6. The value of r does not change if all values of one of the variables are multiplied by the same constant.

7. Because r must be between -1 and 1 inclusive, the value of 1.200 is the result of an error in the calculation of r.

8. The best predicted tip is $12.26. It was found by substituting $84.62 for x in the regression equation.

9. The best predicted tip is $9.76. Because there is not sufficient evidence to support the claim of a linear correlation between the cost of dinner and the tip, the best predicted tip is found by computing the mean of the eight sample tips.

10. Because $r^2 = 0.716$, it follows that 0.716 (or 71.6%) of the variation in tips is explained by the linear relationship between amounts of dinner and amounts of tips. It then follows that 0.284 (or 28.4%) of the variation in tips is not explained by the linear relationship between amounts of dinner and amounts of tips.

Chapter 10: Review Exercises

1. $r = 0.445$. P-value: 0.318 (Table: > 0.05). Critical values: ± 0.754. There is not sufficient evidence to support the claim that there is a linear correlation between size and revenue. It does not appear that a casino can increase its revenue by enlarging its size.

2. a. $y = 63.9 + 0.443x$

b. Best predicted value of revenue: $\bar{y} = 134.7$ million dollars. Because the predicted amount of revenue is 134.7 million dollars for *any* casino size, the prediction is not likely to be accurate.

3. a. $r = 0.450$.

b. With P-value $= 0.192$ (Table: > 0.05) and critical values: $r = \pm 0.632$ (assuming a 0.05 significance level), there is not sufficient evidence to support the claim that there is a linear correlation between time and height.

c. Although there is no *linear* correlation between time and height, the scatterplot shows a very distinct pattern revealing that time and height are associated by some function that is not linear. (The scatterplot appears to depict a parabola. The quadratic regression equation is $y = -4.44x^2 + 9.13x + 0.0482$.)

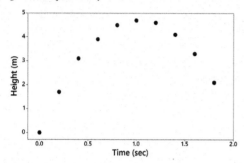

4. a. NICOTINE $= -0.443 + 0.0968$ TAR $- 0.0262$ CO, or
   $\hat{y} = -0.443 + 0.0968x_1 - 0.0262x_2$.

   b. $R^2 = 0.936$; adjusted $R^2 = 0.910$; P-value $= 0.001$.

   c. With high values of R^2 and adjusted R^2 and a small P-value of 0.001, it appears that the regression equation can be used to predict the amount of nicotine given the amounts of tar and carbon monoxide.

   d. The predicted value is 1.39 mg or 1.4 mg rounded, which is close to the actual value of 1.3 mg of nicotine.

Chapter 10: Cumulative Review Exercises

1. a. Is there a difference between the mean IQ score of airline passengers and the mean IQ score of police officers?

   b. Test for a difference between the means of two independent populations using the methods of Section 9-2.

   c. $H_0: \mu_1 = \mu_2$. $H_1: \mu_1 \neq \mu_2$. Test statistic: $t = -1.557$. P-value $= 0.1516$ (Table: P-value > 0.05). Critical values (assuming a 0.05 significance level): $t = \pm 2.239$ (Table: ± 2.262). Fail to reject H_0. There is not sufficient evidence to support the claim that there is a difference between the mean IQ score of airline passengers and the mean IQ of police officers. (This 95% confidence interval could also be used: $-20.0 < \mu_1 - \mu_2 < 3.59$. Because the confidence interval includes 0, there is not sufficient evidence to support the claim that there is a difference between the mean IQ score of airline passengers and the mean IQ of police officers.)

2. a. Was the training course effective in raising the IQ scores? That is, do the "before − after" differences have a mean that is less than 0, showing that the course is effective in raising IQ scores?

   b. Use the methods of Section 9-3 to test the claim that the mean of the "before − after" differences is less than 0, showing that the course is effective with larger "after" scores.

   c. $H_0: \mu_d = 0$. $H_1: \mu_d < 0$. Test statistic: $t = -1.541$. P-value $= 0.0789$ (Table: P-value > 0.05). Critical value (assuming a 0.05 significance level): $t = -1.833$. Fail to reject H_0. There is not sufficient evidence to support the claim that the course is effective with higher "after" scores. (This 90% confidence interval could also be used: $-18.0 < \mu_d < 1.56$). Because the confidence interval includes 0, there is not sufficient evidence to support the claim that the course is effective with higher "after" scores.

3. a. For professional horse jockeys, is there a correlation between weight and number of top three race finishes?

   b. Use the methods of Section 10-1 to test for a linear correlation.

   c. $r = -0.060$. P-value $= 0.869$ (Table: > 0.05). Critical values (assuming a 0.05 significance level): $r = \pm 0.632$. There is not sufficient evidence to support the claim that there is a linear correlation between weight and the number of top three race finishes.

4. a. Because the table lists time series data, a key question is this: What is the trend of the data over time?

   b. Use the methods of Section 2-3 to construct a time series graph that would reveal a trend of the data over time.

   c. A time series graph clearly shows that there is a distinct trend of steadily increasing numbers of digital buyers over time. Businesses should ensure they can market and sell their goods and services online.

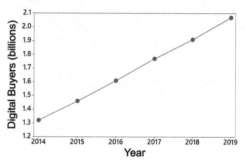

5. a. What is an estimate of the proportion of all adults who have wireless earbuds?

   b. Use the methods of Section 7-1 to construct a confidence interval estimate of the proportion of all adults who use wireless earbuds.

   c. 95% confidence interval estimate of p: $0.280 < p < 0.320$. With 95% confidence, it is estimated that between 28.0% and 32.0% of all adults have wireless earbuds.
   (It would also be reasonable to conduct a hypothesis test, such as a test of the claim that fewer than 50% of adults have wireless earbuds. For that test, the test statistic is $z = -17.95$ and the P-value is 0.0000 so there is sufficient evidence to support the claim that fewer than 50% of adults have wireless earbuds.)

6. a. Is Stephen Curry *significantly tall* in the population of adult males?

   b. Using the methods of Section 3-3, convert Stephen Curry's height to a z score and use the range rule of thumb to determine whether his height is significantly high.

   c. Converting Stephen Curry's height to a z score, we get $z = (x - \mu)/\sigma = (191 - 174.12)/7.10 = 2.38$. Stephen Curry's height is 2.38 standard deviations above the mean, so his height is significantly high.

7. a. Is the mean amount provided by the new device equal to 16 ounces? Is there anything else about the data suggesting that there is a problem with the new device?

   b. Explore the sample data to see if there are any undesirable characteristics. Use the methods of Section 8-3 to test the claim that the mean of the amounts is equal to 16 ounces.

c. H_0: $\mu = 16$ oz. H_1: $\mu \neq 16$ oz. Test statistic: $t = 0.998$. P-value $= 0.3363$ (Table: P-value > 0.20). Critical values (assuming a 0.05 significance level): $t = \pm 2.160$. Fail to reject H_0. There is not sufficient evidence to warrant rejection of the claim that the mean is equal to 16 oz. (This 95% confidence interval could also be used: 15.42 oz $< \mu <$ 17.58 oz. Because the confidence interval includes 16 oz, there is not sufficient evidence to reject the claim that the mean is equal to 16 oz.). Although the mean appears to be OK, exploring the data reveals that the variation appears to be too high. The minimum sample value is 12.6 oz and the maximum is 19.2 oz, and they show that the amount of variation is far too high. Some containers would be dramatically underfilled while others would be overflowing. The filling device must be modified to correct the unacceptably high amount of variation.

8. a. What is an estimate of the proportion of wrong results in the population of all of the drug tests?

b. Use the methods of Section 7-1 to construct a confidence interval estimate of the proportion p of wrong results in the population of all of the drug tests. Decide whether the proportion of wrong results is acceptable.

c. 95% confidence interval estimate: $0.0576 < p < 0.122$. This shows that we have 95% confidence that the percentage of wrong test results is between 5.76% and 12.2%. Because wrong test results could possibly have adverse implications, such as unfair rejection of job applicants, it appears that the proportion of wrong results is unacceptably high.

Chapter 11 Answers

Section 11-1

1. a. Observed values are represented by O and expected values are represented by E.

b. For the leading digit of 2, $O = 62$ and $E = (317)(0.176) = 55.792$.

c. For the leading digit of 2, $(O - E)^2/E = 0.691$.

3. There is sufficient evidence to warrant rejection of the claim that the leading digits have a distribution that fits well with Benford's law.

5. Test statistic: $X^2 = 4.050$. P-value $= 0.908$ (Table: > 0.10). Critical value: $X^2 = 16.919$. There is not sufficient evidence to warrant rejection of the claim that the last digits of the reported heights occur with about the same frequency. There is not sufficient evidence to conclude that the heights were reported instead of being measured.

7. P-value $= 0.516$ (Table: >0.10). Critical value: $X^2 = 16.919$. There is not sufficient evidence to warrant rejection of the claim that the observed outcomes agree with the expected frequencies. The slot machine appears to be functioning as expected.

9. Test statistic: $X^2 = 524.713$. P-value $= 0.0000$ (Table: <0.005). Critical value: $X^2 = 13.277$. There is sufficient evidence to warrant rejection of the claim that the distribution of clinical trial participants fits well with the population distribution. Hispanics have an observed frequency of 60 and an expected frequency of 391.027, so they are very underrepresented. Also, the Asian/Pacific Islander subjects have an observed frequency of 54 and an expected frequency of 163.286, so they are also underrepresented.

11. Test statistic: $X^2 = 11.161$. P-value $= 0.011$ (Table: <0.025). Critical value: $X^2 = 7.815$. There is sufficient evidence to support the claim that the results contradict Mendel's theory.

13. Test statistic: $X^2 = 13.689$. P-value $= 0.134$ (Table: > 0.10). Critical value: $X^2 = 16.919$. There is not sufficient evidence to warrant rejection of the claim that the likelihood of winning is the same for the different post positions. Based on these results, post position should not be considered when betting on the Kentucky Derby.

15. Test statistic: $X^2 = 7.658$. P-value $= 0.054$ (Table: > 0.05). Critical value: $X^2 = 7.815$. There is not sufficient evidence to warrant rejection of the claim that the actual numbers of games fit the distribution indicated by the proportions listed in the given table. It appears that the actual games conform reasonably well with the results expected by theory.

17. Test statistic: $X^2 = 9.500$. P-value $= 0.147$ (Table: >0.10). Critical value: $X^2 = 16.812$. There is not sufficient evidence to support the claim that births do not occur on the seven different days of the week with equal frequency.

19. Test statistic: $X^2 = 5.714$. P-value $= 0.335$ (Table: > 0.10). Critical value: $X^2 = 11.071$. There is not sufficient evidence to warrant rejection of the claim that the color distribution is as claimed.

21. Test statistic: $X^2 = 3650.251$. P-value $= 0.000$ (Table: <0.005). Critical value: $X^2 = 20.090$. There is sufficient evidence to warrant rejection of the claim that the leading digits are from a population with a distribution that conforms to Benford's law. It does appear that the checks are the result of fraud (although the results cannot confirm that fraud is the cause of the discrepancy between the observed results and the expected results).

23. Test statistic: $X^2 = 1.762$. P-value $= 0.988$ (Table: >0.10). Critical value: $X^2 = 15.507$. There is not sufficient evidence to warrant rejection of the claim that the leading digits are from a population with a distribution that conforms to Benford's law. The tax entries do appear to be legitimate.

25. a. 26, 46, 49, 26

b. 0.2023, 0.3171, 0.3046, 0.1761 (Table: 0.2033, 0.3166, 0.3039, 0.1762)

c. 29.7381, 46.6137, 44.7762, 25.8867 (Table: 29.8851, 46.5402, 44.6733, 25.9014)

d. Test statistic: $X^2 = 0.877$ (Using probabilities from table: 0.931). P-value $= 0.831$ (Table: >0.10). Critical value: $X^2 = 11.345$. There is not sufficient evidence to warrant rejection of the claim that heights were randomly selected from a normally distributed population. The test suggests that we cannot rule out the possibility that the data are from a normally distributed population.

Section 11-2

1. $E = 138.906$

3. a. Test statistic: $X^2 = 19.490$. P-value: 0.000. Reject the null hypothesis of independence between whether the dog is correct and whether malaria is present.

b. No. It is possible that the dogs are wrong significantly more than they are correct. However, with the given data, dogs were correct 70.3% of the time when malaria was present, and they were correct 90.3% of the time when malaria was not present, so they do appear to be effective in their identifications.

5. Test statistic: $X^2 = 25.571$. P-value $= 0.000$ (Table: <0.005). Critical value: $X^2 = 3.841$. There is sufficient evidence to warrant rejection of the claim that whether a subject lies is independent of the polygraph test indication. The results suggest that polygraphs are effective in distinguishing between truths and lies, but there are many false positives and false negatives, so they are not highly reliable.

7. Test statistic: $X^2 = 576.224$. P-value $= 0.000$ (Table: <0.005). Critical value: $X^2 = 3.841$. There is sufficient evidence to warrant rejection of the claim of independence between texting while driving and driving when drinking alcohol. Those two risky behaviors appear to be somehow related.

9. Test statistic: $X^2 = 12.162$. P-value $= 0.001$ (Table: <0.005). Critical value: $X^2 = 3.841$. There is sufficient evidence to warrant rejection of the claim that whether students purchased gum or kept the money is independent of whether they were given four quarters or a \$1 bill. It appears that there is a denomination effect.

11. Test statistic: $X^2 = 6.343$. P-value $= 0.012$ (Table: <0.05). Critical value: $X^2 = 3.841$. There is sufficient evidence to warrant rejection of the claim of independence between gender and success in challenging referee calls. However, with success rates of 29.1% for men and 26.7% for women, the difference does not appear to have practical significance.

13. Test statistic: $X^2 = 16.091$. P-value $= 0.001$ (Table: <0.005). Critical value: $X^2 = 11.345$. There is sufficient evidence to warrant rejection of the claim of independence between gender and eye color. However, because the sample data were reported, it is possible that the sample is not representative of the population.

15. Test statistic: $X^2 = 2.925$. P-value $= 0.232$ (Table: >0.10). Critical value: $X^2 = 5.991$. There is not sufficient evidence to warrant rejection of the claim that getting a cold is independent of the treatment group. The results suggest that echinacea is not effective for preventing colds.

17. Test statistic: $X^2 = 20.271$. P-value $= 0.0011$ (Table: <0.005). Critical value: $X^2 = 15.086$. There is sufficient evidence to warrant rejection of the claim that cooperation of the subject is independent of the age category. The age group of 60 and over appears to be particularly uncooperative.

19. Test statistic: $X^2 = 50.446$. P-value $= 0.000$ (Table: <0.005). Critical value: $X^2 = 5.991$. There is sufficient evidence to warrant rejection of the claim of independence between the state and whether a car has front and rear license plates. It does not appear that the license plate laws are followed at the same rates in the three states.

21. Unrounded test statistics: $X^2 = 3.197517514$ and $z = 1.788160371$ so that $X^2 = z^2$. Critical values: $X^2 = 3.841$ and $z = \pm 1.96$ (or ± 1.959963986 from technology), so $X^2 = z^2$.

Chapter 11: Quick Quiz

1. $H_0: p_0 = p_1 = \cdots = p_9$. H_1: At least one of the probabilities is different from the others.
2. $O = 45$ and $E = 50$.
3. Right-tailed.
4. df $= 9$

5. There is not sufficient evidence to warrant rejection of the null hypothesis that the digits are all equally likely. Although we cannot conclude that the sample data support the claim that the digits are equally likely (because we can't support a null hypothesis), it does appear that Statdisk generates the digits so that they are equally likely.

6. H_0: Surviving the sinking is independent of whether the person is a man, woman, boy, or girl.
   H_1: Surviving the sinking and whether the person is a man, woman, boy, or girl are somehow related.
7. Chi-square distribution.
8. Right-tailed.
9. df $= 3$
10. There is sufficient evidence to warrant rejection of the claim that surviving the sinking is independent of whether the person is a man, woman, boy, or girl. Most of the women survived, 45% of the boys survived, and most girls survived, but only about 20% of the men survived, so it appears that the rule was followed quite well.

Chapter 11: Review Exercises

1. Test statistic: $X^2 = 186.332$. P-value $= 0.000$ (Table: <0.005). Critical value: $X^2 = 24.725$. There is sufficient evidence to warrant rejection of the claim that weather-related deaths occur in the different months with the same frequency. The warmer months appear to have disproportionately more weather-related deaths, and that is likely due to the fact that vacations and outdoor activities are much greater during those months.

2. Test statistic: $X^2 = 396.014$. Critical value: $X^2 = 15.507$ (assuming a 0.05 significance level). P-value: 0.000 (Table: <0.005). There is sufficient evidence to warrant rejection of the claim that the observed frequencies fit the distribution from Benford's law. It appears that the data are from matches in which cheating may have occurred.

3. Test statistic: $X^2 = 9.750$. P-value $= 0.002$ (Table: <0.005). Critical value: $X^2 = 6.635$. There is sufficient evidence to warrant rejection of the claim that success is independent of the type of treatment. The results suggest that the surgery treatment is better.

4. Test statistic: $X^2 = 58.393$. Critical value: $X^2 = 7.815$. P-value: 0.000 (Table: <0.005). There is sufficient evidence to warrant rejection of the claim that success is independent of the treatment. Although these results of this test do not tell us which treatment is best, we can see from the table that the success rates of 81.8%, 44.6%, 95.9%, and 77.3% suggest that the best treatment is to use a non-weight-bearing cast for 6 weeks. These results suggest that the increasing use of surgery is a treatment strategy that is not supported by the evidence.

Chapter 11: Cumulative Review Exercises

1. a. Here are two different key questions that are appropriate for the data: (1) Is there a correlation between the scores of the females and the scores of their brothers? (2) For the paired scores, is there a significant difference between the scores of the siblings?
   b. (1) Use the linear correlation coefficient, as in Section 10-1. (2) Use the methods for inferences about differences from matched pairs, as in Section 9-3.

c. (1) Using correlation: $r = -0.481$, P-value $= 0.412$ (Table: >0.05), critical values: $r = \pm 0.878$ (assuming a 0.05 significance level). There is not sufficient evidence to support a claim of a correlation. (2) Test statistic: $t = -0.459$, P-value $= 0.670$ (Table: >0.20), critical values: $t = \pm 2.776$ (assuming a 0.05 significance level). There is not sufficient evidence to support a claim of a difference between the scores of the siblings.

2. a. Are the last digits from a population in which they all occur with the same frequency?

b. Use the goodness-of-fit test, as in Section 11-1.

c. Test statistic: $\chi^2 = 6.500$. P-value $= 0.689$ (Table: >0.10). Critical value: $\chi^2 = 16.919$ (assuming a 0.05 significance level). Fail to reject the null hypothesis that the last digits are from a population in which they all occur with the same frequency.

3. a. Is there a significant difference between the distances run by males and the distances run by females?

b. Use the test for a difference between the means of two independent populations, as in Section 9-2.

c. $H_0: \mu_1 = \mu_2$. $H_1: \mu_1 \neq \mu_2$. Test statistic: $t = -0.536$. P-value $= 0.613$ (Table: P-value >0.20). Critical values (assuming a 0.05 significance level): $t = \pm 2.492$ (Table: ± 2.776). Fail to reject the null hypothesis of no difference. There is not sufficient evidence to reject the claim of no significant difference between the distances run by males and females. (The same conclusion results from a 95% confidence interval: -6.8 miles $< \mu_1 - \mu_2 < 4.4$ miles.)

4. a. Are the variables of workday and shift independent?

b. Use the χ^2 test for a contingency table, as in Section 11-2.

c. Test statistic: $\chi^2 = 4.225$. P-value $= 0.376$ (Table: >0.10). Critical value: $\chi^2 = 9.488$ (assuming a 0.05 significance level). There is not sufficient evidence to warrant rejection of the claim of independence between shift and day of the week.

5. Test statistic: $\chi^2 = 3.409$. P-value $= 0.0648$ (Table: >0.05). Critical value: $\chi^2 = 3.841$. There is not sufficient evidence to warrant rejection of the claim that the form of the 100-yuan gift is independent of whether the money was spent. There is not sufficient evidence to support the claim of a denomination effect. Women in China do not appear to be affected by whether 100 yuan are in the form of a single bill or several smaller bills.

6. a. $128/150 = 0.853$ b. $143/150 = 0.953$

c. 0.727 (not 0.728)

Chapter 12 Answers

Section 12-1

1. a. The chest compression amounts are categorized according to the one characteristic of vehicle size category.

b. The terminology of *analysis of variance* refers to the method used to test for equality of the four population means. That method is based on two different estimates of a common population variance.

3. The test statistic is $F = 3.815$, and the F distribution applies.

5. Test statistic: $F = 0.57$. P-value: 0.638. Fail to reject $H_0: \mu_1 = \mu_2 = \mu_3 = \mu_4$. There is not sufficient evidence to warrant rejection of the claim that the four vehicle size categories have the same mean force on the left femur in crash tests. Size

of the car does not appear to have an effect on the force on the femur of the left leg in crash tests.

7. Test statistic: $F = 28.1666$. P-value < 0.0001. Reject $H_0: \mu_1 = \mu_2 = \mu_3$. There is sufficient evidence to warrant rejection of the claim that the three different types of Chips Ahoy cookies have the same mean number of chocolate chips.

9. Test statistic: $F = 9.4695$. P-value: 0.001. Reject $H_0: \mu_1 = \mu_2 = \mu_3$. There is sufficient evidence to warrant rejection of the claim that pages from books by Clancy, Rowling, and Tolstoy have the same mean Flesch Reading Ease score. It appears that at least one of the authors has a mean Flesch Reading Ease score that is different from the others. With means of 70.73, 80.75, and 66.15, it appears that Rowling is different by having the highest Flesch Reading Ease score, but ANOVA does not justify a conclusion that any particular mean is different from the others.

11. Test statistic: $F = 27.2474$. P-value: 0.000. Reject $H_0: \mu_1 = \mu_2 = \mu_3$. There is sufficient evidence to warrant rejection of the claim that the three different miles have the same mean time. These data suggest that the third mile appears to take longer, and a reasonable explanation is that the third mile has a hill.

13. Test statistic: $F = 0.0558$. P-value: 0.946. Fail to reject $H_0: \mu_1 = \mu_2 = \mu_3$. There is not sufficient evidence to warrant rejection of the claim that the three vehicle size categories (midsize, large, SUV) have the same mean head injury criterion (HIC) measurements in crash tests. For midsize, large, and SUV cars, size category of the car does not appear to have an effect on the HIC measurements.

15. Test statistic: $F = 144.4462$. P-value: 0.000. Reject $H_0: \mu_1 = \mu_2 = \mu_3 = \mu_4$. There is sufficient evidence to warrant rejection of the claim that the four rides have the same mean wait time. At least one of the rides has a mean 10 AM wait time that is different from the others.

17. The Tukey test results show different P-values, but they are not dramatically different. The Tukey results suggest the same conclusions as the Bonferroni test.

Section 12-2

1. The measurements are categorized using *two* different factors of (1) femur side (left, right) and (2) vehicle size (small, midsize, large, SUV).

3. a. An interaction between two factors or variables occurs if the effect of one of the factors changes for different categories of the other factor.

b. If there is an interaction effect, we should not proceed with individual tests for effects from the row factor and column factor. If there is an interaction, we should not consider the effects of one factor without considering the effects of the other factor.

c. The lines are not too far from being parallel except for the mean for the left femur in small cars. That large difference does suggest that there is an interaction effect between femur side and size of vehicle.

5. For interaction, the test statistic is $F = 4.4313$ and the P-value is 0.0103, so there is sufficient evidence to warrant rejection of the null hypothesis of no interaction effect. Because there appears to be an interaction between femur side (left, right) and vehicle size category, we should not proceed with a test for an effect from

the femur side (left/right) and a test for an effect from vehicle size category. It appears that an interaction between the femur side and vehicle size category has an effect on the force measurements. (Remember, these results are based on fabricated data used in one of the cells, so this conclusion does not necessarily apply to real data.)

7. For interaction, the test statistic is $F = 3.6296$ and the P-value is 0.0749, so there is not sufficient evidence to warrant rejection of the null hypothesis of no interaction effect. For the row variable of gender, the test statistic is $F = 5.3519$ and the P-value is 0.0343, so there does appear to be an effect from gender. For the column variable of handedness, the test statistic is $F = 2.2407$ and the P-value is 0.1539, so there does not appear to be an effect from handedness. It appears that the distance between pupils is affected by gender. For distances between pupils, we expect the following: (1) No interaction between genders; (2) No effect from handedness (right, left); (3) There could be differences based on gender. The results are as expected.

9. For interaction, the test statistic is $F = 2.1727$ and the P-value is 0.1599, so there is not sufficient evidence to warrant rejection of the null hypothesis of no interaction effect. For the row variable of gender, the test statistic is $F = 27.8569$ and the P-value is 0.0001, so there does appear to be an effect from gender. For the column variable of handedness, the test statistic is $F = 1.4991$ and the P-value is 0.2385, so there does not appear to be an effect from handedness. It appears that sitting height is affected by gender. For sitting heights, it is reasonable to not expect an interaction between genders and handedness, it is reasonable to not expect that handedness (right, left) would affect sitting heights, and it is reasonable to expect that there could be differences based on gender, so the results are as expected.

11. a. Test statistics and P-values do not change.
    b. Test statistics and P-values do not change.
    c. Test statistics and P-values do not change.
    d. An outlier can dramatically affect and change test statistics and P-values.

Chapter 12: Quick Quiz

1. $H_0: \mu_1 = \mu_2 = \mu_3 = \mu_4$. Because the displayed P-value of 0.000 is small, reject H_0. There is sufficient evidence to warrant rejection of the claim that the four samples have the same mean weight.

2. No. It appears that mean weights of Diet Coke and Diet Pepsi are lower than the mean weights of regular Coke and regular Pepsi, but the method of analysis of variance does not justify a conclusion that any particular means are significantly different from the others.

3. Right-tailed.

4. Test statistic: $F = 503.06$. Larger test statistics result in smaller P-values.

5. The four samples are categorized using only one factor: the type of cola (regular Coke, Diet Coke, regular Pepsi, Diet Pepsi).

6. One-way analysis of variance is used to test a null hypothesis that three or more samples are from populations with equal means.

7. With one-way analysis of variance, data from the different samples are categorized using only one factor, but with two-way analysis of variance, the sample data are categorized into different cells determined by two different factors.

8. Two-way analysis of variance includes a test for an *interaction* between gender and age bracket, but the two separate tests fail to include that test for an interaction.

9. a. Because the effect from an interaction has a P-value of 0.3973, conclude that there is not sufficient evidence to warrant rejection of the null hypothesis of no interaction. Pulse rates do not appear to be affected by an interaction between gender and age bracket.
   b. If there does appear to be an interaction, we should not proceed to test for an effect from the row factor of age bracket and we should not proceed to test for an effect from the column factor of gender. If there is an interaction, we should not consider the effect of either factor without also considering the effect of the other factor.

10. Pulse rates do not appear to be affected by an interaction between gender and age bracket, they do not appear to be affected by age bracket, but they do appear to be affected by gender.

Chapter 12: Review Exercises

1. With test statistic $F = 2.1436$ and P-value 0.096, fail to reject $H_0: \mu_1 = \mu_2 = \mu_3 = \mu_4$. Conclude that there is not sufficient evidence to warrant rejection of the claim that subjects in the four age brackets have the same mean cholesterol level. It appears that for the given age brackets, age does not have a significant effect on cholesterol.

2. Test statistic: $F = 2.3831$. P-value: 0.092. Fail to reject $H_0: \mu_1 = \mu_2 = \mu_3 = \mu_4$. There is not sufficient evidence to warrant rejection of the claim that subjects in the four different age brackets have the same mean cholesterol level. It appears that for those four age brackets, age does not have an effect on LDL cholesterol.

3. For interaction, the test statistic is $F = 0.8476$ and the P-value is 0.6413, so there is not sufficient evidence to warrant rejection of the null hypothesis of no interaction effect. For the row variable of hospital, the test statistic is $F = 0.3549$ and the P-value is 0.7857, so there does not appear to be an effect from hospital. For the column variable of day of the week, the test statistic is $F = 0.8386$ and the P-value is 0.5426, so there does not appear to be an effect from day of the week. It appears that birth weights are not affected by an interaction between hospital and day of the week, they are not affected by the hospital, and they are not affected by the day of the week.

4. For interaction, the test statistic is $F = 1.0605$ and the P-value is 0.3795, so there is not sufficient evidence to warrant rejection of the null hypothesis of no interaction effect. For the row variable of hospital, the test statistic is $F = 0.6423$ and the P-value is 0.5935, so there does not appear to be an effect from hospital. For the column variable of day of weekday/weekend, the test statistic is $F = 0.4097$ and the P-value is 0.5267, so there does not appear to be an effect from whether the day is a weekday or weekend day. It appears that birth weights are not affected by an interaction between hospital and weekday/weekend, they are not affected by the hospital, and they are not affected by whether the day is a weekday or weekend day.

Chapter 12: Cumulative Review Exercises

1. a. 15.9 years, 13.1 years, 22.7 years
   b. 9.9 years, 9.0 years, 18.6 years
   c. 97.4 years^2, 80.3 years^2, 346.1 years^2
   d. Visual inspection of the data shows that among the monarchs, the values of 59 years and 63 years appear to be possible outliers, but they are not outliers according to the criterion of being above the third quartile Q_3 by more than 1.5 times the interquartile range.
   e. Ratio level of measurement

2. Test statistic: $t = 1.136$. P-value = 0.2610 (Table: >0.20). Critical values assuming a 0.05 significance level: $t = \pm 2.006$ (Table: ± 2.069). Fail to reject H_0: $\mu_1 = \mu_2$. There is not sufficient evidence to support the claim that there is a difference between the mean longevity times of presidents and popes.

3. Because the pattern of the points is reasonably close to a straight-line pattern, the longevity times of presidents do appear to be from a population with a normal distribution.

4. 12.7 years $< \mu <$ 19.1 years. We have 95% confidence that the limits of 12.7 years and 19.1 years contain the value of the population mean for longevity times of presidents.

5. a. H_0: $\mu_1 = \mu_2 = \mu_3$
   b. Because the P-value of 0.054 is greater than the significance level of 0.05, fail to reject the null hypothesis of equal means. There is not sufficient evidence to warrant rejection of the claim that the three means are equal. The three populations do not appear to have means that are significantly different.

6. a. 0.5563 (Table: 0.5552)
   b. 0.3434 (Table: 0.3446)
   c. 1/256 or 0.00391
   d. 5.591 g

7. Test statistic: $\chi^2 = 85.945$. P-value: 0.000 (Table: <0.005). Critical value: $\chi^2 = 3.841$. Reject the null hypothesis of independence between physical activity within 7 days after an acute concussion and symptoms 28 days after the concussion. It appears that early physical activity during the week after a concussion does have an effect on symptoms 28 days after a concussion.

8. a. Because the vertical scale begins at 15 instead of 0, the graph is deceptive by exaggerating the differences among the frequencies.
   b. No. A normal distribution is approximately bell-shaped, but the given histogram is far from being bell-shaped. Because the digits are supposed to be equally likely, the histogram should be flat with all bars having approximately the same height.
   c. The frequencies are 19, 21, 22, 21, 18, 23, 16, 16, 22, 22. Test statistic: $\chi^2 = 3.000$. P-value = 0.964 (Table: >0.95). Critical value: $\chi^2 = 16.919$ (assuming a 0.05 significance level). There is not sufficient evidence to warrant rejection of the claim that the digits are selected from a population in which the digits are all equally likely. There does not appear to be a problem with the lottery.

Chapter 13 Answers

Section 13-2

1. a. The only requirement for the matched pairs is that they constitute a simple random sample.
   b. There is no requirement of a normal distribution or any other specific distribution.
   c. The sign test is "distribution-free" in the sense that it does not require a normal distribution or any other specific distribution.

3. H_0: There is no difference between hospital admissions due to traffic accidents that occur on Friday the 6th and those that occur on the following Friday the 13th. H_1: There is a difference between hospital admissions due to traffic accidents that occur on Friday the 6th and those that occur on the following Friday the 13th. The sample data do not contradict H_1 because the numbers of positive signs (1) and negative signs (5) are not exactly the same.

5. The test statistic of $x = 3$ is not less than or equal to the critical value of 1 (from Table A-7). There is not sufficient evidence to warrant rejection of the claim of no difference. Based on the given data, there does not appear to be a significant difference between measured weights and reported weights.

7. The test statistic of $z = -1.47$ results in a P-value of 0.1416, and it does not fall in the critical region bounded by $z = -1.96$ and 1.96. There is not sufficient evidence to warrant rejection of the claim that there is no significant difference between the numbers of words spoken by males and females in couple relationships. Based on the given data, there does not appear to be a significant difference.

9. The test statistic of $z = -1.30$ results in a P-value of 0.1936, and it is not in the critical region bounded by $z = -1.96$ and 1.96. There is not sufficient evidence to warrant rejection of the claim that toast will land with the buttered side down 50% of the time.

11. The test statistic of $z = -2.00$ results in a P-value of 0.0455, and it is in the critical region bounded by $z = -1.96$ and 1.96. There is sufficient evidence to warrant rejection of the claim that the coin toss is fair in the sense that neither team has an advantage by winning it. The coin toss does not appear to be fair.

13. The test statistic of $z = -4.91$ results in a P-value of 0.0000, and it is in the critical region bounded by $z = -2.575$ and 2.575. There is sufficient evidence to warrant rejection of the claim that the median is equal to 98.6°F.

15. The test statistic of $z = -29.67$ results in a P-value of 0.0000, and it is in the critical region bounded by $z = -2.575$ and 2.575. There is sufficient evidence to warrant rejection of the claim that smokers have a median cotinine level equal to 2.84 ng/mL.

17. Second approach: The test statistic of $z = -4.29$ results in a P-value of 0.0000, and it is in the critical region bounded by $z = -1.645$, so the conclusions are the same as in Example 4. Third approach: The test statistic of $z = -2.82$ results in a P-value of 0.0024, and it is in the critical region bounded by $z = -1.645$, so the conclusions are the same as in Example 4. The different approaches can lead to very different results; see the test statistics of -4.21, -4.29, and -2.82. The conclusions are the same in this case, but they could be different in other cases.

Section 13-3

1. a. The only requirements are that the matched pairs be a simple random sample and the population of differences be approximately symmetric.

   b. There is no requirement of a normal distribution or any other specific distribution.

   c. The Wilcoxon signed-ranks test is "distribution-free" in the sense that it does not require a normal distribution or any other specific distribution.

3. The sign test uses only the signs of the differences, but the Wilcoxon signed-ranks test uses ranks that are affected by the magnitudes of the differences.

5. Test statistic: $T = 22$. Critical value: $T = 8$. Fail to reject the null hypothesis that the population of differences has a median of 0. There is not sufficient evidence to warrant rejection of the claim of no difference between measured weights and reported weights of females.

7. Convert $T = 612$ to the test statistic $z = -1.52$. P-value: 0.1285 (Table: 0.1286). Critical values: $z = \pm 1.96$. There is not sufficient evidence to warrant rejection of the claim of no significant difference between the numbers of words spoken by males and females in couple relationships. Based on the given data, there does not appear to be a significant difference.

9. Convert $T = 491.5$ to the test statistic $z = -5.77$. P-value: 0.0000. Critical values: $z = \pm 2.575$. There is sufficient evidence to warrant rejection of the claim that the median is equal to 98.6°F.

11. Convert $T = 19$ to the test statistic $z = -26.01$. P-value: 0.0000. Critical values: $z = \pm 2.575$. There is sufficient evidence to warrant rejection of the claim that smokers have a median cotinine level equal to 2.84 ng/mL.

13. a. 0 and 1275
    b. 637.5
    c. 1110
    d. $\dfrac{n(n + 1)}{2} - k$

Section 13-4

1. Yes. The two samples are independent. (The heights from ANSUR I and ANSUR II are not matched in any way.) Each sample has more than 10 values.

3. H_0: The sample of heights from ANSUR I and the sample of heights from ANSUR II are from populations with the same median.

   H_1: The sample of heights from ANSUR I and the sample of heights from ANSUR II are from populations with different medians.

   H_1: The ANSUR I sample is from a population with a lower median than the median of the second population.

   H_1: The ANSUR I sample is from a population with a higher median than the median of the second population.

5. $R_1 = 172$, $R_2 = 206$, $\mu_R = 168$, $\sigma_R = 20.4939$, test statistic: $z = 0.20$. P-value: 0.845. Critical values: $z = \pm 1.96$. Fail to reject the null hypothesis that the populations have the same median. There is not sufficient evidence to warrant rejection of the claim that the sample of female heights from ANSUR I and the sample of female heights from ANSUR II are from populations with the same median.

7. $R_1 = 253.5$, $R_2 = 124.5$, $\mu_R = 182$, $\sigma_R = 20.607$, test statistic: $z = 3.47$. P-value: 0.0005. Critical values: $z = \pm 1.96$. Reject the null hypothesis that the populations have the same median. There is sufficient evidence to reject the claim that for those treated with 20 mg of Lipitor and those treated with 80 mg of Lipitor, changes in LDL cholesterol have the same median. It appears that the dosage amount does have an effect on the change in LDL cholesterol.

9. $R_1 = 7236.5$, $R_2 = 7298.5$, $\mu_R = 7267.5$, $\sigma_R = 320.868$, test statistic: $z = -0.10$. P-value: 0.923. Critical values: $z = \pm 2.575$. Fail to reject the null hypothesis that the populations have the same median. There is not sufficient evidence to warrant rejection of the claim that cars in two lines have a median waiting time equal to that of cars in a single line.

11. $R_1 = 501$, $R_2 = 445$, $\mu_R = 484$, $\sigma_R = 41.15823$, test statistic: $z = 0.41$. P-value: 0.3409. Critical value: $z = 1.645$. Fail to reject the null hypothesis that the populations have the same median. There is not sufficient evidence to support the claim that subjects with medium lead levels have a higher median of the full IQ scores than subjects with high lead levels. Based on these data, it does not appear that lead level affects full IQ scores.

13. Using $n_1 = 12$ and $n_2 = 15$, we get $U = 131$ and $z = 2.00$. The test statistic from the Mann-Whitney U test is the same test statistic from the Wilcoxon rank-sum test but with opposite sign.

Section 13-5

1. $R_1 = 103.5$, $R_2 = 48.5$, $R_3 = 90$, $R_4 = 83$

3. $n_1 = 7$, $n_2 = 5$, $n_3 = 6$, $n_4 = 7$, and $N = 25$

5. Test statistic: $H = 2.029$. Critical value: $\chi^2 = 7.815$. (Tech: P-value = 0.566.) Fail to reject the null hypothesis of equal medians. There is not sufficient evidence to warrant rejection of the claim that small, midsize, large, and SUV vehicles have the same median HIC measurement in car crash tests.

7. Test statistic: $H = 16.949$. Critical value: $\chi^2 = 9.210$ (Tech: P-value = 0.0002.) Reject the null hypothesis of equal medians. There is sufficient evidence to warrant rejection of the claim that pages from books by those three authors have the same median Flesch Reading Ease score. At least one of the books has a median different from the others.

9. Test statistic: $H = 2.745$. Critical value: $\chi^2 = 11.071$. (Tech: P-value = 0.739.) Fail to reject the null hypothesis of equal medians. There is not sufficient evidence to warrant rejection of the claim that the six different colors of M&M candies have the same median weight. It does not seem feasible that the color would have much of an effect on the weight, so the result is as expected.

11. Test statistic: $H = 2.5999$. Critical value: $\chi^2 = 7.815$. (Tech: P-value = 0.458.) Fail to reject the null hypothesis of equal medians. It appears that the four hospitals have birth weights with the same median.

13. The values of t are 2, 2, 2, 2, and 4, so the values of T are 6, 6, 6, 6, and 60 and $\Sigma T = 84$. Using $\Sigma T = 84$ and $N = 19$, the corrected value of H is 0.703, which is not substantially different from the uncorrected value of 0.694. In this case, the large numbers of ties do not appear to have a dramatic effect on the test statistic H.

Section 13-6

1.

Jackpot	9	1	8	6	5	4	3	2	7
Tickets	9	1.5	8	7	5	3.5	3.5	1.5	6

3. r represents the linear correlation coefficient computed from sample paired data; ρ represents the parameter of the linear correlation coefficient computed from a population of paired data; r_s denotes the rank correlation coefficient computed from sample paired data; ρ_s represents the rank correlation coefficient computed from a population of paired data. The subscript s is used so that the rank correlation coefficient can be distinguished from the linear correlation coefficient r. The subscript does not represent the standard deviation s. It is used in recognition of Charles Spearman, who introduced the rank correlation method.

5. $r_s = -1$. Critical values are -0.786 and 0.786. Reject the null hypothesis of $\rho_s = 0$ (no correlation). There is sufficient evidence to support a claim of a correlation between altitude and temperature.

7. $r_s = -0.644$. Critical values: -0.648 and 0.648. Fail to reject the null hypothesis of $\rho_s = 0$. There is not sufficient evidence to support the claim of a correlation between the quality ranks and the costs. It does not appear that more expensive brands have better quality.

9. $r_s = 1$. Critical values: -0.886, 0.886. Reject the null hypothesis of $\rho_s = 0$. There is sufficient evidence to conclude that there is a correlation between overhead widths of seals from photographs and the weights of the seals.

11. $r_s = -0.434$. Critical values: -0.700 and 0.700. Fail to reject the null hypothesis of $\rho_s = 0$. There is not sufficient evidence to support the claim of a correlation between heights of winning presidential candidates and heights of their main opponents. Hopefully, we do not elect our presidents based on heights or any other physical appearance.

13. $r_s = 0.429$. Critical values: -0.074 and 0.074. Reject the null hypothesis of $\rho_s = 0$. There is sufficient evidence to support the claim of a correlation between distance of the ride and the amount of the tip. It does appear that riders base their tips on the distance of the ride.

15. $r_s = 0.024$. Critical values: -0.207 and 0.207. Fail to reject the null hypothesis of $\rho_s = 0$. There is not sufficient evidence to support the claim of a correlation between ages of Best Actresses and Best Actors at the times they won Oscars. There does not appear to be a correlation between ages of Best Actresses and Best Actors.

17. With $n = 91$, the number of degrees of freedom is 89. Use $t = 1.987$ to get critical values of -0.206 and 0.206, which are very close to the critical values of -0.207 and 0.207 found by using Formula 13-1 on page 678.

Section 13-7

1. No. The runs test can be used to determine whether the sequence of political parties is not random, but the runs test does not show whether the proportion of Republicans is significantly greater than the proportion of Democrats.

3. The critical values are 8 and 19. Because $G = 17$ is not less than or equal to 8 nor is $G = 17$ greater than or equal to 19, fail to reject randomness. There is not sufficient evidence to conclude that the sequence of political parties is not random. The sequence appears to be random.

5. The median is 161.0. $n_1 = 15$, $n_2 = 15$, $G = 16$. From Table A-10, the critical values are 10 and 22. There is not sufficient evidence to reject randomness. There does not appear to be a trend of increasing or decreasing values.

7. $n_1 = 20$, $n_2 = 10$, $G = 16$, critical values: 9, 20. Fail to reject randomness. There is not sufficient evidence to reject the claim that the dates before and after July 1 are randomly selected.

9. $n_1 = 27$, $n_2 = 26$, $G = 22$, $\mu_G = 27.49057$, $\sigma_G = 3.603576$. Test statistic: $z = -1.52$. P-value: 0.1276. Critical values: $z = \pm 1.96$. Fail to reject randomness. There is not sufficient evidence to reject randomness. The runs test does not test for disproportionately more occurrences of one of the two categories, so the runs test does not suggest that either conference is superior.

11. The median is 3291.0. $n_1 = 27$, $n_2 = 27$, $G = 2$, $\mu_G = 28$, $\sigma_G = 3.639407$. Test statistic: $z = -7.14$. Tech: P-value = 0.0000. Critical values: $z = \pm 1.96$. There is sufficient evidence to reject randomness. All of the values below the median occur at the beginning and all of the values above the median occur at the end, so there appears to be an upward trend, and the stock market appears to be a profitable investment for the long term.

13. b. The 84 sequences yield these results: 2 sequences have 2 runs, 7 sequences have 3 runs, 20 sequences have 4 runs, 25 sequences have 5 runs, 20 sequences have 6 runs, and 10 sequences have 7 runs.

    c. With $P(2 \text{ runs}) = 2/84$, $P(3 \text{ runs}) = 7/84$, $P(4 \text{ runs}) = 20/84$, $P(5 \text{ runs}) = 25/84$, $P(6 \text{ runs}) = 20/84$, and $P(7 \text{ runs}) = 10/84$, each of the G values of 3, 4, 5, 6, 7 can easily occur by chance, whereas $G = 2$ is unlikely because $P(2 \text{ runs})$ is less than 0.025. The lower critical value of G is therefore 2, and there is no upper critical value that can be equaled or exceeded.

    d. Critical value of $G = 2$ agrees with Table A-10. The table lists 8 as the upper critical value, but it is impossible to get 8 runs using the given elements.

Chapter 13: Quick Quiz

1. 3, 8.5, 8.5, 3, 6, 1, 5, 10, 7, 3

2. The efficiency rating of 0.91 indicates that with all other factors being the same, rank correlation requires 100 pairs of sample observations to achieve the same results as 91 pairs of observations with the parametric test for linear correlation, assuming that the stricter requirements for using linear correlation are met.

3. a. Distribution-free test

   b. The term "distribution-free test" suggests correctly that the test does not require that a population must have a particular distribution, such as a normal distribution. The term "nonparametric test" incorrectly suggests that the test is not based on a parameter, but some nonparametric tests are based on the median, which is a parameter; the term "distribution-free test" is better because it does not make that incorrect suggestion.

4. $r_s = 1$. There is sufficient evidence to conclude that there is a correlation between the time of travel and the distance traveled.

5. Rank correlation can be used in a wider variety of circumstances than linear correlation. Rank correlation does not require a normal distribution for any population. Rank correlation can be used to detect some (not all) relationships that are not linear.

6. The sign test can be used to test claims involving matched pairs of sample data, it can be used to test claims involving nominal data with two categories, and it can be used to test claims about the median of a single population.

7. Because there are only two runs, all of the values below the mean occur at the beginning and all of the values above the mean occur at the end, or vice versa. This indicates the presence of an upward (or downward) trend.

8. Because the sign test uses only *signs* of differences while the Wilcoxon signed-ranks test uses *ranks* of the differences, the Wilcoxon signed-ranks test uses more information about the data and tends to yield conclusions that better reflect the true nature of the data.

9. The Wilcoxon signed-ranks test is used to test a claim that a population of matched pairs has the property that they have differences with a median equal to zero or to test a claim that a single population of individual values has a median equal to some claimed value, whereas the Wilcoxon rank-sum test is used to test the null hypothesis that two independent samples are from populations having equal medians.

10. One-way analysis of variance can be used instead of the Kruskal-Wallis test. Like many other nonparametric tests, the Kruskal-Wallis test has no requirement that the populations have a normal distribution or any other particular distribution.

Chapter 13: Review Exercises

1. The test statistic of $x = 0$ is less than or equal to the critical value of 0 (from Table A-7). There is sufficient evidence to warrant rejection of the claim that for the population of freshman male college students, there is not a significant difference between the weights in September and the weights in the following April. Based on the given data, there does appear to be a significant difference. The test does not address the specific weight gain of 15 lb.

2. $T = 0$. The critical value is $T = 2$. There is sufficient evidence to warrant rejection of the claim that the median of the differences is equal to 0. There does appear to be a difference. The test does not address the specific weight gain of 15 lb.

3. $r_s = 0.983$. Critical values: -0.700 and 0.700. Reject the null hypothesis of $\rho_s = 0$. There is sufficient evidence to support the claim of a correlation between the September weights and the April weights. The presence of a correlation tells us nothing about the belief that college students gain 15 lb (or 6.8 kg) during their freshman year.

4. Test statistic: $H = 0.465$. Critical value: $X^2 = 5.991$ (Tech: P-value $= 0.792$.) Fail to reject the null hypothesis of equal medians. There is not sufficient evidence to warrant rejection of the claim that the lengths of stay at the three hospitals have the same median.

5. Test statistic: $z = -1.59$. P-value $= 0.1113$. The P-value is not small, so fail to reject the null hypothesis of $p = 0.5$. There is not sufficient evidence to warrant rejection of the claim that in each World Series, the American League team has a 0.5 probability of winning.

6. The test statistic of $x = 3$ is not less than or equal to the critical value of 1 (from Table A-7). There is not sufficient evidence to warrant rejection of the claim that the sample is from a population with a median equal to 15 minutes.

7. Test statistic $T = 15.5$ is not less than or equal to the critical value of 8. There is not sufficient evidence to warrant rejection of the claim that the sample is from a population with a median equal to 15 minutes.

8. $n_1 = 14$, $n_2 = 16$, $G = 17$, critical values: 10, 22. Fail to reject randomness. There is not sufficient evidence to warrant rejection of the claim that odd and even digits occur in random order. The lottery appears to be working as it should.

9. $R_1 = 204.5$, $R_2 = 230.5$, $\mu_R = 255$, $\sigma_R = 22.58318$, test statistic: $z = -2.24$. Tech: P-value: 0.025. Critical values: $z = \pm1.96$. Reject the null hypothesis that the populations have the same median. There is sufficient evidence to warrant rejection of the claim that the recent eruptions and past eruptions have the same median time interval between eruptions. The conclusion does change with a 0.01 significance level.

10. $r_s = 0.714$. Critical values: ±0.738. Fail to reject the null hypothesis of $\rho_s = 0$. There is not sufficient evidence to support the claim that there is a correlation between the student ranks and the magazine ranks. When ranking colleges, students and the magazine do not appear to agree.

Chapter 13: Cumulative Review Exercises

1. $\bar{x} = 4.5574$ g, median $= 4.5185$ g, range $= 0.3860$ g, $s = 0.1192$ g, $s^2 = 0.0142$ g^2

2. The normal quantile plot shows that the points approximate a straight-line pattern, so the weights do appear to be from a population having a normal distribution.

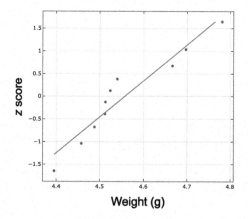

3. H_0: $\mu = 4.5333$ g. H_1: $\mu \neq 4.5333$ g. Test statistic: $t = 0.640$. P-value $= 0.5384$ (Table: P-value > 0.20). Critical values: $t = \pm2.262$. Fail to reject H_0. There is not sufficient evidence to warrant rejection of the claim that the sample is from a population with mean equal to 4.533 g. The claim of 340 g appears to be valid.

4. The test statistic of $x = 4$ is not less than or equal to the critical value of 1 (from Table A-7). There is not sufficient evidence to warrant rejection of the claim that the sample of weights is from a population with a median of 4.5333 g.

5. Test statistic: $T = 27$. Critical value: $T = 8$. Fail to reject the null hypothesis that the population has a median of 4.5333 g.

6. 4.4722 g $< \mu <$ 4.6426 g. Because the confidence interval contains the claimed mean of 4.5333 g, there is not sufficient evidence to warrant rejection of the claim that the population mean is equal to 4.5333 g.

7. Answers vary, but here is a typical answer:
   4.4924 g $< \mu <$ 4.6293 g. Because the confidence interval contains the claimed mean of 4.5333 g, there is not sufficient evidence to warrant rejection of the claim that the population mean is equal to 4.5333 g.

8. The sample mean is 55.15 years. $n_1 = 22$, $n_2 = 17$, and the number of runs is $G = 17$. $\mu_G = 20.17949$, $\sigma_G = 3.029127$. Test statistic: $z = -1.05$. Tech: P-value $= 0.2939$. Critical values: $z = \pm 1.96$. Fail to reject the null hypothesis of randomness. There is not sufficient evidence to warrant rejection of the claim that the sequence of ages is random relative to values above and below the mean. The results do not suggest that there is an upward trend or a downward trend.

9. 2401

10. There must be an error, because the rates of 13.7% and 10.6% are not possible with samples of size 100.

Chapter 14 Answers

Section 14-1

1. a. A run chart is a sequential plot of *individual* data values over time. It is used to monitor process data for any patterns of changes over time.
   b. An R chart is a plot of sample ranges. It is used to monitor the *variation* in a process.
   c. An $\bar{x}$ chart is a plot of sample means. It is used to monitor the *center* in a process.

3. A process is statistically stable (or within statistical control) if it has only natural variation, with no patterns, cycles, or significantly low or significantly high points.

5. $\bar{\bar{x}} = 267.11$ lb, $\bar{R} = 54.96$ lb. For R chart: LCL $= 4.18$ lb and UCL $= 105.74$ lb. For $\bar{x}$ chart: LCL $= 244.08$ lb and UCL $= 290.14$ lb.

7. The R chart does not meet any of the three out-of-control criteria, so the variation of the process appears to be within statistical control.

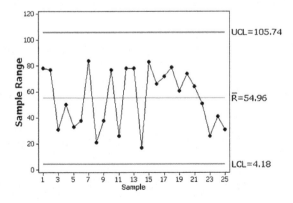

9. $\bar{\bar{x}} = 5.6955$ g, $\bar{R} = 0.2054$ g. For R chart: LCL $= 0.0000$ g and UCL $= 0.4342$ g. For $\bar{x}$ chart: LCL $= 5.5770$ g and UCL $= 5.8140$ g.

11. There are points lying beyond the upper control limit, so the process mean appears to be out of statistical control.

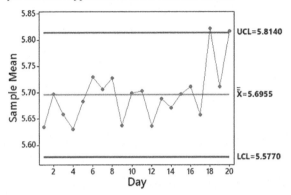

13. Except for a different vertical scale, the s chart is nearly identical to the R chart shown in Example 3.

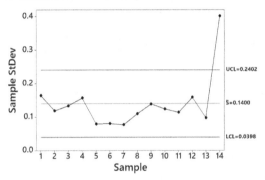

Section 14-2

1. No, the process appears to be out of statistical control. There is a downward trend and there are at least eight consecutive points all lying above the centerline. Because the proportions of defects are decreasing, the manufacturing process is not deteriorating; it is improving.

3. Because the value of -0.00325 is negative and the actual proportion of defects cannot be less than 0, we should replace that value with 0.

5. The process appears to be within statistical control. (Considering a shift up, note that the first and last points are about the same.)

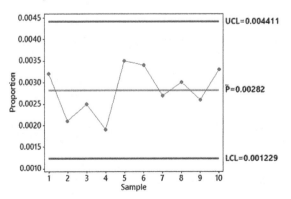

7. The process appears to be out of statistical control because of a downward trend, but the number of defects appears to be decreasing, so the process is improving. Causes for the declining number of defects should be identified so that they can be continued.

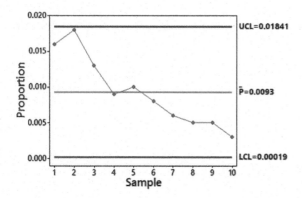

9. The process is out of statistical control because there are points lying beyond the upper control limit and there are points lying beyond the lower control limit. The graph shows a "sawtooth" pattern because presidential elections held every four years tend to attract many more voters than the national elections that do not include a presidential election.

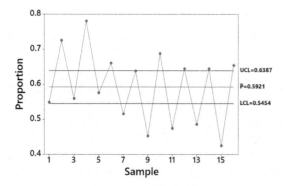

11. Based on the control chart for p it appears that the process is within statistical control. However, the numbers of defects in batches of 100 are significantly high. Although the process is within statistical control, immediate corrective action should be taken to reduce the large numbers of defects.

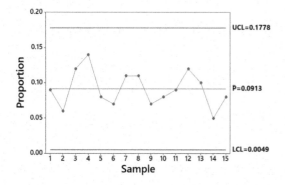

13. Except for a different vertical scale, the basic control chart is identical to the one given for Example 1.

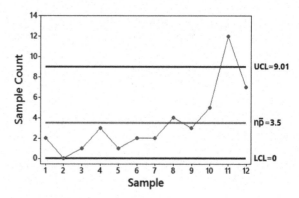

Chapter 14: Quick Quiz

1. Process data are data arranged according to some time sequence. They are measurements of a characteristic of goods or services that result from some combination of equipment, people, materials, methods, and conditions.

2. Random variation is due to chance, but assignable variation results from causes that can be identified, such as defective machinery or untrained employees.

3. There is a pattern, trend, or cycle that is obviously not random. There is a point lying outside the region between the upper and lower control limits. There are at least eight consecutive points all above or all below the centerline.

4. An R chart uses ranges to monitor variation, but an $\bar{x}$ chart uses sample means to monitor the center (mean) of a process.

5. No. The R chart has at least eight consecutive points all lying below the centerline, there are at least eight consecutive points all lying above the centerline, there are points lying beyond the upper and lower control limits, and there is a pattern showing that the ranges have jumped in value for the more recent samples. What a mess!

6. $\bar{R} = 67.0$ ft. In general, a value of $\bar{R}$ is found by first finding the range for the values within each individual subgroup; the mean of those ranges is the value of $\bar{R}$.

7. No. The $\bar{x}$ chart has a point lying beyond the upper control limit, and there are at least eight consecutive points lying below the centerline.

8. $\bar{\bar{x}} = -2.24$ ft. In general, a value of $\bar{\bar{x}}$ is found by first finding the mean of the values within each individual subgroup; the mean of those subgroup means is the value of $\bar{\bar{x}}$.

9. No. The control charts can be used to determine whether the mean and variation are within statistical control, but they do not reveal anything about specifications or requirements.

10. Because there is a downward trend, the process is out of statistical control, but the rate of defects is decreasing, so we should investigate and identify the cause of that trend so that it can be continued.

Chapter 14: Review Exercises

1. $\bar{\bar{x}} = 3157$ kWh, $\bar{R} = 1729$ kWh. R chart: LCL $= 0$ kWh, UCL $= 3465$ kWh. $\bar{x}$ chart: LCL $= 2322$ kWh, UCL $= 3992$ kWh.

2. The process variation is within statistical control.

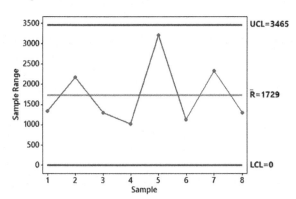

3. There appears to be a shift up in the mean values, so the process mean is out of statistical control.

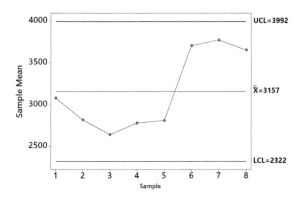

4. There appears to be a slight upward trend. There is 1 point that appears to be exceptionally low. (The author's power company made an error in recording and reporting the energy consumption for that time period.) The process is not within statistical control.

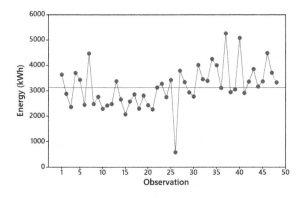

5. The process appears to be within statistical control. However, using the manager's definition of a defect, the rate of defects is far too high, so corrective action should be taken to lower the service time.

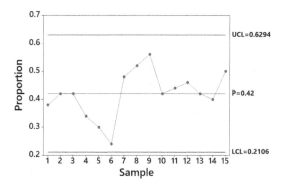

Chapter 14: Cumulative Review Exercises

1. a. 0.08   b. 0.17
   c. 0.0166   d. 0.729
   e. First try to get the case dismissed, then try to arrange for a plea deal. Given the very high conviction rate from trials, a trial should be avoided.

2. $0.440 < p < 0.501$. Because the confidence interval includes 0.5, we cannot conclude that fewer than half of all adults say that nuclear plants are safe.

3. 47% of 1038 is 488, so 488 of those surveyed said that nuclear plants are safe. H_0: $p = 0.5$. H_1: $p < 0.5$. Test statistic: $z = -1.92$. P-value $= 0.0272$ (Table: 0.0274). Critical value: $z = -1.645$. Reject H_0. There is sufficient evidence to support the claim that fewer than half of all Americans say that nuclear plants are safe. This conclusion does contradict the conclusion from the preceding exercise. Because this hypothesis test is a left-tailed test with a 0.05 level of significance, it is equivalent to a confidence interval with a 90% level of confidence, but the preceding exercise used a 95% level of confidence.

4. Yes. The vertical scale does not begin with 0, so the difference between 47% and 49% is visually exaggerated to give a false impression.

5. $r = -0.419$. P-value $= 0.228$ (Table: >0.05). Critical values: $r = \pm 0.632$. There is not sufficient evidence to support the claim that there is a linear correlation between temperature and carbon dioxide. Even if there had been a linear correlation, that would not be basis for concluding that carbon dioxide *causes* a rise in temperatures.

6. $\hat{y} = 16.5 - 0.00412x$. The best predicted value of the temperature in the year with a CO_2 level of 420 is $\bar{y} = 14.878°C$. Because that predicted value is the same for any CO_2 level, it is not likely to be accurate.

7. a. 99.89% (Table: 99.88%)
   b. 0.1587

8. There is a pattern of an upward trend, so the process is out of statistical control.

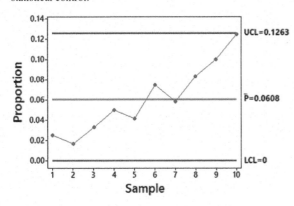

9. $\bar{x} = 7.3$, median $= 6.5$, $s = 4.2$. These statistics do not convey information about the changing pattern of the data over time.

10. H_0: $\mu_1 = \mu_2$. H_1: $\mu_1 > \mu_2$. Test statistic: $t = 2.879$. P-value $= 0.0026$ (Table: <0.005). Critical value: $t = 2.376$ (Table: 2.426). Reject H_0. There is sufficient evidence to support the claim that the mean number of details recalled is lower for the stress group. It appears that "stress decreases the amount recalled," but we should not conclude that stress is the cause of the decrease.

Chapter 15 Answers

Holistic Exercises

1. Test statistic from parametric t test (Section 9-3): $t = -8.484$, critical values are $t = \pm1.996$ (Table: ±2.000), P-value $= 0.000$ and 95% confidence interval is $-1.05°F < \mu_d < -0.65°F$. Nonparametric sign test: Test statistic is $z = -5.86$, critical values are ±1.96, P-value $= 0.000$. Nonparametric Wilcoxon signed-ranks test: Test statistic is $z = -5.98$, critical values are ±1.96, P-value $= 0.000$. Randomization test with 1000 resamplings yields no results at least as extreme as $\bar{d} = -0.85072°F$. Bootstrap 95% confidence interval: $-1.04°F < \mu_d < -0.66°F$ (which can vary). All of the results suggest rejection of H_0: $\mu_d = 0°F$. There appears to be a significant difference between the 8 AM and 12 AM second-day temperatures. It appears that there is generally a significant difference between body temperatures measured at 8 AM and at 12 AM.

3. $r = 0.206$ and critical values are ±0.237 which suggests no correlation. $r_s = 0.252$ and critical values are ±0.238 which suggests that there is a correlation. These results conflict, but a scatterplot shows no clear pattern, so conclude that there is not a correlation.

5. Using 98.20°F we get $P_{99} = 99.64°F$. Using 98.6°F we get $P_{99} = 100.04°F$. The difference is 0.40°F, which is not insignificant, but it probably does not make too much of a difference in practice.

7. Test statistic from parametric t test (Section 8-2): $t = -7.102$, critical values are $t = \pm1.986$ (Table: ±1.987), P-value $= 0.000$ and 95% confidence interval is $97.99°F < \mu < 98.26°F$. Nonparametric sign test: Test statistic is $z = -4.91$, critical values are ±1.96, P-value $= 0.000$. Nonparametric Wilcoxon signed-ranks test: Test statistic is $z = -5.77$, critical values are ±1.96, P-value $= 0.000$. Results can vary, but a randomization test with 1000 resamplings yields no results at least as extreme as 98.12366°F. Bootstrap 95% confidence interval: $97.99°F < \mu_d < 97.25°F$ (which can vary). All of the results suggest rejection of H_0: $\mu = 98.6°F$. It appears that the mean body temperature at 12 AM is different from 98.6°F.

9. Typical results are shown in this chapter in the discussion of simulations. It would be very rare to get a simulated sample with a mean as extreme as 98.2°F, and this shows that the assumption of a mean equal to 98.6°F is probably an incorrect assumption. It appears that the mean body temperature is not 98.6°F.

CREDITS

<table>
<tr><td>Cover Image:</td><td>Bim/Getty Images</td></tr>
</table>

Chapter 1: Image Credits

Shutterstock: GongTo/Shutterstock 1; **Shutterstock:** Gary Blakeley/Shutterstock 5; **Shutterstock:** USBFCO/Shutterstock 6; **Shutterstock:** Wavebreakmedia/Shutterstock 7; **Shutterstock:** Suppakij1017/Shutterstock 15; **Shutterstock:** Khamidulin Sergey/Shutterstock 15; **Shutterstock:** Ollyy/Shutterstock 17; **Alamy Stock Photo:** Allstar Picture Library/Alamy Stock Photo 19; **Shutterstock:** 18percentgrey/Shutterstock 20; **Shutterstock:** Lucky Business/Shutterstock 21; **Getty Images:** Andersen Ross/Stockbyte/Getty Images 27; **Shutterstock:** Triff/Shutterstock 22; **Shutterstock:** Pixsooz/Shutterstock 29; **Shutterstock:** Fujji/Shutterstock 31; **Shutterstock:** Dotshock/Shutterstock 32; **Shutterstock:** Shutterstock 1; **Shutterstock:** Stephen VanHorn/Shutterstock 8; **Shutterstock:** Dmitry Naumov/Shutterstock 16; **123RF:** Andriy Popov/123RF 28; **123RF:** Pavlo Vakhrushev/123RF 30; **123RF:** Sam74100/123RF 23; **Shutterstock:** Juan Camilo Bernal/Shutterstock 4; **Shutterstock:** Oleg Golovnev/Shutterstock 29; **123RF:** Mihtiander/123RF 15; **123RF:** Sherry Yates Young/123RF 18

Chapter 1: Text Credits

Society for Human Resource Management: Based on data from The Society for Human Resource Management 4; **American Medical Association:** From "Registering Clinical Trials" by Kay Dickersin and Drummond Rennie in Journal of American Medical Association, Vol 290, No: 4,pp: 516-523. Published by Journal of American Medical Association, © 2003. 7; **American Medical Association:** Based on data from "Comparison of the Atkins, Ornish, Weight Watchers, and Zone Diets for Weight Loss and Heart Disease Reduction," by Dansinger, et al, Journal of the American Medical Association, Volume 93, Number 1 7; **Dell Publishing:** From Lies, Damn Lies, And Statistics: The Manipulation Of Public Opinion In America. Published by Dell Publishing, © 1976. 8; **U.S. Department of Health & Human Services:** Based on data from National Vital Statistics reports 10; **Oxford University Press:** Based on Teresa L. Dillinger et al., 2000, Food of the Gods: Cure for Humanity? A Cultural History of the Medicinal and Ritual Use of Chocolate, Journal of Nutrition, Vol. 130, No. 8. 10; **American Medical Association:** Based on data from "Comparison of the Atkins, Ornish, Weight Watchers, and Zone Diets for Weight Loss and Heart Disease Risk Reduction," by Dansinger et al., Journal of the American Medical Association, Vol. 293, No. 1 10; **National Council of Teachers of Mathematics.:** The Overtime Rule in the National Football League: Fair or Unfair?" by Gorgievski et al, MathAMATYC Educator, Vol. 2, No. 1 11; **International Cement Review Publishers Limited:** Based on data from ICR Research Group 11; **American Chemical Society:** Based on data from "The Trouble with QSAR (or How I Learned to Stop Worrying and Embrace Fallacy)" by Stephen Johnson, Journal of Chemical Information and Modeling, Vol. 48, No. 1 12; **The New York Times Company:** From Looking for a Date? A Site Suggests You Check the Data by Jenna Wortham in New York Times. Published by The New York Times Company, © 2010. 21; **National Center for Health Statistics:** Based on data from the National Center for Health Statistics 24; **Toluna Quicksurveys poll:** Based on a Toluna Quicksurveys poll 24; **Great Lakes Research:** Based on Brian S. Dorr et al., 2010, Management Effects on Breeding and Foraging Numbers and Movements of Double-Crested Comorants in the Les Cheneaux Islands, Lake Huron, Michigan, Journal of Great Lakes Research, Vol. 36, No. 2. 32; **American Medical Association:** Based on data from "Bipolar Permanent Magnets for the Treatment of Chronic Lower Back Pain: A Pilot Study," by Collacott, Zimmerman, White, and Rindone, Journal of the American Medical Association, Vol. 283, No. 10 33; **American Medical Association:** Based on data from "A Randomized Trial Comparing Acupuncture, Simulated Acupuncture, and Usual Care for Chronic Low Back Pain," by Cherkin et al., Archives of Internal Medicine, Vol. 169, No. 9. 34; **Pfizer Inc:** Based on data from Pfizer, Inc. 34; **USA Today:** USA Today" 37; **American Medical Association:** High-Flow Oxygen for Treatment of Cluster Headache" (Journal of the American Medical Association, Vol. 302, No. 22), 37; **Consumer Reports magazine.:** Based on data from Consumer Reports magazine. 38; **Taylor & Francis Group:** "A Selection of Selection Anomalies" by Wainer, Palmer, and Bradlow in Chance, Volume 11, No. 2. 41; **Starch Research:** Roper Starch Worldwide, 1991 39

Chapter 2: Image Credits

Shutterstock: GongTo/Shutterstock 43; **Shutterstock:** Gallofoto/Shutterstock 46; **Shutterstock:** Valua Vitaly/Shutterstock 57; **Getty Images:** Stockbyte/Getty Images 62; **Shutterstock:** Dmitriy Eremenkov/Shutterstock 78; **Texas Instruments Inc:** Courtesy of Texas Instruments. Used by permission of Texas Instrument. 54; **Shutterstock:** Prachaya Roekdeethaweesab/Shutterstock 47; **Shutterstock:** Blend Images/Shutterstock 49; **Shutterstock:** Prachaya Roekdeethaweesab/Shutterstock 64; **Shutterstock:** DeawSS/Shutterstock 71; **Shutterstock:** DeawSS/Shutterstock 71; **Shutterstock:** laymul/Shutterstock 72; **Shutterstock:** laymul/Shutterstock 72; **123RF:** Welcomia/123RF 43; **Shutterstock:** Antoniodiaz/Shutterstock 66; **Shutterstock:** Shutterstock 74; **Shutterstock:** Karyna Che/Shutterstock 63; **Shutterstock:** Ganna Demchenko/Shutterstock 65; **Shutterstock:** Milos Luzanin/Shutterstock 68

Chapter 2: Text Credits

Samsung: Based on data from Samsung 59; **TE Connectivity survey.:** Based on data from TE Connectivity. 71; **The Ladders.:** Based on data from The Ladders. 71; **Magna Global Inc:** Based on data from Magna Global 73; **USA Today:** From USA TODAY: FBI Vastly Understates Police Deaths in Chases by Thomas Frank in USA Today. Published by USA Today, © 2015. 73; **Cable News Network:** Based on data from CNN 80; **Gabriel García Márquez:** Gabriel García Márquez 65

Chapter 3: Image Credits

Shutterstock: GongTo/Shutterstock 86; **Shutterstock:** Wavebreakmedia/Shutterstock 89; **Shutterstock:** Image Point Fr/Shutterstock 91; **StatCrunch:** Courtesy of StatCrunchTM. Used with permission. 97; **Shutterstock:** Kitch Bain/Shutterstock 106; **Shutterstock:** Alfredo Ragazzoni/Shutterstock 107; **Shutterstock:** Ariwasabi/Shutterstock 110;

Shutterstock: VINCENT GIORDANO PHOTO/Shutterstock 123; **Shutterstock:** Poleze/Shutterstock 126; **Texas Instruments Inc:** Courtesy of Texas Instruments. Used by permission of Texas Instrument. 97; **Texas Instruments Inc:** Courtesy of Texas Instruments. Used by permission of Texas Instrument. 97; **Minitab Corporation:** Courtesy of Minitab Corporation. Used by permission of Minitab Corporation. 97; **Texas Instruments Inc:** Courtesy of Texas Instruments. Used by permission of Texas Instrument. 132; **Shutterstock:** Todd Taulman/Shutterstock 108; **Getty Images:** Melvyn Longhurst/The Image Bank Unreleased/Getty Images 86; **Shutterstock:** ZM_Photo/Shutterstock 90; **Shutterstock:** Forestpath/Shutterstock 92; **Shutterstock:** Dotshock/Shutterstock 94; **Shutterstock:** Leigh/Shutterstock 111

Chapter 3: Text Credits   **Stephen Jay Gould:** From The Median isn't the Message by Stephen Jay Gould. Published by Stephen Jay Gould. 84; **McGraw-Hill Education:** From Investments by Zvi Bodie; Alex Kane and Alan Marcus. Published by McGraw-Hill Education, © 2013. 99; **California Health Interview Survey.:** Based on data from the California Health Interview Survey. 112; **Elsevier:** Based on data from "An Unexpected Rise in Strontium-90 in U.S. Deciduous Teeth in the1990s," by Mangano et. al., Science of the Total Environment. 126; **U.S. News & World Report:** Based on data from U.S. News & World Report 93; **U.S. News & World Report:** Based on data from U.S. News & World Reports 109; **US Department of Transportation:** Based on data from the Department of Transportation 124; **American Medical Association:** Based on anthropometric survey data from Gordon, Clauser et al. 124; **Centers for Disease Control and Prevention:** Based on data from the National Health and Nutrition Examination Survey 127; **Federal Communications Commission:** Data are from the Federal Communications Commission 91

Chapter 4: Image Credits   **Shutterstock:** GongTo/Shutterstock 142; **Shutterstock:** Photomatz/Shutterstock 146; **Getty Images:** Dansin/E+/Getty Images 147; **Shutterstock:** Pakhnyushcha/Shutterstock 147; **Shutterstock:** Worker/Shutterstock 147; **Shutterstock:** PeJo/Shutterstock 148; **Shutterstock:** Ssuaphotos/Shutterstock 149; **Shutterstock:** Bochkarev Photography/Shutterstock 150; **Shutterstock:** Nomad_Soul/Shutterstock 152; **Shutterstock:** Dgbomb/Shutterstock 153; **Shutterstock:** Ssuaphotos/Shutterstock 163; **Shutterstock:** Jim Barber/Shutterstock 164; **Shutterstock:** Chepe Nicoli/Shutterstock 165; **Getty Images:** Srischivan/E+/Getty Images 172; **Shutterstock:** Africa Studio/Shutterstock; **Shutterstock:** Alexander Raths/Shutterstock 173; **Shutterstock:** Philip Gangler/Shutterstock 171; **Shutterstock:** Stephen VanHorn/Shutterstock 176; **Shutterstock:** Bioraven/Shutterstock 182; **Shutterstock:** Serg Shalimoff/Shutterstock 170; **123RF:** Zentilia/123RF 185; **Stats, Triola:** ©Triola Stats. All Rights Reserved. 183; **Shutterstock:** Pshenina_m/Shutterstock 142; **123RF:** Ikiryo/123RF 174; **123RF:** Vitaly Yamzin/123RF 162; **Shutterstock:** EPG_EuroPhotoGraphics/Shutterstock 175; **Shutterstock:** Jason Stitt/Shutterstock 184; **123RF:** Zentilia/123RF 181; **Shutterstock:** 123dartist/Shutterstock 191

Chapter 4: Text Credits   **Genetics & IVF Institute:** Based on data from the Genetics & IVF Institute 143; **Conestoga College:** Based on data from "Are Women Carrying 'Basketballs' . . . ," by Perry, DiPietro, Constigan, Birth, Vol. 26, No. 3 156; **Quest Diagnostics Incorporated:** Based on data from Quest Diagnostics 163; **Bonnier Corporation:** From Popular Science Magazine Vol. 233, No. 1. Published by Bonnier Corporation, © 1988. 164; **The New York Times Company:** From BUSINESS; In the Gaming Industry, the House Can Have Bad Luck, Too by Andrew Pollack. Published by The New York Times Company, © 1999. 165; **Backblaze, Inc.:** Based on data from Backblaze, Inc. 166; **Pfizer Inc:** Based on data from Pfizer 167; **American Academy of Pediatrics:** Based on data from "Texting While Driving and Other Risky Motor Vehicle Behaviors Among U.S. High School Students," by O'Malley, Shults, and Eaton, Pediatrics, Vol. 131, No. 6 167; **Backblaze, Inc.:** Based on data from Backblaze, Inc. 169; **American Medical Association:** Based on data from "Pacemaker and ICD Generator Malfunctions," by Maisel et al., Journal of the American Medical Association, Vol. 295, No. 16. 170; **American Medical Association:** Based on data from "Association Between Helicopter vs Ground Emergency Medical Services and Survival for Adults With Major Trauma," by Galvagno et al., Journal of the American Medical Association, Vol. 307, No. 15. 170; **Harvard Business Review:** Based on data from the Harvard Business Review 175; **Cambridge University Press:** Based on Probabilistic Reasoning in Clinical Medicine by David Eddy, Cambridge University Press. 171; **Taylor & Francis Group:** From "Estimating the Probability of Events That have Never Occurred: When is Your Vote Decisive?" by Andrew Gelman, Gary King & W. John Boscardin in Journal of American Statistical Association, Vol: 93, pp: 1-28. Published by Taylor & Francis group, © 2012. 171; **Statista Inc:** Based on data from Statista 177; **World Health Organization:** Based on data from the Global Status Report on Road Safety 177; **Oxford University Press:** Based on data from "The Denomination Effect" by Priya Raghubir and Joydeep Srivastava, Journal of Consumer Research, Vol. 36. 178; **Electric Power Research Institute.:** Based on data from Arshad Mansoor, Senior Vice President with the Electric Power Research Institute. 180; **Charles R. Honts:** Charles R. Honts (Boise State University) and Gordon H. Barland (Department of Defense Polygraph Institute) 180; **USA Today:** Based on data from USA Today. 196; **Franchise Gator:** Based on data from Franchise Advantage 197; **Sallie Mae:** Based on data from a survey sponsored by Sallie Mae 197; **U.S. Department of Education:** The data are from "The Left-Handed: Their Sinister History," by Elaine Fowler Costas, Education Resources Information Center, Paper 399519 197; **John Wiley & Sons:** Based on data from "How 'Random' is Ryanair's Seating Allocation" by Jennifer Rogers, Significance 197; **Centers for Disease Control and Prevention:** Based on data from the Centers for Disease Control and Prevention 197; **Centers for Disease Control and Prevention:** Based on data from "Carbon Monoxide Test Can Be Used to Identify Smoker," by Patrice Wendling, Internal Medicine News, Vol. 40., No. 1, and Centers for Disease Control and Prevention. 201

Chapter 5: Image Credits   **Getty Images:** Fuse/Corbis/Getty Images 203; **Shutterstock:** GongTo/Shutterstock 203; **Shutterstock:** JHDT Productions/Shutterstock 207; **Shutterstock:** Laborant/Shutterstock 209; **Shutterstock:** B Calkins/Shutterstock 220; **Stats, Triola:** © Triola Stats. All Rights Reserved. 222; **Microsoft Corporation:** © Microsoft Corporation 222; **Stats, Triola:** © Triola Stats. All Rights Reserved. 222; **Shutterstock:** Vitalinka/Shutterstock 222; **Minitab Corporation:** Courtesy of Minitab Corporation. Used by permission of Minitab Corporation. 222; **Texas Instruments Inc:** Courtesy of Texas Instruments. Used by permission of Texas Instrument. 222; **Shutterstock:** Iurii Stepanov/Shutterstock 225; **Shutterstock:** Upthebanner/Shutterstock 225; **Shutterstock:** Andy Dean Photography/Shutterstock 208

Chapter 5: Text Credits   **Business Software Alliance:** Based on data from Business Software Alliance 204; **American Statistical Association:** From "Meta-Analysis of Migraine Headache Treatments: Combining Information from Heterogeneous Designs," by Francesca Dominici, Giovanni Parmigiani, Robert L. Wolpert and Vic Hasselblad in Journal of the American Statistical Association, Vol. 94, No. 445, pp: 16-28. Published by American Statistical Association, © 1999. 209; **TE Connectivity survey.:** Based on a TE Connectivity survey. 214; **Kaspersky Labsurvey:** Based on data from a Kaspersky Labsurvey 215; **Sallie Mae:** Based on data from Sallie Mae 215; **Consumer Technology Association:** Based on data from the Consumer Technology Association 215; **American Medical Association:** Based on data from "Hemispheric Dominance and Cell Phone Use," by Seidman et al., JAMA Otolaryngology—Head & Neck Surgery, Vol. 139, No. 5. 215; **Arity survey of drivers:** Based on data from an Arity survey of drivers 215; **U.S. Department of Health & Human Services:** Based on data from the U.S. Department of Health and Human Services 215; **U.S. Bank:** Based on a U.S. Bank survey of over 2003 adult smartphone owners in the .S. 219; **ICR Research Group:** Based on data from ICR Survey Research Group. 231; **American Academy of Neurology:** Based on data from "Prevalence and Comorbidity of Nocturnal Wandering In the U.S. Adult General Population," by Ohayon et al., Neurology, Vol. 78, No. 20 238; **Quest Diagnostics Incorporated:** Based on data from Quest Diagnostics 238; **Coca-Cola survey.:** Based on a Coca-Cola survey. 221; **U.S. National Center for Health Statistics.:** Based on data from the U.S. National Center for Health Statistics. 239; **American Medical Association:** Based on data from ES14 Chapter 5: Discrete Probability Distributions — "Hemispheric Dominance and Cell Phone Use," by Seidman et al., JAMA Otolaryngology—Head & Neck Surgery, Vol. 139, No. 5 215; **HSS:** HSS 223; **Association for Computing Machinery Inc:** Based on data from the IBM research paper "Passenger-Based Predictive Modeling of Airline No-Show Rates," by Lawrence, Hong, and Cherrier 241

Chapter 6: Image Credits   **Shutterstock:** GongTo/Shutterstock 244; **123RF:** Rui Santos/123RF 248; **Stats, Triola:** ©Triola Stats. All Rights Reserved. 252; **Microsoft Corporation:** © Microsoft Corporation 255; **Shutterstock:** Elena Stepanova/Shutterstock 255; **Shutterstock:** Elena Yakusheva/Shutterstock 256; **Microsoft Corporation:** © Microsoft Corporation 265; **Shutterstock:** Ciurea Adrian/Shutterstock 287; **Stats, Triola:** ©Triola Stats. All Rights Reserved. 298; **Stats, Triola:** ©Triola Stats. All Rights Reserved. 297; **Stats, Triola:** ©Triola Stats. All Rights Reserved. 297; **Shutterstock:** Derek Gordon/ Shutterstock 244

Chapter 6: Text Credits   **American Statistical Association:** From Statisticians and the EPA: What's the Connection Issue -371 by Barry D. Nussbaum. Published by American Statistical Association, © 2008. 248; **StatPearls Publishing LLC.:** Based on anthropometric survey data from Gordon, Churchill, et al. 270; **Elsevier:** Based on data from Applied Ergonomics 271; **StatPearls Publishing LLC.:** Based on anthropometric survey data from Gordon, Clauser, et al. 271; **National Highway Traffic Safety Administration:** Based on data from the National Highway Traffic Safety Administration 280; **Elsevier:** Based on data from Applied Ergonomics 286; **HarperCollins Publishers:** From The Cartoon Guide to Statistics by Larry Gonick and Woollcott Smith. Published by Harper and Collins, © 1993. 287; **Centers for Disease Control and Prevention:** Based on data from the National Health and Nutrition Examination Survey. 291; **American Medical Association:** Based on data from "Neurobehavioral Outcomes of School-age Children Born Extremely Low Birth Weight or Very Preterm," by Anderson et al., Journal of the American Medical Association, Vol. 289, No. 24. 293; **StatPearls Publishing LLC.:** Based on anthropometric survey data from Gordon, Clauser, et al 293; **American Medical Association:** Based on data from "Comparison of the Atkins, Ornish, Weight Watchers, and Zone Diets for Weight Loss and Heart Disease Reduction," by Dansinger et al., Journal of the American Medical Association, Vol. 293, No. 1 293; **StatPearls Publishing LLC.:** Based on anthropometric survey data from Gordon, Churchill, et al. 303; **StatPearls Publishing LLC.:** Based on anthropometric survey data from Gordon, Churchill, et al. 305; **Indiana University:** Based on a study by Dr. P. Soria at Indiana University. 306; **American Medical Association:** Based on data from "Comparisonof the Atkins, Ornish, Weight Watchers, and Zone Diets for Weight Loss and HeartDisease Reduction," by Dansinger et al., Journal of the American Medical Association, Vol. 293, No. 1" 307

Chapter 7: Image Credits   **Shutterstock:** GongTo/Shutterstock 310; **Shutterstock:** Mike Flippo/Shutterstock 313; **Shutterstock:** Stocksnapper/ Shutterstock 315; **Shutterstock:** Mama_Mia/Shutterstock 317; **Stats, Triola:** ©Triola Stats. All Rights Reserved. 317; **Shutterstock:** Juan Camilo Bernal/Shutterstock 371; **Shutterstock:** Robin W/Shutterstock 333; **Stats, Triola:** ©Triola Stats. All Rights Reserved. 349; **Shutterstock:** Gary Blakeley/Shutterstock 335; **Shutterstock:** Rafael Ramirez Lee/Shutterstock 335; **Shutterstock:** ESB Basic/Shutterstock 356; **Texas Instruments Inc:** Courtesy of Texas Instruments. Used by permission of Texas Instrument. 341; **Shutterstock:** Marut Sayannikroth/Shutterstock 332; **123RF:** Teerawut Masawat/123RF 321; **123RF:** Wavebreak Media Ltd/123RF 319; **Shutterstock:** Alphaspirit/Shutterstock 322; **123RF:** Sjenner13/123RF 314; **Shutterstock:** Dmytro Sheremeta/Shutterstock 336

Chapter 7: Text Credits   **The New York Times Company:** From How the Poll Was Conducted in New York Times. Published by The Newyork Times Company, © 2016. 305; **American Medical Association:** From "High-Dose Nicotine Patch Therapy," by Lowell C Dale; Richard D Hurt; Kenneth P Offord; Lawson G M; Croghan I T and Schroeder D R in Journal of the American Medical Association. Published by American Medical Association, © 1995. 319; **Bristol-Myers Squibb Co:** Based on data from Bristol-Myers Squibb Co. 325; **Physicians Insurers Association of America.:** Based on data from the Physicians Insurers Association of America. 325; **Purdue Pharma L.P.:** Based on data from Purdue Pharma L.P. 328; **American Medical Association:** Based on data in "A Close Look at Therapeutic Touch," Journal of the American Medical Association, Vol. 279, No. 13. 326; **Pew Research Centre:** Based on three Pew Research Center polls 328; **Soul Publishing:** Based on data from Soul Publishing 327; **Onedio:** Based on data from Onedio 327; **Gambling Commission:** Based on 2017 data from Gambling Commission study in Great Britain 328; **ICR Research Group:** Based on data from "Sustained Care Intervention and Postdischarge Smoking Cessation Among Hospitalized Adults," by Rigotti et al., Journal of the American Medical Association, Vol. 312, No. 7. 327; **American Statistical Association:** From "Sampling Wildlife Populations" by Bryan Manly and Lyman McDonald in Chance, Vol.9, No. 2,pp: 9-19. Published by American Statistical Association, © 2012. 332;

American Medical Association: Based on data from "Cognitive Behavioral Therapy vs Zopiclone for Treatment of Chronic Primary Insomnia in Older Adults," by Sivertsen et al., Journal of the American Medical Association, Vol. 295, No. 24. 342; **American Medical Association:** Based on data from "Effect of Raw Garlic vs Commercial Garlic Supplements on Plasma Lipid Concentrations in Adults with Moderate Hypercholesterolemia," by Gardner et al., Archives of Internal Medicine, Vol. 167. 342; **Food and Drug Administration.:** Based on data from the Food and Drug Administration. 343; **Nabu Press:** Based on data from Ancient Races of the Thebaid by Thomson and Randall-Maciver 362; **American Medical Association:** Based on data from "Cognitive Behavioral Therapy vs Zopiclone for Treatment of Chronic Primary Insomnia in Older Adults," by Sivertsen et al., Journal of the American Medical Association, Vol. 295, No. 24. 353; **American Medical Association:** Based on data from "Effect of Raw Garlic vs Commercial Garlic Supplements on Plasma Lipid Concentrations in Adults with Moderate Hypercholesterolemia," by Gardner et al., Archives of Internal Medicine, Vol. 167. 353; **Bristol-Myers Squibb Co:** Based on data from Bristol-Myers Squibb Co. 348; **Nabu Press:** Based on data from Ancient Races of the Thebaid by Thomson and Randall-Maciver 362; **Physicians Insurers Association of America.:** Based on data from the Physicians Insurers Association of America. 363; **Motorcycle Industry Council:** Based on data from the Motorcycle Industry Council 364; **ICR Research Group:** Based on data from ICR Research Group 365; **Government Printing Office:** Based on data from the Federal Communications Commission 367

Chapter 8: Image Credits

Shutterstock: GongTo/Shutterstock 372; **Shutterstock:** Azuzl/Shutterstock 381; **Shutterstock:** Wikki/Shutterstock 383; **Shutterstock:** David H.Seymour/Shutterstock 387; **Shutterstock:** Suravid/Shutterstock 393; **StatCrunch:** Courtesy of StatCrunchTM. Used with permission. 375; **123RF:** Alexey Burmakin/123RF 396; **Stats, Triola:** ©Triola Stats. All Rights Reserved. 375; **Shutterstock:** Boscorelli/Shutterstock 398; **International Business Machines Corporation:** Reprint Courtesy of International Business Machines Corporation, © SPSS, Inc., an IBM Company. 407; **SAS Institute, Inc.:** Created using JMP® software. Copyright © SAS Institute Inc. SAS and all other SAS Institute Inc. product or service names are registered trademarks or trademarks of SAS Institute Inc., Cary, NC, USA. 407; **StatCrunch:** Courtesy of StatCrunchTM. Used with permission. 407; **Microsoft Corporation:** © Microsoft Corporation 407; **Stats, Triola:** ©Triola Stats. All Rights Reserved. 413; **Shutterstock:** Zentilia/Shutterstock 410; **SAS Institute, Inc.:** Created using JMP® software. Copyright © SAS Institute Inc. SAS and all other SAS Institute Inc. product or service names are registered trademarks or trademarks of SAS Institute Inc., Cary, NC, USA. 413; **Stats, Triola:** ©Triola Stats. All Rights Reserved. 413; **Minitab Corporation:** Courtesy of Minitab Corporation. Used by permission of Minitab Corporation. 407; **Texas Instruments Inc:** Courtesy of Texas Instruments. Used by permission of Texas Instrument. 407; **Texas Instruments Inc:** Courtesy of Texas Instruments. Used by permission of Texas Instrument. 408; **Minitab Corporation:** Courtesy of Minitab Corporation. Used by permission of Minitab Corporation. 408; **Texas Instruments Inc:** Courtesy of Texas Instruments. Used by permission of Texas Instrument. 408; **Texas Instruments Inc:** Courtesy of Texas Instruments. Used by permission of Texas Instrument. 408; **Minitab Corporation:** Courtesy of Minitab Corporation. Used by permission of Minitab Corporation. 413; **Texas Instruments Inc:** Courtesy of Texas Instruments. Used by permission of Texas Instrument. 413; **Shutterstock:** Wright Studio/Shutterstock 372; **Shutterstock:** Beerkoff/Shutterstock 384; **123RF:** James Steidl/123RF 385; **Shutterstock:** Digital Genetics/Shutterstock 408; **Shutterstock:** Nadya Lukic/Shutterstock 409

Chapter 8: Text Credits

Trafimow, David: From "Psychology Journal Bans P Values" by David Trafimow quoted in Chris Woolston in Nature, Vol: 519, Issue: 7541. Published by David Trafimow, © 2015. 381; **Gibbs, Lisa:** Quote by Lisa Gibbs from Money Magazine. 387; **Pfizer Inc:** Based on data from Pfizer, Inc. 390; **Pfizer Inc:** Based on data from Pfizer, Inc. 400; **Purdue Pharma L.P.:** Based on data from Purdue Pharma L.P. 401; **Pew Research Centre:** Based on three Pew Research Center polls 401; **Physicians Insurers Association of America.:** Based on data from the Physicians Insurers Association of America. 401; **Department of Defense Polygraph Institute.:** Based on data from experiments conducted by researchers Charles R. Honts of Boise State University and Gordon H. Barland of the Department of Defense Polygraph Institute. 402; **American Medical Association:** Based on data in "A Close Look at Therapeutic Touch," Journal of the American Medical Association, Vol. 279, No. 13. 402; **Washington Post:** Based on a poll by the Washington Post 402; **American Medical Association:** Based on data from "Holidays, Birthdays, and Postponement of Cancer Death," by Young and Hade, Journal of the American Medical Association, Vol. 292, No. 24. 403; **American Medical Association:** Based on data from "Sustained Care Intervention and Postdischarge Smoking Cessation Among Hospitalized Adults," by Rigotti et al., Journal of the American Medical Association, Vol. 312, No. 7. 403; **O'Sullivan, Maureen:** From Discover Your Inner Economist: Use Incentives to Fall in Love, Survive Your Next Meeting, and Motivate Your Dentist by Tyler Cowen. Published by Penguin Random House, © 2008. 410; **American Medical Association:** Based on data from "Comparison of the Atkins, Ornish, Weight Watchers, and Zone Diets for Weight Loss and Heart Disease Reduction," by Dansinger et al., Journal of the American Medical Association, Vol. 293, No. 1. 414; **American Medical Association:** Based on data from "Cognitive Behavioral Therapy vs Zopiclone for Treatment of Chronic Primary Insomnia in Older Adults," by Sivertsen et al., Journal of the American Medical Association, Vol. 295, No. 24. 414; **American Medical Association:** Based on data from "Lead, Mercury, and Arsenic in US and Indian Manufactured Ayurvedic Medicines Sold via the Internet," by Saper et al., Journal of the American Medical Association, Vol. 300, No. 8. 415; **Payscale:** Based on data from payscale.com. 415; **ICR Research Group:** Based on data from ICR Survey Research Group. 434

Chapter 9: Image Credits

Shutterstock: GongTo/Shutterstock 440; **Shutterstock:** Sirtravelalot/Shutterstock 444; **Shutterstock:** Sergei Telegin/Shutterstock 446; **Shutterstock:** Alex Staroseltsev/Shutterstock 421; **Stats, Triola:** ©Triola Stats. All Rights Reserved. 444; **StatCrunch:** Courtesy of StatCrunchTM. Used with permission. 450; **Shutterstock:** GJS/Shutterstock 455; **Shutterstock:** Amy Walters/Shutterstock 458; **Shutterstock:** David Lee/Shutterstock 459; **Shutterstock:** Christy Thompson/Shutterstock 461; **Shutterstock:** Spayder pauk_79/Shutterstock 471; **Shutterstock:** Andrey Arkusha/Shutterstock 472; **Shutterstock:** Pressmaster/Shutterstock 473; **Stats, Triola:** ©Triola Stats. All Rights Reserved. 469; **Shutterstock:** Andrey_Popov/Shutterstock 440; **Shutterstock:** Vertes Edmond Mihai/Shutterstock 443; **123RF:** Zamfir Cristian Ion/123RF 447

Chapter 9: Text Credits **Massachusetts Medical Society:** Based on "A Randomized Trial of Ecigarettes versus Nicotine-Replacement Therapy" by Hajek, et al, New England Journal of Medicine 467; **Chance Magazine:** From "Poll Faulting" by Ansolabehere S, Belin TR in Chance, Vol:6, pp:22-8. Published by Chance, © 1993. 444; **American Medical Association:** Based on data from "Effect of Pictorial Cigarette Pack Warnings on Changes in Smoking Behavior" by Brewer et al, Journal of the American Medical Association. 452; **American Society of Tropical Medicine:** Based on data presented at an annual meeting of the American Society of Tropical Medicine, by principal investigator Steve Lindsay 452; **American Statistical Association:** Based on data from "Does Eye Color Depend on Gender? It Might Depend on Who or How You Ask" by Froelich and Stephenson, Journal of Statistics Education, Vol. 21, No. 2 453; **American Statistical Association:** Based on data from "Does Eye Color Depend on Gender? It Might Depend on Who or How You Ask" by Froelich and Stephenson, Journal of Statistics Education, Vol. 21, No. 2 453; **American Psychological Association:** Based on data from "Do We Dream in Color?" by Eva Murzyn, Consciousness and Cognition, Vol. 17, No. 4. 451; **Purdue Pharma L.P.:** Based on data from Purdue Pharma L.P. 451; **American Psychological Association:** Based on data from "Who Wants Airbags?" by Meyer and Finney, Chance, Vol. 18, No. 2. 451; **American Medical Association:** Based on data from "Sustainability of Reductions in Malaria Transmission and Infant Mortality in Western Kenya with Use of Insecticide-Treated Bednets," by Lindblade et al., Journal of the American Medical Association, Vol. 291, No. 21. 452; **American Medical Association:** Based on data from "Hemi-spheric Dominance and Cell Phone Use," by Seidman et al., JAMA Otolaryngology—Head & Neck Surgery, Vol. 139, No. 5. 450; **Oxford University Press:** Based on data from "The Denomination Effect" by Priya Raghubir and Joydeep Srivastava, Journal of Consumer Research, Vol. 36. 451; **U.S. Department of Education:** Based on data from "The Left-Handed: Their Sinister History," by Elaine Fowler Costas, Education Resources Information Center, Paper 399519. 453; **American Medical Association:** Based on data from "Association Between Helicopter vs Ground Emergency Medical Services and Survival for Adults With Major Trauma," by Galvagno et al., Journal of the American Medical Association, Vol. 307, No. 15. 453; **Penguin Random House:** From Freakonomics by Steven D. Levitt, Stephen J. Dubner. Published by Penguin Random House, © 2010. 455; **John Wiley & Sons:** Based on data from "Sweetening the Till: The Use of Candy to Increase Restaurant Tipping" by Strohmetz et al, Journal of Applied Social Psychology, Vol. 32, No. 2 454; **Canadian Center of Science and Education:** Based on data from "Reading on the Computer Screen: Does Font Type Have Effects on Web Text Readability?" by Ali et al, International Education Studies, Vol. 6, No. 3 465; **British Medical Association:** Based on data from "Efficacy of Handrubbing With Alcohol Based Solution versus Standard Handwashing with Antiseptic Soap" by Girou et al, British Medical Journal 465; **British Medical Association:** Based on data from "Bicycle Weights and Commuting Time" by Jeremy Groves, British Medical Journal 466; **American Medical Association:** Based on data from "Bipolar Permanent Magnets for the Treatment of Chronic Lower Back Pain: A Pilot Study," by Collacott, Zimmerman, White, and Rindone, Journal of the American Medical Association, Vol. 283, No. 10. 466; **Taylor & Francis Group:** Based on data from "Item Arrangement, Cognitive Entry Characteristics, Sex and Test Anxiety as Predictors of Achievement in Examination Performance," by Klimko, Journal of Experimental Education, Vol. 52, No. 4. 468; **Oxford university Press:** Based on data from "Effects of Alcohol Intoxication on Risk Taking, Strategy, and Error Rate in Visuomotor Performance," by Streufert et al., Journal of Applied Psychology, Vol. 77, No. 4. 469; **American Psychological Association:** Based on "An Analysis of Factors That Contribute to the Efficacy of Hypnotic An-algesia," by Price and Barber, Journal of Abnormal Psychology, Vol. 96, No. 1. 479; **British Medical Association:** Based on data from "Bicycle Weights and Commuting Time" by Jeremy Groves, British Medical Journal 488; **American Psychological Association:** Based on data from "Effects of Alcohol Intoxication on Risk Taking, Strategy, and Error Rate in Visuomotor Performance," by Streufert et al., Journal of Applied Psychology, Vol. 77, No. 4. 487; **Oxford University Press:** Based on data from "Item Arrangement, Cognitive Entry Characteristics, Sex and Test Anxiety as Predictors of Achievement in Examination Performance," by Klimko, Journal of Experimental Education, Vol. 52, No. 4. 489; **American Medical Association:** Based on data from "Effect of Oral Dexamethasone Without Immediate Antibiotics vs Placebo on Acute Sore Throat in Adults" by Hayward et al, Journal of the American Medical Association 498; **American Medical Association:** Based on data from "Sustained Care Intervention and Postdischarge Smoking Cessation Among Hospitalized Adults," by Rigotti et al., Journal of the American Medical Association, Vol. 312, No. 7 500; **American Public Health Association:** Based on data from "Morbidity Among Pediatric Motor Vehicle Crash Victims: The Effectiveness of Seat Belts," by Osberg and Di Scala, American Journal of Public Health, Vol. 82, No. 3 500; **Pew Research Centre:** Based on data from a Pew Research Center survey 501; **Pew Research Centre:** Based on data from a Pew Research Center survey 501; **Kazaa publisher:** Based on data from the Recording Industry Association of America 502; **American Psychological Association:** Based on data from "Eyewitness Memory of Police Trainees for Realistic Role Plays," by Yuille et al., Journal of Applied Psychology, Vol. 79, No. 6 502; **British Medical Association:** Based on data from "Is Friday the 13th Bad for Your Health" by Scanlon, et al, British Medical Journal, Vol. 307 476; **National Center for Health Statistics:** Based on data from the National Center for Health Statistics 478; **National Center for Health Statistics:** Based on data from the National Center for Health Statistics 478; **Oxford university Press:** Based on data from "Probable Error of the Mean" by W. S. Gosset, Biometrica, Vol. 6 478

Chapter 10: Image Credits **Shutterstock:** GongTo/Shutterstock 506; **SAS Institute, Inc.:** Created using JMP® software. Copyright © SAS Institute Inc. SAS and all other SAS Institute Inc. product or service names are registered trademarks or trademarks of SAS Institute Inc., Cary, NC, USA. 531; **International Business Machines Corporation:** Reprint Courtesy of International Business Machines Corporation, © SPSS, Inc., an IBM Company. 531; **Shutterstock:** John Roman Images/Shutterstock 513; **Shutterstock:** Alexander Raths/Shutterstock 515; **Shutterstock:** Africa Studio/Shutterstock 519; **SAS Institute, Inc.:** Created using JMP® software. Copyright © SAS Institute Inc. SAS and all other SAS Institute Inc. product or service names are registered trademarks or trademarks of SAS Institute Inc., Cary, NC, USA. 531; **International Business Machines Corporation:** Reprint Courtesy of International Business Machines Corporation, © SPSS, Inc., an IBM Company. 531; **Shutterstock:** Zffoto/Shutterstock 533; **Stats, Triola:** ©Triola Stats. All Rights Reserved. 531; **Stats, Triola:** ©Triola Stats. All Rights Reserved. 531; **Getty Images:** David Madison/Photodisc/Getty Images 558; **Shutterstock:** Leah-Anne Thompson/Shutterstock 565; **International Business Machines Corporation:** Reprint Courtesy of International Business Machines

Corporation, © SPSS, Inc., an IBM Company. 531; **Texas Instruments Inc:** Courtesy of Texas Instruments. Used by permission of Texas Instrument. 565; **Texas Instruments Inc:** Courtesy of Texas Instruments. Used by permission of Texas Instrument. 565; **Texas Instruments Inc:** Courtesy of Texas Instruments. Used by permission of Texas Instrument. 565; **Texas Instruments Inc:** Courtesy of Texas Instruments. Used by permission of Texas Instrument. 565; **Minitab Corporation:** Courtesy of Minitab Corporation. Used by permission of Minitab Corporation. 522; **Texas Instruments Inc:** Courtesy of Texas Instruments. Used by permission of Texas Instrument. 524; **Texas Instruments Inc:** Courtesy of Texas Instruments. Used by permission of Texas Instrument. 524; **Shutterstock:** Stephen VanHorn/Shutterstock 506; **Shutterstock:** VLADGRIN/Shutterstock 534

Chapter 10: Text Credits

Chance Magazine: From "Teacher Course Evaluations and Student Grades: An Academic Tango," by Valen Johnson in Chance, Vol. 15, No. 3, pp:9-16. Published by Chance, © 2012. 515; **American Chemical Society:** Based on data from "The Trouble with QSAR (or How I Learned to Stop Worrying and Embrace Fallacy)" by Stephen Johnson, Journal of Chemical Information and Modeling, Vol. 48, No. 1. 528; **Harvard University Press.:** Based on data from The Song of Insects by George W. Pierce, Harvard University Press. 542; **Montana State University.:** Based on "Mass Estimation of Weddell Seals Using Techniques of Photogrammetry," by R. Garrott of Montana State University. 543; **Montana State University.:** Based on data from the U. S Department of Agriculture and the National Science Foundation 527; **U. S. Department of Agriculture:** Based on data from the U. S. Department of Agriculture 528; **Chance Magazine:** From "Poll Faulting" by Ansolabehere S, Belin TR in Chance, Vol:6, pp:22-8. Published by Chance, © 1993. 551; **Montana State University.:** Based on "Mass Estimation of Weddell Seals Using Techniques of Photogrammetry," by R. Garrott of Montana State University. 551; **New York Times:** Based on data from the New York Times 571; **eMarketer:** Based on data from eMarketer 572; **Consumer Technology Association:** Based on data from the Consumer Technology Association 573

Chapter 11: Image Credits

Shutterstock: GongTo/Shutterstock 576; **Shutterstock:** AlexKalashnikov/Shutterstock 582; **Shutterstock:** Serhiy Shullye/Shutterstock 584; **Shutterstock:** Lenetstan/Shutterstock 595; **Shutterstock:** Dundanim/Shutterstock 596; **StatCrunch:** Courtesy of StatCrunchTM. Used with permission. 596; **Texas Instruments Inc:** Courtesy of Texas Instruments. Used by permission of Texas Instrument. 600; **Texas Instruments Inc:** Courtesy of Texas Instruments. Used by permission of Texas Instrument. 594; **Texas Instruments Inc:** Courtesy of Texas Instruments. Used by permission of Texas Instrument. 594; **Shutterstock:** Rohane Hamilton/Shutterstock 576

Chapter 11: Text Credits

American Medical Association: Based on "Autism Occurrence by MMR Vaccine Status Among U. S. Children with Older Siblings With and Without Autism" by Jain et al, Journal of the American Medical Association, Vol. 313, No. 15 577; **Oxford University Press:** From "A Solution to the Too-Good-to-be-True Paradox and Gregor Mendel" by Ira Pilgrim in The Journal of Heredity Vol: 77, Vol: 3, pp: 218-220. Published by Oxford University Press, © 1986. 584; **American Medical Association:** Based on data from "Participation in Cancer Clinical Trials," by Murthy, Krumholz, and Gross, Journal of the American Medical Association, Vol. 291, No. 22. 587; **American Medical Association:** Based on data from "Efficacy of Hip Protector to Prevent Hip Fracture in Nursing Home Residents," by Kiel et al., Journal of the American Medical Association, Vol. 298, No. 4. 598; **Sage Publications:** Based on data from "Identifying Fingerprint Expertise" by Tangen, Thompson, and McCarthy, Psychological Science, Vol. 22, No. 8 601; **American Statistical Association:** Based on data from "Does Eye Color Depend on Gender? It Might Depend on Who or How You Ask," by Froelich and Stephenson, Journal of Statistics Education, Vol. 21, No. 2 602; **Oxford university Press:** Based on data from "Texting While Driving and Other Risky Motor Vehicle Behaviors Among U.S. High School Students," by O'Malley, Shults, and Eaton, Pediatrics, Vol. 131, No. 6. 600; **Oxford University Press:** Based on "The Denomination Effect," by Priya Raghubir and Joydeep Srivastava, Journal of Consumer Research, Vol. 36. 601; **Royal Society:** Based on data from "Why Are Some People Left-Handed? An Evolutionary Perspective," by Laurens and Faurie, Philosophical Transactions, Vol. 364 603; **American Public Health Association:** Based on data from "What Kinds of People Do Not Use Seat Belts?" by Helsing and Comstock, American Journal of Public Health, Vol. 67, No. 11. 602; **British Medical Association:** Based on data from "An Evaluation of Echinacea Angustifolia in Experimental Rhinovirus Infections," by Turner et al., New England Journal of Medicine, Vol. 353, No. 4. 602; **British Medical Association:** Based on data from "Motorcycle Rider Conspicuity and Crash Related Injury: Case-Control Study," by Wells et al., BMJ USA, Vol. 4. 602; **Sage Publications:** Based on data from "I Hear You Knocking But You Can't Come In," by Fitzgerald and Fuller, Sociological Methods and Research, Vol. 11, No.1. 603; **Copper Cauldron Publishing:** Based on data from "Predicting Professional Sports Game Outcomes from Intermediate Game Scores," by Copper, DeNeve, and Mosteller, Chance, Vol. 5, No. 3–4. 603; **National Weather Service:** Based on data from the National Weather Service 605; **American Resaerch Institute:** Based on data from "Preliminary Study to Detect Match-Fixing: Benford's Law in Badminton Rally Data" by Park et al, Journal of Physical Education and Sports; Management, Vol. 3, No. 1" 605; **Oxford University Press:** Based on "The Denomination Effect" by Priya Raghubir and Joydeep Srivastava, Journal of Consumer Research, Vol. 36. 606; **American Medical Association:** Based on data from "Splinting vs. Surgery in the Treatment of Carpal Tunnel Syndrome," by Gerritsen et al., Journal of the American Medical Association, Vol. 288, No. 10 598; **Frontline Medical Communication:** Based on data from "Surgery Unfounded for Tarsal Navicular Stress Fracture," by Bruce Jancin, Internal Medicine News, Vol. 42, No. 14 600

Chapter 12: Image Credits

Shutterstock: GongTo/Shutterstock 610; **SAS Institute, Inc.:** Created using JMP® software. Copyright © SAS Institute Inc. SAS and all other SAS Institute Inc. product or service names are registered trademarks or trademarks of SAS Institute Inc., Cary, NC, USA. 615; **International Business Machines Corporation:** Reprint Courtesy of International Business Machines Corporation, © SPSS, Inc., an IBM Company. 615; **StatCrunch:** Courtesy of StatCrunchTM. Used with permission. 586; **International Business Machines Corporation:** Reprint Courtesy of International Business Machines Corporation, © SPSS, Inc., an IBM Company. 623; **International Business Machines Corporation:** Reprint Courtesy of International Business Machines Corporation, © SPSS, Inc., an IBM Company. 621; **Stats, Triola:** ©Triola Stats. All Rights Reserved. 624; **Texas Instruments Inc:** Courtesy of Texas Instruments. Used by permission of Texas Instrument. 615;

Texas Instruments Inc: Courtesy of Texas Instruments. Used by permission of Texas Instrument. 615; **Minitab Corporation:** Courtesy of Minitab Corporation. Used by permission of Minitab Corporation. 614; **Minitab Corporation:** Courtesy of Minitab Corporation. Used by permission of Minitab Corporation. 614; **Shutterstock:** Benoist/Shutterstock 610

Chapter 13: Image Credits

Shutterstock: GongTo/Shutterstock 642; **Stats, Triola:** ©Triola Stats. All Rights Reserved. Multi; **Stats, Triola:** ©Triola Stats. All Rights Reserved. Multi; **Shutterstock:** Sinisa Botas/Shutterstock 681; **Shutterstock:** ESB Professional/Shutterstock 688; **Stats, Triola:** ©Triola Stats. All Rights Reserved. Multi; **Shutterstock:** Igor Kardasov/Shutterstock 642

Chapter 13: Text Credits

Consumers Union: Based on data from Consumer Reports 680; **Genetics & IVF Institute:** Based on data from the Genetics & IVF Institute. 649; **British Medical Association:** Based on data from "Is Friday the 13th Bad for Your Health" by Scanlon, et al, British Medical Journal, Vol. 307 655; **Physicians Insurers Association of America.:** Based on data from the Physicians Insurers Association of America. 656; **British Medical Association:** Based on data from "Is Friday the 13th Bad for Your Health" by Scanlon, et al, British Medical Journal, Vol. 307 663; **Elsevier:** Based on data from "An Unexpected Rise in Strontium-90 in U.S. Deciduous Teeth in the1990s," by Mangano et. al., Science of the Total Environment. 669; **Montana State University.:** Based on "Mass Estimation of Weddell Seals Using Techniques of Photogrammetry," by R. Garrott of Montana State University. 684; **Consumers Union:** Based on data from Consumer Reports 684; **Consumers Union:** Based on data from Consumer Reports 684; **U. S. Department of Agriculture:** Based on data from the U. S. Department of Agriculture 685; **Harvard University Press.:** Based on data from The Song of Insects by George W. Pierce, Harvard University Press. 685; **Kazaa publisher:** Based on data from the Recording Industry Association of America 692

Chapter 14: Image Credits

Shutterstock: GongTo/Shutterstock 700; **Shutterstock:** Getmilitaryphotos/Shutterstock 703; **Shutterstock:** Blaz Kure/Shutterstock 704; **Shutterstock:** Michael Rosskothen/Shutterstock 707; **Shutterstock:** Moreno Soppelsa/Shutterstock 705; **SuperStock:** Age Fotostock/SuperStock 708; **Shutterstock:** Tupungato/Shutterstock 715; **Minitab Corporation:** Courtesy of Minitab Corporation. Used by permission of Minitab Corporation. Multi; **Shutterstock:** ChameleonsEye/Shutterstock 700

Chapter 14: Text Credits

NASA: Based on data from NASA's Goddard Institute for Space Studies (GISS) 701; **American Society for Testing and Materials:** Adapted from ASTM Manual on the Presentation of Data and Control Chart Analysis, © 1976 ASTM, pp. 134–136. Reprinted with permission of American Society for Testing and Materials. 707; **U.S. Department of the Interior:** Based on data from the U.S. Department of the Interior 711; **U.S. Courts:** Based on data from the Administrative Office of the U.S. Courts 720; **American Psychological Association:** Based on data from "Eyewitness Memory of Police Trainees for Realistic Role Plays," by Yuille et al., Journal of Applied Psychology, Vol. 79, No. 6 721

Chapter 15: Image Credits

Shutterstock: eskay lim/123RF 724; **Stats, Triola:** ©Triola Stats. All Rights Reserved. 727; **Stats, Triola:** ©Triola Stats. All Rights Reserved. 728; **Minitab Corporation:** Courtesy of Minitab Corporation. Used by permission of Minitab Corporation. Multi; **Shutterstock:** Focal point/Shutterstock 724

Appendix A: Text Credits

Pearson Education: Mosteller, Probability With Statistical Applications, 2nd Ed., © 1970. Reprinted and Electronically reproduced by permission of Pearson Education, Inc. Upper Saddle River, New Jersey. 731; **Addison Wesley Publishing:** From Donald B. Owen, Handbook of Statistical Tables. 735; **Oxford University Press:** Based on data from Maxine Merrington and Catherine M. Thompson, "Tables of Percentage Points of the Inverted Beta (F)Distribution," Biometrika 33 (1943): 80–84. 736; **American Cyanamid Company:** Based on data from Some Rapid Approximate Statistical Procedures, Copyright © 1949, 1964 Lederle Laboratories Division of American Cyanamid Company. 740; **Institute of Mathematical Statistics:** From Tables for Testing Randomness of Grouping in a Sequence of Alternatives by Frieda S. Swed and C. Eisenhart in The Annals of Mathematical Statistics, Vol. 14, No.1, pp. 66–87. Copyright © Institute of Mathematical Statistics. 741; **Oxford University Press:** Based on data from Maxine Merrington and Catherine M. Thompson, "Tables of Percentage Points of the Inverted Beta (F)Distribution," Biometrika 33 (1943): 80–84. 739

Appendix B: Text Credits

Elsevier: Data are from "Neuropsychological Dysfunction in Children with Chronic Low-Level Lead Absorption," by P. J. Landrigan, R. H. Whitworth, R. W. Baloh, N. W. Staehling, W. F Barthel, and B. F. Rosenblum, Lancet, Vol. 1, No. 7909. 753; **National Center for Health Statistics.:** Data are from the National Center for Health Statistics. 750; **U.S. Army.:** Data are from the U.S. Army. 750; **U.S. Army.:** Data are from the U.S. Army. 750; **National Center for Health Statistics.:** Data are from the National Center for Health Statistics. 751; **National Center for Health Statistics.:** Data are from the National Center for Health Statistics. 751; **National Center for Health Statistics.:** Data are from the National Center for Health Statistics. 751; **Rohren, Brenda:** Rohren, Brenda, "Estimation of Stature from Foot and Shoe Length: Applications in Forensic Science." Copyright © 2006. Reprinted by permission of the author. 752; **Elsevier:** Data are from "Neuropsychological Dysfunction in Children with Chronic Low-Level Lead Absorption," by P. J. Landrigan, R. H. Whitworth, R. W. Baloh, N. W. Staehling, W. F Barthel, and B. F. Rosenblum, Lancet, Vol. 1, No. 7909. 752; **American Academy of Neurology:** Data provided by M. J. Tramo, W. C. Loftus, T. A. Stukel, J. B. Weaver, M. S. Gazziniga. See "Brain Size, Head Size, and IQ in Monozygotic Twins," Neurology, Vol. 50. 752; **Taylor & Francis Group:** Based on Hoffman, D. J., Policastro, P., Quick, V., and Lee, S. K.: "Changes in Body Weight and Fat Mass of Men and Women in the First Year of College: A Study of the 'Freshman 15.'" Journal of American College Health, July 1, 2006, Vol. 55, No. 1, p. 41. 754; **National Center for Health Statistics.:** Data are from the National Center for Health Statistics. 754; **U.S. Food and Drug Administration.:** Data are from the U.S. Food and Drug Administration. 754; **National Weather Service:** Data are from the National Weather Service 755; **U.S. Census Bureau:** Data are from the U.S. Census Bureau's 2017 American Community Survey. 758; **National Highway Traffic Safety Administration:** Data are from the National Highway Traffic Safety Administration 761; **U.S. Army.:** Data are from the 1969 Vietnam War U.S. Army draft lottery 763; **Masakuza Tani:** Data provided by Masakuza Tani, the Garbage Project, University of Arizona. 763;

SUBJECT INDEX

A

Acceptance sampling, 170
Actual odds against, 153
Actual odds in favor, 153
Addition rule
    complementary events and, 160–161
    defining, 158
    disjoint events and, 159–160
    formal, 158–159
    intuitive, 159
    notation for, 158–159
    summary of, 167
Adjusted coefficient of determination,
    554–555
Airport data speeds, 757
Alcohol and tobacco in movies, 752
α, 256
Alternative hypothesis, 518
    contingency tables, 591
    defining, 377
    goodness-of-fit and, 578
    original claim for, 377–378
Aluminum cans, 759
Analysis of data, 6
    potential pitfalls, 7–9
Analysis of variance (ANOVA)
    history of, 616
    interaction in, 627
    one-way, 612–626
    two-way, 626–636
Area
    between boundaries, 250
    known, 254–256
    with nonstandard normal
        distribution, 260–262
    probability and, 247, 250–253
    z scores and, 249, 250–253
Arsenic in rice, 751
Aspirin, 383
Assignable variation, 704, 707
Attributes, control charts for, 713
Audiometry, 748
Autism, 576–577
Average, 88, 518
Axis, nonzero vertical, 67–68

B

b_1 slope, 529, 530
Balanced design, 628
Bar codes, 183
Bar graphs, 64
Bayes' theorem, 175–177
Bear measurements, 751
Benford's law, 582–584
Bell-shaped distribution, 246
β, 384

Bias

in internet surveys, 314, 317
in missing data, 23
publication, 7
survivorship, 5
Biased estimators, 107, 115, 279–280
Big data, 14, 18, 20–22
    applications of, 21
Bimodal, 91
Binomial probabilities, 731
Binomial probability distribution,
    218–226
    defining, 219
    finding, 220–224
    formula, 220–221
    normal distribution approximation
        of, 303–304
    notation, 219, 303
    rationale for, 225–226
    software/calculator results, 226
Births, 747, 760
Bivariate normal distribution, 510
Blinding, 28
Blocks, 31–32
Body data, 746
Body temperatures, 724, 726–730, 747
Bonferroni multiple comparison test
    critical values in, 620
    one-way ANOVA, 620
    P-values in, 620
Bootstrap resampling
    for claims testing, 395–396, 410, 426
    for constructing confidence intervals,
        318, 335, 350
    in holistic statistics, 728
    in hypothesis testing, 384
    for matched pairs, 474, 495
    randomization vs., 490
    software/calculator results, 360,
        496–497
    for two-samples inferences, 447, 460,
        474, 490, 492–494, 496
Bootstrap sample
    for confidence interval, 356, 357
    defining, 356
    means and, 358–359
    proportions and, 357–358
    requirements, 355
    standard deviation and, 359
Box, George E. P., 613
Boxplots, 121–130
    constructing, 127–128
    defining, 127
    for mean, 619
    modified, 130–131
    skeletal, 130

skewness in, 128
software/calculator results, 132–133
Bribery, 708

C

Callbacks, repeated, 207
Cancer, 681
Candies data set, 758
Car chases, 78
Car crash tests, 610–611
Car data set, 757
Car seats, 582
Case-control study, 30–31
Categorical data, 15–16
    in frequency distributions, 47–48
Causation
    correlation and, 7, 73, 517–518
    interpretation with, 517
Censored data, 103
Census, 4
Centerline, 704
Central Limit Theorem, 283–288
    applications of, 286–288
    defining, 284
    fuzzy, 287
    sample mean and, 285
    sampling distribution and, 285
    universal truths and, 284
Chebyshev's theorem, 113
Chi-square distribution, 345–347, 735
    critical values in, 346
    degrees of freedom in, 346
    formula, 345
    properties of, 417–419
Chi-square test of homogeneity, 595–596
Chocolate chip cookies, 758
Cigarette contents, 751
Claimed distribution
    disagreement with, 579–582
    in goodness-of-fit, 579–582
Claims testing
    with abnormal populations, 421
    bootstrap resampling for, 395–396,
        410, 426
    confidence interval for, 395, 405,
        409, 420
    critical values for, 392, 405, 409
    critical values in, 418
    degrees of freedom in, 417
    equivalent methods, 417
    exact methods, 397–398
    important properties of, 406
    for non-normal population, 409–410
    normal approximation method, 391–396
    notation, 405, 416
    about population means, 404–416, 429–430

APPLICATIONS INDEX

835

Health

TABLE A-3 *t* Distribution: Critical *t* Values

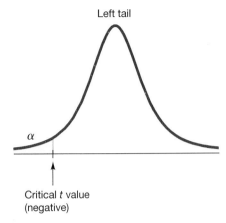

Left tail

α

Critical *t* value
(negative)

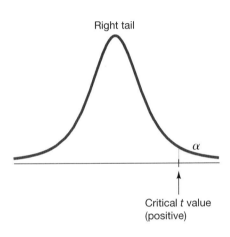

Right tail

α

Critical *t* value
(positive)

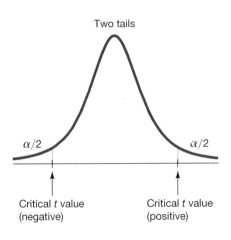

Two tails

α/2   α/2

Critical *t* value   Critical *t* value
(negative)   (positive)

			Area in One Tail		
	0.005	0.01	0.025	0.05	0.10
Degrees of			Area in Two Tails		
Freedom	0.01	0.02	0.05	0.10	0.20
1	63.657	31.821	12.706	6.314	3.078
2	9.925	6.965	4.303	2.920	1.886
3	5.841	4.541	3.182	2.353	1.638
4	4.604	3.747	2.776	2.132	1.533
5	4.032	3.365	2.571	2.015	1.476
6	3.707	3.143	2.447	1.943	1.440
7	3.499	2.998	2.365	1.895	1.415
8	3.355	2.896	2.306	1.860	1.397
9	3.250	2.821	2.262	1.833	1.383
10	3.169	2.764	2.228	1.812	1.372
11	3.106	2.718	2.201	1.796	1.363
12	3.055	2.681	2.179	1.782	1.356
13	3.012	2.650	2.160	1.771	1.350
14	2.977	2.624	2.145	1.761	1.345
15	2.947	2.602	2.131	1.753	1.341
16	2.921	2.583	2.120	1.746	1.337
17	2.898	2.567	2.110	1.740	1.333
18	2.878	2.552	2.101	1.734	1.330
19	2.861	2.539	2.093	1.729	1.328
20	2.845	2.528	2.086	1.725	1.325
21	2.831	2.518	2.080	1.721	1.323
22	2.819	2.508	2.074	1.717	1.321
23	2.807	2.500	2.069	1.714	1.319
24	2.797	2.492	2.064	1.711	1.318
25	2.787	2.485	2.060	1.708	1.316
26	2.779	2.479	2.056	1.706	1.315
27	2.771	2.473	2.052	1.703	1.314
28	2.763	2.467	2.048	1.701	1.313
29	2.756	2.462	2.045	1.699	1.311
30	2.750	2.457	2.042	1.697	1.310
31	2.744	2.453	2.040	1.696	1.309
32	2.738	2.449	2.037	1.694	1.309
33	2.733	2.445	2.035	1.692	1.308
34	2.728	2.441	2.032	1.691	1.307
35	2.724	2.438	2.030	1.690	1.306
36	2.719	2.434	2.028	1.688	1.306
37	2.715	2.431	2.026	1.687	1.305
38	2.712	2.429	2.024	1.686	1.304
39	2.708	2.426	2.023	1.685	1.304
40	2.704	2.423	2.021	1.684	1.303
45	2.690	2.412	2.014	1.679	1.301
50	2.678	2.403	2.009	1.676	1.299
60	2.660	2.390	2.000	1.671	1.296
70	2.648	2.381	1.994	1.667	1.294
80	2.639	2.374	1.990	1.664	1.292
90	2.632	2.368	1.987	1.662	1.291
100	2.626	2.364	1.984	1.660	1.290
200	2.601	2.345	1.972	1.653	1.286
300	2.592	2.339	1.968	1.650	1.284
400	2.588	2.336	1.966	1.649	1.284
500	2.586	2.334	1.965	1.648	1.283
1000	2.581	2.330	1.962	1.646	1.282
2000	2.578	2.328	1.961	1.646	1.282
Large	2.576	2.326	1.960	1.645	1.282

NEGATIVE z Scores

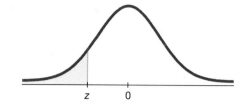

TABLE A-2 Standard Normal (z) Distribution: Cumulative Area from the LEFT

z	.00	.01	.02	.03	.04	.05	.06	.07	.08	.09
−3.50 and lower	.0001									
−3.4	.0003	.0003	.0003	.0003	.0003	.0003	.0003	.0003	.0003	.0002
−3.3	.0005	.0005	.0005	.0004	.0004	.0004	.0004	.0004	.0004	.0003
−3.2	.0007	.0007	.0006	.0006	.0006	.0006	.0006	.0005	.0005	.0005
−3.1	.0010	.0009	.0009	.0009	.0008	.0008	.0008	.0008	.0007	.0007
−3.0	.0013	.0013	.0013	.0012	.0012	.0011	.0011	.0011	.0010	.0010
−2.9	.0019	.0018	.0018	.0017	.0016	.0016	.0015	.0015	.0014	.0014
−2.8	.0026	.0025	.0024	.0023	.0023	.0022	.0021	.0021	.0020	.0019
−2.7	.0035	.0034	.0033	.0032	.0031	.0030	.0029	.0028	.0027	.0026
−2.6	.0047	.0045	.0044	.0043	.0041	.0040	.0039	.0038	.0037	.0036
−2.5	.0062	.0060	.0059	.0057	.0055	.0054	.0052	.0051 *	.0049	.0048
−2.4	.0082	.0080	.0078	.0075	.0073	.0071	.0069	.0068	.0066	.0064
−2.3	.0107	.0104	.0102	.0099	.0096	.0094	.0091	.0089	.0087	.0084
−2.2	.0139	.0136	.0132	.0129	.0125	.0122	.0119	.0116	.0113	.0110
−2.1	.0179	.0174	.0170	.0166	.0162	.0158	.0154	.0150	.0146	.0143
−2.0	.0228	.0222	.0217	.0212	.0207	.0202	.0197	.0192	.0188	.0183
−1.9	.0287	.0281	.0274	.0268	.0262	.0256	.0250	.0244	.0239	.0233
−1.8	.0359	.0351	.0344	.0336	.0329	.0322	.0314	.0307	.0301	.0294
−1.7	.0446	.0436	.0427	.0418	.0409	.0401	.0392	.0384	.0375	.0367
−1.6	.0548	.0537	.0526	.0516	.0505 *	.0495	.0485	.0475	.0465	.0455
−1.5	.0668	.0655	.0643	.0630	.0618	.0606	.0594	.0582	.0571	.0559
−1.4	.0808	.0793	.0778	.0764	.0749	.0735	.0721	.0708	.0694	.0681
−1.3	.0968	.0951	.0934	.0918	.0901	.0885	.0869	.0853	.0838	.0823
−1.2	.1151	.1131	.1112	.1093	.1075	.1056	.1038	.1020	.1003	.0985
−1.1	.1357	.1335	.1314	.1292	.1271	.1251	.1230	.1210	.1190	.1170
−1.0	.1587	.1562	.1539	.1515	.1492	.1469	.1446	.1423	.1401	.1379
−0.9	.1841	.1814	.1788	.1762	.1736	.1711	.1685	.1660	.1635	.1611
−0.8	.2119	.2090	.2061	.2033	.2005	.1977	.1949	.1922	.1894	.1867
−0.7	.2420	.2389	.2358	.2327	.2296	.2266	.2236	.2206	.2177	.2148
−0.6	.2743	.2709	.2676	.2643	.2611	.2578	.2546	.2514	.2483	.2451
−0.5	.3085	.3050	.3015	.2981	.2946	.2912	.2877	.2843	.2810	.2776
−0.4	.3446	.3409	.3372	.3336	.3300	.3264	.3228	.3192	.3156	.3121
−0.3	.3821	.3783	.3745	.3707	.3669	.3632	.3594	.3557	.3520	.3483
−0.2	.4207	.4168	.4129	.4090	.4052	.4013	.3974	.3936	.3897	.3859
−0.1	.4602	.4562	.4522	.4483	.4443	.4404	.4364	.4325	.4286	.4247
−0.0	.5000	.4960	.4920	.4880	.4840	.4801	.4761	.4721	.4681	.4641

NOTE: For values of z below −3.49, use 0.0001 for the area.

(continued)

*Use these common values that result from interpolation:

z Score	Area
−1.645	0.0500
−2.575	0.0050